COGNITIVE NEUROSCIENCE

THIRD EDITION

Marie T. Banich
UNIVERSITY OF COLORADO AT BOULDER

Rebecca J. Compton
HAVERFORD COLLEGE

WADSWORTH
CENGAGE Learning™

Australia • Brazil • Japan • Korea • Mexico • Singapore • Spain • United Kingdom • United States

WADSWORTH
CENGAGE Learning

Cognitive Neuroscience: Third Edition
Marie T. Banich and Rebecca J. Compton

Senior Publisher: Linda Schreiber-Ganster

Executive Editor: Jon-David Hague

Acquiring Sponsoring Editor: Timothy C. Matray

Developmental Editor: Tali Beesley

Assistant Editor: Paige Leeds

Editorial Assistant: Alice McLaughlin

Media Editor: Lauren Keyes

Senior Marketing Manager: Jessica L. Egbert

Marketing Director: Kimberly Russell

Executive Marketing/Communications
  Manager: Talia Wise

Senior Content Project Manager: Pat Waldo

Creative Director: Rob Hugel

Art Director: Vernon Boes

Print Buyer: Karen Hunt

Rights Acquisitions Account Manager, Text:
  Bobbie Broyer

Rights Acquisitions Account Manager, Image:
  Dean Dauphinais

Production Service: Tiffany Timmerman,
  S4Carlisle Publishing Services

Text Designer: Diane Beasley

Photo Researcher: Scott Rosen/Bills Studio
  Group

Text Researcher: Karyn Morrison

Copy Editor: S4Carlisle Publishing Services

Illustrators: S4Carlisle Publishing Services and
  Argosy Publishing

Cover Designer: Denise Davidson

Cover Image: Pasieka/SPL/Getty Images

Compositor: S4Carlisle Publishing Services

For product information and technology assistance, contact us at
Cengage Learning Customer & Sales Support, 1-800-354-9706

For permission to use material from this text or product,
submit all requests online at **www.cengage.com/permissions**
Further permissions questions can be e-mailed to
permissionrequest@cengage.com

Library of Congress Control Number: 2010923540
International Student Edition:

ISBN-13: 978-0-8400-3265-2
ISBN-10: 0-8400-3265-X

Cengage Learning International Offices

Asia
cengageasia.com
tel: (65) 6410 1200

Australia/New Zealand
cengage.com.au
tel: (61) 3 9685 4111

Brazil
cengage.com.br
tel.: (55) 11 3665 9900

India
cengage.co.in
tel: (91) 11 4364 1111

Latin America
cengage.com.mx
tel: (52) 55 1500 6000

UK/Europe/Middle East/Africa
cengage.co.uk
tel: (44) 0 1264 332 424

Represented in Canada by Nelson Education, Ltd.
tel: (416) 752 9100 / (800) 668 0671
nelson.com

Cengage Learning is a leading provider of customized learning solutions with office locations around the globe, including Singapore, the United Kingdom, Australia, Mexico, Brazil, and Japan. Locate your local office at: **www.cengage.com/global**

Cengage Learning products are represented in Canada by Nelson Education, Ltd.

For product information: **www.cengage.com/international**

Visit your local office: **www.cengage.com/global**

Visit our corporate website: **www.cengage.com**

Printed in China
2 3 4 5 6 7 14 13 12

To my brother, John, who is alive in

my memory and in my heart.

When I sat down to write,

you were always sitting next to me.

Marie Banich

To Noah Aldanysh

Rebecca Compton

Brief Contents

Contents

PART II   NEURAL BASES OF MENTAL FUNCTIONS

5   Motor Control   108

6   Early Perceptual Processing   145

9 Language 231

10 Memory 265

Attention   302

Executive Function   336

13   Emotion and Social Cognition   365

PART III   BROAD-BASED PHENOMENA

14   Psychopathology   395

15   Brain Development and Plasticity   428

16 Generalized Cognitive Disorders 466

Preface

THE THIRD EDITION of this book, though extensively revised, retains the spirit, organization, and many of the features of the first two editions. Like the earlier editions, it provides a systematic introduction to the neural basis of mental function. It includes state-of-the-art research from experimental work performed with humans and animals, as well as findings from clinical populations. The goal, as before, is to provide a balanced, synthesized, and integrated view of what we know both about the brain and about cognition.

Although the entire text has been revised and updated, three major changes are especially notable. First, recognizing the importance of visual elements in learning, the third edition features a new, bold, four-color art program. The art is designed to illustrate important concepts, paradigms, and findings, helping students to absorb these elements through accessible visual images. Second, this edition includes two new chapters. Reflecting the ever-expanding growth in research on visual and auditory perception, and the relevance of this knowledge to higher-level cognition, we have included a new chapter on early perceptual processing (Chapter 6). We have also included a new chapter devoted to psychopathology (Chapter 14), a topic that had previously been covered in a more cursory way in the chapter on emotion. Devoting an entire chapter to psychopathology allows students to see how the fundamental principles of cognitive neuroscience covered in earlier chapters can be applied to crucial clinical problems. Finally, the third major change is the addition of a new co-author, Rebecca Compton. Rebecca's 10 years of experience teaching at a selective liberal arts college, in addition to her research expertise in the study of emotion, provide a complement to Marie Banich's teaching experience at a large research university and her established research program on attention and executive functions.

In addition to these major changes, every chapter has been thoroughly updated to reflect current findings in the fast-growing field of cognitive neuroscience. We pay special attention to the integration of findings from a variety of methods, from traditional methods, such as the study of brain-damaged patients, to newer methods such as transcranial magnetic stimulation and diffusion tensor imaging. In this edition, we continue to incorporate more findings about the genetic underpinnings of cognition. Throughout, our intention is to provide students with a thorough and solid grounding in the basic principles and findings of cognitive neuroscience—tools that they can then use to further understand applied and clinical problems.

Text Organization and Features

The book's soul remains very much the same as the first two editions, as the following main features have been retained.

■ The book provides a systematic survey of the neural bases of a wide variety of mental functions.

The overall organization of the book has changed little from the first two editions. The first section of the book, comprising the first four chapters, provides students with a basic foundation for the exploration of cognitive neuroscience and neuropsychology. The first chapter provides information about the basic parts and divisions of the central nervous system; the second chapter, which is new, discusses the fundamentals of neural transmission. These two chapters are probably unnecessary for students who have already completed a course in physiological psychology, though they would serve as a good review, and will be very useful to students who have not. The third chapter acquaints students with the myriad of burgeoning techniques, both standard and novel, that are available to scientists and clinicians in their quest to understand the neural bases of mental function. The fourth chapter gives an overview of lateralization of function.

The second part of the book, Chapters 5 through 13, constitutes a survey of the neural bases of mental function, with each chapter devoted to a distinct mental function. The chapter topics discussed are, in order, motor processes, early perceptual processing, object recognition, spatial cognition and processing, language, memory, attention, executive function, and emotion.

The last part of the book, comprised of the last three chapters, examines broad-based issues in cognitive neuroscience, including development, aging, and clinical syndromes. Instructors may view these chapters as more discretionary than earlier chapters, in the sense that they cover more integrative issues. In our teaching, we've found that the broad-based, applied, and clinical issues are of special interest to many students, as they find it very rewarding to use the knowledge that they have gained from earlier text chapters to approach these issues. Chapter 14, a new chapter, examines mental conditions such as schizophrenia, depression, anxiety disorders, and substance abuse from a cognitive neuroscience perspective. Chapter 15 examines neural plasticity from a life-span perspective, including developmental changes during both childhood and aging. In addition, it discusses recovery of function in children and in adults, and the neural bases of developmental disabilities. Chapter 16 examines syndromes that are characterized by generalized cognitive disorders (rather than the more localized and specific disorders discussed in Chapters 5 through 13), including closed head injury, dementia, demyelinating diseases, and epilepsy.

■ The sequence of the chapters is designed for progressive learning.

The chapters have been carefully sequenced so that information in later chapters builds upon information in earlier chapters. Notably, the processes most linked to motoric and sensory functions are presented earlier, and those that depend on more integrative aspects of brain function, such as executive function and emotion, are presented later. For example, the chapter on object recognition directly precedes that on spatial processing, so that the student is introduced to the ventral and dorsal visual-processing streams in consecutive chapters. The chapter on memory is preceded by the language and object-recognition chapters so that the distinction between generalized memory disorders and the "memory" problems that are specific to certain domains (e.g., anomia in language or agnosia with regard to objects) is clear.

■ The book is designed to actively engage students in the process of learning.

Each chapter begins with an opening case history to pique students' interest and preview the issues discussed in the chapter. For example, the opening case history in Chapter 5 discusses how Muhammad Ali's boxing career led him to have a Parkinsonian disorder, and the opening case history in Chapter 16 discusses the mental decline of Marie's maternal grandmother due to dementia. The text is written in a conversational tone rather than in a technical style, to grab students' interest and retain it. We use analogies extensively so as to present difficult conceptual issues in a tractable manner. Each chapter includes an "In Focus" feature that explores in depth a specific applied issue in cognitive neuroscience, helping students to see the implications of research for everyday life.

To keep students oriented to terminology, key terms are introduced in boldface and defined in a glossary at the back of the book. Chapter summaries allow students to review the material learned or preview what is to be discussed, and outlines at the beginning of each chapter provide a clear conceptual structure of the contents. All these features are designed to make this book as user-friendly as possible.

■ State-of-the-art knowledge in the field is presented without sacrificing accuracy or oversimplifying the material.

As researchers who maintain highly active and visible research programs, we are in a position to ensure that the book discusses not only the "classic" findings in the field, but also the cutting-edge portion of our knowledge. Never, however, are students overwhelmed with a laundry list of findings or with overly technical, arcane issues. Rather, representative studies are used to highlight the nature of current debates, so that students can understand the conceptual issues under consideration and how researchers attempt to reason and draw conclusions based on experimental evidence. Our extensive work in both research and teaching in cognitive neuroscience allows us to present issues in a manner that is precise and sophisticated, yet also accessible and integrative.

What's New in This Edition

Although the approach of the first edition has been retained, this second edition has nevertheless been extensively revamped. The main new additions are as follows.

■ The introduction of a four-color art program.

In this edition, an enhanced and improved four-color art program has been introduced to further promote students' understanding of the material. Important figures from earlier editions have been redrawn, and many new figures have been added. Some figures highlight regions of the brain so the reader can quickly see "where" and "what" in the brain are important. Other figures present data from representative studies in the field, so that students can gain experience in viewing and interpreting data; still others depict important experimental paradigms so that students can quickly grasp how a key study was conducted.

■ Addition of two new chapters.

Two chapters have been added to the text to reflect growing areas of research over the last decade. Chapter 6 is a new chapter covering the early perceptual processing that takes place along pathways between sensory receptors, such as the retina, and primary sensory cortex. This chapter lays the groundwork for understanding how the brain represents the sensory-perceptual world—knowledge that students can build upon in subsequent chapters addressing object recognition and spatial cognition. Chapter 14, a new chapter on psychopathology, examines the application of cognitive neuroscience principles to the understanding of major mental illnesses such as schizophrenia and depression.

■ Ancillary materials to aid in learning.

Book Companion Site at www.cengage.com/psychology/Banich

This website provides instructors and students with a wealth of free information and resources, including tutorial quizzes, flashcards, and glossary.

PowerPoint Lecture Outlines

Microsoft® PowerPoint® slides let you incorporate images from the book right into your lectures:

■ Extensive updating of the material to incorporate the acceleration of knowledge in the field.

The field of cognitive neuroscience continues to explode with new discoveries. As a result, most of the chapters of the book had to be extensively rewritten to incorporate this huge amount of additional knowledge, which is reflected in hundreds of new references reflecting studies using diverse methodologies.

Following is a summary of the main changes to each chapter.

CHAPTERS 1 and 2

- We have polished the writing style to increase accessibility of the "nuts-and-bolts" material covered in these chapters.

CHAPTER 3

- We have updated this chapter to reflect the latest on neuroimaging techniques and methods for modulating brain activity.
- We have added a new section on multimethod approaches.

CHAPTER 4

- We included a new "In Focus" feature on laterality across different species.

CHAPTER 5

- This chapter includes expanded coverage of cortical regions involved in motor control.
- A new section reviews integrated models of motor control.
- A new "In Focus" feature discusses the use of brain signals to control prosthetic limbs.

NEW CHAPTER 6—EARLY PERCEPTUAL PROCESSING

Includes coverage of:

- Visual processing from the retina to the primary visual cortex.
- The clinical phenomenon of blindsight, as an example of applying knowledge from research to understand the organization of visual pathways.
- Auditory pathways from the ear to the primary auditory cortex.
- Auditory-visual interactions.

CHAPTER 7

- Material has been reorganized to focus on four core theoretical questions in the study of object recognition.
- Coverage of new findings shifts the emphasis from a primary focus on brain-damaged patients to more recent findings ranging from single-cell studies in monkeys to neuroimaging.

CHAPTER 8

- The chapter has been rewritten and reorganized to focus material around core questions in spatial cognition.
- New sections on motion perception and on the relationship between space and action were added.
- Discussion integrates new findings from a variety of cognitive neuroscience methodologies.

CHAPTER 9

- Extensive revision reflects newer, more integrated models of language function, as compared to classical models of localized function.
- Expanded coverage of findings from brain mapping methods, including functional magnetic resonance imaging and event-related potentials, is included.

CHAPTER 10

- The entire chapter has been reorganized to highlight the existence of multiple memory systems.
- Expanded discussion of results from brain mapping methods incorporates findings from recent studies and the newest methods.
- We include a more detailed and enhanced discussion of the interrelationships between memory systems.
- A new "In Focus" feature investigates the role of sleep in memory.

CHAPTER 11

- Chapter reorganization emphasizes the integrated functioning of brain regions to support different aspects of attentional control.
- There is expanded coverage of network models of attentional control.
- Information regarding the default network is included.
- A new "In Focus" feature highlights study findings on attention and driving.

CHAPTER 12

- Extensive revisions throughout the chapter incorporate the explosion of new research in this field.
- The chapter has been reorganized to highlight both goal-directed behavior and higher-order thinking.
- A new "In Focus" feature investigates the inhibition of memory.
- We include an entirely new section reviewing the theoretical models of how the frontal lobe is organized for executive function.

CHAPTER 13

- The chapter has been greatly reorganized and updated to reflect major functional components of emotion.
- New sections on emotion regulation and social cognition enhance the basic discussion.
- A new box feature highlights the relationship between social and physical pain.

NEW CHAPTER 14—PSYCHOPATHOLOGY

- This entirely new chapter covers the neural basis of major mental illnesses: schizophrenia, depression, anxiety disorders, and substance abuse.
- Throughout, the new material shows how cognitive neuroscience approaches from previous chapters can be applied to understand clinical syndromes.

CHAPTER 15

This revised chapter includes:

- A new section on the adolescent brain.
- New material on plasticity in the adult brain, incorporating findings on recovery of function in both childhood and adulthood.

CHAPTER 16

- A new "In Focus" feature discusses the consequences of head injury in sports.
- New material discusses risk factors for the development of dementia, including both genetic and environmental factors.

Acknowledgments

This book has benefited greatly from the generous help of many colleagues who reviewed either this or prior editions. We were genuinely touched by the amount of time and effort that these people took to improve the book. Their enthusiasm for the project bolstered us and kept us on our toes. Although we may not have taken all of their advice, we thought carefully about every one of their suggestions. We are most appreciative of their input.

Alaa Ahmed, University of Colorado–Boulder; Daniel Arnstein, University of Groningen; Mark H. Ashcraft, Cleveland State University; Ruth Ann Atchley, University of Kansas; Mark Beeman, Northwestern University; Robert Bohlander, Wilkes University; Robert Bornstein, Ohio State University; Joan C. Borod, Queen's College of CUNY; Marie-Christine Buhot, Centre National de la Recherche Scientifique, France; Brian Butterworth, University College, London; Michael P. Caligiuri, University of California–San Diego; James V. Corwin, Northern Illinois University; Verne C. Cox, University of Texas–Arlington; Suzanne Craft, University of Washington; Tim Curran, University of Colorado–Boulder;

Martha J. Farah, University of Pennsylvania; Deborah Fein, University of Connecticut; Wim Fias, Ghent University; Gili Freedman, University of Texas-Austin; Susan M. Garnsey, University of Illinois; Siegfried Gauggel, University of Technology Chemnitz; Jordan Grafman, National Institute of Neurological Disorders and Stroke; Kenneth F. Green, California State University, Long Beach; Gary Greenberg, Wichita State University; Eleanor Huber, Haverford College; Dai Jones, Cheltenham & Gloucester CHE; Al Kim, University of Colorado–Boulder; Daniel Kimble, University of Oregon; Karen E. Luh, Creighton University; James V. Lupo, Creighton University; Jennifer A. Mangels, Columbia University; Yuko Munakata, University of Colorado; Loraine K. Obler, CUNY Graduate School; Shelley Parlow, Carleton University; Michael Peters, University of Guelph; Graham Ratcliff, Healthsouth Harmarville Rehabilitation Center; Patricia Reuter-Lorenz, University of Michigan; John D. Salamone, University of Connecticut; Martin Sarter, Ohio State University; Carol A. Saslow, Oregon State University (Emeritus); Sid Segalowitz, Brock University; Matthew L. Shapiro, Mount Sinai School of Medicine; Angela Sirigu, Centre de Neuroscience Cognitive, Lyon, France; Myra O. Smith, Colgate University; Chantal Stern, Boston University; Christopher Sullivan, Butler University; James Tanaka, University of Victoria; Eli Vakil, Bar-Ilan University; Janet M. Vargo, University of South Dakota; X. T. Wang, University of South Dakota; David A. Westwood, Dalhousie University; Daniel B. Willingham, University of Virginia.

We thank Doug Bernstein for his insights and wisdom regarding the textbook publishing process, which spared us many headaches, and also Jane Knetzger and Danielle Richardson, invaluable editors on the first two editions. We are very grateful to Jane Potter for inspiring us to pursue work on a third edition. Tali Beesley has been an outstanding editor at Cengage, and the book would not have been possible without her astute insights, organization, dogged persistence, and patience with the authors. Pat Waldo, our project manager, used her skill and acumen to keep everyone on task; we appreciate her enthusiasm for this project and her willingness to go above and beyond at every step of the revision process. For essential support services and research assistance, we are grateful to Cris Fuller, Corrie Fahl, Rob Haley, and Eleanor Huber at Haverford College; and to Kirsten Orcutt and Paula Villar at the University of Colorado–Boulder.

In the end, however, the people most important to this revision are the ones who inspired and believed in us. We depend on these people more than any others when the going gets rough and we need boosts of inspiration, nurturing, humor, or confidence. Rebecca is most deeply indebted to Judy and Richard Ellis, David and Cindy Compton, Gwendolyn Compton-Engle, and Jeremy Meyer, for all their love and support. Rebecca is also grateful to Marie for a decade of mentoring and guidance. Marie is indebted to her co-author Becky, who has been the best co-author one could possibly wish for, and who has aided in making the creation of this new edition a much more enjoyable endeavor. She is also indebted to her students and staff for their patience with her as she pursued this project, and to Laura Edwards, her partner, and Serafina Banich, her mother for reminding her that there are other wonderful things in life besides work—their love and support being two of the most precious to her.

Marie has dedicated this book to the memory of her brother for the personal reasons described below:

My brother died between the publication of the second and third editions of this book as the result of one of the brain disorders we describe—one that runs in my extended family and affects more of us than seems fair. My anguish at my brother's suffering, and my intense anger at my total impotence to help him despite all I supposedly know, is the fuel that now propels me. What also propels me is the example that my brother left me. Damage to the brain fundamentally transforms who we are as people. Yet, despite the mutiny of his brain, my brother held fast to the very end to the vision of the type of person he was and wanted to be and the values he held dear. I will never understand some of the decisions he made along the way, but I do know that despite all the chaos in his mind, he was attempting to follow a principled path. That he persisted for as long as he did, with as few signposts as someone lost in the wilderness and blinded by a whiteout, is to me an example of both perseverance and courage.

My brother's picture sits on my desk at work and I look at it every time I walk in my office before I do anything else, whether it be sit down to craft a paper, talk to a student, design an experiment, analyze data, organize a conference, or return a phone call. It is his memory that compels me to continue on in my scientific endeavors and to undertake yet another edition of this book. I pursue my work with the desire that my stream of tears will transform into a stream of knowledge. In that spirit, perhaps this book will lead some students who read it to become fascinated by the challenge of understanding how our brains profoundly shape human existence, both at the level of the individual and that of society. I hope that as a result at least some of them will rise to the challenge of inventing new ways of influencing the brain's working when it goes awry, inventing treatments that capitalize on what we know about its neural structure or utilizing the principles of the intricate ways in which it processes information to compensate for deficits. Those discoveries will come too late to help my brother, but they may spare other families the grief and heartache we have known.

Marie T. Banich
Rebecca J. Compton

Introduction to the Nervous System

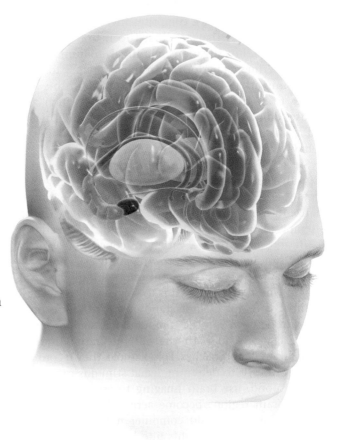

What Is Cognitive Neuroscience?

In this book, we explore how the neurological organization of the brain influences the way people think, feel, and act. **Cognitive neuroscience** is critical to our understanding of this link between brain and mind. Cognitive neuroscience comprises investigations of all mental functions that are linked to neural processes, ranging from investigations in animals to humans and from experiments performed in the laboratory to computer simulations. Much of the early work in this area comes from **human neuropsychology**, which also focuses on understanding mental processes in humans, but with an emphasis on examining the changes in behavior as a result of brain trauma.

Since the mid-1970s, our knowledge in the realm of cognitive neuroscience and neuropsychology has grown rapidly, and so has the number of individuals who specialize in these areas of inquiry. *Cognitive neuroscientists* attempt to understand the relationship between the brain and mind from a variety of conceptual vantage points simultaneously. Borrowing from computer science, they view the brain as an information-processing system whose primary goal is to solve problems. These scientists attempt to understand how the brain is organized to perform specific computations, such as recognizing a face. To do so, they rely on integrating findings from different approaches. For example, they record the activity of cells to determine what stimulus makes the cells respond, use brain imaging to ascertain exactly which brain regions become active during a specific mental task, and build computer models to provide principles and gain insights into how different mental operations might be performed by the brain.

Experimental neuropsychologists work to understand the neural bases of cognition by doing scientific studies comparing individuals who have sustained brain damage with those who are neurologically intact. These researchers use a variety of techniques to divide complicated mental functions into meaningful categories, such as language and memory, and to isolate the contribution of specific brain regions to each of these functions.

Clinical neuropsychologists work in health care settings, such as hospitals and clinics, with individuals who have sustained brain damage through either trauma or disease. They diagnose the cognitive deficits resulting from brain trauma, plan programs of rehabilitation, evaluate the degree to which an individual is regaining function, and determine how environmental factors (e.g., family structure, educational background, and so forth) may moderate or exacerbate the effects of brain dysfunction. In this book, we provide an overview of the current state of knowledge in cognitive neuroscience as derived from findings in both the laboratory and the clinic.

The endeavor of understanding the relationship between the brain and the mind may be undertaken from two distinct vantage points, one that emphasizes the neurological organization of the brain and one that emphasizes the psychology of the mind. The neurologically oriented approach emphasizes the brain's anatomy; therefore, the major objective of this approach is to understand the function of specific circumscribed regions of brain tissue. For instance, a researcher might want to investigate a particular brain structure, such as the hippocampus, to determine its anatomical characteristics, its pattern of connections to other brain regions, and its role in mental functioning. Information derived from this approach can be extremely useful to medical personnel such as neurosurgeons who need to know what functions might be affected by different surgical approaches.

In contrast, the psychologically oriented approach emphasizes the brain's mental capabilities, so the major objective of this approach is to understand how different aspects of cognition, such as language, memory, and attention, are supported by the neurological organization of the brain. For example, cognitive neuroscientists may want to know whether the brain structures supporting the ability to read are the same as, or distinct from, those supporting the ability to write. One way of addressing this question is to determine whether the type of brain damage that impairs the process of reading always impairs the process of writing as well. In fact, reading and writing abilities are not always simultaneously lost after brain damage. This finding tells us that although they may appear to be similar functions, they are controlled by separate brain regions.

In this book we lean more toward the psychologically oriented approach than the neurologically oriented one. This bias can be seen most clearly by taking a quick glance at the table of contents, which includes chapter titles such as "Language," "Memory," and "Attention," indicating that our discussion of the relationship between the brain and the mind emphasizes cognitive functions. If this book were written from a more neurologically oriented approach, the chapters would have been organized by brain regions and been titled "The Basal Ganglia," "The Cerebellum," and "The Frontal Lobes." Although we take a more psychologically oriented approach, a working knowledge and understanding of the neurological organization of the brain is indispensable, for only with that knowledge can we intelligently discuss the relationship between psychological functions and the specific regions of brain tissue that support those functions.

Cognitive neuroscience and neuropsychology, by the very questions they address, fall at the intersection of a variety of fields, including neurology, neuroscience, cognitive psychology, clinical psychology, and computer science. To study such a cross-disciplinary subject, we must be willing not only to examine questions from different perspectives, but also to integrate the information provided from these alternative perspectives. You may find that you are already familiar with some of the concepts raised in the book through previous course work in cognitive psychology, biological psychology, or neuroscience. However, the perspectives taken in this book are likely to be different because we integrate, interrelate, and synthesize material from both biological and cognitive vantage points. For example, when discussing face recognition in Chapter 7, we learn not only which salient features enable people to recognize the face of someone they haven't seen for 30 years, but also which regions of the brain support such feats and why.

Now is a particularly exciting time to study cognitive neuroscience. Vast advances in our knowledge in neuroscience, medical science, cognitive psychology, and computer science provide the opportunity to synthesize findings in ways that were impossible just a few years ago. Research in cognitive psychology has tremendously increased the sophistication of models of mental functioning. For example, we can take a complicated function such as language and divide it into specific subcomponents and subprocesses. At the same time, incredible advances in medical technology now allow us to examine the neuroanatomy and physiological functioning of the brain in ways unimagined even as recently as the 1980s. We discuss these advances in methods in more detail in Chapter 3.

Before we begin to attempt to link cognitive functions to the brain, however, we need a common base of knowledge about the anatomy and physiology of the brain. The first two chapters are designed to provide this knowledge base. The first chapter introduces the specific vocabulary scientists use when discussing the brain—the terms that describe the location of brain structures and their characteristics. Next there is a brief overview of the major regions of the brain, providing a glimpse of each region's major functions. After gaining a general familiarity with the nervous system, the second chapter takes a closer look at how nerve cells communicate with one another, and how disruptions in this process can have important implications for mental functions.

Basic Building Blocks of the Nervous System

The human nervous system, which consists of the brain, spinal cord, nerves, and ganglia, controls the body's response to internal and external stimuli. It is comprised of two main classes of cells: neurons and glia. **Neurons** are the cells in the nervous system that carry information from one place to another by means of a combination of electrical and chemical signals. **Glia**, which outnumber neurons by at least 10 to 1, are support cells.

Neurons have three main parts: a dendritic tree, a cell body, and an axon. The **dendritic tree** is the part

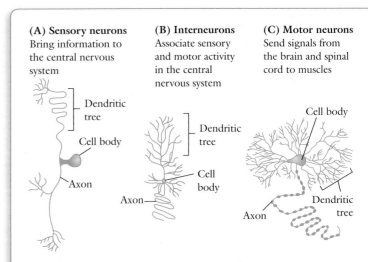

(A) Sensory neurons
Bring information to the central nervous system

Dendritic tree
Cell body
Axon

(B) Interneurons
Associate sensory and motor activity in the central nervous system

Dendritic tree
Cell body
Axon

(C) Motor neurons
Send signals from the brain and spinal cord to muscles

Cell body
Dendritic tree
Axon

● **FIGURE 1.1   Examples of some nervous system cells (not to scale).** (A) Sensory neurons, (B) interneurons, and (C) motor neurons. Note that the appearance of the different kinds of neurons is distinctive; the appearance of each kind of neuron reflects its function. A sensory neuron collects information from a source and passes it on to an interneuron. The many branches of interneurons suggest that they collect information from many sources. Motor neurons are distinctively large and collect information from many sources; they pass this information on to command muscles to move. © 2011 Cengage Learning

of the neuron that receives input from other cells. The **cell body** is the part of the cell containing the nucleus and other cellular apparatus responsible for manufacturing the proteins and enzymes that sustain cell functioning. The **axon** is the appendage of the cell along which information is carried. It can vary in length; in some cases it is very short, extending not much farther than the length of the dendrites and cell body. In other instances the axon is very long, spanning large distances between brain regions.

Some neurons, known as *sensory neurons*, bring information to the central nervous system. Others, known as *interneurons*, associate information within the central nervous system. Finally, there are *motor neurons*, which send information from the brain and spinal cord to the muscles. Although all neurons have these same basic component parts, they come in a variety of sizes and shapes (● Figure 1.1). We examine neurons in more detail in Chapter 2. There we present an overview of how neurons work, highlighting the aspects of neuronal function that are important for discussions in later chapters.

Although glia are not the main carriers of information, they are critical to the functioning of the nervous system. Their tasks include influencing the communication between neurons by modifying the chemical milieu between them (for a good discussion on how this aspect of their functioning affects memory, see Bains & Oliet, 2007), aiding with reorganization after brain damage by removing dead neurons, serving some of the nutritive needs of neurons, and providing structural support. Glia are critical to maintaining the **blood-brain barrier**,

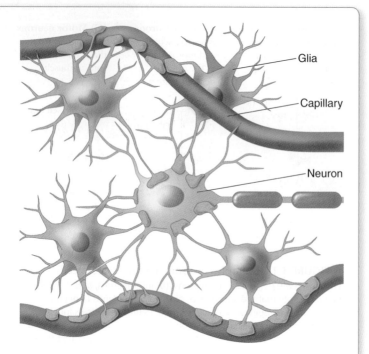

● **FIGURE 1.2   The relationship between glia and neurons.**
Glia support the cell in many different ways. As shown here, they provide
a support matrix around the neuron. In addition, by their close association
with the blood supply they help to maintain the blood-brain barrier.
© 2010 Cengage Learning

which is the mechanism by which many harmful substances, such as toxins, are prevented from reaching the brain. The blood-brain barrier consists of tightly packed glial cells between blood vessels and neurons; this creates a physical obstruction that keeps not only toxins, but also nutrients, drugs, and immune system cells in the bloodstream from directly reaching the nervous system (● Figure 1.2).

Developmentally, glia guide neurons as they migrate from the site of creation to their final position within the brain. Compared with our knowledge about neurons, our knowledge about glia is scant, but it has increased tremendously in recent years and has revealed that glia are much more than just "bit-part" players overshadowed by the leading role that neurons play in the nervous system (for a nice overview, see Stevens, 2003). Now that we know the basic cells that form the nervous system, let's step back and view the system as a whole.

Neuroanatomical Terms and Brain "Geography"

Anytime you begin a long journey, you need a road map to guide your path, plus some understanding of common directional terms such as *north, south, east,* and *west.* So, to begin our trip around the "geography" of the central nervous system, we must identify the major neural

regions and introduce terms that can help to orient us during the journey. Distinguishing between regions of the central nervous system, and in particular the brain, serves a function similar to that of drawing boundary lines on a map. Such lines on a map may tell us about differences not only in the geography of different regions, but also in the behavior, attitudes, and customs of the people on either side of a boundary. Likewise, boundaries between brain regions are often drawn to demarcate differences in the structure and function of brain tissue. Sometimes boundaries between brain regions are based on large and obvious anatomical landmarks, similar to major geographical features such as rivers or mountains on a map. In other cases, the physical distinction between regions is not obvious from the neuroanatomical terrain.

We must first learn the anatomical equivalents of north, south, east, and west. Unlike most geographical maps, which have only two dimensions, the brain has three. Thus, we need terms not only for the brain's left, right, top, and bottom, but also for its back and front. The front of the brain is referred to as **anterior** and the back as **posterior**. Because the head of an animal is situated in front of its tail, regions toward the front can be referred to as **rostral** (toward the head), whereas regions toward the rear are referred to as **caudal** (toward the tail). The top of the brain is referred to as **superior**, and the bottom is referred to as **inferior**. In the human brain, **dorsal** and **ventral** have meanings similar to superior and inferior, respectively. However, in other portions of the central nervous system, such as the spinal cord, *dorsal* and *ventral* are better understood in reference to a four-legged animal or a fish. In these cases, dorsal means toward an animal's back, whereas ventral means toward an animal's stomach. If you have aquatic interests, you can remember that dorsal means top because the dorsal fin of a shark sticks out of the water. Finally, areas in the middle or center of the brain are referred to as **medial**, whereas areas that are toward the outside of the brain are called **lateral** (● Figure 1.3).

Throughout this text, the brain is portrayed in one of three planes. When the brain is sliced ear-to-ear to separate the front from the back, the view is **coronal**. If the brain is sliced so that the top of the brain is separated from the bottom, the view is **horizontal** (also sometimes referred to as *axial* or *transverse*). Finally, if the brain is cut so that the left side of the brain is separated from the right side, the view is **sagittal**. A sagittal slice down the middle of the brain is known as a **midsagittal**, or *medial*, section, whereas a section taken more toward one side is known as a *lateral* section (● Figure 1.4).

Knowledge of these terms can help us understand the location of specific brain structures. For example, when we are introduced to the anatomical structure called the *lateral ventricle* (a *ventricle* is a space within the nervous system that is filled with fluid), we can deduce that it

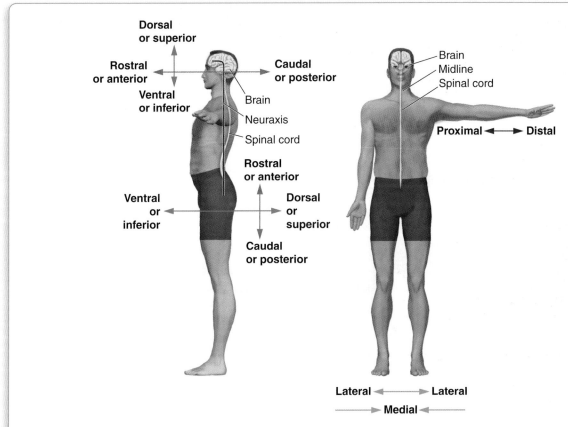

● FIGURE 1.3   Anatomical terms for directions. (Left) In a four-legged animal, dorsal/superior and ventral/inferior typically refer to the areas toward the back and stomach respectively, as shown at the hips of the figure on the left. However, because humans walk upright instead of on all fours, dorsal/superior and ventral/inferior also refer to the top and bottom of the head, respectively. (Right) Shown here are anatomical directions relative to the body midline. © 2010 Cengage Learning

must be positioned away from the midline of the brain (i.e., laterally). As another example, consider how we might go about locating **nuclei**, distinct groups of neurons whose cell bodies are all situated in the same region, in a brain structure called the *thalamus*. As discussed later in this chapter, the thalamus helps to regulate and organize information coming from the outer reaches of the nervous system as it ascends toward the cortex. The thalamus also modifies information descending from the cortex. If we need to find the anterior ventral nucleus of the thalamus, we now know from our discussion of anatomical terms that it should be located at the front and bottom part of the thalamus. You can give yourself a quick test of how well you learned these anatomical terms by trying to locate the dorsal medial nucleus, the ventral lateral nucleus, and the lateral posterior nucleus of the thalamus in ● Figure 1.5.

Other terms we need to know include **contralateral**, meaning on the opposite side, and **ipsilateral**, meaning on the same side. So, for example, the left half of your brain is contralateral to your right hand, whereas it is ipsilateral to your left hand. To make these definitions more concrete, remember the familiar adage that the right side of your brain controls the motor

movements of the limbs on the left side of your body, and vice versa. Put in the terms we just learned, motor control occurs contralaterally.

Unilateral applies to only one side of the brain, whereas **bilateral** applies to both sides of the brain. For example, when injury occurs to one side of the brain, it is unilateral damage, but when injury occurs to both sides, it is bilateral damage. Other terms often used to describe brain regions and their relation to body parts are **proximal**, which means near, and **distal**, which means far. Thus, distal muscles are in your far extremities, such as your hands. Now that we know the spatial terms of directionality in the nervous system, we turn our attention to the major subdivisions of the nervous system.

Major Subdivisions of the Central Nervous System

We now start our journey across the different territories, or regions, of the **central nervous system**. The central nervous system encompasses the brain and the

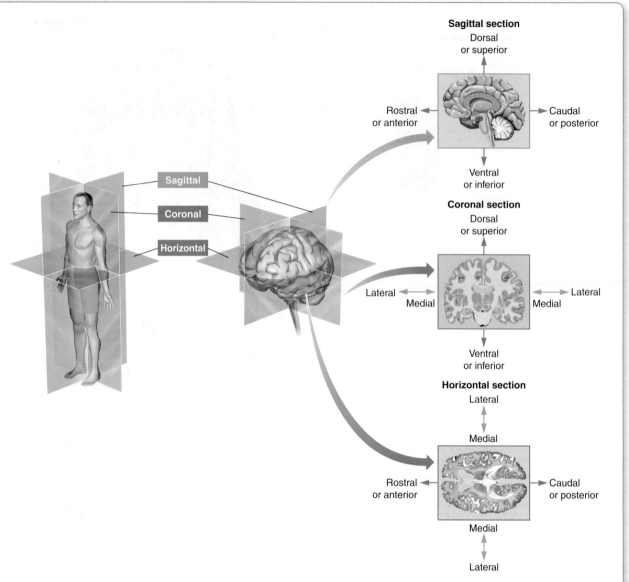

● FIGURE 1.4   **The main planes in which the brain is viewed.** A sagittal section divides left from right, a coronal section divides front from back, and a horizontal section divides top from bottom. The anatomical terms describing the brain as seen in each of these sections are shown on the right.
© 2010 Cengage Learning

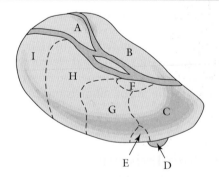

● FIGURE 1.5   **The different nuclei of the thalamus.**
(A) Anterior nucleus, (B) dorsal medial nucleus, (C) pulvinar,
(D) medial geniculate nucleus, (E) lateral geniculate nucleus,
(F) lateral posterior nucleus, (G) ventral lateral posterior nucleus,
(H) ventral lateral nucleus, and (I) ventral anterior nucleus.
© 2011 Cengage Learning

spinal cord, whereas the **peripheral nervous system** comprises all neural tissue beyond the central nervous system, such as neurons that receive sensory information or that send information to muscles, and those that relay information to or from the spinal cord or the brain. Because of its fragility, the entire central nervous system is encased in bone. The spinal cord is enclosed within the spinal column and the brain within the skull. Although these bony structures protect the central nervous system, at times they can cause damage. For example, if the spinal column presses against the spinal cord, it can pinch a nerve and cause pain. Likewise, as discussed in Chapter 16, the brain can be damaged by compression against the skull.

Between the neurons and their bony encasements is **cerebrospinal fluid (CSF)**, which is similar in composition to blood plasma. Essentially, the brain floats in CSF, which makes it buoyant and cushions it from being knocked around every time we move. The fluid-filled spaces that contain CSF are known as **ventricles**, the most prominent of which are the **lateral ventricles** (● Figure 1.6). CSF also serves metabolic needs, allowing nutrients to reach neurons. Typically, cells outside the nervous system receive nutrients from the blood. However, the blood-brain barrier precludes direct transport of nutrients from the blood to the brain. Rather, nutrients from the blood reach nerve cells through CSF.

The blood-brain barrier also acts to deflect bacteria and other infectious agents and to block the entry of toxins into the brain. However, molecules of the immune system, such as antibodies and phagocytes (cells, such as white blood cells, that engulf foreign bodies), also have difficulty crossing the blood-brain barrier. Thus, the immune system is in large part prevented from protecting the central nervous system against infection. When an infection does reach the brain, it can be difficult to arrest because standard treatments used for infections in other regions of the body are unlikely to be effective. By drawing a sample of CSF from a region near the spinal cord (commonly known as a *spinal tap*), a neurologist can determine if the brain is being affected by an infectious or toxic agent. An unusually high bacteria count in the fluid may indicate infection.

Having discussed the basic organization of the nervous system, we now turn to examine the seven main subdivisions of the central nervous system depicted in ● Figure 1.7: (1) the spinal cord, (2) the medulla, (3) the cerebellum, (4) the pons, (5) the midbrain, (6) the hypothalamus and thalamus (diencephalon), and (7) the cerebral cortex. In addition, we discuss two

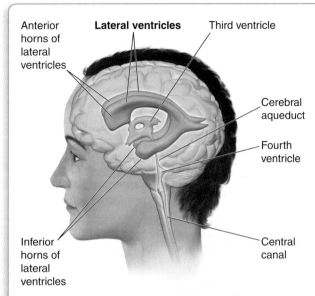

● **FIGURE 1.6   The ventricular system of the brain.** This system of spaces in the brain is filled by cerebrospinal fluid. It consists of the two lateral ventricles, one in each of the cerebral hemispheres, and the third and fourth ventricles positioned along the midline, which are connected via the cerebral aqueduct. The cerebrospinal fluid in the ventricles helps to cushion the brain and also aids in allowing nutrients to reach neurons. © 2010 Cengage Learning

major subcortical systems, the basal ganglia and the limbic system.

■ Spinal Cord

The portion of the nervous system through which most (but not all) sensory neurons relay information on the way to the brain, and through which motor commands

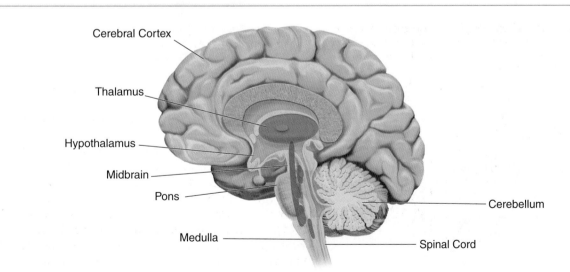

● **FIGURE 1.7   The major subdivisions of the human brain.** A sagittal view of the major subdivisions: the spinal cord, medulla, cerebellum, pons, midbrain, diencephalon (thalamus and hypothalamus), and cerebral cortex. The medulla, pons, and midbrain are often referred to as the *brainstem*. Sometimes the brain is conceived of as having three broad sections: the hindbrain (medulla, pons, and cerebellum), the midbrain, and the forebrain (diencephalon and cerebral cortex). © 2010 Cengage Learning

from the brain are sent to the muscles, is the **spinal cord**. The *spinal column,* the bony structure housing the spinal cord, is composed of many sections, or vertebrae. At each vertebra, sensory information enters the spinal cord and motor information leaves it. If the spinal cord were cut in cross-section, two clumps of nerve cells, one located ventrally and another located dorsally, would be prominent, as shown in ● Figure 1.8. Cells in the dorsal section of the spinal cord (toward the back) receive sensory information. In contrast, cells in the ventral region (toward the stomach) are responsible for conveying motor commands to the muscles as well as receiving input from the brain and from other regions of the spinal cord.

Damage to the spinal cord leaves an individual without sensation in or motor control for all body areas that are connected to the brain by spinal cord segments distal to the point of injury. Impulses from the periphery cannot be carried up the spinal cord past the point of injury and therefore cannot reach the brain. Likewise, information from the brain cannot be relayed down past the point of injury to the muscles. How much of the body is paralyzed and how much sensation is lost depends on where in the spinal cord the damage occurs.

The vertebrae where information from each part of the body enters the spinal cord are shown in ● Figure 1.9. Compression of the spinal column that causes a vertebra to be broken or crushed may result in a damaged or severed spinal cord. For example, when damage to the spinal cord occurs at the level of the fifth cervical vertebra (C-5), the person is often left quadriplegic, without control of muscles in or sensation from either the arms or the legs (see Figure 1.9). If, however, the damage is sustained at a lower level, perhaps waist level (e.g., at vertebra T-12, the twelfth thoracic vertebra), the person is often paraplegic, with loss of sensory information and motor control for just the bottom half of the body.

■ Medulla

For the purposes of this text, we should know a few main facts about the **medulla**, the section of the brain directly superior to the spinal cord. First, it is the region of the brain that contains many (though not all) of the cell bodies of the 12 **cranial nerves**. Whereas the spinal cord is the point of entry and exit for sensory and motor nerves of the body, some cranial nerves are responsible for receipt of sensory information and motor control of the head. Other cranial nerves are responsible for the neural control of internal organs. A list of the 12 cranial nerves and their functions, and a diagram of the region of the brain where their nuclei are located, are presented in ● Figure 1.10.

Second, at the medulla, most of the motor fibers cross from one side of the body to the other, with the result that the left side of the brain controls the right side of the body, and the right side of the brain controls the left side of the body. Third, the medulla controls many vital functions and reflexes, such as respiration and heart

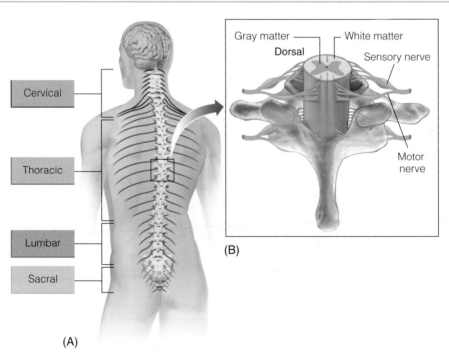

(A)

(B)

● FIGURE 1.8   The spinal cord. (A) The four sections of the spinal cord: cervical, thoracic, lumbar, and sacral. A spinal nerve exists at each vertebra of the spinal column. (B) A cross-section of the spinal cord. Sensory information enters the spinal cord through the dorsal region, and nerves exit through the ventral region to control muscle movements. The gray matter consists largely of cell bodies. The surrounding white matter is composed of myelinated axons that carry information to other levels of the spinal cord and the brain.
© 2011 Cengage Learning

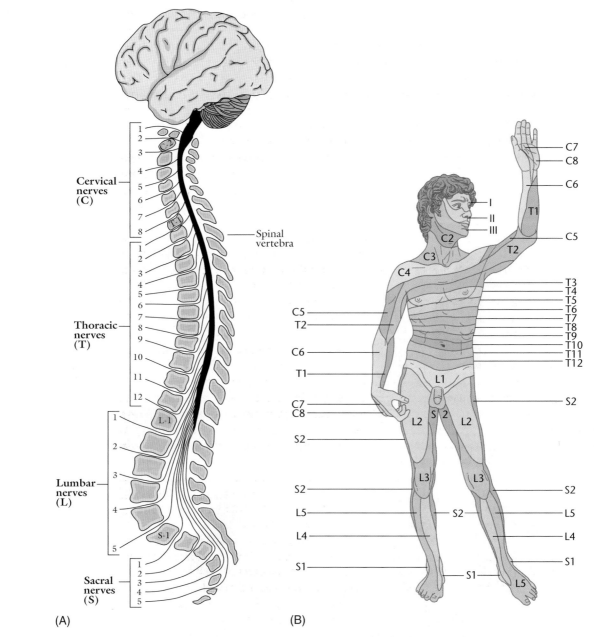

● FIGURE 1.9   (A) Shown on the left are the positions where each of the spinal nerves exits the spinal column. (B) On the right is a map indicating which sensory nerve carries information from that portion of the body to the spinal cord. Determining the locations of sensory loss after trauma to the spinal cord by using such maps helps medical personnel determine the level of the spinal cord at which the damage occurred. Information from the face reaches the brain via the cranial nerves. © 2011 Cengage Learning

rate. Because the medulla serves these functions, damage to it can be fatal. One common accompaniment of either diffuse or specific brain damage is swelling of the entire brain. When this swelling puts enough pressure on the medulla to interfere with its functions, death can result.

Fourth, the medulla is home to part of a set of the neurons known as the **reticular activating system**. These neurons receive input from the cranial nerves and project diffusely to many other regions of the brain. The reticular activating system is important for

overall arousal and attention, as well as for regulation of sleep-wake cycles. Chapter 11 discusses this system in more detail.

■ Cerebellum

Located posterior to the medulla (see Figure 1.7) is the **cerebellum**, a brain region important for the regulation of muscle tone and guidance of motor activity. In large part, it is the region of the brain that allows a pianist to play a piece of music seamlessly or a pitcher to throw a

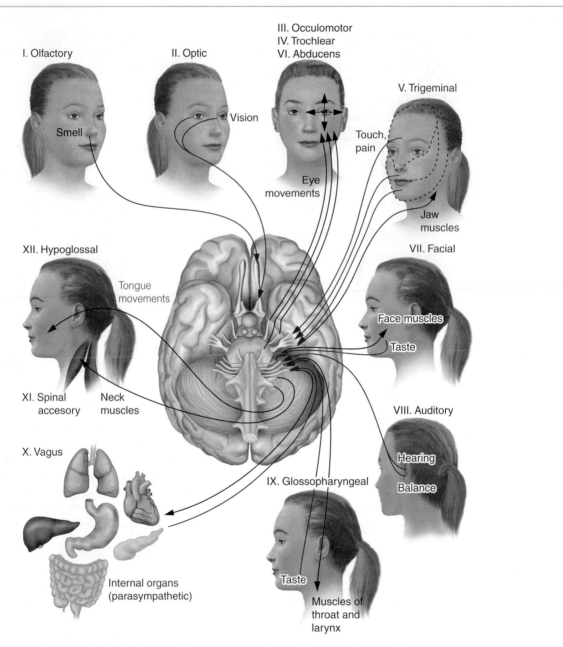

● FIGURE 1.10   Locations at which the 12 cranial nerves enter (sensory) or exit (motor) the brain, and each nerve's functions.   A ventral (bottom) surface view of the brain is shown on the left. The majority of cranial nerves enter at the medulla and the pons. The purple lines represent sensory functions; the red lines show motor functions. Some cranial nerves are sensory only, some are motor only, and some are mixed. © 2010 Cengage Learning

ball fluidly. Damage to the cerebellum does not result in paralysis, but instead interferes with precision of movement and disrupts balance and equilibrium. The classic test used to detect cerebellar damage is one in which the doctor asks a person to alternate between touching his or her own nose, and then the doctor's. Although a person with cerebellar damage can follow this command, the path taken by the hand from one nose to the other will be imprecise and jagged. Damage to the cerebellum also contributes to lack of balance and motor control. A common manifestation of temporary disruption to the cerebellum is seen in *punch-drunk syndrome,* in which an

individual temporarily loses balance and coordination after sustaining a hard blow to the head.

Traditionally, a specific region of the cerebellum, the *lateral cerebellum*, was thought to be primarily involved in motor control and the learning of motor skills (e.g., the skill of precisely serving a tennis ball). More recent evidence suggests that this brain structure may also be linked to certain aspects of cognitive processing, allowing for fluidity and precision in mental processes (Akshoomoff & Courchesne, 1992). The lateral cerebellum may also be critical for timing information, acting as the brain's internal clock (Ivry, 1997).

■ Pons

Directly superior to the medulla and anterior to the cerebellum, we find the many-functioned **pons** (● Figure 1.11). Because of its anatomical location, it acts as the main connective bridge from the rest of the brain to the cerebellum. It is the point of synapse (point of connection between neurons) of some of the cranial nerves, and it acts as an important center for the control of certain types of eye movements and for vestibular functions (e.g., balance). Finally, the pons is the site of the *superior olive,* one of the points through which auditory information is relayed from the ear to the brain. At the superior olive, information from both ears converges, and this convergence allows comparison of the information received from each ear. Such comparison is thought to be important for localization of sounds in the horizontal dimension (Masterton, 1992; also see Chapter 6).

■ Midbrain

Superior to the pons lies the **midbrain** (see Figure 1.11). Like the pons and medulla, this region of the brain contains the nuclei of the cells that form some of the cranial nerves. The midbrain also contains two important structures on its dorsal side, the **inferior colliculus** and the **superior colliculus**, which play a role in orienting to stimuli in the auditory and visual modalities, respectively (● Figures 1.11 and 1.12).

Like the superior olive, the inferior colliculus is a relay point for auditory information as it travels from the ear to the cortex; thus, it appears to be involved in sound localization. However, it also contributes to reflexive movements of the head and eyes in response to sound, which provide us with the rudimentary ability to orient toward salient auditory stimuli.

The superior colliculus is the visual system's equivalent of the inferior colliculus, allowing us to perceive and orient toward large moving objects in the periphery. So, for example, if a car comes speeding toward you from the far left, the superior colliculus signals that something is approaching. The superior colliculus also aids in guiding your eyes toward that large object so that it falls in the center of your vision, a process known as *foveation.* The midbrain visual system cannot, however, make fine discriminations between visual objects (e.g., recognize the object as a car); only after the object is in central vision can it be identified precisely by other brain regions that are specialized for object recognition. The role of the superior colliculus in orienting toward certain types of visual information and guiding the eyes toward objects of interest is revisited in Chapters 6, 8, and 11.

■ Hypothalamus

The general role of the **hypothalamus** (● Figure 1.13) is to control behaviors that help the body satisfy its needs so it can maintain equilibrium. When organisms

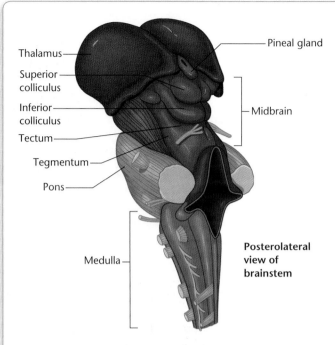

● FIGURE 1.11   Brain stem, including medulla, pons, and midbrain. Note that the cerebellum has been cut away.
© 2009 Cengage Learning

have a particular need, they generally emit a behavior designed to bring the body back to a stable state, known as *homeostasis.* For example, when hungry or thirsty, a person will engage in behaviors that lead to ingesting food or drink; if cold, the person will search for a blanket or a warmer location. The hypothalamus provides the signals telling the brain that these sorts of behaviors are needed.

Let's now examine the role of the hypothalamus in each of a variety of such functions in more detail. One of the main functions of the hypothalamus is to aid in feeding and drinking behavior. For example, research with animals has demonstrated that damage to the ventromedial region of the hypothalamus causes an animal to eat more than is required to maintain a normal body weight; such behavior eventually leads to obesity. Likewise, *lesions* (wounds, damage, or injuries) to dorsal and lateral regions of the hypothalamus can interfere with water intake. Another main function of the hypothalamus is to aid in regulation of body temperature. Some neurons in both anterior and posterior sections of the hypothalamus detect changes in the temperature of the skin or blood and therefore function like a thermostat.

The hypothalamus also has an intimate relationship with the *hormonal system,* which is the system that releases chemical messengers to be carried throughout the body by means of the bloodstream, so as to exert their influence on target organs far from their point of production. The hypothalamus secretes some hormones itself, and it also produces other factors that regulate activity of additional brain regions that secrete hormones. The connections of the hypothalamus with

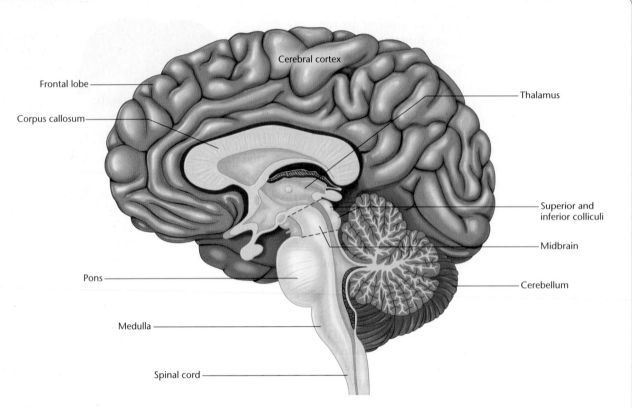

● **FIGURE 1.12   Location of the superior and inferior colliculi.** As shown here in blue in this sagittal slice, the inferior and superior colliculi are located on the dorsal surface of the midbrain, nestled below the cerebral cortex and in front of the cerebellum. These structures help in orienting toward items in the auditory and visual modalities, respectively. © 2009 Cengage Learning

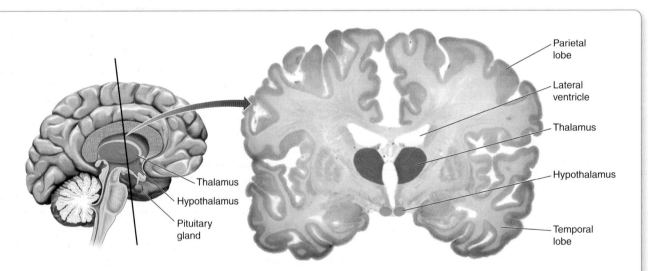

● **FIGURE 1.13   The diencephalon.** The diencephalon is comprised of the hypothalamus and the thalamus. The hypothalamus is involved in controlling behaviors so the body can maintain its equilibrium. It does so, in part, by its connections with the hormonal system, in particular the pituitary gland. The thalamus is a major relay point for information going to and coming from the cortex. The slice shows the position of the structures comprising the diencephalon in relation to the lateral ventricle above it and regions of the cerebral cortex surrounding it. © 2010 Cengage Learning

the pituitary gland are an example of the latter. This linkage of the hypothalamus to the hormonal system helps explain its role in sexual behavior, daily (diurnal) rhythms, and fight-or-flight reactions.

Certain regions of the hypothalamus, such as the *sexually dimorphic nucleus,* vary in size between males and females. This difference is seen in many mammalian species, including humans. Other regions of the hypothalamus, such as the *suprachiasmatic nucleus,* play a role in diurnal rhythms. The suprachiasmatic nucleus receives input from the retina and, in response, controls fluctuations in the release of hormones during the day. Finally, lateral areas of the hypothalamus are important for activating bodily responses such as the fight-or-flight reactions that are automatic for animals in threatening situations.

◼ Thalamus

Along with the hypothalamus, the **thalamus** (see Figure 1.13) is part of the **diencephalon**. It is a large relay center for almost all sensory information coming into the cortex and almost all motor information leaving it. A **relay center** is a brain region in which the neurons from one area of the brain synapse onto neurons that then go on to synapse somewhere else in the brain. Often, the pattern of connections between neurons at relay centers serves to reorganize information before it is sent elsewhere in the nervous system. For example, in the visual system, information from the retina comes, via the optic tract, to synapse onto the **lateral geniculate nucleus** of the thalamus. One layer of the lateral geniculate, the *magnocellular layer,* tends to receive input from cells that are extremely sensitive to low levels of light and quite insensitive to color, whereas the *parvocellular layer* receives information from cells that are color sensitive and need higher levels of light to function. Thus, at this relay point, signals are organized on their way to the brain so that information about color and light intensity are segregated (Zeki & Shipp, 1988). Chapter 6 discusses this organization in more detail.

To give you a better sense of how certain brain regions, including the thalamus, act as relay centers, consider an analogy to the distribution of eggs laid by a group of chickens, each of which has a particular roost. In this case, eggs, rather than information, are being relayed from one point to another. Initially, each hen lays a set of eggs in her nest. These eggs are then sent down the conveyor belt toward the processing plant in a systematic order so that eggs laid by hens with roosts next to each other end up on the belt next to each other. However, as the eggs reach the plant, they are sorted into two piles on the basis of size; therefore, all the small eggs are packaged together and all the large ones are packaged together. Such a system preserves basic information about life in the henhouse (because eggs from hens with adjacent roosts get packaged next to each other), but nonetheless also sorts the information in a novel way (because the eggs are now segregated with regard to size).

The connections of the thalamus are extremely complicated, and understanding all of them could be a course (and textbook) unto itself. For our purposes, remember that the patterns of connections, both to and from the thalamus, are very specific. One particular region of the thalamus receives information from just one sensory system and projects to only one particular region of the cortex.

◼ Major Subcortical Systems

Two important neural systems reside mainly at the level of the midbrain and diencephalon: the basal ganglia, important for motor control, and the limbic system, important for emotions. Because many or all the structures in these systems are located in regions below the cerebral cortex, they are referred to as *subcortical* systems.

The **basal ganglia** consist of the *caudate nucleus,* the *putamen,* and the *globus pallidus,* all of which are structures located near the thalamus (● Figure 1.14). Degeneration or destruction of these areas leads to difficulty in motor control, generally characterized by involuntary movements. Damage to the globus pallidus leads to involuntary twisting and turning of the limbs. In contrast, damage to the caudate nucleus and putamen causes involuntary movements, such as tremors while the person is at rest, as well as the introduction of extra movements into a standard progression of voluntary movement such as walking. Chapter 5 discusses the role of these structures in motor behavior in much more detail.

The **limbic system** is a series of mainly subcortical structures initially believed to be a circuit for integrating emotional information between various parts of the nervous system. Scientists thought that these structures functioned mostly to process emotional information, by linking information from the sensory world and from an individual's internal state with information from the cortex. For example, if a small animal sees a larger one, it must integrate (1) information from its hypothalamus about fear, (2) information from its visual cortex identifying the large animal, and (3) information from the brain regions involved in memory that reminds the small animal whether previous encounters with this type of large animal were dangerous. Although the general concept of the limbic system has been retained, we know now that the structures comprising the limbic system play a much more complicated role in a variety of functions.

Limbic structures include the *amygdala,* the *hypothalamus,* the *cingulate cortex,* the *anterior thalamus,* the *mammillary body,* and the *hippocampus* (● Figure 1.15). We discuss the roles of these structures in more detail in later chapters. For example, the amygdala has been implicated in the control of fear and is thought to play a prominent role in emotional functioning, as discussed in Chapter 13. The hippocampus plays an important

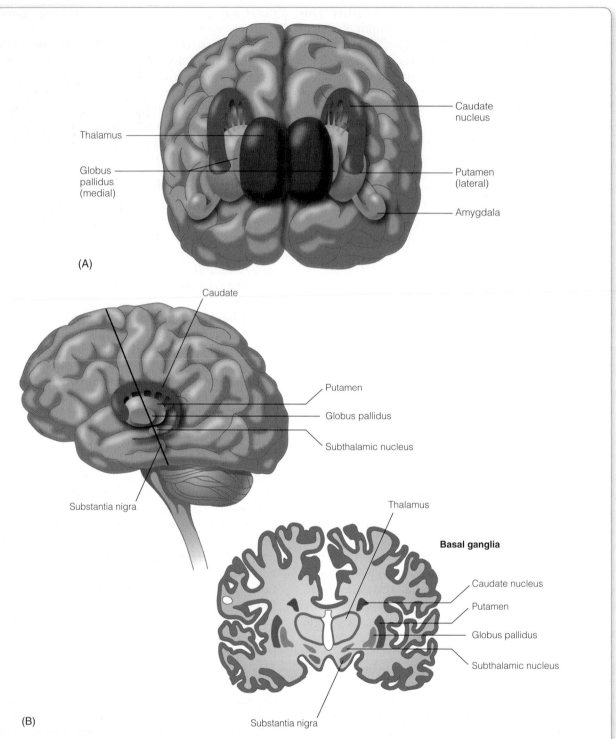

Thalamus

Globus pallidus (medial)

(A)

Caudate nucleus

Putamen (lateral)

Amygdala

Caudate

Putamen

Globus pallidus

Subthalamic nucleus

Substantia nigra

Thalamus

Basal ganglia

Caudate nucleus

Putamen

Globus pallidus

Subthalamic nucleus

(B)   Substantia nigra

● **FIGURE 1.14   The location of basal ganglia deep within the brain.** (A) View from the front of the brain, and (B) view from the side and in coronal view. The basal ganglia are comprised of the globus pallidus, the caudate nucleus, and the putamen as well as the associated subthalamic nucleus and substantia nigra. Notice how they are located lateral and ventral to the thalamus. Also note that the head of the caudate nucleus is anterior and that this structure wraps around to its tail, which is located next to the amygdala.
© 2010 Cengage Learning

role in memory, specifically the formation of new long-term memories, as described in Chapter 10, and the cingulate cortex has been implicated in motor control and in the selection of actions, as discussed in more detail in Chapters 5 and 11.

■ Cerebral Cortex

The cerebral cortex is the region that most often comes to mind when we think of the brain (see Figure 1.7). The cortex plays a primary role in most of the functions

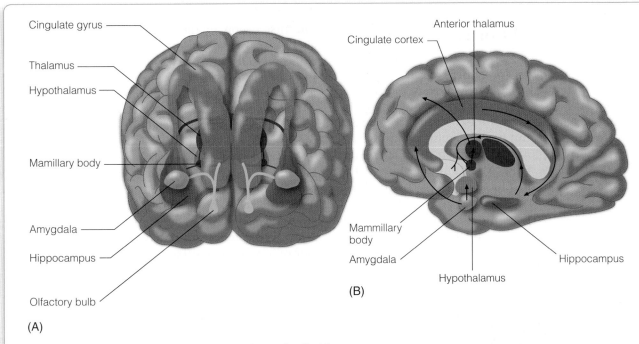

FIGURE 1.15   The structures that constitute the limbic system. The limbic system consists of the amygdala, the mammillary body, the cingulate cortex, the anterior thalamus, the hippocampus, and the hypothalamus. (A) The position of the limbic structures deep within the brain. (B) A diagram of the connectivity between different limbic regions illustrating how they form a system. © 2011 Cengage Learning

discussed in the remainder of this text, such as object recognition, spatial cognition, and attention. The cortex is divided into two physically separated halves, each called a **cerebral hemisphere**. Although at first glance these two hemispheres look similar, we learn in Chapter 4 that they differ in both function and anatomy. Each convolution, or bump, of the brain is called a **gyrus** (plural: gyri) and is basically a giant sheath of neurons wrapped around the other brain structures just discussed. These convolutions serve to pack more brain tissue into a smaller space, much as rolling your clothes allows you to get more of them into your suitcase. Each valley between the bumps is called a **sulcus** (plural: sulci), and if it is deep it is known as a **fissure**. Every brain has the same basic gyral pattern, just as every face has the same basic pattern (i.e., eyes above the nose, mouth below the nose). However, subtle individual variations exist in the gyral pattern, just as facial configuration varies (e.g., some people have wide-set eyes, whereas in others the eyes are close together). The major gyri and sulci of the brain and their names are shown on the inside front cover of your book (Figures A–D). They are located there so it will be easy for you to find the particular portions of the brain under discussion as you go through the book. Notice that the labels for the gyri are in black ink and those for the sulci are in red ink.

Three major fissures serve as prominent landmarks in the brain because they provide a means for conceptualizing distinctions in function between major brain regions. The first of these is the **central fissure**, sometimes called the *Rolandic fissure*, which separates each hemisphere of the brain in an anterior-posterior dimension. In general, areas of the brain in front of the central fissure are more involved in motor processing, whereas those behind are more involved in sensory processing. The second major fissure is the **Sylvian (lateral) fissure**, which separates each hemisphere of the brain in the dorsal-ventral dimension. This division (sometimes alternately called the *fissure of Sylvius*) is important because the area of the brain below the Sylvian fissure is the temporal lobe, which plays an important role in memory, emotion, and auditory processing. The third major fissure is the **longitudinal fissure**, which separates the right cerebral hemisphere from the left. This division is important because each hemisphere has a unique specialization with regard to both cognitive and emotional functioning.

These three major fissures also divide each hemisphere into four major regions, or lobes. The area in front of the central fissure is known as the **frontal lobe**. The area below the Sylvian fissure is the **temporal lobe**. The region directly behind the central fissure but above the Sylvian fissure is the **parietal lobe**. The remaining region of the brain behind the parieto-occipital sulcus is the **occipital lobe** (see Figure C on the inside front cover of the book: "Lateral view of the brain").

A Closer Look at the Cerebral Cortex

Because the cortex plays a prominent role in many functions that we think of as uniquely human, we examine it in more detail. We begin by briefly discussing the anatomical characteristics of the cortex and a system of how cortical regions can be distinguished on the basis of the pattern of cellular organization, often referred to as *cytoarchitectonics*. Then, we examine regions of the cortex according to the functions that each serves. We discuss both the areas of the brain that are important for receiving sensory information from the outside world, and also the areas that are important for controlling the motor output of the body. Finally, we examine an overview of the functions of the remaining areas of the cortex, most of which are devoted to cognitive and emotional function.

■ Cytoarchitectonic Divisions

Although all regions of cortex have five or six layers, or *laminae*, of cells, the relative thickness of each layer, as well as the size and the shape of cells within those layers, varies between brain regions. Neuroanatomists have identified areas of the cortex in which the laminar organization and nature of cells are similar. From these findings has emerged what is known as a **Brodmann map** (named after its creator), which divides the brain into distinct areas (shown on the inside back cover of your book in Figures A and B). Bear in mind that the boundaries on the Brodmann map are neither absolute nor always distinct. Sometimes they reflect smoother transitions; therefore, the borders may be considered "fuzzy."

Although the regions in the Brodmann map are defined entirely on the basis of anatomy, with no regard to function, in some cases regions with distinct cytoarchitectonic characteristics also have distinct functions. In other cases, the correlation between neuroanatomy and function is less clear. One of the main reasons to be familiar with the Brodmann map is that use of this system has become very popular with cognitive neuroscientists as a way to refer to particular regions of brain tissue. Chapter 3 discusses the explosion of research utilizing brain imaging techniques that are designed to determine which regions of the brain are physiologically active during performance of a specific task. To convey the location of these regions to the reader, scientists often refer to the activated brain region by means of the number assigned to that region on the Brodmann map. For example, *Broca's area*, a region of the left hemisphere that is important to speech output, is often referred to in Brodmann's terminology as area 44 (abbreviated as BA 44, for Brodmann Area 44). Alternatively, this same region could be called the *frontal opercular region* (see endpaper on the inside front cover, Figure C: "Lateral view of the brain").

■ Primary Sensory and Motor Cortices

The first region in the cortex to receive information about a particular sensory modality (e.g., visual information) is known as **primary sensory cortex**. The **primary motor cortex** is the region of the cortex that is the final exit point for neurons responsible for fine motor control of the body's muscles. The locations of the primary sensory areas and primary motor cortex are presented in ● Figure 1.16.

The organization of primary sensory regions is dictated by the physical attributes of the world to which our sensory receptors are sensitive. Let's use *audition* (the sense of hearing) to illustrate this point. In some alternative universe, we might have evolved so that the sensory receptors in the cochlea of the ear, known as *hair cells,* were organized to allow certain receptors to respond only to loud sounds and others only to soft sounds. However, in our world this is not the case. Rather, the hair cells in the cochlea of the ear are differentially sensitive to sounds of different frequencies (i.e., low tones vs. high tones), which we perceive as tones of different pitch. Thus, frequency is the attribute of auditory information that is coded by the nervous system. As we will learn in more detail in Chapter 6, the sensitivity of the sensory receptors to frequency is reflected in the organization of primary auditory cortex, in that some regions are active when high tones are heard and other regions are active when low tones are heard.

The primary sensory and motor areas share some general characteristics of organization that are worth noting now, although we leave discussion of the specifics of each system for Chapters 5 and 6. First, all these brain areas are organized so that specific attributes of the physical world are "mapped" onto brain tissue. For example, motor control of a specific region of the body is controlled by a specific region of primary motor cortex. Thus, movement of the index finger is controlled by one specific region of the motor cortex rather than by many areas. Second, these maps are distorted relative to the physical world. They appear to reflect the density of receptors (or effectors) within a system. For example, we have a much higher density of receptors at the fovea, the focal point of our vision, than for more lateral locations. Likewise, much more of the primary visual cortex is devoted to processing visual information from the central part of the visual world as compared with the periphery. Third, the mapping of the world onto brain tissue occurs in an upside-down and backward manner for vision, touch, and motor control. For example, information from the upper right-hand portion of the body or world is processed by primary sensory or motor cortex in the ventral portion of the left hemisphere.

Motor Cortex

The *primary motor cortex* resides directly in front of the central fissure in a long, narrow band called the *motor strip*. It begins deep within the longitudinal

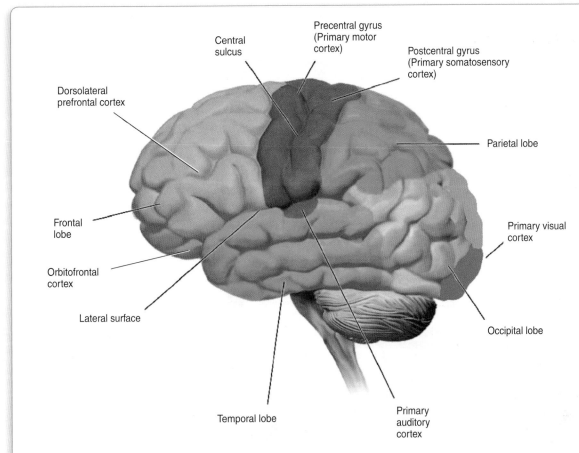

● FIGURE 1.16   Primary sensory and motor cortices. All the primary sensory areas are posterior to the central sulcus, whereas primary motor cortex lies anterior. The position of these primary sensory areas are shown in relation to the four major lobes of the brain: frontal, parietal, occipital, and temporal. © 2010 Cengage Learning

fissure, rises up to the top of the brain, and then continues down to the Sylvian fissure. It falls mainly within Brodmann area 4. Look at ● Figure 1.17C, which depicts the body regions that are controlled by each portion of the motor strip. This map is often referred to as the *homunculus,* meaning "little man." As you look at Figure 1.17C, note that a couple of features bear out the generalizations we just discussed. First, notice that the mapping of the body onto the brain is inverted both with regard to top and bottom and with regard to left and right. The left-right inversion occurs because the left motor strip controls the right side of the body and the right motor strip controls the left side of the body. The top-bottom inversion occurs because the area of the motor strip controlling the toes and feet is at the top end of the motor strip, actually within the longitudinal fissure, and the control of the face is most ventral on the lateral surface of the brain.

Second, notice that the mapping is distorted, in that the area of brain tissue devoted to control of a particular body part is disproportionate to the size of that body part. Notice which regions of the body have large amounts of cortex devoted to their control despite their relatively small size: the face, the larynx, the vocal cords, and the hands. As you may surmise, the distortion of the map depends, in large part, on the degree to which we have fine motor control of a body part. The body parts for which we have a large degree of fine motor control, such as the face and the hand, have a disproportionately larger area of brain tissue devoted to their control than do areas of the body for which we have little fine motor control, such as the thigh.

The functional significance of this distortion can be understood when we consider the extremely precise fine motor control needed to express emotion, speak, and manipulate objects—actions that are performed by the face, the vocal apparatus, and the hands, respectively. Hence, large sections of the motor cortex are devoted to control of these body regions. In comparison, we have little fine motor control of the muscles of our backs, so only a small region of the motor strip is devoted to their control, even though the back is one of the larger regions of the body.

What are the effects of damage to the primary motor cortex? Because the neurons in the motor cortex control the amount of force to be applied by muscles, damage

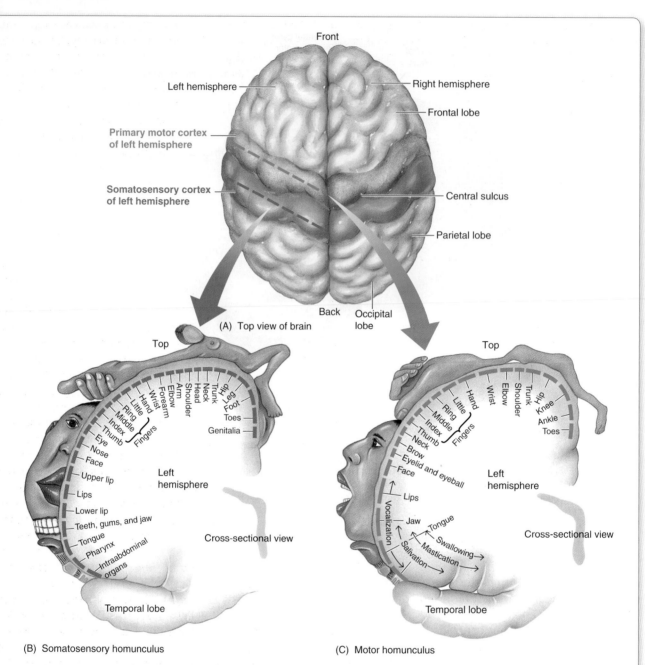

(A) Top view of brain

(B) Somatosensory homunculus

(C) Motor homunculus

● **FIGURE 1.17   Maps of the motor homunculus and the somotosensory homunculus.**
(A) Top view of the brain showing the location of primary motor cortex anterior to the central sulcus and
the primary somatosenory cortex posterior to the central sulcus. (B) Somatosensory homunculus. Notice
that the regions of the body for which we have fine tactile sensitivity, such as the hand and face, have a
large region of somatosensory cortex devoted to them. In contrast, large body parts for which we have
relatively poor tactile sensitivity, such as the trunk, have a relatively small region of the cortex devoted to
them. (C) Motor homunculus. Like the somatosensory homunculus, the motor homunculus is distorted,
with regions of brain tissue that control body parts for which we have fine motor control, such as the hand
and fingers, occupying larger regions of cortex than those for which we have poorer fine motor control,
such as the leg. Also notice that although the distortion is similar to that of the somatosensory homunculus,
it is not identical. © 2010 Cengage Learning

to primary motor cortex leads to muscle weakness on the contralateral side of the body. For example, damage to dorsal regions of the motor strip results in weakness of the bottom part of the body (recall the upside-down orientation of the homunculus), whereas damage to ventral regions of the motor strip often leads to weakness in face and arm muscles. As discussed in Chapter 5, the body has multiple systems for muscle control. Therefore, damage to the motor cortex does not cause total paralysis, because the other motor systems can compensate for the damage. However, the ability to move muscles independently of one another is lost, as are the abilities required for fine motor control, such as is needed to grasp something between the thumb and forefinger. When massive unilateral destruction to the motor strip occurs along with damage to the basal ganglia (as often occurs after stroke), paralysis on the contralateral side of the body is observed and results in a deficit known as **hemiplegia**.

Somatosensory Cortex

The *primary somatosensory cortex* is the portion of the cortex that receives information about tactile stimulation, **proprioception** (the perception of the position of body parts and their movements), and pressure and pain sensations from internal organs and muscles. It is located directly posterior to the central fissure in Brodmann areas 1, 2, and 3.

The skin contains various nerve endings, or *receptors*, that are sensitive to various aspects of tactile information, such as pain, pressure, vibration, and temperature. This information travels to the cortex along two main routes. Crude tactile information, along with information about pain and temperature, is sent to the cortex by neurons that synapse at dorsal regions of the spinal cord. From there information is carried to the thalamus and then to the cortex. Information about fine touch and proprioception enters the spinal column but does not synapse until the medulla, from which point it crosses over and is carried to the thalamus and subsequently onto the cortex.

Like the motor homunculus, the map of the body onto the primary somatosensory cortex is inverted left-to-right and top-to-bottom. The distortion of body parts in the somatosensory map is proportional to the density of touch receptors. In general, areas that have a high density of tactile receptors have large areas of the somatosensory strip devoted to receiving information from them, and areas of the body that have relatively few tactile receptors have relatively small regions of brain tissue devoted to receiving information from them. The mapping of the body's sense of touch onto the somatosensory cortex is illustrated in Figure 1.17B.

If you compare this map with that of the motor strip in Figure 1.17C, you can see that the map of somatosensory cortex looks similar but is not identical to that of the motor homunculus. The differences clearly arise because what is being mapped in the somatosensory strip is sensitivity of touch, not precision of motor control. Nevertheless, striking similarities are apparent. These similarities should not be surprising, because the parts of the body for which we have fine motor control, such as the hands, are the same areas for which we need a fine sense of touch. Agile manipulation of an object requires not only that we be able to move our hands and fingers, but also that our sense of touch be equally fine, so that we have tactile feedback on which to base our movements. If this relationship is not intuitively obvious, consider, for instance, how difficult it is to deftly manipulate something like your car keys in the winter when you are wearing a pair of gloves and your sense of touch is reduced.

What are the consequences of damage to the somatosensory strip? Rather than obliterating all sense of touch, such damage impairs fine discriminations of touch on the side of the body contralateral to the damaged primary somatosensory cortex. So, for example, if you put a piece of cloth in the hand of an individual who sustained damage to the somatosensory strip, that person would know that something had been placed there but would have difficulty determining whether the cloth was velvet or burlap. Furthermore, if touched multiple times in quick succession, that person likely would have trouble determining the number of times she had been touched. Finally, if that individual was touched in two places near each other (e.g., two places on the back of the palm about 5 millimeters [mm] apart), she would have difficulty knowing that the touch had occurred in two separate places. This type of discrimination is known as *two-point discrimination,* and our sensitivity to it varies depending on the body part. The distance required to perceive two points as distinct is smallest for the hands and fingers (with the largest number of receptors) and largest for the shoulders, thighs, and calves (with the smallest number of receptors).

One interesting aspect of the somatosensory map of the body is that it appears to provide a means for understanding some phenomena associated with *phantom limb pain,* a symptom common after the loss of a limb. With phantom limb pain, the person usually perceives the missing limb to be in a particular position and may also perceive that it moves. In addition to pain, the person may also perceive other sensations, such as itching. Reorganization of the primary somatosensory region after limb loss can also lead to some atypical feelings. For example, in the case of a person who has lost a hand, touch on his face leads him to report that he feels the phantom hand. Although at first such a claim may seem odd, it really is not if you think about the organization of the somatosensory strip. By referring to Figure 1.17B, you can see that the primary somatosensory region that receives tactile information from the hand is adjacent to the area that receives information from the face. In this person, the reorganization of the somatosensory strip probably led neurons in regions previously devoted exclusively to receiving tactile information from the hand to interact with neurons

IN FOCUS: Discovery of the "Homunculus"

Our knowledge about the organization of the motor cortex is derived in large part from the search for a therapeutic intervention for a particular disease—epilepsy. Although scientists knew from the late 1800s that the left motor strip controlled the right side of the body and vice versa, the precise nature of the homunculus was revealed only in the course of attempting to obtain a better understanding of epilepsy (Novelly, 1992). Observations of a particular type of epileptic seizure known as *Jacksonian seizure* (named after the famous neurologist John Hughlings Jackson) revealed that the body was mapped onto the brain in an orderly fashion. During an **epileptic seizure**, neurons in the brain fire in an abnormal manner typified by great bursts, or volleys, of firing, often called *spikes*. In Jacksonian seizures, the tremors follow an orderly pattern, starting in one body part, such as the leg, and moving systematically to the trunk, then to the arms and face. Such a pattern indicates that the seizure begins in one part of the motor strip and proceeds along it in an orderly fashion.

In the mid-20th century, the creation of therapeutic interventions to reduce and control epilepsy dramatically revealed the degree of distortion of the brain map of the motor area. Working at the Montreal Neurological Institute, Wilder Penfield pioneered the use of surgical interventions to excise (remove) regions of brain tissue that cause epileptic activity (Penfield & Rasmussen, 1950). Even today, when seizures originate from a specific brain region, often referred to as an *epileptic focus*, and cannot be controlled by drugs, physicians sometimes remove brain tissue at the focus. The rationale for this intervention is that continued seizure activity will recruit otherwise healthy

neurons and cause them to become more prone to seizure activity. Although the neurosurgeon wants to remove the region of brain tissue that is misfiring, he or she must ensure that neither the incisions required to reach the focus nor the removal of the misfiring tissue will have devastating effects. Therefore, the neurosurgeon needs to map out precisely which regions of the brain control which functions. This is especially true for the motor strip, because excision of portions of it can leave a person with severe muscle weakness on the contralateral side of the body.

Let's move into the operating room to see how the mapping is performed. The patient is lying on the operating table, covered with surgical sheets that form a tent of sorts, with one open side around the patient's head. The patient's face protrudes from under one side of the tent, whereas the surgeon is situated on the other side at the opening of the tent. Procedure in this operating room is different from what you might expect: Instead of an unconscious patient on the operating table, this patient is alert and talking! Because the brain has no pain receptors, only local anesthetics are used as the surgeon removes a piece of skull to expose the brain underneath. After the brain is exposed, the surgeon places a tiny piece of metal, known as an *electrode* and connected to a very fine wire, on the brain. Then a sheet with a number is placed on the brain, adjacent to the electrode. Let's assume that the surgeon starts by placing the electrode directly in front of the central fissure at the most dorsal portion of the brain. Although the patient is lying perfectly still, as soon as the surgeon runs some current through the electrode, the patient's leg begins to twitch involuntarily! When the current

is turned off, the twitching stops. The neurosurgeon then announces, "Leg movement at position 4" and moves the electrode more ventrally, leaving the marker in place. She or he now places another marker number on the brain and stimulates at the next spot. The patient's thigh begins to twitch. The neurosurgeon continues in this fashion until the whole motor strip is identified.

The need for such detailed, individualized mapping is obvious if you consider that each individual's brain is as distinct as each person's face. Although neurosurgeons know that the motor strip lies in front of the central fissure, they do not know exactly where it is in any single brain. Consider by analogy the organization of the face. Just as we know that the eyes are always located above the nose, so the neurosurgeon knows that the motor strip is in front of the central fissure. However, this landmark alone is not enough, just as knowing where a person's nose is located does not tell you exactly where his or her eyes are situated. Likewise, precise mapping is needed to determine the extent and range of the motor strip.

In addition to mapping the motor area, a neurosurgeon will also map the primary somatosensory cortex during surgery. In this case, the active cooperation of the patient is even more critical. Only a conscious patient can convey to the surgeon where the sensations, such as a tingle, a tickle, or an itch, are being felt as different regions of the somatosensory strip are stimulated. This mapping technique, originally designed to aid the neurosurgeon in therapeutic interventions for epilepsy, has provided extremely useful information about the organization of the primary motor and somatosensory areas, as well as language areas.

that receive information from the face (Ramachandran, Rogers-Ramachandran, & Steward, 1992).

Visual Cortex

The *primary visual cortex* is the first region of the cortex that processes visual information. It is located in Brodmann area 17 in the occipital lobe (● Figure 1.18A). We leave for Chapter 6 a more detailed discussion of how information gets from the eye to the brain. For now, we

will just highlight some basic attributes of this pathway that are important for understanding the mapping of the visual world onto the primary visual cortex.

To understand the organization of the visual system, take a look at ● Figure 1.18B. When you look straight ahead, the information to the right of fixation, known as the **right visual field**, projects to the left half of the retinas of both your eyes. Information to the left of fixation, known as the **left visual field**, projects to

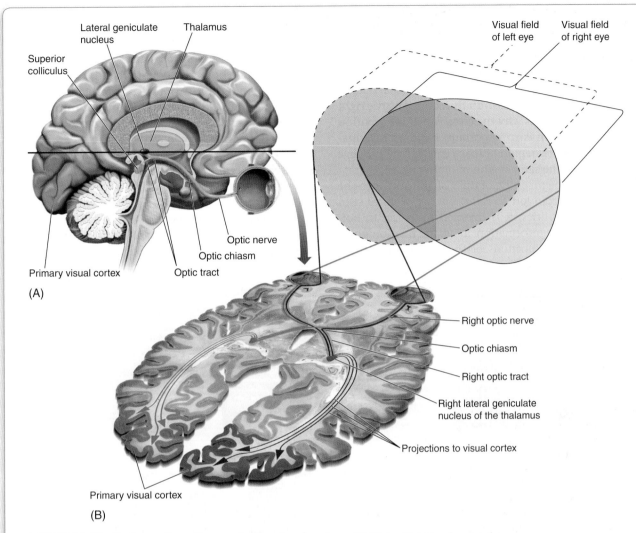

(A)

(B)

● **FIGURE 1.18   Pathway from the eye to the visual cortex.** (A) Midsagittal slice showing the location of the primary visual cortex of the left hemisphere. (B) Here the right visual field is depicted in blue and the left visual field in red. Information from each visual field reaches both eyes, but at the optic chiasm there is a partial crossing of information. The result is that all information from the left visual field projects to the right lateral geniculate nucleus of the thalamus and subsequently to the right primary visual cortex. Likewise, all information from the right visual field projects to the left lateral geniculate and subsequently to the left primary visual cortex. © 2010 Cengage Learning

the right half of the retinas of both your eyes. Except for information in the far periphery of the visual world, all visual information reaches both eyes. The far peripheral portion of the left side of the visual world is detected only by the left eye (in part because the nose precludes the right eye from perceiving that part of the visual world); likewise, the far right side is detected only by the right eye. However, ultimately information from the right visual field is directed solely to the primary visual cortex of the left hemisphere, and information from the left visual field projects only to the primary visual cortex of the right hemisphere.

How does this occur? Information from the inside half of each retina, known as the *nasal hemiretina* (because this half of the retina is near your nose), crosses the midline of the body at the **optic chiasm** and projects to contralateral lateral geniculate nucleus in the thalamus.

In contrast, information from the outside, or *temporal, hemiretina* projects to the ipsilateral lateral geniculate. This aspect of visual system wiring is important because at the lateral geniculate, for the first time, information from one side of space is confined to one half of the brain, and information from the other side of space is confined to the other side of the brain. From the lateral geniculate, information then projects back to the ipsilateral visual cortex (see Chapter 6 for more details).

Because of the organization of the visual system, determining whether a difficulty in vision arises from a problem in the eye or a problem in the brain is relatively easy. If the source of the problem is in the eye, the world will look different depending on whether it is being viewed by only the right or left eye. For example, if part of the retina of the left eye is damaged, the visual problem will be noticeable when viewing the world with just the left eye open, but there will be no problem when just the right eye is open. In contrast, if the problem resides in the brain, the problem is identical no matter which eye is open, because *all* information from a specific region of the visual world converges on the same region of the lateral geniculate or primary visual cortex, regardless of whether it was initially received by the right eye or the left. (This is why the crossover of information at the optic chiasm is so important: it allows information from a specific region of space detected by *each* eye to converge on the same region of brain tissue.)

Not only is the mapping of the visual world onto the brain reversed from left to right, but, as we have seen with other modalities, it is inverted from top to bottom as well. Thus, information above the fixation point projects to ventral portions of the visual cortex, and information below the fixation point projects to dorsal portions of the visual cortex.

Destruction of visual cortex results in an inability to perceive light-dark contrast. If the entire occipital cortex of only one hemisphere is damaged, no visual information can be detected in the contralateral visual field. This condition is known as an **homonymous hemianopsia**. Sometimes just the dorsal or ventral portion of occipital cortex is damaged, in which case just one quadrant of the visual world is lost, a disorder known as **quadranopsia**. In other cases, only small portions of the visual cortex are damaged, resulting in **scotomas**, particular regions of the visual field in which light-dark contrast cannot be detected.

To determine how well you understand the organization of the visual system, take a look at ● Figure 1.19.

(A)   Normal vision

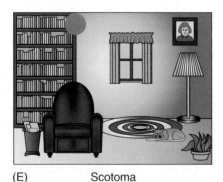

(B)   Quadranopsia

(C)   Homonymous hemianopsia

(D) Far left peripheral visual field deficit

(E)   Scotoma

(F)   Quadranopsia

● **FIGURE 1.19   Visual field disorders.** (A) The visual world as it appears to an individual with an intact visual system. Where would the damage be located to create the views in (B), (C), (D), (E), and (F)?
© 2011 Cengage Learning

Answers:
(B) Ventral regions of the left occipital lobe. (C) all regions of right occipital lobe. (D) damage to the left eye, (E) damage to a small portion of the ventral region of the right occipital lobe. (F) damage to the dorsal region of the left occipital lobe.

Each picture shows a view of the visual world as it appears to a person with damage in a particular portion of the visual system. Try to determine the location of the lesion in the visual system for each situation shown.

Auditory Cortex

The human auditory system is sensitive to sound, which is essentially pressure waves in the air. The physical energy in sound waves causes vibration of the eardrum and the bones in the ear. These vibrations are transformed into pressure waves in a liquid in the cochlea, which contains hair cells that transduce pressure waves into a neural signal. Chapter 6 discusses the route from the ear to the brain in more detail.

For now, it is important to know that unlike other sensory systems, in which information from one side of the body projects solely to the contralateral hemisphere, the auditory system is organized so that there are both ipsilateral and contralateral projections from the ear to the brain. Therefore, auditory information received at the right ear projects to both the left and right hemispheres. The primary auditory cortex of the human brain is located in the superior portion of the posterior temporal lobe in an area called **Heschl's gyrus**, which is located in Brodmann area 41.

Like other primary sensory areas, the *primary auditory cortex* has a specific organization, described as **tonotopic**, meaning that it is organized with regard to the frequency of a tone. In the auditory cortex, information from cells that all respond maximally to the same frequency converge on the same region of cortex. The mapping of auditory cortex is such that the lowest tones are processed rostrally and laterally and tones of increasing frequency are processed more caudally and medially (● Figure 1.20).

Unilateral damage to the primary auditory cortex does not impair the ability to perceive all sound, because of the redundancy provided by both crossed and uncrossed connections in the auditory system. If primary auditory cortex in the right hemisphere is damaged, primary auditory cortex in the left hemisphere can still process sound from both ears, because it receives information both ipsilaterally and contralaterally. So, what types of deficits are observed after damage is sustained by auditory cortex in one hemisphere? First, the softest intensity that can be perceived—that is, the *sound threshold*—becomes higher contralateral to the damaged hemisphere. In addition, the ability to perceive the location of a sound becomes poorer for the contralateral side of space.

If you have had a course in physiological psychology or perception, this finding should not be surprising. The mechanisms used to determine the location of a sound involve a comparison of the difference in the intensity and time at which auditory information arrives at each ear. Quite simply, if a sound is located closer to your right ear than to your left, the sound will be louder at the right ear (and will arrive there sooner).

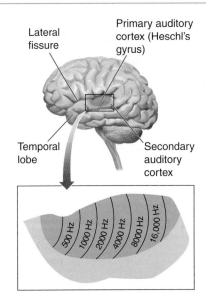

■ **FIGURE 1.20   Location of primary auditory cortex and its organization.** The primary auditory cortex is located within the Sylvian (lateral) fissure. Its organization is tonotopic, with low-frequency tones processed more rostrally and also closer to the scalp, whereas high-frequency tones are processed more caudally and more deeply within the cortex. © 2010 Cengage Learning

Because unilateral damage to primary auditory cortex disrupts the ability to judge the loudness of sounds, you can see why individuals with such damage have difficulty localizing the source of a sound.

Olfactory and Gustatory Cortex

Our brains also have the ability to detect chemical substances in our environment, either those carried in the air, which are detected by the nose, or those contained in the food we eat, which are detected by the tongue. Our sense of smell comes from receptors in the nasal mucosa that send information about odors to the **olfactory bulb**. Each of the two bulbs (one in each hemisphere) is a thin strand of neural tissue located directly below the frontal lobe (● Figure 1.21). From the olfactory bulb, information is projected in one of two directions. One pathway, which probably mediates our emotional responses to smell, travels to various parts of the limbic system. Another projection goes via the medial dorsal thalamus to orbitofrontal regions, which can hence be considered *primary olfactory cortex.*

Olfaction is unique in humans because it is the only sensory system in which information is conveyed ipsilaterally: Information received in the right nostril is sent to the right olfactory bulb, and information received in the left nostril is sent to the left olfactory bulb. Unlike the visual and auditory systems, in which we know that light-dark contrast and sound frequency, respectively, are the critical dimensions of the sensory world that the nervous system processes, the basic

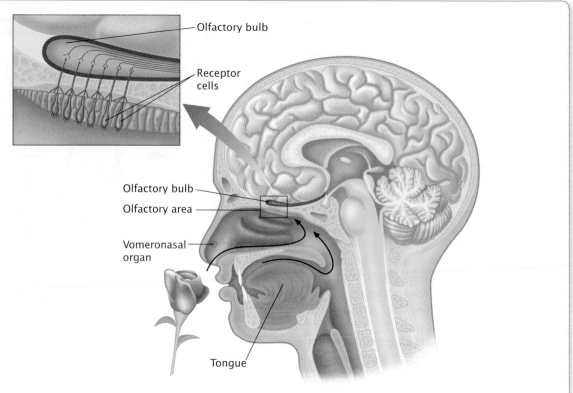

Olfactory bulb

Receptor cells

Olfactory bulb

Olfactory area

Vomeronasal organ

Tongue

● **FIGURE 1.21   The olfactory system.** Human olfactory receptors reside in the nasal cavity where they receive airborne chemicals through the nostril. Their axons form the olfactory nerve, which sends information to the olfactory bulb. © 2011 Cengage Learning

dimension by which smell is mapped onto the nervous system is unknown. What we do know, however, is that damage to primary olfactory cortex impairs odor discrimination in humans.

Our sense of taste comes from receptors in the tongue, known as *taste buds*. Like information from olfactory receptors, the information received by the taste buds and sent to the brain divides into two major branches, one going to portions of the limbic system and the other going to the primary sensory cortex (● Figure 1.22). Primary sensory cortex for taste is located in the anterior portion of a region called the *insula*, which is tucked inside the fold of the Sylvian (lateral) fissure. It probably should not surprise you that information from our sensory receptors of smell and taste go not only to primary sensory cortex but also to portions of the limbic system that are involved in emotional processing. Think, for example, about how one refers to an unpleasant situation as "distasteful" or a dubious proposal or plan as "smelling rotten."

At this point, we have discussed how sensory information is initially received and organized in the cortex. After processing by primary sensory regions, the information is relayed to *secondary sensory cortex*, which, like the primary sensory regions, processes information from only one sensory modality. However, secondary sensory cortex has a more specialized organization.

For example, more than 30 regions of secondary visual cortex have been identified, each of which varies in its sensitivity to important visual attributes such as color, orientation, and motion. However, primary and secondary sensory cortices account for only a small proportion of the overall mass of the cortex. Next, we present an overview of the type of processing performed by the remainder of the cortex.

■ **Association Areas**

An area of the brain where information from multiple modalities is processed is known as an **association area**. As we shall see, these regions of the brain support the abilities that we tend to think of as distinctly human, such as language, compassion, and foresight. Because the occipital lobe is mainly involved in processing visual information, it does not serve as large an associative function as the other three major lobes of the brain. We now turn to a brief overview of the many functions performed by each of these three lobes: the frontal, the parietal, and the temporal.

Frontal Lobe

Researchers and clinicians generally describe the frontal lobe as having three distinct regions: the *primary motor region* (previously discussed), the *premotor region*, and the *prefrontal region*. Prefrontal regions are often further

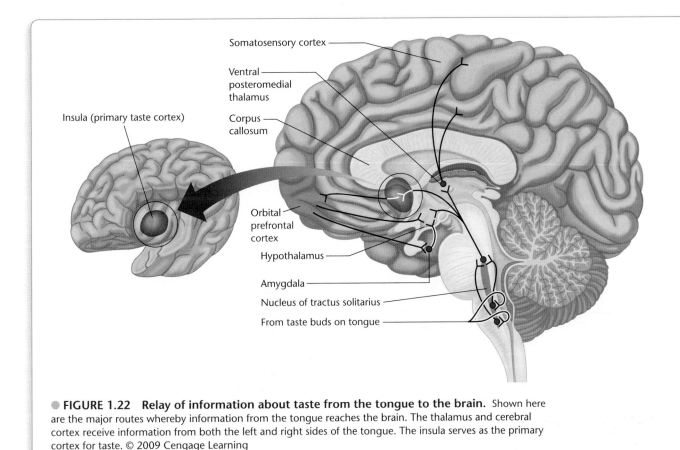

● **FIGURE 1.22** **Relay of information about taste from the tongue to the brain.** Shown here are the major routes whereby information from the tongue reaches the brain. The thalamus and cerebral cortex receive information from both the left and right sides of the tongue. The insula serves as the primary cortex for taste. © 2009 Cengage Learning

divided into dorsolateral, orbital, and medial regions (● Figure 1.23). The distinction among these regions is based on major cytoarchitectonic subdivisions. Recent evidence suggests that these regions may play very different roles in mental functioning. Although we will talk about these subdivisions in more detail later, it is important to note here that dorsolateral regions have been implicated in memory and attentional processing, orbital regions in emotional processing, and medial regions in judgment, decision making, and the detection of errors.

Frontal regions are often considered the source of some of the most uniquely human abilities. A good generalization about the role of frontal regions is that they are associated with the planning, guidance, and evaluation of behavior. Just as the head of a corporation oversees its day-to-day operations and plans long-term goals for it, the frontal lobes are considered the "executive" of the brain. Not only are the frontal regions important for organizing behavior coherently, but research suggests that they may also allow us to extrapolate forward in time, enabling us to predict and consider the future consequences of our current behavior.

The loss of these abilities can be profound. For example, individuals with frontal lobe dysfunction may exhibit little decrement in performance when given standardized IQ tests that assess fact knowledge and academic skills, such as knowing the definitions of

words, understanding how to solve arithmetic problems, knowing how to put together jigsaw puzzles, and so forth. Yet, they may be unable to successfully make a simple trip to the grocery store to get missing ingredients for a recipe or to improvise making the dish without them.

One of the most striking problems in people with frontal lobe damage is difficulty organizing behavior to reach a goal. This can take many forms. Some problems arise from an inability to correctly sequence behavior. Although people with frontal lobe damage may know the components of or steps in a process, they are unable to put the steps together in a coherent manner to achieve a goal. Thus, in making an omelet, a patient with frontal lobe damage might beat the eggs, place them in the skillet, turn up the heat, and then add the butter. As this example illustrates, the individual knows that making an omelet requires eggs, grease, and heat, but cannot organize these components in a systematic way to reach the desired endpoint. Such difficulties also extend to memory. For example, individuals with frontal lobe damage are unable to determine which of two items in a sequence occurred more recently (Milner, Corsi, & Leonard, 1991), even though they can clearly distinguish between items that appeared in a sequence and those that did not (Milner & Petrides, 1984). Moreover, if you show individuals with frontal lobe damage a series of items in which some items randomly appear on

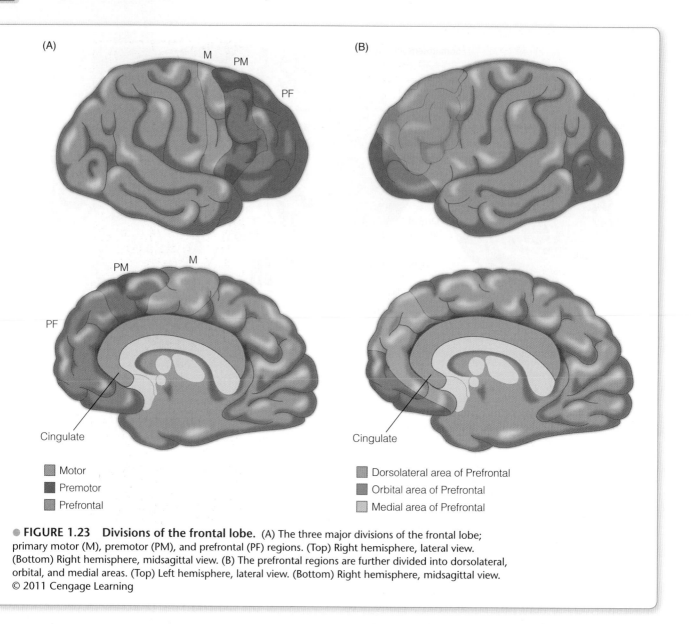

● **FIGURE 1.23   Divisions of the frontal lobe.** (A) The three major divisions of the frontal lobe; primary motor (M), premotor (PM), and prefrontal (PF) regions. (Top) Right hemisphere, lateral view. (Bottom) Right hemisphere, midsagittal view. (B) The prefrontal regions are further divided into dorsolateral, orbital, and medial areas. (Top) Left hemisphere, lateral view. (Bottom) Right hemisphere, midsagittal view. © 2011 Cengage Learning

multiple occasions (e.g., three times, five times, seven times), they have difficulty in estimating how often an item occurred, although they have no difficulty in discerning whether an item was previously viewed (Smith & Milner, 1988).

Another problem observed in people with frontal lobe damage is an increase in what has been called *psychological inertia,* the force that must be overcome to either initiate a process or stop one. This handicap may take many forms. For example, persons with frontal lobe damage may not bathe and change clothes each day of their own volition, though they will do so if directed to by someone else. Such an individual may sit on a couch for hours without initiating any behavior. Initiating behavior seems to take a monumental effort that the person just cannot muster. Conversely, once involved in a behavior, an individual with frontal lobe damage may find it impossible to stop that behavior. Such patients are likely to **perseverate** (perform a behavior repeatedly).

Perserverative behavior is also observed in psychiatric disorders in which there is dysfunction of the frontal lobes, such as in obsessive-compulsive disorders, which are characterized by engaging in the same stereotyped motor behavior (e.g., constantly washing one's hands to rid them of germs) in an attempt to ward off some perceived danger (e.g., Friedlander & Desrocher, 2006). Chapter 14 discusses this further. Young children also perseverate because their frontal lobes are relatively immature (Diamond, 1990). You may have had the experience of hiding a child's favorite toy behind one of many pillows. If the first pillow that the child removes does not reveal the toy, he or she will not try the other pillows, but instead will search for the toy behind the first pillow over and over again. This sort of behavioral loop is exactly the type of perseverative behavior that may be exhibited after frontal lobe damage.

Not only do individuals with frontal lobe damage have difficulty in starting and stopping behavior, but they have more general difficulties in modulating behavior. For example, patients with frontal lobe damage are often socially uninhibited and display socially inappropriate behavior. They may make unwanted sexual advances, tell jokes at inappropriate times, and be insensitive to the social context in which they find themselves. (For example, imagine a man dressed in a business suit, who, after obtaining his boarding pass for an overbooked flight, skips past the remaining long line of haggard customers yelling, "It's Friday, be happy!") This inability to modulate behavior leads to a paradoxical effect: sometimes individuals with frontal lobe damage are insensitive to their social surroundings and at other times they are unduly swayed by those environs. For example, by talking about depressing topics, physicians and other medical personnel may cause an individual with frontal lobe damage to be moved to tears, but they can reverse the effect and put the individual in an ecstatic mood within minutes by talking about the person's favorite possessions or activities.

From what we just learned, you should not be surprised that frontal regions of the brain have been implicated in emotional functioning. Although we discuss the role of the frontal lobes in emotion in more detail in Chapter 13, let's briefly consider some important points. Commonly, the family and other loved ones of an individual who has sustained frontal lobe damage will comment that the individual just does not seem like himself or herself anymore. A formerly quiet and peaceful person may be described as argumentative and prone to outbursts, a previously conscientious and hardworking person may be characterized as irresponsible and lazy, and a previously kind and considerate person may now be called selfish and uncaring. In sum, people often say that the individual with frontal lobe damage has undergone a change in personality. One of the most famous early cases in which such changes were documented was that of Phineas Gage, a railroad worker. While he was helping to clear a way for the railroad in 1848, an explosion blew a steel rod through his skull, damaging sections of his frontal cortex (● Figure 1.24). Family and friends complained that Phineas just "wasn't Phineas anymore." Whereas he had been agreeable and patient before the injury, he was now short-tempered and irritable. The man they knew seemed to have vanished.

The frontal lobes have also been implicated in judgment and decision making. People with frontal lobe damage often display poor judgment. These difficulties appear to result from both disordered cognitive processes and disordered emotional processes. For example, patients with frontal lobe injury are poor at systematically implementing strategies that would enable them to understand contingencies such as the set of conditions that lead to reward. Moreover, there is evidence that they have trouble interpreting those emotional or "gut feelings" that send us signals that "something just isn't right" or integrating them with the facts about a situation (Bechara, 2004). Some have suggested that

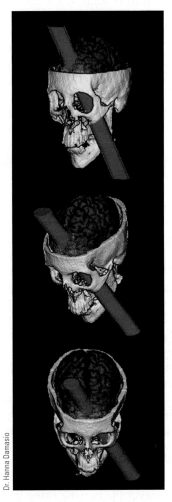

Dr. Hanna Damasio

■ **FIGURE 1.24   The case of Phineas Gage.** Shown here is a reconstruction of the path of an iron rod that destroyed portions of Gage's prefrontal cortex. © 2010 Cengage Learning

medial regions of the frontal lobe are involved in monitoring actions, allowing us to determine whether we have made an error. Such monitoring provides a mechanism for correcting behavior that does not lead to a reward or keeps one from reaching a goal (Taylor, Stern, & Gehring, 2007). In fact, some have argued that this combination of emotional and rational reasoning provided by the frontal regions plays a large role in moral reasoning (Moll & de Oliveira-Souza, 2007).

As this short review illustrates, the frontal regions of the brain are involved in a vast array of behaviors. Rather than being important for specific domains of cognitive activity, such as language, spatial processing, or object recognition, frontal regions provide us with executive capabilities that are used across a vast number of domains and allow us to guide our behavior in a meaningful manner.

Parietal Lobe

The parietal lobe of the cortex plays a role in (1) integrating information from various sensory modalities,

(2) integrating information from the sensory world with information stored in memory, and (3) integrating information about an individual's internal state with information from the external sensory world. Because this integrative function can occur in various ways, the deficits observed after parietal lobe damage are often diverse and difficult to conceptualize as all falling under the same rubric. However, if you keep in mind that the parietal lobe is critical for associating different forms of information, the array of functions performed by the parietal lobe will not seem all that disjointed.

One way to begin to conceptualize the role of parietal cortex is to consider the results of experiments done with macaque monkeys, in which an electrode is placed into the brain to record the activity of a single cell. The investigator determines what type of stimulus makes the cell fire. This procedure is performed for many different cells all over the area of interest, until the researcher can deduce the critical characteristics required to make cells in that region fire. To understand the role of the parietal lobe, we need to consider what we would observe if we recorded from other brain regions as well. Let's suppose that a banana is in a monkey's field of view. If we recorded from a cell in the *inferior temporal cortex* (which, as discussed in the next section, is important for distinguishing between visual forms), we might find a cell that would fire consistently whenever the banana was within the monkey's field of view but would not fire when other visual forms, such as other monkeys, people, or objects, were within view. If we recorded from a cell in the parietal lobe, however, we would find that it too would fire whenever the banana came into view, but if and only if the banana was within the monkey's reach. Alternatively, another cell in the parietal lobe might not fire at the sight of the banana alone, but would fire only if the animal was also hungry. Thus, in both cases, the cell would fire in response to some *conjunction* of attributes: the visual stimulus of the banana *and* its position in space, or the visual stimulus of the banana *and* the animal's internal state (e.g., Lynch, 1980). For this reason, we can say that processing by the parietal lobe is *multimodal* in nature.

In humans, the role of the parietal lobe in multimodal integration is seen in many syndromes that occur after damage to this region, including alexia and agraphia. **Alexia** and **agraphia** are, respectively, the inability to read and the inability to write as a result of brain damage. Chapter 9 discusses both these syndromes in more detail. The fact that alexia and agraphia are caused by parietal lobe damage makes sense if you consider what is involved in reading and writing. What we must do is take a pattern of letters (e.g., d-o-g) and associate it with meaning (e.g., a favorite household pet). Thus, reading and writing, like other functions for which the parietal lobe is important, require different types of information to be linked.

Still another deficit observed after damage to parietal regions is **apraxia**, which is the inability to link skilled motor movement to ideas or representations. Basic motor control is intact; the individual is not paralyzed. Although individuals with apraxia can usually make skilled voluntary movements without difficulty, they cannot pantomime them. For example, an individual with apraxia could easily put a spoonful of sugar into her coffee cup, but when asked to pantomime the same gesture, she might use one finger to represent the spoon, rather than mimicking holding the spoon, twisting it to drop the sugar into the cup, and then rotating it to stir the sugar into the coffee. Apparently, individuals with apraxia lack the capacity to program the motor sequences that allow the representation of an act, even though these persons have the capacity to perform the act itself. Chapter 5 discusses apraxia more thoroughly.

Another ability affected by parietal lobe damage is spatial cognition (see Chapter 8). Damage to parietal regions disrupts the ability to localize points in space, to know the angle of lines, and to understand spatial relations between items. Moreover, parietal regions of the brain also enable us to link spatial maps across different sensory modalities, and to integrate spatial information with motor movements. Consider the situation in which you hear but do not see a bird with a particularly melodic song. You want to know whether this bird is as pretty as it sounds. The parietal lobe will help translate the bird's probable spatial location, as deduced from auditory information, into coordinates in visual space. Moreover, it will aid in translating visual space into motor coordinates so you can move your eyes from their present location to the bird's probable location.

The importance of parietal regions in maintaining a map of space is seen most prominently in the syndrome called **hemineglect**, or **hemi-inattention**. In this syndrome, individuals ignore information on one side of space, usually the left, and act as if that side of the world does not exist. It is not that such individuals have sensory deficits that preclude them from processing information from the neglected region; rather, they do not direct attention to one half of the world, acting as if that region has been erased from their spatial map of the world. More details about spatial processing and hemineglect are given in Chapters 6, 8, and 11.

As you can probably tell from this brief review, damage to the parietal regions can cause a heterogeneous array of syndromes. In general, however, they all are syndromes in which sensory information cannot be integrated either across modalities, with internal representations or memories, or with actions.

Temporal Lobe

Temporal regions of the brain are associated with four main functions: memory, visual item recognition, auditory processing, and emotion. The hippocampus in the temporal lobes was clearly linked to memory by the famous case of H.M. In early adulthood, he underwent bilateral removal of anterior portions of the temporal lobe for the relief of intractable epilepsy. Although the surgery was successful in reducing his seizures, he became unable to learn almost all types of new information, even though most of his memories from the years before the operation were intact. You will learn much more about the role of the temporal lobes in memory in Chapter 10.

In addition to being important for the formation of new long-term memories, temporal regions of the brain play important roles in visual processing, contributing to visual item recognition. Electrical recordings from single cells in the inferior temporal lobes of monkeys have revealed that these cells respond only to highly specific visual stimuli. Unlike cells in the primary visual cortex, which respond to bars of light oriented at particular angles and moving in particular directions, the cells of the inferior temporal lobe respond to very specific shapes, such as a hand, a brush, or a face (Gross, Rocha-Miranda, & Bender, 1972). In fact, some of the cells may respond only to faces of particular people or certain features on a face, such as eyes (Perrett, Mistlin, & Chitty, 1987). In people, damage to temporal regions can lead to deficits in recognizing common objects such as cars and chairs (Farah & Feinberg, 2000), or in knowing that a given face belongs to a specific individual (DeRenzi, 2000). Thus, temporal regions appear to be important for identification of visual items. Chapter 7 discusses the role of the temporal lobe in visual item recognition in more detail.

This specialization of temporal regions for visual item processing and parietal regions for visual location processing seems to reflect a segregation of the processing of visual information in the mammalian brain into two streams or systems, one of which is important for processing the shape of items and the other of which is important for processing the location of items (Ungerleider & Mishkin, 1982). One way to think about these two systems if you are a sports fan is to consider the contrast between a zone defense and a person-to-person defense. The parietal region of the brain treats items much the way a defender in a zone defense does. The job of these parietal regions is to process the location of items in space regardless of who they are. Thus, for parietal regions, localization of objects, not their identities, is important. In contrast, the temporal region of the brain treats items much the way a defender in a person-to-person defense does. These regions are sensitive to a specific person or object regardless of its location in space, just as a defender will stick to his or her target person regardless of where on the court or field that person may wander.

Because auditory processing areas are located in the temporal lobe, damage to this region can have consequences for the processing of auditory material. For example, damage in the temporal lobe can lead to an inability to recognize common sounds, such as a church bell, or to difficulties in the appreciation of certain aspects of music, such as melody.

Also associated with temporal damage are the syndromes of visual agnosia and auditory agnosia. An **agnosia** is a modality-specific deficit in recognizing sounds or objects that occurs in the absence of major deficits in basic sensory processing. What we mean by *modality-specific* is that the person cannot recognize an object in one sensory modality but can recognize it in other modalities.

An individual with *visual agnosia* will be unable to identify an item as a rose merely by looking at it. However, if pricked by a thorn or catching the perfume of the flower, an agnosic individual will instantly recognize it. An important point about agnosia is that the deficit can be attributed neither to the inability to perform basic sensory processing nor to a memory deficit. People with visual agnosia are not blind: they can distinguish light from dark, and can discriminate basic shapes (e.g., square from rectangle; Warrington & James, 1988). For example, when looking at a rose, a person with visual agnosia can see that there is an object, describe its color, and maybe even crudely describe its shape, but cannot use this information to gather a visual impression of a rose. Furthermore, memory for an item is intact. Therefore, if asked which popular flower associated with romance has thorns or what flower makes up the garland placed around the neck of the horse that wins the Kentucky Derby, a person with agnosia could easily answer "rose."

In *auditory agnosia,* an individual knows that a sound has occurred but does not know its significance. For example, a person with auditory agnosia cannot identify a particular sound as a car horn even though she or he knows that some sound just occurred. Likewise, in *tactile agnosia,* which is associated with parietal lobe damage, objects cannot be recognized by touch. What is common to all these agnosias is that basic sensory processing in the affected modality is intact, as are memory processes. Chapter 7 discusses agnosia in more detail.

Finally, temporal regions of the brain have also been implicated in the processing of emotional information, as discussed in more detail in Chapter 13. Some structures in the temporal lobe are portions of the limbic system, which, as we learned earlier in this chapter, can act to integrate information from the sensory world with internal urges (e.g., urges for food, sex, and so forth). More recently, it has been suggested that portions of the temporal lobe are critically important for social and emotional processes, such as having empathy for others or for inferring what another person might be feeling or thinking (Saxe, 2006).

In this chapter we have learned the terms that scientists use to talk about the nervous system and the brain, become familiar with the major subdivisions of the central nervous system, and gained a brief acquaintance with the role that each of these subdivisions plays. Chapter 2 will help us become more knowledgeable about how the main cells that constitute the nervous system communicate with one another.

Summary

What Is Cognitive Neuroscience?

- Cognitive neuroscience comprises all investigations of mental functions that are linked to neural processes—ranging from investigations in animals to humans, and from experiments performed in the laboratory to computer simulations.
- Human neuropsychology is the specific study of linking brain function to mental processes in humans, usually inferred from examining the performance of individuals who have sustained brain damage.

Basic Building Blocks of the Nervous System

- Neurons are the cells that carry information by means of electrical and chemical signals.
- Glia are support cells that serve as a conduit for transfer of nutrients to neurons and help repair damage to the nervous system.

Neuroanatomical Terms and Brain "Geography"

- Toward the front is known as anterior or rostral.
- Toward the back is known as posterior or caudal.
- Near the top of the head is known as superior or dorsal.
- Toward the bottom is known as inferior or ventral.
- Near the middle or midline of the body is known as medial.
- Toward the side of the head is known as lateral.

Major Subdivisions of the Central Nervous System

- The spinal cord is the main route for information coming into and leaving the nervous system.
- The medulla is important for controlling such life-sustaining functions as the beating of the heart and breathing, and for overall alertness and arousal.
- The cerebellum is important for skilled, coordinated motor movement.
- The pons is the brain region at which information from many of the cranial nerves enters the nervous system.
- The midbrain is home to two important structures involved in orienting toward sensory stimuli: the inferior colliculus, which processes auditory information; and the superior colliculus, which processes visual information.
- The hypothalamus is important for motivational behavior, such as seeking food, seeking a sexual partner, and fleeing.
- The thalamus is a major relay center in the brain whereby information from the sensory world is reorganized on its way to the cortex and information from the cortex is reorganized on its way to the periphery.
- Major subcortical systems are the basal ganglia, which is involved in the control of movement; and the limbic system, traditionally thought to be important for emotion but now known to be involved in other functions as well, such as memory.
- The cerebral cortex is the main structure in the human brain; it is involved in processing sensory input, in controlling motor output, and in higher-order mental functions such as object recognition, spatial processing, and memory.

A Closer Look at the Cerebral Cortex

- Primary sensory cortex is the first place in the central nervous system at which information about a particular sensory modality is received from the peripheral receptors.
- Motor cortex is the final exit point for neurons controlling the fine motor functions of the body's muscles.
- Primary somatosensory cortex processes tactile information, including pain, temperature, texture, and the degree of pressure applied.
- Visual cortex processes the contrast between light and dark.
- Auditory cortex processes sound according to its frequency (pitch).
- The frontal lobe is the region of the brain involved in the planning, guidance, and evaluation of behavior.
- The parietal lobe is the region of the brain involved in multimodal processing: integrating information across sensory modalities, memory, and an individual's internal state.
- The temporal lobe is the region of the brain involved in memory, visual item recognition, emotion, and auditory processing, including the processing of music.

Key Terms

agnosia 29	apraxia 28	bilateral 5
agraphia 28	association area 24	blood-brain barrier 3
alexia 28	axon 3	Brodmann map 16
anterior 4	basal ganglia 13	caudal 4

cell body   3
central fissure   15
central nervous system   5
cerebellum   9
cerebral hemisphere   15
cerebrospinal fluid (CSF)   6
cognitive neuroscience   2
contralateral   5
coronal   4
cranial nerves   8
dendritic tree   3
diencephalon   13
distal   5
dorsal   4
epileptic seizure   20
fissure   15
frontal lobe   15
glia   3
gyrus   15
hemi-inattention   28
hemineglect   28
hemiplegia   19
Heschl's gyrus   23
homonymous hemianopsia   22

horizontal   4
human neuropsychology   2
hypothalamus   11
inferior   4
inferior colliculus   11
ipsilateral   5
lateral   4
lateral geniculate nucleus   13
lateral ventricles   7
left visual field   20
limbic system   13
longitudinal fissure   15
medial   4
medulla   8
midbrain   11
midsagittal   4
neurons   3
nuclei   5
occipital lobe   15
olfactory bulb   23
optic chiasm   21
parietal lobe   15
peripheral nervous system   6
perseverate   26

pons   11
posterior   4
primary motor cortex   16
primary sensory cortex   16
proprioception   19
proximal   5
quadranopsia   22
relay center   13
reticular activating system   9
right visual field   20
rostral   4
sagittal   4
scotomas   22
spinal cord   8
sulcus   15
superior   4
superior colliculus   11
Sylvian (lateral) fissure   15
temporal lobe   15
thalamus   11
tonotopic   23
unilateral   5
ventral   4
ventricles   7

Book Companion Site at www.cengage.com/psychology/Banich
This website provides instructors and students with a wealth of free information and resources, including tutorial quizzes, flashcards, and the glossary.

How Neurons Communicate

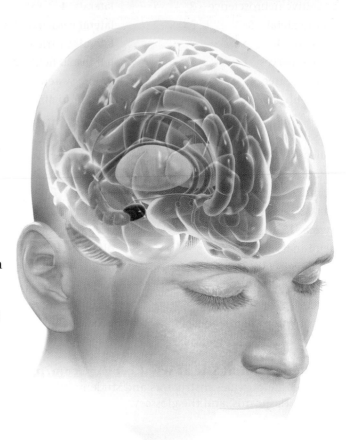

Introduction

In this chapter we will discuss how neurons communicate with one another. You will learn about the electrochemical nature of this communication system as well as how it can be disrupted or enhanced. Understanding how neurons work will allow you to more fully appreciate a number of issues covered in later chapters. For example, once you understand more about the electrical properties of neural conduction, you will see why electroencephalography (EEG) provides a useful measure of brain function and why the brain's activity can be disrupted by transcranial magnetic stimulation. Understanding more about the chemical nature of neural transmission will help you see how the depletion of certain chemicals in the brain may lead to mood disorders such as depression, and why people may find taking certain drugs, such as amphetamines, enjoyable.

Electrochemical Signaling in the Nervous System

Neurons transfer information by means of a combination of electrical and chemical processes. There are two broad principles to this electrochemical signaling: information is relayed within a neuron by means of an electrical signal, whereas one neuron influences another via a chemical signal.

■ How Information Is Transferred within a Neuron

To better understand these principles, we need to examine the neuron in its typical resting state. In the resting state, there is a difference in the electrical charge between the inside and outside of the neuron. This difference in electrical charge is the neuron's **resting potential**, typically about –70 millivolts (mV). You may wonder how a cell in your body could have an electrical charge. The cell membrane of the neuron acts as a barrier separating *ions,* which are electrically charged particles, on the inside from those on the outside. These ions, such as sodium and potassium, can traverse the cell membrane only through special passageways known as *ion channels.* These channels are formed by protein molecules embedded in the cell membrane. In specific configurations, these protein molecules create a passageway that allows ions to flow in and out of the cell. In other configurations, the passageway is blocked, and ions cannot move from one side of the cell membrane to the other.

Ion channels are selective, allowing only certain ions to traverse them. Therefore, the cell membrane contains several types of ion channels, including channels for sodium and potassium ions. Ions are found in different concentrations on either side of the membrane, and when the channels are open, the ions begin to diffuse in the direction that will allow the concentration on both sides of the membrane to reach an equilibrium. Potassium, which has a higher concentration inside the cell than outside, travels out of the cell, whereas sodium, which has a higher concentration outside the cell than inside, flows inward.

Eventually, diffusion would cause these ions to be equally distributed between the inside and outside, much the way a drop of ink eventually disperses equally throughout a glass of water. However, an active mechanism known as the *sodium-potassium pump* works to prevent equal distribution of ions, thereby maintaining the resting potential. This pump sends more positively charged sodium ions out of the cell while allowing fewer positively charged potassium ions into the cell. The net result is that the inside of a neuron stays more negatively charged than the outside. This net imbalance causes a potential, or electrical charge, across the membrane of approximately –70 millivolts.

Input from other neurons can affect the opening and closing of ion channels. The resulting change in the ion concentrations on each side of the membrane drives the neuron's electrical charge away from its resting potential, making it either more negative or more positive. If the cell receives enough stimulation to reduce the voltage across the membrane to about –55 mV, a threshold is passed and the cell "fires." When a cell fires, the electrical charge of the neuron reverses quite rapidly from –55 mV to a peak of +40 mV. After reaching the peak—a state known as *depolarization*—the electrical charge then retreats toward the baseline resting potential, which is known as *repolarization*. The voltage then briefly becomes even more negative than the resting potential, a phase known as *hyperpolarization*. Following hyperpolarization, the neuron returns to the resting potential.

The whole sequence of events just described, from resting potential and back again, is known as an **action potential**. The different phases of the action potential, along with the opening and closing of the different ion channels that drive each of these phases, are depicted in ● Figure 2.1.

This action potential has three very important properties. First, it is self-propagating, which means that once it is set in motion nothing else need be done—much as knocking down one domino causes all the others in a line to fall as well. Second, its strength does not dissipate with the distance that it travels. The peak of the action potential remains +40 mV for its entire trip down the axon. In this characteristic it is quite unlike sound, for example, which loses energy the farther it travels. Third, the action potential is an all-or-nothing response: either the cell "fires" (i.e., has an action potential) or it doesn't. You can think of the action potential as working like a conventional camera. You either press the button down far enough to take a picture or you don't. Once you have depressed the button past a certain point, there is no turning back—the picture is

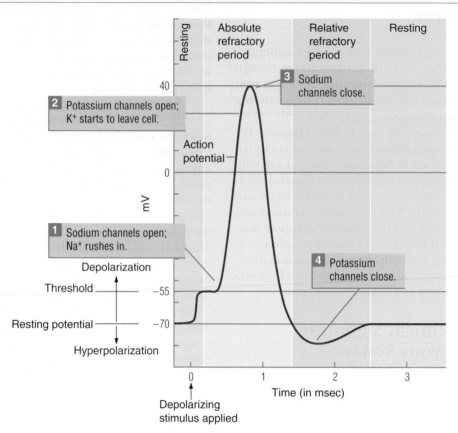

● **FIGURE 2.1** **Phases of the action potential.** (1) When the threshold of activation is reached, sodium (Na+) begins to enter the cell. (2) Potassium (K+) begins to leave the cell. (3) No more sodium enters the cell, and the voltage reaches its peak positive value. (4) The leakage of potassium drives the voltage in the negative direction, hyperpolarizing the cell; potassium channels then close and the cell returns to its resting potential. © 2011 Cengage Learning

taken. If you don't press hard enough to get to the trigger point, it makes no difference how far you partially depress the button—the picture is not taken.

● Figure 2.2 shows the main parts of a neuron in detail. The action potential is first produced at a specific part of the neuron near the cell body called the **axon hillock**. From there, the action potential is carried along the entire length of the axon to the *terminal bouton,* which is the end of the road for the action potential. Here the electrical signal gets transformed into a chemical message. The terminal bouton contains little balloons, known as **synaptic vesicles** (● Figure 2.3), which are filled with neurotransmitter. Some of these synaptic vesicles reside in the bouton, whereas others are fused to the outside wall of the neuron. The action potential causes synaptic vesicles that are fused to the outside walls of the neuron to burst open, pouring their contents into the area between neurons known as the *synaptic cleft.* Once out of the vesicles, neurotransmitter molecules diffuse across the cleft into the vicinity of the neighboring neuron. The side of the cleft that releases the neurotransmitter is known as the *presynaptic side;* the opposite side, containing the outside edge of the

neighboring neuron, is known as the *postsynaptic side.* This region of contact between the neuron containing the terminal bouton, the synaptic cleft, and the postsynaptic region is called a **synapse** (● Figure 2.4).

■ **How Information Is Transferred between Neurons**

At the synapse, **neurotransmitter** molecules are released from the presynaptic neuron and received by the postsynaptic neuron. The membrane of the dendritic trees of the postsynaptic neuron contains regions known as **receptors**. These receptors are specially configured proteins that are embedded within the postsynaptic membrane. As shown in ● Figure 2.5, when neurotransmitter reaches the postsynaptic membrane, it fits into a specific region of the receptor (called the *binding site*), much the way a key fits into a lock. The binding of the neurotransmitter changes the configuration of the receptor, which in turn changes the electrical charge of the postsynaptic neuron in a small local area near the receptor site by altering the flow of ions across the membrane. At this point, the chemical signal is transformed back into an electrical one.

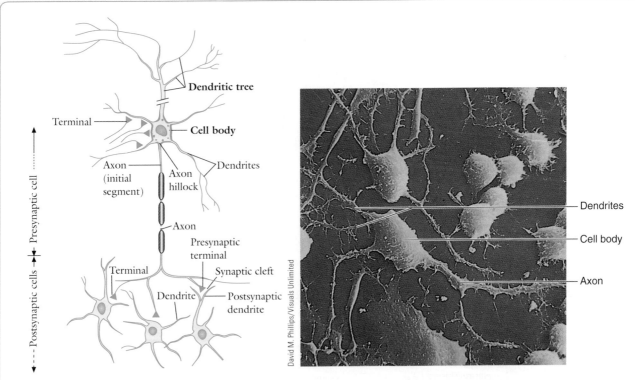

● FIGURE 2.2　Basic parts of a neuron. The dendritic tree, made up of individual dendrites, is the main region that receives information from other cells. The cell body contains the nucleus and the machinery necessary to support basic cell functions. The axon hillock is the location at which a large electrical signal is generated, and the axon is the long shaft of the cell across which this large electrical signal is propagated. The branches at the end of the axon contain bulbous-shaped terminals (terminal boutons or simply boutons), which have vesicles filled with neurotransmitters. These neurotransmitters, which can be either inhibitory or excitatory, are released into the space between adjacent neurons, which is known as the synaptic cleft. The neuron on the terminal side of the cleft is known as presynaptic and the neurons on the opposite side are referred to as postsynaptic. Some synaptic connections are made onto postsynaptic dendrites, whereas others are made directly onto the postsynaptic cell body. An axon can have many branches, synapsing with as many as 1,000 other neurons. © 2011 Cengage Learning

There are two main classes of receptors, one that works directly to produce a local change in the voltage of the dendritic tree of the postsynaptic neuron, and one that works indirectly. These two types of receptors are illustrated in Figure 2.5. **Ionotropic receptors** work directly to either open or close an ion channel. In contrast, **metabotropic receptors** indirectly control the ion channels. Metabotropic receptors are linked to a protein called *guanyl nucleotide-binding protein,* known as **G protein** for short. When the neurotransmitter binds to the receptor, it causes a subunit of the protein, known as the α (alpha) subunit, to break away. The α subunit either binds directly to an ion channel, opening it so that ions can pass, or it activates the channel in a much more roundabout manner by attaching to and activating an enzyme situated in the postsynaptic membrane. An **enzyme** is any molecule that controls a chemical reaction, either by binding together two substances or by cleaving a substance into parts. The enzyme causes the production of another chemical, known as a *second messenger.* This second messenger causes a series of steps to occur that in turn open the ion channel. Although the postsynaptic potentials produced by metabotropic

receptors are slower to start, they end up being longer lasting than those produced by ionotropic receptors.

■ How Postsynaptic Potentials Can Cause an Action Potential

The local changes in the electrical potential that occur near the receptor sites can make the electrical charge of the cell either more positive or more negative than the resting potential. An **excitatory postsynaptic potential (EPSP)** makes the cell's electrical charge a bit more positive—that is, it reduces the difference in electrical charge between the inside and the outside of the cell. This reduction brings the differential closer to the threshold value of −55 mV at which the cell will fire. In contrast, an **inhibitory postsynaptic potential (IPSP)** makes the inside of the cell a bit more negative than the outside and moves the cell farther away from the threshold at which it will fire. Whether a particular neurotransmitter has an excitatory or inhibitory effect depends not on the neurotransmitter but rather on the receptor type to which it binds. We will talk a bit more about the many different types of receptors later in this chapter.

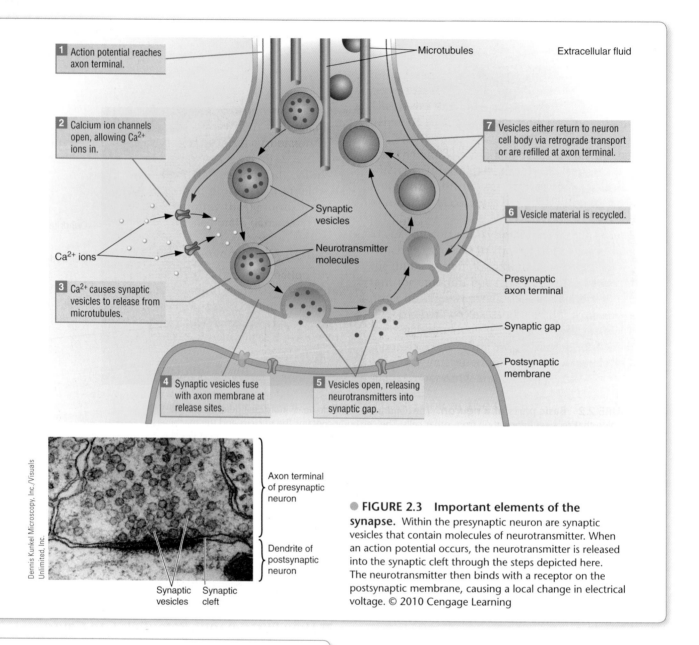

1 Action potential reaches axon terminal.

Microtubules

Extracellular fluid

2 Calcium ion channels open, allowing Ca²⁺ ions in.

7 Vesicles either return to neuron cell body via retrograde transport or are refilled at axon terminal.

Synaptic vesicles

Neurotransmitter molecules

6 Vesicle material is recycled.

Ca²⁺ ions

3 Ca²⁺ causes synaptic vesicles to release from microtubules.

Presynaptic axon terminal

Synaptic gap

Postsynaptic membrane

4 Synaptic vesicles fuse with axon membrane at release sites.

5 Vesicles open, releasing neurotransmitters into synaptic gap.

Dennis Kunkel Microscopy, Inc./Visuals Unlimited, Inc.

Axon terminal of presynaptic neuron

Dendrite of postsynaptic neuron

Synaptic vesicles   Synaptic cleft

● **FIGURE 2.3   Important elements of the synapse.** Within the presynaptic neuron are synaptic vesicles that contain molecules of neurotransmitter. When an action potential occurs, the neurotransmitter is released into the synaptic cleft through the steps depicted here. The neurotransmitter then binds with a receptor on the postsynaptic membrane, causing a local change in electrical voltage. © 2010 Cengage Learning

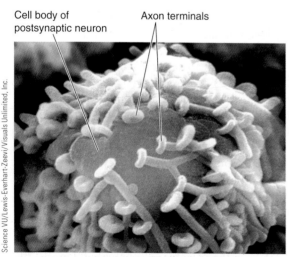

Cell body of postsynaptic neuron

Axon terminals

Science VU/Lewis-Everhart-Zeevi/Visuals Unlimited, Inc.

● **FIGURE 2.4   Neurons communicate at the synapse.** Terminal boutons from many different neurons are shown forming synapses on the cell body of a postsynaptic cell.

Postsynaptic potentials differ from action potentials in three important ways. First, they are graded: The farther they travel from their source, the more they dissipate. Thus, unlike the action potential, which remains constant for the entire course of its journey, postsynaptic potentials weaken as they travel across time and space. Second, postsynaptic potentials are much smaller in magnitude than an action potential, usually in the range of 0.5 to 5 mV. Third, whereas action potentials are always "excitatory," in that they make the cell fire, postsynaptic potentials can be either excitatory or inhibitory.

Because postsynaptic potentials are small and dissipate over space, a single one of them is highly unlikely to cause a cell to fire. Rather, it requires the combined effect of these potentials, both across time and across space, to make a neuron fire. For example, two EPSPs have a greater influence if they occur close together in time than if a

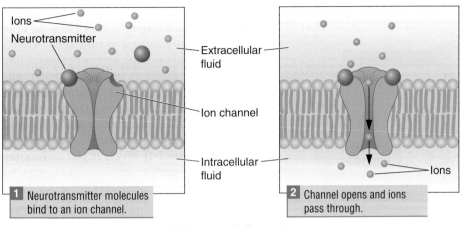

(a) Ionotropic Receptor

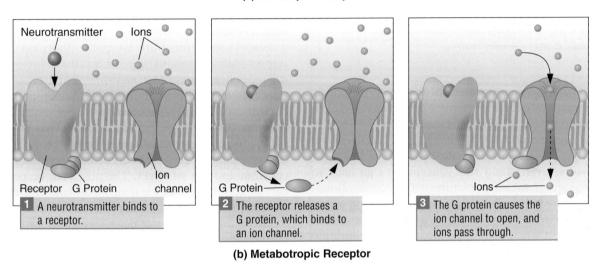

(b) Metabotropic Receptor

● **FIGURE 2.5   Ionotropic and metabotropic receptors.** (A) When neurotransmitters bind with an ionotropic receptor, the receptor opens a channel that allows ions to move through, thereby altering the local membrane potential. (B) When neurotransmitters bind with a metabotropic receptor, several steps take place before the membrane potential is altered. When the neurotransmitter binds with the receptor, the receptor releases G proteins, which act as internal messengers in the cell. G proteins can cause adjacent ion channels to open, and they may also change gene expression. © 2010 Cengage Learning

gap in time separates them. Likewise, if two EPSPs occur at the same part of the dendritic tree, they are likely to have a larger influence th an if they occurred in spatially disparate regions of the dendrite. You can appreciate the complexity of this summation process if you consider that the average neuron has hundreds to thousands of other neurons synapsing upon it. Thus, whether a single cell fires depends not on a single voice from a neighboring neuron, but rather on the chorus of EPSPs and IPSPs produced by its neighbors and on whether those voices occur close together in time and space.

The cacophony of postsynaptic potentials is summated at the axon hillock. If the summed value of EPSPs and IPSPs manages to change the differential in charge across the membrane at the axon hillock from its resting potential of –70 mV to around –55 mV, the cell will fire. If this value is not reached, the cell will not fire. Because the postsynaptic potentials are graded

and lose their potency as they travel from their source to the axon hillock, potentials generated close to the axon hillock have a larger influence on whether or not the cell fires. Consequently, if we go back to our chorus analogy, the cells that synapse closer to the axon hillock have a louder voice in the chorus than those that synapse farther away. In general, excitatory synapses are located on a dendritic tree, whereas inhibitory synapses are located on the cell body. Therefore, IPSPs are more likely to be generated closer to the axon hillock, where they can have a greater effect.

■ Factors That Influence the Responsiveness of a Neuron

Let's consider the way the electrochemical processes of neuronal firing serve to both enable and limit the responsiveness of the neuron. Because the value of the action potential is always the same, neurons cannot code the

(A)

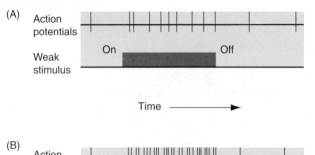

Time ———→

(B)

● **FIGURE 2.6   Neurons code the strength of a stimulus by the rate of firing.** (A) When a relatively weak stimulus is encountered, the cell fires relatively infrequently. (B) When a strong stimulus is encountered, the cell fires many times. © 2011 Cengage Learning

intensity of a stimulus by the size of its electrical response. Rather, neurons code the intensity of a stimulus via the *rate*, or pace, of its firing. When there is a strong stimulus, the cell fires many times in succession; when there is a weak input, it fires only occasionally (● Figure 2.6).

To better understand this concept, let's go back to our analogy of taking a picture with a conventional camera. Consider a situation in which you find a person or vista interesting—you snap a picture or two. But what happens when you find someone overwhelmingly attractive or a vista breathtakingly beautiful? You snap

lots and lots of pictures. Likewise, neurons code their "interest" in a stimulus by how many times they fire.

This firing rate does have an upper limit, which is generally about 200 times per second. The ceiling exists because once an action potential has been initiated, it is impossible to generate another one during the depolarization and repolarization phases. After an ion channel opens and allows the movements of ions, it then becomes blocked and cannot reopen until it is "reset." This is known as the *absolute refractory period* (refer back to Figure 2.1). Much as you cannot take another picture with a conventional camera until it has been forwarded to the next frame, another action potential cannot occur until the channels are reset. During the hyperpolarization phase, another action potential can be produced, but stimulation must be substantially higher than for the prior action potential; this is known as the *relative refractory period*.

Even though there are temporal limits on a cell's responsiveness, certain aspects of the electrochemical processes involved in neuronal firing enable it to respond repeatedly to multiple stimuli. One way of making a cell more responsive is to have a mechanism that can limit the postsynaptic potential. If such a mechanism did not exist, there would be little precision of firing. An event that occurred seconds ago could continue to have an effect. The postsynaptic potential can be terminated by clearing neurotransmitter from the synaptic cleft so that the postsynaptic receptors are freed for another influx of neurotransmitter, which can then produce IPSPs or EPSPs.

Several mechanisms exist for clearing neurotransmitter molecules from the synaptic cleft; these mechanisms are illustrated in ● Figure 2.7. One method is **reuptake**, the rapid removal of neurotransmitter back into the terminal bouton by special transporter molecules that are embedded in the presynaptic membrane. Another mechanism is **enzymatic deactivation**, in which an enzyme cleaves the transmitter molecules so they become incapable of binding to the receptor. This process occurs mainly for one neurotransmitter, **acetylcholine**. An enzyme known as **acetylcholinesterase** divides acetylcholine into its two constituent parts, choline and acetate. This deactivation is a very active process—one molecule of acetylcholinesterase can destroy more than 5,000 molecules of acetylcholine per second! A third mechanism occurs via glial cells in the vicinity of the synapse. A particular type of glial cell known as an *astrocyte* (because it looks like a star) takes up the neurotransmitter and destroys it by breaking it down.

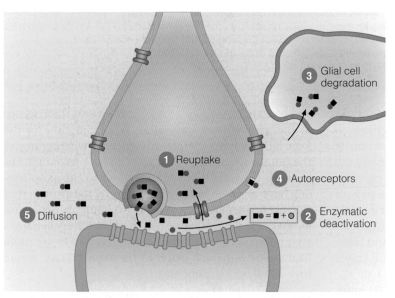

● **FIGURE 2.7   Mechanisms for modulating the amount of neurotransmitter in the synaptic cleft.** (1) Neurotransmitter may be taken up by the presynaptic neurons via special transporter molecules. (2) The neurotransmitter may be broken apart by enzymatic deactivation. (3) Glial cells may take up and destroy neurotransmitter. (4) Neurotransmitter may bind to an autoreceptor. (5) Neurotransmitter may diffuse away from the synapse. © 2011 Cengage Learning

Another way of regulating the responsiveness of cells is through **autoreceptors**. These receptors are located on the presynaptic neuron and bind the same neurotransmitter as released by that neuron. When neurotransmitter released into the synaptic cleft binds to the autoreceptor, it decreases the activity of the presynaptic neuron. These autoreceptors work as a negative feedback mechanism, providing a way to keep the cell from becoming overactivated or overstimulated. Some tolerance effects to drugs are thought to be mediated by autoreceptors, as the cells down-regulate (reduce) their activity in response to repeated exposure to the drug. Finally, neurotransmitter may also be cleared from the synapse by diffusion: it simply floats away, putting it out of range of the receptors.

Neurotransmitters

Up to this point, we have been discussing neurotransmitters in a generic manner, as if they came in only one flavor. Actually, they come in a variety of flavors, and many aspects of neural transmission are influenced by the type of neurotransmitter released into the synapse. Although at one time it was thought that a neuron releases only one type of neurotransmitter, it is now clear that many types of neurons can release two or more neurotransmitters. In this section we discuss those different types of neurotransmitters, their characteristics, the type of receptors to which they bind, and their influence on mental function. You should be aware that there are many more neurotransmitters and other chemicals that modulate neural activity (e.g., peptides) than we discuss here. In the following discussion, we focus primarily on neurotransmitters that play a major role in the functioning of the central nervous system (CNS), while largely ignoring neurotransmitters that play a more prominent role in the peripheral nervous system.

As already mentioned, *neurotransmitters* are the chemicals that neurons release that allow them to communicate with one another. Traditionally, neurotransmitters are defined as having four major characteristics. First, they are chemicals synthesized within the neuron. Second, they are released when the cell is activated by an action potential and they have an effect on a target cell, such as a neighboring neuron or muscle cell. Third, the same response is obtained in the target cell when the transmitter is placed upon it artificially, such as in an experimental situation. Fourth, when the release of the neurotransmitter is blocked, an action potential will not result in activity in the postsynaptic neuron.

Although a variety of chemicals can serve as neurotransmitters, our discussion focuses on two major classes of neurotransmitters found in the CNS. The first is the **amino acids**, the smallest and most basic building blocks of proteins. Amino acids act as the main excitatory and inhibitory neurotransmitters in the brain. The other main class consists of neurotransmitters that

are organized into "systems"; these neurotransmitters are produced by specific sets of neurons whose cell bodies are located subcortically and whose axons project diffusely throughout the cortex.

■ Amino Acids

Amino acids are the most common type of neurotransmitter in the CNS. Because these substances are found in the nervous systems of even very simple organisms, they are likely to have been the first neurotransmitters to evolve. The two main amino acids in the central nervous system that act as neurotransmitters are **glutamate**, which has an excitatory effect, and **GABA** (gamma-aminobutyric acid), which has an inhibitory effect. Two other amino acids that also serve as neurotransmitters are *aspartate,* which is excitatory, and *glycine,* which is inhibitory. Because their role is mainly confined to the brainstem and peripheral nervous system, we will not discuss them in detail.

You might wonder why there are both inhibitory and excitatory neurotransmitters. If only excitatory inputs existed, the system might career out of control. Inhibitory inputs serve to dampen down, or modulate, the system. Think about a car, as an analogy. Imagine that the only way that one could control a car was via the gas pedal—by modulating "excitatory" input. You could indeed take your foot off the gas to slow the car down, but you could not do so very precisely or quickly. There is a need for the "inhibitory" input provided by the brake. Likewise, the nervous system must be able to both ramp up the activity of neurons and tone them down.

Glutamate

The main excitatory amino acid neurotransmitter in the CNS is glutamate. This neurotransmitter is used at approximately 15 to 20% of synapses in the CNS. There are four major glutamatergic receptors. Three are ionotropic and named after the artificial chemicals that stimulate them: NMDA (N-methyl-D-aspartate), AMPA (alpha-amino-3-hydroxy-5-methylisoasole-4-proprionic acid), and kainate receptors. The fourth is the metabotropic glutamate receptor. Binding of glutamate to the AMPA and kainate receptors produces EPSPs. In contrast, the binding of glutamate to the NMDA receptor has special properties that allow it not only to regulate the entry of ions, but also to allow those ions to act as second messengers to change the biochemical and structural properties of the cell. These changes are important for the production of new memories, as they initiate a cascade of events that leads to changes in the shape and number of spines at synaptic sites.

Overactivity of glutamate (and also aspartate) in the brain is thought to play a role in the development of epilepsy, a disease in which an abnormal lowering of a cell's firing threshold causes it to misfire (Morselli & Lloyd, 1985). Drugs that treat epilepsy are known to decrease the amount of glutamate and aspartate released from neurons. Too much glutamate can produce **excitotoxicity**, which is excessive activity of receptors that can literally excite neurons to death. These neurons get "fried" by too much stimulation. In fact, excitotoxicity appears to be an unfortunate consequence of a particular form of brain damage, known as **ischemia**, in which neurons die due to a lack of oxygen, most typically after blockage of a blood vessel in the brain. Glutamate and aspartate build up during ischemia because their reuptake mechanism is energy-dependent and therefore relies critically on oxygen. Without oxygen, these neurotransmitters cannot be effectively cleared out of the synaptic cleft.

Gamma-Aminobutyric Acid (GABA)

The main inhibitory amino acid neurotransmitter is gamma-aminobutyric acid (GABA). About 40% of receptors in the CNS are GABAergic; as you can see, the use of inhibitory input is rather common. GABAergic input is thought to occur mainly via interneurons. The inhibitory control provided by GABA is thought to be important for "fine-tuning" the pattern of activation across the nervous system.

There are two main types of GABA receptors: $GABA_A$ and $GABA_B$. $GABA_A$ is an ionotropic receptor, whereas $GABA_B$ is metabotropic. Both appear to be important in dampening oscillatory, reverberatory excitation between the thalamus and cortex that could lead to the seizure activity associated with epilepsy (e.g., Hosford et al., 1992). Many substances that reduce the activity of the CNS bind to GABA receptors. One such group of substances is **barbiturates**, a class of CNS depressants derived from barbituric acid. Not surprisingly, these drugs reduce seizure activity and induce sedation and sleep. Other substances that bind to GABA receptors are tranquilizing drugs called **benzodiazepines**, such as diazepam (Valium) and chlordiazepoxide (Librium). These drugs are generally used to treat anxiety disorders, but can also be used as antiseizure medication and to promote sleep and muscle relaxation. Alcohol also produces its *anxiolytic* (i.e., anxiety-reducing) and sedative effects by affecting GABA receptors.

Although GABAergic input tends to fine-tune the pattern of brain activation across the brain, in some systems it plays a more direct role. For example, as we will see in Chapter 5, some changes in activation in the motor systems occur via modulation of the constant inhibitory input provided by GABAergic receptors. The system can be freed to function by "taking off the brakes" rather than by "pressing down on the gas," as would occur by excitation.

■ Neurotransmitter Systems

The other main class of neurotransmitters differs from amino acids in that its members are organized into systems. These neurotransmitters are produced by neurons whose cell bodies are located subcortically and in the brainstem, and whose axons project diffusely throughout the cortex. We have already been introduced to one

neurotransmitter of this kind, *acetylcholine,* which is composed of acetate and choline. The three other such neurotransmitters are known as **monoamines**, as they derive from an amino acid that has undergone a chemical transformation via an enzymatic process. The monoamines are **dopamine, noradrenaline** (also known as **norepinephrine**) and **serotonin**. Their molecular structures are very similar; as a result, there are drugs that affect the activity of all of them to some degree. For example, all three are affected by *monoamine oxidase inhibitors (MAOIs),* which are used to treat depression. As you can guess from the name, MAOIs inhibit the activity of monoamine oxidase, an enzyme that breaks down monoamines. The end result is to provide the brain with more monoamines—dopamine, noradrenaline, and serotonin.

Two of these monoamines, dopamine and noradrenaline, derive from the same amino acid, *tyrosine,* and are known as **catecholamines**. Tyrosine is transformed by tyrosine hydroxylase, an enzyme, into L-dopa. (You can easily identify enzymes in our subsequent discussion, because their names all end in "–ase".) As we will learn in Chapters 5 and 16, L-dopa is used to treat Parkinson's disease, a disorder characterized by the death of dopaminergic cells and resulting in difficulties with the initiation of motor control and thought. L-dopa is then transformed by dopa decarboxylase to form dopamine. Finally, dopamine can be transformed into noradrenaline by dopamine beta-hydroxylase. The third monoamine, serotonin, derives from *tryptophan,* and is classified as an **indolamine** (rather than a catecholamine).

Each of these neurotransmitters is released by a different set of neurons that together form a neurotransmitter system: the cholinergic, dopaminergic, noradrenergic, and serotonergic systems. Because these systems project diffusely throughout the cortex, each one can affect a large variety of behaviors, some of which overlap. Nonetheless, each system has been found to have some degree of specificity in influencing behavior. For example, the breakdown of different neurotransmitter systems can result in specific neuropsychological impairments.

Before we turn our attention to the particulars of each of these systems, however, we must introduce the idea of neurotransmitter agonists and antagonists. **Agonists** are chemicals that mimic or facilitate the effect of a neurotransmitter on a target neuron, whereas **antagonists** oppose or diminish the effect on a target neuron. Much has been learned about the functions associated with different neurotransmitter systems by examining the effects of agonists and antagonists on each system.

Cholinergic System

Acetylcholine (ACh) is the neurotransmitter used in the *cholinergic* system. The cell bodies of neurons of the cholinergic system are located mainly in the basal forebrain nucleus and project to almost all portions of the cortex in a very diffuse and nonspecific manner (● Figure 2.8). There are also cell bodies in the septal nuclei that project to the hippocampus. Both these nuclei are located between the hypothalamus and orbitofrontal cortex. Because ACh is released in almost every cortical area, it tends to have a very general effect on neuronal and mental functioning.

There are two different types of ACh receptors, one ionotropic and one metabotropic, each of which is activated by a different drug. The ionotropic ACh receptor is known as the *nicotinic receptor* because it can be stimulated by nicotine, the drug found in tobacco leaves. In contrast, the metabotropic receptor is known as the *muscarinic receptor* because it can be stimulated by muscarine, a drug in the poisonous mushroom *Amanita muscariam.*

The cholinergic system plays an important role in maintaining overall cortical excitability. ACh levels are decreased during anesthesia, when the brain is less active, and are increased by convulsants, which are drugs that produce seizure activity. ACh has also been linked to the production of rapid eye movement (REM) sleep, which is that portion of sleep when we dream and our minds are relatively active.

Given that ACh plays a role in overall cortical excitability, it may not surprise you that activity of the cholinergic system has been linked to paying attention (Sarter, Hasselmo, Bruno, & Givens, 2005). Cholinergic activity appears to be important for overall arousal or vigilance—the ability to stay alert, especially in boring or monotonous situations or over long periods of time (Wesnes & Warburton, 1984). For example, although depletion of ACh does not initially affect the ability of animals to differentiate between a target and nontarget stimulus, it seriously decreases their ability to do so as the task drags on. In humans, nicotine, an acetylcholine agonist, can improve performance on tasks requiring sustained attention, ranging from those that are relatively simple, such as detecting three consecutive even digits in a row (Mancuso, Andres, Ansseau, & Tirelli, 1999), to those that are more complicated, such as landing a plane in a flight simulator late at night after having done the task a couple of times before (Mumenthaler, Taylor, O'Hara, & Yesavage, 1998) (for a recent review of nicotine's effect on cognition, see Poorthuis, Goriounova, Couey, & Mansvelder, 2009). Moreover, the administration of ACh agonists attenuates deficits in patients with Alzheimer's disease who undertake tasks requiring sustained attention (Sahakian & Coull, 1994).

ACh has also been linked to *selective attention,* which is the ability to attend to certain information while tuning out other information. ACh appears to sharpen the responses of cells to the features of stimuli that are most likely to make them fire, while suppressing responses to less prominent features of a stimulus (Sarter et al., 2005). In both humans and monkeys,

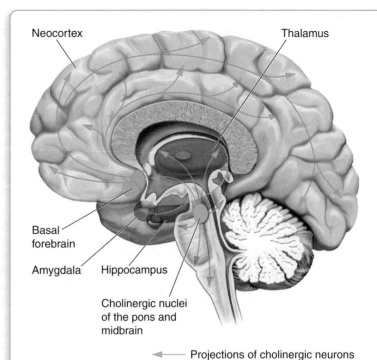

● FIGURE 2.8   Cholinergic pathways in the brain. The cell bodies of cholinergic neurons can be found in the basal forebrain, pons, and midbrain. The axons of these cells project to the limbic system and neocortex and release acetylcholine in those locations. © 2010 Cengage Learning

cholinergic agonists aid the ability to orient toward important sensory information (Witte, Davidson, & Marrocco, 1997). One possible reason that people like to smoke is that nicotine can enhance the ability to filter irrelevant and annoying information from the smoker's awareness, allowing the person to focus on new and important information (Kassel, 1997). Higher-level brain regions, such as the prefrontal cortex, can also modulate activity in the ACh pathway, providing a feedback loop that allows some internal control over the activation of this system (Sarter et al., 2005).

Traditionally, neuroscientists have associated activity of the cholinergic system most closely with memory processing. Acetylcholine depletion is associated with Alzheimer's disease (Spillane, White, Goodhardt, Flack, Bowen, & Davison, 1977), which has devastating effects on memory as well as other functions, as we will learn in Chapter 16. When given to young, healthy individuals, scopolamine, an ACh antagonist drug that blocks muscarinic receptors, can induce deficits in learning new tasks comparable to those seen in older individuals (e.g., Drachman & Leavitt, 1974). These deficits can be reversed by agonist drugs, such as physostigmine, that keep ACh from being broken down in the synaptic cleft. Giving individuals a cholinergic agonist significantly improves learning (Sitaram, Weingartner, & Gillin, 1978).

It is difficult to determine whether the effects of ACh on cognition relate more to attention or to memory. Clearly, if you are not paying attention to information when you first learn it, the information will be difficult to retrieve later on, because it was never well stored in memory. Therefore, some researchers suggest that apparent improvements in memory with cholinergic agents result from improvements in attention rather than memory (Bartus, 2000). Studies have indicated that ACh agonists increase activity in extrastriate regions during a working memory task, suggesting that these drugs augment the process of selecting specific information for storage in memory (Furey, Pietrini, & Haxby, 2000; Thiel, 2003). Therefore, ACh may affect both attentional and memory processes because it modulates an operation required in both: that of selecting, or highlighting, certain types of information while discarding or ignoring other types.

Dopaminergic System

Dopamine is the main neurotransmitter used in the *dopaminergic system*. There are actually three dopaminergic subsystems: the nigrostriatal, mesolimbic, and mesocortical. These subsystems, shown in ● Figure 2.9, are differentiated by the location of their cell bodies, the regions of the brain to which they project, and the effect they have on behavior. In a moment, we will examine each of them in more detail. But first, let's look at some characteristics common to all three subsystems.

Overall Characteristics   There are many different dopaminergic receptors, all of which are metabotropic. The two main families of receptors are the D_1-like and D_2-like.

D_1-like receptors, which are the D_1 and D_5 receptors, increase the production of a second-messenger, cyclic AMP. In contrast, the D_2-like receptors, which are the D_2, D_3, and D_4 receptors, all decrease the production of cyclic AMP.

D_1 receptors are located exclusively on postsynaptic sites, whereas D_2 receptors are located both postsynaptically and presynaptically, where they serve as autoreceptors. Postsynaptically, dopamine can act to produce both excitatory and inhibitory potentials, depending on which receptors are activated. Presynaptically, autoreceptors located on dendrites and cell bodies decrease neural firing by producing hyperpolarization. In contrast, those located in the terminal boutons suppress the activity of the enzyme tyrosine hydroxylase, decreasing the production and ultimately the release of dopamine.

We mention the variety of dopamine receptors because they have been related to a wide variety of mental and emotional functions. In particular, the activity of D_1 and D_2 receptors has been linked to schizophrenia, a disorder discussed in more detail in Chapter 14. Many antipsychotic drugs work as D_2 antagonists. For example, chlorpromazine, one common antipsychotic drug, blocks D_2 dopamine receptors. These drugs often reduce the "florid" symptoms of schizophrenia, which are delusions (such as a belief that "The FBI is reading my thoughts") and hallucinations (such as hearing voices that command a person to act in certain ways). However, they do not much alleviate the cognitive deficits and emotional withdrawal observed in patients with schizophrenia.

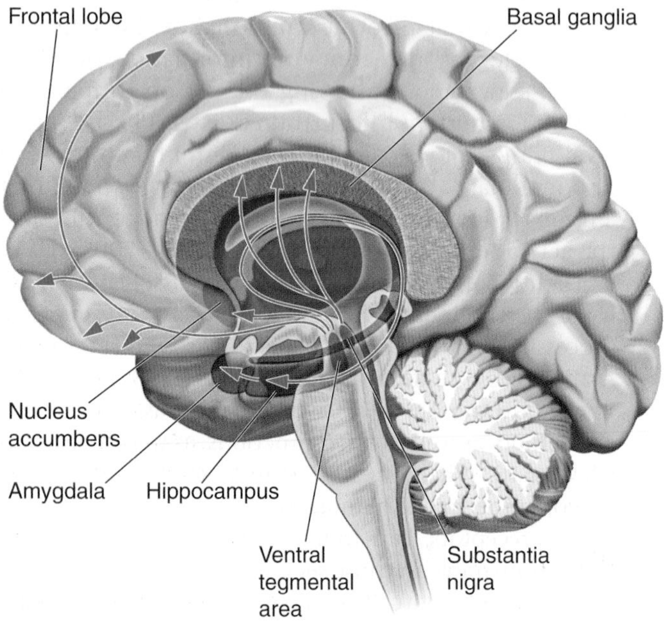

Rather, the severity of these latter deficits in schizophrenic individuals has been linked to the level of binding of D_1 receptors. For example, studies have found that there are more available D_1 receptors in individuals with schizophrenia especially in the frontal cortex (Abi-Dargham et al., 2002). Further, both human and animal studies have linked the availability of D_1 receptors to working memory performance (Abi-Dargham et al., 2002; Sawaguchi & Goldman-Rakic, 1991; Zahrt, Taylor, Mathew, & Arnsten, 1997). Therefore, current research is focused on understanding how the relative balance of D_1 versus D_2 receptor activation may play a role in the symptoms observed in people with schizophrenia (Winterer & Weinberger, 2004).

Designing effective drugs for schizophrenia is very difficult because the D_2 antagonists that are effective antipsychotic medications also have the effect of decreasing D_1 receptor activity. Remember that people with schizophrenia do not seem to be able to bind dopamine to D_1 receptors to an optimal degree to begin with, and that inadequate binding of D_1 receptors is associated with their emotional and cognitive deficits. Therefore, if antipsychotic drugs reduce D_1 receptor action or availability, cognitive and

● **FIGURE 2.9   Dopaminergic pathways in the brain.** Dopaminergic neurons originate in the substantia nigra and ventral tegmental area of the midbrain. Their axons project to the basal ganglia, the limbic system, and the frontal lobes. These systems contribute to motor control, reward behavior, and executive functions, respectively. © 2010 Cengage Learning

Labels: Frontal lobe, Basal ganglia, Nucleus accumbens, Amygdala, Hippocampus, Ventral tegmental area, Substantia nigra

emotional problems can be exacerbated. Consequently, a major challenge in designing new drug therapies for schizophrenia is to find drugs that optimize binding of both D_1 and D_2 receptors, reducing psychotic symptoms without having deleterious effects on cognitive and emotional functioning (e.g., Lidow, Williams, & Goldman-Rakic, 1998; Winterer & Weinberger, 2004).

Other receptors in the D_2 family also have specific effects on aspects of cognitive and emotional processing. One of these, the D_4 receptor, acts postsynaptically and tends to be located in the limbic system and cortex. The expression of the D_4 receptor has been linked to a psychological trait known as "novelty seeking" (Benjamin et al., 1996), which is characterized by exploratory behavior, excitability, and impulsiveness. All of these characteristics are hallmarks of individuals who have trouble regulating their attentional control, so it is not surprising that genetic variability in the nature of D_4 receptors may contribute to inherited aspects of attention deficit hyperactivity disorder (see Barr, 2001, for a review).

Subsystems   The first subsystem that we discuss is the **nigrostriatal system**. The cell bodies of this system are located in the substantia nigra and project to the neostriatum (i.e., the caudate nucleus and putamen, also known as the basal ganglia; refer back to Figure 2.9). You may remember from Chapter 1 that the caudate and putamen play a role in motor functioning, so it may not surprise you that this portion of the dopaminergic system is important in motor control. This subsystem does not control motor output as much as it regulates the selection, initiation, and cessation of motor behaviors. As we will learn in Chapter 5, it is the nigrostriatal dopaminergic subsystem that is affected by Parkinson's disease. In that disorder, the dopaminergic neurons in the substantia nigra die, depleting the caudate and putamen of dopaminergic input and leading to difficulties with motor control.

The second system, known as the **mesolimbic system**, has its cell bodies in the *ventral tegmental area,* which is medial to the substantia nigra. It projects to several parts of the limbic system, including the *nucleus accumbens* and ventral portions of the striatum, amygdala, and hippocampus, as well as prefrontal cortex.

The mesolimbic system has been linked to reward-related behavior. Dopamine levels in the nucleus accumbens increase in response to both natural reinforcers, such as food, drink, and sex, and drugs of abuse, such as amphetamine and cocaine (Spanagel & Weiss, 1999). Activity within the ventral portion of the striatum has been linked to a wide variety of reinforcers. For example, the better one performs on a video game, the greater the release of dopamine and its subsequent binding to D_2 receptors in the ventral striatum (Koepp et al., 1998). This same region of the brain becomes more active when people view a picture of a person they are madly in love with, compared to a picture of a close friend (Bartels & Zeki, 2000). Seeing or ruminating about the person you adore is apparently very rewarding! The portion of the mesolimbic system that projects to the amygdala appears to be important for linking predictive cues to either a rewarding or aversive stimulus (Nader & LeDoux, 1999). Finally, inputs to prefrontal regions help to integrate what the organism is doing at that time with the appropriate behavioral response to the rewarding stimulus. We discuss the reward pathways in more detail in Chapter 13.

One prominent theory of how this dopaminergic subsystem affects mental activity posits that the dopaminergic signal is very specific. It does not code whether a reward has been received nor how an organism acts in response to the reward. Instead, dopamine appears to signal whether the reward *exceeds* or *falls short* of what was expected (Hollerman & Schultz, 1998). Dopamine production associated with an unexpected reward elicits a strong positive dopamine signal in the ventral tegmental area. With repeated presentation and learning this response declines, because with time the reward is no longer unexpected. Conversely, omission of a predicted reward leads to suppression of the dopamine signal. Now you know why a surprising success, like winning a raffle, feels so good!

The cell bodies of the third dopaminergic subsystem, the **mesocortical system,** are also located in the ventral tegmental area. The axons of these cells project to much of the cortex, especially motor and premotor cortex, as well as prefrontal cortex, where they influence a variety of mental functions. One of these functions is working memory, which allows us to keep information "online" for performance of tasks, planning, and strategy preparation for problem solving. Depletion of dopamine, but not of other neurotransmitters, produces a specific deficit in these cognitive functions of the dorsolateral prefrontal cortex (refer back to Figure 1.20), similar to that observed in animals that have had this area surgically removed. This effect has been linked specifically to D_1 receptors (Sawaguchi & Goldman-Rakic, 1991). Moreover, this behavioral deficit can be reversed by giving the dopamine precursor L-dopa or the dopamine agonist apomorphine, but cannot be reversed by other neurotransmitter precursors (Brozoski, Brown, Rosvold, & Goldman, 1979).

Noradrenergic System

Noradrenaline (or norepinephrine) is the neurotransmitter emitted by cells of the *noradrenergic system.* The central noradrenergic system originates primarily in the locus coeruleus (● Figure 2.10). Neurons in the locus coeruleus project to the thalamus, hypothalamus, and the cortex, most notably the prefrontal cortex. There are four main types of noradrenergic receptors: α_1, α_2, β_1, and β_2. All are metabotropic, coupled to G proteins.

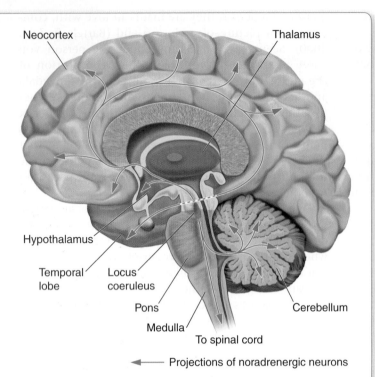

● **FIGURE 2.10   Noradrenergic pathways in the brain.** Neurons that release noradrenaline (norepinephrine) have their cell bodies located in the pons, medulla, and hypothalamus. These neurons project widely throughout the brain and spinal cord, allowing them to modulate overall states of arousal and vigilance. © 2010 Cengage Learning

Adrenergic receptors produce both excitatory and inhibitory effects.

The primary cognitive effect of increased activity in the noradrenergic system is to influence arousal and attention (see Berridge & Waterhouse, 2003, for a review). Overall arousal is increased through action at α_1 receptors in the thalamus and cortex, whereas decreased arousal is associated with decreased release of noradrenaline mediated through presynaptic α_2 autoreceptors. Noradrenaline also plays a role in sleep. The α_2 receptors in the thalamus put the brain in a sleep mode, and noradrenergic cells also shut off during REM sleep. The only difference between waking and dreaming is noradrenaline!

Attention is influenced by α receptors as well. Low doses of clonidine, which down-regulates the release of noradrenaline via α_2 presynaptic autoreceptors, degrades performance when tasks require vigilance (Coull, Middleton, Robbins, & Sahakian, 1995), when attention must be focused on a highly demanding task (Coull, Sahakian, et al., 1995), when attention must be maintained in the absence of sensory input (Smith & Nutt, 1996), and when participants are "alerted" to an upcoming stimulus by a warning cue (Coull, Nobre, & Frith, 2001).

Given the association of noradrenaline with attentional functions, some researchers have suggested that the functioning of noradrenaline also may be disrupted in attention deficit hyperactivity disorder (for more details on this disorder, see Chapter 15). Drugs that affect the noradrenergic system, such as tricyclic drugs that inhibit catecholamine reuptake, have been used clinically to treat attention deficit hyperactivity disorder (Biederman & Spencer, 1999; Biederman et al., 2006).

Functioning of the noradrenergic system in the prefrontal cortex has also been linked to working memory. Research in monkeys suggests that noradrenergic functioning of α_2 receptors in prefrontal cortex aids working memory. This effect is relatively specific: α_2 receptor agonists improve performance on working memory tasks that depend on the prefrontal cortex, but do not improve performance on perceptual and memory tasks that rely on different brain regions (Arnsten, 1998). In contrast, high levels of α_1 receptor binding in prefrontal cortex impairs working memory (Birnbaum, Gobeske, Auerbach, Taylor, & Arnsten, 1999). We have already learned that dopamine also affects working memory and prefrontal cortex. So, how is the effect of the noradrenergic system different? It has been suggested that whereas stimulation of D_1 receptors in prefrontal cortex decreases the "noise" associated with a neural signal, activity of α_2 noradrenergic receptors increases the neuronal "signal" itself.

The activity of the β-receptor system has been linked to long-term memory, especially memory that has an emotional component (Chamberlain, Müller, Blackwell, Robbins, & Sahakian, 2006). For example, administering propranolol, which is a β-adrenergic antagonist, reduces the heightened memory for emotionally charged information in both rats (Cahill, Pham, & Setlow, 2000) and humans (Hurlemann et al., 2005; Reist, Duffy, Fujimoto, & Cahill, 2001).

If the material you've just read seems familiar, you are right. The cognitive effects of the noradrenergic system are suspiciously similar to those of the cholinergic system. At the end of this section we will discuss the reasons for these similarities, as well as interrelations among other neurotransmitter subsystems.

Serotonergic System

Serotonin, or 5-hydroxytryptamine (5-HT), is the neurotransmitter released by the *serotonergic system*. The cell bodies of the serotonergic system are found in several clusters located in the raphe nuclei of the midbrain, pons, and medulla (● Figure 2.11). The most important clusters are found in the dorsal and medial raphe nuclei. For the most part, cells from both the dorsal and medial raphe nuclei project to similar sites in the brain. These include the hypothalamus, hippocampus, and amygdala, all of which are part of the limbic system. However, cells from the dorsal raphe project with greater density to the striatum, cortex, cerebellum, and thalamus, whereas those from the medial raphe project more to the hippocampus and other limbic structures. Because of its diverse sites of projection, this system influences a large variety of behaviors, including arousal; mood; anxiety and aggression; the control of eating; sleeping and dreaming; pain; sexual behavior; and memory.

There are more than 10 different types of serotonergic receptors, all of which are metabotropic except for 5-HT$_3$. Some of these receptors are tightly linked to certain behaviors, whereas others affect a wide variety of behaviors. Here we will touch upon just a few highlights.

One of the functions clearly associated with serotonergic function is sleep. 5-HT levels can influence the level or stage of sleep, including REM sleep, which is associated with dreaming. The dorsal rather than the medial raphe nuclei are especially important for this function. The serotonergic receptors linked to sleep are the 5-HT$_{1A}$ receptors, but these receptors are important in regulating many other behaviors as well, including sexual behavior, appetite, aggression, and pain. Notice that many of these behaviors are controlled by limbic structures and the hypothalamus. They are all regulatory behaviors that help to meet an organism's basic needs.

Serotonin has been linked to mood states, most notably depression, a state in which arousal levels are quite low (i.e., the person has no energy) and mood is continuously blue. We discuss depression in more detail in Chapter 14. Currently, some of the most popular drugs to treat depression are known as *serotonin-specific reuptake inhibitors (SSRIs),* because they do exactly that: they increase the amount of serotonin in the synaptic cleft by inhibiting its presynaptic uptake. You have probably heard of one of the best known SSRIs, fluoxetine, known commercially as Prozac. SSRIs can be very helpful in reducing depression, but because the serotonin system is involved in a variety of regulatory functions, SSRIs have many other consequences as well. SSRIs can interfere with sleep, reduce appetite, and have deleterious effects on sexual performance, making an individual incapable of having an orgasm. Because of individual differences in reactions to various SSRIs, a depressed individual may need to try a number of different SSRIs to find the one that has the most beneficial effect on his or her depression and the least adverse effect on eating, sleep, and sexual function.

With regard to cognitive function, serotonin has been linked most closely to memory, specifically the function of putting new memories into long-term storage (Schmitt, Wingen, Ramaekers, Evers, & Riedel, 2006). For example, individuals given a diet lacking in tryptophan, a precursor to serotonin, show a specific deficit in forming new memories, whereas other cognitive

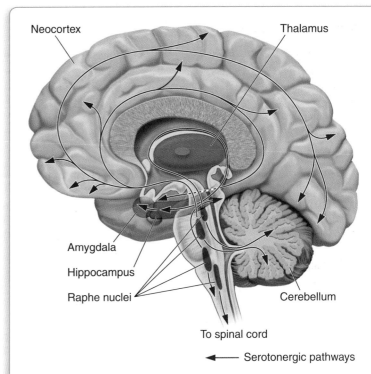

● **FIGURE 2.11   Serotonergic pathways in the brain.** The raphe nuclei in the brainstem contain the cell bodies of most serotonergic neurons. These neurons project to the cerebellum, limbic system, and cerebral cortex; they modulate mood, sleep, and appetite. © 2010 Cengage Learning

functions are unaffected (Riedel, Klaassen, Deutz, van Someren, & van Praag, 1999). Individuals with a history of using the recreational drug "ecstasy" (3,4-methylenedioxy-methamphetamine), which is toxic to serotonergic neurons, tend to exhibit deficits in long-term memory (Zakzanis, Campbell, & Jovanovski, 2007). Finally, deficits in learning and memory associated with aging and Alzheimer's disease appear to coincide with a decline in serotonergic function (Sirviö, 1999), although acetylcholine probably plays a larger role. Drugs that are designed to have a therapeutic effect target the 5-HT$_4$ receptor (Maillet, Robert, & Lezoualc'h, 2004), which occurs with high density within the hippocampus, a structure critical for the formation of new long-term memories (see Chapter 10). Such drugs also target 5-HT$_6$ receptors (Upton, Chuang, Hunter, & Virley, 2008). Because many serotonergic receptors are found in limbic regions, memories that have emotional connotations may be especially affected by compromise of the serotonergic system (Buhot, Martin, & Segu, 2000). Finally, the serotonergic system has also been linked to the hallucinogenic effects of certain drugs. For example, LSD (lysergic acid diethylamide) acts as a direct agonist on 5-HT$_{2A}$ and 5-HT$_{2B}$ receptors.

As you can see, these neurotransmitter systems affect many different regions of the brain and have a variety of effects on cognitive and emotional processing. Table 2.1 summarizes the main attributes of each.

TABLE 2.1	The Four Main Neurotransmitter Systems				
Neurotransmitter System	Transmitter	Site of Origin	Projection Sites	Main Receptor Types	Main Behavioral Effects
Cholinergic	Acetylcholine	Basal forebrain	Diffuse cortical regions	a. Muscarinic b. Nicotinic	Overall cortical excitability, attention, memory
Dopaminergic	Dopamine			a. D_1 family (D_1 & D_5) b. D_2 family (D_2, D_3, & D_4)	Working memory, novelty seeking, attention, psychotic symptomatology
Subsystems NIGROSTRIATAL		Substantia nigra	Dorsal striatum		Motor activity
MESOLIMBIC		Ventral tegmental area	a. Limbic regions b. Ventral striatum		Reward
MESOCORTICAL		Ventral tegmental area	Prefrontal cortex		Working memory, planning
Noradrenergic	Noradrenaline (norepinephrine)			α_1, α_2, β_1, β_2	
		Ventrolateral tegmental area	Hypothalamus		Feeding, sexual behavior
		Locus coeruleus	a. Thalamus b. Hypothalamus c. Cortex		Attention, sleep, working memory
Serotonergic	Serotonin			At least nine different receptors	Sleep, mood, sexual behavior, eating, pain, memory, arousal
		Dorsal raphe nucleus	a. Cortex b. Thalamus		
		Medial raphe nucleus	Limbic system		

Interaction between Neurotransmitter Systems

Although we have treated these neurotransmitter systems as if they were independent, it should be clear from our discussion that they are highly interrelated. For example, we have seen that both dopamine and noradrenaline are implicated in attention deficit hyperactivity disorder, they both have receptors in prefrontal cortex, and they are both derived from tyrosine. Likewise, the serotonergic and cholinergic systems have been implicated in the formation of new long-term memories and sleep, and both project very diffusely to many regions of the brain. Both the cholinergic and the noradrenergic systems influence attention and memory. Given these areas of overlap, much current research is centered on how the various neurotransmitter systems interact (e.g., Olvera-Cortés, Anguiano-Rodriguez, López-Vázquez, & Alfaro, 2008).

Because of these interactions, many new pharmacological interventions, for a variety of disorders ranging from hyperactivity to schizophrenia to depression, either attempt to capitalize on these similarities or try to disentangle them. One approach is to combine drugs to treat a disorder. For example, a possible treatment approach for moderate to severe Alzheimer's disease involves manipulating the cholinergic systems via an anticholinesterase while at the same time providing a glutamate antagonist (e.g., Hsiung & Feldman, 2008). Another approach, employed with Parkinson's disease, is to utilize a more general pharmacological intervention (i.e., a monoamine oxidase inhibitor) at early stages of the disease and a more specific one (a dopamine agonist or levo-dopa) at later stages (Schapira, 2009).

Chemical Modulation of Neural Transmission

Now that we have covered the basics of neural transmission and the different neurotransmitter systems, let us briefly review how communication between neurons can be modulated or disrupted. Many of the examples we provide are for the neurotransmitter acetylcholine. In addition to modulating cortical excitability in the CNS, this neurotransmitter is used outside the CNS at synapses of the neuromuscular junction, which is where neurons synapse onto muscles. When the neuron fires, it causes the muscle tissue to contract. Knowing this will help you appreciate some of the following examples.

There are three main ways of modulating neurotransmission: by affecting presynaptic mechanisms, by modulating the amount of neurotransmitter in the synaptic cleft, and by affecting postsynaptic mechanisms (refer back to Figure 2.7).

Presynaptic mechanisms can be influenced in a number of ways. One way is to regulate the amount of neurotransmitter that is actually produced. For example, ingesting a diet high in choline helps to promote the production of acetylcholine. Foods rich in choline include cauliflower and milk. Another way is to modulate the release of the neurotransmitter into the synaptic cleft. For example, the venom of the black widow spider promotes the release of ACh, allowing it to flood the synaptic cleft. Because the excessive amount available keeps a large amount of ACh bound to the postsynaptic receptors, the person cannot initiate any other motor actions, becomes paralyzed, cannot breathe, and dies.

Finally, the action of autoreceptors can be modulated. Remember from our discussion earlier in the chapter that when a neurotransmitter binds to an autoreceptor, it causes a *decrease* in the release of that neurotransmitter. Some drugs stimulate autoreceptors. The drug binds as if it were identical to the neurotransmitter, which then causes the cell to release less of that neurotransmitter. For example, at low doses clonidine binds the autoreceptors for norepinephrine, inhibiting its release, with a consequent degradation in attention. However, a drug that blocks an autoreceptor, displacing the neurotransmitter so that it cannot bind to the autoreceptor, will enhance the release of neurotransmitter and thus increase firing. The neuron will be stripped of the feedback mechanism that provides information about how much transmitter is in the cleft, and will not adjust release of the transmitter downward. As one example, some experimental antipsychotic drugs, such as amisulpride, at low doses block the D_3 autoreceptor, leading to increased release of dopamine.

A variety of mechanisms can modulate the amount of neurotransmitter in the synaptic cleft. One way is to affect reuptake mechanisms. For example, cocaine blocks reuptake of dopamine, thereby causing stimulatory effects. Another way to modulate the amount of neurotransmitter is to inhibit the action of the enzymes that break them down. For example, insecticides, nerve gases, and herbicides all serve to inhibit acetylcholinesterase, allowing ACh to accumulate in the synaptic cleft. This eventually leads to neuromuscular paralysis. Notice that the end result here is similar to that observed with black widow spider venom. Both nerve gases and black widow spider venom have the same result: they lead to an excess of ACh. However, a different mechanism produces this excess.

The final major way to modulate neuronal activity is via postsynaptic mechanisms. A drug can increase activity by mimicking the effect of a neurotransmitter, thus serving as an agonist. For example, nicotine stimulates receptors to which acetylcholine binds. The physical structure of nicotine is similar enough to that of acetylcholine to allow it to fit into the binding sites of the postsynaptic receptor and be effective in opening the ion channels. Thought of this way, an agonist is like an alternative key that can open the lock. Because nicotine binds to cholinergic receptors, it stimulates this system, leading to effects such as increased attention. In contrast, a drug may block postsynaptic sites, precluding the neurotransmitter from doing so, and thereby act as an antagonist. For example, because it occupies the receptor site, curare prevents acetylcholine from binding postsynaptically. Yet, when in the receptor site, curare does not open the ion channel. Its action is much like having a key that fits in a lock but can't turn there. It is jammed in the lock, preventing the correct key from being used. This jamming of the lock mechanism explains why curare causes paralysis: Acetylcholine cannot bind with the receptor to produce muscle activity.

Myelination

So far we have discussed the mechanics of how information is propagated from one neuron to another. However, we have not considered how information can be carried over long distances in the nervous system. The speed at which neurons propagate electrical signals down their axons depends on the degree to which the axon is insulated by a fatty sheath called **myelin**. The larger the myelin sheath is, the greater the speed with which the electrical signal is propagated down the axon. The axons of some neurons have no myelin sheath. Unmyelinated neurons typically are small and do not carry information over long distances; rather, they generally synapse on nearby neurons. In contrast, neurons whose axons project to distant places in the nervous system are typically myelinated, because myelination decreases the time needed to transport information from one neuron to the next.

To demonstrate the increase in speed afforded by myelin, let's consider a specific type of neuron in the brain known as a **pyramidal cell**, which, among other things, is involved in controlling muscle movement. The axon of a pyramidal cell that controls movement of the right leg must extend from the brain to the bottom reaches of the spinal cord, a distance of more than 3 feet, or approximately 1 meter (m). Unmyelinated fibers convey information at the rate of only about 0.5 millimeter per millisecond (mm/ms). If the pyramidal neuron were unmyelinated, it would take approximately 2,000 ms (i.e., 2 seconds) to convey information from the brain to the base of the spinal cord (2,000 ms $\times$ 0.5 mm/ms = 1 m). Such a time delay would mean that

IN FOCUS: Can Herbs Improve Your Memory, Attention, and Mood?

Balm is sovereign for the brain, strengthening the memory and powerfully chasing away the melancholy (John Evelyn, 1699).

Although we may think that the use of herbal supplements and therapies is a new and trendy approach to treating a variety of disorders, it is actually a time-honored tradition, as attested to by this quotation. Long used in Eastern medicine, and now increasingly in Europe and to a lesser degree in the United States, herbal supplements are being favored in some cases over standard pharmaceutical products. For example, in the United Kingdom, rosemary, lemon balm (a member of the mint family), and sage are used by herbalists and aromatherapists for memory problems. Probably one of the most commonly touted substances for reducing memory problems is ginkgo, which is derived from the leaf of the *Ginkgo biloba* tree, a plant native to China. It is widely prescribed in Europe, especially in France and Germany, for dementia. St. John's wort, an aromatic perennial native to Europe, is frequently used in Germany and other European countries to treat mild to moderate depression. Its effects have been known for a very long time, as evidenced by discussions of the herb by ancient Greek and Roman physicians such as Hippocrates and Galen. Kava, derived from a shrub native to Polynesia and the Pacific Islands and traditionally taken as a beverage mixed with water and coconut milk, is used to reduce anxiety and induce calm. Ginseng, derived from the root of a Chinese perennial, has been used to increase energy (see Beaubrun & Gray, 2000, for a brief review). Do these herbs have the claimed effect on thinking and mood, and if so, how do they work?

There is much controversy surrounding the answer to this question. One source of controversy is the fact that in the United States such substances are not regulated by the Food and Drug Administration, so dosages and purity are not monitored. However, it appears that in some cases, these herbs may have therapeutic effects. For example, there are some reports that ginkgo special extract EGb 761 slows the mental decline of individuals with Alzheimer's disease (LeBars et al., 1997). Its effectiveness in slowing the disease in people with mild to moderate Alzheimer's has, in some cases, been found to approximate the level achieved with standard pharmaceutical products, whose main action is to inhibit acetylcholinesterase (Wettstein, 2000; Mazza, Capuano, Bria, & Mazza, 2006). However, it is not clear whether ginkgo aids cognitive performance in individuals who appear to be healthy; one large-scale study failed to find evidence that ginkgo enhances cognitive performance in healthy older adults (Solomon, Adams, Silver, Zimmer, & DeVeaux, 2002). In addition, a longitudinal study found that ginkgo did not protect against the development of dementia in elderly people (DeKosky et al., 2008). This study included more than 3,000 participants, age 75 or older, who were randomly assigned to receive either ginkgo or a placebo. Most of the participants had normal cognition at the beginning of the study, though some were characterized by mild cognitive impairment. The researchers followed these participants over about a six-year period, and found that participants in both the gingko and placebo groups were equally likely to develop dementia. These results cast doubt on the possibility that ginkgo can be used preventatively. Other longitudinal studies of the possible preventative effects of ginkgo are ongoing (e.g., Vellas et al., 2006), but the results will not be known for a number of years.

Another herb, St. John's wort, has been used to treat depression. A study of patients in clinics in Germany found that St. John's wort was as effective as standard antidepressants and had fewer side effects than conventional medications for treating mildly to moderately depressed individuals (Woelk, 2000). Additional studies have confirmed the beneficial effects of this herb for treating mild cases of depression (Kasper et al., 2008). However, St. John's wort does not appear to be effective with more severely depressed people (Shelton et al., 2001; see Linde, Berner, Egger, & Mulrow, 2005, for review).

So how do these herbs affect the brain? It appears that many of them work on some of the neurotransmitter systems discussed in this chapter. Sage inhibits acetylcholinesterase (Perry, Court, Bidet, & Court, 1996) and binds with muscarinic cholinergic receptors (Wake et al., 2000); balm inhibits acetylcholinesterase as well as binding with nicotinic receptors (Perry et al., 1996). Ginseng facilitates the release of acetycholine (Benishin, Lee, Wang, & Liu, 1991) as well as the binding to muscarinic acetylcholine receptors (Kumar, Ghosal, & Bigl, 1997). Thus, many herbs that are thought to help memory affect the cholinergic system. St. John's wort inhibits the uptake of serotonin and noradrenaline, a mechanism of action similar to more commonly prescribed antidepressant drugs (Neary & Bu, 1999). Furthermore, some of these herbs have a very specific effect: for example, Indian ginseng affects only the cholinergic system, having no effect on GABAergic or glutaminergic receptors (Kumar et al., 1997), whereas ginkgo appears to specifically affect the cholinergic system, rather than affecting all monoamine systems (Fowler et al., 2000).

Interestingly, some herbs may affect the CNS through mechanisms other than neural transmission. For example, ginkgo causes dilation of the blood vessels, which may allow more oxygen to reach the brain. Ginkgo also appears to help in dealing with molecules known as "free radicals" that can interfere with oxygen metabolism. Defects in oxygen metabolism may contribute to a large number of neurodegenerative disorders.

So, should you suggest to your older relatives that they start gobbling down scads of ginkgo, sage, St. John's wort, and ginseng to ward off the mental declines that can accompany aging? Probably not. As with any drugs, dosage and interactions with other drugs, as well as effects on other bodily systems, are important. For example, one 36-year-old woman who ate 70 to 80 ginkgo nuts in an attempt to improve her health unfortunately had a very unexpected outcome: the herb induced seizures four hours later (Miwa, Iijima, Tanaka, & Mizuno, 2001). St. John's wort can affect blood pressure, intensify the effects of anesthetics, and increase the skin's sensitivity to sunlight. It can also interact with many other drugs because it interferes with a metabolic pathway in the liver that is used by many drugs to enter the body. Ginseng can interfere with the functioning of cells in the blood that aid in clotting. Therefore, as with many other products, let the buyer beware!

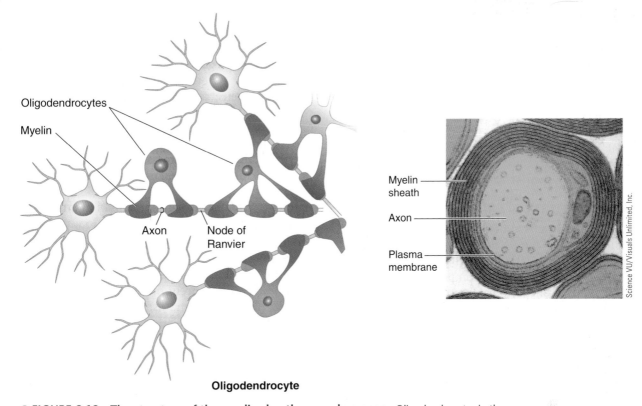

Oligodendrocytes
Myelin
Axon
Node of Ranvier
Oligodendrocyte

Myelin sheath
Axon
Plasma membrane

Science VU/Visuals Unlimited, Inc.

FIGURE 2.12   The structure of the myelin sheath around an axon. Oligodendrocytes in the brain form a short section of the myelin sheath on each of a number of adjacent neurons by wrapping a paddlelike process around each axon. Gaps between sections of myelin, known as nodes of Ranvier, help the electrical signal to be propagated at a constant strength along the axon. © 2010 Cengage Learning

people could not move or react very quickly. The myelination of pyramidal neurons allows information to be relayed at about 50 mm/ms, reducing the time between the generation of the signal in the brain to its arrival at the spinal cord more than a hundredfold, to about 200 ms.

The myelin sheath is not produced by the neuron, but rather by a particular class of glia. In the brain, these are known as **oligodendrocytes**. A portion of the oligodendrocyte wraps itself around the axon much like a strip of carpet wrapped around a cardboard tube; such wrapping creates a discrete section of myelin (● Figure 2.12). The more turns there are around the neuron, the greater the insulation and therefore the greater the conduction speed. Gaps between myelinated sections of an axon are known as **nodes of Ranvier**. Because the electrical signal must jump across these nodes, they serve to keep the electrical signal constant in size rather than degrading as it travels down the axon.

Because myelin is fatty, it is white. Areas of the brain through which myelinated fibers run are known as the *white matter* of the brain. Concentrations of unmyelinated cell bodies constitute the *gray matter*. When a group of cells sends their axons to the same place, the group of axons is known as a **fiber tract**, and because these axons usually traverse long distances, they tend to

be myelinated. For example, the *corpus callosum,* which is the main fiber tract connecting the two hemispheres of the brain, is composed mainly of myelinated fibers, which allow a speedy transfer of information from a neuron in one hemisphere to a distant neuron in the other hemisphere.

Later in this book, we discuss the myelination of neurons in the contexts of development and specific neurological disorders. As discussed in Chapter 15, myelination of the brain follows a developmental course in which sensory and motor regions myelinate early in life, but the connections between more distant regions involved in higher cortical processing do not become fully myelinated until as late as the teenage years or early twenties (Giedd et al., 1996). The result is that regions of the brain become functionally more connected during development (Paus et al., 1999). Some of the disease states we discuss later, such as multiple sclerosis (see Chapter 16), cause the myelin surrounding a neuron to be thinned in a patchy or haphazard manner. This process leads to a significant disruption in neural processing, affecting both motor function and cognitive function (e.g., Peyser & Poser, 1986). In fact, in individuals with multiple sclerosis, a greater degree of demyelination is associated with poorer scores on measures of quality of life (Mowry et al., 2009).

Summary

Electrochemical Signaling in the Nervous System

- Information is conveyed within a neuron via an electrical signal.
- An action potential, which is often referred to as the cell "firing," consists of a change in the differential electrical charge across the cell membrane from −70 millivolts to +40 millivolts and back again.
- An action potential causes neurotransmitter to be released. The neurotransmitter chemical diffuses across the synaptic cleft and binds with specific receptors on the postsynaptic side of neighboring neurons.
- This chemical binding causes the production of postsynaptic potentials, which summate in time and space and can cause an action potential.
- The responsiveness of a neuron is limited by the time needed to "reset" before it can fire again.
- The effect of postsynaptic potentials is temporally limited by reuptake of the neurotransmitter by the presynaptic neuron, enzymatic deactivation of the neurotransmitter, uptake of the neurotransmitter by nearby glial cells, and diffusion away from the synaptic cleft.

Neurotransmitters

- Neurotransmitters are chemicals that are synthesized within the neuron and when released produce an action potential.
- Amino acids are the most common type of neurotransmitter in the CNS. The main excitatory amino acid in the CNS is glutamate, whereas the main inhibitory amino acid is gamma-aminobutyric acid (GABA).
- The other types of neurotransmitter are arranged into systems: acetylcholine is one type, and the monoamines—dopamine, norepinephrine, and serotonin—constitute the other type. The cell bodies for the neurons producing these neurotransmitters originate in subcortical and brainstem regions and project diffusely throughout the cortex.

Chemical Modulation of Neural Transmission

- Presynaptic modulation can occur by affecting the amount of neurotransmitter produced, the release of neurotransmitter into the cleft, or the feedback regulation that is controlled by autoreceptors.
- Modulation can occur in the synaptic cleft by affecting reuptake mechanisms or the breakdown of neurotransmitter.
- Postsynaptic modulation occurs by a substance binding with receptors or by blocking the receptor site.

Myelination

- Myelination is the process whereby oligodendrocytes wrap themselves around the neurons to provide an insulating fatty sheath around axons.
- Myelination reduces transmission time of information to and from disparate sites in the nervous system.
- Myelinated axons are referred to as white matter, in contrast to cell bodies, which are gray matter.

Key Terms

acetylcholine   38
acetylcholinesterase   38
action potential   33
agonists   40
amino acids   39
antagonists   40
autoreceptors   39
axon hillock   34
barbiturates   40
benzodiazepines   40
catecholamines   40
dopamine   40
enzymatic deactivation   38
enzyme   35

excitatory postsynaptic potential (EPSP)   35
excitotoxicity   40
fiber tract   49
G protein   35
GABA   39
glutamate   39
indolamine   40
inhibitory postsynaptic potential (IPSP)   35
ionotropic receptors   35
ischemia   40
mesocortical system   43
mesolimbic system   43
metabotropic receptors   35

monoamines   40
myelin   47
neurotransmitter   34
nigrostriatal system   43
nodes of Ranvier   49
noradrenaline/norepinephrine   40
oligodendrocytes   49
pyramidal cell   47
receptors   34
resting potential   33
reuptake   38
serotonin   40
synapse   34
synaptic vesicles   34

Book Companion Site at www.cengage.com/psychology/Banich
This website provides instructors and students with a wealth of free information and resources, including tutorial quizzes, flashcards, and the glossary.

Methods

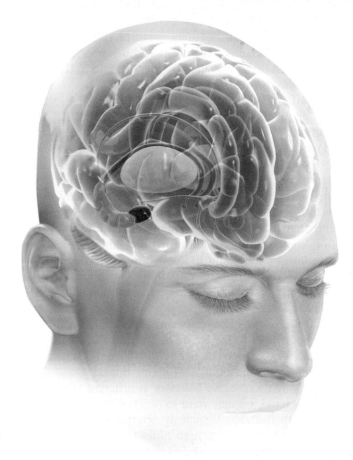

Introduction

In this chapter we discuss the different methods that can be used to understand how the brain influences the way we think, feel, and act. Because cognitive neuroscience is an interdisciplinary field of research, it requires integration of information about the brain with information about behavior. Depending on the question under investigation, we may examine different kinds of information about the brain and behavior. We may want to obtain information about the brain at the neuroanatomical, neurochemical, or neurophysiological level. At a neuroanatomical level, we may need information about the integrity of brain structures, their connections to other brain regions, and their relationship to particular behavioral patterns.

For example, knowing that people have specific difficulties in recognizing faces after sustaining trauma to the ventral regions of the right temporal lobe may allow us to infer a connection between that cognitive process and that brain region. We may also require information about the brain at the neurochemical level. For example, we may want to know how the dysregulation of the neurotransmitter dopamine contributes to the symptoms of schizophrenia. Finally, at the neurophysiological level, we may observe which brain regions are electrically or metabolically active during performance of a specific task. For example, we may want to know the degree to which the right hemisphere is electrically responsive during a musical judgment task.

We can also observe behavior at different levels. On the one hand, we may want to observe sensory processing in an individual, such as determining whether a person can distinguish high tones from low tones. On the other hand, we may need to examine more central aspects of mental processes, such as the integrity of the memory system. In still other cases, we may want to deconstruct specific mental abilities, such as determining whether a memory deficit is limited to learning new information or extends to retrieving previously learned information as well.

To investigate each of these issues requires particular tools: Research methods are the tools of cognitive neuroscientists. The research methods and ideas introduced in this chapter will be referred to throughout this book as we explore the neurocognitive underpinnings of mental activity. During all our discussions, understanding the strengths and limitations of different research methods is important; the adage "You need the right tool for the job" is as apt in cognitive neuroscience as in carpentry. If you have ever tried to use a knife or a dime when you needed a screwdriver, you know that the correct tool can mean the difference between success and failure or between ease and hardship. In cognitive neuroscience, the proper tool may be a particular clinical population, a specific brain imaging technique, or a certain experimental method.

Cognitive neuroscientists must consider how the information they gather in any investigation is influenced by the choice of a particular population and a particular method. Each choice biases the researcher toward observing some aspects of functioning and not others. Consider, as an analogy, that the form of transportation you choose to take from one city to another influences what you see along the way. Taking a plane from one city to another will allow you to clearly see differences in the topography of land, and to distinguish between plains and forest, whereas taking a car will allow you to see differences in the regional architecture of buildings such as farmhouses and row houses. Given the limitations imposed by any single method of neurocognitive inquiry, you may wonder how scientists can be certain of the conclusions that they draw about brain-behavior relationships. Are these scientists as foolhardy as the inhabitants of the Emerald City in *The Wizard of Oz*, who thought the city was emerald because they were wearing green eyeglasses?

As we discuss in more detail later in this chapter, cognitive neuroscientists rely upon a strategy akin to changing your eyeglasses often. In general, researchers aim to gather information on the same question by using a variety of methods with a variety of populations. This technique—examining whether all the answers obtained from a set of interrelated experiments lead to the same conclusion—is known as the **method of converging operations**. When researchers have examined a question from multiple perspectives and all answers point to the same verdict, the researchers can be relatively confident that they understand a basic aspect of the relationship between the brain and behavior. Let's consider an example of converging operations by examining three representative findings, from different methods, regarding the role played by the parietal lobe in directing attention to particular regions of space. Simultaneously, we'll also consider the potential pitfalls of each method.

First, research with monkeys indicates that the response of neurons in the posterior parietal cortex varies depending on the region of space to which the animal is directing its attention (e.g., Lynch, Mountcastle, Talbot, & Yin, 1977). Suggesting that this region plays a leading role in directing attention, it appears to synchronize its activity with that of visual areas (Saalmann, Pigarev, & Vidyasagar, 2007). Extrapolating from animals, however, may sometimes be problematic because their repertoire of behavior and the organization of their brains may differ from those of humans. Second, brain imaging in neurologically intact individuals reveals an increase in the metabolic activity of the parietal region when a person directs attention to a specific portion of visual space (Corbetta, Miezin, Shulman, & Petersen, 1993), and such activation varies with how well they exert such attention (Huddleston & DeYoe, 2008). However, brain imaging techniques usually provide an "average" of activity across a number of individuals, so conclusions about precise anatomical locations can sometimes be difficult to make. Third, it was originally noted that after a person sustains a unilateral parietal lobe lesion, he or she often ignores the contralateral portion of visual space (e.g., Vallar & Perani, 1986), and newer, higher-resolution neuroimaging techniques support that association (Mort et al., 2003). However, findings from patients with brain damage are always subject to variability among individuals, both in the extent of the neurological damage and in the diversity of the individuals' experiences before and after the damage. Although the evidence from any one of these studies alone is not convincing, evidence from all three methods converges on the same conclusion: namely, that the parietal region plays an important role in directing attention to a given region of space. When such convergence occurs, researchers can have more confidence that the answer arrived at is accurate and that the inherent biases of each method are not so great as to obscure their usefulness. Notice that such a converging body of work usually cannot be performed by a single scientist; rather, it depends on a community of scientists with different areas of expertise.

We now turn our discussion to the specific subject populations and the specific methods used to examine the relationship between the brain and behavior. In this endeavor, we need three critical ingredients. First, we need a population of individuals on which to test a hypothesis. The group of participants we choose will vary depending on the question we are asking. Second, we need a means of gathering information about the brain of each individual. Depending on the question, we may want information about brain structure, brain function, or both. Third, we need a way to measure behavior. In some cases, we may want to use specific measures of behavior, and in other cases, large batteries of tests. In the remainder of this chapter, we survey the options available for each of these three critical ingredients and outline the advantages and disadvantages conferred by each choice.

Populations of Research Participants

In this section of the chapter we examine the specific advantages and disadvantages of using three major populations—individuals with circumscribed brain damage, neurologically intact individuals, and nonhuman animals—to investigate questions in cognitive neuroscience.

■ Patients with Circumscribed Brain Damage

Understanding mental functioning by examining brain-damaged patients has a long and venerable history, stretching back some 2,000 years. In the time of the Romans, Galen, a physician who ministered to the wounds of the gladiators, noticed that contestants sustaining injury to the arm, leg, or torso retained their powers of thought, whereas those who sustained injury to the head or the brain did not. From these observations, he inferred that the brain was linked to thought.

Galen's approach was a precursor of the logic we use today to determine which regions of the brain are important for a given mental function. If damage to a particular brain region results in an inability to perform a specific mental function, scientists usually assume that the function must have depended on that brain region. This approach is known as the **lesion method**. During the history of neuropsychological investigation, this method has proved very powerful in expanding knowledge about the neurological bases of thought and emotion. It has led us to conceptualize the brain as being composed of different subsystems, or *modules*, each supporting a different mental function. Although scientists have different ideas about exactly what constitutes a module (e.g., Fodor, 1985), for our purposes it can be considered a portion of a processing system that is dedicated to a single function not performed elsewhere within that system (e.g., reading, verbal short-term memory, or face recognition). Furthermore, we now realize that these subsystems are located in specific regions of brain tissue, a concept called **localization of function**.

The brain was not always believed to work in the manner just described. In the early twentieth century, scientists debated whether functions were localized or whether the brain worked by **mass action**, meaning that all pieces of brain contributed to all functions. One of the most notable supporters of the mass action viewpoint was the psychologist Karl Lashley, who did much of his work in this area in the 1920s and 1930s (Lashley, 1929). He argued that the nature of cognitive deficits following brain damage hinged not on which region of the brain was destroyed but rather on the extent of the damage: The larger the amount of tissue destroyed, the greater were the decrements in performance. In contrast, researchers supporting the idea of localization of function argued that the site of brain damage, not just the overall amount of destruction, predicted the nature and degree of the deficit observed.

Today, although we know that mental functions are localized in the brain, we also know that no brain region acts in isolation. Because of improved techniques for measuring lesions (or in the case of animals, creating lesions), and because of more sophisticated methods for measuring behavior, researchers have realized that not all lesions have the same effect on behavior. Thus, behavioral differences must occur because of differences in brain structure. However, despite evidence of distinct subsystems in the brain, we must not forget that the brain is comprised of about 50 billion *interconnected* neurons. In fact, as we discuss later in this chapter, many computational models that represent the brain's functioning in an abstract fashion, using computer simulations, are precisely designed to capture the nature of this diffuse processing. Consider by analogy a car. Although it is made of specific parts or systems such as an engine, a drive train, wheels, and a suspension, all these parts are useless for travel unless they are interconnected in a specific manner so that the power from the engine can be transferred to the drive train to move the wheels.

Throughout this book, we will see that certain cognitive abilities, such as language, have been conceived traditionally as being organized in a modular fashion, with specific subcomponents such as those required for the comprehension of spoken language, the production of spoken language, reading, and writing each being performed by relatively distinct brain regions. In contrast, other cognitive functions, such as certain aspects of attention, are much more diffusely organized across many brain regions. Thus, we must remember that the brain relies both on localization of function and on distributed processing to carry out cognitive function in a seamless fashion.

Uses of the Lesion Method

The main strength of the lesion method is that it allows a specific region of brain tissue to be directly linked to a specific aspect of mental processing. We can directly observe that when a particular region is damaged, a particular mental process is lost. Our ability to make such a linkage has been critically important to understanding many aspects of human cognition and emotion. Unlike animal models, in which scientists carefully create lesions in a certain region of the brain and then observe the effect on behavior, the lesion method in humans requires investigators to rely on cases of brain damage that result from unfortunate circumstances, such as war, accident, injury, or disease. Therefore, the researcher has no control over the location, extent, and cause of the lesion in any given patient. Typically, scientists work with medical personnel to identify patients who can be asked to participate in a research project. The success of this method depends critically on the cooperation, courage, and goodwill of these patients. Even though testing will starkly reveal the extent of their disabilities and will not benefit them personally, they nonetheless participate, hoping that the knowledge gained will help others.

When using the lesion method, a researcher can take one of two conceptual approaches: one emphasizes knowledge about neural substrates, the other knowledge about cognitive function. The approach chosen has a large influence on the population recruited for a study. Throughout this book, we give many examples of these two different conceptual approaches, so we discuss them next in more detail.

If the researcher chooses to emphasize neural substrates, by asking, "What functions are supported by a particular piece of brain tissue?," then she or he assembles a group of individuals in whom the site, cause, and extent of damage are as similar as possible. A classic example of this approach is work by Brenda Milner and colleagues at the Montreal Neurological Institute, who examined the role of the temporal lobe in memory. Their population consisted of patients with epilepsy who underwent a "planned lesion"—unilateral surgical removal of portions of the temporal lobe because these portions were the center of epileptic activity. Using this approach, Milner and colleagues demonstrated that removal (that is, excision) of regions in and around the hippocampus within the temporal lobe leads to difficulties in forming new long-term memories. By comparing excisions of the left hippocampus with excisions of the right, they also demonstrated that whether verbal or visual memory is impaired depends on the hemisphere of the excision (e.g., Milner, 1978).

To determine whether the behavioral disruption is linked specifically to the brain structure under investigation, such studies usually include groups of patients with damage elsewhere in the brain. Returning to the previous example, Milner and colleagues typically included one or more groups of individuals with unilateral damage to a different brain region, such as the frontal lobe. Because individuals with damage to these other regions did not exhibit problems in forming new long-term memories, the researchers concluded that the hippocampal region specifically supports the formation of new long-term memories.

Such an approach allows us to identify a particular brain region as critically important to a specific component of cognition, and thus it can provide invaluable information to physicians, clinical neuropsychologists, and other medical professionals. For example, neurosurgeons must know which cognitive functions are likely to be disrupted if a particular region of brain tissue is excised. Likewise, knowing the site of brain damage allows clinical neuropsychologists to predict which intellectual abilities are likely to be compromised, to tailor their evaluation of cognitive deficits, and to plan for appropriate rehabilitation.

The other conceptual approach to the lesion method emphasizes cognitive function. When taking this approach, researchers select a group of individuals who exhibit the same behavioral symptoms, with little regard for the location of the brain damage. For example, *hemineglect,* as discussed in Chapter 1, causes individuals to ignore information on one side of space. Although most common after damage to parietal regions of the right hemisphere, hemineglect can occur after damage to many other brain regions, including the basal ganglia, the frontal lobes, and the thalamus. Researchers interested in the cognitive consequences of hemineglect may assemble a group of individuals who have hemineglect regardless of the site of the lesion. For example, researchers might conduct a study to determine whether the neglect can be minimized if there are fewer objects in the environment. Obtaining answers to this question can be useful in designing effective methods of rehabilitation. Although this approach does not emphasize the neural organization of the brain, it may nonetheless be able to provide such information. Similarity of the location of damage across patients with a common behavioral deficit can help to identify the set of neural structures likely to participate in that given function.

Comparing patterns of cognitive disability and cognitive sparing across individuals with lesions in different locations can provide important insights into the architecture of the mind. **Double dissociation** is a particularly powerful method that allows researchers to determine whether two cognitive functions are independent of one another (e.g., Shallice, 1988; Teuber, 1955). A double dissociation occurs when lesions have converse effects on two distinct cognitive functions: one brain lesion causes a disruption in Cognitive Function A but not Cognitive Function B, whereas a different lesion causes a disruption in Cognitive Function B but not Cognitive Function A. From such a pattern, we can infer that the functions can be independent, because the viability of one cognitive function does not depend on the viability of the other.

To make the concept of a double dissociation more concrete, let's consider a classic example, the dissociation between Broca's aphasia and Wernicke's aphasia. Both of these conditions involve disruptions in language processing (see Chapter 9). As a starting point, we might hypothesize that all aspects of language processing rely on the same region of the brain. If this were the case, we would predict that if a person lost the ability to understand language, he or she would also lose the ability to speak. However, Broca's aphasia and Wernicke's aphasia illustrate that the ability to produce speech and the ability to comprehend speech are distinct. In Broca's aphasia, comprehension of spoken language is, for the most part, intact. However, individuals with this syndrome have great difficulty producing speech. Persons with Wernicke's aphasia display the opposite pattern. Such individuals cannot understand what is said to them but nonetheless fluently produce grammatically correct sentences (although, as we will learn later, these sentences are usually nonsensical). Considering these two conditions together, we see that disruptions in speech output are independent of whether a disruption in speech comprehension occurs, and vice versa.

The importance of the lesion method in expanding our knowledge in cognitive neuroscience cannot be underestimated. It has led to classic conceptualizations about the neural underpinnings of language, memory, and perception, to mention just a few areas (see Damasio & Damasio, 1989, for further discussion). Even today, when we have many new techniques for imaging the brain's structure and function, the lesion method remains an important tool for cognitive neuroscientists (Rorden & Karnath, 2004). Yet for all its power, this method, like any other, has its limitations. We now turn to a discussion of these limitations.

Difficulties with the Lesion Method

The lesion method imposes two major limitations on researchers. First, variability in characteristics of the participant population, as well as variability in the location and extent of the damage, can make straightforward inferences difficult. Second, although the lesion method has an obvious intuitive appeal and appears to allow straightforward inferences about the relationship between the brain and behavior, in some cases this logic can lead us to inaccurate conclusions. We discuss both sets of problems in turn.

Compared with lesion experiments done with nonhuman animals, research performed with people who have sustained brain damage is "messy" because the sample is much less homogeneous along a number of dimensions. In animal experiments, the population usually consists of littermates (which are genetically similar) raised in the same environment, given the same lesion at the same age, provided with the same experiences before and after the lesion, and assessed behaviorally at the same age. Thus, genetic and environmental characteristics of the sample are made as comparable as possible.

In contrast, populations of individuals who have sustained brain damage are quite different. Individuals typically vary widely in age, socioeconomic status, and educational background. Prior to brain damage, these individuals had diverse life experiences. Afterward, their life experiences tended to vary too, depending on the type of rehabilitation they received, their attitudes toward therapy and recovery, and their social support networks. Compared with research animals or the human participants of standard psychology experiments (typically college sophomores), individuals with brain damage who participate in studies on the neural underpinnings of human cognition are quite a heterogeneous group. Even if we compare groups of individuals who have similar demographic characteristics, such as age, educational background, and gender, the participants still differ on a myriad of other individual characteristics. Therefore, two individuals who sustained lesions in the same location might nonetheless exhibit different degrees of deficit as a result of their varying experiences.

Furthermore, lesions sustained by humans are much less specific, both in extent and origin, than those created in animal experiments. Although a researcher can assemble a group of patients in whom the lesion is in more or less the same location (e.g., the temporal lobe), the size and severity of the lesions are likely to vary widely. In animals, we can induce lesions in a uniform manner (e.g., apply electrical current to destroy brain tissue), whereas in humans the cause of damage can range from a bullet wound to a stroke to an infectious disease to surgical removal of a region necessitated by epilepsy or tumor. These different events yield very different types of damage. For example, damage from stroke has more diffuse effects and has a higher probability of involving subcortical regions than damage inflicted by a bullet does. Often researchers attempt to assemble groups of individuals with similar causes of brain damage, yet in some cases doing so may be impossible.

Thus, many factors—the diversity of characteristics among people who sustain brain damage, the heterogeneity of the causes of damage, and variability in the size and location of lesions—can impede our ability to isolate the specific neural structures that influence a given behavior. When a relationship is uncovered, however, it is more likely to be robust because it was discerned despite variations in populations and differences in the nature of the damage.

The second major limitation of the lesion method is that we cannot directly observe the function performed by the damaged portion of the brain. Rather, all that can be observed is how the rest of the brain performs *without* that particular area. From these observations we then infer the previous role of the damaged region. Although such inferences are usually sound, they may have certain limitations and liabilities. First, only the regions of the brain *critical* to a given cognitive function can be identified, not the entire set of brain regions that may participate in that function. Second, behavioral impairment may result after damage to a region not because that region is critical to the task, but rather because that region *connects* other brain regions that must interact for the function to be performed correctly. Finally, a brain region's contribution to a particular cognitive function may be "silent," or masked, if the task can be performed in more than one manner. Individuals may remain competent at performing a given task by using an alternative strategy to that used before damage.

To appreciate the limitations of the lesion method in identifying all the brain regions that are involved in performing a task, think about putting on a play. If the person playing the main character is ill (and there is no understudy), the show cannot go on; therefore, we can identify that person as critical for the performance of the play. But if one of the stagehands or prop masters becomes ill, the curtain still goes up, even though clearly the missing individual contributed to the production. The show can continue because the chores of the remaining crew are likely to be shuffled to compensate for the absence of this individual. Similarly, if brain damage destroys a region that participates in but is not critical to the performance of a function, behavior can appear to be more or less intact, because other brain regions can act to take over or support that function.

Another serious limitation of the lesion method is that it does not allow us to discern whether damage to a particular region of the brain alters performance because that region is critical to task performance or because it contains axons, known as *fibers of passage,*

that connect two or more brain regions critical for the function. When damage occurs, information carried by these fibers, in effect, cannot be transmitted from one brain region to another. The result is a behavioral deficit called a **disconnection syndrome**. To understand this concept more clearly, consider a situation in which severe weather prevents food from the farms from reaching the city. Perhaps the farms were destroyed and are no longer producing food. This case would be similar to a brain lesion having damaged a portion of the brain critical for performance of a task. Alternatively, assume that the farms are intact but the highway between the farms and the city was ruined and thus the food cannot be transported. This situation would be similar to what occurs in a disconnection syndrome. Throughout this book, there are many examples of disconnection syndromes, including *split-brain syndrome* (discussed in Chapter 3 on lateralization of function) and *conduction aphasia* (discussed in Chapter 9 on language). We can sometimes identify disconnection syndromes by referring to brain anatomy. If the region of the brain that leads to cognitive deficits contains few cell bodies and many nerve fiber tracts, a disconnection syndrome is a more likely explanation for the deficit.

A final limitation of the lesion method is that it may cause us to underestimate the role of a specific brain region in a given cognitive function. We may underestimate a region's contribution either because a person compensates by using a different strategy (that relies on intact areas) to perform the task, or because of reorganization of the brain tissue itself. For example, suppose that after damage to Region A of the brain, a person navigates around her or his world without much difficulty, leading us to assume that the functioning of Region A is unrelated to the cognitive skill of navigation. Yet, in actuality, Region A *is* important for navigation, playing a role in constructing the geographical relationship between objects or places (e.g., that the post office is to the east of the main shopping center). However, Region B of the brain provides the ability to navigate point to point by means of landmarks (e.g., the post office is six blocks past the church). It is possible to uncover the distinct roles of Regions A and B in navigation only if we carefully break down general cognitive skills into their components and test each component individually, a task that sometimes can be difficult. Alternatively, a brain region may be critical for a function, but after damage the brain reorganizes so that the function is now performed by other regions that normally would not support the task. We discuss the issue of reorganization of function that can occur after brain damage in more detail in Chapter 15.

Single-Case versus Group Studies

Our discussion of the lesion method would be incomplete without a review of what we can learn from single-case and/or group studies of individuals with brain damage. In **single-case studies**, a single individual with brain damage is studied intensively with a variety of neuro-psychological tests. For example, the case of H.M., who received a bilateral temporal lobectomy (see Chapter 10), provided invaluable insights over 30 years into the role of the temporal lobe in memory. Because the memory loss he experienced after the surgery was so profound, no other individual has ever had this surgery, making him a unique but highly important case. In contrast, in **group studies**, individuals with brain damage who have similar characteristics (e.g., lesions in similar areas) are studied as a group. Some researchers argue that group studies may obscure patterns of behavior or cause misleading interpretations of data because the group average may be a composite that is rarely, if ever, found in any one individual (e.g., Caramazza & Badecker, 1989). Suppose, for example, as illustrated in Table 3.1, that researchers test a group of nine individuals with localized brain damage and a control group of nine neurologically intact people on three tasks. Looking at the bottom of the table, you can see that the average percentage correct for each of the three tasks is lower for the group with brain damage than for the control group. However, no single individual with brain damage performs more poorly than the controls on all three tasks! Rather, you should be able to identify three subgroups of patients: one group that does poorly on Task 1 (Individuals 1–3), one that does poorly on Task 2 (Individuals 4–6), and a third that does poorly on Task 3 (Individuals 7–9). Because of difficulties such as these, some researchers endorse the single-case study approach.

However, the single-case-study approach also has its difficulties (see Zurif, Gardner, & Brownell, 1989). One problem is that we cannot be sure that the pattern observed for a single individual represents people in general. For example, we know that left-handers, who constitute about 10% of the population, have a neural organization for cognitive function distinct from that of right-handers. If handedness, genetics, or some special environmental influence causes an individual's brain organization to be atypical, the pattern of disability after damage may be atypical as well. This issue is especially a problem when the behavioral syndrome and its causative lesion are so rare that they have been observed in only one or two individuals. In such cases, our power of interpretation is significantly restricted.

If both group and single-case studies have limitations, what are researchers to do? One approach, known as the **multiple-case-study approach**, is to validate research findings on a series of patients, each of whom is also treated as a single-case study. In this approach, data for each individual within each group are provided, so that researchers can determine the variability across individuals as well as the degree to which the overall group average typifies the behavior of individuals within the group (● Figure 3.1).

Multiple-case studies can also be used to examine whether a relationship exists between a cognitive deficit and some other factor of interest, such as the amount of tissue destroyed. For example, in a previous example in this chapter, Milner and colleagues found that the degree of hippocampal damage is proportional to the degree of memory loss, providing additional evidence of this region's role in memory formation (e.g., Pigott & Milner, 1993). A single-case study cannot address this question; it can reveal only whether the hippocampal region is related to memory, not whether the degree of damage predicts the severity of the memory problem.

■ Neurologically Intact Individuals

Studying neurologically intact individuals can also aid our understanding of the linkage between mental function and brain structure. In studies using the lesion method, neurologically intact people provide the important control group that allows us to determine the degree to which the performance of individuals with

TABLE 3.1	Hypothetical Example of Potential Distortion of Performance Patterns When Group Averages Are Used		
	Performance as Measured by Percentage Correct		
Individual with Brain Damage	**Task 1**	**Task 2**	**Task 3**
1	20	75	70
2	25	70	80
3	30	80	75
4	75	25	75
5	80	30	70
6	70	20	80
7	75	80	25
8	70	75	30
9	80	70	20
Average of nine individuals with brain damage	58.3	58.3	58.3
Average of nine neurologically intact individuals	78	80	83

The average score for the nine individuals with brain damage does not adequately reflect the performance of any given individual. Although the average for individuals with brain damage is lower than that for neurologically intact individuals on all three tasks, all individuals with brain damage score as well as neurologically intact individuals on two of the three tasks.

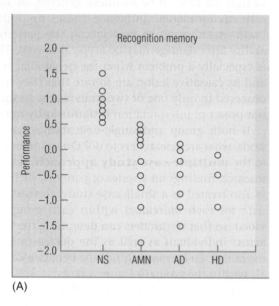
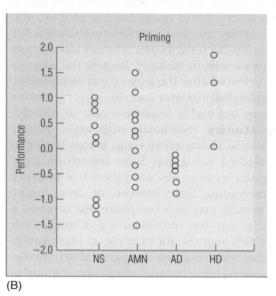

(A)   (B)

● **FIGURE 3.1   An example of the multiple-case-study approach.** To determine the extent of differences between patients with brain damage (AMN, patients with amnesia; AD, patients with Alzheimer's disease; HD, patients with Huntington's disease) and neurologically intact subjects (NS), the researcher treats each member of the group as a single-case study as well. (A) On a measure of recognition memory, every patient is performing at a level worse than that of the neurologically intact controls (0 indicates average performance, positive values represent above-average performance, and negative values below-average performance). (B) In contrast, on a measure of memory "priming" (i.e., facilitation of processing of material due to prior exposure), much more variability exists across the groups; the result is an overlap between the performance of the neurologically intact participants and that of the different patient populations. Whereas individuals with brain damage can clearly be characterized as having poorer recognition memory than controls, the same is not true for memory priming. © 2011 Cengage Learning

brain damage is compromised. Clearly, a problem is much more severe if, after brain damage, an individual performs worse than 98% of the individuals in a neurologically intact reference group than if he or she performs worse than 40% of those individuals. The larger the control group assembled for any given test, the more certainty researchers can have in such comparisons.

Well-designed neuropsychological studies must include careful consideration of the characteristics of the individuals composing the neurologically intact control group. These individuals must be matched, on a case-by-case basis, as thoroughly as possible with the individuals with brain damage for demographic variables such as age, gender, and educational history. In this manner, the study hones in on the degree to which the brain damage, and not other factors, affects performance. When choosing a control group, we may also want to select individuals who are experiencing stresses similar to those of individuals who recently suffered brain damage. Because individuals under stress often perform poorly on cognitive tasks, a well-designed study should demonstrate that any cognitive deficit can be attributed to the brain damage and not to the stresses associated with illness, medical treatment, financial concerns, or changes in family dynamics. For this reason, neurologically intact individuals gathered from a different medical population are often good controls because

they are under similar stresses but do not have brain damage. One example of such a population is patients who, like those with brain damage, are receiving rehabilitation, but who are receiving such treatment because of bodily injury rather than brain injury.

Neurologically intact individuals may aid our understanding of brain-behavior relations in other ways besides acting as a control group. They can shed light on how individual variations in the neuroanatomical structure of the brain are related to cognition. For example, differences among individuals in the neuroanatomy of language-related brain regions can predict how well or how quickly they can learn foreign speech sounds (Golestani, Molko, Dehaene, LeBihan, & Pallier, 2007). Finally, when brain imaging techniques (discussed later in this chapter) are used with neurologically intact individuals, scientists can obtain evidence on how brain structures work together under *normal* conditions. Such insights cannot be obtained from individuals with brain damage.

■ Nonhuman Animals

Until this point, we mainly have considered how studying people can aid our understanding of the neural underpinnings of cognition. However, studies performed with nonhuman animals, most notably monkeys, can also aid in this endeavor. Although the brains of monkeys and humans are distinct, they appear to share several basic organizational principles, some of which are exhibited in all mammalian brains (● Figure 3.2). Because monkeys can be trained to perform sophisticated cognitive tasks, classically many mental functions have been investigated with these animals, such as object recognition (e.g., Gross, Rocha-Miranda, & Bender, 1972), attention (Moran & Desimone, 1985), and memory (Mishkin, 1982), a tradition that continues today. Of course, some mental functions, such as language, are more difficult, if not impossible, to study in nonhuman species.

For many of the reasons mentioned earlier in this chapter, such as better control over environmental conditions, the size and nature of lesions, and previous life experiences, research with animals can be more straightforward than that with people. In addition, certain techniques that we discuss later in this chapter, such as single-cell recordings, can be readily performed with animals, but only with very restricted groups of people. As with research involving humans, researchers must adhere to careful guidelines concerning the ethical treatment of their animal subjects. Researchers are responsible for designing and following protocols to ensure that the animals experience the minimum amount of pain possible and are not unduly traumatized by the procedures.

Now that we have discussed the different populations of individuals that are used to examine brain-behavior relationships, we turn our attention to the different methods available for both research and clinical work that inform us about brain anatomy, brain function, and behavior.

Techniques for Assessing Brain Anatomy

Our ability to link brain structure and function has been revolutionized since the mid-1970s because of the advent of different brain imaging techniques. Such imaging techniques are useful to researchers using the lesion method because they allow the location of damage to be pinpointed much more precisely than previously possible in living people. Prior to this revolution, researchers had to wait for postmortem examination of the brain to localize damage that had occurred years or decades prior, or they had to guess the location of brain damage from scant medical records or exams. To appreciate the advances provided by these brain imaging methods, look at ● Figure 3.3, which depicts the older methods. Older methods only informed us about what part of the skull was missing due to entry of a bullet or another missile, without providing any hint of the extent or depth of the brain damage. Methods that allow us to see the internal structures of the brain are useful not only for identifying damaged structures, but also for assessing the size and shape of neural structures in neurologically intact people.

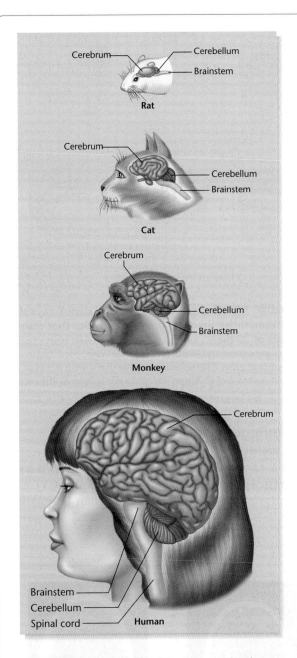

● **FIGURE 3.2 Similarity of brain organization across mammalian species.** Because the overall organization of the brains of other mammals is similar to that of humans, research with other species can help us to understand which portions of the brain are important for which mental functions. Like studies with humans, all such research must be approved by an ethics committee, which ensures that the animals are treated as humanely as possible. © 2009 Cengage Learning

The intricacies of some of the new brain imaging techniques can take a career to master. The goal of this section of the chapter is to present a practical overview of how these techniques work, the basic principles behind them, and, most importantly, the type of information they provide. We also consider the advantages and disadvantages of each technique. We begin our discussion with the first of the modern brain imaging techniques, computerized axial tomography.

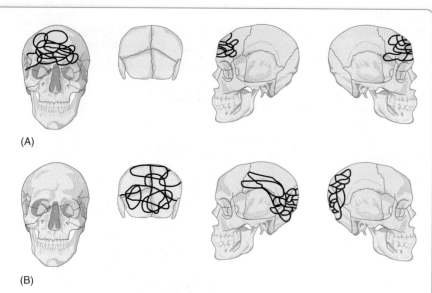

(A)

(B)

● **FIGURE 3.3 Composite diagrams of skull X-rays showing the entrance (and sometimes the exit) points of missiles that caused damage in two groups of 20 men.** X-rays were used in the days before brain imaging techniques to infer the extent and location of brain damage. Localization was not precise and allowed only gross differentiation such as that shown between (A) individuals with anterior lesions and (B) those with posterior lesions. © 2011 Cengage Learning

which is less dense than blood, which is less dense than bone. In a CAT scan, dense tissue such as bone appears white, whereas material with the least density, such as CSF, appears black. Typically, CAT scans provide a series of "slices" of the brain (usually between 9 and 12), stacked one above the other. In CAT scans, regions of the brain that were damaged long ago appear darker than the surrounding tissue because they are filled with less dense CSF (● Figure 3.4A). In contrast, areas in which a hemorrhage has recently occurred are indicated by lighter areas, because blood is denser than brain tissue (● Figure 3.4B). The advantage of CAT scans is that they are relatively inexpensive and available in most hospitals. Furthermore, there are no restrictions on who can receive a CAT scan, in contrast to other methods discussed later.

■ Computerized Axial Tomography

The density of brain structures can be determined with X-rays in a process called **computerized axial tomography** (**CAT**, also sometimes called **CT**). Cerebrospinal fluid (CSF) is less dense than brain tissue,

■ Magnetic Resonance Imaging

Although CAT scanning was a breakthrough, in many ways it has been superseded by **magnetic resonance imaging (MRI)**, a technique that relies on the use of magnetic fields to distort the behavior of protons. The information recorded about how long the protons take to recover from this distortion is then used to create an image of the anatomy of the brain. The description of how this technique works is somewhat more complicated than that for CAT, so we examine it in a bit more detail.

MRI relies on three magnetic fields. The first is the **static field**, a constant magnetic field. MRI machines are classified by the strength of this field. Clinical machines typically are 1.5 tesla (T), with "high-field" research machines generally being either 3 or 4T (for a reference point, the magnetic field of the earth is 0.0001T) and some experimental machines work at a field strength of 7T or higher (● Figure 3.5). This static magnetic field causes all the magnetically sensitive particles to align themselves in the same direction. A perturbation to this field is provided by the second magnetic field, the **pulse sequence**, an oscillating magnetic field. The time it takes for the protons to revert to their original state, the *relaxation time,* is recorded through a radio-frequency coil that acts as a **receiver coil**. This coil is positioned around or near a portion of the individual's head.

Because hydrogen atoms in different substances have different relaxation times, we can adjust the various parameters of the pulse sequence to maximize the ability to image certain substances, such as

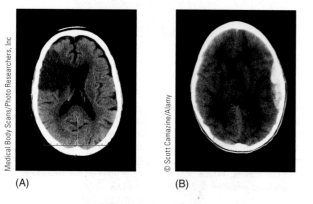

(A)   (B)

Medical Body Scans/Photo Researchers, Inc

© Scott Camazine/Alamy

● **FIGURE 3.4 Slices of a computerized axial tomography (CAT) scan.** (A) Low-density regions appear dark on a CAT scan. Here the dark region in the frontal lobe of the left hemisphere indicates the site of damage as a result of stroke. Because brain tissue in this region was lost, it filled with cerebrospinal fluid, which is less dense than the surrounding brain tissue. (B) High-density regions appear bright on a CAT scan. Here a collection of blood (known as a *hematoma*) appears as an area of increased brightness in the right temporal lobe, as blood is more dense than brain tissue. Notice that the presence of the hematoma causes a displacement of the lateral ventricle on that side of the brain.

water if we are interested in obtaining information about the density of brain tissue, or fat if we are interested in imaging white matter. The intensity of the signal received by the receiver coil indicates the concentration of the particular substance in the brain, but by itself the signal intensity cannot provide information on the location in the brain from which it is coming. This information is provided by the third magnetic field, the **gradient field**, which varies in intensity over the area being imaged. It provides a way to identify particular locations, thus enabling identification of the location from which signals are emanating. The combination of spatial information from the gradient field and the signal intensity received after a series of radio-frequency pulses allows a three-dimensional image of the brain to be reconstructed (for a more advanced but readable discussion of this method and some of its applications, see www.howstuffworks .com/mri.htm).

MRI has two main advantages over CAT. First, MRIs do not require X-rays, so they do not involve transmitting high-energy ionizing radiation through the body. Second, the clarity of the picture—that is, the *spatial resolution* of the image—is superior in MRIs. If you look at ● Figure 3.6A, which is a coronal section of the brain from an autopsy, you can see how well a similar slice provided by MRI, in ● Figure 3.6B, compares with what is revealed by anatomical dissection.

Not everyone can be subjected to an MRI scan. Because magnetic fields interfere with electrical fields, individuals with pacemakers (which generate electrical signals to the heart) cannot undergo MRI. Also, any individual with metal in her or his body that is not connected to hard tissue (e.g., a clip on an artery or a metal shaving in the eye such as might be received from welding) cannot have an MRI taken, because the attraction of the metal to the magnet could cause it to move or dislodge. (Metal embedded in hard tissue, such as the fillings in teeth, is not a problem.) Other than these exceptions, MRI is the anatomical imaging technique of choice because of its superior imaging capabilities and the lack of high-energy ionizing radiation.

A more recently developed anatomical MRI method called **diffusion tensor imaging (DTI)** has the potential to provide information not only about the structural integrity of brain regions, but also about the anatomical connectivity between different brain regions. This method detects the

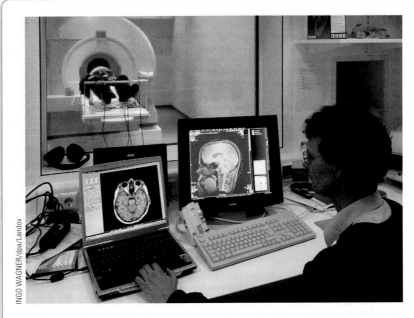

● **FIGURE 3.5   A typical setup for magnetic resonance imaging (MRI).** The technician or researcher works in a control room at a console where images of the participant's brain can be viewed. This keeps the researcher outside of the magnetic field of the MRI machine, which is in a separate room, viewed as shown in this picture through a glass window. For neuroimaging studies, an individual's head and torso are positioned within the large round cylinder, which contains the magnet that produces the static field. A set of goggles is often positioned over the participant's eyes so that he or she can view a stimulus required for performing either cognitive or emotional tasks.

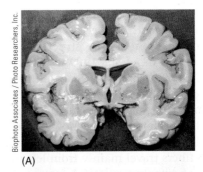

(A)

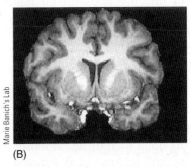

(B)

● **FIGURE 3.6   A comparison of the clarity obtained in anatomical dissection and magnetic resonance imaging (MRI).** (A) A coronal section through the brain achieved by anatomical dissection. The temporal lobes, Sylvian fissure, putamen, globus pallidus, lateral ventricles, and frontal lobes can be seen. (B) The same coronal slice as imaged by MRI. Note how precisely the MRI reveals anatomical detail.

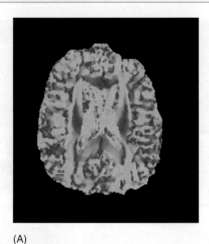

(A)

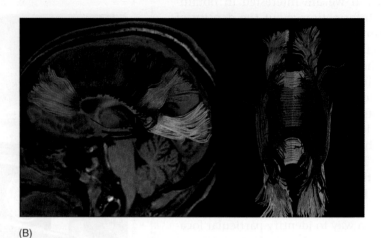

(B)

● **FIGURE 3.7A   Examples of diffusion tensor imaging.** Shown here is a horizontal slice of the brain at the level of the thalamus. Fibers going left to right are shown in red, those going top to bottom are shown in blue, and those going front to back are shown in green. Notice that the anterior and posterior portions of the corpus callosum are shown in red, that subcortical-cortical connections from the thalamus are shown in blue, and fibers connecting frontal and posterior regions are shown in green. Courtesy of Marie Banich's Lab.

● **FIGURE 3.7B   An example of DTI tractography.** Shown here is an example of DTI tractography of the corpus callosum. As you can see, there is a topography to callosal fibers, such that anterior regions of the callosum connect anterior regions of the brain and posterior regions of the callosum connect posterior regions of the brain. The fibers are color-coded by the regions that they connect: prefrontal lobe (coded in green), premotor and supplementary motor areas (light blue), primary motor cortex (dark blue), primary sensory cortex (red), parietal lobe (orange), occipital lobe (yellow), and temporal lobe (violet). Notice that orbitofrontal regions lack callosal connections and that the fibers in posterior sections of the callosum loop down to connect temporal regions (shown in purple). *Source:* Hofer, S. & Frahm, J. (2006). Topography of the human corpus callosum revisited—comprehensive fiber tractography using diffusion tensor magnetic resonance imaging. Neuroimage, 32, Figure 1A and 1B, pg. 991.

main axis or direction along which water diffuses in nerve fibers. The axis along which water diffusion is greatest indicates the main directional orientation of white-matter tracts, while the degree of diffusion provides information on the structural integrity of those tracts (Conturo et al., 1999). ● Figure 3.7A illustrates regions of the brain that have diffusion mainly along the left/right (shown in red), top/bottom (shown in blue), and front/back (shown in green) axes. For example, the corpus callosum, shown in red, is a large myelinated nerve fiber tract connecting the hemispheres, so fibers travel mainly from left to right. Diffusion tensor imaging is useful for many purposes. For example, it can be used to investigate the effects of demyelinating disorders such as multiple sclerosis (e.g., Coombs et al., 2004); to examine changes in white-matter tracts during childhood, adolescence, and both early and late adulthood (McLaughlin et al., 2007); and to detect disorders that arise from a partial or complete disconnection between brain regions (e.g., Molko et al., 2002).

By building upon such diffusion tensor information through a method referred to as *diffusion tensor imaging* **tractography**, information on probable white-matter tracts can be ascertained. Construction of the probable tracts is based on a number of assumptions, the most basic of which is that regions that are part of the same white-matter tract will have similar tensor

information in adjacent regions (for a review see Ciccarelli, Catani, Johansen-Berg, Clark, & Thompson, 2008). An example of the use of this method to image the white-matter tracts that form the corpus callosum is shown in ● Figure 3.7B.

Techniques for Assessing Physiological Function

The brain imaging techniques we just discussed provide a picture of the anatomical structure of the brain. However, they cannot tell us about brain function. As an analogy, consider devices that measure the thickness of metal on a car's body as an index of how much a car has been affected by rust. Although these devices provide information about the structural integrity of the car, much the way anatomical brain imaging techniques provide information about the structural integrity of the brain, they cannot tell us how well the car runs. A similar limitation befalls anatomical brain imaging techniques.

For many reasons, cognitive neuroscientists often want to know how well the brain is functioning. But, just as is the case with cars, there exist many different ways to evaluate function—by the amount of "fuel" consumed, by the level of certain critical substances, and by the degree of electrical activity. Just as we might want to know how much fuel the car is using, we may want to know how much of the brain's fuel, such as oxygen or glucose, is being consumed by different regions. As we might want to know the amount of antifreeze in the cooling system of our car, so we might want to measure the concentration of a specific neurotransmitter, such as dopamine, in the brain. Likewise, while we might want to see whether our car battery is holding a charge, in the case of the brain, we might measure whether aberrant electrical signals are being generated, or we might want to record the sum of the brain's electrical activity.

Notice that we have been talking about the mechanics of how the car functions, not its overall behavior. We have not discussed ways to measure overall performance: how a car handles in sharp turns, how quickly it brakes, how it climbs steep, narrow roads. Similarly, in this section of the chapter we discuss methods for measuring the mechanics of brain function rather than its overall performance at such tasks as remembering or paying attention.

■ Functional Brain Imaging Methods

Not only has there been a revolution in the ability to image the brain anatomically, but there has also been a revolution in the ability to measure the functioning of the brain. In this section, we discuss methods that discern which areas of the brain are physiologically active by measuring changes related to blood flow and the metabolic changes in compounds used by different brain regions. By far, the technique most commonly used by cognitive neuroscientists is **functional magnetic resonance imaging (fMRI)**, which uses a variation of the MRI techniques just discussed. Another method is **positron emission tomography (PET)**, which uses a radioactive agent to determine the brain's metabolic activity. PET was developed earlier than fMRI and still remains useful for certain types of investigation.

Although these functional brain imaging techniques are often used to study individuals with known or suspected brain damage, these techniques can also be used to great advantage to study neurologically intact individuals. The techniques allow researchers to observe the degree to which a brain region in a neurologically intact individual is activated by a task, so that its contribution to task performance under normal circumstances can be directly observed. This technique contrasts with the lesion method, in which inferences about a brain region's contribution to a task are made as a result of dysfunction. Functional brain imaging methods also allow researchers to observe the entire network of brain structures that participate in performing a particular cognitive function, by revealing all brain regions that are active.

Positron Emission Tomography

PET's greatest advantage is that it allows researchers to determine the amount of a specific compound of interest, such as a neurotransmitter like dopamine, that is being used by specific brain regions. Similar to CAT, PET relies on the use of high-energy ionizing radiation, although in this case the radiation is emitted by a substance introduced into the body rather than by radiation passing through it. In PET imaging, molecules altered to have a radioactive atom are introduced into the blood supply and carried to the brain. These radioactive molecules become stable and nonradioactive by releasing a positively charged particle called a *positron*. When the positron collides with an electron, two photons of light are produced that travel in exactly opposite directions. Brain areas of high metabolic activity emit many photons of light, whereas those that are less active emit fewer. From the data received by the detectors, computers extrapolate backward to determine the point from which the photons emanated, allowing the activity of various brain regions to be determined.

The time required to obtain a picture of the brain's functioning is linked to how quickly a given isotope goes from a radioactive state to a nonradioactive state (known as its *half-life*), because a significant number of photons must be detected to create an image. The process of acquiring a PET image is shown in ● Figure 3.8A, and an image generated from this process is shown in ● Figure 3.8B.

A related technique, *single photon emission computed tomography (SPECT)*, is essentially a much scaled-down version of the same technique as PET, using a small set of sensors rather than a ring of sensors. The smaller number of sensors reduces the spatial resolution, or clarity, of the obtained brain image. Moreover, the isotope used with these techniques usually takes longer to decay than the isotopes used with PET; therefore, the picture of the brain activity is less precise because it is averaged over a much longer time interval than with PET.

PET has two main advantages. First, it allows researchers to examine how the brain uses specific molecules (provided that a radioactive [i.e., positron-emitting] version of the molecule can be created). PET has been used in this manner quite successfully in studies of psychiatric disorders to examine the distribution of neurotransmitter binding (see Gatley et al., 2005). If we are interested in the distribution of a neurotransmitter, such as dopamine, we can introduce a radioactively tagged substance that binds to receptor sites (e.g., Wong et al., 1986). This technique has shown, for example, that medicines that reduce hallucinations and delusions in individuals with schizophrenia work specifically by binding to the dopaminergic D_2 and D_3 receptors (see Chapter 2, page 42, for a discussion of different types

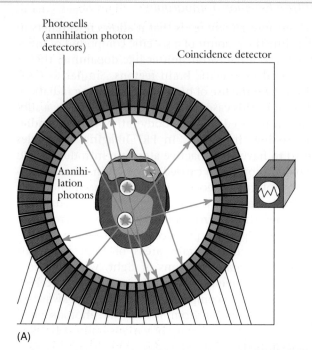

Photocells
(annihilation photon
detectors)

Coincidence detector

Annihi-
lation
photons

(A)

● **FIGURE 3.8A   An explanation of how positron emission tomography is used to measure brain activity.** A radioactive substance is introduced into the bloodstream and carried to the brain. Typically, this molecule is a radioactive form of a physiologically inert sugar, such as 2-deoxy-2-fluoro-D-glucose with a radioactive fluorine atom (^{18}F) attached, or water containing a radioactive isotope of oxygen ($H_2{}^{15}O$). These substances become nonradioactive by emitting a positively charged ion, known as a positron. As the positron travels from the molecule, it collides with an electron, which has a negative charge of the same value, and they annihilate each other. As first realized by Einstein, the annihilation of matter produces energy—in this case, two photons of light that travel from the site of annihilation exactly 180 degrees opposite each other. The coincidence of arrival of two photons 180 degrees apart is detected by a ring of photocells surrounding an individual's head. Brain regions that are very active give off many photons, whereas those that are less active give off fewer. By extrapolating backward, researchers can determine the source of the photons. © 2011 Cengage Learning

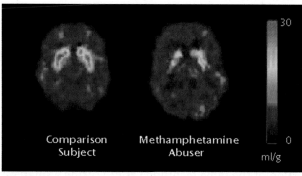

Comparison
Subject

Methamphetamine
Abuser

30

0

ml/g

(B)

● **FIGURE 3.8B   Example of a PET image.** This PET scan comes from a study in which radioactive carbon was attached to a drug that can provide a measure of the activity of dopaminergic cells. Low levels of activity are depicted by blue and green; higher levels of activity are shown by yellow and red. Notice that even after 80 days of detoxification, there is less activity of dopaminergic neurons in the brain of a methamphetamine abuser than in someone who does not use drugs. One of the strengths of PET is that it allows insights into neurotransmitter function in the brain. © 2011 Cengage Learning

of dopaminergic receptors) (Stone, Davis, Leucht, & Pilowsky, 2008).

A second advantage of PET is that it provides information on absolute levels of brain metabolism. Increased neural activity is associated with local changes in blood flow, oxygen use, and glucose metabolism (e.g., Sandman, O'Halloran, & Isenhart, 1984), all of which can be measured with PET. Because PET can provide an absolute measure of regional cerebral blood flow (rCBF), rCBF can be compared from one person (or population of people) to the next. For example, let's say a scientist is interested in investigating whether smoking causes a significant decrease in oxygen supply to the brain, and whether that effect increases with age. Using PET, the scientist could directly compare the rCBF in younger versus older individuals as well as smokers versus nonsmokers. Then he or she might go on to investigate whether such changes in rCBF are related to performance on cognitive tasks.

Although PET was used in the early 1990s to investigate the neural bases of cognitive function (for a readable account, see Posner & Raichle, 1994), it has been eclipsed by fMRI for a variety of reasons. First, like CAT, PET involves ionizing radiation; therefore, the number of scans an individual can undergo per year is limited to somewhere between two and five scans. This makes it difficult to do studies that require multiple scans to examine changes over time, such as changes that might accompany recovery from brain damage, training, or rehabilitation regimens. Second, the temporal and spatial resolution of PET is poorer than functional MRI. The time periods required to obtain a picture of brain activity (which is determined by an isotope's half-life) are typically quite long. For example, 2-deoxy-2-fluoro-D-glucose will yield a picture of brain activity averaged over about 40 minutes, and ^{15}O provides an image of brain activity averaged over a minute and a half, as compared to 2 seconds for functional MRI. In addition, whereas functional MRI provides spatial resolution on the order of a couple of millimeters, the spatial resolution of PET is on the order of 5 mm. New approaches that fuse data from

PET or SPECT scans with high-resolution CT scans are being devised to overcome the problem of poor spatial resolution (e.g., Maurer, 2008). An additional drawback is that PET requires an ongoing ability to create a radioactive isotope that can be continually infused into the individual for the duration of the task. Such a procedure requires a machine called a *cyclotron*, which is expensive and often available only at major medical centers. Although PET has numerous limitations, it is still the preferred technique for examining neurotransmitter function in the brain.

Functional Magnetic Resonance Imaging

Although we previously discussed MRI as a means of obtaining images of brain anatomy, a variation of this method, known as *functional magnetic resonance imaging (fMRI),* allows examination of certain aspects of brain function. Because changes in neuronal activity are accompanied by local changes in other physiological functions, such as cerebral blood flow and blood oxygenation (e.g., Fox, Raichle, Mintun, & Dence, 1988), these local changes can be used to infer the activity levels of different brain regions. In the past decade or so, there has been a veritable explosion of research using a particular fMRI method known as BOLD (Blood Oxygen Level Dependent), which takes advantage of the fact that oxygenated and deoxygenated blood have different magnetic properties (for discussion of this issue and fMRI methodology, see Bandettini, 2007). It should not surprise you that blood has magnetic properties if you consider that a lack of iron in the blood causes anemia, which is the reason that many people, especially women, are encouraged to ensure that their diet contains enough iron. As we learned earlier in this chapter, MRI works by imposing a static magnetic field and then perturbing it. It turns out that deoxygenated blood makes the static magnetic field inhomogenous, making it more difficult to detect a signal change, whereas oxygenated blood does not have such an effect. When a particular area of the brain is active, the local increase in oxygen-rich blood is greater than the amount of oxygen that can be extracted by the brain tissue. Thus, the relative proportion of oxygenated blood to deoxygenated blood increases in that local region, and it is this decrease in deoxygenated blood that allows increased signal clarity from which a picture of brain activity can be derived (e.g., Kwong et al., 1992). For example, when neurons in primary visual cortex fire in response to light, more oxygen is delivered to this region. Researchers can detect the *increase* in the signal due to decreased presence of deoxygenated blood, compared to the previous state when there was no light, the neurons were less active, and more deoxygenated blood was present.

Because it detects a change in the signal from one state to another, the use of fMRI requires that we always compare two conditions: the condition of interest, such as "light on," to a baseline, such as "light off." In many of the studies discussed later in this book, we will notice that researchers attempt to isolate the brain region involved in a particular function by carefully picking a baseline task against which to measure changes in brain activation associated with the task of interest. The selection of the baseline is critical for interpretation of the results. For example, if one wants to determine those regions *specifically* involved in processing faces above and beyond other objects, then brain activation while viewing faces must be compared to a baseline of brain activation while viewing nonface objects. In contrast, if the researcher wants to determine all the brain regions involved in visually analyzing a face, then brain activation while viewing faces has to be compared to a baseline of brain activation while viewing a very basic visual form such as a cross.

Notice that fMRI cannot measure a neuronal response directly; rather, it indexes a *hemodynamic response,* the response of the vascular system to the increased need for oxygen of neurons in a local area. This response is slow, generally starting about 2 seconds after a stimulus is presented, peaking at about 6–8 seconds, and falling back to baseline by about 14–16 seconds. Although this response is drawn out over seconds, we can nonetheless obtain a measure of brain activity on about a second-by-second basis (● Figure 3.9). This temporal resolution is much faster than PET, although it is slow compared to some other methods, such as EEG, that we discuss later in this chapter.

For a number of reasons, fMRI is a particularly exciting method for making brain-behavior inferences. First, it is a widely available method, as scans can be obtained

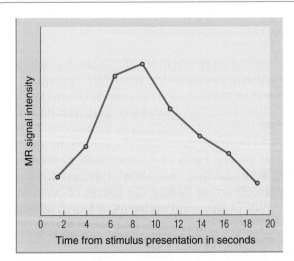

● **FIGURE 3.9   Time course of the fMRI signal from the onset of a stimulus.** Notice that there is a lag such that the increase in relative oxygenation, which is picked up as an increase in MR signal intensity, starts only 2 seconds after the stimulus onset, peaks about 8 seconds later, and then returns to baseline after about 16 seconds. © 2011 Cengage Learning

IN FOCUS: Participating in a Functional Magnetic Resonance Imaging Study

What is it like to participate in fMRI studies of brain function? I have been involved in these studies both as a researcher and as a participant, so I can provide a short description of some of this work from both perspectives. As an experimenter, it is often very helpful to be an initial "pilot" participant before actual data collection starts. It provides a way of checking to make sure that everything is in working order, and also allows you to determine what difficulties might arise during the course of the experiment. This was especially true for me and my colleagues back in 1993 when we first started doing studies using fMRI. It was a relatively new technique then, so before asking anyone else to participate in a study using this new technique, we wanted to see for ourselves what it would be like. That way, we would know exactly what our participants would experience. Because the magnet is quite a different environment than the standard cognitive neuroscience laboratory, we also wanted insights into the ways in which a "typical" cognitive neuroscience experiment would be transformed by having to perform it in the magnet.

Our first study was very simple; it was designed to determine whether we could detect changes in blood oxygenation over the occipital lobe while a person stared at a checkerboard of red and green squares that reversed color seven times a second. I was one of the first participants. I could not just go and sit in the magnet to be tested. First, I had to carefully look over a checklist to make sure that I did not have characteristics that would preclude a scan. Such characteristics included having ever had a metal clip placed on any blood vessel during surgery, having a pacemaker, and even having "permanent" eyeliner! Next, I had to check that I had nothing on my person or in my pockets that would be attracted to the magnet or would be influenced by the strong magnetic field—this included belt buckles, jewelry, pens, credit cards, watches, coins, and paper clips, among other things. Such precautions are very important because the strength of the magnetic field in a 1.5 Tesla magnet (the strength of a standard clinical magnet) can pull a pen into the center of the magnet at more than 100 miles per hour, with unfortunate consequences for both pieces of equipment. Denuded of any metallic objects, I then entered the magnet room. There I was given a pair of earplugs, as MRI scans are very loud. At this point, I was positioned on my back on a table outside the magnet, which is a rather large cylinder, about 8 ft tall by 8 ft wide, with a small hole (known as the *bore*) in the middle, into which the person is placed (see accompanying figure, which, by the way, is not me).

To obtain good fMRI images, it is very important that the person's head remain motionless. My colleagues placed pillows around my head to stabilize it before the receiver coil of the magnet, which is like an enlarged baseball catcher's mask, was put around my head. Finally, two angled mirrors positioned directly above my eyes were adjusted so that I could view a screen, positioned near my feet, on which the visual stimuli would be projected (Nowadays video goggles tend to be used instead for displaying stimuli). Then I was moved into the machine headfirst. My head was placed in the middle of the magnet, which is where the best image can be obtained. Because I'm not tall, I was literally swallowed up into the magnet—my feet were just barely sticking out of the bore.

I found the experience of being moved into the magnet somewhat disconcerting. The bore of the magnet is a small semicircular opening that leaves little room for even the smallest arm movements and places your nose just inches from the top of the magnet. If you are a spelunker (that is, a cave explorer), you'd probably feel comfortable, but for people who have any tendency to claustrophobia, the experience can be a bit nerve-racking. I must admit that the first time I was rolled into the

---

with clinical MRI machines that have the appropriate hardware to enable the procedure. Second, it is a noninvasive technique, because no high-energy radiation is involved. Third, multiple scans can be run on a single individual, avoiding the limitations imposed by PET. Multiple scans allow scientists to examine changes in the brain over time, such as those that occur with learning, and allow clinicians to observe changes occurring during the course of recovery or as a result of treatment regimens. A fourth advantage of fMRI is that it provides a measure of brain activity over seconds rather than minutes as is the case with PET. Finally, the precision of scans obtained from fMRI enables us to examine brain-behavior relationships in individuals, which makes fMRI particularly useful for clinical interventions such as neurosurgery (e.g., Matthews, Honey, & Bullmore, 2006).

Although use of the BOLD contrast to examine brain activity is widespread, it does have a drawback: it can only provide information about the *relative* concentration of oxygenated and deoxygenated blood. Absolute measurements of the amount of oxygen delivered to the brain across individuals, such as younger and older individuals, are not available. Other fMRI methods, such as *arterial spin-labeling techniques,* provide information about brain perfusion that can be directly compared across individuals (Petersen, Zimine, Ho, & Golay, 2006). However, this information cannot be collected as quickly as the BOLD signal and provides poorer spatial resolution.

Because MRI can be tuned to specific atoms, it can also be utilized to examine the concentration of other biologically active substances via a method known as *magnetic resonance spectroscopy* (for a review, see Gujar, Maheshwari, Björkman-Burtscher, & Sundgren, 2005). These methods are limited, however, in two ways. First, they provide only very gross information on the location of these substances within the brain (e.g., within the

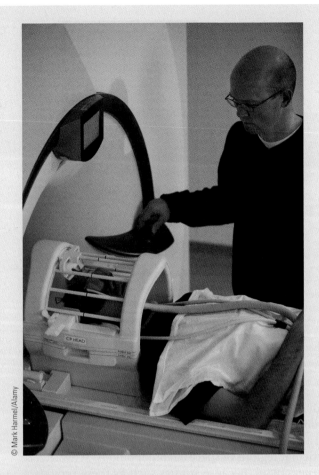

© Mark Harmel/Alamy

magnet, my heart started to race and I felt uncomfortable. But I chatted to my colleagues and forced myself to think about being safely and snugly tucked into bed rather than trapped in a magnet. By keeping my mind on that train of thought, I subsequently found the magnet a comfortable place to relax.

Once the screen at my feet was positioned for optimal viewing, the studies began. MRIs work by setting up a homogeneous static magnetic field around an object. Because a body and a head in the magnet disrupt that field, the machine has to be "shimmed," or adjusted, to take into account the peculiarities of the individual's head and body, and to optimize the signal that the machine will receive. While this was being done, the machine made low, deep "a-clump, a-clump, a-clump" noises, like the sound of a large steel horse slowly loping around a racetrack. After the shimming, an anatomical scan of my brain was taken. The first time I participated in this procedure, my colleagues thoughtfully let me know through an intercom system that the structural scan revealed that I did indeed have a brain!

Because we were interested in visual processing, the machine was programmed to take a "slice" of my brain's activity that would pass through the calcarine fissure (see figures on the inside front cover of this book), which is where the primary visual areas of the brain are located. During each pair of scans, I first had to close my eyes, a task designed to provide a baseline of the activity level in my occipital cortex when it receives no visual input. Then a checkerboard was flashed to measure the response of my occipital cortex to visual stimulation. This comparison between a baseline condition and a control condition is a hallmark of the design of fMRI studies. The noise made by the machine became different, more tinny and staccato than previously. To round out the day, a high-resolution anatomical scan of my brain with 128 slices was obtained so that a computerized three-dimensional rendering of my entire brain could be constructed. About an hour after we started, my colleagues told me through the intercom that we were done, came into the magnet room, and wheeled me out of the magnet. Although being in the magnet was relaxing, I was glad to get out, stretch my legs, and hear more familiar noises.

Source: MTB

frontal lobe). Second, to be detectable by this method, the concentration of the substances must be quite high. For example, it remains to be seen whether these methods will be able to detect neurotransmitters. One substance that has been examined using this technique is *N*-acetylaspartate (NAA). This amino acid, which is found only within the nervous system, has the second highest concentration of any free amino acid (i.e., one that is not bound to another substance) in the nervous system. Although its exact role in neuronal processes is unknown, a reduction in NAA appears to index pathological processes acting upon neurons and glia, as in demyelinating disorders such as multiple sclerosis (De Stefano, Bartolozzi, Guidi, Stromillo, & Federico, 2005), and its concentration can predict performance on cognitive tasks (Ross & Sachdev, 2004). The importance of magnetic resonance spectroscopy may increase in the future as high-field MR systems (i.e., 7T or higher) become more commonplace. These high-field systems will enhance the ability to detect substances at lower concentrations than is currently available with more standard magnets (e.g., 1.5 or 3T).

■ Electromagnetic Recording Methods

The methods we have discussed so far examine the metabolic activity of the brain. In other cases, however, we may want to record the electrical activity of the brain that results from neuronal firing or the magnetic fields induced by that electrical activity. In animals, we can place electrodes directly into or onto cells and determine what types of stimuli make a cell fire. In humans, we typically record the summed electrical activity of many neurons. Compared with the brain imaging techniques just discussed, electrical measures in humans (including EEG, event-related potentials, and magnetoencephalography) do a relatively poor job of identifying where activity is occurring in the brain. Nevertheless, the electrical methods provide an accurate measure of brain activity

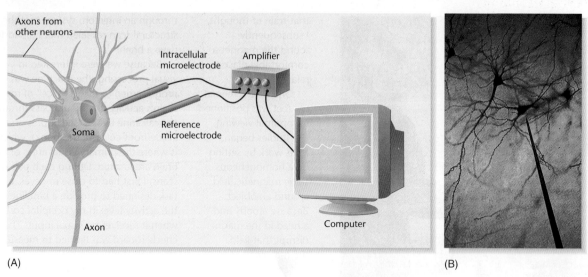

● FIGURE 3.10   Single-cell recording. (A) Shown on the left is a diagram of how information is recorded from single cells. The tip of an electrode, which is otherwise insulated, is placed in contact with the cell while the tip of another insulated electrode outside the cell serves a reference. This information is fed into an amplifier and the activity is output on a computer monitor which shows the size of the electrical activity over time. (B) A photograph showing the tip of an electrode in contact with a cell body. Courtesy of David Hunter Hubel, Department of Neurobiology, Harvard Medical School.

on a millisecond-by-millisecond basis, much more rapidly than even the fastest fMRI methods, and thus offer neuroscientists the best available *temporal resolution* of brain activity.

Single-Cell Recordings

Many of the animal studies discussed in this book examine the electrical responses of cells in particular regions of the brain. In these studies, an electrode is placed into the brain region of interest and the experimenter records the electrical output of the cell or cells that are contacted by the exposed electrode tip (● Figure 3.10). After establishing a baseline firing rate for a given cell, researchers then determine what properties of a stimulus make the cell fire maximally above that baseline. Researchers use this technique to examine various issues. They may want to determine whether the cells are sensitive to input in only one sensory modality or are multimodal in sensitivity; whether they respond to information from only specific places in the sensory world or from broad regions of space; and whether a cell's response is modified depending on whether or not the animal's attention is directed toward the stimulus.

Studies involving single-cell recording techniques in animals have been enormously helpful in providing information about the organization of many brain regions. For example, such studies have demonstrated that cells in primary visual areas are responsive to basic orientation of bars of light, whereas cells in higher-order visual regions are responsive to much more elaborate forms (e.g., Desimone, Albright, Gross, & Bruce, 1984); that frontal regions play a role in keeping information

available in memory during a short delay period (e.g., Funahashi, Bruce, & Goldman-Rakic, 1991); and that parietal areas are important for directing arm movements to particular regions of space (Georgopoulous, Schwartz, & Kettner, 1986). Because studies such as these provide a basis for conceptualizing how particular regions of the human brain may be organized for certain cognitive functions, we discuss them throughout this text where appropriate.

In humans, opportunities for such studies are limited. However, there are cases in which electrodes are implanted into the brain for about a week prior to surgery for the removal of epileptic tissue, and cases in which electrodes are placed on the surface of the brain during an operation to better isolate the source of seizure activity (● Figure 3.11). Such procedures allow precise localization of tissue that generates seizure activity and avoid the removal of useful, undamaged tissue. These procedures can also provide scientists with knowledge of the stimulus properties that make cells fire in a given brain region (e.g., Allison, McCarthy, Nobre, Puce, & Belger, 1994; Quian Quiroga, Reddy, Kreiman, Koch, & Fried, 2005). In addition, small amounts of current can be passed through the electrodes, allowing observation of the associated behavior. For example, researchers have isolated regions of the left hemisphere involved in language processing by identifying regions that, when stimulated electrically, result in an arrest of speech (Ojemann, 1983). Because opportunities to study the firing of single cells in humans are so limited, researchers often rely instead upon measurements of electrical activity of the whole brain via methods to which we now turn.

Electroencephalography

Recordings of the brain's electrical activity are often used clinically to detect aberrant activity, such as that associated with epilepsy and sleep disorders. Experimentally, they are used to detect certain psychological states, such as drowsiness and alertness, because each of these states is associated with particular patterns of electrical activity.

In **electroencephalography (EEG)**, the electrical signals produced by the brain are typically recorded by metal electrodes positioned on the scalp (● Figure 3.12) and then amplified. Each electrode (sometimes called a *lead*) acts as its own recording site or channel. The number of electrodes used varies from around 20 to more than 100 in high-density-array recording systems. Additionally, one electrode is attached to an electrically inactive site, such as the mastoid bone (located behind the ear), which acts as a reference that provides a baseline against which the activity at each of the other electrodes can be compared. In high-density arrays, the activity at one electrode may be averaged against the activity at all other sites. An electrode simply placed on the skin is an inappropriate reference because it covers muscles, whose contractions are induced by electrical signals. To avoid mistaking eye movement for brain activity, researchers usually place an electrode near the eye muscles, which allows EEG signals from the time periods when eye movements occur to be eliminated from further analysis.

The **electrical potential** recorded at an electrode on the scalp is the summed or superimposed signal of the postsynaptic electrical fields of similarly aligned neuronal dendrites. Recorded at the scalp as a waveform, the electrical potential has a particular voltage (which is a measure of its size) and a particular frequency, meaning that it oscillates at a specific rate (measured in Hertz [Hz] or cycles per second). The frequency and form of the EEG signal vary according to a person's state. During sleep, very slow frequencies of *delta activity*, at 1 to 4 Hz, predominate. When a person is relaxed, with his or her eyes closed, slow frequencies, or *alpha activity*, at 9 to 12 Hz, are much more common. When a person is awake, the EEG shows a mixture of many frequencies, but those that are relatively fast (15 Hz), known as *beta activity*, tend to predominate. Recently, research has suggested that synchronous oscillations between groups of neurons in the 30–100 Hz range, known as *gamma activity*, may play an important role in perception and attention, specifically in the conscious perception of alternative views of objects (see Jensen, Kaiser, & Lachaux, 2007, for a review) (● Figure 3.13A).

Clinically, EEG can detect epilepsy, which can be conceptualized as an electrical storm in the brain. Neurons normally fire in a synchronous manner, leading to

● **FIGURE 3.11**   **An example of an electrode array placed directly on the surface of the brain in an individual with epilepsy.**

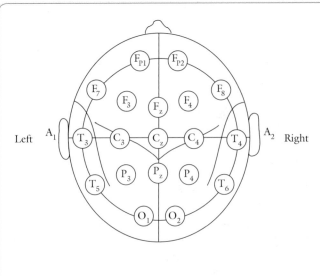

Left A_1 A_2 Right

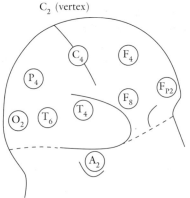

C_z (vertex)

● **FIGURE 3.12   Standard placement of electrodes during electroencephalography recording for a 20-lead system.** Electrodes over the left hemisphere are labeled with odd numbers, those over the right hemisphere are labeled with even numbers, and those on the midline are labeled with a *z*. The uppercase letter is an abbreviation for the location of the electrode: A, auricle; C, central; F, frontal; Fp, frontal pole; O, occipital; P, parietal; and T, temporal. © 2011 Cengage Learning

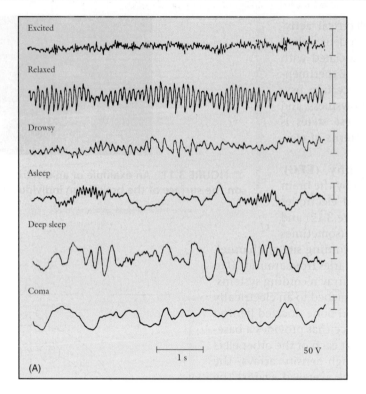

● FIGURE 3.13A Examples of EEG recordings. Characteristic EEG activity during various mental states. Note the cyclicity of activity that can be observed, for example, when an individual is in a relaxed state. © 2011 Cengage Learning

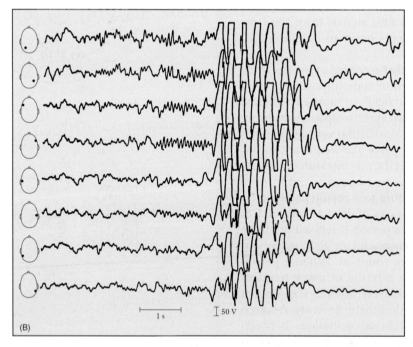

● FIGURE 3.13B An example of the "spiking" activity that accompanies epilepsy, shown as a discrete increase in the voltage of the EEG. In this case, the seizure occurred over many regions of the brain simultaneously, as can be seen by the occurrence of high-voltage activity over all electrodes. The position of the electrode for each line of recording is indicated by a dot on the diagram of the head on the left. The square shape of the wave during seizure activity is an artifact caused by limitations of the recording apparatus, which could not adequately record the intensity of the voltage associated with this seizure. More typical waveforms during seizure activity can be seen in the third recording from the bottom, in which square waves are less prominent. © 2011 Cengage Learning

the alpha, beta, and delta waveforms just discussed. In epilepsy, however, rather than firing in a synchronous rhythm, neurons fire in large quantities at once (a burst, or "spike") at random times. The result is an increase in the amplitude of firing that can be observed on the EEG record (● Figure 3.13B). After an individual is treated with anticonvulsants, the EEG can be performed again to ensure that the spiking activity has decreased.

EEG can also be used to examine experimental questions. Because alpha waves indicate that a person is relaxed and resting, the absence, or suppression, of alpha activity is often used as an indicator of the degree of activation of the brain. The degree of **alpha suppression**, as it is known, is examined to determine how active the brain is under different conditions. For example, in the chapter on emotion (Chapter 13), we discuss evidence that when individuals are depressed, they exhibit greater alpha suppression over right frontal areas than over left frontal areas. This finding indicates that depression is accompanied by greater activation of right frontal regions than of left frontal regions.

Event-Related Potentials

Whereas EEG recordings provide a continuous measure of brain acti-vity, **event-related potentials (ERPs)** are recorded in reference to a specific event (● Figure 3.14). ERPs are recordings of the brain's activity that are linked to the occurrence of an event, such as the presentation of a stimulus. Therein lies their greatest strength: they can provide some idea of *when* processes occur in the brain. The common alignment and firing of dendritic fields in the brain after this event create a **dipole**, which is a small region of electrical current with a relatively positive end and a relatively negative end (hence *di*pole, or *two*-pole, system). Electrodes placed on the scalp can detect this dipole.

As time from the onset of the stimulus elapses, the active groups of neurons, and hence the locations of the dipoles, change. Thus, the waveform recorded on the scalp changes as well. The waveform can be divided into **components**, which are characteristic portions of the wave that have been linked to certain psychological processes, such as attention and memory. ERP

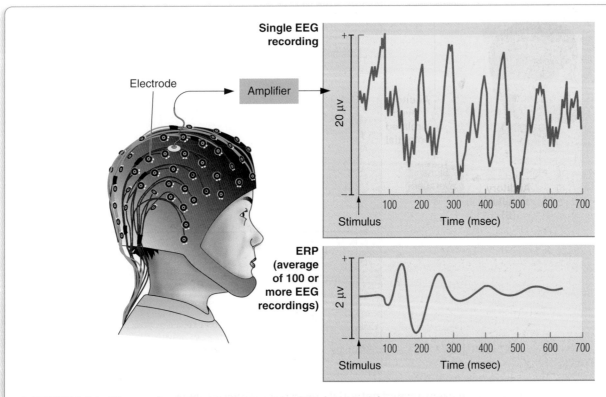

● **FIGURE 3.14 The method of recording event-related potentials.** The ongoing electroencephalography (top) is recorded on the scalp and then sent through an amplifier. As shown at the top, the voltage (on the y axis) varies over time (shown on the x axis). To obtain the event-related potential (bottom), the electrical signal is recorded for a discrete period (e.g., 700 msec) following a specific event, such as the onset of the stimuli. This is often referred to as "time-locked" because the recording is locked to a particular point in time. Signals from numerous such time periods (often a hundred or more) are then averaged, because ERPs are too small to be detected in the ongoing EEG. The resulting ERP waveform is then obtained, which measures the consistent response of the brain in the second or so after the event, in this case, the presentation of the stimulus. © 2010 Cengage Learning

components are usually given names that have two parts: a letter and then a subscript number (e.g., P_{300}). The letter is always a *P* or an *N* to denote whether the deflection of the electrical signal is positive or negative. The number represents, on average, how many milliseconds (ms) after stimulus presentation the component appears. (Sometimes component names are abbreviated to represent, on average, how many *hundreds* of milliseconds after stimulus presentation they occur. In this case, for example, a P_{300} will be referred to as a P_3.)

Components are often divided into two categories: exogenous and endogenous. **Exogenous components** are linked to the physical characteristics of a stimulus and usually occur early in the waveform. Because they are evoked by an external stimulus, they are sometimes referred to as *evoked potentials*. In contrast, **endogenous components** appear to be driven by internal cognitive states, independent of stimulus characteristics. They typically occur later in the waveform. An example of a typical waveform with the different components is presented in ● Figure 3.15.

Next, let's discuss the major classes of important components, starting with those that occur earliest in time. The very early components, occurring within 100 ms of stimulus onset, are linked to sensory processing. This property makes them useful in assessing the integrity of nerve fiber pathways from the sensory receptors to the brain. For example, the points where neurons synapse as information is relayed from the cochlea of the ear to the cortex are, in order, the cochlear nuclei (and superior olive) at the level of the medulla, the inferior colliculus, the medial geniculate nucleus of the thalamus, and then Heschl's gyrus, the primary auditory region of the brain. Information takes time to reach each of these relay points, and when it does, a characteristic component of the waveform is produced. Hence, an abnormality in one of these early components implicates a disruption at a specific relay point in the flow of information from the sensory receptors to the cortex.

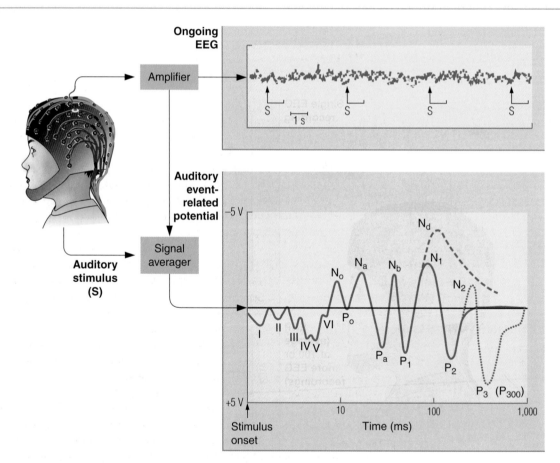

● **FIGURE 3.15   Components of an event-related potential.** The ongoing electroencephalography (top) is recorded from the scalp and passed through an amplifier. Every time a stimulus occurs (denoted by an S in the ongoing EEG), the electrical signal is recorded for a discrete period (e.g., 1 second). Signals from all such time periods are then averaged. The resulting ERP from an auditory stimulus is shown below, with time plotted logarithmically to allow differentiation of the (N_o, P_o, N_a, P_a, N_b) (exogenous) responses from the brainstem (Waves I–VI) and early components (<100 ms postpresentation) that indicate the response of the brain to sensory characteristics of the stimulus as compared to later (P_1, N_1, P_2, N_2, P_3) (endogenous) components (>100 ms postpresentation) that tend to be linked more to cognitive processes. © 2011 Cengage Learning

Components that appear approximately 100 ms after a stimulus is presented include the P_{100} and N_{100}. At this point, ERPs are no longer driven solely by sensory information, but can also be modulated by attention. The P_{100} component is a positive deflection observed between 80 and 140 ms postpresentation, whereas the N_{100} is a negative deflection observed about 100 ms postpresentation for auditory stimuli and between 160 and 200 ms postpresentation for visual stimuli. Scientists can observe the effect of attention on these components by asking individuals to pay attention to information presented in one location but not another, such as attending to information presented to the right ear but not the left. When an individual's attention is directed to the location at which the stimulus is presented, the size of the P_{100} and N_{100} are increased relative to when that same stimulus is presented but the individual's attention is directed elsewhere (Mangun & Hillyard, 1990). Notice that the stimulus in both cases is identical—all that varies is whether the individual is attending to its location.

The N_{200}, a negative deflection at about 200 ms postpresentation, is known as the *mismatch negativity*. It occurs when an individual is presented with an item that is physically deviant from that of the prevailing context. For example, if someone is listening to a series of tones, most of which are low in pitch, a high-pitched tone will elicit an N_{200}. Unlike the N_{100}, this effect occurs regardless of whether the individual is attending to the location in which the deviant stimulus appears (e.g., Näatanen, Gaillard, & Mantysalo, 1978).

One of the most studied components is the P_{300}, which is a positive deflection found approximately 300 ms poststimulus. Although researchers disagree on exactly what the P_{300} measures, it appears to be related to attention and the updating of memory, as it occurs when a person modifies his or her current model of the environment to include new incoming information (Donchin & Coles, 1988). The P_{300} occurs in numerous situations; however, the classic situation that elicits a P_{300} is an experimental procedure called the *oddball paradigm*. In this paradigm, an individual hears a series of tones at consecutive intervals, most of which are at one pitch (e.g., a "beep") and a minority of which are at another pitch (e.g., a "boop"). A larger P_{300} generally occurs to the oddball, the boop, than to the regular items, the beeps. Typically a P_{300} is observed when the individual must pay attention to an item, the oddball, and that oddball is distinct from the information currently held in memory (necessitating the updating of memory).

The P_{300} is distinct in two ways from the mismatch negativity that occurs when physical deviance is detected. First, a P_{300} can be elicited by the lack of sensory stimulation, such as silence. If, for example, a person hears a series of tones punctuated periodically by silence when a tone should occur, a P_{300} is elicited by the silence because memory must now be updated. Furthermore, whereas the mismatch negativity appears to occur relatively automatically, regardless of whether an individual is paying attention to the items, the person must be engaged in processing the stimulus for a P_{300} to occur. Because of this feature, it has been used as an index of how much attention an individual is devoting to processing a stimulus (e.g., Kramer, Wickens, & Donchin, 1985).

Another late component that has been linked to psychological processing is the N_{400}. This negative-going component appears approximately 400 ms after stimulus presentation and occurs when individuals detect semantic anomalies. So, for example, if your ERP were being recorded at this moment, an N_{400} would probably be observed as you read the last word of the following sentence: "Running out the door, Patty grabbed her jacket, her baseball glove, her cap, a softball, and a skyscraper." In contrast, the N_{400} would be absent if the same sentence ended with the word "bat." The amplitude of the N_{400} increases with the deviance of a word relative to the prior context of the sentence. For example, your N_{400} for the following sentence, "Running out the door, Patty grabbed her jacket, her baseball glove, her cap, a softball, and a lamp," would be smaller than your N_{400} for the first sentence, because *lamp* is less deviant a word than *skyscraper* (i.e., Patty could actually grab a lamp, but not a skyscraper). However, an N_{400} would still be elicited by the second sentence because you would expect Patty to grab another piece of softball equipment, not a piece of furniture (e.g., Kutas & Hillyard, 1980).

A review of the components and the psychological processes with which they are associated is presented in Table 3.2. (A more detailed review of ERPs and their relations to psychological processes is presented in Fabiani, Gratton, & Federmeier, 2007.)

ERPs are extremely useful because they provide some information about the time course with which information is processed in the brain. For example, we have learned that attention acts to enhance processing of task-relevant materials by at least 150 milliseconds postpresentation. Still, ERPs do have some drawbacks. The pattern of brain activity on the scalp cannot tell us with certainty the location of the dipole or dipoles within the brain that are generating such a pattern. Any given pattern of activity on the scalp could mathematically be produced by a variety of generators or sets of generators within the brain, a difficulty known as the *inverse problem*. For this reason, researchers have focused on utilizing computer models of the head that make certain simplifying assumptions to help them more precisely localize the neural generator or generators withinthe brain (e.g., Scherg, 1992). An example of dipole modeling of the source of a component is shown in ● Figure 3.16. The additional information provided by high-density recording systems, which often have up to 128 leads, aids in the modeling process (e.g., Potts, Liotti, Tucker, & Posner, 1996).

TABLE 3.2		Basic Components and Psychological Processes Associated with Event-Related Potential (ERP) Components	
ERP Component	Time Period (Ms)*	Eliciting Conditions	Associated Mental Processes
Sensory components	0–100	After the receipt of sensory information	Transmission of sensory information from the periphery to the cortex
N_{100}–P_{100}	100–300	When subjects are paying attention to the portion of the stimulus stream in which the material was presented	Selective attention
Mismatch negativity (N_{200})	200–300	When a stimulus is physically deviant from other recent stimuli; it is not much affected by whether the individual is paying attention to the portion of the stimulus stream in which the deviant item is presented	Detection of physical deviance
P_{300}	300–800	When individuals must pay attention to the rarer of two events, even if that rare event is the absence of sensory stimulation (e.g., silence)	Memory of context updating
N_{400}	400–600	When items deviate in meaning from what is expected	Detection of semantic deviance

*Indicates time postpresentation.

Another approach, called *time-frequency analysis*, combines aspects of the approaches used in ERPs and EEG. Like ERPs, activity is examined over time, locked to a specific event. But rather than the summed signal of all activity, the strength of activity in different EEG frequencies is computed. Certain cognitive processes or differences between groups appear to be better characterized by changes in the frequency at which neurons are firing, rather than the absolute level of activity. For example, in ● Figure 3.17, you can see such a time-frequency plot of activity for regions of dorsolateral prefrontal cortex during performance of a task that requires attention. Notice that about 200 ms after presentation of the stimulus, there is a broad shift in the frequency of activity. Before this point, most of the activity occurs in

the range of alpha (8–12 Hz), but after that point there is suppression of this activity, which as we learned earlier indicates that individuals are involved in effortful behavior.

Magnetoencephalography

Rather than recording the electrical potentials to index brain activity, a related method **magnetoencephalography**, known as MEG, records the magnetic potentials produced by brain activity. Remember when discussing ERPs, we mentioned that the synchronous activity in aligned fields of dendrites creates a dipole, which consists of a region that is relatively negatively charged at one end and relatively positively charged at the other end. If you have taken physics,

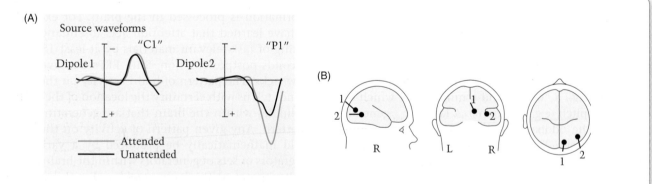

● **FIGURE 3.16   Results of a dipole modeling procedure.** In this experiment, individuals were shown a simple visual stimulus (a circular checkerboard) and told to attend to information on the left side of space. (A) Shown here are the responses to attended items, depicted by the blue line, and unattended items, depicted by the black line. Dipole 1 models the source of the C1 waveform. Notice that its amplitude does not vary depending on whether an item is attended or not. Dipole 2 models the source of the P1 waveform, which reflects attentional modulation of sensory processing as indicated by the larger response to attended than unattended information. (B) The location of these two dipoles as seen from a lateral, coronal, and horizontal perspective. The location of Dipole 1 is near the midline of the brain and near the calcarine fissure, consistent with a position within primary visual cortex. Dipole 2, however, is positioned more laterally, consistent with a location in secondary visual processing areas. © 2011 Cengage Learning

you will have learned that a magnetic field exists around such a differential electrical potential, as shown in ● Figure 3.18A. This magnetic field can be used to locate the dipole because the dipole resides midway between the extreme high points of intensity of the magnetic field, as shown in ● Figure 3.18B. Although originally systems contained only one or two sensors, modern systems now contain more than 200 sensor arrays. As you can see in ● Figure 3.19, the apparatus for collecting MEG data is quite large, mainly because the sensors, known as *superconducting quantum interference devices (SQUIDS)*, have superconducting properties only at very low temperatures. Hence, they must be encased in large cylinders that contain liquid helium, a substance found at 4 degrees Kelvin or colder.

Recording magnetic fields has some advantages and disadvantages over recording electrical potentials. Whereas electrical currents produced in the brain are carried in varying degrees through brain tissue, cerebralspinal fluid, the skull, and the scalp, the strength of magnetic fields is not as influenced by these variations in tissue. Moreover, the strength of magnetic fields falls off from their source in a systematic manner (with the square of the distance), so the strength of the magnetic field recorded on the outside of the head can help provide some information about how deep within the brain the source is located. However, because the size of the magnetic fields produced by the electrical activity in the brain is very small—in the range of 50–500 femtoTeslas (fT), which is 1 billionth the size of the earth's magnetic field—an MEG device requires a special magnetically shielded room. This room, usually made of aluminum (which is a nonmagnetic metal), shields not only against the earth's magnetic field but also other electromagnetic radiation, such as microwaves, radiation contained by electrical currents in everyday buildings, and the magnetic field generated by the sun. Another drawback of MEG can be seen if you refer back to Figure 3.18—it cannot detect activity of cells that are oriented with their long axes radial to the surface because the magnetic field will not "emerge" from the brain allowing them to be recorded by sensors.

The two most common clinical uses of MEG are (1) to localize the source of epileptic activity and (2) to locate primary sensory cortices so they can be avoided during neurosurgical intervention (e.g., Tovar-Spinoza, Ochi, Rutka, Go, & Otsubo, 2008). MEG is especially helpful in cases where neither EEG nor a brain imaging method such as fMRI or PET can definitely locate the source of epileptic activity or the location of primary sensory cortices.

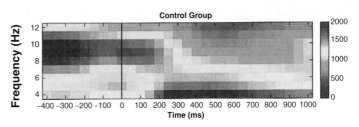

● **FIGURE 3.17   Time-frequency analysis plot.** Shown here is the time-frequency analysis plot of activity that is time-locked to stimulus presentation (shown by the bar at time 0) of an attentionally demanding task. Time is plotted along the x axis and the frequency of electrical activity (Hz) is plotted along the y axis. The color represents the power or activity at a particular time for a particular frequency. As shown by the bar at the right, blue indicates the least activity and red indicates the most. Here there is a broad shift away from activity in the alpha band (8–12 Hz) about 200 ms after stimulus presentation. Courtesy of Heller/Miller Lab

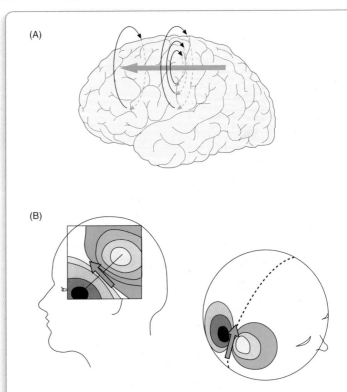

● **FIGURE 3.18   Relationship between electrical dipoles and magnetic fields.** (A) The orientation of a magnetic field that occurs around a dipole. The magnetic field, shown here as solid and dashed lines, emanates in a clockwise manner around a dipole, shown here as an arrow, with the arrowhead representing the positive pole of the dipole. In physics this is known as the "right-hand rule," because if you stick the thumb of your right hand out to represent the dipole, with your thumb being the positive end, the curling of your remaining fingers represents the magnetic field around that dipole. (B) How the localization of an electrical dipole is derived from the distribution of the magnetic fields. The electrical dipole is located midway between the extremes of the magnetic signal. Just the way electrical signals are positive or negative, magnetic fields also have a sign: negative is shown here in black and positive in bluish-white. In this figure, the intensity of the magnetic field is illustrated by the intensity of the color. Notice that the intensity of the magnetic fields drops off very close to the electrical dipole. © 2011 Cengage Learning

● **FIGURE 3.19   Magnetoencephalography.**
(A) Apparatus necessary to record MEG showing the location of the SQUIDS, which detect the magnetic signals in the helmet-shaped bottom of the helium dewer, so they can be as close as possible to the participant's head. (B) The process of using MEG to record a response to an auditory tone. © 2010 Cengage Learning

(A) Subject Undergoing MEG Procedure

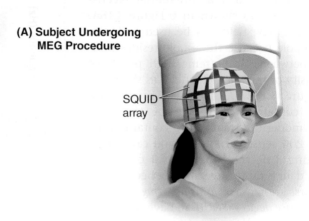

SQUID array

(B) MEG Analysis of a Response to a Tone

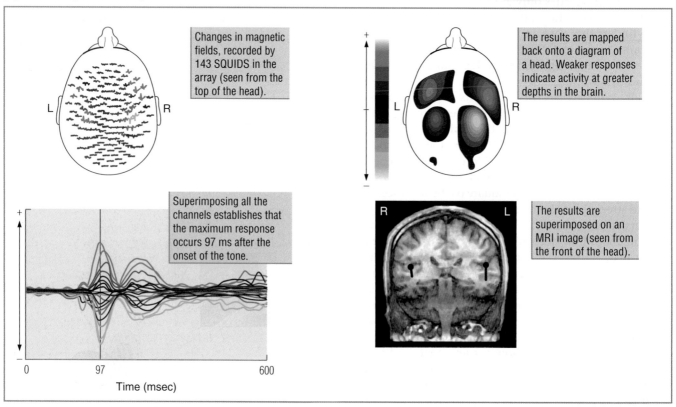

Changes in magnetic fields, recorded by 143 SQUIDS in the array (seen from the top of the head).

The results are mapped back onto a diagram of a head. Weaker responses indicate activity at greater depths in the brain.

Superimposing all the channels establishes that the maximum response occurs 97 ms after the onset of the tone.

The results are superimposed on an MRI image (seen from the front of the head).

Time (msec)

In research, MEG has been used to understand a variety of cognitive processes, including language, object recognition, and spatial processing among others, in neurologically intact individuals. (See Ioannides, 2007 for a discussion of how MEG works and its application to cognitive neuroscience). It has also been used to understand more about the neurophysiology underlying psychiatric disorders such as schizophrenia. For example, one particular component of a MEG waveform, the M100, is thought to index the raw perceptual memory for auditory stimuli that lasts 150 ms or so after stimulus presentation (Lu, Williamson, & Kaufman, 1992). In people with paranoid schizophrenia, this component is generated at an atypical location in Heschl's gyrus (which, as

you may remember from Chapter 1, is the location of primary auditory cortex) (e.g., Reite et al., 1994, 1997). Such findings lend support to the theory that people with paranoid schizophrenia have difficulties in filtering early sensory information appropriately (e.g., Boutros, Belger, Campbell, D'Souza, & Krystal, 1999; Freedman, Waldo, Bickford-Wimer, & Nagamoto, 1991; see Chapter 14).

■ Optical Recording Methods

Currently there is one technique that can provide cognitive neuroscientists with the ability to simultaneously obtain information about the source of neural activity as well as its time course. In this method, called **optical imaging**, a laser source of near-infrared light is positioned on the scalp. Detectors composed of optic fiber bundles are located a few centimeters away from the light source. These detectors sense how the path of light is altered, either through absorption or scattering, as it traverses brain tissue (● Figure 3.20).

This method can provide two types of information. First, it can provide information similar to that obtained by the BOLD signal in fMRI, by measuring the absorption of light. This signal is known as the *slow signal* and is so named because the time course is on the order of seconds: it starts about a second and a half after neuronal activity commences and subsides seconds after it stops. As with the BOLD signal, it is thought to reflect increased blood flow to areas engaged by task demands. However, unlike BOLD, which provides information only on the ratio of oxyhemoglobin to deoxyhemoglobin in the blood, optical imaging can actually tease them apart, because the degree to which light is absorbed by each of these substances can be determined separately. Second, it can measure the scattering of light, which is related to physiological characteristics such as the swelling of glia and neurons that are associated with neuronal firing. This information is known as the *fast signal* because it occurs simultaneously with neuronal activity (Andrew & MacVicar, 1994).

A newer method, *event-related optical signal* or *EROS*, takes advantage of this fast signal to record information locked to an event, much the way ERPs record the time-locked electrical response to a stimulus. The EROS method provides information about the source of activity within millimeters while providing temporal information on the order of milliseconds (typically recorded every 20 ms or so). It has been used to provide information about the timing of responses in different regions of visual cortex that is consistent with that obtained in ERP studies, and has also been used to examine memory and attentional processes (for a review of how this method works, its validation, and its application to studying human cognition, see Gratton & Fabiani, 2001). For example, EROS was recently used to reveal rapid interactions between posterior and anterior brain regions involved in language (Tse et al., 2007). However, this method has a major limitation: it cannot be used to obtain information about subcortical regions because too much light gets absorbed on the way to and from structures deep within the brain.

Techniques for Modulating Brain Activity

The more dramatic types of methodologies employed in cognitive neuroscience actually modulate or change brain activity in neurologically intact individuals. The

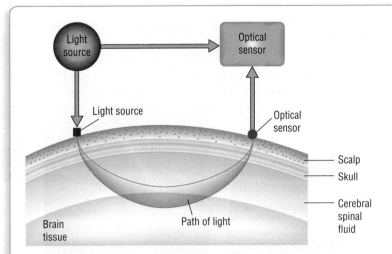

● **FIGURE 3.20   The principles of optical imaging.** A light source at the surface of the head emits near-infrared light that travels through the skull into the brain. The light then passes through the brain and emerges at the surface, where it can be detected. The path that the light takes through the brain can vary depending on a number of factors, including the geometry of the head. Hence, the set of possible paths is shown here as a crescent-shaped gray area. The optical signal is analyzed to determine how much light is absorbed, which results in a decrease in intensity, or how much the light is scattered from its ideal path, which causes a delay in its receipt at the sensor. © 2011 Cengage Learning

best of example of this type of approach is **transcranial magnetic stimulation (TMS)**. TMS can be conceptualized as working in a way opposite from MEG. Whereas MEG records the magnetic fields produced by the electrical activity of the brain, in TMS a pulsed magnetic field over the scalp induces an electrical field, which alters the pattern of brain activity in the underlying tissue. This magnetic field is created by a coil or series of coils placed on the scalp. An example of a TMS setup is shown in ● Figure 3.21.

The induced electrical field alters the membrane potential of neurons, causing them to depolarize synchronously, which in turn changes the probability that they will fire. Once the pulsed magnetic field is discontinued, the neurons can return to their previous state. Although TMS has been referred to as causing a "reversible" lesion, which would suggest that it blocks neuronal activity, it is better understood as scrambling neuronal activity—it causes neurons to fire in a random pattern rather than in a coherent manner.

There are two main types of TMS: *single-pulse TMS,* in which the stimulation is delivered at a precise time during performance of a task, and rTMS, which stands for *repetitive TMS* and involves multiple pulses with rates up to 50 Hz for tens, hundreds, or thousands of milliseconds. Although TMS can actually facilitate brain activity, such as inducing muscle movement, it can also disrupt activity. For example, a person who is speaking normally, and then receives TMS applied over Broca's area, becomes unable to produce speech (Pascual-Leone, Gates & Dhuna, 1991)! Demonstrating that TMS may

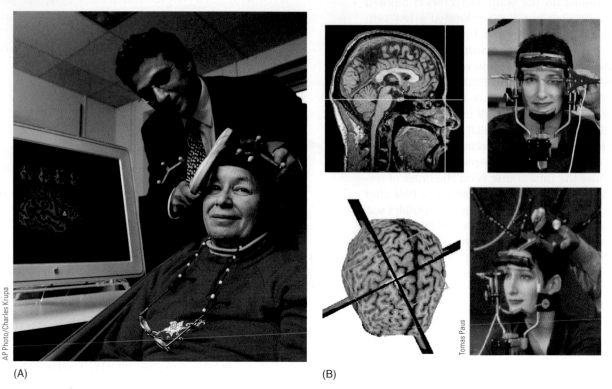

(A)   (B)

● **FIGURE 3.21   Transcranial magnetic stimulation (TMS) can be used to alter ongoing brain activity.** (A) On the left, an experimenter positions a coil over a participant's head. (B) Generally, a structural MRI scan (top left) is used to find landmarks on a person's head, which are used as a reference. The person's head is then placed in a stereotaxic frame (top right) with regard to such a reference point. Next, the site at which TMS is to be delivered is identified with regard to the person's brain anatomy (bottom left) and then the coil is placed at that coordinate within the stereotaxic frame (bottom right). © 2009 Cengage Learning

either disrupt or enhance activity, TMS applied over primary visual cortex can either lead to a transient scotoma (a blind spot in the visual field) or phosphenes, which are spots of light within the visual field, depending on the nature of the pulse sequence (for a recent review of the basics of this method, see Hallett, 2007).

One of the major advantages of TMS is that it can be used to confirm findings from the lesion method and implicate a brain region as playing a critical role in a specific mental function. If a brain area is critical for a particular mental function, then applying TMS to the region should disrupt that function. For example, PET and fMRI studies have indicated that primary visual cortex becomes active when an individual imagines an object, "picturing" it in his or her mind's eye (e.g., Kosslyn, Thompson, Kim, & Alpert, 1995). But perhaps primary visual cortex does not play a critical role in mental imagery; maybe it just becomes active as a result of back projections from more anterior visual areas, which are required to create a visual image. To resolve this ambiguity, researchers applied TMS over primary visual cortex and found that it disrupts ● visual imagery, indicating that these brain regions are in fact critically involved in producing visual imagery (Kosslyn et al., 1999).

This method has generated much excitement because of the many questions it can help to answer and because of its potential clinical applications. TMS can provide insights into how the brain reorganizes, either with learning or as a result of sensory deprivation (see Siebner & Rothwell, 2003 for a discussion). For example, applying TMS to primary visual areas in normal individuals does not interfere with their reading Braille, an alphabet felt with the fingers. We would anticipate such a result, as reading Braille would of course rely heavily on tactile regions of the brain. However, TMS applied to the visual cortex of blind individuals actually interrupts the reading of Braille (Cohen et al., 1997)! Such a finding suggests that as a result of sensory deprivation and exposure to Braille, the visual cortex of blind individuals has reorganized from processing visual information to processing nonvisual information.

TMS can also provide important information about whether a behavior is critically dependent on a particular brain region or whether it results from the interaction between brain regions. For example, hemineglect (to which you were introduced in Chapter 1) typically occurs after a right hemisphere lesion, leading individuals to ignore information on the left side of space. If paying attention to this side of space depends critically on an intact right hemisphere, then once the right hemisphere is damaged, patients should never be able to orient attention leftwards. Amazingly, the severity of neglect can be reduced transiently by applying TMS to the left hemisphere of these patients (Oliveri et al., 2001). Such findings suggest that neglect results not so much from right-hemisphere dysfunction, but rather from an imbalance of activation between the hemispheres. If the activity level of the left hemisphere is decreased via TMS to equalize the activation level of both hemispheres, neglect is reduced. Because the interconnectivity and functional interrelations between brain regions are sources of major unanswered questions in cognitive neuroscience today, TMS has an important role to play in increasing our understanding of the organization of the human brain.

TMS also can be used therapeutically. For example, successive trains of high-frequency rTMS can be applied over left frontal regions to offset the decreased activity of this region that is associated with depression (e.g., George et al., 1997; for a longer discussion, see Chapter 14). As a brief overview, a recent meta-analysis across 30 studies performed over the past 15 years indicates that this method is an effective treatment and at least as potent as a subset of antidepressive medications (Schutter, 2008). Because of its promise, it is now approved therapeutically for use in many countries across Europe, in Canada, New Zealand, Australia, and Israel, though as of the publication date of this book it had not been approved for use in the United States. (For a recent review of TMS as a clinical tool for treatment of depression, see Fitzgerald & Daskalakis, 2008.)

Because TMS alters brain function, it must be used with caution. Initially studies indicated that both single-pulse TMS in patients (Fauth, Meyer, Prosiegel, Zihl, & Conrad, 1992) and too high a rate of stimulation of rTMS in neurologically intact individuals (Wasserman, Cohen, Flitman, Chen, & Hallett, 1996) could induce seizures. On a less severe level, in humans TMS can lead to mild headache (due to activation of scalp and neck muscles), muscle twitches, or nausea. Therefore, it must be utilized very carefully, and strict guidelines have been drawn up to minimize the potential for such adverse effects (Wasserman, 1998). These guidelines appear to be effective, as recent research reveals only mild side effects both in neurologically intact control groups (Anderson et al., 2006) and in patients with clinical conditions such as depression (Janicak et al., 2008).

TMS also has some limitations as a tool for cognitive neuroscientists. As currently designed, the stimulating coils affect only the region of the brain closest to the surface. At present, it is not possible to stimulate deeper cortical neurons or subcortical structures without affecting the neurons that are on top of them. Also, it is not possible to precisely control what regions of the brain are affected by TMS, making it a rather broad-brush-stroke tool (for a review of TMS in cognitive neuroscience research, see Robertson, Théoret, & Pascual-Leone, 2003).

In summary, in this section we discussed various techniques for assessing or modulating brain function.

Because we need the proper tool for the job, the relative advantages and disadvantages of each method must be considered for each question to be investigated. A summary of the information provided by each method, as well as its spatial and temporal resolution, is presented on the inside back cover of this book. Table 3.3 lists the advantages and disadvantages of each method.

Multimethod Approaches

As Table 3.3 shows, there is no one perfect method that can provide a cognitive neuroscientist with answers to all questions of interest; each method has its advantages and drawbacks. In recent years, researchers have started to use a *multimethod approach,* using multiple tools in tandem. (This is sometimes referred to as a *multimodal approach.*) One common coupling combines electromagnetic methods of recording brain activity, which provide excellent information about the timing of brain events, with fMRI, which is better at providing information about the location of brain activity. In some cases, both types of information may be very important for the question under investigation. For example, as we will learn in Chapter 11, attention is supported by a circuit of brain regions. It has been suggested that some parts of this circuit exert control over other parts of the circuit. Although fMRI can do an excellent job of identifying all the portions of the circuit, it cannot identify which ones act first and which ones act second. To demonstrate that certain portions of the circuit lead and other portions follow requires a tool that provides information about the timing of the neuronal response, namely ERPs or some related method. In this case, a researcher may choose to run identical experiments, one using ERP recordings and one using a complementary method such fMRI or PET. In such cases, the data obtained from fMRI or PET about the location of brain activity during a mental process are utilized to constrain the set of potential locations for the possible dipoles. The researcher can then examine whether the ERP data collected on the scalp are consistent with such a dipole. If there is a good fit, the researcher has information about both the probable location and the time course of a given mental process (see Crottaz-Herbette & Menon, 2006, for an example of such an approach).

Another multimethod approach involves combining TMS with other methods to provide information on the connectivity between brain regions. The logic underlying these studies is to decrease or interrupt activity of one brain region using TMS, and then to examine the change in the pattern of activity across the whole brain with another imaging method, such as PET. Those brain regions intimately connected with and influenced by the region receiving TMS should also show decreases in activity.

As an analogy, imagine that I want to determine which students in the class tend to talk to one another. I could temporarily disable the cellular phone of one person in the class, much the way TMS can disrupt the activity of a

TABLE 3.3	Advantages and Disadvantages of Different Methods Used in Cognitive Neuroscience

Methods of Assessing Brain Anatomy

	Advantages	Disadvantages
CAT (computerized axial tomography)	Can be used with almost all individuals	a. Involves the use of ionizing radiation b. Does not provide high spatial resolution
Anatomical MRI (magnetic resonance imaging)	a. Can be used to detect different substances b. Allows white-matter tracts to be visualized via diffusion tensor imaging c. Does not involve radiation d. Good spatial resolution	a. Cannot be used with individuals who have metal in their bodies or pacemakers b. Can induce claustrophobia in some individuals

Methods of Assessing Brain Physiology

Functional Brain Imaging	Advantages	Disadvantages
PET (positron emission tomography)	Can be used to assess many aspects of physiological function	a. Involves the use of ionizing radiation (which limits an individual to 4–5 scans per year) b. Provides images that are averaged over times longer than thought processes require
fMRI	a. Provides good spatial resolution in relatively short periods b. Can be performed repeatedly on the same individual c. Widely available	a. Cannot be used with individuals who have metal in their bodies or pacemakers b. Limited ways of measuring physiological function BOLD: (1) Provides information only on relative oxygenation of the blood; (2) measures the brain's hemodynamic response that occurs on the order of seconds Spectroscopy: Does not provide precise information on location of chemical substances

Electromagnetic Recordings	Advantages	Disadvantages
Single-cell	Provides information on the type of stimulus to which a cell responds	Cannot be used in humans except under very specific circumstances
EEG (electroencephalography)	a. Provides information on the general state of the person (e.g., alert, drowsy) b. Provides excellent temporal resolution	a. Difficult to determine the souce of activity from within the brain b. Difficult to detect activity of cells oriented parallel to the brain's surface
ERP (event-related potentials)	a. Provides information that has been linked to specific psychological processes such as memory and attention b. Provides excellent temporal resolution	a. Difficult to determine the source of activity from within the brain b. Difficult to detect activity of cells oriented parallel to the brain's surface
MEG (magnetoencephalography)	a. Provides better information than EEG/ERP about the source of the signal b. Not as susceptible to differences in conduction of tissue intervening between the brain and scalp	a. Set up is large and elaborate, requiring a shielded room b. Cannot detect cells with orientations radial to the brain's surface

Optical Imaging	Advantages	Disadvantages
Slow signal (metabolic)	a. Noninvasive b. Inexpensive c. Portable d. Allows the concentration of oxygenated and deoxygenated blood to be calculated separately	a. Cannot provide information on subcortical structures b. Can measure only the hemodynamic response of the brain
Fast signal EROS	a. Noninvasive b. Inexpensive c. Portable d. Detects a neuronal response rather than a hemodynamic response	a. Cannot provide information on subcortical structures

Methods of Modulating Brain Activity

	Advantages	Disadvantages
TMS (transcranial magnetic stimulation)	a. Can be used to confirm findings from lesion method b. Can be used therapeutically to treat clinical syndromes c. Can provide information on brain reorganization d. Provides information about the functional connectivity of brain regions e. Can be used to determine whether a deficit results from dysfunction of a region or disconnection of brain regions	a. Very small but possible potential for adverse effects on brain functions (e.g., induce seizures) b. Can only stimulate regions close to the surface c. Does not allow for precise localization of effects

single brain region. I can now determine which individuals in the class talk to the person whose phone has been disabled, by examining which individuals are receiving fewer phone calls than normal. In the case of the brain, PET or some other method is used to determine which brain regions are showing a decrease in activation (rather than, in our analogy, a decrease in phone calls received). This logic has been utilized very effectively by researchers. For example, rTMS over left mid-dorsolateral frontal cortex has been linked to modulation of activity in limbic and cingulate regions as measured by PET (Paus, Castro-Alamancos, & Petrides, 2001), which appears to be one of the mechanisms by which rTMS alleviates the symptoms of depression (Paus & Barrett, 2004). Recently, TMS has been used together with ERPs to similar effect (see Taylor, Walsh, & Eimer, 2008, for a longer discussion of using ERPs and TMS in conjunction).

You may wonder why researchers do not use multimodal techniques as a matter of course—it would seem the best way to answer questions. Unfortunately, multimethod techniques usually require using twice as much equipment, collecting and analyzing twice as much data, undertaking additional analyses to link them together, and often the cooperation of research participants to do multiple sessions of similar tasks in each modality. Hence, the benefits of a multimodal approach, in terms of the additional knowledge that can be gained, must justify the effort required.

Techniques for Analyzing Behavior

Just as we need precise tools to measure brain anatomy and physiology, we also need precise tools to examine behavior. Careful and thoughtful behavioral testing is one of the most powerful tools for analyzing how the brain constrains and influences the way we think.

■ The Role of Cognitive Theories

Theories of cognitive and emotional function play an important role in both research and clinical practice. Throughout this book, we discuss different theories of mental function. They help to guide investigations into the relationship between the brain and behavior by conceptualizing overarching cognitive functions such as "language" or "spatial ability" as actually consisting of a set of more specific cognitive capacities. To understand the neural underpinnings of functions such as language or spatial ability, we often must break them down into smaller subcomponents, which can then be mapped onto brain function. For example, psycholinguists often describe language as being composed of three parts: phonology, syntax, and semantics. *Phonology* refers to the rules governing the sounds of language, *syntax* its grammar, and *semantics* its meaning. As we discuss in the chapter on language, individuals with brain damage may have deficits in only one of these domains.

Why is it so important to be aware of cognitive theories? Let's suppose that a naive cognitive neuroscientist or neuropsychologist does not know or consider psycholinguistic theories of language and encounters an individual who cannot correctly repeat a sentence spoken to her. Our researcher or clinician might conclude, erroneously, that the patient does not "understand" the words in the sentence. However, if this scientist knew from theories of language that the ability to use grammar correctly can be separable from the knowledge of what words mean, the clinician or researcher would test both the patient's ability to repeat the sentence and also her comprehension—for example, by asking her to point to a picture that depicted what she had just heard. If she could point to the picture depicting the sentence even though she could not repeat the sentence, it would provide evidence that she could indeed understand the meanings of words. At this point, the researcher or clinician could go on to systematically test for difficulties in other aspects of language processing, such as grammar or syntax.

Not only do cognitive theories inform neuropsychological investigations, but neuropsychological investigations can in turn inform cognitive theories, especially differentiating those that are plausible from those that are not. For example, as discussed in the chapter on language, data from neuropsychological studies support the conceptualization of syntax and semantics as distinct aspects of language, because brain damage can disrupt one of these abilities while leaving the other intact.

■ Assessment of Behavior in Brain-Damaged Populations

In this section, we discuss some of the methods commonly used to assess the effects of brain damage. We focus on approaches that help cognitive neuroscientists to understand the organization of the brain and its linkage to mental function, but we also discuss how such methods are used clinically.

We might assume that the deficits a person has sustained due to brain damage can be ascertained simply by observing behavior, but this is not the case. Think for a moment about the many possible reasons a patient might not be able to provide a name when shown a picture of an animal, such as a zebra. Perhaps the visual attributes of the stimulus cannot be processed because occipital regions were damaged and the person is blind. Or maybe basic visual processing is intact, but the patterns of light and dark cannot be interpreted as the black-and-white stripes of a zebra. Alternatively, maybe the physical form can be perceived (which we know because the patient can correctly choose a horse and not an elephant as looking similar to the zebra) and the patient's memory for zebras is intact (which we know because when asked which African animal is similar to a horse and has stripes, the patient correctly points to the word *zebra*), but the patient cannot identify that particular form as a zebra. Or perhaps the verbal label cannot be specifically accessed (that is, if you said "zebra," the patient could point to a picture of one, but if shown a picture of a zebra, he or she couldn't name it). Finally, the patient may have sustained some damage to the vocal musculature that does not allow production of the sound sequence denoted by *zebra*, even though she or he knows that the picture is that of a zebra. As this example demonstrates, what appears on the surface to be a simple problem may actually stem from numerous complex sources. Often the job of both clinical and experimental neuropsychologists is to carefully tease apart the possibilities and pinpoint the probable locus of the deficit.

Regardless of whether a brain-damaged individual's abilities are being examined for research or for clinical purposes, a **neuropsychological assessment** is generally performed to determine the degree to which damage to the central nervous system may have compromised a person's cognitive, behavioral, and emotional functioning. This assessment is designed to provide a profile of which abilities have been compromised and which ones are intact. Different approaches are used, but typically the assessment surveys a variety of different abilities, administers some measure of general intelligence, and then does more specific tests in the domain that seems to be most affected, such as language. A larger discussion of neuropsychological assessment is beyond the scope of this textbook. However, if you are interested in the approaches used and the tests employed in neuropsychological assessment, the definitive reference, often considered the "bible" for clinical neuropsychologists, is the volume by Muriel Lezak and her co-authors (Lezak, Howieson, Loring, Hannay, & Fischer, 2004), now in its fourth edition.

Most neuropsychological tests were designed for use in the clinic, with the goal of casting a wide net to detect any type of brain dysfunction of either neurological or psychiatric origin. To do so, neuropsychologists often administer a **neuropsychological test battery**. Probably the most widely used neuropsychological test battery is the *Halstead-Reitan battery*, which examines a range of abilities from simple tests of sensory function to complex tests of reasoning, from tests of verbal function to tests of spatial function, and from tests of immediate recognition to tests of memory (see Table 3.4) (Boll, 1981). Other test batteries, such as the Luria-Nebraska, can be administered in about four hours, half the time of the Halstead-Reitan. The tasks on the Luria-Nebraska are divided into 12 content scales: motor functions, rhythm and pitch, tactile and kinesthetic functions, visual functions, receptive language, expressive language, reading, arithmetic, writing, memory, intermediate memory, and intelligence. This battery is a formalized set of tests that reflects the philosophy of Alexander Luria, who believed the brain to be composed of three functional and interrelated systems: a brainstem system that is important for overall tone and arousal, an anterior system that is important for the planning and output of behavior, and

a posterior system that is important for the reception of information and its processing (Golden, 1981). In addition to providing data about the absolute level of performance, test batteries can provide data on the qualitative nature of performance—that is, the strategies an individual uses to perform a task. Such information can be important in gaining a more precise understanding of the cognitive deficit.

A neuropsychological battery will often contain some estimate of intelligence. The Wechsler family of intelligence tests are probably the most widely used to assess intellectual abilities and include the WPPSI-III (Wechsler Preschool and Primary Scale of Intelligence—Third Edition [Wechsler, 2002]), for children aged 3 years 7 months to 7 years 3 months; the WISC-IV (Wechsler Intelligence Scale for Children—Fourth Edition [Wechsler, 2003]), for children aged 6 years to 16 years 11 months; the WAIS-IV (Wechsler Adult Intelligence Scale—Fourth Edition [Wechsler, 2008]), and the WNV (Wechsler Nonverbal Scale of Ability [Wechsler & Naglieri, 2006]). To provide you with a feel for the types of abilities measured by such tests, the subtests of the WAIS-IV are presented in Table 3.5. The WISC-IV and WPPSI-III contain many of the same subtests, with some minor modifications and substitutions. The pattern of performance across the various subtests provides information on a person's strengths and weaknesses.

When deficits are more subtle, they may be difficult to detect. Consider the case of a midlevel manager for a small business who, after a car accident, performs about average on the WAIS-IV. How can a clinical neuropsychologist differentiate between the possibility that this person initially had average intelligence and the possibility that brain damage compromised his functioning? To make such a distinction, neuropsychologists and cognitive neuroscientists may use a test to obtain an **estimate of premorbid functioning**—that is, a reasonable guess as to how well the person was performing before the injury. The Vocabulary subtest of the WAIS is often used to estimate premorbid IQ, because the abilities it measures seem relatively resistant to brain damage, even that which affects many different arenas of intellectual functioning, such as occurs in Alzheimer's disease. Another test used to estimate premorbid functioning is the National Adult Reading Test (Nelson, 1982), which is an oral reading test consisting of 50 words, most of which are short and irregular in that they do not follow normal rules of pronunciation (e.g., *ache*). Because the words cannot be sounded out, the ability to read them indicates some previous familiarity with them and hence provides an estimate of premorbid abilities (Crawford, 1992). When estimates of premorbid intelligence are much higher than present test scores, the results suggest that the brain damage adversely affected the individual's intellectual abilities.

Cognitive neuroscientists are often interested in obtaining an even more fine-grained analysis of the precise components of cognitive or emotional functions that have

TABLE 3.4	Components of the Halstead-Reitan Neuropsychological Test Battery	
Test	**What It Measures**	**How the Ability Is Measured**
MMPI-2 (Minnesota Multiphasic Personality Inventory—Second Edition)	Psychiatric symptomatology, such as depression and schizophrenia	The individual answers a large number of yes-no questions to provide a profile relative to individuals who have been diagnosed with specific psychiatric disorders.
Categories Test	Abstract reasoning	The individual views four items on the screen and pushes one of four buttons: different sets of items require different responses (e.g., push the button corresponding to the atypical item, push the button corresponding to the Roman numeral on the screen). The only feedback provided is a bell for correct answers and a buzzer for incorrect responses.
Rhythm Test	Auditory perception and timing	The individual decides whether two patterns of sounds are similar.
Speech Sounds Perception Test	Verbal abilities Attentional abilities	In each trial, the individual chooses a previously heard sound from among a number of choices. The sounds are nonsense syllables that begin and end with different consonants.
Finger Tapping Test	Motor function	The tapping rate of each index finger is determined.
Grip Strength Test	Motor function	The strength with which a dynamometer can be squeezed by each hand is assessed.
Trail Making Test	Visual search Attention	*Part A:* The individual's ability to draw a line connecting consecutively numbered circles is assessed. *Part B:* The individual's ability to connect, in an alternating manner, numbered and lettered circles (e.g., A1B2C3) is examined.
Aphasia Screening Test	Language	The individual's ability to use and perceive language, to pantomime simple actions, and to reproduce simple geometric forms is assessed.
Tactile Perception Test	Tactile ability	The individual is tested as to whether he or she can identify objects by touch (each hand separately), can identify letters traced on the fingertips (with the eyes closed), and can perceive being touched on different fingers of both hands.
Tactual Performance Test	Tactile memory Spatial localization	Without any visual input (blindfolded or eyes closed), the individual must place a set of felt shapes into a single board from which they were cut out. Afterward, with eyes open and the board obscured from view, the individual must draw each shape at its correct location on the board.
Sensory-Perceptual Exam	Sensory loss Hemineglect	The individual's perception of simple information in the visual, tactile, and auditory modalities is examined. To determine whether neglect is present, the investigator presents stimuli to just one side of the body or to both sides simultaneously.
WAIS-IV (Wechsler Adult Intelligence Scale—Fourth Edition)	General intellectual abilities	Eleven subtests are used to assess various intellectual functions of the individual (see Table 3.5).

been disrupted. An alternative strategy to the test-battery approach, which is more conducive to cognitive neuroscience research, is **customized neuropsychological assessment**. In such assessment, the examiner initially uses information from a small set of tests (e.g., WAIS-IV, Boston Diagnostic Aphasia Exam) to generate hypotheses about the set of particular abilities that were compromised by the brain damage. Each hypothesis is then evaluated with a specific neuropsychological test, and, depending on the individual's performance, the hypothesis is either pursued further by means of another test or abandoned (e.g., Lezak et al., 2004). If it is abandoned, a new hypothesis is generated, and the cycle is repeated until the behavioral deficit is well characterized. In such a situation, not only the level of performance, but also the manner in which an individual performs tasks can provide important clues to the nature of the underlying deficit.

Although cognitive neuroscientists can be tempted to use neuropsychological tests to examine the range of abilities in neurologically intact populations, there is a hazard in doing so. These tests typically have been designed to detect a low level of functioning—one that is so far below the average as to indicate brain damage. These tests may be insensitive to variations in abilities across neurologically intact individuals, who may all perform at a high level regardless of true individual variation in ability.

Techniques for Modeling Brain-Behavior Relationships

In this final section of the chapter, we discuss another major method in cognitive neuroscience, the use of computer modeling techniques to simulate the action of the brain and its processes. Researchers create such simulations, generally known as **neural networks**, to

TABLE 3.5	Wechsler Adult Intelligence Scale IV (Fourth Edition)	
Subtest	What It Measures	How the Ability Is Measured
Verbal Comprehension Scales		
Vocabulary	Vocabulary	The individual defines a series of orally and visually presented words, such as *commerce.*
Similarities	Abstract thinking	The individual answers questions such as "How are celery and a carrot alike?"
Information	Factual knowledge	The individual answers questions such as "If you were to go from New York to Los Angeles, in which direction would you be traveling?"
Working Memory Scale		
Arithmetic	Arithmetic abilities; freedom from distractibility	The individual solves math problems, such as the following, in his or her head, without the aid of a pen and paper: "If it takes 18 days for 12 workers to manufacture one automobile, how many workers would it take to manufacture an automobile in 6 days?"
Digit span	Verbal short-term memory; freedom from distractibility	The individual hears a string of digits ranging in length from three to eight and must repeat the string to the experimenter. In half the trials, the string must be repeated in the same order as presented (e.g., hear: "2-5-3" and respond: "2-5-3"), and in the other half in the opposite order (e.g., hear: "2-5-3" and respond: "3-5-2").
Perceptual Reasoning Scale		
Visual puzzles	Visual processing	The individual views an abstract picture and must choose the set of pieces that comprises the picture
Block design	Visuomotor ability; spatial processing	The individual is given cubes that are red on two sides and white on two sides and two that are half red and half white (the color divide goes along the diagonal). The cubes must be arranged so that their top surfaces match a picture.
Matrix reasoning	Visual processing; abstract reasoning skills	The individual views an incomplete gridded pattern with a section missing. He or she has to choose the correct missing piece of the picture out of five possible choices.
Processing Speed Scale		
Symbol search	Visual processing	The individual views two groups of symbols, a target group and a search group. He or she must indicate whether either of the target symbols appears in the search group by marking yes or no.
Coding	Mental processing speed; visuo-motor coordination	The individual is shown a template in which the numbers 1–9 are each associated with a unique symbol. Then the individual is shown a series of numbers and must fill in the associated symbol below each number.

help them test theories of neuropsychological functioning and to derive general principles regarding brain-behavior relationships.

Computational modeling has a number of important strengths. First, when researchers create a model, they must be very explicit about the assumptions underlying their reasoning, and about the factors that they think contribute to a neural mechanism underlying mental processing. Basically, you can think of these models as keeping a researcher honest. Second, models can be manipulated systematically in ways that may be impossible to do with animals or people. For example, lesions that do not occur or that occur rarely in real life can be simulated in a model. Finally, the outcome of modeling can provide researchers with novel predictions about the relationship between the brain and behavior that can be tested via many of the other techniques that we have discussed (e.g., by examining patients who have lesions or by using neuroimaging techniques). In later chapters we will discuss how computational models can provide better insight into the interrelationships between brain and behavior. The drawbacks of such models are that they obviously are only an abstraction of the brain or of a cognitive process. In addition, it is hard to determine how well any model "fits" or "explains" behavior, as no clear criteria for evaluating their validity is available.

Let's explore the nature of these models in a bit more detail. Brain processes can be modeled at different levels. Some neural networks model the electrical processes in dendrites (e.g., Anton, Granger, & Lynch, 1993), others model the electrical properties of neurons (e.g., Gerstner, Kempter, van Hemmen, & Wagner, 1996), and still others model the interactions in a well-specified circuit of neurons that controls some very fundamental behavior (e.g., the oculomotor circuit in the brainstem that is the final common pathway for movement of the eyes; Qian, 1995). These types of models are not of much concern to us here, as they attempt to describe the behavior of the nervous system rather than to model mental functioning in humans.

A variety of **computational models** can be used to simulate mental functions in humans (for an accessible overview, see Hinton, 1992). Here we will focus on **connectionist networks**, which are composed of interconnected layers of units that exhibit neuron-like behavior (for a book-length treatment of how such models are used in cognitive neuroscience, see O'Reilly & Munakata, 2000). The basic component of most computational models is a "unit," which one can think of as exhibiting behavior like an individual neuron. These units receive input from other units, which are summed to produce a net input. The summed input is then transformed via an *activation function* that produces an activation value, which is sent on to other units. Typically such models utilize a sigmoid activation function, which as you can see from ● Figure 3.22 allows maximal changes in activation to occur over the range of intermediate input values, with relatively little change when the input to a unit is very weak or very strong. As you will soon learn, this function aids in helping the system "settle" into a stable state.

These units are wired together in layers. Most models have an input layer that simulates the receipt of information from the outside world, an output layer that simulates the response of the system, and a "hidden" layer that is involved in the transformations necessary to perform the computation under investigation (● Figure 3.23). Units in one layer are connected to those in another via connection weights, which indicate the degree of influence that a unit in one level has on a unit in another level. The values of these weights usually vary between −1 and +1. If positive, activity in the first unit will increase activity of the next unit. If negative, then activity in the first unit will decrease activity of the next unit. If the absolute value of the weight is large (0.9), then a large amount of the activity in the first unit will be passed on to the next one. In contrast, if the absolute value of the connection weight is small (0.1), then not much of the activity of the first unit will be passed on to the other.

Let's look a little more closely at all of the layers in a model to understand their interrelation. The input layer typically encodes something about the external environment. In computer models it is impossible to code actual physical attributes of the physical world, so physical attributes are represented by an arbitrary code. Typically, each unit is assigned a value of either 1 or 0. For example, let's say that a stimulus might be in one of four positions: far left, left center, right center, or far right. The input layer would consist of four units. We might have the values for each unit be "1000" to indicate far left, "0100" to indicate left center, "0010" to indicate right center, and "0001" to indicate far right. In this example, there is an actual correspondence between the spatial location and the position of the "1" in the array. However, the four arrays could be used to represent green, red, blue, and yellow, or any other dimension of a stimulus.

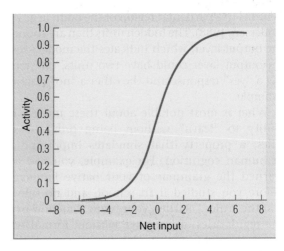

● **FIGURE 3.22 The sigmoid activation function that translates the sum of the input values to a unit of a neural network into an output value.** Notice that the main changes in activation occur across a range of intermediate input values (e.g., between −2 and +2), rather than more extreme input values (e.g., less than −2 or greater than +2). This feature causes activation of the unit to remain relatively stable when the inputs are either very high or very low, but very responsive to changes when inputs are in an intermediate range. © 2011 Cengage Learning

Each node in this array then feeds information to the hidden layer. Notice that the hidden layer receives input from multiple input units, allowing it to integrate such information. Exactly what these hidden units "represent" is often obscure, although in some cases

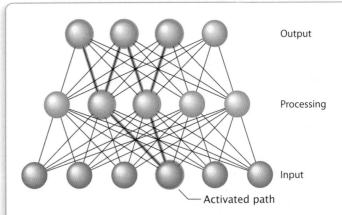

● **FIGURE 3.23 A simple connectionist network.** In this hypothetical connectionist network, units are depicted as circles. Lines represent the connections between units, and the strength of the connection weights is depicted by the thickness of the line. The input layer represents some type of information that is received by the system. The value for each unit in the input layer is typically either "1" or "0." The output layer represents the response of the system. Here, for example, one unit could represent a "far left" response, another could represent a "middle left" response, and the remaining two a "middle right" and "far right" response, respectively. The exact type of information that is coded by the middle layer, known as the hidden layer, is generally not easily determined. © 2008 Cengage Learning

they can actually end up simulating the properties of neurons in a particular region of the brain (e.g., Zipser & Andersen, 1988). The hidden units then are connected to the output layer, which indicates the model's response. An output layer could have two units, one representing a "yes" response and the other a "no" response, for example.

What is most notable about these models is their ability to "learn" without being provided specific rules, a property that simulates important aspects of human cognition. For example, you had actually learned the grammar of your native language long before you studied it in school, and no one taught you the "rules." Rather, your brain somehow extracted the regularities of language without formal training. These computational models learn in much the same manner: by extracting the regularity of relationships with repeated exposure. In computational modeling this exposure occurs via "training" in which certain input patterns are provided over and over again. Learning within the system occurs via adjustment of the connection weights between units, typically those between layers. Notice that learning occurs not because of changes in the activation functions of the units themselves, but rather because of changes in the interrelationships between and among units. It is thought that similar changes occur in the nervous system with learning, via a process known as *neuronal plasticity.* Such changes are thought to occur either because the influence of one neuron on another is increased (i.e., through increased efficacy of the synaptic connection) or because of a sprouting of new connections between neurons or a withdrawal of existing connections. We will talk more about this issue of plasticity in Chapter 15. In computational models, changes in synaptic efficiency are simulated by changes in the absolute value of the connection weight. A shift from a connection weight of 0 (i.e., no connection, no influence) to a nonzero weight is the equivalent of sprouting a new connection, whereas the reverse is akin to withdrawing a synaptic connection.

One of the most common methods for learning in computational models is *supervised learning.* In this approach, the system is provided with an input and allowed to compute through to a final output. The output obtained is then compared to the output that *should* have been given (e.g., the output yielded a "yes" response and the correct response would have been "no"). Next, small adjustments are made in the connection weights between units. If input from one unit helped push a connected unit toward the correct output, its connection weight is slightly increased; if it helped push a connected unit toward an incorrect output, its connection weight is slightly decreased. This process is performed over and over again until the system settles into a relatively stable state, in which increased training does not change the performance of the system much. However, this approach has been criticized because most real-life learning situations do not involve explicit feedback about what is right and what is wrong (unless perhaps your teacher is standing right over you!).

Other computational models work by an alternative process called *Hebbian learning,* named for the neuroscientist Donald Hebb. Hebb argued that when activity in neuron A is consistently associated with the firing of neuron B, a change occurs such that the influence of neuron A on neuron B is increased. In Hebbian learning models, when the activity of units co-occurs frequently, the connection strength of one unit upon the other is increased.

Performance of a computational model is evaluated in a number of ways. One way is to determine whether the pattern of results mimics that seen in people. Another is to pit models against each other and determine which one makes the fewest "errors" or reaches a stable state most quickly. By these standards, computational simulations can successfully model a remarkable amount of human behavior, ranging from learning the pronunciation rules and reading skills for the English language (Seidenberg & McClelland, 1989), to recognizing objects (e.g., Reisenhuber & Poggio, 2000), to accounting for our ability to store and retain new information in longterm memory (O'Reilly & Rudy, 2000). In addition, these models can mimic patterns of behavior seen after brain damage, such as dyslexias that impair reading ability (McLeod, Shallice, & Plaut, 2000) and attentional disruptions that lead to hemineglect (Mozer, Halligan, & Marshall, 1997). In these cases, the models are "damaged" by reducing the number of connections or adding "noise" to the system, such as adding variability to the input/ output function of units.

Obviously, a vast array of tools is available to cognitive neuroscientists as they work to discover how the neural organization of the brain influences how we think and what we feel. In subsequent chapters, the experiments we discuss will utilize the broad span of techniques discussed in this chapter. These methods are somewhat complicated and you may need to flip back to this chapter to remind yourself of what these methods can and cannot tell us. Knowing the strengths and limitations of each method will help you to evaluate the strength of the experimental evidence discussed in the remaining chapters of this book.

Summary

Introduction

■ The relationship between the functional architecture of the brain and behavior can be investigated through the use of a variety of populations and techniques. Depending on the question researchers want to answer, the focus may be on the neuroanatomy or neurophysiology of the brain, or on the way in which the brain affects behavior.

■ Various techniques are often used in combination because converging evidence from different techniques is the most powerful tool for uncovering fundamental aspects of brain-behavior relationships.

Populations of Research Participants

■ Patients with delineated brain damage allow researchers to determine which functions are lost as a result of damage to specific brain regions. This method cannot identify all brain regions that participate in a function, but rather identifies only the areas critical for task performance.

■ Neurologically intact individuals provide (1) a baseline against which to compare performance of individuals who sustain brain trauma, (2) information on the basic neuroanatomical organization of the brain, and (3) when used in conjunction with brain imaging techniques, evidence on how brain structures work together.

■ Nonhuman animals can provide useful information about the brain-behavior relationship because human brains share certain characteristics with other mammalian and primate nervous systems, especially those of monkeys.

Techniques for Assessing Brain Anatomy

■ These methods provide information about the structural integrity of the brain.

■ Computerized axial tomography (CAT) uses X-rays to provide information about the density of tissue, which can differentiate bone, blood, brain tissue, and cerebrospinal fluid.

■ Magnetic resonance imaging (MRI) uses magnetic fields to provide a picture of the distribution of specific substances, such as water and fat, in the brain.

Techniques for Assessing Physiological Functioning

■ Functional brain imaging methods provide information about the physiological activity in the brain that occurs as a byproduct of neuronal firing, and thus provide very good information about *where* in the brain activity is occurring.

■ Positron emission tomography (PET) uses a radioactively tagged molecule to provide a measure of physiological activity of different brain regions. It can be used to examine consumption of glucose and oxygen as well as binding of specific neurotransmitters.

■ Functional magnetic resonance imaging (fMRI) typically works by detecting differences in the magnetic properties of oxygenated and deoxygenated blood, allowing the identification of brain regions where neurons are active.

■ Electromagnetic recording methods record the electrical signals or the magnetic fields that accompany neuronal firing, providing very precise information on *when* neuronal activity is occurring.

■ Single-cell recordings, which are used mainly in animals but in rare cases with people, involve inserting an electrode into single cells so researchers can determine what type of stimulus will make that cell fire.

■ Electroencephalography (EEG) is used to examine the frequency of the summed electrical signal of synchronous firing in the dendrites of populations of neurons. It is useful for distinguishing states of alertness, drowsiness, and sleepiness and can be used for detecting the electrical spiking that occurs in epilepsy.

■ Event-related potentials (ERPs) are electrical potentials that are recorded in response to an event and are time-locked. Different portions of the ERP signal are linked to specific sensory or cognitive processes.

■ Magnetoencephalography (MEG) provides information about the magnetic potentials that are associated with electrical activity in the brain. Different portions of the MEG signal are linked to specific sensory or cognitive processes.

■ Optical recording methods supply information about the absorption and scattering of light through the brain. These can be used to infer regional changes in oxygenated and deoxygenated blood that occur on the order of seconds, and information about changes associated with neuronal firing that occur on the order of milliseconds.

Techniques for Modulating Brain Activity

■ Transcranial magnetic stimulation (TMS) disrupts brain activity through magnetic fields on the scalp that interfere with the electrical firing of neurons. It can be used to identify those regions of the brain that are critical to performance of a task.

Techniques for Analyzing Behavior

■ Cognitive theories play a large role in helping to dissect the different component processes of mental functioning.

■ Clinical assessment of behavior is done either via a test battery that samples a large number of mental functions without going into a detailed examination of any one function, or a customized approach that assesses very specific cognitive functions in addition. In either case, a measure of general intelligence often also is obtained.

Techniques for Modeling Brain-Behavior Relationships

■ Computational models, composed of neuronlike units, can be used to make predictions about the way the brain supports mental functions and to simulate what happens after brain damage.

Key Terms

alpha suppression   71

components   71

computational models   84

computerized axial tomography (CAT, CT)   60

connectionist networks   85

customized neuropsychological assessment   83

diffusion tensor imaging (DTI)   61

dipole   71

disconnection syndrome   56

double dissociation   55

electrical potential   69

electroencephalography (EEG)   69

endogenous components   72

estimate of premorbid functioning   82

event-related potentials (ERPs)   71

exogenous components   72

functional magnetic resonance imaging (fMRI)   63

gradient field   61

group studies   57

lesion method   53

localization of function   53

magnetic resonance imaging (MRI)   60

magnetoencephalography (MEG)   74

mass action   53

method of converging operations   52

multiple-case-study approach   57

neural networks   83

neuropsychological assessment   82

neuropsychological test battery   82

optical imaging   76

positron emission tomography (PET)   63

pulse sequence   60

receiver coil   60

single-case studies   56

static field   60

transcranial magnetic stimulation (TMS)   77

tractography   62

Book Companion Site at www.cengage.com/psychology/Banich

This website provides instructors and students with a wealth of free information and resources, including tutorial quizzes, flashcards, and the glossary.

Hemispheric Specialization

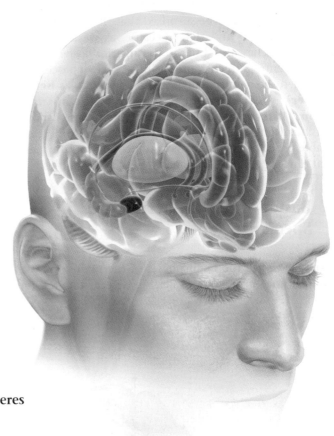

Close to the edge, a little off center,
More than a dreamer, a real believer,
Visual but I take heart,
I've been born right brained in a left brain world, it's true!
—*Carrie Newcomer, folksinger, 1991*

AS THE LYRICS to this song attest, it is common knowledge that the cerebral hemispheres are specialized for different aspects of cognitive and emotional functioning. We should not be surprised that the brain's functions differ left and right, because, as we learned in Chapter 1, they also differ in the anterior-posterior and dorsal-ventral dimensions. The difference in processing between the hemispheres is often referred to as **hemispheric specialization**, or **lateralization of function**. This chapter provides an overview of basic aspects of hemispheric specialization, which you will learn more about in later chapters that focus on specific mental functions, such as language and spatial abilities.

Basics of Hemispheric Specialization

At first glance the hemispheres of the brain look like mirror images, but this impression is deceiving in some important ways. Actually, the hemispheres are distinct in their neuroanatomy, neurochemistry, and function.

Asymmetry in the gross anatomy of the cerebral hemispheres has been noted for more than 100 years (see Toga & Thompson, 2003, for review). The right frontal lobe tends to extend farther forward and is wider than the left frontal lobe, whereas the left occipital lobe extends farther back and is wider than the right occipital lobe (● Figure 4.1A). In most individuals, the Sylvian fissure extends farther in the horizontal dimension in the left hemisphere but takes more of an upward turn in the right hemisphere (Hochberg & LeMay, 1975; Rubens, Mahowald, & Hutton, 1976) (● Figure 4.1B). This asymmetry has a long evolutionary history, having been observed in australopithecine fossils dating back as far as 3.5 million years (Holloway, 1983). In addition, the region at the end of the Sylvian fissure in the temporal lobe, known as the **planum temporale** (temporal plane), is usually larger on the left than on the right, sometimes by as much as 10 times (Geschwind & Levitsky, 1968) (● Figure 4.2). The planum temporale in the left hemisphere is important for language comprehension, and individuals who have a larger left than right planum temporale are likely to rely more on the left hemisphere when processing language (Foundas, Leonard, Gilmore, Fennell, & Heilman, 1994). Another

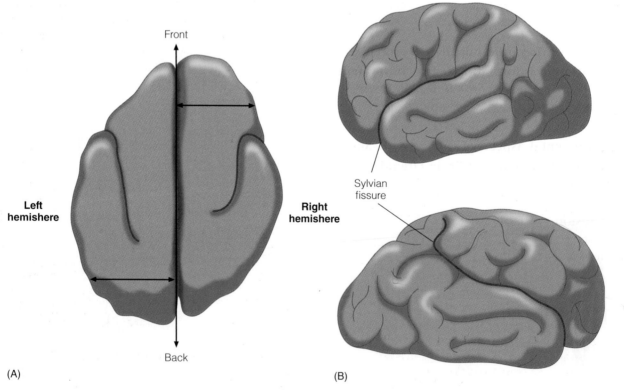

(A) Front · Left hemishere · Right hemishere · Back

(B) Sylvian fissure

● **FIGURE 4.1   Some anatomical asymmetries of the human brain.** (A) The right frontal region typically extends farther forward and is wider than the left frontal region, whereas for the occipital region the opposite is true: this region of the left hemisphere extends farther back and is wider. (B) The Sylvian fissure extends farther horizontally in the left hemisphere (top), whereas in the right hemisphere (bottom), it takes more of an upward turn. © 2011 Cengage Learning

language-related area that is larger on the left than the right side is Broca's area in the frontal lobe, which is implicated in speech output (Amunts, Schleicher, Burgel, Mohlberg, Uylings, & Zilles, 1999).

The left and right sides of the brain appear to differ not only in large-scale anatomical structures, but also in some micro-level features. Columns of cells are more widely spaced in auditory areas of the left hemisphere than the right, and the left hemisphere contains more large pyramid-shaped cells than the right (see Hutsler & Galuske, 2003, for review). The functional significance of such asymmetries is not yet clear. However, one possibility is that the wider spacing of cortical columns in left auditory regions allows for better separation of different auditory inputs, thus giving rise to a more fine-tuned representation of sounds. Neurons in Broca's area of the left frontal lobe show greater branching of dendrites than those in the homologous region of the right hemisphere (Scheibel, 1984), possibly indicating that neurons in this region have a larger or more specialized processing capacity.

Neurochemical differences between the hemispheres also abound, mainly expressed as asymmetries in neurotransmitter concentrations. For example, higher concentrations of norepinephrine can be found in certain regions of the right thalamus than the left (Oke, Keller, Mefford, & Adams, 1978). A portion of the basal ganglia has greater concentrations of dopamine and more dopamine receptors in the left than the right (Glick, Ross, & Hough, 1982; Wagner et al., 1983). These findings imply that mental processes more dependent on dopamine, such as those that require a readiness for action, are lateralized to the left hemisphere. In contrast, processes more dependent on norepinephrine, such as those that aid a person in orienting toward new or novel stimuli, are lateralized to the right hemisphere (Tucker & Williamson, 1984). Some neurochemical asymmetries differ by brain region. For example, serotonin binding is greater in the left hemisphere than the right in primary and secondary auditory cortex, but this binding is greater in the right hemisphere than the left in adjacent regions of the temporal lobe (Fink et al., 2009).

Most dramatic, however, are differences in function between the hemispheres, a distinction that was first observed in the late 1800s. We now turn back the pages of time to explore how the distinct specialization of each hemisphere was uncovered.

■ Historical Perspective

The idea that the hemispheres have different functions first caught the attention of the scientific community in the 1860s, when Paul Broca, a French neurologist and anthropologist, provided evidence that the left hemisphere is critical in language processing. Broca's discovery was sparked by an unusual patient whom he met on his rounds. The man could utter only the syllable "tan," yet it was clear that he could understand language because he could follow simple verbal commands. Because he did not exhibit paralysis of the vocal musculature or the vocal tract, Broca realized that the problem arose from the brain function controlling speech output. Soon after Broca met him, the man died, at which point Broca autopsied his brain. He noticed that the damage was confined to a specific region of the left hemisphere (● Figure 4.3). Broca then accumulated brains from several other individuals who had the same type of language problem. In each case, the damage was

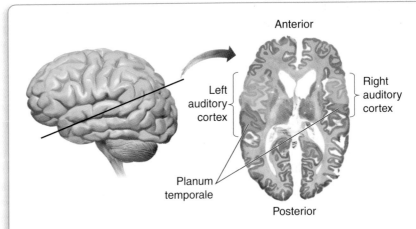

● **FIGURE 4.2 Asymmetries in the planum temporale.** The planum temporale, or "temporal plane," has a larger area on the left than the right side of the brain in most people. © 2010 Cengage Learning

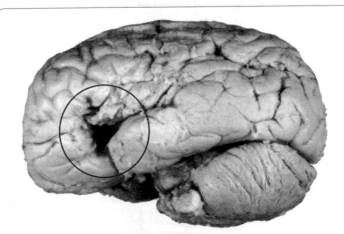

● **FIGURE 4.3 The brain of Broca's patient "Tan."** This patient was no longer able to say anything other than the syllable "tan"; his functioning, along with physical evidence from his autopsy, led Broca to propose that a left-hemisphere region is crucial for speech. Source: Dronkers, N.F., Plaisant, O., Iba-Zizen, M.T. & Cabanis, E.A. (2007). Paul Broca's historic cases: high resolution MR imaging of the brain of Leborgne and Lelong. Brain, 130, Figure 3, pg. 1436. By permission of Oxford University Press.

restricted to the same brain region, always located in the left hemisphere. Individuals with damage to the analogous area of the right hemisphere displayed no difficulties in language.

The importance of the left hemisphere for language processing was confirmed by other neurologists. Karl Wernicke noticed that damage to yet another region of the left hemisphere caused a syndrome different from that discovered by Broca. In Wernicke's syndrome, individuals lose almost all ability to comprehend language, although they retain their ability to speak fluently (however, what they say makes little or no sense). Like Broca, Wernicke found that this syndrome occurred only after left-hemisphere damage.

Near the end of the 1860s, the English neurologist John Hughlings Jackson introduced the idea of **cerebral dominance**, which is the concept that one hemisphere dominates or leads mental function. At that time language was considered to be the quintessential mental act. As a result, the left hemisphere came to be viewed as the dominant hemisphere, and even today you may

find a research article in which the right hemisphere is referred to as the "nondominant hemisphere." Although Jackson documented the deficits that occur after right-hemisphere damage in the late 1800s, these findings were generally ignored. The prevailing thought was that the right hemisphere was important only for receiving sensory information from the left side of space and for controlling motor movement of the left half of the body. In this view, the right hemisphere was like a spare tire, available in case the left hemisphere sustained damage, but having few functions of its own (see Harrington, 1987, for a fascinating history of 19th-century thinking about the brain's duality).

Research in the late 1950s and early 1960s, nearly a century after the discoveries of Broca and Wernicke, revealed that each hemisphere has its own specialization, thus dramatically changing scientists' conceptions of the brain. For example, Brenda Milner and colleagues at the Montreal Neurological Institute demonstrated that surgical removal of temporal regions of the right hemisphere for the relief of epilepsy disrupted memory for unfamiliar faces and other stimuli that could not be easily named (e.g., Milner, 1968; see also Benton, 1969; Hécaen, 1962). Probably the most dramatic demonstration of differences in function between the hemispheres came from research at the California Institute of Technology, done by Roger Sperry and associates, who tested the competency of each hemisphere in a unique set of patients (e.g., Sperry, 1974). The findings from this research were so definitive and compelling that they contributed to Sperry's winning the Nobel Prize for Physiology and Medicine in 1981. We turn next to this body of research.

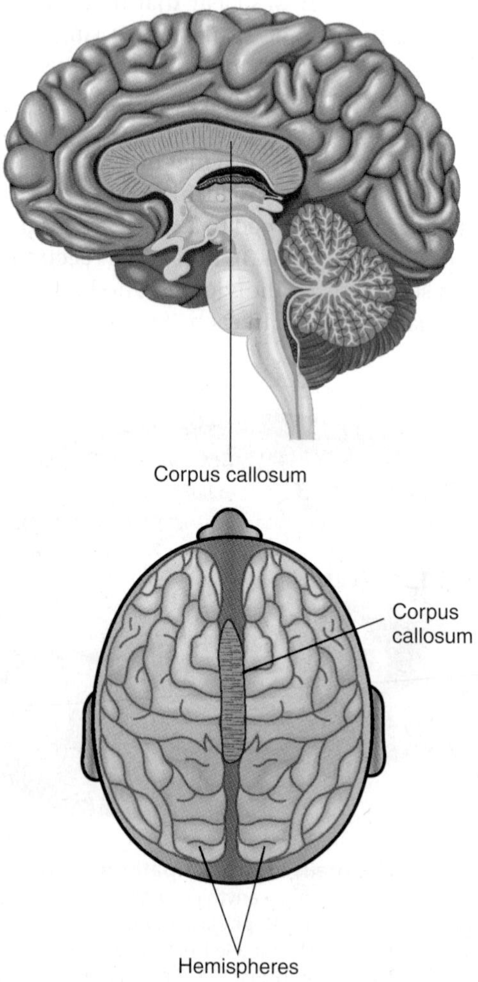

■ Studies of Patients with Split-Brain Syndrome

Sperry's interest in hemispheric specialization arose through his attempts to elucidate the function of the **corpus callosum**, the massive tract of more than 250 million nerve fibers that connects the hemispheres. While studying this structure in cats and monkeys, Sperry found it was critical in the transfer of information between the brain's hemispheres. Around the same time, the neurosurgeons Joseph Bogen and Philip Vogel were severing the corpus callosum in a small group of people for a different reason: to control intractable epileptic seizures. These patients' seizures did not diminish with anticonvulsant medication and were so frequent and severe as to make any semblance of a normal life impossible. The surgical procedure performed by Bogen and Vogel became known as the **split-brain procedure** because it severed the primary route by which the left and right cerebral hemispheres interact, thereby splitting the brain in half. This procedure is also sometimes referred to as *commissurotomy* because it severs the corpus callosum, one of the brain's *commissures* (structures that connect the hemispheres). ● Figure 4.4 shows the location of the corpus callosum.

Corpus callosum

Corpus callosum

Hemispheres

● **FIGURE 4.4   Location of the corpus callosum.**
The callosum is severed in the split-brain procedure. © 2009 Cengage Learning

When the callosum is intact, the hemispheres can coordinate their processing, shuttling information back and forth with great speed over millions of nerve fibers. However, with the callosum severed, information initially directed to one hemisphere cannot be sent to the other; essentially, the information is trapped within a single hemisphere. Using techniques that take advantage of the neuroanatomy of the human nervous system, Sperry and colleagues were able to direct information to only one hemisphere at a time, and were thereby able to determine each hemisphere's individual competencies.

Basic Findings

One of Sperry's first goals was to determine lateralization of speech output in the split-brain patients, as language had been thought since Broca's time to be lateralized to the left hemisphere. Sperry and his colleagues asked the patients to feel objects with one hand, either just the left or just the right. The objects were hidden from view so that the only source of information about them was tactile. With this procedure, objects felt by a given hand are perceived exclusively by the contralateral hemisphere. Thus, objects felt by the right hand of a patient with split-brain syndrome would be perceived only by the left hemisphere and those felt by the left hand would be perceived only by the right hemisphere. Strikingly, patients were able to name the objects placed in the right hand but not those placed in the left.

Did the object in the left hand go unreported because the right hemisphere did not understand what the object was? Or was the right hemisphere unable to verbalize what it understood? To distinguish between these possibilities, the researchers changed the task so that the patient had to demonstrate the correct use of familiar objects, such as pencils, cigarettes, and drinking glasses. The researchers found that objects placed in the left hand could be used correctly, an indication that the right hemisphere can demonstrate its knowledge of the object nonverbally even though it is mute (Gazzaniga, Bogen, & Sperry, 1962).

Although the right hemisphere is much more than a spare tire, its linguistic capacity is somewhat limited (for debate, see Gazzaniga, 1983a, 1983b; Levy, 1983; Zaidel, 1983b). First, as we have already learned, the right hemisphere cannot control speech output. Second, it cannot understand complicated grammatical constructions (e.g., "The dog that the cat chased ran under the table behind the garage that was condemned by the sheriff last week") (Zaidel, 1978). Rather, its grammatical abilities are limited to simple distinctions (e.g., differentiating between "The boy went to the store" and "The boy did not go to the store"), and its vocabulary is limited mainly to concrete words (that is, words that represent real objects or actions) (e.g., Zaidel, 1990). Finally, the right hemisphere seems unable to break words down into their constituent sounds, a task known as *phonologic processing,* which is required to determine whether two words rhyme (e.g., Levy & Trevarthen, 1977).

Because the right hemisphere's language capability was revealed to be relatively poor in split-brain patients, researchers began to focus their attention on what the right hemisphere *could* do. Additional experiments demonstrated that the right hemisphere excels at spatial or nonverbal tasks. For example, when given a task in which blocks must be arranged to form a pattern, the right hand performed in a hapless and disorganized manner. In contrast, the left hand performed the task rapidly and accurately. In addition, the left hand, but not the right, could depict three-dimensional structures in a two-dimensional plane, such as drawing a cube on a piece of paper (Gazzaniga, 1970).

Other studies revealed that the right hemisphere was superior on spatial tasks even when no manual manipulation was required. In a series of studies, patients with the split-brain syndrome were asked to view chimeric faces (i.e., faces composed of two different sides, such as those in ● Figure 4.5). Although these figures seem strange to us, remember that the hemispheres of a split-brain patient cannot communicate, so they do not realize that they are viewing different faces. When split-brain patients were asked to point to the face that had been shown, accuracy was much greater with the left hand than the right hand. This pattern held not only for faces but also for abstract forms (Levy, Trevarthen, & Sperry, 1972). Therefore, the results of research on patients with the split-brain syndrome demonstrated the complementarity of the hemispheres for different aspects of mental functioning. The left is superior at processing verbal material, but the right has expertise in the spatial domain.

Caveats in Interpretation

Although studies of patients with the split-brain syndrome provide compelling and dramatic data, we must keep certain caveats in mind when interpreting these results. One potential problem is that the brains of these patients may not be typical, due to their long-standing history of epileptic seizures. Furthermore, to sever the corpus callosum, which is located deep within the longitudinal fissure (refer back to Figure 4.4), the surgeon must *retract* (pull back) the hemispheres, which provides the opportunity for damage to regions other than the callosum.

A second set of problems arises because of the small population of patients who have been extensively tested. Most individuals who undergo split-brain surgery have IQs so low as to preclude them from participating in research studies. Further compounding this problem, results from split-brain patients can sometimes be difficult to interpret because different patients may exhibit distinct patterns of performance. For example, the right hemisphere's language competency varies among split-brain patients (Sidtis, Volpe, Watson, Rayport, & Gazzaniga, 1981). Therefore, we need to be careful not to overgeneralize when drawing conclusions from studies of these patients.

"Whom did you see?"   "Point to the person you saw."

"It was the child."

(A)   (B)   (C)

● **FIGURE 4.5   Examining the competency of each hemisphere in a patient with split-brain syndrome.** (A) An example of a chimeric stimulus, composed of two half-faces that are perceived by opposite hemispheres. (B) When asked to report verbally which face was seen, the patient reports the face that was seen by the left hemisphere (right visual field). (C) When asked to point with the left hand to the face that was seen, the patient points to the face that was seen by the right hemisphere (left visual field). Accuracy is higher when pointing with the left hand to the face seen in the left visual field, compared to pointing with the right hand to the face seen in the right visual field. This finding indicates a right-hemisphere superiority for face recognition. Source: Reception of bilateral chimeric figures following hemispheric deconnexion, Levy J, Trevarthen C, Sperry RW. Brain. 1972; 95(1):61–78. By permission of Oxford University Press.

Despite these caveats, research with split-brain patients remains very important (see Gazzaniga, 2005, and Reuter-Lorenz & Miller, 1998, for more recent reappraisals of split-brain research). Because studies of patients with split-brain syndrome provide information on the functioning of a reasonably intact but isolated hemisphere, they continue to be a powerful tool in our attempts to understand asymmetry of function in the human brain.

■ Research with Individuals Who Have Lateralized Lesions

While dramatic demonstrations of lateralization of function were being provided by split-brain research, studies with other neurological patients were also revealing the distinct capabilities of the hemispheres. Although scientists had known for some time that left-hemisphere lesions compromise language functioning, other methods provided converging evidence. One such method is the **Wada technique,** used to determine which hemisphere is responsible for speech output in patients about to undergo tissue removal to control epileptic seizures. Although the left hemisphere is almost always dominant for speech (except in left-handers), the surgeon wants to know this unequivocally before beginning surgery. In the Wada technique, illustrated in ● Figure 4.6, a barbiturate (typically sodium amytal) is injected into one of the carotid arteries that lead from the heart to

the brain. Because the blood supply from the heart to the brain is unilateral, the barbiturate anesthetizes only one hemisphere. If the person becomes mute, the anesthetized hemisphere is inferred to be responsible for speech output. Research with this method has revealed that the left hemisphere is dominant for speech in 95% of right-handers, a finding consistent with evidence from patients who sustain unilateral brain damage (Rasmussen & Milner, 1977). Because the Wada test is very invasive, much work is being performed to determine whether fMRI can be used instead to localize critical language areas prior to neurosurgery (e.g., Benke et al., 2006; Gaillard et al., 2004; Wilke, Lidzba, Staudt, Buchenau, Grodd, & Krageloh-Mann, 2006). Magneto-encephalography is also being explored as a means of identifying areas of language localization, because it is much less invasive than the Wada test and easier than fMRI to use with children (e.g., Ressel, Wilke, Lidzba, Preissl, Krägeloh-Mann, & Lutzenberger, 2006). Nevertheless, the Wada test remains a mainstay in neurosurgical settings (Paolicchi, 2008).

Studies of patients with brain damage have also demonstrated that right-hemisphere lesions have different consequences than left-hemisphere lesions. Whereas left-hemisphere lesions disrupt language-related processing, right-hemisphere lesions disrupt many spatial and visuospatial abilities. For example, individuals with right-hemisphere damage are poor at making judgments about line orientation (Benton, Hannay, & Varney, 1975), have difficulty recognizing objects that are not in a standard or canonical form (Warrington & Taylor, 1973), and are poor at distinguishing between faces that were previously viewed and those that were not (Yin, 1970). In addition, patients with right-hemisphere damage have difficulty distinguishing different pitches of sound or tones of voice (Ross, 1981) and cannot interpret the emotional expression of faces (Bowers, Bauer, Coslett, & Heilman, 1985). This body of research revealed that the right hemisphere has cognitive abilities just as sophisticated as those of the left hemisphere, albeit in nonverbal, nonlinguistic domains.

■ Research with Neurologically Intact Individuals

Examination of hemispheric differences in neurologically intact individuals is relatively easy because in most sensory modalities, information from one sensory half-world is directed initially to the primary sensory regions of the opposite hemisphere. The large body of evidence garnered in this manner provides a third converging approach that illustrates the specialization of the hemispheres for different cognitive and emotional processes. Before discussing this evidence further, though, we first discuss the methods used to investigate lateralization of function.

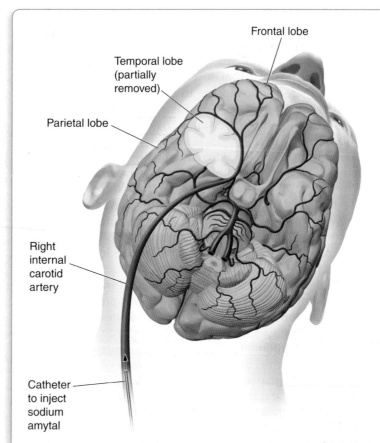

● **FIGURE 4.6   The Wada technique.** As shown from below the brain, sodium amytal is injected into one of the internal carotid arteries in the neck, which allows researchers anesthetize one hemisphere of the brain at a time to determine if speech is disrupted. This procedure is used to determine speech lateralization prior to neurosurgery. © 2010 Cengage Learning

Methods

Lateralization of function is mainly investigated in the visual, auditory, and tactile modalities. Measuring hemispheric differences in the visual modality takes advantage of the arrangement of the neural pathways from the eye to the brain (see Figure 1.18). Information in the right visual field (RVF) projects exclusively to the primary visual cortex of the left hemisphere, whereas information presented in the LVF projects exclusively to the primary visual cortex of the right hemisphere. Studies that take advantage of this neural arrangement involve presenting information separately in each visual field, a technique often referred to as the **divided visual field technique**.

We can infer how well each hemisphere processes information by comparing either the speed or the accuracy of performance for items presented in the RVF versus the LVF. For example, if recall of information is superior when presented in the RVF than when presented in the LVF, the left hemisphere is assumed to be specialized for processing that type of information. Note that what we actually observe is an asymmetry in the perception of information depending on which part of the sensory system we stimulate; these differences in performance are therefore often referred to as **perceptual asymmetries**. Because different parts of the sensory system project to different hemispheres, the perceptual asymmetries are interpreted as reflecting hemispheric differences.

In the divided visual field technique, information must be presented for 200 ms (one-fifth of a second) or less because this precludes movement of the eyes from one position to another. Only if the eyes are maintaining fixation on a single point will the region of space that constitutes the RVF and the LVF stay static. To ensure that the presented information is initially received by only one hemisphere, the researcher usually positions stimuli somewhat lateral (at least 1 or 2 degrees) from midline. This way, the stimuli will fall exclusively within one visual field even if the individual moves his or her eyes slightly off fixation.

Similar logic can be applied to investigate hemispheric differences in the somatosensory (touch) modality. In **dichaptic presentation**, a person is asked to feel two items simultaneously, one in each hand, and then to identify these items in some manner (e.g., Witelson, 1974). Often, the items are behind a screen or the person is blindfolded so that information can be obtained only through touch. Because tactile information from the left side of the body projects to the primary somatosensory region of the right hemisphere, an advantage in processing information presented to the left hand is generally interpreted as a right-hemisphere superiority for the task (and vice versa).

Examining hemispheric differences in the auditory modality is a bit more complicated. As you may remember from Chapter 1, information from each ear connects both to the primary auditory cortex of the contralateral hemisphere and to the primary auditory cortex of the ipsilateral hemisphere. If each ear connects to both hemispheres, how are we to interpret differences in the ability to report information from each ear? Under special conditions known as **dichotic presentation**, the situation is simplified (● Figure 4.7). In dichotic presentation, *different* information is presented simultaneously to each ear so that each hemisphere receives two competing pieces of information, one from the ipsilateral ear and one from the contralateral ear. Because of this competition, information traveling to a hemisphere from the ipsilateral ear is suppressed relative to information from the contralateral ear (Milner, Taylor, & Sperry, 1968). Thus, information from the right ear is processed almost entirely by the left hemisphere and information from the left ear is processed almost entirely by the right hemisphere.

Research Findings

Studies examining perceptual asymmetries have been quite effective in revealing differences in the processing capabilities of the hemispheres. As you might expect based on what you have already learned, processing of verbal materials tends to be superior when directed initially to primary sensory regions of the left hemisphere, whereas nonverbal information tends to be processed better when directed initially to the right hemisphere. For example, in the visual modality, studies usually find an RVF (or left-hemisphere) advantage for words and an LVF (or right-hemisphere) advantage for faces (Levine & Banich, 1982; Levine, Banich, & Koch-Weser, 1988). In the tactile modality, a right-hand advantage is found for identifying letters drawn on the palm (e.g., O'Boyle, Van Wyhe-Lawler, & Miller, 1987) and for identifying dichaptically presented letters made of sandpaper (Gibson & Bryden, 1983). In contrast, when individuals must feel two complex shapes simultaneously and match them to a visual array or otherwise identify them, a left-hand advantage appears (Gibson & Bryden, 1983; Witelson, 1974). In the auditory modality, the response to words and other speech sounds is better when the sounds are presented to the right ear (e.g., Kimura, 1967; Studdert-Kennedy & Shankweiler, 1970), whereas response to nonverbal sounds, such as animal noises, environmental sounds (e.g., doors opening, train whistles), and musical tones, is more accurate when the material is presented to the left ear (e.g., Gordon, 1980). These advantages are typically small, on the order of a

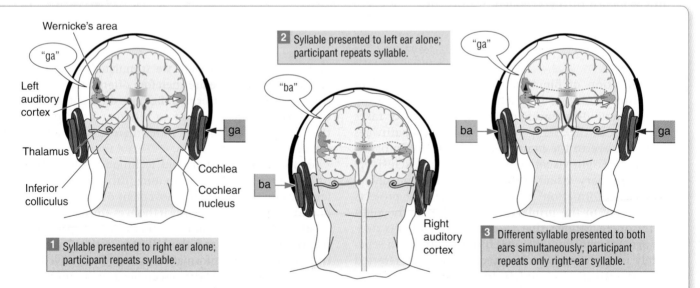

● **FIGURE 4.7   Ipsilateral suppression in the dichotic listening technique.** When a syllable is presented to either the right or the left ear (monaural stimulation), the person can easily report the syllable. The auditory information from each ear is sent to both hemispheres via both contralateral and ipsilateral connections. However, when the two ears are simultaneously stimulated with different syllables (dichotic stimulation), people typically have trouble reporting both syllables. Under dichotic conditions, the syllable presented to the right ear is usually reported more accurately than the syllable presented to the left ear, because the right-ear syllable has better access to the verbal left hemisphere. The syllable presented to the left ear is not reported as well because information carried through ipsilateral fibers is suppressed under dichotic conditions, and therefore the left hemisphere does not have direct access to the left-ear syllable. © 2010 Cengage Learning

10% difference in accuracy or 20- to 30-ms difference in reaction time. They are nonetheless impressive considering that the hemispheres are connected by the 250 million nerve fibers of the corpus callosum.

How do such perceptual asymmetries arise in neurologically intact individuals, given the vast network of interconnections between the hemispheres? No single account is agreed upon, but researchers have a number of ideas. One idea, referred to as the **direct access theory**, assumes that the hemisphere receiving sensory information processes it. When information is received by the hemisphere less suited to a task, performance is poorer than if it is received by the hemisphere better suited to the task. Another idea, the **callosal relay model**, assumes that information received by the hemisphere less adept at a given task is transferred to the opposite hemisphere. This callosal transfer degrades the information and leads to poorer performance than if the information is received by the hemisphere more suited to the task (see Zaidel, 1983a, for a discussion of these issues). A third type of model, known as the **activating-orienting model**, suggests that an attentional set or bias can contribute to perceptual asymmetries (Kinsbourne, 1975). According to this theory, engaging in a particular type of process (e.g., word recognition) causes greater activation in the hemisphere best suited to the task (e.g., the left hemisphere). This increased activity is thought to result in an attentional bias to the side of space contralateral to the more active hemisphere (i.e., the right side). As a result, perceptual information on that side of space is more salient, allowing it to be processed better.

Characterization of Hemisphere Differences

Up to this point, we have implied that the hemispheres are specialized for processing different types of material: verbal versus nonverbal. However, the situation isn't quite that simple. The current consensus is that the hemispheres differ not so much in *what* type of information they process, but rather in *how* they process information. Current theories suggest that the hemispheres have different modes of processing (e.g., holistic versus piecemeal) and that these two distinct modes provide complementary information about the world.

One major theory of hemispheric differences posits that the left hemisphere processes information in a piecemeal and analytic fashion, with a special emphasis on temporal relationships; the right hemisphere is thought to process information in a gestalt and holistic fashion, with a special emphasis on spatial relationships. These different modes of processing can be observed by comparing the performance of patients with unilateral damage to either the left or right hemisphere. For example, look at the figures in ● Figure 4.8, which are

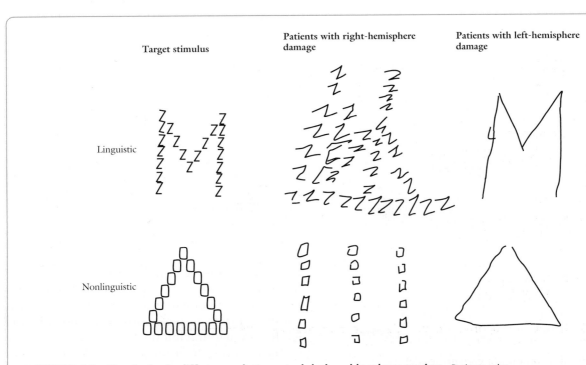

● **FIGURE 4.8   Hemispheric differences between global and local processing.** Patients who sustain damage to the right hemisphere can correctly draw the local, or component, parts of the objects, as illustrated by the correct drawing of the Zs and the rectangles. However, the overall global form is incorrect; it is neither an M (in the case of the linguistic stimulus) nor a triangle (in the case of the nonlinguistic stimulus). In contrast, patients who sustain damage to the left hemisphere can correctly draw the global form of the items but not the local, or component, parts. © 2011 Cengage Learning

often referred to as *hierarchically organized figures*. After sustaining a right-hemisphere lesion, individuals have difficulty paying attention to the global form of the item (i.e., an *M* or a triangle) but have no difficulty paying attention to the local pieces or parts (i.e., the *Z*s or the rectangles). Conversely, after left-hemisphere damage, patients have difficulty paying attention to the parts (i.e., the *Z*s and the rectangles) but no difficulty with the global form (i.e., the *M* and the triangle) (Robertson & Lamb, 1991). Regardless of whether the stimulus is linguistic or nonlinguistic, the hemispheres take complementary roles in processing. Metaphorically, the right hemisphere pays attention to the forest while the left hemisphere pays attention to the trees.

Currently, researchers agree that both hemispheres contribute simultaneously to performance on almost all tasks, albeit in different manners. This makes sense: it means that the right hemisphere is not just taking a nap while we are reading, and the left hemisphere is not just snoozing while we recognize a friend's face. Going around in such a half-brained manner doesn't seem a very good strategy! Instead, each hemisphere contributes in some way to nearly all complex mental functions. Even those functions traditionally thought of as relying on one hemisphere, such as verbal and spatial abilities, actually seem to intimately involve both hemispheres. For example, the processing of metaphor, the comprehension of a storyline, and the ability to make inferences across sentences are all language-related

processes that rely more on the right hemisphere (see Beeman & Chiarello, 1998a, 1998b). Similarly, the ability to discern top from bottom, right from left, and front from back are all spatial relations that rely more on the left hemisphere (Chabris & Kosslyn, 1998).

Within a cognitive neuroscience framework, researchers have attempted to understand what types of computational biases might underlie these hemispheric differences. One early influential theory of this sort, the **spatial frequency hypothesis**, proposes that the hemispheres differ in their ability to process a particular attribute of visual information known as *spatial frequency* (e.g., Sergent, 1983). Visual information has a low spatial frequency if, over a given expanse of space, it oscillates slowly from dark to light. In contrast, it has a high spatial frequency if information switches quickly from dark to light.

To obtain a better appreciation of visual information of high spatial frequency versus that of low spatial frequency, look at ● Figure 4.9. Visual information of low spatial frequency generally provides a broad outline of form without much detail. You can get a rough approximation of low spatial frequency information by squinting your eyes and looking at this page. Notice that you can perceive broad general forms but not details. Visual information of high spatial frequency provides the details.

Sergent's theory hypothesizes that the right hemisphere is more adept at processing low spatial frequency, whereas the left hemisphere is specialized for processing high spatial frequency. This distinction is somewhat akin to an earlier suggestion that in general the right hemisphere is specialized for coarse coding of information, whereas the left is specialized for fine coding of information (Semmes, 1968). Research suggests that it is less important whether the frequency of information is high or low on an absolute scale, and more important whether it is relatively high or low within a given context (Kitterle, Hellige, & Christman, 1992). It seems, then, that when viewing a scene or listening to sounds (Ivry & Lebby, 1993), the brain first identifies the range of spatial frequencies present, and then each hemisphere takes responsibility for its set of frequencies within that range. This idea has been expanded into a theory known as the **double filtering by frequency theory**. This theory posits that after task-relevant information has been identified, filtering causes information of relatively higher spatial frequency to be preferentially processed by the left hemisphere and information of relatively lower spatial frequency to be processed by the right hemisphere (Ivry & Robertson, 1998; Robertson & Ivry, 2000). This filtering leads to the right-hemisphere advantage for holistic processing and the left-hemisphere advantage for piecemeal processing. Now that we have a greater appreciation for how

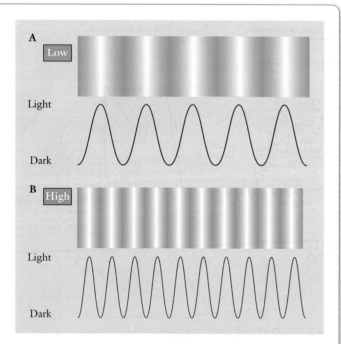

● **FIGURE 4.9   Information of varying spatial frequency.** (A) Information of low spatial frequency. (B) Information of higher spatial frequency. As you can see, the change from light to dark occurs less often in A than in B.
© 2011 Cengage Learning

both hemispheres contribute to performing almost all cognitive tasks, we turn our attention to how the activities of each hemisphere are integrated.

Integration of Information between the Hemispheres

Although our hemispheres are clearly specialized for different processes, our actions and everyday experiences reflect the unified processing of a single brain, not the output of two distinct minds. Thus, we must address the question of how the hemispheres manage to communicate with each other and coordinate processing to yield a seamless response. We focus here on two aspects of this issue. First, we examine the properties of the corpus callosum, the main conduit through which the hemispheres communicate, and then we examine the functions served by interaction between the hemispheres.

■ Nature of Information Carried over the Corpus Callosum

The corpus callosum is the main nerve-fiber tract that transfers information between the cerebral hemispheres, although other subcortical commissures can transfer some rudimentary information. Structurally, anterior sections of the callosum connect anterior sections of the brain, and posterior sections of the callosum connect posterior sections of the brain (● Figure 4.10). Because of this organization, different types of information are transferred across different parts of the callosum depending on the brain regions connected by that section of the callosum. For example, information about motor signals is transferred in the middle of the callosum (known as the *body*), whereas visual information is transferred in the back of the callosum (a region known as the *splenium*).

Researchers can determine the nature of information transferred by the callosum by asking patients with the split-brain syndrome to compare items directed to different hemispheres. If the patients are incapable of

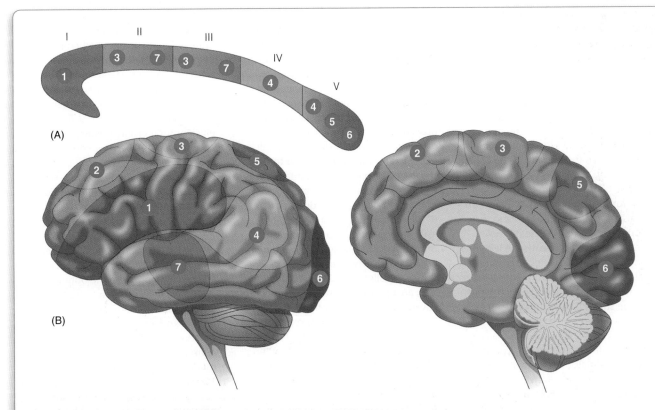

● **FIGURE 4.10   Different brain regions connected by different sections of the corpus callosum.** (A) Diagram of the corpus callosum. The number shown in each section indicates the brain region depicted in (B) (lateral view on left, midsagittal view on right), which are connected through that section of the callosum. The connections occur in a topographic manner: Anterior sections (I) of the callosum connect anterior sections of the brain (Region 1, which is frontal), middle sections of the callosum (II and III) connect brain regions that are more central (Regions 3 and 7), and posterior sections of the callosum (IV and V) connect posterior sections of the brain (Regions 4, 5, and 6). Some brain regions, such as the frontal region labeled 2, have few, if any, callosal connections. © 2011 Cengage Learning

IN FOCUS: Why Have a Lateralized Brain?

Brain asymmetry was long assumed to be a uniquely human characteristic. This mistaken belief probably resulted from an initial focus on language as the main function that differed between the hemispheres, together with a dose of human arrogance and desire to see ourselves as unique.

Asymmetries are also clearly observed in other primates, including gorillas, chimpanzees, and monkeys. Like humans, the great apes show an anatomical asymmetry of the planum temporale (Hopkins, Marino, Rilling, & MacGregor, 1998) and Broca's area (Cantalupo & Hopkins, 2001). Evidence of specialization of function includes left-hemisphere specialization for the recognition of vocal calls in macaque monkeys (Poremba, Malloy, Saunders, Carson, Herscovitch, & Mishkin, 2004), better discrimination of faces by the right hemisphere of split-brain monkeys (Hamilton & Vermeire, 1988), and a left-hemisphere advantage for processing local information in the chimpanzee (Hopkins, 1997).

But asymmetry in the nervous system is not found only among primates; it exists in many forms among more distantly related species, such as birds, fish, amphibians, and reptiles (Vallortigara, 2000). For example, control of the vocal system in songbirds is lateralized to the left side of the brain (Nottebohm, 1971, 1977). Schools of fish have biases, as a group, for turning left or for turning right when they swim (Bisazza, Cantalupo, Capocchiano, & Vallortigara, 2000); likewise, tadpoles have a turning bias towards the left when diving back into the water after surfacing (Malaschichev & Wasserug, 2004). Toads are more agile at catching prey through "tongue strikes" when the prey appears to the toad's right side (perceived by the left hemisphere), although the toads are more likely to act aggressively toward members of their own species on the left side (Vallortigara, Rogers, Bisazza, Lippolis, & Robins, 1998). Across a range of vertebrate species, the right hemisphere appears to be specialized for predator detection and escape behaviors, whereas the left hemisphere is specialized for prey catching and foraging (Vallortigara & Rogers, 2005).

The ubiquity of lateralization raises fascinating questions about why natural selection favored the development of asymmetry in many different corners of the animal kingdom (Vallortigara & Bisazza, 2002). Do species share the characteristic of lateralization through homology—that is, shared descent from an ancestral vertebrate species that was lateralized—or was lateralization a solution that evolution came up with independently at different times and places because it solved a commonly occurring problem? Answering this question with certainty is difficult, because it requires a more exhaustive survey of existing species as well as inferences about species that no longer exist. In either case, the fact that laterality exists in so many species indicates that it must have conferred some benefit to animals, such that it persisted over many generations in many species.

Although we cannot know for sure, there are various speculations about what benefits are provided by lateralization (see Vallotigara & Rogers, 2005, for a review and commentary). In other species, the advantages of lateralization can be demonstrated experimentally by interfering with lateralization and observing the consequences. For example, in normally developing chicks, searching for food is lateralized to the left hemisphere and maintaining vigilance for a predator is lateralized to the right hemisphere; disruption of the normal pattern of asymmetry leads to poor performance on both of these tasks, suggesting an advantage to hemispheric division of labor (Rogers, Zucca, & Vallortigara, 2004). Even in fruit flies, an asymmetric brain appears to be advantageous, as disrupting lateralization has negative consequences for memory performance (Pascual, Huang, Neveu, & Préat, 2004)!

Acquiring evidence about the evolutionary adaptiveness of lateralization in humans is more difficult. One viewpoint suggests that lateralization in humans may have been advantageous because it allowed for the best expression of complex manual or vocal skills that are crucial for communication (Corballis, 1997). Other theorists have placed more emphasis on motor functions, arguing that precise manual manipulation and throwing would be more efficient if feedback were received from somatosensory regions in the same hemisphere (Wilkins & Wakefield, 1995) and that motor functions would be best performed by a single hemisphere so as to avoid possible interhemispheric conflict (Corballis, 1991). For example, chimps who strongly prefer one hand over the other when foraging for food such as termites do so more efficiently than chimps who do not have a strong hand preference (McGrew & Marchant, 1999). In contrast, other researchers emphasize language lateralization, suggesting that having language perception and production in the same hemisphere would provide more reliable feedback than if these functions were lateralized to different hemispheres (Annett, 1985). Researchers in this camp also suggest that the temporal precision required by language functions might have been impeded by delays in interhemispheric communication if language areas were not co-lateralized (Ringo, Doty, Demeter, & Simard, 1994). Finally, some theorists have suggested that because both language and motor skills rely on efficient sequencing abilities, language and handedness became co-lateralized to the same hemisphere (Kimura, 1993).

The question then becomes, why isn't everyone in the population right-handed and strongly lateralized? One possibility is raised by evolutionary neuropsychologist Michael Corballis, whose theory contends that neither extreme lateralization nor absence of lateralization provides the optimal brain organization. According to his theory, left-hemisphere dominance is achieved at the expense of right-hemisphere functions, while reduced cerebral asymmetry imposes a cost in verbal and manual manipulative abilities (Corballis, 1997). Some studies have supported this theory, showing that extreme right-handedness is associated with poor spatial and mathematical skills, whereas certain verbal difficulties are associated with a lack of right-handedness (for a dissenting interpretation, however, see Provins, 1997).

comparing two items sent to opposite hemispheres, such integration must rely on the callosum, which has been severed in these patients. If the patients can make such a comparison, that comparison must rely on commissures other than the callosum, such as those shown in ● Figure 4.11. Studies have revealed that detailed information required to uniquely identify an item can be transferred between the hemispheres only by the callosum, although more general information can be transferred through subcortical commissures (see Gazzaniga, 2000, for a review). For example, patients with the split-brain syndrome cannot determine whether two faces, each directed to a different hemisphere, are the same person (e.g., whether the face that each hemisphere is viewing is Madonna). However, the subcortical commissures may be able to transfer some dichotomous information, such as whether the face is of a younger or older adult, is a female or a male, or is an emotionally negative or positive image (Sergent, 1990; Sperry, Zaidel, & Zaidel, 1979). From these studies we can conclude that the corpus callosum is the major conduit for transfer of higher-order information between the hemispheres, but that other brain commissures are capable of transferring basic and rudimentary information.

■ Functions of Interhemispheric Interaction

Part of the corpus callosum's function in interhemispheric interaction is to act much like an office messenger service, providing photocopies of each hemisphere's experience for the other and sending information that allows the hemispheres to coordinate processing. We first discuss this function of the callosum and then explore its additional roles.

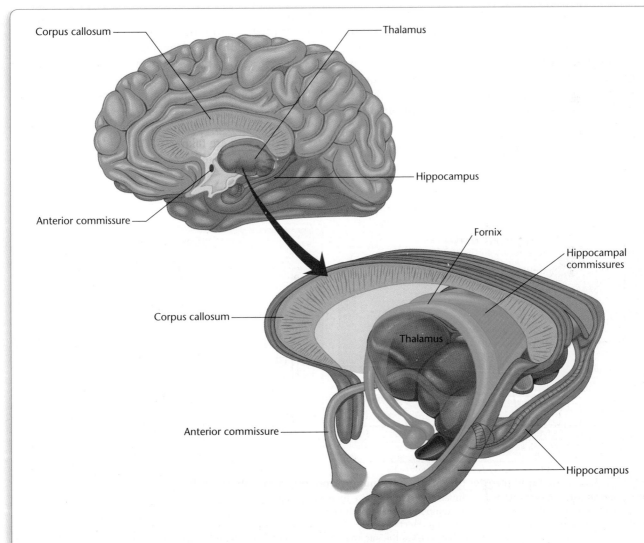

● **FIGURE 4.11   Location of the main commissures in the brain.** Although the corpus callosum is the main connection between the two sides of the brain, other connecting pathways, such as the anterior and hippocampal commissures, also may be routes for interhemispheric information exchange. © 2009 Cengage Learning

The callosum keeps the hemispheres informed of each other's doings by allowing information received by one hemisphere to be immediately transferred to the other. One way this fast transfer can be demonstrated is by examining event-related potentials (ERPs) to sensory stimuli. A response recorded over the hemisphere contralateral to presentation of a stimulus is followed only a few milliseconds later by a response over the other hemisphere (e.g., Saron & Davidson, 1989) (● Figure 4.12). The difference in time between the peak of the ERP recorded over the hemisphere that received the information and the opposite hemisphere is an estimate of callosal transfer time, which ranges from 5 to 20 ms in the average adult. Although this transfer is swift, sometimes information acquired by means of callosal transfer may be somewhat degraded, much as a photocopy may be of poorer quality compared with the original (e.g., Banich & Shenker, 1994).

However, interaction between the hemispheres is not limited merely to message transfer service. Interhemispheric interaction may enhance the overall processing capacity of the brain under highly demanding conditions (see Banich, 1998, for a review). Demanding conditions include those in which processing is relatively complex, when information must be simultaneously processed within a short period, or when a task is difficult because of the need to ignore other information that is distracting or irrelevant.

To examine how interaction between the hemispheres enhances the brain's capacity to process information,

two types of trials are contrasted (● Figure 4.13). On some trials (called *across-hemisphere trials*), critical items are directed to opposite hemispheres and have to be compared; on other trials (called *within-hemisphere trials*), the critical items are directed initially to just one hemisphere. Across-hemisphere trials require interhemispheric communication, whereas within-hemisphere trials do not. When a task is relatively easy, such as deciding whether two items look physically identical (e.g., 2 and 2), processing is faster on within-hemisphere trials. Yet when the task is more complicated, such as determining whether the sum of two numbers equals 10 or more (e.g., 2 and 8), an across-hemisphere advantage is observed (e.g., Banich & Belger, 1990; Belger & Banich, 1992, 1998). This advantage of interhemispheric communication is especially evident in populations in which the capacity of a single hemisphere is reduced, such as in elderly adults (Reuter-Lorenz, Stanczak, & Miller, 1999) or young children (Banich, Passarotti, & Janes, 2000). Conversely, in diseases that affect the integrity of the corpus callosum, such as multiple sclerosis or phenylketonuria, the poor ability of the hemispheres to coordinate processing may contribute to the attentional difficulties observed in individuals with these syndromes (Banich, 2003).

Why is within-hemisphere processing faster and more efficient for easy tasks, but across-hemisphere processing superior for difficult ones? As a simple analogy, assume that you are taking a 20th-century history class and your professor tells you to do your assignments in

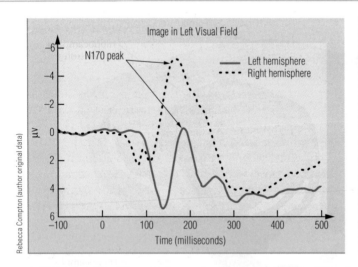
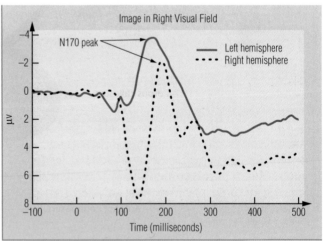

● **FIGURE 4.12   The rapid transfer of sensory information from one hemisphere to the other.** Shown here are event-related potentials (ERPs) in response to images of faces presented in one visual field. The waveforms were recorded over the temporal lobes of both hemispheres. The N170 peak in the waveform occurs sooner over the hemisphere that directly receives the visual information (the contralateral hemisphere), compared to the hemisphere that receives the information only after it is transferred across the corpus callosum. For example, a face image that is presented to the left visual field will evoke an N170 peak sooner over the right hemisphere than the left hemisphere, and vice versa. The time it takes for information to be sent over the callosum is estimated by the time difference between the left- and right-hemisphere peaks, approximately 15 to 20 milliseconds.

teams. If your task is easy, such as writing a one-paragraph summary of the major events of World War II, it will probably take you less time to just sit down and write it yourself, rather than having to communicate with a friend and work on the paragraph together. But suppose you have the more difficult task of writing a 40-page term paper on the same topic. The time and effort required for coordinating with your friend will be small relative to the time you will save by having your friend research and write half the paper. Likewise, as tasks get harder, the brain seems to work better when both hemispheres contribute (see Banich & Brown, 2000, for a more detailed discussion of this model).

To summarize, the studies we have just discussed demonstrate that the brain's functioning does not depend exclusively on the specialization of the different regions of the brain; rather, it also depends on the nature of their interaction. The processing capacity of the brain is enhanced when the hemispheres interact, though only when task demands are high. In other words, the brain's activity is not simply the sum of all the parts!

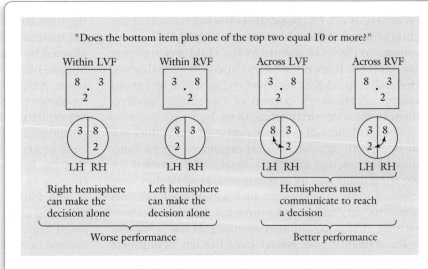

● **FIGURE 4.13   Example of interhemispheric interaction aiding in the performance of demanding tasks.** In a task of interhemispheric interaction, two types of trials are compared. In within-hemisphere trials, the critical pieces of information are directed initially to only one hemisphere and the correct decision can be reached without interhemispheric interaction. In across-hemisphere trials, each hemisphere receives only one of the critical pieces of information, so the hemispheres must communicate with one another for the task to be performed correctly. Performance is better on within-hemisphere trials compared to across-hemisphere trials when the task is easy, such as indicating whether two digits are identical. However, performance is better on across-hemisphere trials when the task is harder, such as making a decision about whether the sum of the bottom and either of the top two numbers is greater than 10. These findings indicate that interhemispheric interaction helps in the performance of more demanding tasks. © 2011 Cengage Learning

Developmental Aspects of Hemispheric Specialization

Now that we have examined the manner in which the hemispheres are specialized and how they interact, we need to consider whether such patterns are observed from an early age or whether they change as a person develops. In an influential book, *Biological Foundations of Language,* Eric Lenneberg (1967) hypothesized that the hemispheres of the brain are equipotential at birth. According to this view, each hemisphere holds the capacity to perform the same functions as the other. Lenneberg suggested that lateralization increases until puberty, after which it remains constant. He based this hypothesis, in part, on evidence that younger children who sustain left-hemisphere damage have less severe deficits than older children and adults with similar lesions. He posited that the recovery in younger children occurred because the right hemisphere, which he assumed was not yet fully specialized, took over language processing.

However, subsequent investigations suggest that the basic specialization of the hemispheres is in place at birth and that the degree of specialization is not modified much with development, except in cases of profound environmental influence such as traumatic injury to the brain. The evidence for the lack of an increase of lateralization of function comes from four major areas (Segalowitz & Gruber, 1977).

The first piece of evidence that a child's brain is lateralized at birth comes from neuroanatomy. As we discussed earlier in the chapter, neuroanatomical asymmetries exist in certain regions of the human brain, such as the planum temporale. We would expect that if lateralization develops with age, these neuroanatomical asymmetries would become more pronounced with age. However, this is not the case; asymmetry in the planum temporale can be observed in newborns (Witelson & Pallie, 1973) and even before birth (Wada, Clarke, & Hamm, 1975). Thus, neuroanatomically, an infant's brain is already lateralized.

The second piece of evidence comes from studies examining the size of perceptual asymmetries in children. If asymmetry develops with age, the size of the left-hemisphere advantage for verbal material and the right-hemisphere advantage for spatial information would be smaller in younger children than in older children. However, a vast review of studies with school-age children revealed that perceptual asymmetries do not increase with age during this period of development (Witelsen, 1977). Of course, this does not mean that the child's brain is static over this time. Indeed, both hemispheres continue to mature as the child acquires new skills in both linguistic and nonlinguistic domains (see Holland et al., 2007). However, what seems to remain fairly constant is the pattern of asymmetric involvement in these developing functions.

The third piece of evidence that asymmetry does not increase with age comes from measurements of functional asymmetries in infants. Researchers recorded the electrical brain activity of young infants while they were exposed to verbal materials, such as nonsense syllables (e.g., "pa" or "ba"), or to nonverbal materials, such as musical chords. In children as young as one week old, brain activation was greater over the left hemisphere for verbal material and over the right hemisphere for nonverbal material (Best, Hoffman, & Glanville, 1982; Molfese, Freeman, & Palermo, 1975). Other investigators relied on normal baby behaviors, such as sucking on a pacifier, to examine perceptual asymmetries. When young babies are interested in something, they suck at a fast rate; when they get used to a stimulus, their sucking rate decreases. When verbal material was played, the sucking rate was more affected by changes in sound in the right ear than in the left. In contrast, when nonverbal material was presented, the sucking rate was more affected by changes in the left ear (Bertoncini, Morais, Bijeljac-Babic, McAdams, Peretz, & Mehler, 1989; Entus, 1977). Likewise, studies using fMRI and optical imaging methods have found evidence of left-hemisphere specialization even in very young infants (Dehaene-Lambertz, Dehaene, & Hertz-Pannier, 2002; Peña et al., 2003). The results of these studies suggest that the hemispheres of infants are specialized, just as they are in older children.

The fourth piece of evidence comes from studies of young children who were born with one extremely small and malformed hemisphere. Because this malformed hemisphere often becomes a focus for epileptic activity, the prognosis for these children is better if the hemisphere is removed at birth, a procedure known as **hemispherectomy** (● Figure 4.14). If the hemispheres are equipotent at birth, the performance of children with just a left hemisphere should be identical to those with just a right hemisphere, even years after the hemispherectomy. However, on language tasks, most notably those involving syntax, children who have only a left hemisphere outperform children with only a right hemisphere (Dennis & Kohn, 1975; Dennis & Whitaker, 1976). Likewise, children with only a left hemisphere do not acquire spatial skills to the degree of children with only a right hemisphere (Kohn & Dennis, 1974). Children with hemispherectomy do acquire better skills than do adults with damage to the same hemisphere, indicating that in early development the opposite hemisphere is able to take over (at least to some extent) the functions that would normally be served by the lost hemisphere. Nevertheless, differences in cognitive abilities between those with left versus right hemispherectomy indicate that the hemispheres are not equipotent at birth.

Considered collectively, the evidence argues strongly that the human brain is already asymmetric prior to birth. But how does nature set up an asymmetric nervous system during embryonic development? Examining asymmetries in other vertebrate species can yield clues about developmental mechanisms that can give rise to left-right asymmetries. For example, specific genes are known to influence a molecular signaling pathway leading to asymmetry in the zebrafish brain in an area near the pineal gland; asymmetry in that region in turn induces asymmetric development in nearby brain regions (Halpern, Liang, & Gamse, 2003). Still, genes are not the only factors that can cause the development of neural asymmetries. In chick embryos, because of the position of the chick in the egg, the right eye is exposed to greater amounts of light than the left eye, and this sets off a cascade of asymmetries in the development of the chick's visual system (Halpern, Güntürkün, Hopkins, & Rogers, 2005). Although it is still unknown what

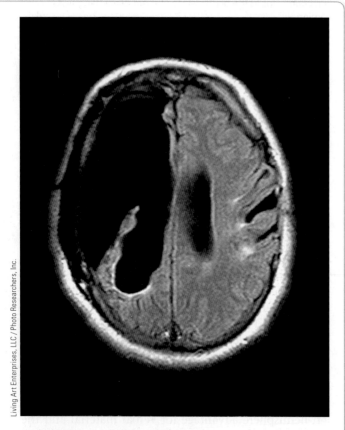

Living Art Enterprises, LLC / Photo Researchers, Inc.

● **FIGURE 4.14   Hemispherectomy.** In cases of severe epilepsy in early life, sometimes doctors resort to an extreme procedure that involves removal of one hemisphere of the brain.

factors trigger the development of asymmetry in the human brain, researchers have identified genes that are expressed asymmetrically in the human embryonic brain at 12 to 14 weeks of gestation, providing clues for future research (Sun et al., 2005).

As the preceding sections of this chapter have made clear, differences in processing between the two hemispheres of the human brain are a fundamental aspect of brain organization, and these asymmetries are in place very early in life. We next turn our attention to the ways in which this basic pattern of brain organization varies among individuals.

Individual Differences in Brain Organization

We have described the pattern of lateralization of function that is observed for most individuals, but this brain organization is not observed in *all* individuals. Some variability in brain organization appears to be linked to specific individual characteristics. In this section we discuss two of these factors: handedness and gender.

■ Handedness

Scientists have known for some time that the brain organization for left-handed individuals is distinct from that for right-handed individuals. Historically, left-handers have been characterized in a none-too-flattering way. For example, the Latin word for left is *sinister,* whereas the French word is *gauche.* In certain cultures such as in India, the left hand is never used to eat a meal (nor is it extended to someone for a handshake) because it is the hand reserved for bathroom functions. Even in the early to mid-20th century, individuals who wrote with the left hand were considered evil, stubborn, and defiant, and consequently they were often forced to write with the "correct" (right) hand. Left-handers often were subjected to such indignities because they constitute a minority of the population, approximately 10% (see McManus, 2002, for a fascinating discussion of left and right in cultures and nature).

Although left-handers have been unfairly labeled with negative stereotypes, they do appear to have somewhat different brain organization than right-handers. For right-handers, verbal processing is almost always lateralized to the left hemisphere and visuospatial processing to the right; this is not the case for left-handers. Rather, their brain organization is heterogeneous, some being the same as that of typical right-handers, some the opposite, and some different altogether. For example, speech output is controlled by the left hemisphere in 95% of right-handers and by the right hemisphere in 5%. Among left-handers, 70% have speech controlled by the left hemisphere, 15% by the right, and 15% by either hemisphere (Rasmussen & Milner, 1977). Thus, when we

average across all these types of left-handers, as a group they appear to be less lateralized than right-handers (e.g., Bryden, 1965). However, a given left-hander may not be less lateralized than a given right-hander.

Because on average left-handers are less lateralized than right-handers, the consequences of brain injury for a given function may not be as dire for left-handers. For example, after damage to the left hemisphere, left-handers may exhibit less severe language deficits than right-handers, because language output may be controlled by one hemisphere and language comprehension by the other (e.g., Naeser & Borod, 1986). Yet, such apparent sparing of function is misleading. Following left-hemisphere damage, left-handers typically exhibit more severe visuospatial deficits than right-handers (Borod, Carper, Naeser, & Goodglass, 1985).

Although we know that the brains of left-handers differ from those of right-handers, the reasons for such variation are beyond our grasp. Most researchers assume that there is at least some genetic component to handedness. However, although various genetic models have been proposed, none seems to perfectly account for the distribution of right- and left-handed children, given the handedness of their parents. One prominent model (Annett, 1985, 1995) assumes that individuals either inherit from each parent what is called a right-shift (RS) gene, or they do not inherit the gene. The RS gene shifts cerebral dominance for language to the left hemisphere, with a concomitant shift toward right-handedness. Individuals who inherit two RS genes will be likely to be strongly right-handed, those who inherit one RS gene will be less likely to be right-handed, and those who inherit no RS genes will exhibit a random distribution of handedness. A similar model assumes that handedness is controlled by two genetic codings, or alleles. One allele, D, specifies dextrality (right-handedness) and another, C, specifies chance (McManus, 1985). The D allele is similar to the RS gene, and the C allele is comparable to the *absence* of an RS gene, except that the C allele must be specifically inherited. In general, these models assume that there is an intrinsic bias toward an asymmetry (in this case rightward), and the genes code for whether or not that bias is expressed. At this point, these theoretical models are intended to describe and explain the distribution of handedness in the population, but so far no one has identified specific genes that make a person left or right handed.

■ Gender

One of the more heated debates about individual variations in brain organization revolves around differences between the genders. For many years, researchers have debated whether lateralization of function is less pronounced in females than in males. If so, females would be more akin to left-handers and males more akin to right-handers.

Although some researchers report a pattern of sex differences consistent with this hypothesis, others find no differences between men and women, and some even find women to be more lateralized (see McGlone, 1980, for the diverse spectrum of viewpoints on this issue). Two reviews of hundreds of divided visual field studies (Hiscock, Israelian, Inch, Jacek, & Hiscock-Kalil, 1995) and dichotic listening studies (Hiscock, Inch, Jacek, Hiscock-Kalil, & Kalil, 1994) revealed that, depending on the criterion used as support for gender differences, between 5% and 15% of these studies yield results consistent with the idea that females are less lateralized than men. These authors concluded that although statistically the average degree of lateralization in a group of men may differ from that in a group of women, gender differences account for little of the variability (1–2%) in patterns of lateralization of function among individuals.

Other research has focused on asymmetry of specific cortical structures. One such structure for which gender differences have been reported is the corpus callosum. Originally, the callosum was reported to be larger in women than in men (deLacoste-Utamsing & Holloway, 1982), but that effect was found to be limited to only the most posterior portion of the callosum, the splenium (e.g., Allen, Richey, Chai, & Gorski, 1991). Other researchers found individual differences that involve both sex and handedness: portions of the callosum were reported to be larger in non-right-handed men than in right-handed men, but the same was not true of women (e.g., Habib, Gayraud, Oliva, Regis, Salamon, & Kalil, 1991; Witelson & Goldsmith, 1991). However, this effect is not always consistently observed (Bishop & Wahlsten, 1997), and the functional significance of any of these differences is uncertain. More recent evidence suggest that subcortical regions such as the amygdala (which is involved in processing emotional information) may show anatomical asymmetries that differ between men and women (Cahill, 2006).

Differences in brain function between the genders have also been reported, but there have been difficulties in replication here as well. For example, some studies indicated differences between the genders in regional brain activation when the participants were at rest (Gur et al., 1995) and during processing of linguistic information (Shaywitz et al., 1995). However, others using larger samples have not observed such effects (e.g., Frost et al., 1999).

When interpreting the results of studies on gender differences in brain function, we must consider whether men and women may exhibit distinct patterns of brain activation on these tasks not because they have differentially organized brains, but because they have learned to use different strategies to perform the same task. For example, men may navigate in terms of compass-point directions (e.g., go northeast), whereas women may use a more point-to-point strategy (go straight down Main Street toward the church and then turn right at Grove Avenue). To definitively demonstrate that the genders have distinct brain organizations, researchers will have to show that dissimilar brain regions are activated in the genders even when both groups are using identical strategies.

Although public imagination on the issue is often fueled by sensational stories in the popular press, the debate regarding gender differences in brain organization has not been satisfactorily resolved. The bodies of men and women clearly differ in a number of anatomical features and physiological functions, and we would probably not be surprised to find that such differences apply to the brain as well. However, what is critically important is how differences in brain lateralization are interpreted. When differences are observed, they tend to be relatively small, and the variations among individuals within a gender are typically much greater than any variation between men and women as a group.

Conclusion

In this chapter, we reviewed many of the fundamental differences between the hemispheres, which involve both their anatomy and their function. With a basic understanding of the principles of cerebral asymmetry, you are prepared to learn more about asymmetries in the context of specific mental functions, such as spatial perception, attention, language, and emotion, discussed in later chapters.

Summary

Basics of Hemispheric Specialization

- Hemispheric differences were first demonstrated in the 1860s, when Paul Broca reported that damage to a posterior region of the left, but not the right, frontal lobe disrupted the ability to produce fluent speech.
- Karl Wernicke later observed that damage to a temporo-parietal region of the left hemisphere produced the opposite syndrome: disrupted language comprehension with intact production.

- These findings led to the idea of cerebral dominance, which is the notion that one hemisphere dominates or leads mental function.
- Studies of split-brain patients, in whom the massive nerve-fiber connection between the hemispheres known as the corpus callosum is severed for the relief of intractable epilepsy, revealed the left hemisphere to be superior for language processing, and the right hemisphere to be superior at visuospatial tasks.

- Research with individuals with lateralized lesions indicates that left-hemisphere lesions disrupt language processing, whereas right-hemisphere lesions disrupt a variety of abilities, including face recognition, judgment of line orientation, recognition of objects, and tonal processing of auditory material.
- Hemispheric specialization can be demonstrated in neurologically intact individuals by directing sensory information so that it is received initially by a single hemisphere.
- Generally, processing of verbal material is superior when presented to the right hand, right ear, or in the right visual field. In contrast, processing of spatial material tends to be superior when presented to the left hand, left ear, or in the left visual field.

Characterization of Hemisphere Differences

- The hemispheres appear to differ not in the type of information they process (verbal vs. nonverbal) but in the nature of how they process information: the left hemisphere is most adept at analyzing information in a piecemeal, detailed, and time-locked manner, whereas the right hemisphere is most adept at analyzing information in a holistic, gestalt, and space-based manner.
- One prominent theory suggests that these hemispheric asymmetries exist because the hemispheres filter incoming sensory information in different manners; the right hemisphere preferentially processes whatever portion is of lower frequency, and the left preferentially processes whatever portion is of higher frequency.

Integration of Information between the Hemispheres

- The callosum is critical for transferring information that can be uniquely characterized (e.g., a picture of Madonna's face), as compared with that categorized dichotomously (e.g., a female face rather than a male face).
- Interaction between the hemispheres increases the brain's processing capacity when tasks are demanding or difficult, but not when they are relatively easy.

Developmental Aspects of Hemispheric Specialization

- The basic pattern of hemispheric specialization appears not to change much during development.
- Anatomical asymmetries can be observed in utero and at birth, behavioral asymmetries can be observed in infants and remain constant during childhood, and children with only a single hemisphere develop skills associated with that hemisphere to a higher degree than those associated with the absent hemisphere.

Individual Differences in Brain Organization

- On average, left-handers have less of a division of labor between the two halves of the brain than right-handers do.
- Although it is often suggested that women are less lateralized than men, there is much debate about the validity of this claim.

Key Terms

activating-orienting model   97
callosal relay model   97
cerebral dominance   92
corpus callosum   92
dichaptic presentation   95
dichotic presentation   96
direct access theory   97

divided visual field technique   95
double filtering by frequency theory   98
hemispherectomy   104
hemispheric specialization   90
lateralization of function   90

perceptual asymmetries   95
planum temporale   90
spatial frequency hypothesis   98
split-brain procedure   92
Wada technique   94

Book Companion Site at www.cengage.com/psychology/Banich
This website provides instructors and students with a wealth of free information and resources, including tutorial quizzes, flashcards, and the glossary.

Motor Control

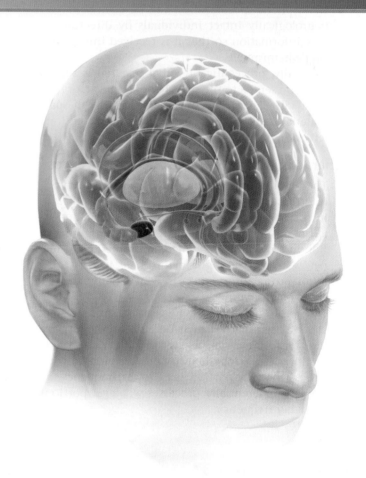

THE LIFE STORY OF MUHAMMAD ALI, one of the 20th century's most famous boxers, interweaves not only boxing and politics, but also the neural basis of motor control. Ali, who was known as Cassius Clay before his conversion to Islam, rose to prominence as an Olympic boxer. He eventually turned pro and became a world champion. Ali said that his boxing strategy was to "float like a butterfly, sting like a bee," meaning that his fancy footwork allowed him to flutter around the ring evading his opponents' punches until he could move in for a knockout. At the height of his career, Ali was drafted to serve in the United States armed forces in Vietnam, but he refused induction because of his religious beliefs. Convicted of draft evasion, he was stripped of his crown, and not allowed to box in a sanctioned match for the next three years.

During his exile from the ring, Ali's ability to "float" deteriorated substantially. When he was allowed to resume his boxing career (shortly before the Supreme Court overturned his conviction), he adopted a different fighting style that capitalized on the strength he had gained during his hiatus from professional bouts. This new style, however, would have deleterious effects later in his life. Ali would let an opponent get him against the ropes in the early rounds, either blocking or absorbing an onslaught of punches that would have felled most men. This technique became known as the "rope-a-dope" style, because a boxer was traditionally considered a fool if he allowed himself to get caught against the ropes (Figure 5.1). However, Ali would patiently wait for the later rounds when his foe was exhausted, frustrated, and getting sloppy. Then he would throw the punch that sent his opponent reeling to the mat.

After his retirement from boxing, Ali became a popular speaker on the lecture circuit. As time passed, however, people began to notice that he was slurring his words and stumbling. When signing autographs, he was slow and his penmanship became more and more illegible. Naive observers assumed that Ali was drunk, but heavy drinking was never his style. Medical examinations revealed that Ali had sustained neurological damage and was most likely displaying signs of Parkinson's disease. In Parkinson's disease, motor control is disrupted so that previously simple motor acts become extremely difficult. The three basic attributes of Parkinson's are slowness of movement, rigidity of movement, and tremors—rhythmic, oscillating movements (which are usually observed when a person is at rest). Generally, Parkinson's is observed in older people as a progressive neurological disorder. But Ali, although well past the years when most boxers are in the ring, was only middle-aged. So what could explain these symptoms?

As best his neurologists could surmise, years of boxing had taken their toll on Ali. Although he had never been knocked out, the barrage of punches Ali absorbed with his rope-a-dope style had the cumulative effect of damaging regions of his brain important for motor control. As we discuss later in this chapter, Parkinsonian symptoms begin to manifest themselves when a substantial proportion of the dopaminergic neurons in the substantia nigra are destroyed. As cells die, the remaining cells try to do all the work, but at some point the amount of damage is too great to be compensated for and motor control deteriorates. Thus, although Ali sustained the damage during his long and illustrious boxing career, only afterward did the effects of this damage become apparent (Hauser, 1991).

Focus On Sport/Getty Images

 FIGURE 5.1   Muhammad Ali, the boxer, receiving a blow to the head from his opponent, Alfredo Evangelista. The repeated punishment that Ali endured in receiving such blows, over the course of his boxing career, led him to exhibit symptoms related to Parkinson's disease after retirement.

Introduction

Muhammad Ali's Parkinson's disease was caused by destruction to just one of the many brain regions that permit the great diversity of motor skills that humans display. Before we discuss these various brain regions, let us first consider some of the types of movements that humans can exhibit. In some motor acts, such as hitting a tennis serve, you must coordinate movement of the gross and postural muscles in a smooth and seamless fashion. When learning to serve, you break down the process into a series of steps: Start to toss the ball, dip your legs, bring the racquet behind your back, push up on your legs, extend the racquet skyward, rotate your torso, and hit the ball. Consider how different such a step-by-step process is from the smooth, well-learned tennis serve of professionals like Venus Williams and Roger Federer. Rather than a concatenation of separate movements, the swing of a tennis pro or even a good amateur player appears to be one smooth, continuous motion. As we learn later in this chapter, such smooth, rapid movements are aided by the cerebellum.

Other actions require that fine motor movements be precisely timed. Touch-typing (that is, when you type with ten fingers instead of pecking with two), unlike a tennis serve, requires little gross muscle movement because the position of your hands remains relatively static. Typing speed is increased by reducing the time between individual keystrokes. One way to accomplish this increased speed is to adjust the typing of a given key on the basis of the keystrokes that precede and follow it. Our ability to make such adjustments implies that we create an overall motor program of the series of movements that we want to produce, then invoke this program when a series of finger strokes is executed. As we learn later, these motor programs are probably produced by a specific brain region known as the **supplementary motor area (SMA)**. This area transmits information about the motor program to other brain regions, eventually allowing activation of the specific muscles required to execute the program.

In other motor acts, performance is linked to specific external cues, such as when you press on the gas pedal upon seeing a green light and step on the brake upon seeing a red light. When movements require us to break well-learned habits or contravene our normal associations (e.g., pressing the gas pedal for a *red* light and stepping on the brake for a *green* one), when movements are novel, or when movements are less well rehearsed, the anterior cingulate is called into action.

Motor acts often involve multiple brain regions because they require many types of motor control to occur simultaneously, such as control over both the fine and gross muscles. However, as this brief introduction should illustrate, specific brain regions play a more prominent role in certain motor acts than in others. We begin this chapter by reviewing the major brain regions involved in motor control and by pointing out the important contribution each makes. Afterward, we examine clinical syndromes in which motor processing is disrupted. These syndromes fall into two major categories: those resulting from damage to subcortical regions of the brain and those resulting from damage to the cortex. The subcortical syndromes that we discuss—Parkinson's disease, Huntington's disease, and Tourette's syndrome—all involve a disruption in the form of movements. These syndromes may lead to slowness or imprecision in movement, or to movement that should not occur (e.g., tremors). In contrast, the cortical syndromes impair the conceptualizing, planning, and sequencing that underlie learned movements. In these cases, individuals may, for example, have difficulty playing the piano or knowing how to program muscles to salute.

Brain Structures Involved in Motor Control

As we mentioned, many brain regions are involved in motor control. In this section, we review the primary brain structures involved in such control, starting with those located subcortically and then discussing those in the cortex.

■ Subcortical Regions

Before discussing the role of different brain regions in motor control, we must first understand the basic underlying mechanism that makes muscles move. Muscles are composed of muscle fibers that can be either in a contracted or an uncontracted state. Muscle fiber contraction is caused by an impulse from a neuron. Typically, one motor neuron innervates a number of muscle fibers. The number of muscle fibers innervated can vary from only two or three, for muscles involved in very fine motor control, to more than a hundred for large antigravity muscles. A motor neuron and the muscle fibers it innervates are referred to as a **motor unit**. The synapse between a neuron and muscle fibers is larger and has a more specialized structure than a typical synapse. It is called the **neuromuscular junction** (● Figure 5.2). For muscles to move, information must be relayed from the nervous system to the muscles across the neuromuscular junction. Without such control, paralysis occurs.

Motor Tracts

Motor movements planned in the brain are sent to target muscles to be executed. This information is relayed along pathways known as *motor tracts*. To better conceptualize the role these pathways play in motor control, we might consider them akin to the messenger that carries information to the infantry in the army (in this case the muscles), which carries out the orders but does not initiate or create them. Instead, the subcortical and cortical regions that we discuss later are the key regions for determining the form, sequencing, and planning

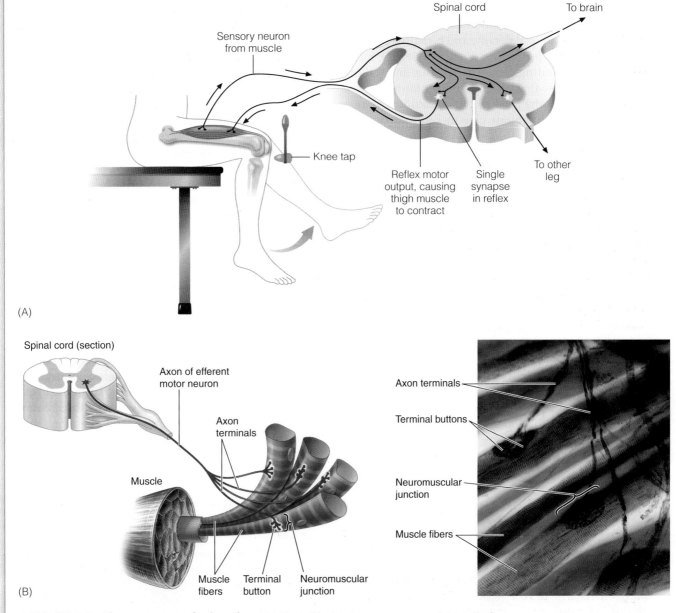

● **FIGURE 5.2   The neuromuscular junction.** (A) The cell body of a motor neuron originates in the spinal cord. It travels along a spinal nerve to the muscles it innervates. (B) When the axon reaches a muscle, the motor neuron divides into many axon terminals, providing a series of unique connections with each muscle fiber, an area known as the *neuromuscular junction*. Within each neuromuscular junction, the axon terminal further divides into fine branches, each of which ends in a terminal button. When an action potential reaches the terminal button, acetylcholine is released into the synaptic cleft. Acetylcholine then binds with nicotinic cholinergic receptors in special troughs in the membrane of the skeletal muscle, known as *motor endplates*. This causes an action potential in the muscle membrane, resulting in muscle contraction. © 2010 Cengage Learning

of these movements. The subcortical regions can be thought of as lieutenants who make sure that their platoons are moving along in proper form, whereas the cortical regions are more like generals who plan the actions of vast numbers of platoons.

Two major sets of pathways link the brain to muscle. The first of these are the lateral pathways, the cell bodies of which are located mainly in the primary motor cortex. From there, the tract crosses entirely from one side of the brain to the opposite side of the body in the medulla. Thus, damage to cell bodies of this tract (which are in motor cortex) results in deficits in motor movement on the opposite side of the body. This tract is responsible for the fine motor movement of distal (i.e., far) limb muscles, such as those that move the arms, hands, fingers, lower leg, and foot. Damage to the **lateral corticospinal tract** has profound effects on the ability to reach, grasp, and manipulate objects.

The other main pathway, the **medial pathway**, is more involved in control of movements of the trunk and proximal (i.e., near) limb muscles. It projects both contralaterally and ipsilaterally, and is mainly involved in the control of posture, as well as bilateral movements such as standing, bending, turning, and walking (● Figure 5.3). Now that we know how information gets from the brain to the muscles, let's examine the roles that different brain regions play in controlling motor movement.

Cerebellum

Looking much like a small cauliflower attached to the back of the brain, the **cerebellum** plays an extremely important role in motor control, especially in the coordination of muscle movement timing, the planning of motor movements, and the learning of motor skills.

There are three main divisions of the cerebellum, named according to the source of input to the region (● Figure 5.4A). The *vestibulocerebellum* is the phylogenetically oldest part of the cerebellum. It is comprised of portions of the **flocculus** and **nodulus**. As the name implies, this region receives input from the vestibular nuclei in the brainstem and then projects back to this region. Not surprisingly, then, damage to this region leads to difficulty with balance and to postural instability.

The *spinocerebellum*, located in medial regions of the cerebellar hemispheres, receives somatosensory and *kinesthetic* information (which is information about body movement derived from the muscles, skin, and joints) from the spinal cord and projects back to the spinal cord. Damage to this region results in difficulty with the smooth control of movement. More medial areas are involved in movement of proximal muscles, such as coordinating movement of the trunk and leg muscles for walking (for a review of the cerebellum in posture and locomotion, see Morton & Bastian, 2004). When individuals sustain damage to this region, they walk in steps that are often short and irregular, and their movements are erratic. More lateral areas are involved in movement of more distal muscles, such as arm movements. In particular, the ability to position the arms, as well as the regulation of agonist and antagonistic muscles in sequence, is disrupted.

The *cerebrocerebellum* receives input from many different regions of the cortex, including both motor and association cortices. This region is involved in the regulation of highly skilled movement that requires complex spatial and temporal sequences involving sensorimotor learning. These activities include motor abilities such as throwing a pitch, serving a tennis ball, and juggling, as well as fluent writing and speaking.

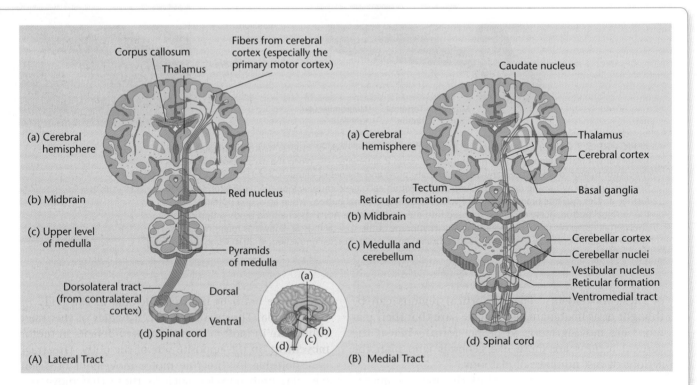

● **FIGURE 5.3   The two major motor pathways from brain to muscle.** (A) The lateral tract crosses from one side of the brain to the opposite side of the spinal cord and controls precise movement in the extremities, such as hand, fingers, and feet. (B) The medial tract produces bilateral control of trunk muscles for postural adjustments and bilateral movements such as standing, bending, turning, and walking. Inset shows location of cuts a, b, c, and d. © 2009 Cengage Learning

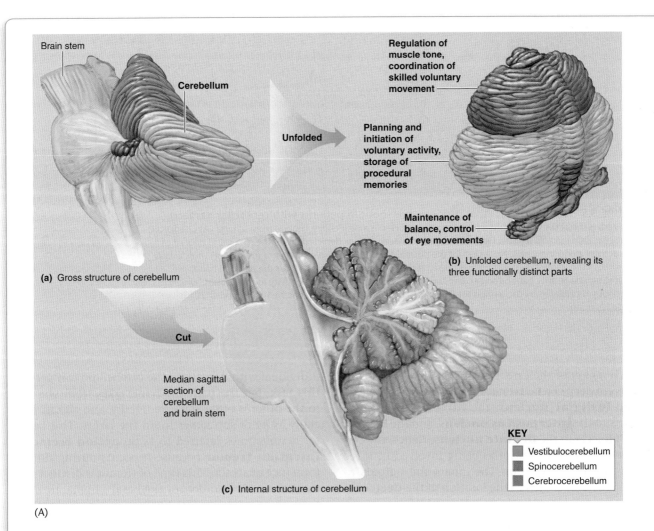

(a) Gross structure of cerebellum

Brain stem

Cerebellum

Unfolded

Regulation of muscle tone, coordination of skilled voluntary movement

Planning and initiation of voluntary activity, storage of procedural memories

Maintenance of balance, control of eye movements

(b) Unfolded cerebellum, revealing its three functionally distinct parts

Cut

Median sagittal section of cerebellum and brain stem

(c) Internal structure of cerebellum

KEY
- Vestibulocerebellum
- Spinocerebellum
- Cerebrocerebellum

(A)

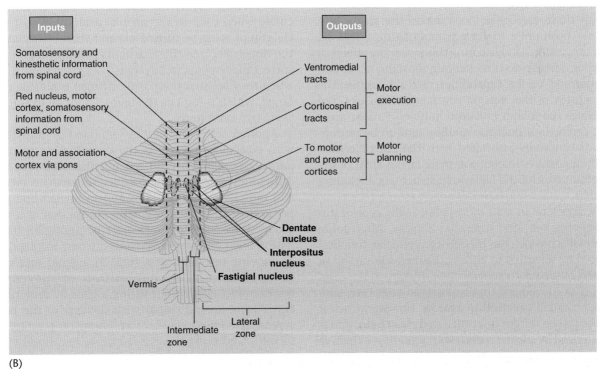

Inputs

Outputs

Somatosensory and kinesthetic information from spinal cord

Red nucleus, motor cortex, somatosensory information from spinal cord

Motor and association cortex via pons

Ventromedial tracts

Corticospinal tracts

Motor execution

To motor and premotor cortices

Motor planning

Dentate nucleus

Interpositus nucleus

Fastigial nucleus

Vermis

Intermediate zone

Lateral zone

(B)

● **FIGURE 5.4   Structure of the cerebellum showing its inputs and outputs.** (A) The three main divisions of the cerebellum (B) The deep cerebellar nuclei within the cerebellar hemispheres. © 2011 Cengage Learning

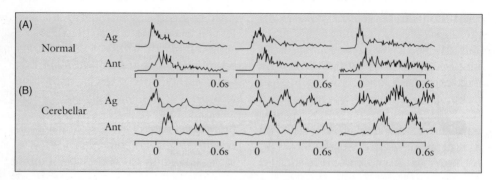

● FIGURE 5.5   The mechanics that produce overshoot in patients with cerebellar damage.
Shown here is the activity of agonist and antagonist muscles in a single-joint motion from a hand (A) unaffected
by cerebellar damage and (B) affected by cerebellar damage. Time is depicted along the x axis and degree of
muscle activity along the y axis. Note that for the normal hand, the activity of the antagonist (Ant) muscle lags
behind that of the agonist (Ag), acting as a brake on the movement. In contrast, for the affected hand, the
antagonist muscle activity comes too late and too strongly. This induces more activity in the agonist, which
then is poorly modulated by the antagonist, leading to overshoot of the target as well as tremor. © 2011
Cengage Learning

Each region of the cerebellar hemisphere projects to a different deep cerebellar nucleus: The **vermis** projects to the **fastigial nucleus**, the **intermediate zone** projects to the **interpositus nucleus**, and the **lateral zone** projects to the **dentate nucleus**. Hence, the cerebellum can be thought of as being involved in three somewhat separable loops. The inputs and outputs to the cerebellum, as well as the location of the **deep cerebellar nuclei**, are shown in ● Figure 5.4B.

A few general principles about the cerebellum are worth noting. First, the projection of information through these cerebellar loops makes the cerebellum perfectly positioned to have a modulating effect on motor processing. Underscoring this point, the effects of cerebellar damage do not eradicate movements; rather, they degrade motor capabilities. Second, unlike the motor cortex, which acts on contralateral muscles, the cerebellum modulates *ipsilateral* muscles. Finally, areas of the cerebellum near the midline tend to be responsible for functions associated with the body's center, including posture. In contrast, more lateral areas of the cerebellum control the lateralized structures, including the limbs.

Now let's look in a bit more detail at the type of difficulties observed after cerebellar damage. After doing so, we will consider the models of cerebellar function proposed by scientists to encompass the wide variety of disorders observed. In general, the difficulty in the coordination of movement that is observed after cerebellar damage is called **cerebellar ataxia**. However, when it involves speech output it is called as **dysarthria**, and is characterized by slurred speech with sometime explosive variations in voice intensity (Spencer & Slocomb, 2007).

As mentioned in Chapter 1, neurologists often screen for cerebellar damage by having an individual touch his or her nose and then the neurologist's nose. An individual with damage to the cerebellum can perform this task, but the path the hand takes from one nose to the other is often staggered, jerky, and zigzag, especially as he or she zeroes in on the target. This behavior is sometimes referred to as an **action tremor** or **intention tremor** because it occurs during the performance of an act. This type of tremor is distinct from that seen with disorders of the basal ganglia, in which the tremor is much more likely to occur at rest. Moreover, the individual often overshoots the target. This overshooting occurs because individuals cannot calculate when each of the agonist and antagonist muscle groups must be turned on and then off to land at the target. Because these patients cannot program the correct movements in advance, they try to adjust only when they see that their arm or finger is almost at the target, which is too late (● Figure 5.5 for an example of these two symptoms).

Another set of difficulties exhibited by individuals with cerebellar damage is the coordination of multijoint movements. It has been hypothesized that these difficulties represent an inability to produce the correct muscle torques of limbs and to predict and compensate for the various dynamic interaction of torques produced by different limbs. Because multijoint coordination breaks down, movements are best accomplished by moving one joint at a time in a serial manner, a strategy known as **decomposition of movement**. For example, rather than lifting a glass by moving the entire arm, an individual with damage to the lateral cerebellar cortex may place an elbow on a table, lean forward, and bring the glass to his or her mouth. With the elbow stationary, the number of joints that must be moved is decreased, which increases the likelihood of a successful movement (Bastian, Martin, Keating & Thach, 1996).

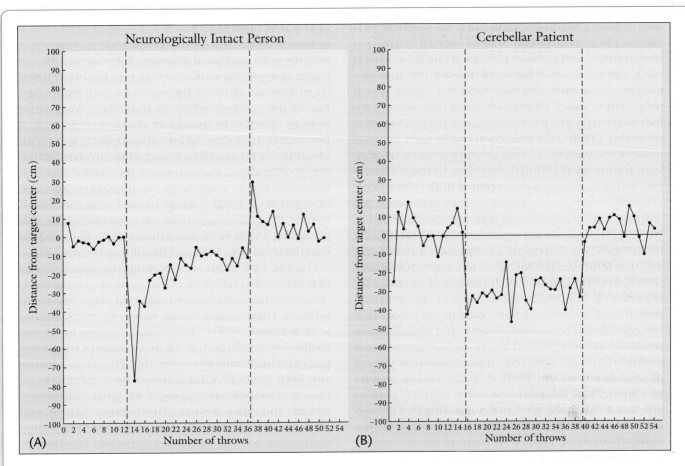

● **FIGURE 5.6   Role of the cerebellum in motor learning.** Shown here are plots of dart-throwing accuracy for a series of throws by two individuals. The first dashed line indicates when the individual puts on the prism spectacles, and the second dashed line when they are taken off. (A) Plot for a neurologically intact individual. After putting on the prisms, the person's throw is far off target, but with practice, the individual's aim improves. After the eyeglasses are removed, the throw is off again but quickly becomes recalibrated. (B) Plot for an individual with cerebellar damage. The introduction of the eyeglasses leads to inaccurate throws, which are not adjusted with practice. Because no learning has taken place, the individual's accuracy returns to the preprism baseline almost immediately after the eyeglasses are removed. © 2011 Cengage Learning

Third, damage to the cerebellum can hamper the learning of new movements (e.g., Deuschl, Toro, Zeffiro, Massaquoi, & Hallett, 1996). Let's consider the case of throwing a dart at a target. The ability to coordinate eye fixation on a target with arm movement is an acquired skill. An individual with cerebellar damage who had decent eye-hand coordination prior to injury can throw a dart with relative accuracy, but if this task is changed a bit so it requires new sensorimotor learning, deficits appear. For example, if a person is wearing prism eyeglasses that displace the view of the world 15 degrees to one side, hitting the target will require a recalibration of the relationship between the position of the gaze and the arm movement. With practice, neurologically intact individuals can gradually make this adjustment, whereas patients with cerebellar damage cannot (● Figure 5.6).

Finally, the lateral portion of the cerebellum may be important in sensorimotor learning and skills that require such learning. Eye-blink conditioning is a classic example of the role of the cerebellum in such learning

(Gerwig, Kolb, & Timmann, 2007). In this paradigm, an animal (or person) hears a tone, which then predicts that a puff of air will be delivered to the eye. Blinking the eyes reduces the aversive effects of the air puff, but only if the timing of the blink relative to the tone is appropriate. It is well known that damage to the cerebellum interferes with the ability to learn to make an anticipatory response at the correct time interval and interferes with the response after it has been learned. Thus, it has been suggested that the cerebellum plays a critical role in sensorimotor learning because it promotes understanding of the nature of the temporal relationship between events. Supporting this idea, neuroimaging studies have demonstrated that as the temporal lag between hand and eye movements increases, making hand-eye coordination more difficult, the involvement of the cerebellum in task performance also increases (Miall, Reckess, & Imamizu, 2001).

How are we to integrate all these diverse symptoms into a unified understanding of cerebellar function?

There are a few different theories, which we describe briefly here. One theory argues that the cerebellum is involved in predictive movement; that is, it is involved in movement that must be planned in advance. This is often referred to as a **forward model** (because you are predicting what will happen in the future, which is forward in time). This theory holds that the cerebellum helps to predict the sensory consequences of motor plans (Ito, 2008). That prediction can be used to determine if the motion is being performed correctly (e.g., I am feeling what I think I should be feeling). Thus, if you decide to pick up a full carton of milk from a table, you have—in advance—a model of how that should feel and how much force you will need to pick it up. The forward model includes sensory information that is likely to accompany a movement. Having such a model can help the brain to "subtract out" any sensory feedback that is irrelevant to task performance. Have you ever noticed that it is nearly impossible to tickle yourself? In part, that is because you create a motor model that has a sensory consequence. Because you already know what the sensory consequences of tickling yourself would be, you are relatively impervious to the results of your motor action. There is less cerebellar activity in response to a self-produced tactile stimulus than to one that is externally generated, suggesting that the cerebellum plays a role in the development of the mental model (Blakemore, Wolpert, & Frith, 1998).

Importantly, this forward model of the cerebellum is uninfluenced by feedback from the periphery, such as sensory and kinesthetic information. Once the movement has started, the cerebellum is not involved in online adjustment of the movement. That function is performed by the parietal lobe, an issue discussed later in this chapter. Rather, it is thought that the cerebellum computes an error signal between how well it predicted the movement and the end result of the movement. This error signal then provides information on how the predictive model should be changed or updated for the next action (Bastian, 2006).

Such a theory is consistent with what is observed in patients with cerebellar damage. For example, in the prism example, they are unable to take the information about how far off their aim was (in regard to the dart hitting the target) to adjust their model of what motor movement would be needed on the next throw to land the dart closer to the target. Also supporting such an idea is the fact that, after learning a task involving hand-eye coordination, the region of the cerebellum that became active as assessed by neuroimaging depended on whether the hand was leading the eye, or the eye was leading the hand, suggesting that the cerebellum was predicting the state of one effector (e.g., the hand) to lead the other (e.g., the eyes) (Miall & Jenkinson, 2005).

Another idea is that the cerebellum is a timing device that in essence provides a clock for events, giving information on the initiation and cessation of movement for different effectors (e.g., arms, hands) in motor control (Ivry & Spencer, 2004). For example, lesions to the cerebellum compromise the ability to perform simple but precisely timed tapping movements. The cerebellum has also been implicated in control of the correct pronunciation of syllable strings, based on what syllable will precede and follow a particular utterance (Ackermann, Mathiak, & Riecker, 2007). However, such a timing mechanism may be used for a variety of mental processes as well, providing information on event timing in which temporal goals are explicitly represented (Ivry, Spencer, Zelaznik, & Diedrichsen, 2002). Evidence for this larger role of the cerebellum comes from studies in which cerebellar lesions impair the ability to make judgments about the temporal duration of events, such as whether the time gap between the presentation of two tones is longer or shorter than a reference interval (e.g., 400 ms) or which of two successive displays of dots is moving more quickly across the screen.

If such a timing mechanism is disrupted, it would explain why the initiation and cessation of different muscle groups' action cannot be well coordinated. This hypothesis would also explain the many neuroimaging studies that have reported activation of the cerebellum (particularly in lateral regions) during higher-level cognitive tasks (Stoodley & Schmahmann, 2009) (● Figure 5.7), as well as the changes in cerebellar anatomy and function have been noted in a number of developmental and psychiatric disorders. These include autism, dyslexia, attention deficit hyperactivity disorder, and schizophrenia (discussed in later chapters), which are all characterized by symptoms that are not mainly motoric in nature (Gowen & Miall, 2007).

Regardless of which of these theories ultimately turns out to be a better description of cerebellar function, they highlight the role played by the cerebellum in the coordination and learning of motor movements and in the timing of movements (see Mauk, Medina, Nores, & Ohyama, 2000, for a longer discussion of the interrelations between these functions).

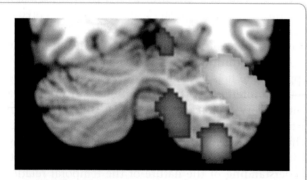

● **FIGURE 5.7 The lateral region of the cerebellum is more involved in higher-order cognition functions.** Shown here are the regions involved in motor control (depicted in red) and language (depicted in green), respectively, as determined by a meta-analysis in which activity across distinct neuroimaging studies is plotted. Notice that language involved more lateral regions. Image by Stoodley and Schmahmann, adapted from data presented in Stoodley & Schmahmann (2009, NeuroImage)

Basal Ganglia

The **basal ganglia** are a complex collection of sub-cortical nuclei, consisting of the **caudate nucleus**, **putamen**, and **nucleus accumbens** (known collectively as the *striatum*), the **globus pallidus** (or *pallidum*), the **substantia nigra**, and the **subthalamic nucleus**. The position of the basal ganglia within the cortex is shown in ● Figure 5.8. Like the cerebellum, the basal ganglia are in a position to modify movement because they form a series of somewhat separable loops with cortical regions. The basal ganglia receive input from cortical regions, with distinct cortical regions projecting to different regions of the caudate and putamen. Output from the basal ganglia occurs via the globus pallidus to the thalamus, which then projects back to the cortex. Each loop consists of input from a cortical region to which information then returns (● Figure 5.9 shows a diagram of these connections). Five such loops have been identified: a motor circuit, an oculomotor circuit, a dorsolateral prefrontal circuit, a lateral orbitofrontal circuit, and an anterior cingulate circuit (Alexander, DeLong, & Strick, 1986).

In addition to input from the cortex, the striatum receives input from the substantia nigra via the **nigrostriatal bundle**, whereas the globus pallidus receives input not only from the striatum but also from the subthalamic nucleus (Alexander, DeLong, & Strick,

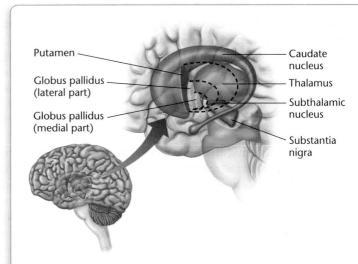

● FIGURE 5.8   Basal ganglia in relation to other brain structures. The basal ganglia surround the thalamus and are surrounded by the cerebral cortex. © 2009 Cengage Learning

1986). In addition to affecting cortex, output from the basal ganglia can affect other motor regions of the brain. For example, their output can influence eye movements via the superior colliculus. The basal ganglia, thus, are at the crossroads of the neural circuits involved in motor control (for a description of the multiple anatomical

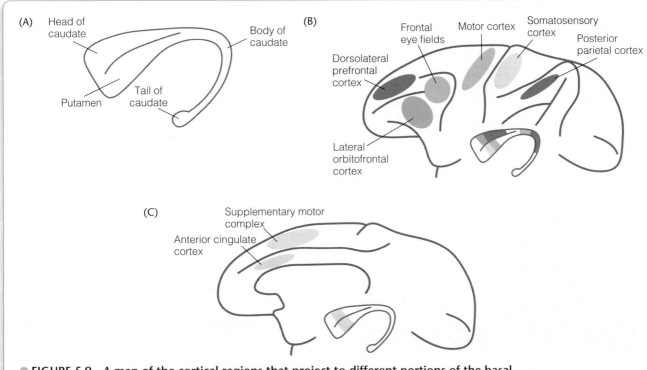

● FIGURE 5.9   A map of the cortical regions that project to different portions of the basal ganglia in the monkey. (A) A schematic of the anatomy of the striatum. (B) Connections of lateral cortical regions to the striatum. (C) Connections of medial cortical regions to the striatum. In (B) and (C), the striatum is color-coded to indicate the cortical region from which it receives projections. *Source:* Utter, A. A., & Basso, M. A. (2008) The basal ganglia: an overview of circuits and function. NEUROSCIENCE AND BIOBEHAVIORAL REVIEWS, 32, Figure 2, p. 335. Reprinted by permission of Elsevier.

connections of the basal ganglia, see Alexander & Crutcher, 1990, or Middleton & Strick, 2000), which positions them perfectly to modulate motor activity.

Unlike the cerebellum, which plays a role in movements that are not modified once they have been initiated, the basal ganglia are more important for the accomplishment of movements that may take some time to initiate or stop. The basal ganglia are thought to have multiple roles in motor control: "setting" the motor system with regard to posture; preparing the nervous system to accomplish a voluntary motor act; acting as an autopilot for well-learned sequential movements; controlling the timing of and switching between motor acts; and, because both motor and nonmotor information feed into the basal ganglia, assisting in motor planning and learning, especially when motor acts have motivational significance (i.e., lead to a reward) or have a large cognitive contribution (i.e.,

learning new input-output rules that override well-learned behavior; see Graybiel, Aosaki, Flaherty, & Kimura, 1994). Overarching theories of basal ganglia function suggest that the basal ganglia facilitate the synchronization of cortical activity underlying the selection of appropriate series of movements or thoughts (Brown & Marsden, 1998), or that they "chunk" individual actions into coordinated, stereotyped, and habitual units of action (Graybiel, 1998).

To best understand the role of the basal ganglia in movement and movement disorders, look at ● Figure 5.10 (see Utter & Basso, 2008, for a review of basal ganglia anatomy, a consideration of how damage to this region leads to different motor disorders, and a discussion of controversial issues regarding basal ganglia anatomy and function). The caudate and putamen, which receive most of the basal ganglia's input, connect by two routes to the main output region of the basal ganglia, which is the internal section of the globus pallidus. One route, the *direct* route, directly connects these two regions in an inhibitory fashion. The internal section of the globus pallidus then has inhibitory connections to motor nuclei of the thalamus, which excite the cortex. As a result, activity in the direct route normally causes inhibition of the internal sections of the globus pallidus so that it can no longer inhibit the thalamus from exciting the cortex. Therefore, activity in this route contributes to sustaining or facilitating ongoing action (because inhibition of the thalamus is decreased). The other route, the *indirect* route, involves inhibitory connections of the caudate and putamen to the external (rather than the internal) section of the globus pallidus. This region has inhibitory connections to the subthalamic nucleus, which in turn has excitatory connections to the internal section of the globus pallidus. Thus, normal activity in the indirect pathway causes the subthalamic nuclei to activate the internal section of the globus pallidus, which suppresses thalamic activity. This pathway is thought to be important for suppressing unwanted movement.

Damage to the basal ganglia produces various motor disorders, depending on which regions of the ganglia are affected. Parkinson's disease is characterized by **akinesia** (the inability to initiate spontaneous movement), **bradykinesia** (slowness of movement), and **tremors** (rhythmic, oscillating movements). Classical models of Parkinson's disease argue that it occurs mainly because there is little or no dopaminergic input into the section of the putamen from which the direct pathway emerges. This dopamine deficiency is caused by the death of cell bodies in the substantia nigra, which projects to the basal ganglia

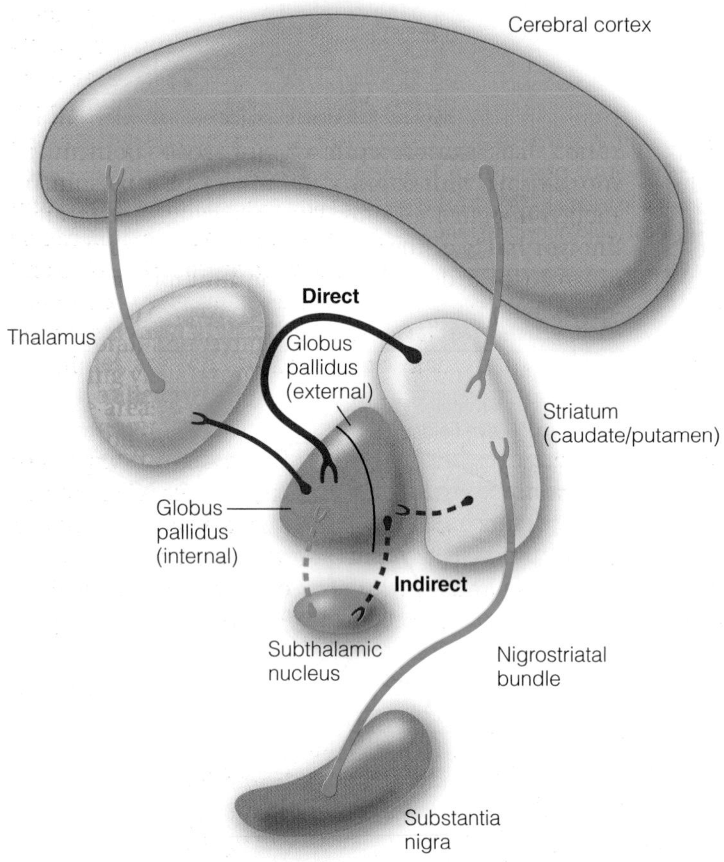

● **FIGURE 5.10 Connections between different sections of the basal ganglia.** Inhibitory connections (indicated by a red line) and excitatory connections (indicated by a green line). Two routes exist between the caudate and putamen (which receive all the input to the basal ganglia) and the internal section of the globus pallidus (the main output region of the basal ganglia). One route is a direct route (inhibitory) between these two regions. The other is an indirect route from the caudate and putamen to the external section of the globus pallidus (inhibitory), to the subthalamic nucleus (inhibitory), then finally to the internal section of the globus pallidus (excitatory). The globus pallidus has inhibitory connections to motor nuclei of the thalamus. The motor nuclei of the thalamus excite the cortex.
© 2011 Cengage Learning

through the nigrostriatal bundle. The death of cells in the substantia nigra (meaning "black substance") can be seen easily on autopsies of patients with Parkinson's disease, because this region does not stain the usual dark color seen in neurologically intact individuals. Because there is no input to the direct pathway, the indirect pathway becomes overactive (refer to Figure 5.10), causing much activity in the internal portion of the globus pallidus, which in turn inhibits the thalamus and results in decreased motor activity (Albin, Young, & Penney, 1989).

If the striatum of the basal ganglia itself is damaged, as in Huntington's disease, a different set of motor problems is observed. **Hyperkinesias** (involuntary, undesired movements) are common. One type of hyperkinesia is **chorea** (derived from the Greek *khoros,* meaning "dance"), which produces uncontrollable, jerky movements such as twitching and abrupt jerking of the body. Another type is **athetosis**, characterized by involuntary writhing contractions and twisting of the body into abnormal postures.

In Huntington's disease, there is a selective loss of striatal neurons that bind gamma-aminobutyric acid (GABA). These neurons give rise to the indirect pathway from the striatum to the globus pallidus, leading to underactivity in this pathway. More specifically, the loss of inhibitory input to the external globus pallidus causes excessive inhibition of the subthalamic nucleus. With this nucleus deactivated, the output from the globus pallidus is decreased. Decreased output in turn lessens inhibition of the thalamus and leads to more motor activity (refer to Figure 5.10) (Albin, Young, & Penney, 1989).

The role of the basal ganglia in the initiation and termination of movements, particularly those oriented toward a goal or in response to a stimulus, can be well illustrated by the symptoms observed when there is dysfunction of the basal ganglia. For example, a person with Parkinson's disease may take a long time to begin to walk across a floor; however, once started, the individual may continue like a runaway train. People with Parkinson's also may have difficulty with cursive

writing, because they cannot maintain a steady velocity of production through the transitions from one stroke to another (● Figure 5.11).

Just as the basal ganglia may help to shift between different movements in a sequence, they may help shift to a new rule or conceptual set that must guide behavior (e.g., Owen, Roberts, Hodges, Summers, Polkey, & Robbins, 1993); it is thought that they do this by helping to clear out information currently being held in prefrontal regions involved in working memory (Frank, Loughry, & O'Reilly, 2001). This idea is made more plausible by the fact that individuals with Huntington's and Parkinson's exhibit difficulties in cognitive as well as motor functions. Later in this chapter we discuss their difficulties in motor control, but we save the discussion of the cognitive difficulties associated with these disorders for Chapter 16.

The basal ganglia are especially important for the control of movement that is guided internally rather than by external sensory stimuli. This is well illustrated in diseases that affect the basal ganglia. For example, patients with Parkinson's will be much better at initiating walking if there are markers on the floor to which they must move. Likewise, a person with Parkinson's disease may be unable to initiate the leg movement required to kick a stationary ball, but if the ball is rolled toward him or her, the ball will act as a trigger, and the person will respond with a kick (a nice illustration of this phenomenon can be seen in the movie *Awakenings,* starring Robert DeNiro and Robin Williams). Conversely, the chorea observed in Huntington's disease may result from an inability to suppress a response to somatosensory and kinesthetic stimuli.

■ Cortical Regions

In contrast to the basal ganglia, which are important for internally guided movements, the major role of cortical regions in motor control is in planned and guided skilled movements and those that require the linkage of sensory inputs with motor outputs. Cortical regions support a range of motor abilities, including picking up

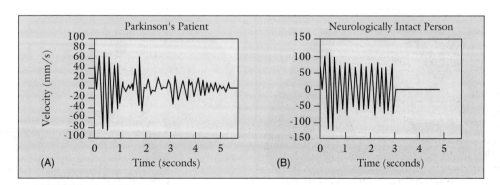

● **FIGURE 5.11   The disruption in writing as a result of Parkinson's disease.** The writing of the word "minimum" (A) by an individual with Parkinson's disease, as compared to (B) a neurologically intact individual. In a person with Parkinson's, there is an inability to maintain the velocity of the movement as transitions occur across letters, whereas in a neurologically intact individual the velocity can be kept constant across those transitions. © 2011 Cengage Learning

an object, using a tool, producing a gesture in response to a verbal command, moving the eyes to explore the image of a face, and moving around the environment. As befits this long list of abilities, a large set of cortical regions is involved in motor control. Before we describe each of their roles in more detail, we first need to become familiar with their locations in the brain.

Take a look at ● Figure 5.12. Regions involved in motor control are distributed across the frontal lobe, located on both the lateral and the medial surfaces. We'll start with a description of the regions on the lateral surface. First, notice the location of the primary motor cortex, directly in front of the central fissure, which encompasses most of Brodmann area 4. Although the majority of primary motor cortex is located on the lateral surface of the brain, it wraps from the dorsal section of the lateral surface down the horizontal fissure to the medial surface (where the representation of the leg and foot are located—refer back to Figure 1.17). Directly in front of primary motor cortex on the lateral surface is premotor cortex, located within Brodmann area 6. At the ventral end of this region but above Broca's areas are the frontal eye fields (also contained within Brodmann area 6; see Paus, 1996).

Now let's look at the medial surface. Above the corpus callosum and below the cingulate sulcus, extending as far back as the central fissure, is the **anterior cingulate cortex**. It resides mainly in Brodmann areas 24 and 32, but also has portions in 25 and 33. Above the cingulate and in front of the primary motor region is the supplementary motor complex, located in Brodmann area 6. One other portion of the brain is involved in motor control, but it is not located within the frontal lobe. These are regions of the parietal lobe within Brodmann areas 7 and 40.

Each of these regions makes a different contribution to motor control, as we will see in detail in the following sections. Generally, the premotor region, supplementary motor area (SMA), and frontal eye fields are involved in the planning, preparing, and initiating of movement. The anterior cingulate is important for selecting particular responses and monitoring whether the execution of those actions occurred appropriately. Primary motor cortex controls the force and direction with which the motor plans are executed. Finally, parietal regions are involved in linking motor movements to extrapersonal space and sensory information, as well as linking motor movements to meaning, as occurs in gesture.

Primary Motor Cortex

Primary motor cortex (sometimes referred to as M1) is the region of the brain that provides the command signal to drive motor neurons to make muscles move. As we learned in Chapter 1 (see Figure 1.17), motor cortex is organized so that different subregions of motor cortex control action of specific portions of the body, such as the fingers, arms, or legs. But exactly what do motor neurons code for, and how do they do so? The coding of motor movement occurs in the form of a neuronal population vector.

Each neuron is tuned to fire maximally to movement in a certain direction. For every movement, though, it is the summed activity (the vector) across the entire set of neurons (the population) that influences or determines the direction of the movement (● Figure 5.13). For every movement, then, each and every neuron votes. If the movement is to be in a neuron's preferred direction, it fires a lot and has a loud vote; if the movement is not in the direction preferred by the neuron, it fires less and has a quieter vote (Georgopoulos, Schwartz, & Kettner,

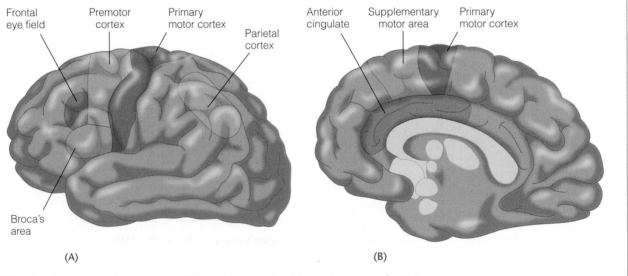

Frontal eye field   Premotor cortex   Primary motor cortex   Parietal cortex   Anterior cingulate   Supplementary motor area   Primary motor cortex   Broca's area

(A)   (B)

● **FIGURE 5.12   The major regions of the cortex involved in motor control.** (A) Left hemisphere, lateral view. (B) Right hemisphere, midsagittal view. © 2011 Cengage Learning

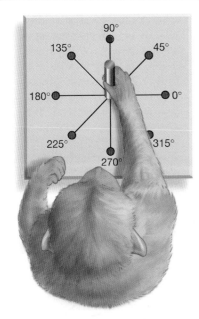

(A) The Monkey and Apparatus

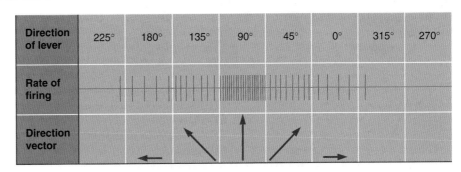

(B) Responses of a Single Cell

Movement direction	Response of Cell 1	Response of Cell 2	Population vector (sum of two responses)
90°			
0°			

(C) Individual Direction Vectors and Population Vectors from Two Neurons

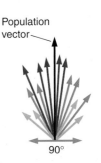

Population vector

90°

(D) Vector Representing Summed Activity from a Population of Neurons

● **FIGURE 5.13   The direction of movement is encoded by populations of neurons** (A) Monkeys are trained to move the joystick in response to a small light moving around a circle. (B) Although single-cell recordings indicate that neurons respond most vigorously to a preferred direction, they also indicate that cells respond to directions that vary as much as 45 degrees from the preferred direction. (C) Responses of single cells can be combined into population vectors. (D) The summed response of the population of neurons accurately predicts the direction of the monkey's movement. In other words, the population of cells essentially tallies up individual cell "votes" regarding the best direction to move. © 2010 Cengage Learning

1986). If a monkey has to rotate the direction of movement in a systematic, continuous manner (e.g., slowly turn 90 degrees clockwise), the activity of the population vector shows a systematic change reflecting the rotation (Georgopoulos, Lurito, Petrides, Schwartz, & Massey, 1989).

From a computational perspective, there has been much debate about exactly what the activity of neurons in M1 tells muscles to do—that is, what these neurons are coding for. These cells seem to be sensitive not only to the direction of movement or the degree of muscle force and torque (rotational force) of joint acceleration, but also to overall trajectory and distance to target, among other things. Furthermore, activity of M1 can be sensitive to sensory information, suggesting that it may be involved in sensory-motor integration (Shen & Alexander, 1997). At the most basic level, neurons in M1 may code for the force of movement (Scott, 2000). More recent work, however, demonstrates that this cannot be the whole story. For example, when a constant load is applied to certain muscles, the activity across the population of neurons can vary depending on whether the monkey is maintaining a posture or is reaching (Kurtzer, Herter, & Scott, 2005). This tells us that force is not the only factor coded by neurons in primary motor cortex (see Scott, 2008, for a longer discussion).

Recent research also suggests that the classical conception of the organization of the motor cortex may have to be revisited as well. Whereas short-duration stimulation of motor cortex leads to movement of particular body parts depending on the regions stimulated, longer trains of stimulation (on the order of 500 ms or longer) reveal more complex coordinated movements that are of critical importance for the animal, including hand-to-mouth movements, reaching motions, and motions to protect the body from attack (● Figure 5.14). Therefore, some researchers have suggested that motor cortex is organized for ethologically relevant behaviors, rather than on the basis of specific body parts per se (Graziano, 2006).

Control of movement by primary motor cortex may also be more flexible than previously thought. Even

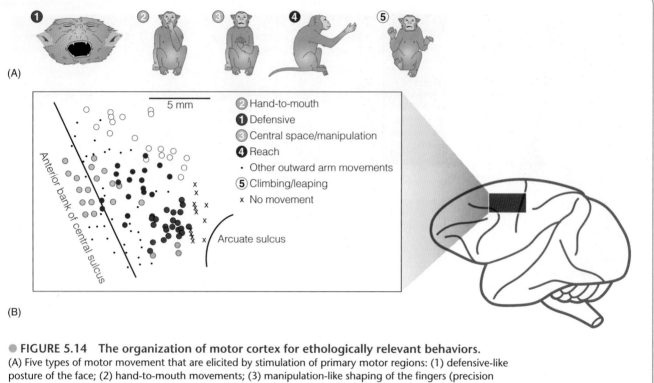

● **FIGURE 5.14   The organization of motor cortex for ethologically relevant behaviors.**
(A) Five types of motor movement that are elicited by stimulation of primary motor regions: (1) defensive-like posture of the face; (2) hand-to-mouth movements; (3) manipulation-like shaping of the fingers (precision grip) and movement of the hands to central space; (4) outward reach with the hand opened to allow for grasping; and (5) climbing or leaping-like posture of all four limbs. (B) A map of the regions of motor cortex that elicit these movements when stimulated: (left) The gray square on the cortex indicates the region of the motor cortex that is shown in the square to the right. (right) Circle and symbols represent areas of stimulation, with color and shape indicating the type of movements elicited by stimulation at that site. Notice the systematic topography with similar motions occurring within distinct subregions. *Source:* Figure 2 and 3 from Graziano, M. (2006). The organization of behavioral repetoire in motor cortex. ANNUAL REVIEW OF NEUROSCIENCE, 29, page 109. Reprinted by permission of Annual Review.

though primary motor cortex programs the control of muscle movement, it can be influenced by cognitive aspects of performance (see Georgopoulos, 2000, for a review). For example, in adults, learning a new motor skill can change the size of the cortical regions in primary motor cortex that represent each finger (e.g., Karni, Meyer, Jezzard, Adams, Turner, & Ungerleider, 1995, 1998). The regions of cortex devoted to fingers that are often used will expand, whereas those controlling fingers that are used less often will retract. (We discuss this issue of changes in the neural substrates underlying mental function, known as *plasticity*, in more detail in Chapter 15.) In addition, the connection between motor cortex and muscles is influenced by feedback of information received from the periphery, meaning that it is more fluid than previously thought (Graziano, 2006). Thus, although the classical model of the organization and function of motor cortex that we presented in Chapter 1 provided a good heuristic, it is clear that the true story is a bit more complicated and not yet fully understood.

Supplementary Motor Complex and Premotor Areas

When the primary motor cortex is damaged, the individual cannot control the force of muscle exertion, and the result is weakness and imprecise fine motor movements.

Of course, skilled movement requires more than being able to move the muscles: it also requires coordination and timing of muscle movements. For example, merely having the ability to move our muscles is clearly insufficient if we want to give a speech or play the piano. Such complicated motor tasks require a plan of action. Areas of the cortex distinct from primary motor cortex but connected to it are believed to be important for the creation of such plans. After first reviewing the concept of a motor plan, we examine the areas involved in creating such plans: the supplementary motor complex and premotor regions.

Concept of a Motor Plan   A plan of action, or **motor program** as it is often called, is an abstract representation of an intended movement. It must contain not only general information about the goal that a series of movements is intended to achieve, but also specific information about the neuromuscular control that will allow the goal to be reached (see Keele, 1968). Suppose that the goal of the plan is to type the sentence, "The lazy white cat just languished in the sun as the bunny bolted across the yard." In this case, the motor program should contain information about which fingers will move, the order in which they will move, the direction in which they will move, the timing between movements, and so forth.

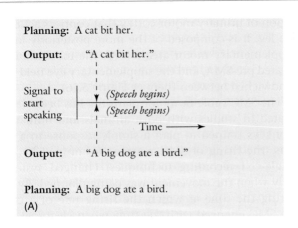

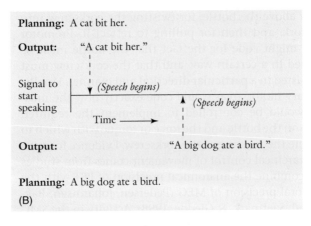

● **FIGURE 5.15 Testing for the existence of a motor program.** (A) If the brain just plans a step or two ahead, the time required to initiate an utterance should not be affected by the length of the utterance—in this case, four versus six words. (B) In contrast, if the brain must plan the entire utterance before initiating speech, the longer the utterance, the longer the delay before its initiation. This is the pattern that scientists observe. © 2011 Cengage Learning

Evidence that the human brain creates an overall plan of a series of complicated motor movements comes primarily from studies examining motor control in the oral and manual domains. One phenomenon suggestive of motor planning is **coarticulation**, which refers to differences in how the vocal muscles produce sounds (most notably vowels) depending on what precedes or follows them. For example, the sound of the vowel "u" requires the lips to be rounded (unless you are a ventriloquist!). In contrast, consonants can be produced acceptably with or without lip rounding. Thus, if a series of consonants precedes a vowel requiring lip rounding, the consonants will be produced with rounded lips. Look at yourself in the mirror as you say "construe." Notice that your lips are rounded as you begin to say "str" of the second syllable. Now look in the mirror at the shape of your lips as you say "constrict." When you said the "str" of this word, your lips were not rounded, because the vowel "i" did not require it.

Examples such as these indicate that some preplanning of speech must have occurred. The question that arises is how far in advance this preplanning occurs. Are motor commands generated in a chainlike manner, allowing movements to be planned only a couple of steps ahead rather than requiring the entire sequence to be planned before an action begins? Or is the *entire* utterance planned in advance? (See Wright, 1990, for further discussion.) The answer appears to be that humans can indeed plan an entire motor sequence before initiating action. Researchers in one study told their participants to produce a fluent stream of words, but only after a signal let them know to do so. The utterances were well practiced so that the subjects could produce them fluently. The critical variable in the study was the time an individual took to begin to say the utterance after the signal appeared. The researchers reasoned that if the motor plan were being continually created "online," the number of words in an utterance would not influence how long a person took to start the utterance. The person would plan speech "on the fly," keeping a step or two ahead of what he or she was actually saying. Such a strategy would be invoked in the same way regardless of whether an utterance consisted of three words or seven. However, if a motor plan of the entire utterance is created before the person begins to speak, the time to initiate speech would be related to the length of the utterance. Because short utterances would require little time to plan, an individual would begin to speak these more quickly than a longer utterance, which would require more time to plan. The logic behind these experiments is shown in ● Figure 5.15. Results indicated that the time it took to begin speaking increased linearly with the number of words in the utterance, such that each word increased the latency to begin speaking by a set amount. The conclusion is that the brain generates an entire plan of action before movement commences rather than creating the plan as actions are being performed (e.g., Sternberg, Monsell, Knoll, & Wright, 1978).

As mentioned previously, the regions of the brain that are involved in creating these motor plans lie outside the primary motor cortex. As a brief overview, the supplementary motor complex (SMC) comes up with the motor plan at the most abstract level—that of sequencing the critical pieces. The premotor areas then code for the types of actions that must occur to meet that motor plan, and primary motor regions execute the commands to move the muscles. For example, if one wanted to uncork a bottle of wine, the SMC might code for the motor sequence needed: to steady the bottle with one hand and to use the other hand to position the cork-screw above the bottle, for twisting the corkscrew into the cork, and then for pulling to retract it. Premotor areas might code for the fact that the bottle must be grasped in a certain way, and that the corkscrew must be twisted in a particular direction and manner. Finally, primary motor areas would code exactly how the muscles would be controlled to implement the required grasp on the bottle and the force or torque with which to execute the twisting of the corkscrew. Evidence for such a hierarchical control of movement comes from studies that combine the anatomical precision of PET with the temporal precision of MEG (Pedersen, Johannsen, Bak, Kofoed, Saermark, & Gjedde, 1998). Activity in the SMC is observed 100–300 ms before an action commences. Activity in the premotor cortex is observed from 100 ms prior to the onset of movement, whereas activity in the primary motor cortex commences at movement onset and continues for another 100 ms. We now examine the function of each of these regions in more detail.

Supplementary Motor Complex One of the main regions of the brain that plays a role in planning, preparing, and initiating movements is the **supplementary motor complex (SMC)**, which is located mainly

on the medial surface of the brain, just anterior to the region of primary motor cortex that controls actions of the leg. It is composed of the more posteriorly located supplementary motor area (SMA), the more anteriorly located pre-SMA, and the supplementary eye field (SEF), sandwiched between them (● Figure 5.16).

The SMC's role in motor planning has been demonstrated in studies with both animals and humans. In monkeys trained to plan a simple response to a stimulus, the firing of SMC neurons (examined by using single-cell recording techniques) changed systematically when the movement was being planned. By comparing the time at which the firing rate of a cell in the SMC changed with the time when electrical activity began in the limbs associated with the movement (remember, neuronal firing is necessary for a muscle to move), researchers determined that the firing rate in the SMA changed *before* electrical activity was recorded at the limb (Tanji, Taniguchi, & Saga, 1980). Thus, these data indicate that the SMC is involved in planning movement prior to initiation of an action. More specifically, the SMA becomes active before the movement of the hand or foot, while the SEF becomes active before movement of the eyes. The region of SMA that becomes active depends on the limb that will be used, as it is organized somatotopically: stimulation of caudal sites causes activity in the hindlimb, whereas stimulation of the rostral sites, bordering the pre-SMA, causes movements of the forelimbs and orofacial region (e.g., Mitz & Wise, 1987).

Other evidence from research on monkeys suggests that the SMA and pre-SMA play an important role in action sequences. For example, particular neurons in SMA and pre-SMA may fire before a given sequence that starts with a particular action (say, turn), but only when that action is followed by a specific sequence (say turn-pull-and then push a lever, but not turn-push-pull) (Shima & Tanji, 2000) (● Figure 5.17A). Furthermore, some neurons in this area fire specifically to the position in a sequence in which an action occurs (e.g., the second action) regardless of the nature of the actual action itself (e.g., a push, a pull, or a turn) (Clower & Alexander, 1998) (● Figure 5.17B). These findings all point to an important role for the supplementary motor complex in the sequencing of actions. Moreover, neurons in this region appear to code information flexibly, as their activity changes while learning new stimulus-response associations and during the learning of novel sequences (Chen & Wise, 1996).

Research with humans provides a similar picture of the role of the SMC in the planning of complex movement. First, functional brain imaging studies indicate that this area becomes active during tasks that require complicated motor sequencing. For example, an increase in SMC activity is observed when an individual must guide a finger by touch (not vision) to a specific

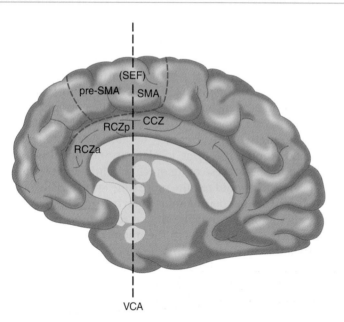

● **FIGURE 5.16   The brain regions that comprise the supplementary motor complex.** Shown here is the location, on the medial surface of the brain, of the supplementary motor area (SMA), the supplementary eye field, and the pre-SMA. The border between the pre-SMA and SMA is generally taken to be determined by a vertical line that extends from the top of the brain's surface to the anterior commissure, known as the vertical commissure anterior line or VCA line. Notice that these regions lie directly above the anterior cingulate regions RCZa and RCZp (anterior and posterior rostral cingulate zones, respective) and area CCZ (caudal cingulate zone). *Source:* Nachev, Kennard, Hussain, "Functional role of the supplementary and presupplementary motor areas," Nature Reviews Neuroscience 9, figure 1a, page 857.

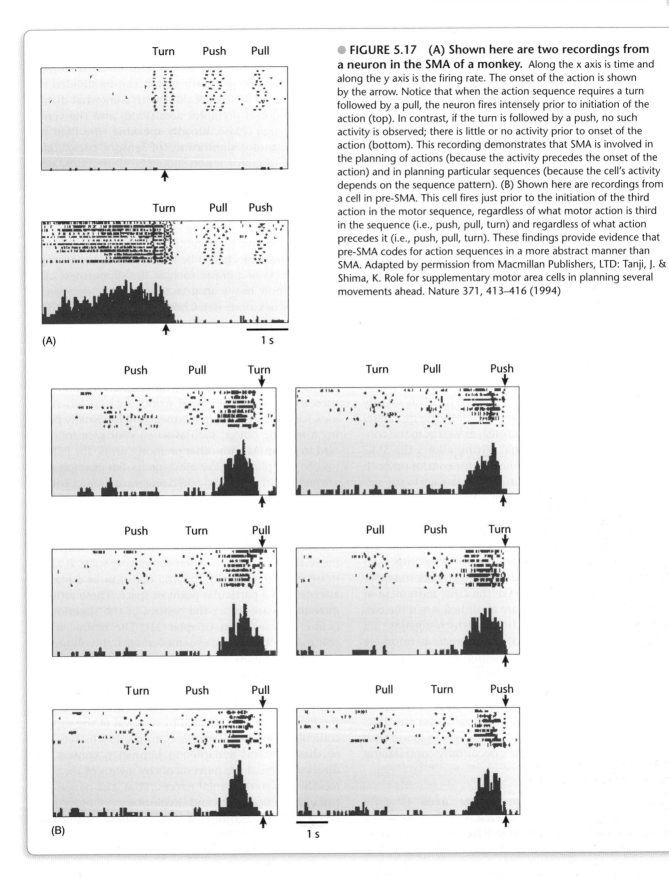

● **FIGURE 5.17** **(A) Shown here are two recordings from a neuron in the SMA of a monkey.** Along the x axis is time and along the y axis is the firing rate. The onset of the action is shown by the arrow. Notice that when the action sequence requires a turn followed by a pull, the neuron fires intensely prior to initiation of the action (top). In contrast, if the turn is followed by a push, no such activity is observed; there is little or no activity prior to onset of the action (bottom). This recording demonstrates that SMA is involved in the planning of actions (because the activity precedes the onset of the action) and in planning particular sequences (because the cell's activity depends on the sequence pattern). (B) Shown here are recordings from a cell in pre-SMA. This cell fires just prior to the initiation of the third action in the motor sequence, regardless of what motor action is third in the sequence (i.e., push, pull, turn) and regardless of what action precedes it (i.e., push, pull, turn). These findings provide evidence that pre-SMA codes for action sequences in a more abstract manner than SMA. Adapted by permission from Macmillan Publishers, LTD: Tanji, J. & Shima, K. Role for supplementary motor area cells in planning several movements ahead. Nature 371, 413–416 (1994)

place within a grid of rectangular rods, or when he or she must repetitively touch the limb of one hand to the fingertips in a 16-sequence set of movements (Roland, Larsen, Lassen, & Skinhøj, 1980). Thus, the SMC is specifically involved in *complex* movements. No increase in SMC activity occurs during a simple repetitive task, such as pressing a spring between the thumb and index fingers once per second.

Second, the SMC is active even when participants are asked to imagine, but not actually perform, a complex finger-sequencing task. Although blood flow to the SMC increases about 20% under these conditions, blood flow does not increase in primary motor cortex unless the person actually performs the task (Roland, Larsen, Lassen, & Skinhøj, 1980). Moreover, when individuals are told to generate self-paced movement, activity was enhanced in pre-SMA when individuals were attending to their intention to make the next move, as compared to actually making the movement itself (Lau, Rogers, Haggard, & Passingham, 2004). Neuroimaging studies have also demonstrated that when one must alter movement plans for the hand and eyes, activity occurs in the pre-SMA and the supplementary eye field respectively, presumably because new motor programs must be generated. In these studies, people are asked to either stop a motor task that has already been initiated, override a typical motor response with a rarer one, or change their movements (e.g., move in the opposite direction from which they initially started) (see Nachev, Kennard, & Husain, 2008, for a longer discussion of the role of SMA and pre-SMA in motor control).

Unlike motor cortex, the output of which is mainly contralateral, each SMC projects to both the ipsilateral and the contralateral motor cortex, as well as to the contralateral SMC. This neuronal wiring allows the SMC in one hemisphere to influence motor control on both sides of the body. Whereas unilateral damage to the primary motor areas produces difficulties only on the contralateral side of the body, unilateral damage to the SMC in nonhuman primates mainly produces difficulty in bimanual coordination. Animals with such damage are unable to execute different movements of the fingers on each hand because the hands no longer work independently, but rather tend to make the same movement at the same time. The deficits are abolished when the corpus callosum is sectioned, a finding which suggests that connections between the SMCs in each hemisphere are also important for coordinating hand movements (Brinkman, 1984). In humans, activity in the SMC also is linked to the planning of movement of both hands. Even in tasks in which only one hand is moving, an increase in blood flow occurs *bilaterally* over the SMC in each hemisphere. In contrast, changes in blood flow over the primary motor cortex occur only contralateral to the hand that is moving.

Premotor Regions The **premotor area** is aptly named, not only because that describes its position in front of the motor area, but also because its role is to send commands to the primary motor area, making it just prior in the chain of command. It is located on the lateral surface of the brain just in front of primary motor cortex (whereas the supplementary motor complex is located in a similar position but on the brain's medial surface). Activity in premotor cortex looks identical to that in primary motor cortex during the production of

an action; however, like the SMC, it differs from primary motor cortex in that it exhibits activity prior to the onset of the movement. Recent research with monkeys suggests that the premotor region can be divided into two somewhat distinct regions with somewhat distinct roles: the dorsal premotor area (PMd) and the ventral premotor area (PMv). Broadly speaking, the PMd processes the motor significance of sensory cues, coding what type of motor action should be chosen or selected based on sensory information. For example, based on visual characteristics, one would plan a different type of grasp to pick up a pencil as compared to planning a grasp to pick up a cup. The PMv appears to be involved in implementing these motor programs and adjusting them so that objects can be manipulated. For example, some aspects of a grasp, such as the slipperiness of an object or how heavy an item is, cannot be determined by visual cues alone (see Chouinard & Paus, 2006, for a longer discussion).

One portion of dorsal premotor regions is known as the **frontal eye field (FEF)**, which, as its name suggests, controls the voluntary execution of eye movements (Paus, 1996). These eye movements include those used in scanning the visual world, such as when you look for a friend's face in a crowd; and in visually pursuing a moving object, such as when your gaze follows a bird in flight. As with other premotor areas, the FEFs are involved in planning eye movements. For example, they are particularly involved when one must predict where a constantly moving item is going to go next and planning eye movements to that location (Ilg & Thier, 2008).

The voluntary eye movements controlled by the frontal eye fields are distinct from the reflexive eye movements that occur when something such as a loud noise or a large, bright, moving object pulls a person's attention to a particular point in space. These reflexive movements are under the control of the superior colliculus (discussed in Chapter 11). The neural system controlling voluntary eye movements (involving the frontal eye fields) and the system controlling reflexive eye movements (involving the superior colliculus) can work independently. For example, eye movements that occur when the frontal eye fields are stimulated in the monkey are not affected by removal of the superior colliculus (Schiller, True, & Conway, 1980). Yet, both of these systems synapse on brainstem centers that direct the actual eye movements by means of the third, fourth, and sixth cranial nerves. Thus, the neural control of both voluntary and involuntary eye movements appears to occur through a final common output pathway, even though they can work separately.

If each of these two systems can control the eye-movement centers in the brain stem, why doesn't massive conflict occur? The conflict seems to be avoided because the frontal eye fields have precedence: they strongly influence the superior colliculus. In humans, damage to the frontal eye fields makes it difficult to suppress automatic eye movements that occur when an attention-grabbing stimulus appears in the periphery, because the frontal eye fields cannot inhibit the response (Paus et al., 1991). In monkeys, cells in the frontal eye fields excite the cells in the superior colliculus that are important for moving the eyes in the same direction while inhibiting the cells important for movements in other directions (Schlag-Rey, Schlag, & Dassonville, 1992). (For a nice review of the different portions of motor cortex involved in eye movements, see Schall & Boucher, 2007).

Turning our attention to ventral regions of the premotor area, research with monkeys has isolated within the PMv a set of neurons known as *mirror neurons* that fire both when a monkey performs a particular action and when the monkey observes another organism performing that same action. In some cases, the correspondence between the performed and the observed actions must be very tight in order for the mirror neurons to respond to both. For example, a mirror neuron will fire only when the same precision grip involving the index finger and thumb is used both by the monkey and the experimenter. In other cases, the activation is broader: any type of grasping exhibited by the experimenter will cause neural firing. However, activity in these neurons will not be evoked just by viewing the object, by watching another animal mimicking a gesture, or by observing an action that is directed toward an object (Rizzolatti & Lupino, 2001), suggesting that there must be strong correspondence between the monkey's actions and the actions of another organism to induce firing in these motor neurons.

Neuroimaging studies with humans find greater activation in Brodmann area 44 (Broca's area) in humans, typically considered the likely human analog to PMv, when hand motions must be imitated as compared to just being observed. For example, this area exhibited more activation when a person lifts a specific finger in response to seeing that finger being lifted in a video, as compared to lifting a specific finger in response to seeing a photograph of fingers with an "x" on the finger that should be lifted (Iacoboni, Woods, Brass, Bekkering, Mazziotta, & Rizzolatti, 1999). Furthermore, TMS to this area disrupts the ability to imitate finger movements (Heiser, Iacoboni, Maeda, Marcus, & Mazziotta, 2003). In addition, this region exhibits activity when observing actions that can be produced by an individual, regardless of the species producing it. For example, greater activity in Brodmann area 44 is observed when a person observes a video clip of either another person, a monkey, or a dog biting an object, compared to a static image of the biting action. The degree of activity observed is proportional to how much the action falls within an individual's repertoire of motor behavior. For example, activity in this region was observed while an individual watched someone reading out loud, to a lesser degree when the individual watched a monkey smacking its lips, and not at all when the individual observed a dog barking (Buccino et al., 2004).

What purpose would such neurons serve? They appear to provide a neural substrate for understanding actions being performed by others and for imitating them. This ability is a basic prerequisite for any communication system: there must be shared understanding and implementation of a communicative code, in this case, a code of motor actions. This system may help an individual not only to understand the goal of the motor act, but also to understand the intention behind it (e.g., grasping a cup to drink versus grasping a cup to start cleaning up a spill). Some researchers propose that the mirror neuron system may be dysfunctional in individuals with autism, who have an impaired ability to understand and relate to other individuals in the social and emotional realm (see Chapter 15). The degree to which an intact mirror neuron system is required for adequate social interactions is an open question, but an intriguing one (for more discussion, see Iacoboni & Dapretto, 2006; Rizzolatti & Fabbri-Destro, 2008).

Anterior Cingulate Cortex

The role of the anterior cingulate cortex in cognitive functioning is one of the most hotly debated topics at present. Until fairly recently, the function of the cingulate in humans was mostly a mystery. Because of its location on the midline of the brain, it was rarely damaged in isolation, making it nearly impossible to determine the effect of a lesion to this region. Since the advent of brain imaging techniques, though, its important role in cognitive function has become much more obvious. Even a cursory look at the brain imaging literature reveals that the cingulate becomes activated across a huge range of tasks (e.g., Paus, Koski, Caramanos, & Westbury, 1998). The debate regarding cingulate function probably occurs in part because this structure covers a large expanse of brain tissue. Although referred to in general terms as the *anterior cingulate,* it has many distinct regions. Some of these regions are more likely to be involved in attentional control and emotional regulation, which we discuss in Chapters 11 and 13, respectively. Here we focus on the role that the anterior cingulate plays in motor control.

The posterior portion of the anterior cingulate is specifically implicated in the control and planning of motor movements, especially when they are novel or require a good deal of cognitive control. Whereas lesions of the cingulate cortex interfere with motor function, extra activity in this region, such as that generated during epileptic seizures, causes increased motor activity. Moreover, stimulation of the anterior cingulate gyrus in monkeys leads to vocalization as well as to movements of the body, some of which are complex (e.g., sucking). Evidence that the region is involved in the preparation for movement comes from single-cell recordings. Activity is observed in the anterior cingulate cortex before the beginning of hand movements, regardless of whether they are initiated internally by the animal (i.e., in self-paced tasks) or occur in response to a sensory signal from the environment (Vogt, Finch, & Olson, 1992).

Evidence from neuroimaging also suggests that the anterior cingulate cortex plays a role in modulating motor commands in humans, especially when the movements to be produced are novel or unrehearsed and therefore influenced by cognitive factors (Paus, 2001). In one of the first such demonstrations, scientists used PET scanning to record regional brain activity while people performed motor tasks that required manual, oral, or ocular movements (Paus, Petrides, Evans, & Meyer, 1993). For each manner of movement (oral, manual, or ocular), the researchers administered two types of tasks: one that was well practiced and one that was not. For example, in the well-practiced oral task, after hearing "A," subjects responded "B," or after hearing "L," they responded "M." In the novel task, the stimuli were the same, but the task demands were different. In this task, when individuals heard "A," they responded "M," and when they heard "B," they responded "L."

The study revealed two important findings. First, it revealed that the anterior cingulate cortex has a specific topography. Tasks requiring manual movements activated the most caudal region of the anterior cingulate cortex, those requiring oculomotor movements the most rostral, and those requiring speech the area between. Hence, like the organization of primary motor and premotor areas, the organization of the anterior cingulate region appears to be topographic (but see Barch, Braver, Akbudak, Conturo, Ollinger, & Snyder, 2001, for a different conclusion). Second, the researchers found that this region was most active when a novel response was required (saying "M" in response to "A") but was not very active when the response had been ingrained over the course of a lifetime (such as saying "B" in response to "A") or over hundreds of trials preceding the PET scan. These findings suggest that the anterior cingulate cortex plays a role in linking motor and cognitive behavior, especially when that linkage is novel or recently learned.

One of the authors of this textbook (MTB) has also performed a study suggesting a very central role for the anterior cingulate in the selection of a motor response (Milham et al., 2001). In our study, individuals had to press one of three buttons to indicate the ink color (blue, green, yellow) in which a word is presented (e.g., "green" in blue ink), a task called the *Stroop task,* which is known to activate the anterior cingulate. We compared regional brain activation for three types of trials: incongruent trials in which the distracting word names a competing response (e.g., the word "blue" appears in yellow ink); incongruent trials in which the distracting word names a different color, but not a competing response (e.g., the word "red" in blue ink); and neutral trials in which the distracting word had no relationship to color (e.g., the word "lot" in blue ink). We reasoned that if the anterior cingulate is *specifically* involved in response-related processes, it should show more

activation when the color word names a competing response than when it does not. Furthermore, as long as the word does not conflict with the response, activation should be similar whether or not the word names a different color (e.g., whether the word is "red" or "lot"). Indeed, we found that posterior portions of the anterior cingulate exhibited exactly such a pattern of activity, reinforcing the idea that it plays a prominent role in response-related processes.

Notice that in both the cases described here, the individual must override the predominant or prevailing response (overriding the bias to say "B" to "A" and instead reply "M"; overriding the bias to select the motor response associated with the word rather than the motor response associated with the ink color). Activation is also observed when the information that should guide the response is somewhat ambiguous (Banich, 2009). These findings suggest that the role of the cingulate is not to program a specific motor response, per se, but rather to aid in selecting among competing response alternatives.

The motor system must be able not only to generate and select a response, but also to evaluate whether such a selection is correct. Recent work has suggested that the cingulate is also involved in relating actions to their consequences, such as determining whether the action led to an error or, conversely, produced a response that was in line with the goals of the task or led to positive reinforcement (Rushworth, Walton, Kennerley, & Bannerman, 2004). Other researchers suggest that the anterior cingulate does not merely determine the value of the outcome of the action, but also reflects the subjective value attributed by an individual to the response. This subjective value is reflected in a specific ERP component, known as the *error-related negativity (ERN)*, which is elicited by the cingulate following performance mistakes (Holroyd & Coles, 2008). We discuss the cingulate's role in evaluating performance in more detail in Chapter 12 on executive control. For now, it is important to know that the regions of the anterior cingulate involved in response evaluation appear to be somewhat more anterior than those involved in overriding or selecting atypical responses (Stevens, Kiehl, Pearlson, & Calhoun, 2009).

Right Inferior Frontal Cortex

Not only is it important to be able to sequence and direct motor actions, but on occasion it is also necessary to interrupt or stop an ongoing motor action. Recent evidence suggests that regions of the right inferior frontal lobe (in particular BA 44 and 45), also referred to as *ventrolateral prefrontal cortex*, may have a special role in such control over motor action.

A variety of converging evidence supports the role of this region in interrupting or inhibiting motor actions. Inhibitory control abilities are often assessed via a task known as the *stop-signal paradigm,* in which participants are told to press a button whenever a stimulus appears. However, on a minority of trials, a tone (or some other cue) occurs after the stimulus, and signals that individuals should now interrupt or abort their motor action. This cue serves as the "stop" signal. Numerous neuroimaging studies have reported activity in right inferior frontal regions, part of the ventrolateral prefrontal cortex, for conditions in which actions must be interrupted (that is, the stop-signal trials); this activity is not seen in conditions in which actions do not require interruption. Such effects are found regardless of what type of movement must be disrupted, either manual or ocular (e.g., Leung & Cai, 2007). Moreover, rTMS over this region interferes with the ability to inhibit a response (Chambers et al., 2007).

These findings are consistent with effects observed in patients who have sustained brain damage to the right inferior frontal region. The larger the amount of damage in this region, the more difficulty the patients have in stopping their behavior (Aron, Fletcher, Bullmore, Sahakian, & Robbins, 2003) (● Figure 5.18) (for a good review of the role of this area in inhibition, see Aron, Robbins, & Poldrack, 2004). However, most paradigms that involve response inhibition require individuals to inhibit responses on a minority of trials. Therefore, right inferior frontal cortex could be implicated in these tasks not because it is involved in inhibition per se, but rather because it processes information signaling low-frequency events (see, for example, Chikazoe et al., 2009). Until clearer evidence for this alternative explanation appears, however, it would seem reasonable to ascribe a role in motor inhibition to right inferior frontal regions.

Parietal Lobe

The role of the parietal lobe in motor programming is twofold: First, it is involved as an interface between movement and sensory information; second, it contributes to the ability to produce complex, well-learned motor acts. These two aspects of motor control appear to rely on different regions of the parietal lobe, the former on the superior regions and the latter on the inferior regions. These regions, and the intraparietal sulcus that divides them, are depicted in ● Figure 5.19.

As demonstrated in both monkeys and humans, the superior parietal lobe acts to integrate sensory information with motor movements so that the limbs or eyes can be guided correctly during motor acts. To do so, information from spatial maps in different modalities must be integrated (we discuss more about the role of parietal regions in regard to spatial processing in Chapter 8). For example, when a person reaches for an object, the object's location is taken from visual information and is in eye-centered coordinates. It must be translated into a spatial map in hand-centered coordinates so that the motor action can be directed to the correct location.

It appears from single-cell recordings that there is a gradient across cells in the superior parietal lobe with regard to their sensitivity to these two frames of reference (those that are eye-centered and those that are hand centered). Cells that are most sensitive to the difference between the target and hand position are located more toward the dorsal surface of the brain,

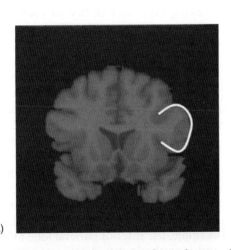

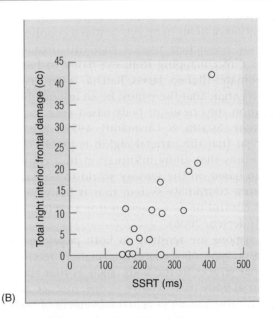

(A)   (B)

● **FIGURE 5.18   The role of right inferior frontal cortex in the inhibition of response.** (A) The region of right inferior frontal cortex for which volume of tissue loss was calculated in individuals who had sustained brain damage. (B) The larger the volume of tissue loss in right inferior frontal cortex (shown on the y axis), the greater the difficulty in inhibiting responses, as indexed by the stop-signal reaction time (SSRT) on the x axis. The SSRT provides an index of how quickly an individual can abort a motor response after receiving a signal to do. From Aron, A.R., Robbins, T.W., & Poldrack, R.A. (2004). Inhibition and the right inferior frontal cortex. Trends in Cognitive Sciences, 8, 170-177. Figure 1, pg. 171. Reprinted by permission of Elsevier.

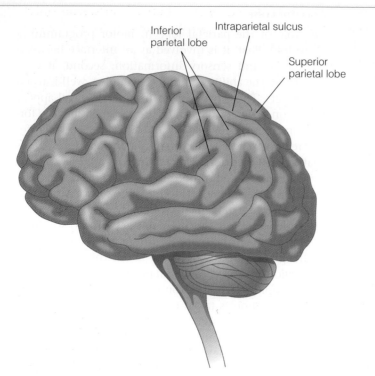

● **FIGURE 5.19   Superior and inferior regions of the parietal lobe involved in motor programming.** In both monkeys and humans, the superior parietal lobule (SPL) is important in controlling movements in space, whereas the inferior parietal lobule (IPL) is important in the ability to produce complex, well-learned motor acts. Neuroanatomically, they are divided by the intraparietal sulcus (IPS). © 2011 Cengage Learning

they are not. (The classic work is this area was performed by Mountcastle and colleagues, 1975.)

Damage to the superior parietal region in humans causes individuals to lose the ability to guide their limbs in a well-controlled manner, and is often accompanied by a tendency to misreach (Levine, Kaufman, & Mohr, 1978). In concordance with animal studies, functional imaging studies also provide evidence that different regions of the parietal lobe are sensitive to the type of cue that aids in reaching. More anterior and medial regions of the superior parietal lobe (often referred to as the *precuneus*) appear to use proprioceptive information to guide reaching, whereas a more posterior parietal region bordering on the occipital region relies more on visual information. This difference in activation across regions has been shown both in individual studies that directly contrast the two conditions (Filimon, Nelson, Huang, & Sereno, 2009) and in a meta-analysis of functional imaging studies (Blangero, Menz, McNamara, & Binkofski, 2009). Along with findings from studies with brain-damaged patients who have difficulty in reaching, these imaging studies implicate the superior parietal lobe in guiding reaching behavior.

Damage to more inferior regions of the parietal lobe can affect the ability to perform complex, well-learned motor acts. Damage to inferior parietal regions may cause apraxia. *Apraxia* is a syndrome in which an individual is unable to perform certain complex, learned motor tasks when asked to do so (Lezak, 1983) despite intact motor innervation of the muscles, an intact ability to coordinate sensorimotor actions spontaneously, and an ability to comprehend what is being asked. Apraxia is discussed in more detail later in this chapter.

The neural control of these aspects of motor function is lateralized, because apraxia often results after damage to the *left* inferior parietal lobe. Researchers have hypothesized that the left parietal lobe links different types of information, such as visuokinesthetic information and internal conceptual representations, to motor programs. Considered this way, the performance of complex, learned acts falls well within the domain we characterized in Chapter 1 as the purview of the parietal lobe—namely, that of a multimodal association area. For example, the inferior parietal lobe might link the visual and kinesthetic information of a match and a matchbook cover with the motor act that involves lighting the match using the matchbook cover. Such linkages do not require a physical object, because the parietal lobe may also link motor acts to internal representations such as those occurring during pantomime or gesture (e.g., waving good-bye) (Heilman & Rothi, 1985).

whereas those located more ventrally appear to be coding the position of items in an eye-centered coordinate system. Some researchers suggest that this organization allows direct mapping from eye-based to hand-based coordinates (Buneo, Jarvis, Batista, & Andersen, 2002); others argue that there must be an intermediate transformation into head- or body-based coordinates (e.g., McIntyre, Stratta, & Lacquaniti, 1997). Regardless, it is clear that the parietal region is involved in transformations that allow information in a coordinate system based on the sensory world to be transformed into a coordinate system that is body-based and allows control of motor action (for a review, see Buneo & Andersen, 2006).

Parietal regions are sensitive to both *proprioceptive information,* a type of sensory information received from internal sensors in the body, such as that about the position of body parts relative to one another, and *kinesthetic* information about actual movement of body parts. Proprioceptive information can be sent forward to premotor and primary motor regions to enable the selection of appropriate motor programs, which in turn provide feedback to parietal regions. The motor feedback, as well as proprioceptive and kinesthetic information, can be used to ensure that movements are being executed according to plan and to enable correction if

Given the deficits in pantomime and gesture after parietal damage, it has been suggested that this region may be critical for generating a mental model of motor movements. For example, individuals with parietal lobe lesions were asked to imagine pressing each finger against the thumb sequentially in beat with a metronome whose speed was increased every five seconds. The participants were asked to determine the speed at which, in their imagination, their fingers could not move quickly enough keep up with the metronome. Then they were asked to perform the task, and the actual breakpoint in their performance was compared to that which they had imagined. Their estimates were quite poor, indicating that their mental model of movements had been disrupted (Sirigu, Duhamel, Cohen, Pillon, Dubois, & Agid, 1996). Converging evidence is provided by neuroimaging studies indicating that the inferior parietal area (BA 40) becomes active when an individual has to imagine making complete sequential movements of the finger (Gerardin et al., 2000) or grasping an object (Decety et al., 1994). This same region in the left hemisphere is involved when one must plan to or actually use a tool, regardless of whether performed by the right hand or the left (Johnson-Frey, Newman-Norlund, & Grafton, 2005). Because the left hemisphere is activated regardless of the hand employed, it suggests that such a motor control system is mainly lateralized to the left hemisphere, consistent with the location of the lesion that causes apraxic behavior.

The parietal lobe plays a role in online adjustment of motor actions with reference to the forward model constructed by the cerebellum (discussed earlier in this chapter at page 116). As we discussed, a forward model helps one to predict the sensory consequences of motor plans (e.g., I am feeling what I think I should be feeling). Thus, if you decide to pick up a full carton of milk from a table, you have a model of how it should feel when you do so and how much force you will need to pick it up. If the carton turns out to be empty, you quickly realize that it does not fit with your model and adjust your actions accordingly. As we discussed earlier, the cerebellum does not seem to be able to make such adjustments after an action is initiated. Rather, the left parietal lobe appears to play a large role in this adjustment process (Desmurget & Grafton, 2000). This role of the parietal lobe was demonstrated in a study in which individuals were to move their arms to a visual target. Unbeknownst to them, after they started to move their arms, the target's location was moved. They therefore needed online adjustment of the motor program, based on the change in visual input, to correctly reach the target. If during this time period TMS was applied over the left posterior parietal cortex to disrupt activity in this region, no adjustments were observed for the contralateral arm movement—it was incorrectly directed to the same position where the target originally was located (Desmurget, Epstein, Turner, Prablanc, Alexander, & Grafton, 1999).

Having a model of motor actions, such as is created by parietal regions, is also important if one wishes to control motor actions to produce a desired sensory outcome. This control can be achieved via an **inverse model**, which conceptually is the opposite of a forward model. In an inverse model, you construct the desired state at each point along a trajectory and translate those states into specific motor commands. Rather than predicting the sensory states to be expected based on a motor program (a forward model), in this case you determine what motor actions are required to reach a particular state (an inverse model). For example, in visually controlled actions, one needs a model of how motor movements can be generated so that the arms will end up in the place to which they are being guided by sight (see Wolpert & Ghahramani, 2000, for a discussion of the range of computational problems that must be solved by the motor system, and the different possible ways of doing so).

Motor skill learning appears to involve both the ability create feedforward models that will predict what sensory experience will accompany motor movements, and also the ability to use sensory feedback to determine if the motor movements had their intended effects. These abilities appear to involve different neural systems. In one neuroimaging study, researchers told people that they had to keep a cursor centered on a screen within a goal area. This task was made difficult because the researchers used a complex, but repeating mathematical function that perturbed the position of the cursor on the screen. Using mathematical modeling, the researchers could disentangle what portion of motor learning was related to feedforward versus feedback components. Consistent with what we have already discussed, improvements in feedforward learning (predicting upcoming sensory experience) appeared to rely in part on left inferior parietal regions, whereas the superior parietal region and the right intraparietal sulcus were more involved in learning from sensory feedback (Grafton, Schmitt, Van Horn, & Diedrichsen, 2008).

■ Integrated Models of the Motor System

At this point, we have reviewed the major regions of the brain that are involved in movement and have briefly outlined some of the motor disorders that occur after damage to these brain regions. It is important to keep in mind that despite the different roles each brain region plays, there is substantial overlap. For example, sequential movement requires the integrated functioning of many different brain regions. To gain an appreciation for how each of these individual brain regions might contribute to sequential motor processing, see Table 5.1.

We can consider the contributions of each region from a number of different perspectives. First, we can view them as aiding in different types of movement. For example, we have discussed the cerebellum as being important for movements that are not modified in response to sensory feedback, such as rapid movements, whereas the basal ganglia and parietal region play roles in modifying movement. Second, we can consider

TABLE 5.1	Functions of Major Brain Regions Involved in Movement
Brain Region	**Computation**
Movement Planning	
Inferior parietal regions	Generating an internal model of the movement
Supplementary motor area	Selecting the order of movements
Premotor area	Selecting the types of movements required (e.g., a grasp)
Frontal eye fields	Voluntarily controlling saccades
Posterior regions of the anterior cingulate cortex	Initiating novel responses and overriding prepotent responses
Movement Specification and Initiation	
Cerebellum	Timing of patterns of muscle activation
Basal ganglia	Switching between different patterns of movement initiation and cessation
Motor cortex	Initiating motor execution of the force and/or direction of movement
Movement Monitoring	
Anterior cingulate cortex	Detecting when an action is erroneous
Parietal cortex	Using sensory feedback to adjust movement online

the roles of these different regions within a hierarchy that contains different representations of movement at different levels of abstraction. For example, we noted that the SMA creates a general motor plan (e.g., pick up the glass of water), that premotor regions specify the type of movement required (e.g., a grasp), and that primary motor regions implement the muscle movements to carry out the plan.

Yet another perspective is derived from computational models of actions, such as models of **optimal feedback control** (Todorov & Jordan, 2002). This viewpoint conceptualizes the motor regions of the brain working together as a circuit to reach a goal, which can be met by a number of different movement options. Regardless of what motor movements are used, however, attaining those goals requires certain computations to be performed, such as estimating the state of the system, predicting the results of actions, determining rewards and costs of action, and optimizing performance. According to the *optimal feedback control model*, different regions of the motor circuit are responsible for different computations. The basal ganglia are thought to help estimate the costs of motor commands and the reward to which they will lead. The cerebellum is proposed to play a role in system identification, building internal models of the sensory consequences of motor commands and modifying those models through learning. The parietal cortex appears to estimate the state of the system by comparing the expected sensory feedback with the actual sensory feedback. Finally, information from the parietal cortex is then fed to premotor regions and primary motor cortex to alter the ongoing motor actions if the current ones are not optimal (see Shadmehr & Krakauer, 2008).

Regardless of which of these models ultimately provides a more compelling account of motor behavior, this discussion underscores a point that we will return to many times in this text: no brain region is an island unto itself. Rather, performance of the complex cognitive abilities demonstrated by the human mind requires a multiplicity of brain regions acting in a coordinated manner.

Motor Disorders

We now turn our attention to the neurological basis of some of the more common motor disorders. In this discussion, we divide motor disorders into two categories: those that occur because of damage or disruption to subcortical areas, and those that occur after cortical damage. As discussed at the outset of this chapter, we can broadly characterize subcortical motor disorders as affecting the form and timing of movements, whereas cortical motor disorders affect the conceptual clarity of motor acts, either by disrupting the sequencing of complex motor acts or by disrupting the ability to have a motor act represent a concept.

■ Subcortical Motor Disorders

In this section we discuss the motor disorders that are characterized mainly by damage to subcortical regions: Parkinson's disease, Huntington's disease, and Tourette's syndrome.

Parkinson's Disease

As we learned earlier, **Parkinson's disease** results from damage to the cells of the substantia nigra, which stops producing the neurotransmitter dopamine (for a good review of all aspects of the disorder, see Lees, Hardy, & Revesz, 2009). The damage and the disease may result from a variety of causes. In some cases, the disease runs in families, and recent research has been examining genes that might cause a genetic predisposition to the disorder. In other cases, the disease appears to be related to toxins, trauma, and inflammation. Still other cases may be viral in origin. In the 1910s and 1920s, individuals with *encephalitis lethargica* (also known as *von Economo's disease*) caught the flu and exhibited Parkinsonian symptoms either soon thereafter or as long as 20 years later.

Parkinson's disease can also be caused by drugs that individuals voluntarily ingest. For example, in the mid-1980s, young adults in their twenties and thirties began appearing in hospital rooms exhibiting symptoms of the disease, especially those related to lack of movement. Because such symptoms are highly unusual in this age group, doctors looked for a commonality among the patients and discovered that all were drug users. These afflicted individuals were dubbed "the frozen addicts." Some detective work revealed that these cases of Parkinson's disease could be linked to a synthetic heroin that was contaminated with the compound MPTP (1-methyl-4-phenyl-1,2,3,6-tetrahydropyridine), which, when converted by the body into MPP$^+$ (methylphenylpyridinium), is toxic to dopaminergic cells.

The behavioral effects of the disease typically are not evident until 60% of nerve cells and 80% of dopamine are lost (for a recent review of the pathophysiology of Parkinson's disease, see Bartels & Leenders, 2009). The delay in symptom onset occurs because the brain tries valiantly to compensate for the loss of dopamine in a number of ways, such as by having the remaining dopaminergic neurons increase their synthesis of dopamine or by decreasing the inactivation or clearance of dopamine once it crosses the synaptic cleft (Zigmond et al., 1990). At some point, however, often later in life, when a person reaches age 60 or 70, these compensatory mechanisms fail. At this point, cell loss, which is a normal part of the aging process, reduces the population of cells in the substantia nigra below a critical point, and behavioral effects are observed.

The movement disorder of Parkinson's disease has four major symptoms: tremors, **cogwheel rigidity**, akinesia, and **disturbances of posture**. These symptoms are generally observed on both sides of the body. However, in some cases, the dopamine depletion occurs in just one half of the brain, so symptoms are evident only on the contralateral side of the body; this condition is known as *hemi-Parkinsonism*. Let us now examine each of the symptoms in more detail.

As mentioned earlier, *tremors* are repetitive rhythmic motions that result from oscillatory movement of agonist and antagonist muscles. They are so predominant that it led James Parkinson to originally call the disease "shaking palsy." Parkinsonian tremors generally affect the arms and hands. These tremors are usually not seen during deliberate and purposeful movements, but are quite obvious when the person is at rest (e.g., just sitting in a chair listening to a conversation). Hand tremors are often described as "pill-rolling" because they resemble movements of an individual who is rolling a pill between the thumb and forefinger.

The rigidity observed in Parkinson's disease occurs because increased muscle tone in the extensor and flexor muscles makes the person appear stiff. In fact, the mechanical nature of the movements is referred to as *cogwheel rigidity*. If you try to move a limb of someone with Parkinson's disease, the movement is resisted. If you push hard enough, however, the limb can be moved, but only so far until once again the movement is resisted. When sufficient force is applied, the limb can be moved again. Thus, rather than moving smoothly, the limb moves in specific, rigid steps, much as a cogwheel does.

Another symptom of Parkinson's disease is *akinesia*, a poverty or lack of movement, or *bradykinesia*, a slowness of movement. Some Parkinson's patients sit motionless, like mannequins in a store window. Even facial movements can diminish to such a degree that these individuals are said to have a *Parkinsonian mask*. As we saw in the case of Muhammad Ali, this lack of movement can disrupt communication. Speech is affected because individuals have trouble producing sounds, and writing is affected because the production of letters is slow and labored.

Parkinsonian symptoms also include difficulty in posture and locomotion. Unlike tremors, which mainly affect the arms and hands, these other difficulties affect muscle groups throughout the body. The posture of a person with Parkinson's disease suffers because he or she has difficulty counteracting the force of gravity. For example, the person's head may droop or the person may bend so far forward as to end up on his or her knees. The posture required for sitting or standing may be impossible to maintain without support. The ability to make postural adjustments may also be impaired. For example, individuals with Parkinson's disease may fall when bumped because they cannot right themselves quickly after losing balance. Movements that require postural transitions are also difficult, such as standing up from a seated position. Walking is compromised not only because it requires continual postural adjustments, but also because it requires a series of movements, which akinesia renders difficult. When patients with Parkinson's disease walk, they tend to shuffle, much as normal individuals do when walking on ice or in other situations in which maintaining balance is difficult. For an example of how someone with Parkinson's disease appears, see ● Figure 5.20.

● **FIGURE 5.20   The presentation of a person with Parkinson's disease.** Notice the frozen face and stooped, flexed posture. *Source:* Figure 1 From Lees, A. J., Hardy, J. & Revesz, T. (2009). Parkinson's disease, Lancet, 373, page 2057/ Illustration courtesy of Nathalie Lees. With permission from Elsevier.

IN FOCUS: Using Brain Activation to Control Prosthetic Limbs

Imagine a science fiction movie in which the main character is a cyborg—half human, half machine. Its hands are not only shaped to allow it to perform all the actions of a human hand, but they are also outfitted with other features, such as retractable claws for latching, scratching, and climbing, and pinchers that enable grasping and crushing. And how does the cyborg command its bionic arm to make both human and nonhuman motions? By wires that run from its brain to its arm, so that simply thinking the movement it wishes to produce makes them happen!

Although this may sound like science fiction, part of this scenario is happening today. Within recent years, there has been a flurry of activity in the creation of brain-computer interfaces, especially those designed to control artificial limbs. To date, most of the work has been confined to rodents and monkeys, but more recent research has demonstrated the utility of this approach in humans as well. These advances have been spurred by greater understanding of the neural mechanisms involved in motor control, increased ability to record brain activity from multiple sites, and the increase in the power and speed of computers that allows complicated brain activity to be analyzed quickly and processed for output without a delay (often referred to as "real-time processing"). In turn, the quest to build a better brain-computer interface has provided additional insights into the principles of brain structure and function (Nicolelis & Lebedev, 2009).

Some brain-computer interfaces are designed with the idea of using intact

motor cortex to send signals either to a limb that has been paralyzed due to spinal cord damage (which precludes the signal from the motor cortex from reaching the limb) or to a prosthetic device (when the limb has been severed) (see Daly & Wolpaw, 2008, for a larger discussion of brain-computer interfaces in neurological rehabilitation). As we learned earlier in this chapter, motor control occurs via activity across a population of neurons. Newer multiarray recording technologies allow the pattern of neural firing across such a population to be recorded. In monkeys, such arrays can be placed in primary motor cortex that controls the movement of limbs or in premotor areas involved in the planning of motor acts.

The information from neural activity from these different areas is then linked with information on where the animal is reaching. To do this, researchers employ complex computational algorithms that, over time, learn the association between the neural pattern of activity and the action that is being performed. As a result of such training, the neural signals can then be used to guide movement of a robotic arm (Wessberg et al., 2000). Further research recording from the parietal "reach" area has demonstrated that neural signals can be used to predict the intended endpoint of a reach (Musallam, Corneil, Greger, Scherberger, & Andersen, 2004) as well as the trajectory of that reach (Mulliken, Musallam, & Andersen, 2008).

Even more exciting are findings that take electrical output from the brain

and use it to control a paralyzed arm (Moritz, Perlmutter, & Fetz, 2008). In this experiment, electrodes were implanted into the motor cortex that controls wrist movement in monkeys. Monkeys were trained to control the discharge rate of those neurons by means of the location of a visual cursor on the screen. In this training, they were rewarded when their performance matched a target rate of discharge. Next, a nerve block was given that disrupted the neural connection between the brain and the wrist. Although the cells in motor cortex continued to fire, no wrist movement was observed, confirming that disruption of the connection between the brain and wrist leads to paralysis of the hand. Then information from the electrodes in motor cortex was connected directly to another set of electrodes that had been implanted in the hand, bypassing the blocked neural pathway between the brain and the hand. With some training, the monkeys learned to use the firing rates of cells in their motor cortex to control their wrist movement! (● Box Figure 5.1.)

In the system just described, an intact animal is trained with the brain-computer interface before the event that leads to paralysis. Obviously, in the everyday life of people such a system would only be utilized after paralysis or loss of a limb. As a result, a number of issues must be overcome before such techniques can be used in humans. For example, if stroke leads to paralysis of the contralateral hand, only one hemisphere remains to control movement of both the contralateral and

---

Although Parkinson's disease has been described as having four major symptoms, not all of these symptoms are typically observed in any one person. Some patients have a rigid-bradykinetic-predominant form of the disease, in which their main symptom is slowness, whereas others have a more tremor-predominant form. These two varieties of Parkinson's differ not only with regard to behavior, but also in their biochemical bases, in the degree of intellectual impairment observed, and in the clinical course of the disease. The clinical course may decline more sharply and the intellectual impairment may be more severe in patients with the rigid-bradykinetic-predominant form than in those with the tremor-predominant form (Huber, Christy, & Paulson,

1991). In addition, different portions of the basal ganglia are affected in these two disease forms (Bernheimer, Birkmayer, Hornykiewicz, Jellinger, & Seitelberg, 1973; Jellinger, 1999). Moreover, the severity of akinesia and bradykinesia is correlated with the clinical progression and dopamine depletion, whereas the severity of tremor is not (Deuschl, Raethjen, Baron, Lindemann, Wilms, & Krack, 2000).

Let's go back and consider how disruption of the basal ganglia might lead to the symptoms of Parkinson's disease. As discussed earlier in the section on the basal ganglia, the classical conception of Parkinson's disease is that it results from overactivity in the indirect pathway, which leads to the cessation of

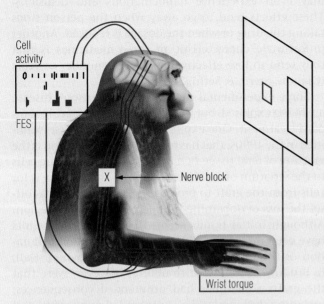

● **BOX FIGURE 5.1   An experiment demonstrating brain-controlled functional stimulation of muscle.** In this brain-computer interface, electrodes from motor regions of monkey cortex feed into a computer that analyzes brain activity. The monkey is trained to alter the pattern of brain activity by being rewarded for keeping a cursor in a particular location on the screen. A nerve block then disconnects the signals from the brain from reaching the hand, which is indicated by paralysis of the wrist. Next, the information from the computer is linked to muscles of the hand. After a little practice, the monkey is able to control the wrist just by altering the pattern of brain activity. Adapted from figure 1a Moritz, C. T., Perlmutter, S. I., & Fetz, E. E. (2008). Direct control of paralyzed muscles by cortical neurons. Nature, 456, page 639.

movements differ. Moreover, it has been demonstrated that individuals can learn to use the pattern of activity associated with contralateral movements to control a cursor, and separately that they can learn to do likewise with neural activity associated with ipsilateral movements. These findings pave the way for stroke patients to potentially control a prosthesis or their own paralyzed limb (Wisneski, Anderson, Schalk, Smyth, Moran, & Leuthardt, 2008).

Other researchers are trying less invasive methods, such as scalp-recorded EEG, to have brain signals control not a limb but an external device such as a robot. This is a first step in working toward use of patterns of brain activity to control other devices, such as a patient's own wheelchair (Cincotti et al., 2008). In addition, information about motor cortex activity derived from real-time fMRI can be used to control the movement of a robotic arm (Lee, Ryu, Jolesz, Cho, &

Yoo, 2009). However, these findings have less direct applicability to the design of prosthetic devices, because people cannot spend their days living within an MRI machine! Nonetheless, they point to the likelihood that multiple measures of brain activity can be used to control prosthetic devices.

In the end, success or failure of these approaches will probably depend on three factors. First is the issue of whether the brain-computer interfaces can extract enough information from the brain to enable the sophisticated control required for tasks of everyday living without undue risk to the individual. Implanted electrodes may provide better fidelity of the patterns of brain activity required for control of a prosthesis, but at the cost of invasive brain surgery. In contrast, the less invasive scalp-recorded EEG may not provide as clean or discrete a pattern of neural signals. These trade-offs will have to be explored. Second, these systems will have to be durable enough to remain intact during the movements of everyday life (outside the closely controlled environment of the laboratory or hospital), and small enough to allow people to move around the world with the interface. Third, it remains to be seen whether such systems will enable movements that occur with the speed, accuracy, and flexibility of an intact system (Ryu & Shenoy, 2009). The hope for many individuals who have lost control of their limbs due to neurological damage, and for those who have lost limbs, is that scientists will make significant headway in solving these problems in the near future.

ipsilateral hands. Hence, the neural signals that are related to motor activity of the contralateral hand must be distinguished from those associated with the ipsilateral hand. Recent research on patients with electrodes implanted over frontal cortex (for surgery associated with epilepsy) suggests, fortunately, that the neural signatures for ipsilateral and contralateral

---

movement. However, such a model does not explain the tremor observed in Parkinson's disease. Clearly, there must be somewhat separable mechanisms for these two sets of symptoms. One possibility is that tremor is an attempt by other motor regions downstream from the basal ganglia to compensate for the low levels of actvitity associated with akinesia (Rivlin-Etzion, Marmor, Heimer, Raz, Nini, & Bergman, 2006). Another is that tremor is caused by the disruption of circuits between the cerebellum and the thalamus. Supporting such an idea is the fact that lesions of the ventrolateral thalamus, which receives input from the cerebellum, reduce or suppress tremor (Bergman & Deuschl, 2002).

More recent research suggests that the causes of Parkinson's disease may be more than just a reduction of activity in the indirect pathway. Studies of monkeys that have been treated with the toxin MPTP—the same substance ingested by the "frozen addicts"—reveals an increase in the proportion of neurons in the basal ganglia that fire in bursts (Wichmann & Soares, 2006). This bursting pattern can be decreased through treatment with dopaminergic drugs, and a concomitant decrease in Parkinsonian symptoms is seen as well (Heimer, Rivlin-Etzion, Bar-Gad, Goldberg, Haber, & Bergman, 2006). Moreover, recordings from the brains of humans who are about to undergo surgical interventions to treat Parkinson's indicate that the reintroduction of dopaminergic drugs after they have been withdrawn reduces the synchrony of neuronal activity. In addition, the degree to which such synchrony is disrupted predicts the decrease in akinesia and rigidity (Kuhn, Kupsch, Schneider, & Brown, 2006). These findings suggest that Parkinson's may not be caused solely by a reduction of activity in certain portions of the basal ganglia, but by a change in the activity across neurons within the basal ganglia.

Although Parkinson's disease cannot be cured, it can be ameliorated, typically by drug therapy designed to increase the level of dopamine. Because the nigrostriatal pathways are damaged, dopaminergic pathways are underactive. To augment the level of dopamine, which cannot cross the blood-brain barrier, physicians give these patients a metabolic precursor of dopamine, **L-dopa**. This precursor can reach the brain when taken orally, and can stimulate pre- and postsynaptic dopaminergic receptors. Monoamine oxidase (MOA-B) inhibitors are also given to reduce the breakdown of dopamine in the synapse and by glia (Schapira, 2009).

Unfortunately, these drugs have numerous side effects. They may alter a person's mood, leading to euphoria or depression. Sometimes they interfere with memory and the ability to pay attention. In other cases, they lead to disorders in impulse control (such as binge eating, pathological gambling, hypersexuality, and compulsive shopping). In extreme cases, an individual may even experience hallucinations and delusions. These effects tend to go away when the person stops taking the drug or when the dosage is reduced. Another unfortunate characteristic of these medicines is that they tend to lose effectiveness after a number of years (Olanow, Stern, & Sethi, 2009).

Some experimental therapies for Parkinson's disease are being explored, but they are far from becoming standard treatment. One exploratory treatment, first examined in the 1990s, that has received much attention is the grafting of fetal tissue rich in dopamine-producing cells to the striatum of an affected person. The strategy is for cells from the graft to produce dopamine and thus offset the loss of dopamine-producing cells in this region. Although initial results seemed promising, the results have been mixed and did not always result in amelioration of the disorder (Deierborg, Soulet, Roybon, Hall, & Brudin, 2008). More troubling, however, were that the grafts sometimes had unintended consequences, including dyskinesias (i.e., unintended movement) and changes in cognition and mood. Because such brain transplants are irreversible (unlike medications, which can be discontinued), there are serious ethical considerations concerning how this potential therapy should be presented and discussed with patients (Duggan et al., 2009). Although postmortem studies on the brains of people who have had such surgery revealed that the grafts do indeed take hold (● Figure 5.21), they also showed evidence of pathological changes in these same nerve cells. These findings suggest that there may be additional pathological processes involved in Parkinson's beyond the simple loss of dopaminergic neurons (Braak & Del Tredici, 2008). For all the reasons just discussed, some researchers and clinicians question whether cell grafts will have long-term efficacy and become a viable treatment for Parkinson's disease.

Other approaches involve attempts to alter the degree of brain activity. To reduce tremor, portions of the thalamus are ablated in a procedure known as *thalatomy*. And to address bradykinesia and akinesia, the internal segment of the globus pallidus (GP$_i$) is ablated in a procedure known as *pallidotomy*. However, more recent approaches try to spare brain tissue and instead use *deep brain stimulation*. As we mentioned briefly, this procedure involves chronically implanted electrodes that are used to artificially produce high-frequency stimulation in the subthalamic nuclei (which project in an inhibitory fashion to the GP$_i$). Typically, during the surgery the physician positions electrodes within the subthalamic nucleus and sends mild current through them to determine the effect on motor behavior. In this manner, the physician can determine the site that produces the best response in terms of reducing Parkinsonian symptoms with the fewest side effects. A pulse-generator implant is then used to provide continual and patterned input to the site (which can disrupt the bursting pattern, discussed earlier, that

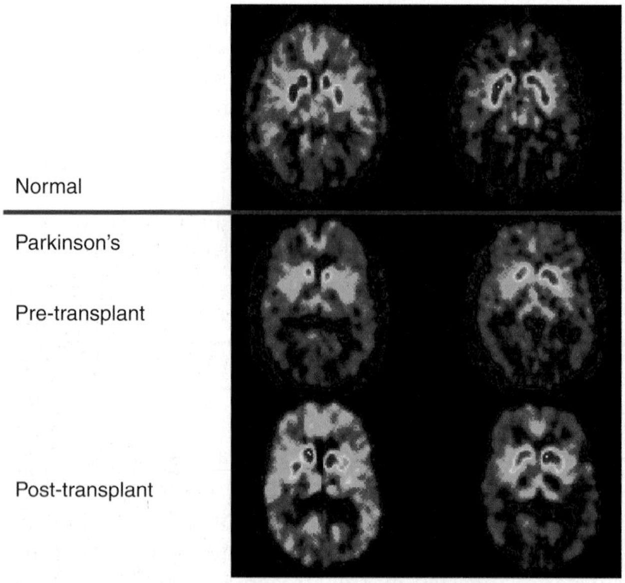

● FIGURE 5.21 Fetal cell implants are used to treat Parkinson's. Using a radioactive version of the dopamine precursor L-dopa as a tracer, researchers can evaluate the level of dopamine activity in the brain. These images compared a healthy participant (top) to a patient with Parkinson's disease both before and after treatment with fetal cell implants. Increased activity is indicated by red and yellow. Notice the increased activity in the basal ganglia in the posttransplant image. Images provided courtesy of Sanjiv Sam Gambhir, M.D., Ph.D., Stanford University.

Normal

Parkinson's

Pre-transplant

Post-transplant

is often associated with Parkinson's). This method appears to be quite effective, although potential side effects include stimulation spreading to surrounding structures, negative neurocognitive changes, and the invasiveness of the procedures (Benabid, Chabardes, Mitrofanis, & Pollak, 2009). However, deep brain stimulation appears to be more effective than standard treatments in terms of reducing the amount of time during which individuals exhibit troublesome movements (Weaver et al., 2009).

Finally, there are indications that intensive training for certain affected behaviors exhibited by Parkinson's patients can have wide-reaching effects. For example, Parkinson's patients typically speak very softly and in a monotone, which can make them difficult to understand. As a result, communication with friends and family deteriorates and other aspects of social interaction are compromised. One type of training to address this issue, which occurs during multiple sessions per week over two to three months, is designed to increase the volume, prosody, and intelligibility of vocal output. Not only does this intervention help with vocal output, but the effects of such training appear to generalize, as they also lead to enhancements in other areas, such as improved swallowing and increased facial expression (Fox, Raming, Ciucci, Sapir, McFarland, & Farley, 2006). Recent research suggests that the therapy works not by increasing activity in the basal ganglia, but rather by increasing activity in regions of the right hemisphere, most notably motor, premotor, and dorsolateral regions of the frontal lobe as well as auditory cortex. Increased engagement of cortical regions appears, at least to some degree, to compensate for loss of function associated with the basal ganglia (Narayana et al., 2009).

Huntington's Disease

An inherited neurologic disease caused by degeneration of the striatum (● Figure 5.22), **Huntington's disease** produces abnormal movements, cognitive deficits (eventually dementia), and psychiatric symptoms. As with our discussion of Parkinson's disease, we concentrate here on the motor aspects of Huntington's and leave a description of the intellectual and cognitive deficits for Chapter 16. Although Huntington's disease is rare (1.6 cases per million), when the Huntington's gene is inherited, it always expresses itself. This gene acts much like a time bomb that remains relatively dormant until some time between the ages of 30 and 45 years, when the symptoms begin to manifest themselves in earnest. Afterward, the disease involves a slow decline for 10 to 15 years and eventually leads to death.

The main motor symptom of Huntington's disease is *chorea*, a variety of rapid, jerky movements that appear to be well coordinated but are performed involuntarily and ceaselessly in an irregular manner. Although individuals with Huntington's disease initially seem to be fidgeting, the movements eventually increase until they are almost incessant. They never involve just one muscle; rather, they affect whole limbs or parts of a limb. Eventually, all movement becomes uncontrollable and the chorea affects most of the body, including the head, face, trunk, and limbs. In the later stages, not only is the person unable to communicate through speaking or writing, but other basic movements required for independent living, such as walking and swallowing, are also lost (Walker, 2007).

Although chorea is considered the classic motor sign in Huntington's disease, individuals with this condition

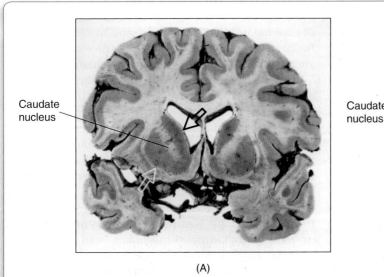
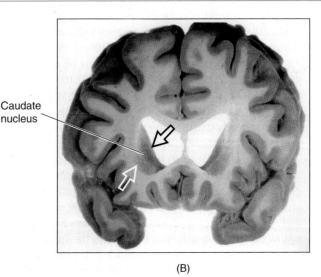

Caudate nucleus

Caudate nucleus

(A)

(B)

● **FIGURE 5.22** **Huntington's disease causes degeneration of the caudate nucleus of the basal ganglia.** On the left is the image of a healthy human brain; on the right is a figure of someone with Huntington's. Notice that the caudate nucleus is much smaller than normal and that lateral ventricles have increased to take up the extra space in the individual with Huntington's disease. © 2010 Cengage Learning

have additional motor difficulties. Some of these occur in the realm of initiation and execution of movement. For example, while neurologically intact individuals can use a cue to aid in performing a sequential button-pressing procedure, Huntington's patients are unable to use such advance information to initiate and execute movements. These difficulties may be a marker for the disease because they may even precede the onset of chorea, which is generally considered the definitive motor symptom of the disorder (Bradshaw et al., 1992). Other difficulties are manifested in learning a sequence of motor actions, which once again may precede the onset of full symptoms of the disease (Feigin et al., 2006).

Limb movements are not the only aspect of motor control affected in Huntington's disease; the speed and initiation of voluntary eye movements are also affected. As we discussed earlier in this chapter, voluntary eye movements are under the control of frontal brain regions. These regions are likely to be affected in Huntington's disease because the basal ganglia, which are damaged, project to the frontal eye field. For example, when required to visually track a target that moves predictably between positions, patients with the disease cannot direct their eyes to the correct location at the correct time. However, normal movements occur to an unexpected stimulus that appears in the periphery, which are under the control of the superior colliculus, a region unaffected in Huntington's disease (Tian, Zee, Lasker, & Folstein, 1991).

Brain imaging techniques have been used for some time to monitor the progression of Huntington's disease. For example, the reduction in the size of the caudate has been linked to the severity of both motor and cognitive deficits (e.g., Starkstein et al., 1988). In addition, the size of the basal ganglia in individuals who are carriers of the Huntington's gene but not yet exhibiting motor symptoms is smaller than in control individuals (Jurgens et al., 2008). More recent work suggests that the degree of atrophy across individuals may be linked to genetic factors. Huntington's is caused by what can be considered a genetic "stutter": a sequence of repeating base pairs that varies in length. The longer this repeating sequence, the greater the atrophy; this is observed both in individuals who are already manifesting motor symptoms (Jech et al., 2007) and in those who are not yet doing so (Henley et al., 2009). These studies also highlight the fact that although atrophy is most pronounced in the striatum, atrophy is observed in other brain regions as well, including the thalamus, cingulate cortex, and premotor cortex, among other regions (Douaud et al., 2006). Huntington's disease causes a slow decline to death, and there is no treatment or cure. However, drugs that deplete or block dopaminergic transmission are often given to aid in reducing the severity of the motor symptoms (Philips, Shannon, & Barker, 2008).

Currently, researchers are trying to learn more from individuals with Huntington's disease about the multiple ways in which the learning of motor sequences and acts can be performed by the brain. Because these individuals have disrupted cortico-striatal pathways, acquisition must rely on other systems, such as cortico-cerebellar motor pathways (Doyon, 2008). In fact, recent neuroimaging studies have shown differential reliance on thalamo-cortical pathways in presymptomatic individuals with Huntington's disease who are learning motor tasks (Feigin et al., 2006). Studies such as these reveal the variety and complexity of the ways in which motor actions and processes can be implemented by the brain.

Tourette's Syndrome

This relatively rare disorder manifests itself as a variety of vocal and motor **tics,** which are repetitive involuntary movements of a compulsive nature that wax and wane in severity. **Tourette's syndrome** can vary in severity from a few tics that occur only when the individual is tired or tense to between 30 and 100 tics per minute. Unlike the other motor disorders discussed so far, all of which affect people in their middle to late adult years, Tourette's syndrome manifests in childhood, usually before the age of 11 years (for a review covering all aspects of this disorder, see Singer, 2005).

Tics can take various forms. Simple motor tics, usually present by age 6 or 7, involve just one portion of the body, such as repetitive blinking of the eyes, twitching of the nose, or shrugging of the shoulders. More complex tics involve several muscle groups and seem to be more purposeful. These can include complex hand gestures, or repetitive touching of people or objects. Although the tics typically involve the face and head, the limbs and even the entire body may be affected. For example, movements akin to those seen in pogo dancing or the head banging of punk rockers can be observed (Hoekstra, Anderson, Limburg, Korf, Kallenberg, & Minderaa, 2009). Vocal tics are usually observed a bit later, but they too can be simple or complex. Simple tics usually involve actions like throat clearing or sniffing, whereas more complex ones can include *echolalia,* the repeating of what has just been said, and *coprolalia,* obscene speech. Because of the unusual behavior of these children, they are often misdiagnosed as having psychiatric disorders.

Because these motor tics occur involuntarily, repetitively, and in a stereotyped manner, Tourette's syndrome was long thought to involve dysfunction of subcortical motor regions (rather than cortical motor regions, which are more involved in voluntary motor movement). Although neither a definitive neural substrate nor cause has been isolated, a variety of evidence points to basal ganglia dysfunction. First, like Huntington's, the tics of Tourette's syndrome are most effectively reduced by treatment with agents that block or reduce dopamine (Bruggeman, van der Linden, Buitelaar, Gericke, Hawkridge, & Temlett, 2001). Second, although inconsistent, anatomical neuroimaging studies reveal reduced volume of the caudate in children and adults with Tourette's syndrome compared to unaffected adults. Moreover, in a longitudinal study in which individuals were followed over time, the size of the caudate in childhood predicted the severity of tics in adulthood. Third, functional neuroimaging studies with fMRI show differences in activity in the striatum, thalamus, and related cortical regions in individuals with Tourette's syndrome compared to non-affected individuals. PET studies suggest alterations of metabolism in these regions as well as supplementary motor cortex and orbitofrontal regions (for review, see Adams, Troiano, & Caine, 2004; Albin & Mink, 2006).

As we learned earlier in this chapter, there are five major cortico-striatal-thalamo-cortical circuits that serve sensorimotor, motor, oculomotor, cognitive, and limbic processes. Moreover, there is a somatotopic organization within those loops. The manifestations of tics may reflect this organization, and the failure to inhibit specific subsets of these loops may cause tics of a particular nature. For example, facial tics may reflect a failure of circuits that include ventromedial areas of the caudate and putamen, which receive projections from portions of the motor and premotor regions that control orofacial movements. Similarly, vocalizations that are profane in nature may involve motor areas as well as the limbic loop (Mink, 2001). Because the basal ganglia are thought to combine or "chunk" stimulus-response associations into more complex behavioral sequences that are executed as stereotyped habitual units, tics may represent either an inappropriate form of such habit learning or the inability to inhibit such habits (Marsh et al., 2004).

The tics of Tourette's differ from the motor movements observed in Huntington's disease, in that not only are they specific to a part of the body, but they also have a motivational or emotional component associated with them. Tics occur with greater frequency during times of emotional arousal or upset, when a person is anxious, excited, or fatigued. Furthermore, many individuals have a premonition before the tic, which feels like an urge, tension, impulse, or itch. Once the tic is emitted, this feeling disappears, leading to relief. Because of such feelings, some researchers have described the nature of tics not as involuntary but rather as "unvoluntary." Similar to compulsive behaviors, in which anxiety about a certain item (e.g., germs) is relieved by an action (e.g., handwashing) (see Chapter 14), people with Tourette's syndrome claim that the more they try to suppress a tic, the greater their compulsion to produce it. In fact, half or more of people with Tourette's exhibit some aspects of obsessive-compulsive disorder. In addition, among individuals with Tourette's, there is an increased incidence of attention deficit hyperactivity disorder, which may also involve dysregulation of systems involving motivation and reward (see Chapter 15). All of this evidence suggests that Tourette's involves dysfunction of not only motor and sensorimotor cortico-striatal-thalamo-cortical circuits, but of limbic loops as well (Singer, 2005).

The cause or causes of Tourette's syndrome remain unclear. Much work suggests that there is a genetic component, as the disorder appears to run in families. At present, however, there is no one clear mechanism of genetic transmission and there may be multiple susceptibility factors that lead to the disorder. Given that the disorder is more prevalent in males than females, some researchers have suggested that it may be caused by an alteration in androgenic steroids during fetal development. In addition, recent research has centered on investigating whether there is an alteration of autoimmune mechanisms (mechanisms in which the body mistakenly treats portions of itself as if they were pathogens or invaders to be destroyed) as result of infection (Leckman, 2002). Although the causes of Tourette's syndrome remain elusive, dysfunction of the basal ganglia and associated regions are highly implicated.

■ Cortical Motor Disorders

As we have learned, most subcortical motor disorders manifest as slowness of movement or as an increase in movements. Cortical motor disorders have a different effect, tending to disrupt the ability to pursue specific plans of motor action or to relate motor action to meaning. We first examine one specific cortical disorder of motor control, alien limb syndrome, and then a family of such disorders, the apraxias.

Alien Limb Syndrome

One of the rarer and more unusual disorders of motor function is **alien limb syndrome** (for a review, see Biran & Chatterjee, 2004). Patients afflicted with this disorder feel as if one of their limbs, usually a hand, is alien, either because it seems to move on its own, feels as though it does not belong to its owner, or seems to have its own personality. Patients with this disorder commonly complain that their limbs do not obey them or that they make involuntary and complex movements. The most typical movements displayed by the alien limb are groping and grasping. As described in one case study, "[t]he left hand would tenaciously grope for and grasp any nearby object, pick and pull at her clothes, and even grasp her throat during sleep" (Banks, Short, Martinez, Latchaw, Ratcliff, & Boller, 1989, p. 456). Under extreme conditions, the limb can take on a personality. In one case study, a patient thought her left arm was named Joseph and was a baby. When her limb acted in strange ways, she would make up a story to explain the alien limb's behavior in the context of her belief about the limb's personality. For example, when this arm acted on other parts of her body (like pinching her nipples), she interpreted this action as baby Joseph's biting her while nursing. In almost all cases, only one limb is affected, and it is located contralateral to the site of the lesion, which is typically caused by a stroke, tumor, or neurodegenerative condition.

Another common symptom among patients with this disorder is competition between the hands or difficulty in bimanual control. For example, one person noted that, while driving, one hand tried to turn the car to the left, while the other tried to turn it to the right. In other cases, each hand would try to hold a glass from a different side, or the hands would fight over which one would pick up the telephone. Not only do the difficulties in bimanual coordination result in power struggles, but they may also manifest as mirror movements, in which one hand mimics the motions of the other (Doody & Jankovic, 1992).

At present, no consensus exists about exactly which neural structures must be damaged for alien limb syndrome to occur (Kikkert, Ribbers, & Koudstaal, 2006). The syndrome is usually observed after damage to the corpus callosum and medial frontal cortex including the supplemental motor area (SMA) (Brainin, Seiser, & Matz, 2008), but it has also been observed after damage to the thalamus or parietal lobe. The different locations of the lesions, as well as some differences in presentation, suggest that there may be subtypes of the disorder (Aboitiz, Carrasco, Schröter, Zaidel, Zaidel, & Lavados, 2003). Nonetheless, the predominance of a callosal lesion and damage to medial frontal areas accords well with our earlier discussion of the role of the SMA in motor control (see page 122). This region is involved in purposeful planning of motor movements and has been implicated in the control of bimanual movements.

No cure exists for alien limb syndrome, and it can be difficult to control. For the most part, the interventions must be customized to the specific problems of the individual (see, for example, Pappalardo, Ciancio, Reggio, & Patti, 2004). One approach is to keep the limb "busy" performing a repetitive motor activity or holding an object. Another approach is to attempt to increase control over the limb by concentrating on it or by directing it with verbal commands.

Apraxia

Some persons develop an inability to perform *skilled, sequential, purposeful* movement, an inability that cannot be accounted for by disruptions in more basic motor processes such as muscle weakness, abnormal posture or tone, or movement disorders (such as tremors or chorea). This disorder, called **apraxia**, is more common after damage to the left hemisphere, although,

as we discuss later, the type of apraxia exhibited varies depending on the exact region damaged.

Two main pieces of evidence suggest that apraxia is a higher-order motor deficit rather than a deficit associated with lower-level aspects of motor control. First, apraxia usually exhibits itself bilaterally. If the deficit were at a low level and concerned the control of specific muscles, it would be expected to be observed only for the limbs contralateral to the site of damage. Second, low-level motor processes are mostly intact in patients with apraxia, who can spontaneously perform skilled motor movements. They encounter difficulty only when the movement must be performed purposefully, as when imitating someone or in response to a verbal command (Poeck, 1986).

Dichotomous Classifications of Apraxia Apraxia can take many forms, and there is an ongoing debate as to how to classify them. A number of classification schemes dichotomously categorize the disorder. For example, some classification schemes focus on the part of the body affected (e.g., a limb vs. the face). Others categorize apraxias depending on whether simple or multisequence movements are affected, whereas still others distinguish between apraxias exhibited when objects are used and apraxias that are seen when objects are not used (for a recent review, see Petreska, Adriani, Blanke, & Billard, 2007). Here we briefly highlight and review these distinctions.

As mentioned, one method of classifying apraxia is by reference to the part of the body that is affected. If facial movements are disordered, the condition is known as oral (buccofacial) apraxia; if limb movements are affected, it is known as limb apraxia.

Oral (buccofacial) apraxia is associated with difficulty in performing voluntary movements with the muscles of the tongue, lips, cheek, and larynx. As is usually the case in apraxia, automatic movements are preserved. However, tasks such as sticking out the tongue, clearing the throat, and blowing a kiss are impaired. These difficulties may also extend to oral movements used to manipulate or act upon objects, such as blowing out a match or sucking on a straw.

Limb apraxia disrupts the ability to use the limbs to manipulate items such as screwdrivers, scissors, and hammers (e.g., DeRenzi & Lucchelli, 1988). It can also disrupt the ability to perform a more complex series of movements, such as opening a can of soup or opening a door with a key (e.g., Lehmkuhl & Poeck, 1981). In addition, limb apraxia affects the ability to use motor movements in a symbolic way, as in gestures like waving good-bye or saluting, and in pantomime (e.g., Heilman & Rothi, 1985). In pantomime, individuals with this type of apraxia commonly use a body part to represent the object that they would be manipulating. For example, if asked to imitate putting a spoonful of sugar into a cup of coffee and then stirring it, an individual with limb apraxia will extend the index finger below the others, as if to represent the spoon, and will move it around in a circular manner rather than rotating the wrist as would occur in a correct pantomime (● Figure 5.23).

Correct pantomime   Apraxic behavior

(A)   (B)

● **FIGURE 5.23   Example of apraxic behavior.** When attempting to pantomime, an individual with apraxia often uses a limb to represent an object. © 2011 Cengage Learning

Their performance tends to be better when they actually perform the task, presumably because of the visual and tactile-kinesthetic cues they receive under those conditions. The person with limb apraxia may also have difficulty copying and imitating meaningless motor movements or unfamiliar hand or arm positions (e.g., Kimura, 1977; Kolb & Milner, 1981).

Oral apraxia usually results from a frontotemporal lesion. More specifically, the lesion includes the frontal and central opercula, a small area of the superior temporal gyrus adjacent to these two frontal regions, and the anterior part of the insula, which is the region tucked into the Sylvian fissure (Tognola & Vignolo, 1980). In contrast, limb apraxia is generally associated with damage to left parietal or parietotemporal regions (● Figure 5.24) (e.g., DeRenzi, Motti, & Nichelli, 1980; Hecaen & Rondot, 1985).

Nature of Underlying Deficit in Apraxia

Other ways of categorizing apraxia are based on what underlying function is disturbed. A classic way of distinguishing between types of apraxia was introduced in 1905 by Liepmann, who differentiated between ideational and ideomotor apraxia. He suggested that **ideational apraxia** (sometimes also called *conceptual apraxia*) impairs the ability to form an "idea" of the movement, so that a person cannot determine which actions are necessary and in what order they should occur. For example, a person might try to eat using a toothbrush. A person may be unable to light a candle because he or she might not be able to sequence the necessary events (e.g., tear a match out of a matchbook, close the matchbook cover, strike the match against the cover, bring the match to the candle's wick).

Conversely, Liepmann conceptualized **ideomotor apraxia** as a disconnection between the idea of movement and execution of the movement. He believed that in this case, single simple actions, mainly gestures, would be impaired because the commands for action could not reach the motor center. These problems would be most pronounced for motor actions that were the least concrete (e.g., gestures, meaningless movements) or that had to be imitated, while the production of most everyday motor actions would be relatively undisturbed. Unlike individuals with ideational apraxia, these individuals would be able to sequence complex movements, although the constituent acts would be disrupted.

Regrettably, it is unclear whether Liepmann's types represent two separate syndromes. Some theorists have suggested that ideational apraxia might be just a more severe version of ideomotor apraxia (Zangwill, 1960). Still others differentiate between ideational apraxia and ideomotor apraxia based on whether the apraxia involves the use of objects (DeRenzi, Pieczuro, & Vignolo, 1968). For these researchers, the cardinal symptom of ideomotor apraxia is an inability to perform or imitate gestures, such as making the sign of the cross or saluting, that are conceptual in nature and that do not act upon an object. (These are sometimes called *intransitive gestures,* because, like intransitive verbs, they do not have an object upon which they act.) In contrast, ideational apraxia is defined by an inability to use an actual object, such as a hammer, a toothbrush, or a pair of scissors (which are considered *transitive gestures*).

Another conceptualization (Leiguarda & Marsden, 2000) suggests that the cardinal symptom of ideational apraxia is an inability to associate objects with their corresponding actions (somewhat similar to the conclusions of DeRenzi and colleagues). However, unlike DeRenzi, these researchers view ideomotor apraxia as mainly disrupting the speed and timing with which movements are made, either in real life or as a pantomime. According to them, patients with ideomotor apraxia are likely to make movements at irregular speeds (e.g., slow and hesitant buildup of hand velocity), in atypical orders, and with atypical configurations (e.g., loss of interjoint coordination, decoupling of hand speed and limb trajectory, use of body parts as objects).

Still another conceptualization considers what Liepmann called ideomotor apraxia to be a loss of "visuokinesthetic motor" memories, which are stored in the angular and supramarginal gyri of the parietal lobe. Under this conceptualization, these memories of action patterns contain not only information about the

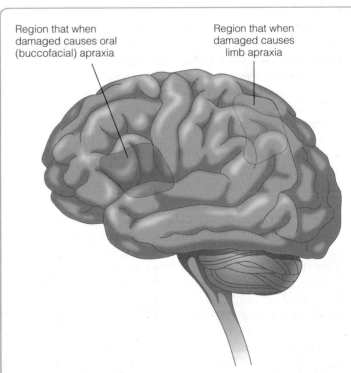

Region that when damaged causes oral (buccofacial) apraxia

Region that when damaged causes limb apraxia

● **FIGURE 5.24 Locations of lesions associated with oral (buccofacial) and limb apraxia.** A lesion in the frontotemporal region produces oral apraxia, whereas limb apraxia is often caused by a left parietal or parietotemporal lesion. © 2011 Cengage Learning

selection and production of specific gestural actions, but also linkages to information about the visual and kinesthetic feedback that will occur during performance of the motor act (Heilman & Rothi, 1985). If damage to parietal regions causes the stored action pattern to be lost, the person exhibits an apraxia in which she can neither perform gestures correctly nor discriminate between them (e.g., knowing the difference between the gesture for brushing one's teeth and that for flipping a coin). If this parietal region is intact but damage disconnects it from motor centers in the frontal cortex, the person will be able to discriminate between correctly and incorrectly performed gestures made by others (because the stored program is intact) but will not be able to produce correct gestures (because the stored program cannot reach motor areas) (Heilman, Rothi, & Valenstein, 1982).

Finally, more recent ideas suggest a quite different view that apraxia results from difficulty in understanding categorical spatial relationships either between objects, between multiple parts of objects, and/or between the hand and objects or their parts. These difficulties would lead to trouble in tool use because the relationship between the hand and objects are not understood, while difficulties in gestures would arise from not comprehending the spatial relationships between body parts (Goldenberg, 2009).

As should be obvious, researchers have not yet formed a clear consensus on how to divide the apraxias into meaningful subtypes. Because of the difficulties in distinguishing between types of apraxias on theoretical grounds, some researchers instead categorize them on descriptive grounds. Thus, rather than talking about ideational versus ideomotor apraxia (which may mean different things to different people), some researchers use descriptive terms such as "apraxias of symbolic actions" or "apraxias of object utilization" (e.g., Dee, Benton, & Van Allen, 1970). Another approach taken to understanding the apraxias is to determine what type of information (sensory, conceptual, memorial) cannot be linked with motor output (e.g., Westwood, Schweizer, Heath, Roy, Dixon, & Black, 2001; Heath, Roy, Westwood, & Black, 2001).

Lesions That Lead to Apraxia

As you might expect, there is also no agreement on the lesion location that leads to apraxic behavior. In fact, apraxia can be observed after damage to a large variety of regions, although apraxia typically is observed after damage to parietal or frontal regions of the left hemisphere. More recent research has suggested a contribution for subcortical regions, such as the basal ganglia, in apraxic behaviors (Hanna-Pladdy, Heilman, & Foundas, 2001). What can be said with some certainty is that the production of skilled motor movement probably requires a set of regions spanning a wide variety of brain regions, including the parietal, prefrontal, motor, and subcortical regions, each contributing in

a different manner to the planning, retrieval, and/or implementation of motor action plans (Gross & Grossman, 2008). Depending on the specifics of the motor task, some of these regions may be more involved than others, and the configuration in which they are employed may vary. For example, learning to play a tune on the piano, which does not rely so much on visual feedback, may tax different portions of the **praxis** system than learning to juggle, which requires much more eye-hand coordination. Likewise, for someone who does not do it often, giving a salute may require retrieving the kinesthetic and spatial information associated with that action, but for someone in the military who performs that action habitually, it may rely on subcortical regions. As such, it is not surprising that different varieties of apraxic disorder do not map neatly onto particular regions of brain tissue.

Other Varieties of Apraxia

Some syndromes referred to as apraxia, in which a person has difficulty performing complex motor acts, appear to arise primarily from difficulty in spatial processing. Two examples of such syndromes are constructional apraxia and dressing apraxia. In **constructional apraxia**, items cannot be correctly manipulated with regard to their spatial relations. For example, wooden blocks cannot be manipulated to copy an arrangement created by someone else. In **dressing apraxia**, the affected individual has difficulty manipulating and orienting both clothes and his or her limbs so that clothes can be put on correctly (e.g., opening a jacket so that the arm can be inserted, and properly putting an arm out and bending it at the elbow to put on the jacket). These syndromes are generally observed after right-hemisphere lesions and are often associated with spatial-processing difficulties and hemineglect. Many neuropsychologists and cognitive neuroscientists do not consider these apraxias per se, but rather motor manifestations of visuoconstructive disorders.

Still other apraxias result from a disconnection syndrome rather than from difficulties in motor programming. We have already discussed the idea that in certain cases of apraxia, visuokinesthetic programs may not reach motor areas because of a disconnection between parietal and frontal areas. Another type of apraxia that results from a disconnection syndrome is **callosal apraxia**. Unlike other apraxias, which affect motor control bilaterally, this apraxia selectively disrupts the ability to perform movements or manipulate objects with the left hand in response to verbal commands. Callosal apraxia is associated with damage to the corpus callosum; hence, some have suggested that it occurs because of a disconnection between the left hemisphere, which is specialized for skilled motor sequencing, and the right hemisphere, which controls motor functioning of the left hand (e.g., Rubens, Geschwind, Mahowald, & Mastri, 1977). According to this explanation, when a person is verbally instructed to perform a skilled motor act, the left hemisphere interprets the command and relays it to left parietal regions so that the appropriate motor program can be assembled. Once formed, the motor command is forwarded to the premotor and motor cortices of the left hemisphere. These areas receive an intact program, so there is no apraxia of the right hand. However, because of the callosal disconnection, the motor programs are trapped in the left hemisphere and have no way of reaching the right hemisphere, which controls the left hand. Because motoric information cannot reach the right hemisphere, the left hand is apraxic. ● Figure 5.25 diagrams the essential anatomical relations of this syndrome.

As we have learned in this chapter, the control of action occurs because of activity across a variety of structures in the brain. Subcortical and cerebellar regions tend to form loops with other regions of the brain to modify action. In contrast, cortical regions are more involved in the planning and execution of motor acts.

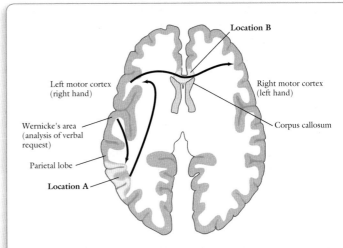

● **FIGURE 5.25 Anatomical mechanisms of unilateral and bilateral apraxia.** Wernicke's area analyzes a verbal request and transmits this information to the left parietal region (Location A), where the correct movements are selected. If this region is damaged, bilateral apraxia results. In contrast, in unilateral apraxia of the left hand, the left parietal region is intact, so information about the correct movements is sent forward to the left motor cortex, where the motor commands are executed. Hence, the right hand is not apraxic. However, because of a lesion of the corpus callosum (Location B), the information cannot be relayed to the right hemisphere and apraxia of the left hand results.
© 2011 Cengage Learning

Summary

Brain Structures Involved in Motor Control

■ Motor tracts transmit information from the brain to muscles.

■ The cerebellum is important for gross posture, the smooth coordination of movements, rapid movements that must be planned with little chance for feedback, the learning of skilled motor movements, and timing of movements.

■ The basal ganglia are important for controlling the initiation and cessation of motor movements that are internally guided; they also play a role in motor planning and learning.

■ Primary motor cortex controls the force and direction of movement of specific muscles.

■ The supplementary motor complex (SMC) is thought to provide a motor plan for an action, which is an abstract representation of an intended movement that is preprogrammed before the motor act is initiated.

■ Premotor regions are thought to specify the type of motor action (such as a grasp) that is necessary to perform a task. A portion of the premotor area, known as the frontal eye field, programs voluntary eye movements such as those involved in scanning visual space.

■ The anterior cingulate cortex plays an important role in the selection of motor responses, especially when they are novel or atypical.

■ The parietal lobe plays multiple roles in motor control. It links movements with a representation of the space in which those movements occur; links information about motor programs with visuokinesthetic and other sensory information about the motor acts, and links a motor act with its conceptual significance.

■ Complex action requires the coordinated effort of all these regions in an integrated manner.

Motor Disorders

■ Subcortical motor disorders affect the form and timing of movements, whereas cortical motor disorders affect the conceptual clarity of motor acts, either by disrupting the sequencing of complex motor acts or by disrupting the ability to have a motor act represent a concept.

■ Parkinson's disease, which occurs because the putamen does not receive dopaminergic input due to the death of cells in the substantia nigra, results in an inability to initiate spontaneous movement (akinesia), a slowness of movement (bradykinesia), and rhythmic oscillating movements (tremors).

- Huntington's disease, which occurs because of damage to the striatum, results in involuntary, undesired jerking and writhing movements.

- Tourette's syndrome, a rare disorder that manifests itself in childhood, is characterized in less severe cases by tics and twitching of the face, the limbs, and other regions of the body. In more severe cases, the patient makes vocalizations such as cries, grunts, and curses.

- Alien limb syndrome, which results from damage to the SMA, causes an individual's appendage to seem to move of its own free will in ways that are destructive or unhelpful, often disrupting coordinated bimanual activity.

- Apraxia is a disorder that typically results from left inferior parietal lesions or left frontal lesions and prevents the individual from performing sequential skilled motor acts.

- Some classifications of apraxia emphasize the body part that is affected, others emphasize whether the idea of movement is lost or whether there is a disconnection between the idea of a movement and its execution, and still others emphasize the difference between movements required to use objects as compared with those that have symbolic significance.

- Other disorders that are not true apraxias are constructional apraxia, in which items cannot be correctly manipulated with regard to their spatial relations; and dressing apraxia, in which limbs and clothes cannot be manipulated to dress.

- In callosal apraxia, the ability to perform movements or manipulate objects with the left hand in response to verbal commands is lost.

Key Terms

Book Companion Site at www.cengage.com/psychology/Banich
This website provides instructors and students with a wealth of free information and resources, including tutorial quizzes, flashcards, and the glossary.

Early Perceptual Processing

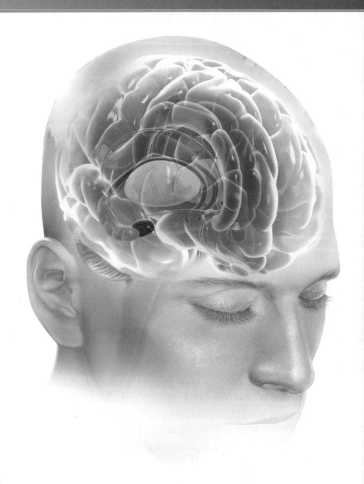

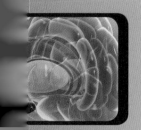

DURING A SERIOUS CAR ACCIDENT, Ron received a blow to the back of his head on the right side. As a result of damage to his right visual cortex, he became completely blind for all objects in his left visual field, often bumping into things on his left. Yet, because the damage was restricted to visual cortex, he processes all other information normally, such as sounds coming from his left side or objects felt with his left hand.

After his accident, Ron visited a researcher who wanted to carefully determine what Ron could and couldn't see. The researcher flashed a light at many different locations on a screen and asked Ron to indicate when he saw it. Ron had no problem seeing the light whenever it fell in his right visual field. However, when a light was flashed in the left visual field, and the tester asked, "Do you see anything there?," Ron's response was always: "No, sorry, I don't see anything." It didn't matter whether Ron had both eyes open or was viewing the screen with just one eye; he always reported not seeing anything in the left half of space.

Despite Ron's insistence that he was blind to everything on the left, the examiner prodded Ron to answer questions anyway. First, the examiner told Ron that he would be shown a small square within the left visual field; Ron should decide whether it was moving up or down. "But I can't see anything!" Ron responded with some exasperation. "Well, OK, but just go ahead and guess on each trial anyway," replied the examiner. Ron complied. Next the examiner told Ron that for the next set of trials, he should decide whether an object in the left visual field was colored or gray. Ron thought to himself, "This is pretty stupid, since I don't see anything," but he guessed anyway. For the next set of trials, the examiner asked whether a line presented in the left field was oriented vertically or horizontally. Finally, for the last set of trials (which Ron thought was utterly ridiculous), the researcher asked him to point to the location in his "blind" visual field where he thought an object might be. At the end of the session, Ron said, "I'm not exactly sure what all this was about, because, as I told you, I can't see anything."

"This may surprise you, Ron," the researcher replied, "but actually you guessed correctly more often than not!"

THE MAN YOU have just read about exhibits a phenomenon known as **blindsight**, which involves the retention of some visual capabilities without the conscious experience of seeing (Weiskrantz, 1986). What makes cases such as these so fascinating is that they raise a fundamental question: "What does it really mean to "see"?

When you open your eyes in the morning, the visual world appears to you, seemingly without any effort. The immediacy and apparent ease of visual awareness makes it hard to believe that a large proportion of your brain is working very hard to solve the complex problems of vision. In the brains of humans and other primates, visual processing is highly developed, with the neural machinery that supports vision taking up a large proportion of cortex. The immense amount of brain tissue dedicated to sight enables us to have the exquisitely detailed color vision that is one of the hallmarks of being a primate.

The topic of perception is so complex that it cannot be covered adequately within a single chapter. The first part of this chapter gives an overview of the basic elements of the visual system, following information as it enters the eye and ascends through various steps until it reaches the cortex. As you will learn, there are two main visual processing pathways in the cerebral cortex. One of these pathways is important in recognizing the identity of objects, and is discussed in Chapter 7; the other path is important in locating objects in space, and is covered in Chapter 8. Together, these three chapters should help you to appreciate the astonishing computations that go into your everyday experience of seeing, and will also help you to understand the many different ways in which visual perception can go awry.

Although vision is especially well developed in primates, auditory perception (hearing) is also paramount. The second part of this chapter reviews the fundamentals of the auditory system, with an emphasis on similarities and differences between visual and auditory processing. Throughout our discussion of the many steps of perceptual processing, you will notice a theme emerging: namely, that the brain deals with the complexities of perception by breaking the problem down into parts, with different systems tackling different aspects of perception. We can see this pattern—which we call *parallel processing*—at every level of the visual system, beginning with the retina in the eye and extending through the higher levels of the cortex that are dedicated to processing visual information. Parallel processing is evident in the auditory system as well. Toward the end of this chapter, we will also learn about how information from different senses, such as vision and hearing, are integrated.

The Retina

The **retina** at the back of the eye is really an extension of the brain (● Figure 6.1). Retinal tissue is derived from neural tissue during embryological development, and the retina acts as an information processor, much like the rest of the brain. We tend to think of the eye as merely registering light and sending that information to the brain, but computations actually go on within the retina itself, so that the brain receives information that has already been partly digested and transformed. Although a detailed analysis of retinal processing is beyond the scope of this chapter, we discuss next some basic and important points (for more details, see Field & Chichilnisky, 2007; Sterling, 2004).

■ Photoreceptors

Parallel processing begins in the retina with the division of the sensory receptors into rods and cones, which are collectively known as **photoreceptor** cells (● Figure 6.2). There are approximately 120 million rods and 6 million cones in the human eye. As you may already know, both rods and cones contain pigments that absorb light. When photons of light are absorbed, a cascade of chemical changes inside the rod or cone leads to changes in membrane polarization and the release of neurotransmitter, signaling to the next layer of cells within the eye. Therefore, rods and cones take light energy and transform it into the electrochemical energy used in the nervous system.

The rods and cones differ in three main ways. First, they contain different pigments, which makes their response to light differ. The rods contain just one pigment, called *rhodopsin*, which is sensitive to very small amounts of light. In broad daylight, this pigment becomes saturated and the rod system no longer functions. At that time, processing is taken over by the cones. There are three different types of cones, each containing a different pigment. The three types of cone pigment are sensitive to wavelengths in different portions of the light spectrum: short-wavelength, medium-wavelength, and long-wavelength light. Short-, medium-, and long-wavelength cone pigments are most sensitive to light that we perceive as blue, green, and red, respectively. It is the pattern of activity across these three types of receptors that ultimately enables exquisite color vision.

The distribution of rods and cones across the retina also differs. Cones are packed more densely in the center of the retina, a region known as the **fovea**, whereas

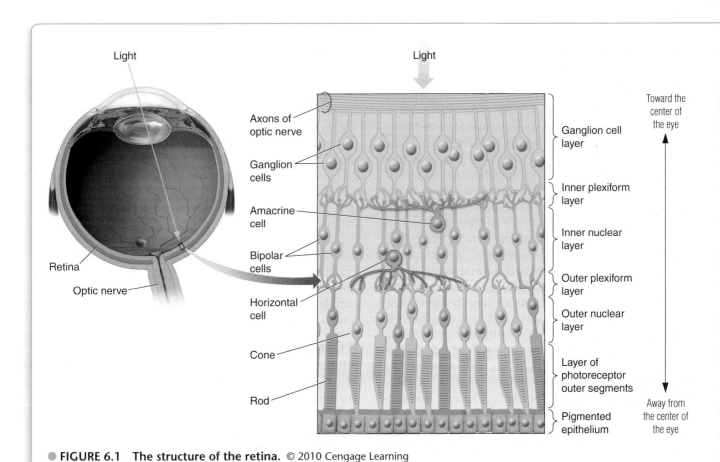

● **FIGURE 6.1   The structure of the retina.** © 2010 Cengage Learning

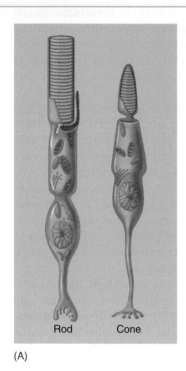

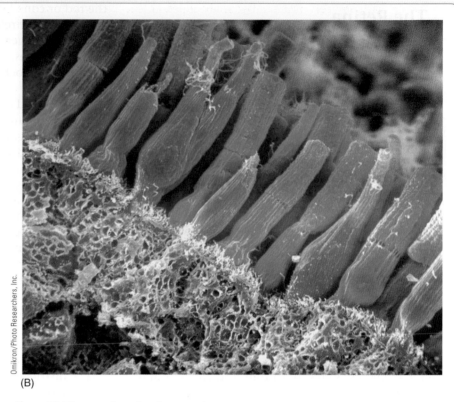

Omikron/Photo Researchers, Inc.

(B)

● **FIGURE 6.2   Rods and cones in the retina.** (A) Diagram of a rod and a cone photoreceptor.
(B) Photograph of rods (shown in green) and cones (shown in blue) from an electron microscope. © 2009 Cengage Learning

rods are distributed more in the periphery. Finally, rods and cones are hooked up to the retina's output layer of cells, called **ganglion cells**, in somewhat different ways. Many rods feed into each ganglion cell, whereas only a few cones feed into each ganglion cell.

The differences in how rods and cones are wired up to other cells is partly what gives the rod and cone systems different properties. Because many neighboring rods feed into one ganglion cell (via intermediate cell layers), low levels of light registered by many rods can summate and cause a response in the ganglion cell. This feature, together with the supersensitivity of rhodopsin to tiny amounts of light, allows the rod system to be more useful under low light levels, such as at night. However, there is a trade-off for the rod system: It is less sensitive to fine details. Because so many rods feed into one ganglion cell, information about the precise location of the light is lost. In contrast, only a few cones feed into each ganglion cell. By having less summation across multiple photoreceptors, the cone system preserves more fine-grained information about where on the retina light has been detected. The trade-off for the cone system, however, is that it cannot function under low light conditions, because the summation of information from the cones is not sufficient to make a ganglion cell fire. Thus, the rod and cone systems have cleverly evolved to serve different aspects of vision.

To see the difference between the rod system and the cone system, try going outside at night and looking up in the sky. Find a dim star somewhat in the periphery of your vision, and then look at it directly. You should notice that you can see the star if you look slightly away from it, but it disappears when you try to focus directly on it. Given what you have learned about the rod and cone systems, can you explain why this happens? Consider that the rod system is especially sensitive to low light levels, but that rods tend to be distributed away from the center of the retina. When you look slightly away from that dim star, its light is falling on the periphery of the retina where the rod system dominates. However, when you look directly at it, the dim starlight is falling on your fovea, where the cone system dominates. Although individual cones might still be responsive to that dim light, these cones do not summate as much as rods do, so the signal is lost. This example illustrates one of the differences between rods and cones, and also reminds us that what we perceive is completely dependent on the organization of our visual system to register and process that sensory information.

■ Ganglion Cells

Whereas the rods and cones are the "input" part of the retina, the *ganglion cells* are the "output," sending information along from the eye to the brain. As you can see in Figure 6.1, there are actually several layers of cells in between the photoreceptors and the ganglion cells, but space does not permit us to examine their operations in detail. The ganglion cell bodies are located in the retina, and their axons stretch out from the retina toward the brain, forming the *optic nerve*.

Retinal ganglion cells come in two main types, again illustrating the concept of parallel processing in the visual system. The two types of ganglion cells are called M cells and P cells (see Kaplan, 2004, and Martin & Grünert, 2004, for reviews). Many vision researchers refer to the **M and P ganglion cells** as *parasol cells* and *midget cells,* respectively, but we use the M and P terminology to make clearer how these two types of cells form functional pathways with similarly named cells in the thalamus. The M ganglion cells tend to be responsive to coarse patterns, and they are tuned to detect rapid motion, a feature that likely derives from how they are wired to subsets of intermediate cells in the retina (see Demb, 2007; Masland, 2004). P cells, in contrast, preserve color information that is coded by the cone system. As we will see, M and P cells send their output to different destinations within the brain.

Although we have described the ganglion cells as if there were only two main types, in fact the situation is much more complex. The M (parasol) and P (midget) ganglion cells are the best-characterized ganglion cells, and they constitute about 80% of all ganglion cells, but there are at least a dozen other types (Nassi & Callaway, 2009; Dacey, Peterson, Robinson, & Gamlin, 2003). One additional type of ganglion cell is the so-called small bistratified type that has a unique projection to the thalamus, as we will see in a later section. These small bistratified cells appear to carry some color information, especially pertaining to blue and yellow. Each of the remaining dozen or so ganglion cell types are anatomically distinct, but their functional differences are not currently well understood. The presence of so many distinct ganglion cell types is an indication of the enormous complexity of processing that occurs before visual information even exits the eye.

■ Receptive Fields

Before we leave the retina, there is one more property of cells in the visual system that is important to understand. Every cell in the visual system—whether a photoreceptor, ganglion cell, or cell higher up in the visual pathway—has a property known as its **receptive field**. The receptive field refers to that specific region of visual space to which a particular cell responds. That is, each cell only cares about patterns of light in a particular location and is essentially "blind" to light outside of that area. Remember that the receptive field is not a part of the cell. Rather, it is a part of visual space in which light will affect the cell's firing rate.

Receptive fields are easiest to understand at the level of the photoreceptors. Light must be absorbed by a particular rod or cone for that photoreceptor to respond. Because the retina is composed of millions of photoreceptors, light from particular locations in space will only stimulate specific subgroups of rods or cones. Remember that ganglion cells receive inputs from specific sets of rods or cones. Thus, an individual ganglion cell will only respond to light from a particular area of space—that of its receptive field. If we were able to record activity from one particular ganglion cell in your eye while we shined a light on different spots on your retina, we would find that most of the time this ganglion cell does not get too excited. However, when the light strikes a certain portion of the retina—the portion that contains the rods or cones that send information to that particular ganglion cell—the ganglion cell will start firing rapidly. Keep in mind that the light has not directly struck the ganglion cell. Rather, the ganglion cell is responsive to light in that particular location of the visual world because of the photoreceptors that feed into it. Because each ganglion cell gets input from a set of neighboring photoreceptors (rather than from photoreceptors in different locations across the retina), the pattern of activity across ganglion cells can code for the location of light in the visual world.

To add another wrinkle, the receptive fields of ganglion cells are a bit more complex than we have just described. In particular, the receptive fields of retinal ganglion cells have what is referred to as a *center-surround* structure. What this means is that whereas light in a particular spot in visual space will excite the ganglion cell, light in the donut-shaped area encircling that center spot will actually inhibit the cell. This type of cell has what is known as an "on-center, off-surround" receptive field. (There are also cells that have an "off-center, on-surround" receptive field type; these cells are inhibited by light in the center of the receptive field, and excited by light in the donut-shaped surround.) Although the details are beyond the scope of this chapter, the center-surround structure of ganglion cell receptive fields arises from a combination of excitatory and inhibitory inputs that the ganglion cells receive from the photoreceptors and other intermediate cells in the retina. Take a few minutes to review ● Figure 6.3 to see the different responses that different patterns of light stimuli will evoke from a typical retinal ganglion cell.

You might ask: What is the point of having a **center-surround receptive field**? Is this just a bizarre side effect of how cells are organized, or does it accomplish some useful function? It turns out that the center-surround structure of retinal ganglion cell receptive fields can help to enhance contrast; that is, to highlight borders between light and dark areas. Because retinal ganglion cells fire best in response to spots of brightness surrounded by darkness (rather than to uniform fields of brightness), these cells are sensitive to contrast. This is an especially useful characteristic of retinal ganglion cells, because most objects and events in the visual world that we care about are defined by edges and borders (as we discuss in more detail in Chapter 7). As you can see, even at the initial stages of visual processing, at the level of the retina, we have mechanisms that are specially designed to enhance contrast at borders. This is another good illustration of the fact that the information the brain receives from the retina has already been partly transformed.

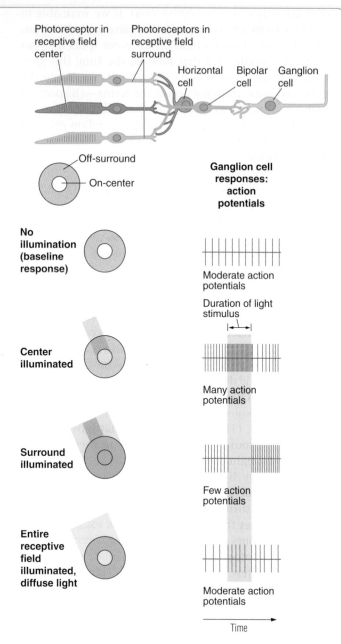

Photoreceptor in receptive field center

Photoreceptors in receptive field surround

Horizontal cell   Bipolar cell   Ganglion cell

Off-surround

On-center

Ganglion cell responses: action potentials

No illumination (baseline response)

Moderate action potentials

Duration of light stimulus

Center illuminated

Many action potentials

Surround illuminated

Few action potentials

Entire receptive field illuminated, diffuse light

Moderate action potentials

Time

● FIGURE 6.3   Receptive fields of ganglion cells.
Light shining on the excitatory center of the receptive field produces strong firing in the cell, whereas light in the inhibitory surround region causes the cell to slow down its firing to below its baseline rate. When light covers both the center and surround regions, the combination of excitatory and inhibitory effects results in a modest response by the cell. © 2010 Cengage Learning

Pathways from the Retina to the Brain

Where does information about the visual world go once it leaves the eye? As we discussed briefly in Chapter 1, there are two main destinations for visual information that travels out of the eye along the optic nerve: the superior colliculus and the lateral geniculate nucleus (which then extends to primary visual cortex). ● Figure 6.4 illustrates these destinations. In addition, minor projections extend to other brain regions. For example, retinal ganglion cells also send information to the suprachiasmatic nucleus of the hypothalamus, which helps to entrain bodily rhythms to daily cycles of light and dark. Here, though, we focus on the two main destinations for visual information, which demarcate the beginning of two separate anatomical paths for processing vision.

■ The Tectopulvinar Pathway

The **tectopulvinar path** allows people to orient quickly to important visual information. For example, imagine that you are working one evening in your kitchen, and you suddenly notice a small dark shape appear above you in your peripheral vision. You immediately turn your head and eyes toward its location, and see a bat! Before you even recognized what the shape was, your brain had already responded to it by shifting your eyes, head, and attention toward that spot. This kind of rapid visual orientation is enabled by the pathway that sends visual information from the retina directly to a midbrain region known as the *superior colliculus,* part of the tectum (giving the tectopulvinar path part of its name). This path is very fast-acting and is especially sensitive to motion and appearances of novel objects in the visual periphery.

Given that the tectopulvinar path is sensitive to motion but not fine detail, you should not be surprised to learn that it receives most of its input from M ganglion cells. Moreover, each half of the superior colliculus is more sensitive to information from the temporal than the nasal hemifield, an asymmetry that is not observed in the geniculostriate pathway that we discuss next (Sylvester, Josephs, Driver, & Rees, 2007). This asymmetry fits with behavioral findings that people are faster to orient to information that falls in the temporal hemifield than in the nasal hemifield (Rafal, Henik, & Smith, 1991). Intuitively, it makes sense that a system designed to rapidly orient to peripheral stimuli would be less sensitive to information coming from the part of the world near the nose, and more sensitive to information in the periphery.

Although traditionally the superior colliculus is considered to be responsive mainly to visual stimuli, it is also a site for integration of the auditory and visual senses. For example, the superior colliculus becomes active when auditory information is temporally synchronous with visual information (Dhamala, Assisi, Jirsa, Steinberg, & Kelso, 2007). Some individual neurons within deep layers of the superior colliculus are responsive to both auditory and visual inputs in a synergistic way, such that the neuron's response to combined audiovisual stimulation is greater than would be expected according to its response to either auditory or

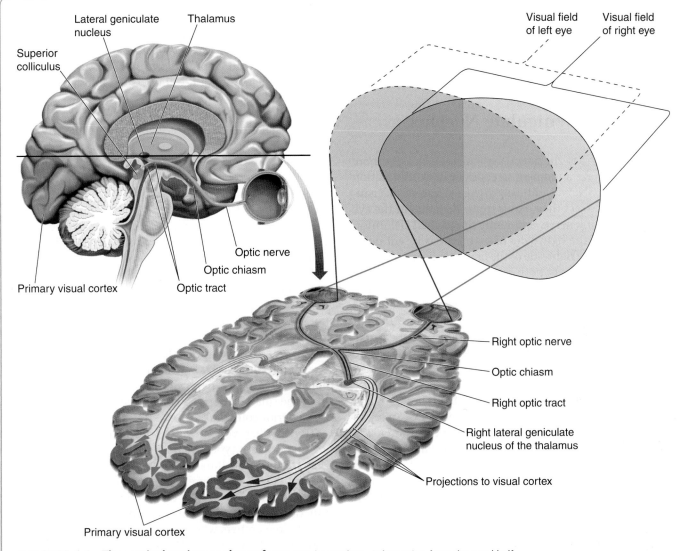

● **FIGURE 6.4   The geniculostriate pathway from eye to cortex.** Information from the nasal half of each retina (the half closest to the nose) crosses over to the LGN on the other side of the brain at the optic chiasm, whereas information from the temporal half of the retina (the half closest to the temples) travels straight back to the ipsilateral LGN. © 2010 Cengage Learning

visual stimulation alone (e.g., Stanford, Quessy, & Stein, 2005; see also Zangenehpour & Chaudhuri, 2001). These multisensory properties are especially adaptive for orienting. For example, if you heard a loud "boom" at the same time as you saw a flash of light in your peripheral vision, it would be a good idea to look quickly in that direction.

From the superior colliculus, the tectopulvinar pathway extends "upstream" to the pulvinar nucleus in the thalamus and to cortical areas that govern eye and head movements (Sommer & Wurtz, 2004). The superior colliculus also sends projections "downstream" to brainstem areas that control eye muscles. This connectivity allows a person to orient the eyes toward peripheral regions of space where important new objects or events may be occurring, so that those regions can be brought into central vision. Once in central vision, the objects can receive more detailed analysis via the other main visual pathway, the geniculostriate pathway.

■ **The Geniculostriate Pathway**

Approximately 90% of optic nerve fibers project to the **geniculostriate pathway**, which enables our conscious experience of seeing (see Figure 6.4). Through the geniculostriate path, we are able to perceive color and all the fine-grained features that we use to recognize the identity of objects and other important details in our visual world. The axons in the geniculostriate portion of the optic nerve terminate in a complex structure in the thalamus, the **lateral geniculate nucleus (LGN)**. From there, the information continues to the primary visual cortex, also known as the

striate cortex. Therefore, the geniculostriate path gets its name because it extends to the lateral geniculate and then to the striate cortex. Because the LGN and striate cortex are each highly complex in their own right, we will deal with them individually in the next two sections.

Lateral Geniculate Nucleus

Before looking at the lateral geniculate nucleus in more detail, let's take a moment to consider how information gets to the LGN. We've already discussed how retinal ganglion cells project their axons from the retina in the eye along the optic nerve, and terminate in the LGN. Information from the right sides of both retinas is sent on to the LGN on the right side of the brain, while information from the left sides of both retinas is sent on to the LGN on the left side of the brain. For this to occur, some information must cross over from the left eye to the right side of the brain, and likewise from the right eye to the left side of the brain. The crossover point is called the **optic chiasm**, illustrated in Figure 6.4. Once the optic nerve fibers cross at the optic chiasm, they are referred to as the *optic tract,* rather than the optic nerve. As a result, the right LGN receives information only about the left half of the world (from both eyes) whereas the left LGN receives information only about the right half of the world (from both eyes). This segregation continues throughout much of the visual system; consequently, information about the two halves of the visual world is not joined together until much later, at the areas of the cortex responsible for higher levels of visual processing.

The LGN has a beautifully layered structure (● Figure 6.5). It consists of six main layers that are stacked on top of one another, and then folded into a knee-like shape. (The word

geniculate comes from the Latin root for "knee"). Researchers have also discovered small cell layers in between the main LGN layers. These are referred to as *koniocellular* or *K-cell layers* (Hendry & Reid, 2000; Kaplan, 2004). Although at present their function is not well understood, we will discuss the relevance of K-cell layers to blindsight later in this chapter.

How do the main layers of the LGN differ from one another? First, each layer receives input from only one eye. Some layers receive input from the contralateral eye, and some receive input from the ipsilateral eye, but all layers receive information from the contralateral visual field. So, for example, what differs between the layers in the left LGN is whether they are representing the right side of the visual world as seen by the right eye (contralateral) or as seen by the left eye (ipsilateral). Of course, the complementary pattern is evident in the right LGN.

Second, the LGN layers receive different kinds of inputs from the retina. The bottom two layers (magnocellular layers) receive input from the M retinal ganglion cells, whereas the top four layers (parvocellular layers) receive input from the P retinal ganglion cells. The koniocellular layers, which lie in between the main magnocellular and parvocellular layers, receive input from the small bistratified ganglion cells as well as from the superior colliculus.

Given what you already know about the M and P ganglion cells, you should not be surprised to learn that the magnocellular LGN layers are important for motion detection, whereas the parvocellular layers are important for perceiving color and fine detail. This functional difference was demonstrated experimentally by researchers who selectively damaged either the magnocellular or parvocellular LGN layers in monkeys (Schiller, Logothetis, & Charles, 1990). When the magnocellular layers were damaged, the monkeys had trouble distinguishing the direction in which a stimulus (a pattern of random dots) was moving. In contrast, when the parvocellular layers were damaged, the monkeys had difficulty distinguishing between patterns that differed only in color or in fine details (high spatial frequencies). Once again, we see how different types of processes are anatomically segregated in the structure of the visual system.

Each of the main layers in the LGN contains a **retinotopic map** of half of the visual world.

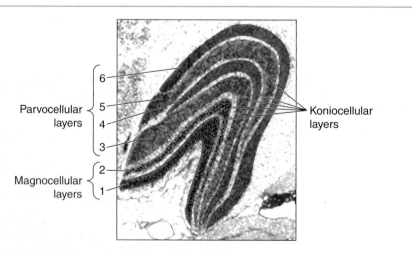

● **FIGURE 6.5   The layered structure of the LGN.** Layers 1 and 2 are the magnocellular layers, whereas 3–6 are the parvocellular layers. Input from the contralateral eye is processed in layers 2, 3, and 5, whereas input from the ipsilateral eye is processed in layers 1, 4, and 6. © 2010 Cengage Learning

By *retinotopic*, we mean a map that is laid out spatially like the retina itself. Neighboring cells in an LGN layer receive input from neighboring ganglion cells in the retina, so they code for neighboring regions of the visual world, preserving the spatial organization of light patterns in the world. In other words, the spatial information coded by the retina does not get all jumbled up when it arrives at the LGN. The retinotopic organization of the LGN was first mapped out in monkeys. To understand how cells are organized in relation to one another, the experimenter painstakingly records from one cell, then another, and then another, and tries to discern systematic relationships in terms of what stimuli excite neighboring cells. More recently, fMRI studies have confirmed that the same basic organization of the LGN holds in humans. Although fMRI does not have the exquisitely fine spatial resolution of single-cell recording, researchers using fMRI have established that each LGN receives information only from the contralateral visual field, and that information in the lower and upper fields activates superior and inferior portions of the LGN, respectively (Chen, Zhu, Thulborn, & Ugurbil, 1999; Kastner, Schneider, & Wunderlich, 2006).

Despite the marvelous organization of the LGN, many people have wondered what the LGN is really good for. Receptive field properties of cells in the LGN are much like receptive fields of retinal ganglion cells, so it doesn't seem that information is really transformed in any new way at this stage of the visual pathway. So, why have this stopover point on the way to the cortex? One clue comes from the fact that most of the inputs that the LGN receives come from the cortex, not the retina (Sherman & Guillery, 2004; Sillito & Jones, 2004). Interestingly, the inputs that the LGN receives from the cortex also seem to be segregated, such that different populations of cortical cells send input to different layers of the LGN (Briggs & Usrey, 2009).

The functional significance of these feedback connections from the cortex is still under investigation, but one possibility is that they allow the cortex to influence the input that it will receive from the LGN. These downward projections from the cortex may boost the representation of some features or dampen the representation of other features coming from the retina. For example, shifts of spatial attention can cause changes in LGN activity, as measured by fMRI studies in humans. When participants are instructed to direct attention to a stimulus in one visual field, activity is increased in the contralateral LGN, compared to when attention is directed away from that same stimulus location (O'Connor, Fukui, Pinsk, & Kastner, 2002). Because the "instructions" to direct attention toward a stimulus must come from higher-level brain regions (not from the retina itself, for example), we can infer that the influence of those higher-level brain regions is being exerted via either direct or indirect top-down modulation of the LGN (see Kastner et al., 2006, for discussion).

There is still much to be learned about the functions of these projections that descend to the LGN, but they are an important reminder that vision is not just a process of piecing together a visual image from the bottom up; that is, from retina to cortex (Sillito, Cudeiro, & Jones, 2006). Rather, top-down influences—from the cortex to prior waystations in the visual stream—can shape the type of visual information that the cortex ultimately receives.

Primary Visual Cortex (Striate Cortex)

Visual information finally reaches the cortex once it has passed through the LGN. The first destination within the cortex is the primary visual cortex in the occipital lobe. Specifically, projections from the parvocellular and magnocellular LGN layers enter layer 4 within the six-layered cortex, and synapse with cells there. The primary visual cortex goes by many names, including V1 (because it is the first area in the cortex that receives visual information), Brodmann area 17, and striate cortex. *Striate* means "striped," and refers to the appearance of this section of the cortex when viewed under a microscope (● Figure 6.6).

Projections from the LGN to the primary visual cortex maintain their spatial organization. That is,

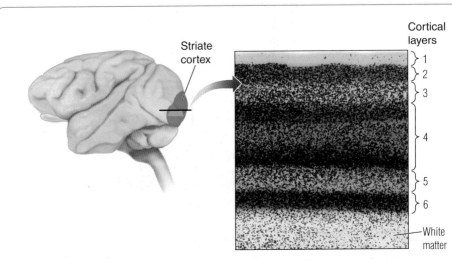

● **FIGURE 6.6** Striate cortex is so named because of its striped appearance.
© 2010 Cengage Learning

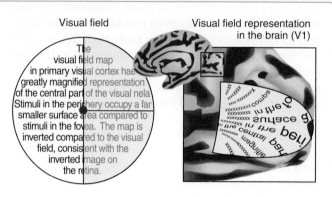

Visual field

Visual field representation
in the brain (V1)

The visual field map in primary visual cortex has greatly magnified representation of the central part of the visual nela. Stimuli in the periphery occupy a far smaller surface area compared to stimuli in the fovea. The map is inverted compared to the visual field, consistent with the inverted image on the retina.

● **FIGURE 6.7   Retinotopic layout of the primary visual cortex.** If the viewer is focused on the dot at the center of the visual field, information to the left of that fixation point will be represented in the right striate cortex. The top half of the left visual field will be represented on the lower bank of the calcarine fissure (shown unfolded), whereas the bottom half will be represented on the upper bank. Note also the cortical magnification, that is, the overrepresentation of the foveal region compared to the periphery. *Source:* Fig. 6 from B.A. Wandell et al. (2009) Visual cortext in humans. Encyclopedia of Neuroscience, 10, 251–257. Reprinted by permission of Elsevier.

the left half of the visual world is represented in the right striate cortex, and vice versa. The striate cortex contains a map that is retinotopically organized, just like the LGN layers. In fact, the mapping is so precise that we can specify the **cortical magnification factor**, which describes the millimeters of cortical surface that are devoted to one degree of angle in the visual world. This cortical magnification value varies dramatically for regions of the fovea compared to the periphery, on the order of 100 to 1. This means that much more of primary visual cortex is devoted to representing information from the center of the visual field than from the periphery (● Figure 6.7 for an illustration). This organization makes sense, because the fovea of the retina is packed with many photoreceptors, providing rich, fine-grained, and detailed information from the center of the visual field. In contrast, much less information from the periphery of the visual field reaches primary visual cortex.

■ Organization of Striate Cortex

Visual information is represented in the striate cortex in complex ways that are somewhat different from the LGN's representation. Through pioneering work by Nobel Prize-winning neurophysiologists David Hubel and Torsten Wiesel, it is known that the receptive field properties of striate cortex cells differ from those of LGN cells. (For reviews of Hubel & Wiesel's findings and the impact of their work, see Hubel, 1982; Kandel, 2009; Wurtz, 2009).

There are several types of striate cortex cells, referred to as **simple**, **complex**, and **hyper-complex** (or *end-stopped*) **cells**. What they all have in common is that

their receptive fields are no longer tuned to spots of light, as LGN cells are; instead, they are responsive to bars of light oriented in particular ways. A simple cell's receptive field is bar-shaped, with an excitatory center and inhibitory surround, but the cell will only fire if the bar is oriented in a particular way (● Figure 6.8A). Different simple cells respond to bars of different orientations. Complex cells are like simple cells in that they respond best to certain line orientations, but complex cells are less picky about where exactly the line is located, they do not have on and off regions, and they show a preference for lines that are moving in a particular direction, such as from left to right (● Figure 6.8B). Hyper-complex, or end-stopped cells, are like simple cells, but prefer lines of certain lengths; as a line gets longer, at a certain point a hyper-complex cell will become less excited by it.

As illustrated in ● Figure 6.9, within the chunk of cortex representing each spatial location, there is a systematic organization of cells that respond to all the various line orientations. Cells that prefer a given line orientation are grouped together, forming *orientation columns*. Neighboring columns contain cells with similar orientation preferences, so that across a small chunk of cortex, all the various orientations are represented. Orientation columns also contain cells that are tuned to respond best to certain directions of motion. In addition, cells are segregated into columns according to which eye sends them input. These columns are referred to as *ocular dominance columns*. Putting all of this together, we have an exquisite organization in which a *hypercolumn* contains cells that are all tuned to respond to stimulation at a particular spatial location; within that hypercolumn, there are subcolumns of cells that prefer particular orientations and that receive inputs from particular eyes. Furthermore, running vertically through these hypercolumns are also areas cleverly known as "blobs," which contain cells that are especially involved in coding color information. The entire retinotopic map is made up of a series of these hypercolumns, each corresponding to a different retinal location (see Ts'o, Zarella, & Burkitt, 2009 for a review).

In addition to the properties represented in the hypercolumns (orientation, ocular dominance, spatial location, and color), there is another property that cells respond to differentially, and that property is spatial frequency. As you may remember from Chapter 4, *spatial frequency* refers to how abruptly visual information changes from light to dark; coarse patterns contain low spatial frequencies, whereas fine-grained patterns contain high spatial frequencies. Some cells in primary visual cortex seem to respond best to low spatial frequencies and some respond best to high spatial frequencies. At present, it is unclear how these frequency-preferring cells are distributed across visual cortex and how their organization is related to hypercolumns (Sirovich & Uglesich, 2004). However, cells that receive information from the fovea—which provides

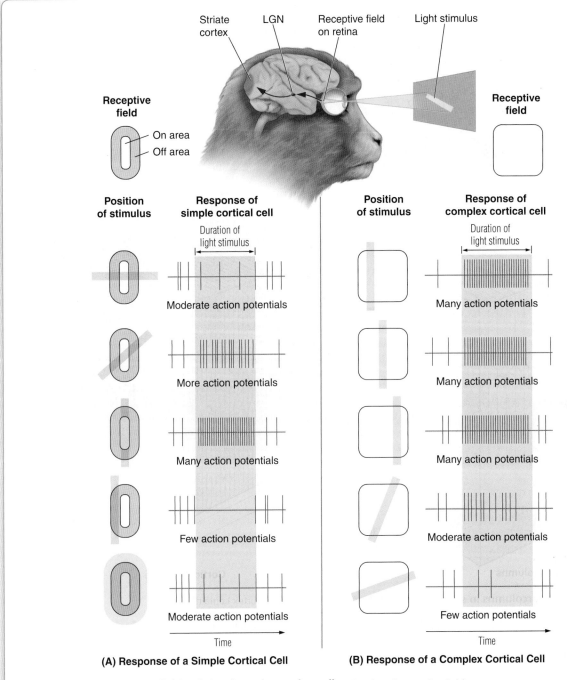

● **FIGURE 6.8 Receptive fields of simple and complex cells.** Simple-cell receptive fields (panel A) are constructed such that the cell responds best to a bar of light oriented in a particular direction and surrounded by darkness. Complex cells (panel B) are less selective about the placement of the line, but still prefer a certain orientation. © 2010 Cengage Learning

the most detailed information about the visual world—tend to be sensitive to information of higher spatial frequency than cells that receive information from the periphery, which tend to be sensitive to information of lower spatial frequency.

Given this beautifully organized map, it is tempting to think that a little person inside your brain could look down on the striate cortex and figure out the pattern in the visual world by noticing which cells are firing, indicating the presence of oriented lines and edges at certain spatial locations. In theory, someone who was given all the information represented in striate cortex could deduce much about the actual scene out in the world (see Kamitani & Tong, 2005). However, there is no little person inside your brain who watches the striate cortex. There are only other brain regions. As we will see in later chapters, other brain regions use the information provided by the striate cortex in the service of

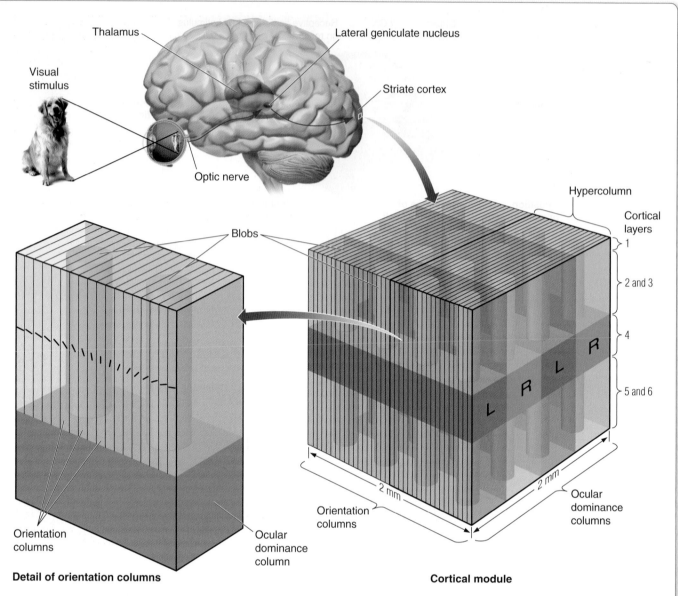

● **FIGURE 6.9   Hypercolumns in striate cortex.** A 2 mm × 2 mm chunk of cortex contains subcolumns corresponding to ocular dominance and orientation columns. Each subcolumn contains cells that are especially responsive to lines of particular orientation as seen by either the left or the right eye. © 2010 Cengage Learning

certain goals, such as object recognition and spatial navigation.

■ Binocular Integration in Striate Cortex

One important aspect of the organization of primary visual cortex is that information from the two eyes is integrated, unlike the LGN in which inputs from the two eyes are kept segregated in separate layers. At the level of the LGN, there is no way for visual information from the two eyes to be directly compared. Why is it ultimately important to compare information from the two eyes? Another way of asking this question is to ask why we even have two eyes in the first place.

The main reason for having two eyes is to enable depth perception. To reach for a cup, you need to know

how far away it is so that you know how far to stick out your arm. However, the retina only records the spatial location of light patterns in two dimensions. Depth must be computed by the brain, because it is not directly coded by the retina. One of the most important cues for depth computation is **binocular disparity**. Binocular *disparity* refers to the fact that the image that falls on each retina is slightly different, because the eyes are positioned in different locations. The images on the two retinas are more discrepant when items are close to the viewer and less discrepant when they are farther away.

Some cells in striate cortex are especially tuned to certain amounts of binocular disparity. These kinds of cells are binocular, in the sense that they receive inputs from both eyes. Because different binocular cells code for different amounts of binocular disparity, a population of such cells can represent all possible depths of an oriented line. Although higher-level cortical brain regions are necessary to make further use of this binocular disparity information (Parker, 2007), disparity information is first computed in striate cortex.

Contextual Modulation of Cells in Striate Cortex

Another characteristic of cells in striate cortex is that their responsiveness can be modified by context (Lamme, 2004). Although information outside a cell's receptive field cannot alone cause the cell to fire, such information can modulate the cell's response when presented together with the cell's favored stimulus. To illustrate this idea, consider a cell that fires maximally to the location and orientation of the line in the center of ● Figure 6.10A. When this line falls within the cell's receptive field, the cell responds by increasing its firing; nevertheless, the magnitude of that response to the line can be modulated by the surrounding context. For example, studies have found that in the monkey striate cortex, a cell whose classical receptive field corresponds to the line in part A of Figure 6.10 will fire less strongly when the surrounding lines all go the same way, as in part B. This corresponds to our perception: the line segment seems more salient in panel A, when it appears against a blank background, compared to panel B, when it appears as part of a group. Likewise, the cell's response to the array in part C is stronger than its response to panel B, again aligning with our perception that the line "pops out" more in C than in B.

Contextual modulation and its influence on striate cortex cells may even help to explain what perceptual psychologists refer to as *figure-ground segregation* (Lamme, 2004). In ● Figure 6.11A, you probably perceive a square, or figure, against a background. The orientation of the lines within the square differs from the orientation of the lines outside the square, creating the sense of a square shape against a background. Now, imagine a striate cortex cell whose receptive field corresponds to the small circle indicated in the center; that is, the cell responds best to lines of that orientation in that location. Will this cell's response differ depending on whether the whole array looks like A or B? The answer is yes. When the preferred stimulus—lines oriented a particular way—appears to be part of a figure, the cell responds more strongly than when the preferred stimulus appears to be part of a background. Keep in mind that the stimulation provided by information in the receptive field itself is exactly the same in these two cases; the only thing that differs is the surrounding context.

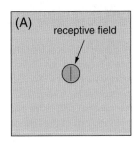
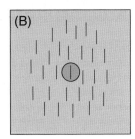
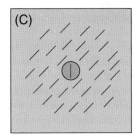

● **FIGURE 6.10   Perception of a line segment depends on its context.** In panel A, the line in isolation is easy to distinguish from its background, whereas in panel B, it is less distinguishable from the other lines. In panel C, the middle line segment "pops" out of the array. Single-cell recordings in monkeys show that the surrounding elements influence the activity of a cell whose receptive field corresponds to the center line segment. *Source:* Figure 45.1, panels a, b & c from Lamme, V.A. (2004). Beyond the classical receptive field: Contextual modulation of V1 responses. In L.M. Chalupa & J.S. Werner (Eds.), The Visual Neurosciences (pp. 720–732). Copyright © 2003 Massachusetts Institute of Technology, by permission of The MIT Press.

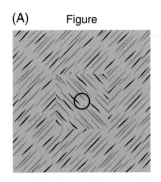
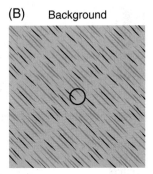
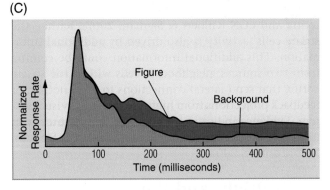

● **FIGURE 6.11   Perception of figure and ground.** In the example in the left, in (A), you perceive a square against a background, whereas the example on the right, in (B), appears to be all background. As illustrated in (C), cells whose receptive fields are tuned to the center of this array will fire more strongly when the oriented lines in their receptive fields are perceived to be part of a figure, compared to when those same lines appear to be part of a background. *Source:* Figure 45.3, panels b & c from Lamme, V.A. (2004). Beyond the classical receptive field: Contextual modulation of V1 responses. In L.M. Chalupa & J.S. Werner (Eds.), The Visual Neurosciences (pp. 720–732). Copyright © 2003 Massachusetts Institute of Technology, by permission of The MIT Press.

IN FOCUS: Seeing What's Not There: Visual Illusions and the Striate Cortex

Do you ever see things that aren't really there? Well, yes. The most benign example is a phenomenon known as perceptual filling-in of the blind spot. Studies of the role of striate cortex in this phenomenon provide fascinating clues about how the brain can create a perception of visual features even when those features are not actually registered on the retina.

As you may know, each of your two eyes has a **blind spot**, created by an area in the retina where there are no photoreceptors. This is the point at which all the ganglion cell fibers are gathered together in a bundle to exit the eye as the optic nerve (look back at Figure 6.1). In daily life, you do not even notice your blind spot. Why not? It could be because you have two eyes, and the blind spot is placed in a slightly different location in each eye. However, if you close one eye, you still do not notice the other eye's blind spot at all: there is no noticeable "hole" in your perception of the visual world. Your visual system perceptually fills in this missing information as if the background just continued on through the blind spot. You can experience this phenomenon for yourself using the image in ● Box Figure 6.1.

Recent evidence indicates that this filling-in process is carried out, at least in part, in primary visual cortex (Komatsu, 2006). Clever studies have recorded signals from individual cells in the monkey striate cortex in regions of the retinotopic map that correspond to the blind spot (Komatsu, Kinoshita, & Murakami, 2000; Matsumoto & Komatsu, 2005). When the monkey views a stimulus that falls in part across the monkey's blind spot, such

as a line with a particular orientation, the striate cortex cells coding for that stimulus still fire. In other words, even though this stimulus is not represented at the level of the retina (because it falls on the blind spot), the primary visual cortex still codes for that feature as if it were there. Results from human brain imaging also find that striate cortex is activated by features that fall within the blind spot (Tong & Engel, 2001; see also Meng, Remus, & Tong, 2005).

● **BOX FIGURE 6.1   Illustration of filling-in of the blind spot.** Try closing your right eye and fixating your gaze on the blue center of the yellow circle on the right. Now, move the page closer to your face. At some point (about 15 cm), you should notice that the pink circle in the center on the left disappears, and the rectangle appears uniformly striped. You can also try to find the blind spot in your right eye by closing the left eye and repeating the procedure focusing on the pink circle on the left side of the figure. At some point, the blue circle in the middle of the yellow one on the right should disappear. *Source:* Adapted by permission from Macmillan Publishers, LTD: Komatsu, H. (2006). Komatsu, H. (2006). The neural mechanisms of perceptual filling-in. Nature Reviews Neuroscience, 7, 220–231.

These contextual effects tell us that the activity of cells within the striate cortex is not just driven by bottom-up inputs that individual cells receive from the retina and LGN (Gilbert & Sigman, 2007). Rather, the striate cells' activity is also driven by additional information. This additional information could be coming from two sources: neighboring cells within the striate cortex that send lateral connections to one another, or feedback projections from higher levels of the visual system. Evidence indicates that both of these sources can influence the activity of striate cells (Gilbert & Sigman, 2007; Lamme, 2004).

Blindsight and the Visual Pathways

At this point, it can be useful to think back on the case study of blindsight at the beginning of this chapter. Remember that individuals with blindsight have no conscious experience of "seeing," because of extensive damage to the striate cortex, yet they are able to make rudimentary visual discriminations. The phenomenon of blindsight helps us to think about the functions served by different visual pathways in the brain,

because to understand blindsight we must understand what pathways are responsible for the patients' intact visual abilities.

People who have damage to the primary visual cortex typically experience **cortical blindness**, which just means blindness of cortical origin rather than due to a problem in the eye or optic nerve. If both sides of the primary visual cortex are damaged, this cortical blindness will extend across the whole visual field. If only one side is damaged, the patient will be *hemianopic* for the opposite (i.e., contralateral) visual field, as discussed in Chapter 1. These patients report being blind for all information in the affected visual field, with no sense of either dark or light.

Among patients with cortical blindness, only a small proportion display *blindsight*, in which special testing reveals that some aspects of vision appear to be preserved, even though the patient's subjective experience is of being blind. In the most basic sense, cortical blindness tells us that the primary visual cortex is necessary for conscious awareness of the visual world. But blindsight also tells us that an intact primary visual cortex is not necessary for *all* aspects of vision, because some aspects of vision appear to be preserved even when the primary visual cortex is damaged.

How can this happen, if those features are not actually registered on the retina? Although the actual mechanism is still unknown, one possibility is that the cells representing that particular feature are stimulated by spreading activation from excited cells nearby, leading to a kind of interpolation of the missing feature (Spillmann, Otte, Hamburger, & Magnussen, 2006). Another possibility is that cells representing the blind spot have large receptive fields that extend beyond the blind spot, and thus their activity is influenced by stimulation right around the blind spot (Komatsu, 2006).

It is useful to have the blind spot filled in, because it would be distracting to walk around with two little holes in your view of the world. However, the phenomenon of filling-in can also make it harder to notice certain kinds of brain damage. For example, imagine someone who sustains a small lesion to a part of the retinotopic map in LGN or striate cortex. Such person would have a **scotoma** (a blind spot) in a certain part of the visual field. Often such people do not even notice these acquired blind spots because the brain fills them in. Such a scotoma may be discovered only through systematic testing of the visual field by an ophthalmologist.

Other illusory phenomena also illustrate that conscious perception is not driven solely by the bottom-up input from the retina. One example comes from the study of **binocular rivalry**. Imagine that you looked into a special machine that showed a picture of a rose to your right eye and a picture of a lemon to your left eye. First, note that this kind of situation would never happen in the natural world; you would never normally see a rose and a lemon occupying the same space in the world. Your visual system is not really set up to handle this situation, because it evolved to cope with situations that actually exist in the natural world. Still, your visual system does not crash completely when presented with this bizarre scenario. Rather, it does something interesting: It creates a perception that oscillates back and forth between seeing the lemon and seeing the rose.

Vision scientists have used binocular rivalry as a special trick to test how neural firing in different brain regions coincides with conscious perception. Here we have a scenario where the visual input remains the same—rose and lemon together—but the conscious perception oscillates—rose, lemon, rose, lemon. Research using binocular stimuli has shown that activity in striate cortex is influenced by which pattern the person is consciously perceiving (Polonsky, Blake, Braun, & Heeger, 2000). This suggests that the striate cortex is not just coding for what appears on the retina (because in the case of binocular rivalry, the retinal image remains unchanged); rather, it is coding for the features that are consciously perceived. Controversy still exists about whether changes in striate cortex activation actually cause the shift in conscious perception between the rival stimuli, or whether the striate cortex is responding to higher-level brain regions that drive the change in perception (see Lee, Blake, & Heeger, 2007). Regardless, these studies make clear that the brain is actively constructing a representation of the visual world.

Although there is some variability in the preservation of visual functions across different patients with blindsight, a review of the extensive testing done on these patients suggests several common areas of preserved function (Weiskrantz, 2004). Patients with blindsight can localize spots or bars of light by pointing or moving their eyes toward the targets; they can distinguish the orientations of lines that differ by about 10 degrees; they can distinguish when a target is moving or stationary; and they can make some basic color judgments, such as determining whether a square is red or gray. Patients may also show some knowledge of visual form; for example, a patient might adjust the hand appropriately for grasping a particular object in the blind field. In all of these areas, performance is above what would be predicted by chance, but still far below what normal vision would support. Furthermore, in all cases the patients report that they are completely guessing and have no perceptual experience of "seeing" in the blind field.

Researchers disagree about what part of the visual system carries out the preserved functions in people with blindsight. One possibility is that the tectopulvinar system is still intact, while the geniculostriate system is disrupted. This explanation has intuitive appeal because it fits with known segregation of function between these pathways. It also fits with the idea that the tectopulvinar system carries out a more basic function that might not require or involve higher-order visual awareness.

Evidence supporting the role of the tectopulvinar pathway in at least some blindsight patients comes from a study that used diffusion tensor imaging to trace visual pathways (Leh, Johansen-Berg, & Ptito, 2006). In this study, researchers examined projections arising from the superior colliculus (part of the tectopulvinar path) in three groups: patients with blindsight following hemispherectomy, patients with hemispherectomy but with no residual visual abilities in the contralateral visual field, and control patients with no brain damage. In patients with blindsight abilities, the superior colliculus in the damaged hemisphere was connected by fiber pathways to a variety of cortical regions in the opposite hemisphere, such as primary visual cortex and visual association areas (● Figure 6.12). These connections seemed to be even more pronounced than in non-brain-damaged control subjects. In contrast, in hemispherectomy patients with no residual vision, the superior colliculus in the damaged hemisphere did not appear to show significant connectivity with cortical regions. These results are consistent with the idea that blindsight depends on projections from the

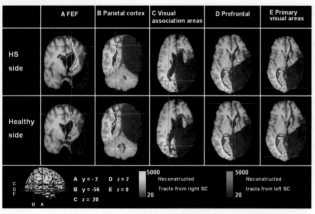

(A)

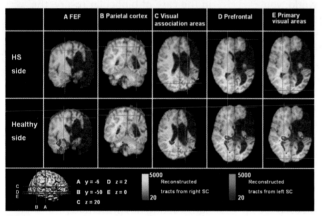

(B)

● **FIGURE 6.12   Intact projections from the superior colliculus in blindsight.** Panel (A) shows intact anatomical pathways connected to the right superior colliculus (in red) and the left superior colliculus (in blue) for a patient with blindsight (residual vision) after hemispherectomy (HS). Panel (B) shows the absence of such pathways in a patient with a hemispherectomy but no blindsight capabilities. In both patients, the dark gray area represents the missing tissue due to the hemispherectomy. *Source:* Leh, S.E., Johansen-Berg, H., & Ptito, A. (2006). Unconscious vision: New insights into the neuronal correlate of blindsight using diffusion tractography. Brain, 129, 1822–1832.

that process motion (Sincich, Park, Wohlgemuth, & Horton, 2004). Therefore, it may be that preserved motion detection in blindsight is carried out by a geniculate pathway that bypasses the striate cortex and therefore remains intact when the striate cortex is damaged.

Other researchers propose instead that the intact functions in blindsight are carried out by islands of intact tissue within the damaged striate cortex itself (Gazzaniga, Fendrich, & Wessinger, 1994). In this view, blindsight does not represent the functioning of an extrastriate system, rather, it represents the functioning of a striate system that is limping along as best it can, sort of like an army battalion that keeps fighting even after its troops have been decimated. Some evidence in favor of this view was provided by a study showing that one blindsight patient, patient CLT, appeared to have a small region of spared vision within the blind field, as well as having areas of striate cortex within the damaged hemisphere that appeared normal on MRI scans (Fendrich, Wessinger, & Gazzaniga, 1992). Another study found that although a patient (patient MC) was functionally blind in the field contralateral to the damaged hemisphere, her damaged primary visual cortex still responded to visual stimulation in a retinotopic manner (Radoeva, Prasad, Brainard, & Aguirre, 2008).

However, other researchers have pointed out that blindsight has been demonstrated in patients who have had an entire cerebral hemisphere surgically removed; in these cases, there is most certainly no lingering striate cortex tissue to support vision (Stoerig, 1993; Ptito & Leh, 2007). A functional imaging study with one blindsight patient (FS) found no evidence of striate cortex activity in the damaged hemisphere, despite using visual stimuli that would produce robust striate responses in normal people (Stoerig, Kleinschmidt, & Frahm, 1998). Other researchers found striate activity in one blindsight patient but not in another (Morland, Lê, Carroll, Hoffmann, & Pambakian, 2004). Thus, while striate sparing may be evident in some blindsight patients, it does not seem to be a tenable explanation for all patients with this syndrome.

Perhaps these explanations for blindsight are not mutually exclusive; there may be more than one possible pathway that can support residual vision in patients with damage to the primary visual cortex. Because it is rare, blindsight has been investigated in only a small number of patients. Each one has a slightly different pattern of brain damage and even different perceptual experiences. Some claim that they can see nothing in the blind field, whereas others report a vague sense of something "being there" while still denying that they can "see" it (Weiskrantz, 2004). This heterogeneity of patients allows for few generalizations at present. A more philosophical question is why some kinds of visual processing, such as those supported by the striate cortex, seem to give rise to conscious experience

tectopulvinar path to cortical regions. Additional evidence comes from findings that these blindsight patients cannot make distinctions that depend upon signals from short-wavelength-sensitive cones, which do not send any information to the superior colliculus (Leh, Mullen, & Ptito, 2006). In other words, the intact visual abilities in these patients seem to be limited to those kinds of visual information to which the superior colliculus has access.

Another pathway that might mediate the intact visual capabilities in blindsight involves the LGN. Although the major projection from the LGN goes to the primary visual cortex, the LGN also appears to send minor projections to other cortical visual areas. Recent data indicate that in monkeys, the koniocellular or K-cell layers of the LGN project directly to extrastriate cortical areas

while others do not. This question is much harder, and perhaps impossible, to address with scientific methods.

Visual Areas beyond the Striate Cortex

The striate cortex is the first cortical processing center for vision, but it is by no means the last. Dozens of additional cortical regions have been implicated in aspects of vision. Striate cortex provides a representation of numerous features of the visual world, but that information must be further processed and transformed before it can be fully useful in understanding and acting upon the world.

■ Multiple Maps of the Visual World

One of the fascinating findings by vision scientists is that there are many maps of the visual world within the brain. We have focused in detail on the retinotopic maps in LGN and primary visual cortex, but similar maps also exist in regions beyond the striate cortex—that is, in so-called "extrastriate" regions of visual cortex.

● Figure 6.13 illustrates the location of several of these additional regions, named V2, V3, and V4, in the macaque monkey brain. Each of these areas is retinotopically mapped, like V1. For example, area V2 in the right hemisphere contains a map of the left visual field, as does area V3. Generally speaking, the dorsal half of each of these regions represents the lower visual field and the ventral half represents the upper half of the visual field.

Like retinotopic maps elsewhere in the brain, the maps in V2, V3, and V4 have been investigated using single-cell recording in monkeys, in which the receptive fields of individuals cells are located and compared with those of neighboring cells. More recently, researchers have used fMRI to study retinotopic mapping in the human cortex. To identify retinotopic maps with fMRI, researchers systematically present stimuli that differ in their eccentricity (degree of distance from the fovea) as well as stimuli that differ in their polar angle (location on a wedge shape). The kinds of stimuli typically used in these experiments are shown in ● Figure 6.14. Researchers present many combinations of these kinds of stimuli in an attempt to determine the part of the visual field to which a certain region of the cortex is most responsive (Wandell & Wade, 2003).

One obvious question has probably occurred to you. What is the point of having all of these retinotopic maps? (And there are known to be many more than these three!) Does each area—V1, V2, and V3—serve a different function? Do they represent different properties of the visual world? The answer is that we do not really know the functions of all these visual maps. However, for some extrastriate areas, researchers have posited particular functions. For example, an extrastriate area known as area MT (also

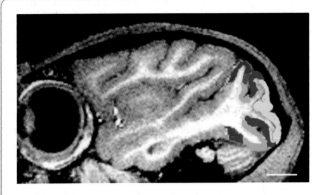

● **FIGURE 6.13   Location of striate and extrastriate visual areas in the macaque monkey cortex.** Note that unlike V1 (shown in yellow) areas V2 (blue), V3 (green), and V4 (red) are split into dorsal and ventral halves. *Source:* Wandell, B.A., & Wade, A.R. (2003). Functional imaging of the visual pathways. Neurologic Clinics of North America, 21, 417–443. Reprinted by permission of Elsevier.

called V5) has been linked to motion perception, as we will discuss in much more detail in Chapter 8. Area V4 has been posited to play a special role in color perception, although that claim has been controversial. In the next section, we focus on the role of V4 in color perception to illustrate the challenges posed by attempting to associate a particular extrastriate region with a particular perceptual function.

■ Area V4: A Special Module for Coding Color?

Observations of brain-damaged patients originally gave rise to the idea that a subregion of visual cortex

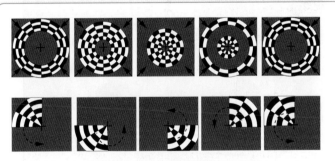

● **FIGURE 6.14   Types of stimuli used to map out retinotopic coordinates in cortical regions in humans.** On the top are stimuli that differ in eccentricity. Notice that the stimulus in the middle will mainly stimulate foveal areas, whereas those on the two ends are likely to stimulate peripheral areas. Comparing the brain regions activated by these two types of stimuli provides information on which portion of brain tissue represent the fovea and which represent the periphery. On the bottom are stimuli that differ in polar angle. These stimuli are used to determine which quadrants of the visual world are mapped onto which portion of visual cortex. *Source:* Wandell, B.A. & Wade, A.R. (2003). Functional imaging of the visual pathways. Neurologic Clinics of North America, 21, 417–443.

may be especially responsible for color vision. Patients with *achromatopsia* have damage to the visual cortex that results in a perceptual experience that is devoid of color (for reviews, see Bouvier & Engel, 2006; Cowey & Heywood, 1997). Such patients report that the world appears in shades of gray, and they often have trouble naming colors or differentiating stimuli on the basis of color alone. Because these patients typically have damage to the posterior ventral cortex, it is logical to infer that some subregion within this area plays an important role in color perception.

At the same time, it is important to note that there do not appear to be any cases of "pure" achromatopsia, in which every other aspect of vision is perfectly normal except color perception. Instead, individuals with achromatopsia tend to also have problems with aspects of spatial vision and pattern recognition (Bouvier & Engel, 2006). The absence of a pure case of achromatopsia could be because acquired brain damage is seldom precise, and therefore is likely to affect nearby visual regions as well as a presumably small "color area." Alternatively, the absence of a pure case may suggest that there is no "color area" that processes color information exclusively. We must look to methods besides the lesion method to further address this question.

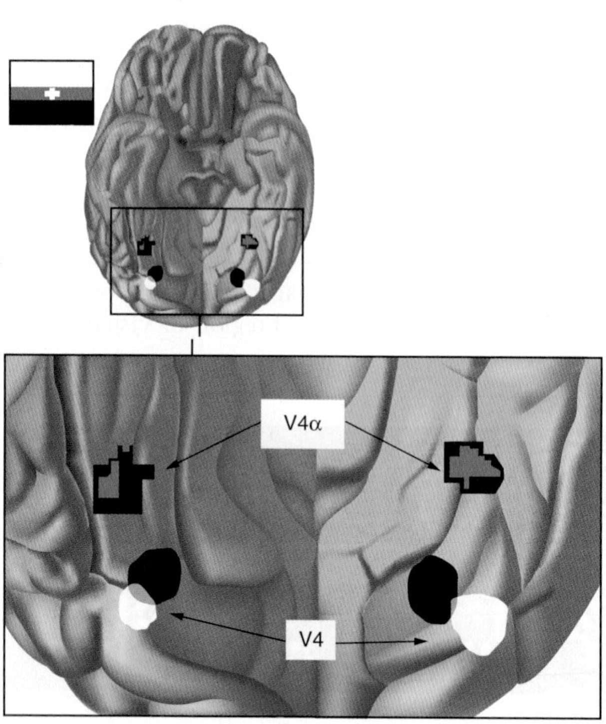

More than 30 years ago, researchers identified cells within the V4 area of the macaque monkey that appeared to be especially sensitive to color (Zeki, 1973). Even more exciting, these cells seemed to demonstrate color constancy (Zeki, 1983; see also Kusunoki, Moutoussis, & Zeki, 2006). *Color constancy* refers to a perceptual phenomenon in which a color appears similar across many different lighting conditions. For example, your favorite red sweater looks "red" whether you see it lit by a dim incandescent bulb or by a bright fluorescent bulb, despite the fact that the source of illumination differs quite dramatically and therefore the wavelengths reflected back by the sweater also differ dramatically. Because your perception of the sweater as "red" persists across these different conditions, your brain must be computing color by taking into account the wavelengths and intensity of the background illumination. The discovery that cells in the V4 area exhibit color constancy—preferring a particular color regardless of the illumination—suggested that this region might be crucial for the computations necessary for color constancy. Subsequent studies that combined fMRI and single-cell recording in monkeys found that V4 is composed of clusters of cells that are color-sensitive interspersed with clusters of cells that are not color-sensitive (Conway, Moeller, & Tsao, 2007). Beyond suggesting that V4 may not be composed of a uniform set of cells, these recent findings also remind us of the limitations of single-cell recording, in which only a small number of the millions of cells in a given region are sampled.

To examine color processing in humans, neuroimaging studies have typically compared conditions that involve making color discriminations to conditions that involve grayscale stimuli whose brightness levels must be discerned (e.g., Bartels & Zeki, 2000; Beauchamp, Haxby, Jennings, & DeYoe, 1999; Hadjikhani, Liu, Dale, Cavanaugh, & Tootell, 1998; McKeefry & Zeki, 1997). Such studies have reported that the color condition activates areas on the ventral surface of the occipital lobe. These areas of activation correspond fairly well with the location of lesions in patients with achromatopsia (Bouvier & Engel, 2006).

However, controversy persists about what these areas should be called, whether they are truly homologous to the monkey V4 area in the sense of sharing a common evolutionary origin, and whether they are functionally equivalent to monkey V4 (see Wandell & Wade, 2003, for a review). One group of researchers (Bartels & Zeki, 2000) reported two separate clusters of activity on the ventral surface of the human brain, a posterior region that is retinotopically organized and perhaps comparable to monkey V4, and a more anterior region that is less clearly retinotopically organized and that the researchers referred to as V4α (● Figure 6.15). Other researchers reported a region of color-sensitive

● **FIGURE 6.15 Color-sensitive regions of the ventral visual cortex.** This study by Bartels and Zeki (2000) found two regions that were sensitive to color information. A more posterior region, called V4, has a retinotopic organization, as seen by the finding that stimulation of the upper (white) and lower (blue) visual fields lead to responses in slightly different subareas of this region. The more anterior color-sensitive region (labeled V4α) does not appear to be retinotopically mapped, because stimulation of upper and lower visual fields leads to overlapping activation. *Source:* Fig. 5 from Bartels, A., & Zeki, S. (2000). The architecture of the colour centre in the human visual brain: New results and a review. European Journal of Neuroscience, 12, 172–193.

activation that was anterior to the presumed V4 location and that they referred to as "V8" (Hadjikhani et al., 1998). Despite the continuing controversy in this area, two things seem clear: there are color-sensitive regions in ventral visual cortex, and those regions likely include areas anterior to V4 as well as V4 proper. This latter conclusion fits with evidence from monkey studies that report the involvement of more anterior areas (beyond V4) in color perception (e.g., Conway et al., 2007; Tootell, Nelissen, Vanduffel, & Orban, 2004).

It is also clear that the idea that V4 is the brain's "color center" is far too simplistic. On the one hand, cells in V4 of the monkey are also responsive to properties other than color, such as line orientation, depth, and spatial frequency (e.g., David, Hayden, & Gallant, 2006; Desimone & Schein, 1987; Hegdé & Van Essen, 2005). On the other hand, cells in earlier areas of the visual stream also appear to code for color information (as do regions more anterior to V4). For example, monkey studies suggest that about half of the cells in areas V2 and V3 are sensitive to color, as shown by the fact that they fire more strongly to some colors than others (Gegenfurtner & Kiper, 2004). Therefore, V4 does not appear to be unique in its color sensitivity. Rather, color is an attribute that is coded at several levels of the visual processing stream, beginning with the cones in the retina and extending through parvocellular layers of the LGN, the striate cortex, and extrastriate areas V2 and V3, as well as V4 and more anterior regions (e.g., Conway & Tsao, 2006).

So, what conclusion should we reach regarding area V4 and color perception? Human neuroimaging and patient studies clearly imply an association between ventral extrastriate subregions and color processing, but the exact nature of the association—how to define different subregions, and what unique contribution each one makes to color perception—is still subject to debate among vision scientists. While this controversy persists, we should avoid the trap of thinking simplistically that somehow, all on its own, the V4 region is responsible for color vision and nothing else. A more distributed model of color perception, with V4 playing an important role, is most likely. Although we have focused in depth on area V4, the lessons of this discussion extend to other visual cortical regions as well, as researchers face the challenges of associating structure with function in visual perception. Simplistic structure-function associations are unlikely to hold up over time, and researchers must strive to integrate findings across species and methodologies to gain a fuller picture.

■ Divergence into the "What" and "Where" Pathways

The complexity of the organization of visual regions in the brain can seem mind-boggling, as shown in
● Figure 6.16, which represents a preliminary sketch

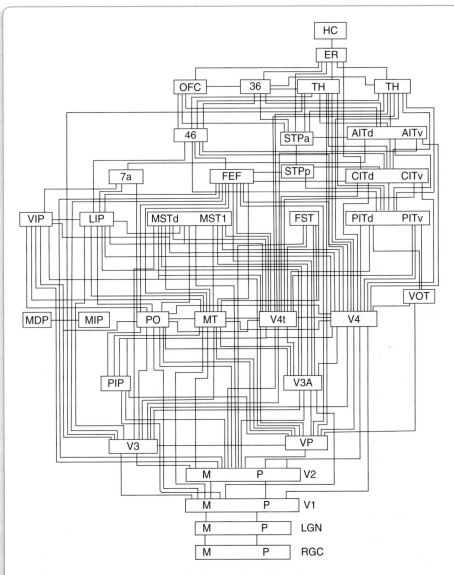

● **FIGURE 6.16 Illustration of the complexities of the visual cortex.** Each box is a separate cortical region that is known to play a role in vision, and the lines represent known pathways between these regions. These data are based on anatomical findings in the macaque monkey reported by Felleman and Van Essen (1991). *Source:* Felleman, D.J., & Van Essen, D.C. (1991). Distributed hierarchical processing in the primate cerebral cortex. Cerebral Cortex, 1, 1–47. Reprinted by permission of Oxford University Press.

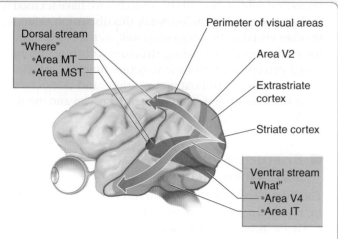

● **FIGURE 6.17   Illustration of dorsal and ventral streams for visual information.** © 2010 Cengage Learning

of anatomical connections between various visually responsive regions of the macaque cortex (Felleman & Van Essen, 1991). The human visual system is likely to be just as complex, if not more so. Amidst this complexity, researchers have identified two main routes along which information travels when it leaves the striate cortex. The striate cortex projects both "downward," or ventrally, in the brain toward the inferior temporal cortex, and also upwards, or dorsally, in the brain toward the parietal lobe (● Figure 6.17). Area V4, which we discussed in the previous section, is one step along the ventral pathway that continues to extend into the temporal lobes past this bifurcation point.

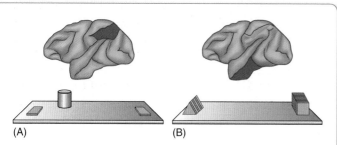

● **FIGURE 6.18   Tasks sensitive to dorsal vs. ventral stream damage in monkeys.** (A) In the landmark-discrimination task, the monkey sees two identical food-well covers and a landmark. A reward is hidden in the food well closer to the landmark. The position of the landmark varies randomly from trial to trial, sometimes closer to the left food well and sometimes closer to the right well. When monkeys sustain bilateral damage to the posterior parietal region, shown in red, they cannot perform this task. (B) In the object-discrimination task, the monkey sees two distinct food-well covers, one of which it has been familiarized with prior to the trial. A reward is hidden under the food-well cover that was not previously viewed. This task is known as a *nonmatch-to-sample paradigm* because the animal must choose the well covered by the object that was not viewed previously. When monkeys sustain bilateral damage to inferotemporal areas, shown in red, they cannot perform this task. © 2011 Cengage Learning

As information travels along either of these two pathways out of the striate cortex, it undergoes further transformations to serve the goals of higher-level vision. Each step along either pathway takes the information one step farther away from the "raw materials" encoded by the retina and toward the higher-level, more abstract representations of the visual world that we will return to in Chapters 7 and 8. Processing that occurs along these two paths, the ventral and dorsal paths, is thought to serve two main goals of vision: identifying objects and representing their spatial locations (Ungerleider & Mishkin, 1982; Ungerleider & Pasternak, 2004). These functions are sometimes referred to as the "what" and "where" functions, answering the two main questions: "What kind of object am I looking at?" and "Where is it located in visual space?"

Original evidence for the dissociation between dorsal and ventral paths came from studies of monkeys with brain lesions. In this research (Mishkin, Ungerleider, & Macko, 1983), monkeys were trained to complete two different visual discrimination tasks, one that required understanding spatial locations and another that required understanding objects and shapes (● Figure 6.18). In the first task, monkeys were shown two food wells with identical covers, and a small tower was situated closer to one of two wells. The position of the tower was moved from one trial to the next, but on each trial the food was hidden in the well closest to the tower. Thus, to obtain the food, the monkey had to understand spatial positions. Damage to the parietal region (dorsal stream) disrupted performance on this task, whereas damage to the temporal lobe (ventral stream) did not.

In the second task, the monkey was shown an object (such as a striped pyramid) in a central location. This object was then placed over one food well, and another object (e.g., a checkered rectangle) was placed over the other food well. In each trial, the food was hidden under the novel object (in this case, the checkered rectangle). This procedure is known as a **nonmatch-to-sample paradigm** because in order to get the food, the monkey has to choose the item that doesn't match the previously shown sample object. Normal performance on the task requires an ability to discriminate between the two shapes. Monkeys with temporal lobe damage performed poorly on this task, whereas those with parietal lobe damage performed normally. Thus, this elegant double dissociation provides evidence that dorsal and ventral streams are crucial for spatial understanding and object recognition, respectively.

Neuroimaging studies in humans confirm the basic dissociation between the dorsal and ventral pathways. For example, in one study, participants viewed pictures of objects presented on a screen (Marois, Leung, & Gore, 2000). On some trials, the object's identity changed (from a chair to a car, for example), and on other trials its spatial position changed. Although either type of change produced increases in activity in both ventral and dorsal stream areas, the magnitude of the increase depended on whether the identity or location had changed. As illustrated in ● Figure 6.19, identity changes led to greater increases in lateral occipital and inferior temporal cortex activity compared to location changes, whereas location changes led to greater increases in superior occipital and posterior parietal cortex activity.

Although initial studies conceptualized the dorsal and ventral streams as "where" and "what" pathways, many researchers currently conceptualize the dorsal path as a "how" pathway rather than a "where" pathway, because it is closely linked with motor areas of the brain that govern how we act upon the visual world (Goodale & Milner, 1992; Goodale & Westwood, 2004). The functions of the ventral and dorsal paths will be covered in much more depth in Chapters 7 and 8, which focus on object recognition and spatial cognition, respectively. At this point, it is useful to see these two paths as another example of parallel processing within the visual system.

Auditory Processing

Research on the neural bases of perception has long been dominated by studies of vision, because primates like us are known to have exquisite visual capabilities. But audition, the perception of sounds, is also a crucial sensory function of the primate brain and is essential for some relatively unique human capacities, such as language. Here we review some of the most important findings in research on the neural basis of auditory perception.

It can be useful to consider why we have both auditory and visual senses. What additional information about the world does audition provide that we can't get from vision? One obvious limitation of vision is that it is restricted to what your eyes are viewing. Vision gives you no information about what is going on behind you. Likewise, vision yields little information about what is happening far away, whereas sounds can travel some distance. Also, though this may seem obvious, vision is not very useful at night. We evolved in a world where both dangers and opportunities could exist behind our backs, hidden in bushes, at far distances across the landscape, or under cover of darkness. Therefore, the ability to perceive sounds is an extremely advantageous complement to the ability to perceive patterns of light. Auditory processing is also essential to the perception of speech, which we will consider in detail in Chapter 9.

■ Computational Problems in Audition

The auditory system must solve some of the same kinds of computational problems as the visual system.

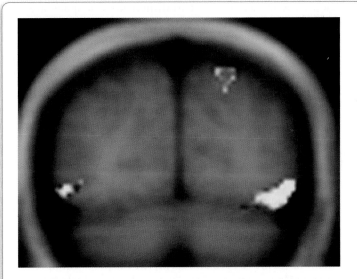

● **FIGURE 6.19 Dissociation between areas sensitive to object orientation and object identity.** In this study, participants viewed pictures of objects. On some trials, the object's identity changed, whereas on other trials, its spatial location changed. The figure shows the ventral stream area that was more activated by identity changes than by location changes (in yellow/red) and the dorsal stream area that was more activated by location changes than by identity changes (in purple/blue). *Source:* Fig 4. from Marois, R., Leung, H.C., & Gore, J.C. (2000). A stimulus-driven approach to object identity and location processing in the human brain. Neuron, 25, 717–728.

Different sensory features, such as the pitch, loudness, and timing of sounds, must be processed in order to recognize specific auditory events, like the sound of an alarm ringing or a child crying. This need to represent various features of the stimulus is similar to the visual system's need to represent features such as contrast, line orientation, brightness, and color. The representation of these important features is constructed by the brain from elemental inputs coded by sensory receptors (spots of light striking photoreceptors in the case of vision, or sound waves stimulating the hair cells in the inner ear in the case of audition).

The auditory system, like the visual system, also has to be able to separate "figures" from their backgrounds. For example, visual perception allows us to discern an apple against the background of the whole tree. Similarly, auditory perception allows us to separate a single sound stream, such as a person's voice, from the ambient background noise.

Auditory perception must also allow us to locate sounds in space, just as vision is also concerned with the location of objects in the world. For example, it is useful to know whether the roar of that lion is coming from behind you or to your left. The problem of spatial localization is even more challenging for audition than for vision, because space is not coded directly on the initial array of sound receptors within the ear, whereas at least two dimensions of space are coded directly on the retina. Therefore, a representation of auditory space must be computed by the brain. As we will see shortly, computations necessary for spatial localization are initiated very early in the auditory system.

■ Organization of the Auditory Pathways

Auditory processing begins in the ear, as you probably suspected. The ear is a very complex organ (● Figure 6.20), and we will focus here only on its most important features. Within the inner ear is the **cochlea**, which contains the cells that translate sound energy into neural impulses. The cochlea is wound up into a spiral, and has a set of membranes that move in relation to one another when sound waves enter the ear. When these membranes move back and forth, the motion stimulates **hair cells** (● Figure 6.21). These cells have little hairs called *cilia* sticking out of them, and the movement of the cilia in response to sound vibrations ultimately causes the cell to emit action potentials. The axons of

the hair cells synapse on spiral ganglion cells, which make up the auditory nerve, just as the axons of retinal ganglion cells make up the optic nerve.

Most importantly for our purposes, sound vibrations of different frequencies cause stimulation of different subsets of hair cells within the cochlea. That is, high frequencies stimulate a different set of hair cells than low frequencies. If you could unroll the cochlea, you would find that hair cells that are sensitive to high-frequency sound are located near the base of the cochlea, whereas those sensitive to low-frequency sound are located near the apex (tip) of the cochlea. Therefore, by knowing which sets of hair cells were stimulated, the brain can determine which frequencies are present in the sound. This organization creates a **tonotopic map**, much the way that the pattern of light across the retina forms a retinotopic map. In the case of audition, the map represents sound frequencies.

Auditory information passes through several stopover points on its way from the ear to the auditory cortex

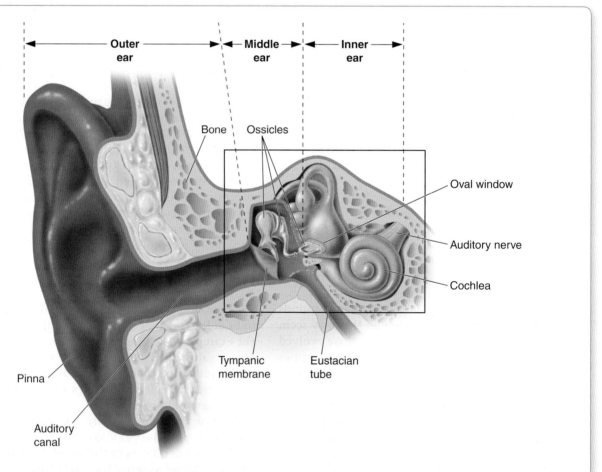

● **FIGURE 6.20   The anatomy of the ear.** Sound enters the ear canal both directly and by reflection off the pinna (outer ear). In the ear canal, sound causes vibration of the tympanic membrane, which in turn causes vibration of the bones (ossicles) of the inner ear. These vibrations are then transferred to the cochlea via the oval window. © 2010 Cengage Learning

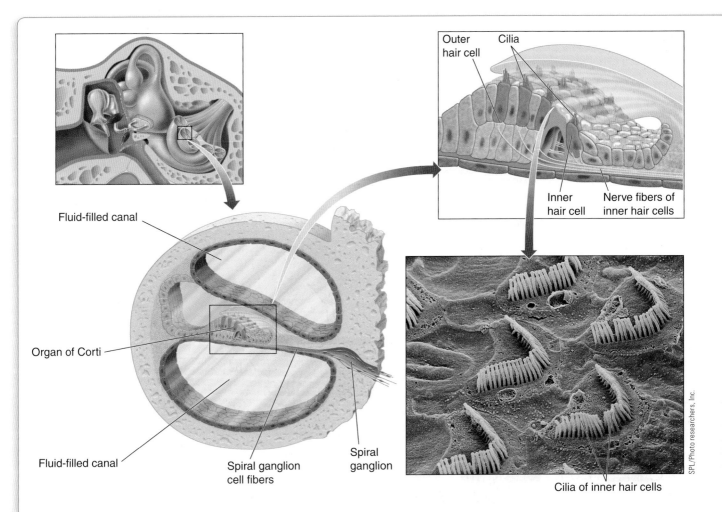

Outer hair cell   Cilia

Inner hair cell   Nerve fibers of inner hair cells

Fluid-filled canal

Organ of Corti

Fluid-filled canal

Spiral ganglion cell fibers

Spiral ganglion

Cilia of inner hair cells

SPL/Photo researchers, Inc.

● **FIGURE 6.21   The cochlea.** Residing in the middle of the cochlea is the organ of Corti, which contains the hair cells that respond to sound. It is surrounded on both sides by fluid-filled canals that contain lymph-like liquid. Movement of the cilia of the inner hair cells is transduced into an electrical signal. This signal is relayed to spiral ganglion cells, the axons of which form the basis of the auditory nerve.
© 2010 Cengage Learning

(● Figure 6.22). Two of these locations are in the brainstem. First, the auditory nerve synapses in the **cochlear nucleus** in the medulla, and from there a pathway sends the information onward to the **superior olivary nucleus**, also in the medulla. Note that between the cochlear nucleus and the olivary nucleus, the pathway extends both contralaterally and ipsilaterally, such that information from both ears is shared with both left and right olivary nuclei. From there, the information travels to the **inferior colliculus** in the midbrain, and then onward to the **medial geniculate nucleus** of the thalamus. From there, the information is finally sent to the primary auditory cortex, which we discuss in more detail in a later section.

At this point it is helpful to note both similarities and differences between the auditory and visual pathways. Some steps in these two pathways seem similar; for example, the inferior colliculus in the midbrain receives auditory information whereas (just above it)

the superior colliculus receives visual information. The close proximity of the inferior and superior colliculi allows for some rudimentary audiovisual interactions that can assist in orienting to stimuli in the environment. Further, the medial geniculate nucleus of the thalamus receives auditory information, whereas the lateral geniculate nucleus of the thalamus receives visual information, and both of these thalamic nuclei project to the primary sensory cortex for that modality.

Another feature that the auditory and visual systems share, to some extent, is the presence of descending projections. In this chapter we have focused on the ascending pathway, from the ear to the cortex. However, there are also descending projections that send modulatory influences all the way down each step of the auditory processing chain. In this way, top-down signals representing the effects of attention, expectations, and contextual factors can shape the information that is proceeding upward from the ear to the cortex.

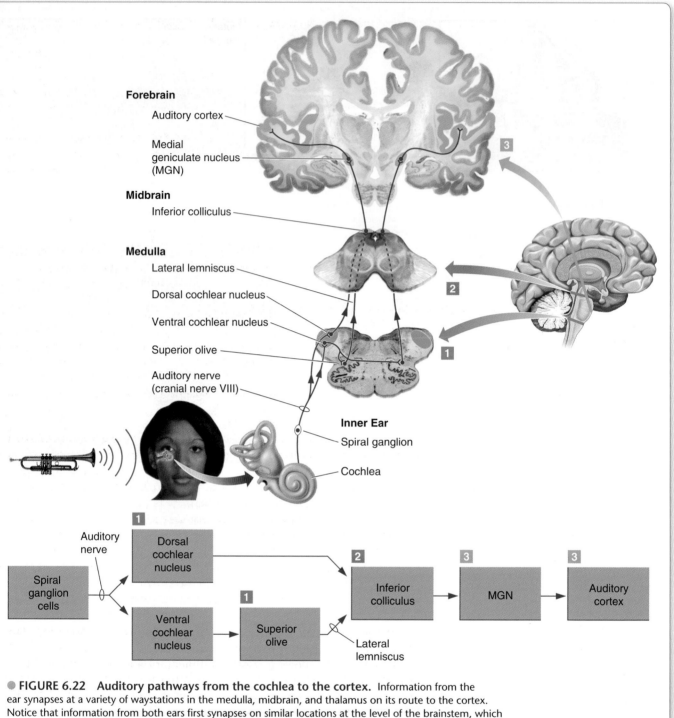

● **FIGURE 6.22 Auditory pathways from the cochlea to the cortex.** Information from the ear synapses at a variety of waystations in the medulla, midbrain, and thalamus on its route to the cortex. Notice that information from both ears first synapses on similar locations at the level of the brainstem, which provides a mechanism for determining the spatial location of sound. © 2010 Cengage Learning

These top-down projections may serve a function similar to that of the projections from the visual cortex to the LGN in the visual system.

Beyond these similarities, we can also see some differences between visual and auditory pathways. For example, there are more stopover points between the ear and the auditory cortex than between the eye and the visual cortex. This means that some computations may be going on in earlier stages, such as the brainstem,

in the auditory system. Furthermore, auditory information from both ears is shared at the level of the brainstem, whereas visual information from both eyes is not integrated until the level of the visual cortex.

■ Brainstem Computation of Spatial Location

As mentioned earlier, the spatial location of a sound source must be computed by the auditory system, because the cochlea itself does not directly map spatial

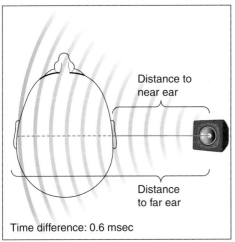
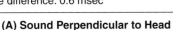

Time difference: 0.6 msec

(A) Sound Perpendicular to Head

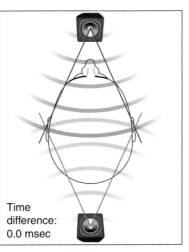

Time difference: 0.0 msec

(B) Sound Directly in Front of or Behind Head

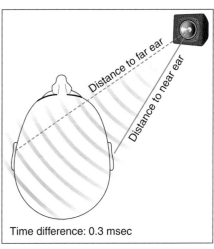

Time difference: 0.3 msec

(C) Sound at 45 Degrees from Head

● **FIGURE 6.23 Localizing sound by comparing inputs from the two ears.** In (A), the sound reaches the right ear approximately 0.6 ms before it reaches the left ear. In (B), sounds either directly ahead or directly behind will reach the right and left ears simultaneously. It can often be difficult to tell whether a sound is coming from directly ahead or directly behind; luckily, turning your head a little can eliminate the confusion. In (C), the sound at about a 45-degree angle to the right will strike the right ear about 0.3 ms earlier than the left ear. © 2010 Cengage Learning

locations in the same way that the retina does. Here we discuss the informational cues that the auditory system can use to localize sounds, as well as evidence from other species that these computations can be carried out in the brainstem.

The fact that we each have two ears is essential to the ability to localize sounds. The auditory system calculates sound location by comparing the inputs from the two ears, just as the visual system calculates the dimension of spatial depth (which is not coded on the retina) by comparing inputs from the two eyes. Because the ears are located on opposite sides of the head, a single sound source will have a different impact on each ear, depending on where the sound source is located. As illustrated in ● Figure 6.23, a sound coming from the right side of your head will reach your right ear slightly before it reaches your left ear. It will also be louder when it reaches your right ear, because the head will block some of the sound from reaching the left ear. Therefore, by comparing **interaural** ("between the ears") **time differences** and **interaural intensity differences**, the auditory system can deduce the spatial location of a sound source. This computation requires exquisite precision in timing, because interaural time differences are typically less than one millisecond.

The auditory system also relies upon a more complex set of cues that reflect how sound is shaped by the head and ear. A sound coming from above and a sound coming from below will each be shaped differently by the structure of the outer ear, and these cues are analyzed by the auditory system to determine spatial location in the vertical dimension. There is an easy way to prove to yourself how much this shaping of sound by the outer ear influences your sound localization ability. Find a friend and ask him or her to shake some keys in front of you, either right in front, above, or below you while your eyes are closed. You should have no difficulty telling the location of the keys. Now try the same thing, but this time fold your ears over to block the ear canal, and notice what happens.

Evidence from other species suggests that brainstem structures are capable of basic computation of spatial location. Many studies have been carried out in species of predatory birds, such as owls, that have excellent spatial localization abilities (Konishi, 2003). Imagine an owl perched high on a tree branch at night, listening for the rustle of a small mouse far below. The owl needs to know exactly where the mouse is so that it can swoop down suddenly to catch its prey. Part of the owl's exceptional spatial localization may reflect species-specific adaptations—for example, the ears of an owl are tilted asymmetrically, one upward and one downward, to further aid in distinguishing sounds. However, much of what has been learned about the owl's brainstem computations regarding auditory space appears to apply to mammals as well (Schnupp & Carr, 2009).

Brainstem areas compute spatial location in part by using so-called **delay lines** and cells called **coincidence detectors** that take into account the different arrival times of a sound at the left and right ears.

(A)

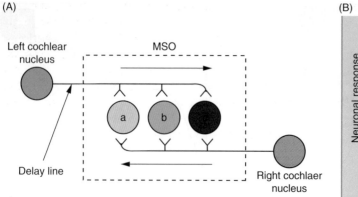

(B)

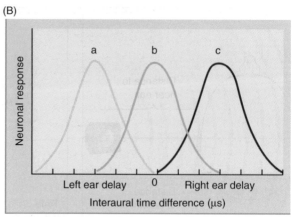

● **FIGURE 6.24   Model of delay lines and coincidence detectors in brainstem.** (A) Signals from the right and left cochlear nuclei are sent along axons, referred to as *delay lines,* in the medial superior olivary nucleus (MSO) in the brainstem. Cells in this nucleus (such as cells a, b, and c) are excited by simultaneous stimulation from both input lines. (B) Cells a, b, and c respond maximally to different interaural time differences. For example, cell a responds best when sound arrives first at the right ear, and then after a brief delay at the left ear. Such a scenario causes the inputs from the cochlear nuclei to arrive at the same time at cell a. In contrast, cell b responds best when the sound arrives simultaneously at the left and right ears, and cell c responds best when the sound arrives first at the left ear and then at the right ear after a short delay. Because interaural time differences are a cue to the location of the sound, these cells code for different sound locations. *Source:* Cohen, Y.E., & Knudsen, H.I. (1999). Maps versus clusters: Different representations of auditory space in the midbrain and forebrain. Trends in Neuroscience, 22, 128–135. Reprinted by permission of Elsevier.

A schematic depiction is shown in ● Figure 6.24. The basic idea is that certain cells respond preferentially to particular timing discrepancies between signals from the two ears. To understand the concept of delay lines and coincidence detectors, consider this analogy. Imagine two runners whose starting positions are at opposite ends of a football field. If the two people start running toward one another at the same time (and at the same rate), they will meet in the middle, at the 50-yard line. However, if one runner gets a head start, the two runners will not meet in the middle. Rather, they will meet somewhere closer to the runner who started late, because the head start will allow the first runner to cover more distance. If you wanted to know which runner started first, you could simply look at where the runners met. If they met at the 50-yard line, then you would know that the runners started at the same time. But if they met at the 25-yard line (three-quarters of the way down the field), you would know that one of the runners had a head start (and you would know which one).

Now, imagine that instead of runners, there are sounds arriving at the two ears, and they are traveling toward one another not on a football field but as signals traveling along axons, "delay lines" that reach into the midbrain and make contact with a line of cells along their path. Imagine that each cell along the path is positioned in a spot analogous to a yardline on the football field. Furthermore, each cell is stimulated by the traveling signal, and it is maximally stimulated when the signals from the right and left ears arrive at

the cell simultaneously. Such cells are often referred to as "coincidence detectors" because they respond best to the coinciding of inputs from the two ears. A cell right in the middle of this path (equivalent to the 50-yard line in the football field example) would be maximally excited when the signals from the two ears started down their paths at the same time, because the two signals would meet each other at this middle cell in the series and they would both stimulate that cell simultaneously. But another cell, let's say one positioned analogous to the 25-yard line, would be most excited when the signal from one ear got a head start, because the head-start signal could get further along the pathway (toward the "25-yard line" cell) before it met up with the later-starting signal.

Essentially, knowing which of the coincidence detectors is maximally activated is equivalent to knowing where the left-ear and right-ear signals meet up along the delay lines, which in turn tells you which signal got a head start. Now remember that the "head start" represents the interaural time difference, which is a cue to the location of the sound. Logically, then, activity in cells along the delay lines codes for the spatial location of the sound source.

Through careful work with animal models such as the barn owl, researchers have determined that such coincidence detectors are present in the superior olivary nucleus (called the laminar nucleus in the owl), which is the first point at which information from the two ears can be compared (for reviews, see

Cohen & Knudsen, 1999; Konishi, 2003) (refer back to Figure 6.22). Thus, at the level of the brainstem, a map of auditory space is essentially computed by comparing the inputs from the two ears. Subsequent steps in the auditory processing sequence make further use of this spatial location information. For example, the inferior colliculus also contains a map of auditory space that is then integrated with the visual map of space in the superior colliculus. Intuitively, it makes sense that spatial location would be coded very early in the processing stream, because it is so important for rapid response to auditory events.

The delay-line model is an elegant computational model explaining how spatial location can be coded rather simply. Of course, the more you think about it, the more you will realize that things can't be quite so simple. For example, let's say that you hear a low-pitched sound to your left, but a high-pitched sound to your right. How can the auditory system identify their separate spatial locations if both signals are traveling along the delay lines? One clue is that there are multiple delay lines in the olivary nucleus, each corresponding to a different sound frequency. Hence, the low-pitched sound is processed through a different set of coincidence detectors than the high-pitched sound, allowing each sound to be localized separately. In addition, as mentioned previously, the brain can use interaural intensity (loudness) differences as well as interaural time differences as a cue to location. Interaural intensity differences also appear to be coded by the olivary nucleus, albeit by a different sector of that nucleus than timing differences (Cohen & Knudsen, 1999). Finally, the brain can also use more complex cues, such as the changing composition of the sound as it bounces around either the left or right outer ear. The neural coding of these more complex spatial location cues is not currently well understood.

■ Organization of Auditory Cortex

Once auditory information has ascended through subcortical paths, it arrives at the auditory cortex, just beneath the Sylvian fissure in the temporal lobe. The layout of auditory cortex has been studied in other mammals, including primates, through single-cell recording. Neuroimaging studies in humans have also addressed the organization

of auditory cortex, although studying auditory perception in a neuroimaging environment poses some challenges. For example, the machinery required to conduct fMRI studies can generate a lot of noise. In addition, it can be difficult to create naturalistic sounds (for example, sounds perceived as coming from various distances) within the constraints of a magnetic resonance imaging system. Nevertheless, studies in humans and other species generally converge on a few key principles of auditory cortex organization (for review, see Recanzone & Sutter, 2008).

First, auditory cortex can be subdivided into a few regions, illustrated in ● Figure 6.25. These regions are called the **core**, the **belt** (which surrounds the core), and the **parabelt** (which surrounds the belt) (for review, see Hackett & Kaas, 2004; Romanski & Averbeck, 2009). The core itself can be further subdivided into areas A1 (primary auditory cortex) and regions anterior to A1, referred to as the rostral and rostrotemporal fields. The core region receives input from the medial geniculate nucleus, whereas the belt region receives most of its input from the core, and the parabelt receives input from the belt. So, there appears to be a rough hierarchy extending from the medial geniculate to the core, then to the belt, then to the parabelt. However, the belt and parabelt regions also receive some direct input from the medial geniculate, so the hierarchy is not completely rigid.

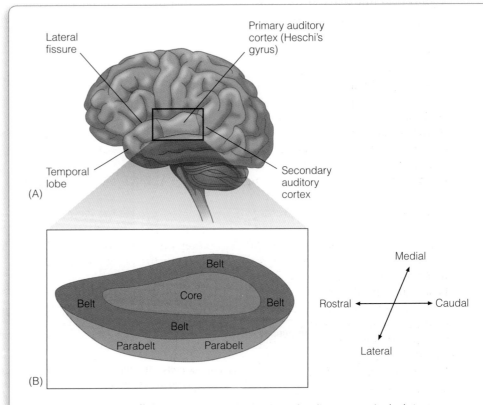

● **FIGURE 6.25 Auditory cortex.** (A) The position of auditory cortex in the human brain. (B) This representation of auditory cortex in the macaque monkey includes the central core area, surrounded by the belt and parabelt. © 2010 Cengage Learning

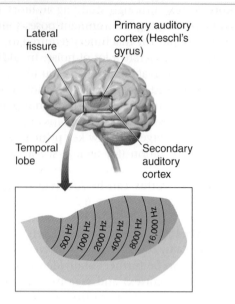

● **FIGURE 6.26   Tonotopic mapping in auditory cortex.** Cells that are all maximally responsive to the same frequency are localized in similar bands or regions. Note that cells maximally responsive to lower frequencies are located more rostrally, whereas those responsive to higher frequencies are located more caudally. © 2010 Cengage Learning

All three of the areas within the core contain *tonotopic maps.* ● Figure 6.26 illustrates a tonotopic map within area A1. A tonotopic map is somewhat analogous to a retinotopic map in the visual cortex, in the sense that they both map out certain features of the sensory world in a

systematic way. However, whereas a retinotopic map is essentially a map of space (that is, a map of the retina), the tonotopic map is not a map of space. Rather, it is a map of sound frequencies. The *frequency* of a sound refers to how fast sound waves oscillate, and roughly corresponds to our perceptual experience of pitch; high-frequency sounds are perceived as high pitches, and low-frequency sounds as low pitches. In primary auditory cortex, each cell responds best to a certain frequency of sound, and neighboring cells respond to similar frequencies. In a sense, the tonotopic map is a map of the cochlea, because the cochlear cells are also organized by frequency.

Cells in a tonotopic map can be thought of as having receptive fields, but these receptive fields are not spatially defined as in the visual system. Rather, individual cells have preferred sound frequencies, such that only frequencies within a particular range will excite the cell; other frequencies will produce no response from the cell. For each cell, we can create a graph that shows the cell's sensitivity across different sound frequencies (● Figure 6.27). This graph is often referred to as the cell's **tuning curve**.

Cells in different parts of the auditory cortex have different kinds of tuning curves. Within area A1, cells are sharply tuned to specific frequencies, whereas in the belt and parabelt regions, cells are more broadly tuned, responding to a variety of stimulus frequencies. In A1, cells also tend to respond best to pure tones (tones composed of only one frequency), whereas in the surrounding regions, cells tend to respond best to more complex stimuli that incorporate several individual sound

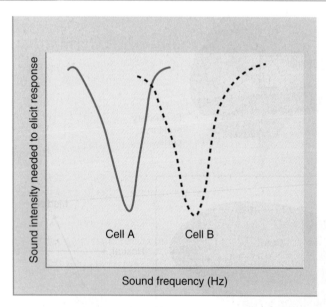

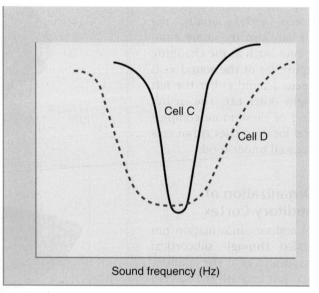

● **FIGURE 6.27   Tuning curve of auditory cortex cells.** This figure schematically illustrates the sensitivity of hypothetical auditory cortex cells to different sound frequencies. The curve represents the sound intensity that is needed to provoke a response from each cell, as a function of the sound frequency. The low point on the curve indicates the sound frequency to which the cell is most responsive. Cell A is more responsive to lower sound frequencies than cell B; cell C has a sharp tuning curve, whereas cell D has a shallow tuning curve.

frequencies. If the belt and parabelt areas are damaged in monkeys while the core is left intact, the monkeys are able to detect individual sounds, but they have difficulty recognizing complex patterns, such as tone sequences (Kaas, Hackett, & Tramo, 1999). Other studies in monkeys have shown that cells within the lateral belt area are especially responsive to the sounds of monkey vocalizations (Romanski & Averbeck, 2009). Thus, as in the visual system, there is a hierarchy in which early cortical stages seem to represent simpler features, whereas later cortical stages represent more complex combinations of features.

In humans, the lateral belt and parabelt regions are thought to correspond to the planum temporale, an anatomical region that is known to be especially important in speech perception. The planum temporale on the left side of the brain is activated by speech sounds, while this region of the brain in both the left and right hemispheres is also activated in response to other complex auditory stimuli like sound patterns, music, and environmental sounds (Griffiths & Warren, 2002). Thus, this region seems crucial in auditory pattern recognition.

One hypothesis about the organization of auditory cortex proposes that spatial and nonspatial features of a stimulus are handled in somewhat separate streams (Hackett & Kaas, 2004; Rauschecker & Tian, 2000). According to this idea, information about spatial location is processed in more caudal/posterior regions of the auditory cortex, whereas nonspatial features (such as sound patterns) are represented in more rostral/anterior sectors of auditory cortex. This organization is analogous to the "what" and "where" segregation of function in the visual system. Some evidence for this view is found in the anatomical projections of the auditory cortex. Caudal auditory cortex projects to areas known to be important in spatial localization, such as the parietal cortex and frontal eye fields, whereas rostral auditory cortex projects to association areas of the temporal lobe and orbitofrontal regions (Hackett & Kaas, 2004). In addition, recordings from single cells in the monkey offer some support for this notion. Researchers recorded the activity of cells in the lateral-belt region of auditory cortex while monkeys listened to communication calls from other monkeys. Cells in the anterior portion of the belt were more responsive to the specific type of call, whereas cells in the posterior region of the belt were more sensitive to the spatial location (Tian, Reser, Durham, Kustov, & Rauschecker, 2001).

Some imaging studies in humans have also provided evidence for the idea of a dissociation between auditory spatial localization versus auditory object recognition. For example, one study found that an auditory localization task activated the inferior parietal lobe and middle and inferior frontal gyrus, whereas an auditory recognition task activated middle temporal gyrus and the precuneus area (Maeder et al., 2001). Although not all imaging studies consistently support a clear dissociation between spatial localization and object recognition (e.g., Middlebrooks, 2002; Zatorre, Bouffard, Ahad, & Belin, 2002;

for discussion, see Griffiths, Warren, Scott, Nelken, & King, 2004), recent evidence combining fMRI and MEG results provides some strong support for such a distinction (Ahveninen et al., 2006). Participants heard a vowel emanating from a specific location in space. Next they heard a target that was either an identical item, a different vowel from the same location, or the same vowel in a different location. Posterior regions of both Heschl's gyrus and the superior temporal gyrus responded more when the items differed in spatial location than when they were different vowels, suggesting that these regions are sensitive to "where" an auditory item is located. In contrast, anterior regions of both Heschl's gyrus and superior temporal gyrus responded more when the items differed in the vowel presented rather than spatial location, suggesting that these regions are more sensitive to "what" an auditory item is. These responses occurred very quickly, within 70 to 150 milliseconds of stimulus onset, with information in the "where" pathway activated approximately 30 milliseconds before that in the "what" pathway. The researchers suggested that perhaps information from the "where" pathway can be fed to the "what" pathway to help direct attention to auditory objects that need to be identified. More research is needed to better characterize the extent of these "what" and "where" auditory pathways, and to understand more about the ways in which they interact.

■ Auditory-Visual Interactions

We tend to think of auditory and visual processing as taking place in largely separate streams within the brain, but at some point sounds and sights must be associated with one another. Such integration is necessary to associate the visual image of your dog, for example, with the sound of his bark. In a traditional hierarchical model, this multisensory integration was thought to take place at higher-level association regions of the brain, such as the association cortex in the temporal and parietal lobes. According to this convergent model, auditory and visual inputs are first processed in their separate cortical areas, and then those areas converge upon higher-level association areas. Although this model clearly and accurately captures many aspects of multisensory integration, recent studies imply that interactions between auditory and visual processing can take place at earlier stages. According to interactive models, processing in one sensory modality (e.g., vision) can influence the information that is being simultaneously processed in another modality (e.g., audition).

An example of multisensory processing in auditory cortex comes from a study that examined responsiveness to vocalizations in monkeys (Ghazanfar, Maier, Hoffman, & Logothetis, 2005; see also Ghazanfar, Chandrasekaran, & Logothetis, 2008). Researchers recorded signals from populations of cells in the core and belt regions of monkey auditory cortex while the monkey either heard the sound of another monkey's grunt, viewed a silent video of the other monkey making the grunt sound, or heard the grunt together with the video. Not surprisingly, the sound without video activated cells in the auditory cortex, whereas the video without any sound did not activate auditory cortex cells. Most interestingly, though, the response of auditory cortex cells to the sound was altered by the simultaneous presence of the video. Some cell populations showed an enhanced response when the grunt sound was accompanied by the video, and others showed a suppressed response (● Figure 6.28). Thus, cells in auditory cortex are influenced by visual information. Future research will help to determine whether such visual influences on auditory processing are due to direct connections between unimodal visual and auditory cortical areas, or whether they are due to descending projections from multimodal areas (such as temporal and parietal association areas).

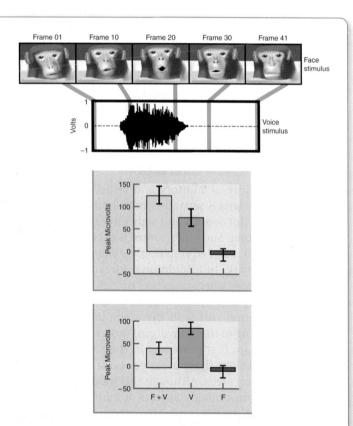

● **FIGURE 6.28 Effect of audiovisual stimulation on the response of auditory cortex cells in the monkey.** In this study, monkeys either heard a vocalization (voice alone – V), viewed a silent video of the monkey making that vocalization (face alone – F), or heard the vocalization along with the video (face + voice – F + V). One type of auditory cortex cell, shown on the top, exhibited an enhanced response when the voice and face image were presented together, compared to the voice alone. Another type, shown on the bottom, exhibited a reduced response when the voice and face image were presented together, compared to the voice alone. *Source:* Ghazanfar, A.A., Maier, J.X., Hoffan, K.L., & Logothetis, N.K. (2005). Multisensory integration of dynamic faces and voices in rhesus monkey auditory cortex. Journal of Neuroscience, 25, 5004–5012. Reprinted by permission of Society for Neuroscience.

This particular study focused on visual influences on auditory processing. However, it is also possible for auditory information to affect visual processing. Recently researchers have shown that primary visual cortex (V1), particularly the region that represents the peripheral visual field, receives anatomical projections from auditory cortex (Falchier, Clavagnier, Barone, & Kennedy, 2002). In addition, V1 cells appear to be responsive to auditory information in at least some circumstances. One study recorded the activity of V1 cells in a task in which a monkey had to orient its gaze to a stimulus in the periphery (Wang, Celebrini, Trotter, & Barone, 2008). Cells in V1 responded more quickly when the stimulus was a combined audiovisual stimulus than when it was solely a visual stimulus. However, the auditory information had no effect on V1 responses when the monkey simply sat passively during the task rather than being required to orient its gaze. These findings suggest that audiovisual interactions in V1 may occur only when multisensory integration is functionally useful for performing a task.

Other studies have examined multimodal integration in brain regions that lie beyond the primary sensory areas, specifically regions that receive convergent input from auditory and visual areas. One example of this approach is research on multimodal coding in the ventrolateral prefrontal cortex (VLPFC; see Romanski, 2007, for review). Although the VLPFC is primarily involved in controlling motor functions, some cells within this region appear to be responsive to certain kinds of sensory information that is important for communication. For example, cells in a subregion of the VLPFC of the monkey are sensitive to the sounds of other monkeys' vocalizations. Interestingly, this subregion lies adjacent to another subregion containing cells that are especially responsive to images of monkey faces.

By recording from cells in both these areas while presenting audio only, visual only, and combined audiovisual stimuli, researchers demonstrated that some cells in VLPFC are multisensory (Sugihara, Diltz, Averbeck, & Romanski, 2006). For example, a cell that is primarily visual, responding maximally to a monkey face, may modulate its firing rate when a monkey vocalization is simultaneously presented. Likewise, a cell that is primarily auditory, responding maximally to a monkey voice, may modulate its firing rate when a face is presented along with the voice. Interestingly, audiovisual combinations that did not involve faces or voices (such as pictures of random dots paired with hand claps) did not excite the cells as much as face-voice pairings. These results are especially exciting because the ventral frontal lobe is known to be important in language production, as we will discuss in more detail in Chapter 9. Thus, one function of multisensory integration in the VLPFC may be to facilitate communication.

Though there is still much to be learned about how the sensory modalities interact, it now seems clear that there are several possible mechanisms for their interaction, from the midbrain superior colliculus to the primary sensory cortex to higher-level multimodal integration areas. Ultimately, such studies will help us to understand the neural basis of multimodal perceptions, which are central to our everyday experience in which sights and sounds are perceived together seamlessly.

Conclusions

Both the auditory and visual systems must extract meaningful information from a massive amount of ever-changing input, whether it be patterns of light or sound waves. As we have seen, both sensory systems tackle these problems through a combination of serial processing, in which information ascends through a hierarchy of successive stages, and parallel processing, in which different processing streams are specialized to handle different aspects of the sensory stimulus. The representation of light and sound patterns (along with other sensory information such as smell, touch, and taste) allows us to understand the surrounding environment and forms the essential raw materials for other processes such as memory and language. In the next two chapters, we focus in more detail on brain systems involved in recognizing objects and understanding the spatial structure of the world around us.

Summary

The Retina

- The retina is derived from neural tissue and processes visual information before that information reaches the brain.

Photoreceptors

- Rods and cones are cells that contain light-sensitive pigments. Absorption of light by these pigments produces a neural signal that is communicated to other cells in the retina.
- Rods and cones have different pigments. The three cone pigments are sensitive to different wavelengths of light, thereby supporting color vision.
- Rods are distributed in the periphery of the retina, whereas cones are distributed in the center or fovea.
- Rods have a higher degree of convergence onto ganglion cells than do cones. This summation in the rod system allows detection of low light levels but loses information about precise location.

Ganglion Cells

- Ganglion cell bodies are located in the retina, and their axons make up the optic nerve.
- M ganglion cells are sensitive to motion and coarse patterns, whereas P ganglion cells code for color and finer details.

Receptive Fields

- A cell's receptive field refers to the region of space which, when stimulated with light, results in a change in the cell's firing rate.
- Photoreceptors have receptive fields that correspond to simple spots of light at certain locations in visual space.

- Ganglion cells have receptive fields with a center-surround organization, in which light located in a central spot in the visual field will have a different effect on the cell's firing than light located in the donut-shaped surrounding area. This center-surround organization makes the cells especially excited by contrast between light and dark.

Pathways from the Retina to the Brain

- There are two main paths out of the retina. The tectopulvinar pathway extends from the retina to the superior colliculus in the midbrain, whereas the geniculostriate pathway extends from the retina to the lateral geniculate nucleus in the thalamus.

Lateral Geniculate Nucleus

- The LGN is a stopover point that organizes incoming information from the retina and sends it to the cortex.
- The LGN has a complex structure, with six layers that each contain a retinotopic map. Two layers, called magnocellular layers, receive input from M ganglion cells. Four other layers, called parvocellular layers, receive input from P ganglion cells. Magnocellular layers are important for motion perception, whereas parvocellular layers are important for color and form perception.
- The LGN receives massive feedback projections from the visual cortex, allowing the cortex to shape the information that is streaming in through the LGN.

Primary Visual Cortex (Striate Cortex)

- The striate cortex is the first cortical region to receive visual information.
- The striate cortex in each hemisphere contains a retinotopic map of half of the visual world.

- Cells in the striate cortex have different kinds of receptive fields than cells in the retina or LGN. Simple cells respond best to bars of particular orientations, complex cells respond best to oriented bars moving in particular directions, and hyper-complex cells respond best to oriented bars of particular lengths.
- The striate cortex contains cells that are sensitive to certain amounts of binocular disparity, or discrepancy between left-eye and right-eye images. Binocular disparity information is important in coding for depth.

Contextual Modulation of Cells in Striate Cortex

- Cells in the striate cortex can change their firing rates depending on the surrounding context. This may help explain the well-known contextual influences on perception, and is likely due to top-down input from higher cortical regions as well as lateral connections within the striate cortex.

Blindsight

- Patients with blindsight exhibit some rudimentary visual capacities even though they experience being blind in the affected visual field.
- There is controversy about whether residual vision in blindsight is due to an intact tectopulvinar path, an intact path from the LGN to extrastriate areas, or islands of spared function within striate cortex.

Visual Areas beyond the Striate Cortex

- Multiple retinotopic maps exist in extrastriate cortex, including in areas V2 and V3. The unique function of each separate map is not well understood.
- Regions on the ventral surface of the brain are especially activated by color stimuli, and damage to these regions can lead to deficits in color vision, called achromatopsia. Controversy persists about whether these brain areas are true "color modules" and how they correspond to monkey visual area V4.
- From the striate cortex, two main paths emerge. The ventral path extends toward the inferior temporal lobe and is concerned with object recognition, whereas the dorsal path extends toward the parietal lobe and is concerned with spatial perception and action.

Auditory Processing

- The auditory system must solve computational problems similar to those of the visual system, including representing multiple features of the sensory world so that objects and their locations can be understood.
- The auditory pathway begins at the cochlea in the inner ear, and extends to the cochlear nucleus in the medulla, the superior olivary nucleus in the medulla, the midbrain inferior colliculus, the medial geniculate of the thalamus, and auditory cortex.
- Spatial location can be computed at the level of the brainstem by comparing the timing and intensity of sounds that arrive at the left and right ears.
- The auditory cortex contains a primary auditory processing area within the core, as well as secondary processing areas known as the belt and parabelt. Primary auditory cortex appears to code simpler features, such as the frequencies of pure tones, whereas secondary areas code for more complex sound patterns.
- Researchers have proposed a distinction between "what" and "where" processing pathways within the auditory cortex, but this distinction seems to be less clear-cut than in the visual system.
- Auditory and visual information processing streams can intersect with one another at several points, including the superior colliculus in the midbrain, the primary sensory cortices, and higher-level multimodal cortical regions.

Key Terms

belt 171

binocular disparity 156

binocular rivalry 159

blind spot 158

blindsight 146

center-surround receptive field 149

cochlea 166

cochlear nucleus 167

coincidence detectors 169

complex cells 154

contextual modulation 157

core 171

cortical blindness 158

cortical magnification factor 154

delay lines 169

fovea 147

ganglion cells 148

geniculostriate pathway 151

hair cells 166

hyper-complex cells 154

inferior colliculus 167

interaural intensity difference 169

interaural time difference 169

lateral geniculate nucleus (LGN) 151

M and P ganglion cells 149

medial geniculate nucleus 167

Book Companion Site at www.cengage.com/psychology/Banich
This website provides instructors and students with a wealth of free information and resources, including tutorial quizzes, flashcards, and the glossary.

Object Recognition

7

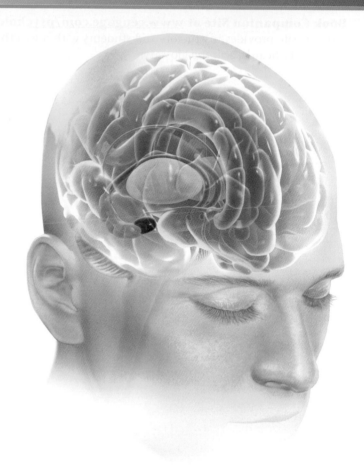

ONE CRISP AUTUMN NIGHT, Betty is yearning for a midnight snack when she remembers that some deliciously spiced tart apple pie is sitting in her refrigerator. She thinks, "That would be wonderful right now with a hot cup of tea!" Although for most people getting the pie out of the refrigerator and making a cup of tea would be simple, for Betty it will be a difficult task.

She walks into the kitchen and identifies the refrigerator by its large size and black color. But now she knows that she must find the pie, and doing so will not be easy. As she peers inside the refrigerator, she sees a large, round object but deduces from its red color that it must be the leftover pizza pie, not the apple pie. Searching a bit more, she sees a tan, round-shaped object and reaches for it. But alas, as soon as she feels how flexible it is, she realizes that it's the package of tortillas, not the desired pie. Searching some more, she spies another tan, round-shaped object. This one feels stiff, like a pie pan, and is covered with plastic wrap. She pulls it out, takes off the plastic wrap, and sniffs. Ah, it is the pie she has been searching for! She carefully places it on the breakfast table.

Now for the cup of tea. Because Betty knows that the stove is to the left of the refrigerator, her usual strategy is to leave the teakettle sitting on the stove so that she can easily find it. Unfortunately, it's not there. "Ah," she sighs, "why didn't I just put the teakettle back where it belongs?" Now she begins to feel all the objects on the counter next to the stove. Hmm, that one feels tall and thin and a little greasy—must be the bottle of olive oil. Another one feels cylindrical and as if it's made of paper—must be either the large container of salt or the carton of oatmeal. Soon thereafter, she feels the distinctive curved arm of the teakettle and its wide, round body. Next to it, she feels the box of tea bags. That was fortunate, she thinks, or I would have spent the next five minutes searching for the tea bags. She carefully places the box of tea bags on the stove; the box is now easily identifiable because its bright green color stands out against the white stove.

She then turns around to the sink, which she knows is located directly across from the stove, and fills the teakettle with water. Waiting for the water to boil, she puts her hand in the silverware drawer, feels for the tines of a fork, and takes one out. Soon, the teakettle whistles. She makes her cup of tea, walks over to the breakfast table, and gets ready to eat her piece of pie. That was a bit of a trial and tribulation, she thinks, but after the first bite of pie and sip of tea, she knows that all her effort was worthwhile.

AT THIS POINT, you are probably wondering what strange disorder this woman has. As you think about this story, a number of possibilities may come to mind. Maybe she has a visual problem and is blind. This seems unlikely. She recognized the pizza pie (if only by its distinctive round shape and red color) and incorrectly grabbed an item that looked similar to the apple pie, a package of tortillas, rather than something quite different in shape and size, like a milk carton. Another possibility is that she has a memory problem and can't remember where things are located or the specific attributes of an item. This possibility seems unlikely, too. She remembered the locations of the stove and the sink. Furthermore, her memory for specific items must be intact because she recognized the apple pie as soon as she smelled it and the kettle as soon as she felt it.

This woman's neurological syndrome is not due to a problem in basic aspects of visual perception or memory. Her disorder is visual agnosia, a syndrome that deprives an individual of the ability to use information in a particular sensory modality (in this case, vision) to recognize objects. The goal of this chapter is to examine the neural mechanisms that allow people to recognize objects through vision as well as other modalities. Our discussion concentrates on visual object recognition because it has been better studied than recognition through other senses.

The brain is confronted with a number of difficult problems when attempting to recognize a visual object. The most basic of these is that the brain must form a three-dimensional representation of objects in the world from the two-dimensional information that falls on the retina. Thus, the brain must construct or add in information about an object's depth. But there are additional problems as well. One major problem is that items must be recognized no matter where they fall on the retina and no matter how much of the retina they fall upon. For example, a cat sitting in your lap projects onto a much larger area of your retina than a cat sitting on a chair across the room. Yet, in both cases, you must recognize the object as a cat. In addition, objects must be recognized regardless of their orientation. You must recognize a cat regardless of whether the cat is facing you with its eyes clearly visible or facing away from you so you see the back, rather than the front, of its head. Finally, you must recognize an object as the same even when it appears in different configurations. Your brain needs to recognize that a cat sitting on its haunches, facing forward, is the same object as the cat lying curled up in a ball. In sum, although the same object can project upon the retina in various ways, the brain must none-theless interpret the object as being the same, regardless of variations in retinal size, retinal position, orientation, and configuration.

As discussed at the end of Chapter 6, the ventral stream in the visual cortex is primarily concerned with recognizing objects through vision. In this chapter, we first discuss some of the basic characteristics of the ventral stream in humans and other primates. We then consider what can be learned about object recognition from the study of people who have agnosia, or object recognition deficits. The chapter then turns to major theoretical questions in the study of object recognition, including how complex objects are represented by patterns of neural firing, how the brain is able to recognize objects under many different kinds of conditions, and whether there are parts of the ventral stream that are specialized for certain categories of visual objects, such as faces.

The "What" Ventral Visual System

Information departing from primary visual cortex is funneled into two distinct processing streams, one that courses ventrally toward anterior temporal regions and one that courses dorsally toward parietal regions. The **ventral visual-processing stream** (depicted in ● Figure 7.1) consists of the areas of the occipital, occipitotemporal, and temporal regions that are devoted to processing visual stimuli. Certain characteristics of cells in these areas seem to be especially adaptive for object recognition. As we move forward in the ventral stream, recording from individual cells along the stream, we can observe several important trends.

The first trend is that cells in posterior regions fire to relatively simple stimuli, but cells further along the

ventral stream fire to more complex and specific stimuli. So, whereas the areas just beyond primary visual cortex, such as V2, are likely to respond to one or more simple stimulus qualities (e.g., color, texture, length, width, orientation, direction of motion, spatial frequency), the cells in inferotemporal regions fire only in response to much more complex visual stimuli.

In fact, cells in the inferotemporal cortex of monkeys seem to exhibit maximal response to very specific forms, such as hands or faces (Gross, Bender, & Rocha-Miranda, 1969; Gross, Rocha-Miranda, & Bender, 1972; for review, see Gross, 2008). The selectivity of these cells' responses was a serendipitous discovery. The researchers were having difficulty determining what type of stimulus would make cells in the inferotemporal region fire, and in frustration one of them moved a hand across the monkey's visual field. To their amazement, they found that the cell fired more strongly than it had to any other object! They then tested other complex visual stimuli and found that in all cases the cell fired only in response to highly specific forms (● Figure 7.2). These findings raised the possibility that complex objects may be coded for by small sets of individual cells that are specifically tuned to those objects, an issue that we discuss in greater depth later in this chapter.

The second trend is that receptive fields become larger as we move further along the ventral stream. As discussed in Chapter 6, the **receptive field** of a cell is the area of visual space to which the cell is sensitive. Cells in primary visual cortex have very small receptive fields, whereas cells positioned farther along the ventral visual-processing stream respond to larger areas of space. ● Figure 7.3 provides a schematic comparison of the relative sizes of the receptive fields for cells in posterior and anterior regions of the ventral visual stream. In primary visual cortex, cells that represent the foveal region may have receptive field sizes of less than one degree of visual angle. (Keep in mind that the entire visual field is approximately 180 degrees wide.) In contrast, receptive fields of individual cells in the monkey's inferotemporal cortex can range up to 26 degrees of visual angle (Op de Beeck & Vogels, 2000; for estimates in humans, using data from fMRI or surface electrodes, see Smith, Singh, Williams, & Greenlee, 2001; Yoshor, Bosking, Ghose, & Maunsell, 2007). The receptive fields of cells in the inferior temporal cortex almost always include the foveal, or central, region of processing (Desimone & Gross, 1979; Op de Beeck & Vogels, 2000). In contrast to the peepholes of the primary visual cortex, which are distributed all over space, the receptive fields of the inferotemporal area can be considered analogous to a large picture window or glass wall that runs the length of one side of a house and always provides a view of what is directly in front.

A large receptive field is useful for object recognition because it may allow an object to be identified regardless of its size or where it is located in space (e.g., Gross & Mishkin, 1977). Consider that when you look

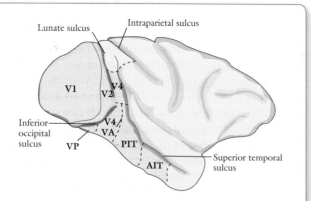

● **FIGURE 7.1   Ventral processing stream of the brain in the macaque.** The ventral processing stream (shown here as more darkly shaded, on a lateral view of the right hemisphere) goes from V1, V2, V3, VP, and V4 to the posterior and anterior inferotemporal areas (PIT and AIT, respectively).
© 2011 Cengage Learning

through a peephole, you see just a small portion of an object—a portion that is often too small to allow you to determine what you are viewing. Such is the problem with the small receptive field sizes of the primary visual cortex. However, as your field of view increases, so does your ability to detect whole objects, because the relationships among their parts can be appreciated. Thus, having a large receptive field allows the cell to respond to objects on the basis of their global shape, rather than just the size or location of local contours. A receptive field that includes the central region of visual space also aids object recognition. We typically direct our eyes so that an object we want to identify lands on the fovea or central region of the retina, where acuity is best.

Nevertheless, having a very large receptive field has a consequence: it means that some information about an item's position in space is lost. If a particular cell in the ventral stream responds to an object regardless of where in space it is located, it is impossible to tell where the object is located based on the firing of that cell. Cells in the ventral stream do preserve some spatial information, because their receptive fields are not nearly as wide as the entire visual field (Op de Beeck & Vogels, 2000). However, spatial coding is not as precise in the ventral stream as in primary visual cortex. Luckily, the dorsal stream preserves spatial information, as we discuss in more detail in Chapter 8.

Another attribute of cells in the ventral processing stream is that they are often sensitive to color (e.g., Edwards, Xiao, Keysers, Földiák, & Perrett, 2003). Color aids in object recognition because it allows us to separate an object from its background, a process often referred to as **figure-ground separation**. Consider an average street scene including parked cars, trees, buildings, and parking meters. Color may aid in quick identification of a car if it is yellow or white, a color distinct from the red brick building, the gray parking meter, the tan sidewalk, and the green trees that surround the car.

Given these properties of individual cells within the ventral stream, you may wonder how all the cells are organized within the cortical tissue. As you remember from Chapter 6, the primary visual cortex is exquisitely organized into columns, such that cells within a cortical column tend to respond best to the same line orientation and spatial location as one another. Do ventral stream areas have a kind of columnar structure as well? Structure within inferotemporal cortex is more difficult to discern than the structure of primary visual cortex. Because the preferred stimuli for cells in inferotemporal cortex are complex rather than simple features, it is less clear what set of images to use for testing cell preferences or finding what properties could be mapped systematically across the cortical surface. Nevertheless, some evidence indicates a columnar structure in which nearby cells tend to respond best to similar properties. For example, researchers recorded the

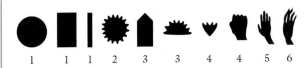

● **FIGURE 7.2 Examples of stimuli used to test the responsiveness of cells in the inferotemporal region of the macaque.** These stimuli are arranged from left to right in order of the degree to which they elicited a response, from 1 (no response) to 2 and 3 (little response) to 6 (maximal response). Note that the forms that make the cell fire are complicated and specific. © 2011 Cengage Learning

response of inferotemporal cortex cells to a set of 60–80 visual images, noting which cells respond best to which images, and found that neighboring cells tend to have somewhat similar response preferences (Kreiman, Hung, Kraskov, Quiroga, Poggio, & DiCarlo, 2006; Tamura,

(A)

(B)

● **FIGURE 7.3 Receptive field size of cells in primary visual cortex compared with that of cells in the inferotemporal region.** The *receptive field* is the region of space to which the cell is sensitive. If the optimal stimulus for an object falls outside its receptive field, the cell does not respond. In these pictures, the receptive field of a cell is indicated by a dashed circle. For purposes of this figure, areas within the receptive field are denoted by the colored regions, whereas those outside the receptive field are denoted by grey regions. (A) In primary visual cortex, the size of a cell's receptive field is small. (B) In contrast, the receptive field of a cell in the inferotemporal region is much larger, usually encompassing a wide expanse of visual space that always includes the midline. © 2011 Cengage Learning

Kaneko, & Fujita, 2005; see also Fujita, Tanaka, Ito, & Cheng, 1992; Sato, Uchida, & Tanifuji, 2009). However, the organization of cells across inferotemporal cortex is still not fully understood.

To better understand the importance of the ventral stream in object recognition, we next turn to the study of deficits in recognition that occur following brain damage. Such deficits help to solidify the case that the ventral stream is crucial for object recognition, and they also raise important theoretical issues about object recognition that we will turn to in the second half of this chapter.

Deficits in Visual Object Recognition

The earliest evidence supporting the role of the ventral stream in object recognition came from neuropsychological patients with deficits in object recognition. These patients typically have damage that includes areas within the ventral stream of the cortex. **Visual agnosia** is an inability to recognize objects in the visual modality that cannot be explained by other causes, such as an inability to do basic visual processing, a memory disorder, attentional problems, language difficulties, or general mental decline. Because the object can be recognized through

other senses, the deficit is **modality specific**, meaning that it manifests in only one of the senses.

For example, a woman with visual agnosia might be able to describe an object as a fuzzy brown, white, and black ovoid balanced on four short, stocky cylinders with a triangular-shaped appendage at one end and a very thin, very pointy, appendage, constantly in motion, at the other end. This description illustrates that her rudimentary visual abilities are intact. Furthermore, if this fuzzy ovoid nuzzled up to her so that she could feel its wet nose and whiplike tail, or if she heard its plaintive "boooaaaaahhhhhh, wooooaaaaaahhh, woooooooaaahhh" she would probably have little trouble identifying it as a dog, and possibly even as a beagle. Thus, although the woman cannot recognize the beagle in the visual modality, she can do so by the sense of touch or sound.

The word *agnosia* is Greek, meaning "without knowledge." One of the most famous figures in psychology, Sigmund Freud—a man not traditionally known for his contributions to neuropsychology—first used this word to describe the neuropsychological disorder. He chose to call this syndrome agnosia because he argued that it was not the result of disruptions in sensory processes but rather reflected an inability to gain access to previous knowledge or information about a sensory experience.

Traditionally, visual agnosias have been divided into two types: apperceptive and associative. This distinction dates to the 1890s and has been attributed to Lissauer. He suggested that **apperceptive agnosia** is a fundamental difficulty in forming a *percept* (a mental impression of something perceived by the senses). Although visual information is processed in a rudimentary way (e.g., distinctions between light and dark can be made), the data cannot be bound together to allow the person to perceive a meaningful whole. In contrast, in **associative agnosia** basic visual information can be integrated to form a meaningful perceptual whole, yet that particular perceptual whole cannot be linked to stored knowledge. If we consider this distinction differently, persons with apperceptive agnosia in some sense have trouble "seeing" integrated objects, whereas persons with associative agnosia can "see" objects but do not know what they are looking at. We now discuss these two main types of agnosia in more detail. (For the definitive, book-length review on agnosia, see Farah, 2004.)

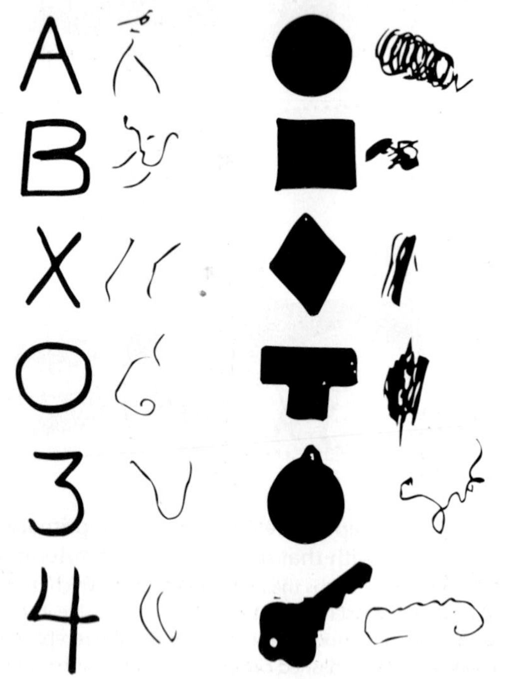

■ Apperceptive Visual Agnosia

In apperceptive agnosia, rudimentary visual processing is intact at least to the degree that basic perceptual discriminations involving brightness, color, line orientation, and motion can be made. However, the person has lost the ability to coalesce this basic visual information into a percept, an entity, or a whole. People with apperceptive agnosia have little or no ability to discriminate between shapes, regardless of whether they are objects, faces, or letters, and they have no ability to copy or match simple shapes (● Figure 7.4).

● **FIGURE 7.4   Example of the inability of a person with apperceptive agnosia to copy even the most basic forms.** The objects that the patient was asked to copy are on the left of each column, and the patient's attempts to do so are on the right. © 2011 Cengage Learning

These individuals often perceive local features of an object correctly, but they suffer from an inability to group them together into the percept of a whole object (Farah, 2004). As an example of this deficit, look at ● Figure 7.5. An individual with apperceptive agnosia would not perceive the pattern as "this" because of the discontinuity between the parts of the "T" and the "H." He or she would read it as the number "7415," because that ability relies on perceiving the simplest of visual features, line orientation. Generally, individuals with such a severely compromised ability to recognize objects have diffuse damage to the occipital lobe and surrounding regions, a pattern of damage that most often occurs with carbon monoxide poisoning (Farah, 2004).

The term *apperceptive agnosia* has also been applied to individuals who have damage not in the ventral processing stream, but rather in right parietal regions. These individuals have specific difficulty in recognizing objects from unusual vantage points (Warrington, 1982; Warrington & Taylor, 1973, 1978). Their deficits probably arise because of difficulties in spatial processing that preclude them from extracting some of the spatial invariants among object parts. As a result, they have difficulty recognizing objects from unusual perspectives.

■ Associative Visual Agnosia

In associative agnosia, individuals retain the ability to perform the perceptual grouping that persons with apperceptive agnosia find difficult. Copying a picture, such as the anchor shown in ● Figure 7.6, is relatively easy for a patient with associative agnosia, even though the same task would be impossible for a person with apperceptive agnosia. However, a patient with associative agnosia would be unable to draw the same picture from memory. This difficulty does not arise from a general problem in memory; when asked, for example, what an anchor is, an individual with associative agnosia can provide a reasonable definition, such as "a brake for ships" (Ratcliff & Newcombe, 1982). In some cases, people with associative agnosia are able to extract enough information from a visually presented item to determine its superordinate category (e.g., mammal, insect, or bird) but cannot correctly determine other attributes (e.g., whether it is tame or dangerous) (Warrington, 1975).

Because patients with this disorder can copy objects and can detect identical items from a set of similarly shaped objects, researchers originally presumed that their visual processing was intact—it was its linkage to semantic information in memory that was defective. More recent evidence suggests that the perceptual abilities of these people, although better than those of patients with apperceptive agnosia, are not truly normal. First, although patients with associative agnosia can perform matching and copying tasks, they use an exceedingly slow point-by-point or part-by-part comparison, which suggests that they are not obtaining

● **FIGURE 7.5   Limited local form perception in an apperceptive agnosic patient.** The patient cannot read this visual pattern as the word "this" but rather reads it as "7415." © 2011 Cengage Learning

a percept of the entire form. This strategy is different from that of neurologically intact individuals, who tend to draw the broad features first and then fill in the details.

Second, their deficits in object recognition become more severe as the input from a visual stimulus becomes

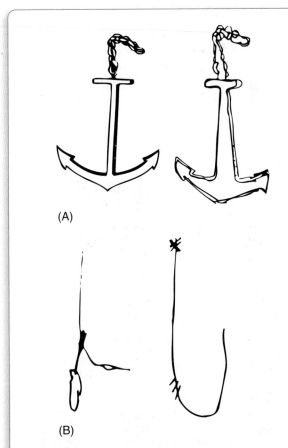

● **FIGURE 7.6   Drawing abilities of a person with associative agnosia.** (A) The patient's copy (right) of the model (left). Compared with the copying ability of a person with apperceptive agnosia (see Figure 7.4), this patient's ability to copy is much better. Yet, despite the patient's ability to copy the figure and assert that an anchor is "a brake for ships," he could identify neither the model nor his copy as an anchor. (B) The patient's attempts to respond to the request to draw an anchor. He was unable to retrieve the correct visual form from memory. © 2011 Cengage Learning

more impoverished. They are best at recognizing real objects, next best with photographs, and worst with line drawings (which are most impoverished). Third, their errors are often ones of visual similarity, such as misidentifying a baseball bat as a paddle, knife, or thermometer, rather than as a bat. Finally, they have difficulty in matching objects that have no semantic associations, such as unfamiliar faces and complex novel shapes. If their visual processing were intact and the problem arose solely from a disconnection between visual form and semantics, they should have no trouble in matching these items (Farah, 2000).

■ Differences between Apperceptive and Associative Agnosias

To review, the main difference between apperceptive and associative agnosia lies in the type of visual information that can be processed. People with classic apperceptive agnosia can process crude visual information, such as color and line orientation, but lack the ability to derive the more complex visual information required to extract shape information, such as contour. In contrast, people with associative agnosia can perceive much more detailed information than those with apperceptive agnosia, as proven by their ability to match items and to copy drawings with a fair degree of accuracy. In addition, they can extract some information about general shape, because when they misidentify an item, they generally assume it to be an object that looks similar in shape (e.g., misidentifying a pig for a sheep). Given these differences in processing abilities between persons with apperceptive agnosia and associative agnosia, we would expect the site of brain damage to differ between these two populations, and indeed this is the case (see ● Figure 7.7). Patients with apperceptive agnosia usually have diffuse damage to the occipital lobe and surrounding areas, whereas the lesion site for associative agnosia varies but typically involves the occipitotemporal

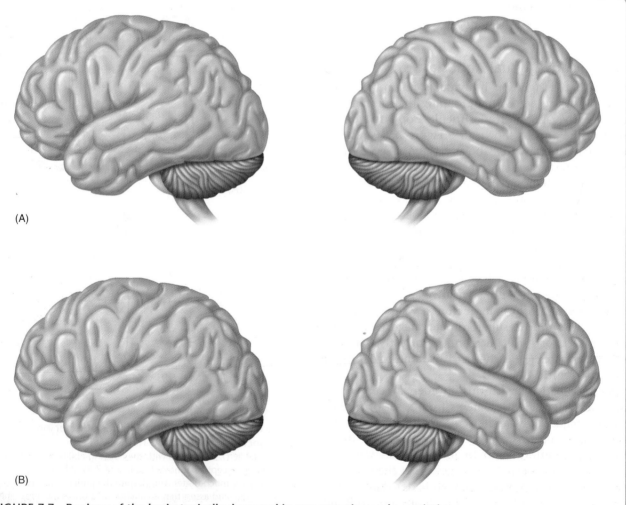

(A)

(B)

● **FIGURE 7.7   Regions of the brain typically damaged in apperceptive and associative agnosia.** (A) In apperceptive agnosia, damage occurs diffusely across occipital regions. (B) In associative agnosia, the damage tends to be bilateral at the occipito-temporal border. The typical lesion in associative agnosia is more anterior than the lesion in apperceptive agnosia. © 2011 Cengage Learning

regions of both hemispheres (Farah, 2004). Nonetheless, what is common to both syndromes is loss of the ability to link visual information to meaning.

■ Prosopagnosia: Agnosia for Faces

So far, we have discussed agnosia as a deficit in which the person loses the ability to recognize or identify all information within a specific modality. However, at least one type of visual agnosia is specific to a particular class of visual items, namely faces. This disorder is known as **prosopagnosia**, and it is a selective inability to recognize or differentiate among faces, although people with this disorder retain the ability to correctly identify other objects in the visual modality. People with prosopagnosia typically can determine that a face is a face, which suggests that some aspects of high-level visual processing are intact. In fact, they may even be able to determine the sex or relative age (old or young) of a person's face and the emotion that it is expressing (e.g., Tranel, Damasio, & Damasio, 1988). Yet, they have lost the ability to recognize a particular face as belonging to an individual person. The impairment can be so severe that the patient with prosopagnosia may not be able to recognize her spouse, children, or even her own face!

Like other individuals with agnosia, those with prosopagnosia do not have a general memory deficit. They can remember information about specific individuals and can recognize these people through other sensory modalities. Commonly, people with prosopagnosia attempt to compensate for their deficit by relying on distinctive visual nonfacial information, such as a person's hairstyle or a distinctive piece of clothing, or by relying on information in a nonvisual modality, such as voice or gait (Damasio, Damasio, & Van Hoesen, 1982).

Most cases of prosopagnosia are acquired, meaning that prior to brain damage the patient's performance was normal. In recent years, though, researchers have identified individuals who appear to be "face-blind" without any known brain damage, a condition referred to as **developmental** (or **congenital**) **prosopagnosia** (Duchaine & Nakayama, 2006). People with this disorder report that they have had great difficulty recognizing faces for their entire lives, although they have no difficulty recognizing other visual objects. They have built up a lifetime's worth of compensatory strategies to recognize other people without having to rely on facial cues, instead relying on other cues such as voices or characteristic styles of movement. Although these patients have no evident brain damage, we can infer that something must have gone awry in the development of face-recognition mechanisms in the brain (Behrmann & Avidan, 2005). Future studies of families in which more than one member shows evidence of developmental prosopagnosia may help to identify genetic mechanisms contributing to the development of normal and abnormal face recognition (Duchaine & Nakayama, 2006; Grueter et al., 2007).

One intriguing aspect of acquired prosopagnosia is that in some cases these patients can show some evidence of limited face recognition even though they do not have conscious access to that information. Such evidence challenges the classic conception of agnosia, which assumes that agnosia results from a disruption in the ability to link perceptual patterns to information in memory. This implicit processing of faces has been demonstrated in two major ways: through physiological measurements and through behavioral priming studies.

Although people with prosopagnosia perform at chance levels when asked to verbally identify which faces are familiar and which are not, in some cases their skin conductance response is greater to the faces of people they knew before their brain damage than to unknown faces (Tranel & Damasio, 1988). The electrodermal skin conductance response measures the increased skin conduction that occurs when the skin becomes sweatier, a response that is under control of the autonomic nervous system. Thus, at least at the level of an autonomic response, these individuals appear to be able to identify previously-known faces, despite no conscious recognition of those faces. Likewise, a measure of cortical activity, the P300 ERP response, differed for familiar and unfamiliar faces in one prosopagnosic patient (Bobes et al., 2004; ● Figure 7.8). As you may remember, the P300 response is strongest to "oddball" stimuli presented within a sequence of similar stimuli. In this study, the prosopagnosic patient viewed a series of unfamiliar faces, with familiar faces interspersed as "oddballs" within the series. The P300 response was larger to the familiar faces, indicating that the patient's brain was treating them as a category separate from the unfamiliar faces.

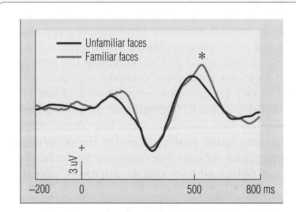

● **FIGURE 7.8   P300 response to familiar faces in a prosopagnosic patient.** Even though the patient does not have a memory of the previously familiar faces, the P300 event-related potential distinguishes between unfamiliar and familiar faces, suggesting that familiar faces are recognized implicitly at some level. *Source:* Bobes, M.A. et al, 2004. Brain potentials reflect residual face processing in a case of prosopagnosia. Cognitive Neuropsychology, 21, 691–718.

Other evidence for implicit recognition of faces in patients with prosopagnosia is the existence of interference effects that could occur only if the individual had some kind of access to information about facial identity. In one study, the task required a prosopagnosic patient to read a person's name aloud, and then classify the person by occupation (e.g., a musician or a politician). The name was positioned beside a face of someone from either a different occupation or the same occupation. Even though this prosopagnosic individual could neither identify the faces nor sort them according to occupation, the face nonetheless influenced performance in reading the name. Like neurologically intact adults, the patient took longer to read an individual's name when it was situated next to the face of someone in a different occupation (De Haan, Young, & Newcombe, 1987).

The results of all these studies suggest that a subset of patients with prosopagnosia retain some information about faces in memory, although it is not available in a way that allows for the explicit naming or categorizing of faces. These cases of prosopagnosia do not fit well with a model that presumes a total disconnection between the perceptual features of a face and its associated biographical information in memory. Perhaps these individuals can only encode a scant amount of visual information from a face. Alternatively, the threshold for recognizing a face may be greatly increased. This could preclude conscious access to the information under ordinary conditions, but still allow the low-level information that is processed to influence performance under certain conditions (see Farah, O'Reilly, & Vecera, 1993, for a computational model demonstrating this possibility). We revisit the issue of implicit memory in more detail in Chapter 10.

In sum, researchers are interested in the syndrome of prosopagnosia for a number of reasons. Studies of patients with prosopagnosia seem to indicate that the ability to identify an item as belonging to a specific category (e.g., determining that the visual pattern is a face) is distinct from the ability to remember the particulars about members within that category (e.g., determining that the face you are viewing is John's and not Tim's). In addition, implicit "recognition" in prosopagnosics raises interesting questions about how stored information is consciously retrieved. Finally, the occurrence of prosopagnosia suggests that faces may be a special type of visual object, an issue that we discuss in more detail later in this chapter.

■ Category-Specific Deficits in Object Recognition

So far we have discussed agnosia as a deficit in which the person loses the ability to recognize or identify information within a specific modality. However, in other cases a person has trouble identifying a certain category of objects even though the ability to recognize other categories of items in that same modality is undisturbed. This disorder is known as a **category-specific deficit** (for reviews, see Caramazza & Mahon, 2003; Humphreys & Forde, 2001). An example would be difficulty in identifying fruits and vegetables but not in identifying human-made objects. These deficits are perplexing because they are difficult to understand within the framework in which we previously considered agnosias.

When discussing agnosias, we emphasized that they do not arise from a fundamental disruption in basic sensory processing, but rather from an inability to form a percept and/or link that percept to meaning. How then are we to understand these category-specific deficits? First, the ability to form percepts must be intact, because objects outside specific categories can be recognized. For example, a person who cannot recognize apples and oranges can recognize cars and trains, indicating that the overall ability to form a visual percept must be intact. Second, in limited cases, the percept can be linked to meaning, because items in the unaffected category can be recognized.

Most category-specific deficits do not appear to be true agnosic deficits. In some cases, the deficits arise from difficulties within the semantic memory system (i.e., the system for meaning). For example, Warrington and Shallice (1984) found patients who could neither recognize pictures of a particular class of objects, nor provide an adequate definition of those items when told the names of the objects (unlike agnosics). Such findings suggest that these individuals have lost access to memory for the affected class of items. In other cases, individuals cannot name certain categories of items, such as fruits and vegetables, but their deficit is limited to naming and therefore appears to be a problem in word retrieval, a *selective anomia*, rather than a problem in semantic memory (e.g., Hart, Berndt, & Caramazza, 1985).

How could such category-specific deficits in memory arise? Currently there are two competing viewpoints. One possible explanation is that memory is organized into domain-specific neural circuits, so that the "living things" section is distinct from the "nonliving things" section (Caramazza & Shelton, 1998) and either one can be selectively damaged. In particular, this account argues that specific neural systems exist for items that were important during our evolutionary history, such as animals, other people, and particular plants. In fact, it is five times more common to have impaired recognition of natural things (e.g. animals, birds, fruit) with spared recognition of human-made things than the reverse (Laws, 2005).

A problem with this account is that patterns of deficit do not always seem to follow simple rules. For example, one patient cannot recognize fish, flowers, or fruit, all of which are living, yet he recognizes body parts perfectly well, even though these are also living. Likewise, although he can identify nonliving items such as clothing, kitchen utensils, and vehicles, he cannot identify musical instruments (Warrington & Shallice, 1984). Nevertheless, a comprehensive review of all patients with category-specific deficits found that certain patterns emerge (Capitani, Laiacona, Mahon, & Caramazza, 2003). Most cases involve dissociations between the ability to recognize animals, the ability to recognize fruits and vegetables, and the ability to recognize artifacts (e.g., tools, furniture).

An alternative explanation is that when a person is accessing memory, information from different modalities may have a differential weight or influence and those influences may differ by class of item (see Farah & McClelland, 1991, for a discussion and computational model). For example, when recognizing human-made objects such as crayons, hammers, and tables, we generally differentiate them according to function, or what actions we perform with them. However, this is not the case for living things. The best way to distinguish a leopard from a lioness and a tiger is by sensory attributes in the visual modality (the leopard has spots, the lioness is all one tawny color, and the tiger has stripes). According to this explanation, a more severe deficit might arise in recognizing animals than in identifying writing utensils, because the information in memory relies more heavily on the visual attributes of the item (Warrington & Shallice, 1984).

Supporting this view, case studies indicate that functional knowledge about an object can be maintained even when perceptual understanding of the object is deficient. For example, one patient with visual agnosia was able to describe what objects are used for (that is, their function); for example, when shown a pot and frying pan, she could say that "both of them are for cooking." However, she was unable to access perceptual knowledge, such as whether two objects were perceptually similar (Peru & Avesani, 2008). In fact, when shown pairs of pictures and asked to explain how they are perceptually similar, the patient tended to describe functional similarities rather than perceptual similarities, regardless of whether the pairs of objects were living or nonliving.

Brain imaging data also indicate that different brain regions are activated when recognizing living versus nonliving things, with greater activity in perceptual areas for living things and greater activity in motor areas for nonliving things (Martin, Wiggs, Ungerleider, & Haxby, 1996; Perani et al., 1995; see also Phillips, Noppeney, Humphreys, & Price, 2002). Furthermore, for living items, activity is observed in left fusiform gyrus regardless of whether the participant is asked about visual attributes (e.g., Does a parrot have a curved beak?) or nonvisual attributes (e.g., Are pandas found in China?). However, for nonliving items, fusiform activation was observed only when the question was about visual attributes, not when it was about nonvisual attributes (Thompson-Chill, Aguirre, D'Esposito, & Farah, 1999). Such findings suggest that access to perceptual features of living items occurs more automatically than for nonliving items.

Yet even this explanation is not quite satisfactory. We still need to be able to explain why some patients have trouble recognizing fruits and vegetables but can recognize other items such as flowers, all of which are probably differentiated on the basis of visual attributes; and why other patients can recognize certain objects such as keys and pens but not airplanes and helicopters, even though they all are probably differentiated on the basis of function. One possible explanation is that particular channels of information within a sensory modality may be more affected by a brain lesion than other channels. Because color may be the visual attribute that best distinguishes among fruits, whereas shape may best distinguish among flowers, recognition of fruits versus flowers may be affected differently depending on whether the brain damage affects color or shape-processing areas (Warrington & McCarthy, 1987).

As you can see, there are several competing explanations for category-specific recognition deficits, and the issues are far from settled. Nevertheless, such deficits continue to attract attention because they are so striking when observed in patients. From a scientific standpoint, the study of such deficits has the potential to help researchers better understand how different kinds of information about an object are stored in memory and contribute to visual recognition of the object.

Theoretical Issues in Object Recognition

Evidence reviewed so far has told us that the ventral visual stream carries out visual object recognition, and that damage to this region can have profound effects on the ability to recognize objects in everyday life. However, there is much more to learn about how objects are actually represented in the neural tissue of the ventral stream. In the remaining sections, we focus on four interrelated questions that are being actively researched and debated in the cognitive neuroscience of visual object recognition. First, how is a specific object represented within the visual stream: is a single object represented by the activity of only a few cells, or is a larger swath of the neural tissue involved in representing any given object? Second, how does the ventral stream achieve perceptual invariance (the ability to recognize objects regardless of their orientation, position, or size)? Third, is object perception based on understanding the individual parts of an object and then fitting those parts together, or is it based on a more holistic representation? Finally, we address the controversial issue of category specificity, the question of whether there are segments of the ventral stream that are dedicated to and specialized for processing certain kinds of stimuli, such as faces.

■ Sparse versus Population Coding for Objects

One basic question in object recognition is how individual cells in the ventral stream are involved in coding for the vast array of objects that a person (or monkey) is able to identify. What kind of code does the brain use? One way of thinking about this question is to ask whether the brain uses sparse coding or population coding (Reddy & Kanwisher, 2006). By **sparse coding**, we mean that a small but specific group of cells responds to the presence of a given object. Each object would excite a small set of cells, such that activity in that small set of cells would represent that particular object in our perception. According to a highly simplified version of this idea, cell #3 fires whenever an apple is present, whereas cell #9 fires whenever an orange is present (●Figure 7.9A). The alternative point of view, **population coding**, theorizes that the pattern of activity across a large population of cells codes for individual objects (●Figure 7.9B). According to the population coding viewpoint, the same cells participate in coding for different objects. For example, cells 1–10 might all be responsive to both apples and oranges, but the pattern of activity across these cells will differ in some way if the object is an apple rather than an orange.

To better distinguish these viewpoints, it is useful to think of the extreme positions. The extreme version of sparse coding is the **grandmother cell theory** (see Barlow, 1985). According to this idea, there is a particular cell in the ventral processing stream whose

job is to fire when you see your grandmother. Some other cell fires when you see your grandfather, and another cell fires to your Uncle Bob, and so on. In many ways, this idea seems to be a logical extension of the trends we see in the visual stream: as we move forward within the stream, cells respond to more complex and specific stimuli because they take in more information from cells earlier in the ventral processing stream. However, if you think about it logically, it doesn't make sense for the brain to have just one cell (or even a few) that identifies your grandmother. For starters, what happens when that particular cell dies? Do you suddenly become unable to recognize your grandmother, while still recognizing grandpa and Uncle Bob? It seems unlikely that the brain would have evolved a system in which representations could be so easily disrupted. Also, what happens when you learn to recognize a new object? Are there undedicated cells just waiting around to be assigned a new object to represent? That also seems unlikely. For these reasons, no one actually believes that the extreme version of the grandmother cell idea could be correct.

Let's also consider what an extreme population coding system might look like. Imagine that every cell in the ventral stream is involved in coding for every object. Each possible object would generate a unique pattern of activity across the millions of cells in the ventral stream. In Chapter 5, we learned about a similar population coding scheme to code for planned actions in primary motor cortex. A population coding scheme

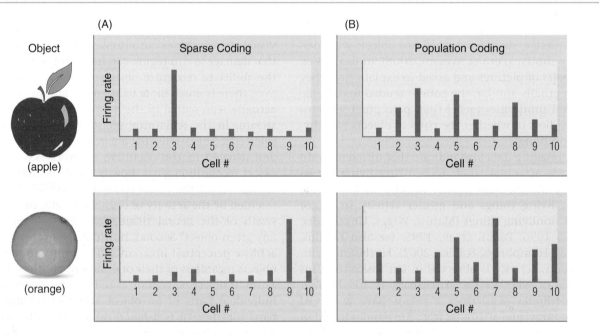

● **FIGURE 7.9   Schematic depiction of sparse versus population coding.** In sparse coding (A), a single cell (or small set) represents a specific object. For example, cell #3 codes for "apple" whereas cell #9 codes for "orange." In population coding (B), different objects are coded by the pattern of activity across a population of cells, rather than by any individual cell.

would be more resilient than the grandmother cell system, because losing a couple of cells would not alter any given representation very much (Pouget, Dayan, & Zemel, 2000). However, this extreme idea has other problems. Keep in mind that ultimately, the point of representing visual information is not just to represent it, but to be able to link that information with other information elsewhere in the brain. For example, you need to be able to link the sight of an apple with the taste of an apple, with its smell, with the word "apple," and with the action of biting an apple. If all the millions of cells in the ventral stream had to be involved in coding for the visual image of "apple," then all those cells would have to be somehow hooked up to cells in the taste system, the smell system, the language system, and the motor control system. That is, there wouldn't be specific connections between "apple" cells in the ventral stream and "apple" cells in the taste or language areas, because all the ventral stream cells would be needed to code for the sight of an apple. Such a system would be pretty unwieldy.

As is often the case when extreme positions make little sense, the answer probably lies in between. Representing "apple" probably involves more than one cell but less than all the cells in the ventral stream. But what do researchers actually know about the coding of individual objects by populations of cells? Most of the findings that pertain to the question of sparse versus population coding come from single-cell recording studies in monkeys. Human neuroimaging studies have a difficult time addressing this question, because the resolution of hemodynamic neuroimaging methods is too coarse to resolve neural activity at the level of individual cells.

As mentioned earlier, it has been known for a few decades that individual cells in the inferotemporal regions of the monkey brain respond best to specific complex stimuli such as hands and faces (Gross, Bender, & Rocha-Miranda, 1969; Gross, Rocha-Miranda, & Bender, 1972). However, it is hard to tell whether a cell's response is truly specific to only one kind of object unless the experimenter tests the cell with all possible objects, which is not feasible. One recent study tried to address this issue by testing cells in the monkey inferior temporal cortex with more than 1,700 pictures. These researchers found that many cells were quite specifically attuned to faces or to other complex shapes (Földiák, Xiao, Keysers, Edwards, & Perrett, 2004). Of course, both monkeys and humans can recognize well over 1,700 objects. So, while this study went farther than most in testing a large number of stimulus images, it still does not approximate the vast number of images that we easily recognize in daily life.

Taking another approach, other researchers have attempted to see whether changing activity in certain cells could change a monkey's perception of a complex image. If so, this could suggest that those specific cells are crucial in representing a specific perception. In one study of this type, researchers demonstrated that stimulating face-preferring cells in a monkey's inferotemporal cortex could make the monkey more likely to categorize an ambiguous picture as a face (Afraz, Kiani, & Esteky, 2006). These findings indicate that activity in specific cells can contribute to creating the perception of specific objects.

Although most of these studies have been carried out with monkeys, on rare occasions single-cell recording is conducted with human epileptic patients. In some epileptic patients, recording electrodes are implanted to track the presence of abnormal electrical activity associated with seizures. Researchers can take advantage of these situations by recording from those sites when different stimuli are presented. In a fascinating study of several patients, researchers found that individual cells had quite a high degree of specificity of response to certain objects (Quiroga, Reddy, Kreiman, Koch, & Fried, 2005). One cell even had a strong preference for the face of the actress Jennifer Aniston, when seen from several different viewpoints, but did not respond to pictures of other actresses nor to pictures of Aniston together with actor Brad Pitt (● Figure 7.10). Maybe this is not a "grandmother cell," but is it the "Jennifer Aniston cell"?

Several factors complicate the interpretation of this study. First, the cells in this study were located not in the inferotemporal cortex of the ventral stream, but instead in the hippocampus in the medial temporal lobe, where the electrodes had been implanted for seizure recording. For ethical reasons, the researchers couldn't just move the electrodes over to the ventral stream areas out of scientific curiosity. Therefore, while the study can tell us something about specificity of coding in the memory system, which the ventral stream feeds into, it doesn't tell us whether the ventral stream itself contains cells with such highly specific responses. In addition, as the researchers themselves point out, given the limited time that they tested the patient and given how many thousands of faces a person can recognize, it seems unlikely that they just happened upon the right actress who matched the cell where the electrode had been implanted. Rather, it seems more plausible that the tested cell probably responds to other faces too, but just not the others that were in their testing set.

Despite indicating that cells can have high degree of selectivity for specific objects, these studies do not tell us that we should accept a strong version of the grandmother cell theory. Other research demonstrates that gathering information over a population of cells within the ventral stream provides the best way to distinguish between different objects. For example, one group of researchers recorded from a few hundred randomly selected neurons in the inferotemporal lobe in monkeys, while presenting the monkeys with 77 different pictures of objects grouped into 8 categories, such as food, toys, monkey faces, and human faces (Hung, Kreiman, Poggio, & DiCarlo, 2005). The researchers fed

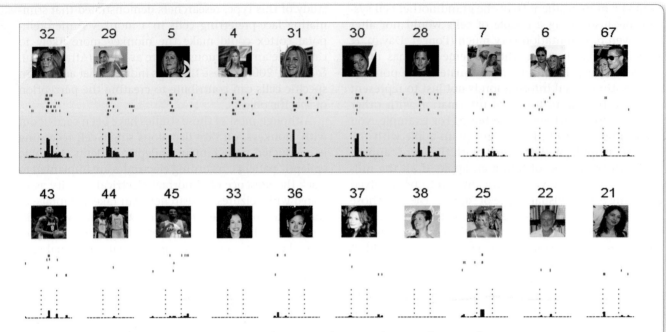

● **FIGURE 7.10   Responses of a single cell in a human epileptic patient to pictures of faces.** This cell in the medial temporal lobe responds preferentially to pictures of the actress Jennifer Aniston, although it does not respond to other famous people or when Aniston is viewed together with Brad Pitt. The number above each picture indicates its position in the series. Adapted by permission from Macmillan Publishers, LTD: Quiroga, R.Q., Reddy, L., Kreiman, G., Koch, C., & Fried, I. (2005). Invariant visual representation by single neurons in the human brain. Nature, 435, 1102–1107.

the pattern of activity across the population of cells into a computer program, and the computer program was able to use the pattern of activity across the cells to correctly identify the category of each object as well as its specific identity. For example, based on the activity of 256 cells, the program could categorize the objects with 94% accuracy, and could correctly identify the specific object 72% of the time. Crucially, the researchers found that as more cells were added to the array, the ability to distinguish between different objects increased exponentially. This indicates that it is a pattern of activity across the whole set of cells, rather than the activity of object-specific "grandmother cells," that most efficiently codes for object identity.

Researchers have also begun to study how patterns of firing in a population of cells can develop rapidly as information is extracted from a visual image. One study with monkeys found that after a visual image is presented, a population of cells in the inferotemporal cortex first coded for general features of the image in a way that supported object categorization, and then coded for the specific object (Matsumoto, Okada, Sugase-Miyamoto, Yamane, & Kawano, 2005). For example, the population pattern might first provide information that allows the distinction between faces and food objects, and then 100–200 milliseconds later the pattern across the same cells could provide more specific information that distinguishes between oranges and bananas. This raises the intriguing possibility that the same population of cells can code different kinds of information at different times while processing an image. In this conceptualization, the representation of certain features of an object is distributed not only across many cells, but across time as well.

■ The Problem of Invariance in Recognition

An amazing aspect of our visual recognition is the ability to identify objects under myriad conditions. For example, you can easily recognize an apple regardless of whether it is depicted as the logo on a computer, seen in a bowl of fruit in front of you, or depicted in a painting. This is known as *form-cue invariance*, because the brain's categorization is constant regardless of the form of the cue that represents that object. People are also easily able to recognize objects seen from different angles, at different positions or sizes, and under different kinds of illumination, a phenomenon known as *perceptual constancy*. The ability to recognize objects across so many varying conditions implies that at some level, our mental representation of objects is fairly abstract, in the sense of being removed from or independent of the original stimulus conditions.

One method that is especially useful in studying form-cue invariance and perceptual constancy is the adaptation method (see Krekelberg, Boynton, & van Wezel, 2006). The adaptation method takes advantage of the fact that the brain's response to an item decreases (adapts) with repeated viewing of the item. In a typical adaptation study, participants first view a particular item for some period of time to become adapted to it, and brain activity decreases correspondingly (● Figure 7.11). If the same item is then presented

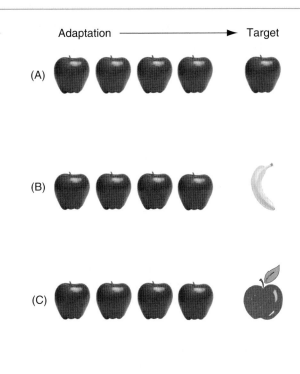
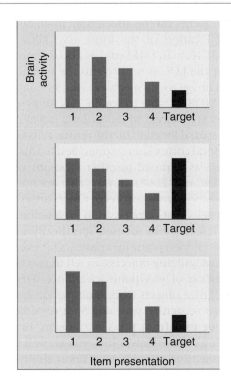

● **FIGURE 7.11** **The logic of the fMRI adaptation method.** Participants are adapted to a particular visual image, and then either the same image is shown again as the target (row A) or a different image is shown as the target (row B). Brain activity decreases, or adapts, to the repeated image, but it increases again (recovers from adaptation) with the presentation of the new item. To test whether a brain region shows form-cue invariance, researchers present a target that is the same object as the adapted item, but in a different visual form (such as a line drawing versus a photograph). If adaptation persists, as shown in row C, the brain region is treating the adapted item and target item as similar, and therefore is showing form-cue invariance.

again, brain activity remains at a low level, because the neurons within that region that code for the item are adapted to its presence. If a new object is presented, however, brain activity increases. The idea is that neurons within that brain region that code for the new object have not been adapted, and therefore they show a strong response to the new object.

Now, consider how this method can be used to test whether a brain region shows form-cue invariance. Logically, if a portion of the brain exhibits invariance, it should show just as much of an adaptation effect when presented with two different instances of the same object (e.g., line drawing of an apple and photograph of an apple) as when presented with two identical representations of the object. In other words, if a brain region continues to show adaptation to a new depiction of the same type of object, the brain region is treating that new depiction just like the old version to which it was already adapted, and therefore it is showing evidence of form-cue invariance.

Neuroimaging studies using the adaptation method have shown that a particular region within the ventral stream seems to display perceptual constancy and form-cue invariance. This region, the lateral occipital complex (LOC), is located at the posterior portion

of the fusiform gyrus, directly anterior to Brodmann area 19, and it shows evidence of perceptual constancy across variations in size, location, viewpoint, and illumination (Grill-Spector, Kushnir, Edelman, Avidan, Itzchak, & Malach, 1999; Mazer & Gallant, 2000). In addition, activation in the LOC exhibits a similar response to both line drawings and photographs of the same object, indicating form-cue invariance (Kourtzi & Kanwisher, 2000). This evidence indicates that at least some portions of the ventral stream exhibit constancy in response to different versions of an object that mirrors our perceptual constancy.

Some research has focused specifically on the problem of position invariance, which refers to our ability to recognize an object regardless of where it appears in the visual field. Despite the fact this ability is easily evident in our everyday lives, researchers are still puzzling over how the visual system is able to achieve such invariance. As we've already discussed, ventral stream cells have larger receptive fields than primary visual cortex cells, which allows the ventral stream cells to respond to an object across a broader area of space than would be possible based on primary visual cortex cells alone. But at the same time, research has shown that individual cells within the ventral stream do tend to have preferred spatial locations; that is, their responses to complex visual forms can be affected by small changes in the spatial location of the form (e.g., DiCarlo & Maunsell, 2003). Human fMRI studies also demonstrate that activity in the LOC is sensitive to the retinal position of a visual image (Grill-Spector et al., 1999; Sayres & Grill-Spector, 2008). Other research has shown that when monkeys are trained to recognize a novel object in a particular spatial location on the retina, cells within the inferotemporal cortex later respond best to that form at that location, as opposed to other locations on the retina (Cox & DiCarlo, 2008). In ways that are not fully understood, position-invariant recognition arises from ventral stream cells that have position preferences.

Additional research has focused specifically on the vexing problem of viewpoint invariance. Our everyday experience in recognizing objects can tell us two things about the question of viewpoint invariance. First, we can easily recognize objects from multiple viewpoints. That is, you can recognize your dog Spot regardless of whether you see him from the side, face on, or from behind. Despite all those viewpoints, you know it is still Spot. At the same time, though, your brain also notices viewpoints. For example, you can easily tell the difference between a view of Spot when you see him from behind (such as when you are walking him) and a view of Spot from the front (such as when he is running up to you to get a treat). So, your representation of objects is flexible enough that you can easily tell the viewpoint from which you're seeing Spot, as well as realizing that it is still Spot no matter which way you look at him.

Scientists who study object recognition have long been concerned with whether neural representations of objects are primarily viewpoint-invariant or viewpoint-dependent (Peissig & Tarr, 2007). That is, do neural representations of an object depend on the viewpoint from which the object is seen? This debate centers around the issue of how the brain takes the two-dimensional information from the retina and creates a three-dimensional representation of an object so that it can be recognized from any viewpoint.

One classic explanation assumes that the brain actually creates a viewpoint-invariant three-dimensional representation of an object that is built up from two-dimensional information. For example, it may be that the brain first extracts viewpoint-specific information, and then uses that representation to build a more abstract three-dimensional representation that is independent of viewpoint. A computational model that posited this basic idea was proposed by computer scientist David Marr (1982). According to Marr, extraction of a full three-dimensional image happens in several stages. First, the visual system constructs a **primal sketch** of features in the visual world, which segments dark from light regions and groups them together via gestalt principles. From information in that primal sketch, the system deduces the relative depth of different surfaces and edges, and constructs a representation of what parts

of an object are in front or behind. Finally, the system develops a full **three-dimensional (3-D) representation** of that object that is not specific to a viewpoint, but is more abstract and viewpoint-invariant.

Other researchers argue that recognition of objects from multiple viewpoints does not depend on having a full 3-D viewpoint-independent representation of the object, but rather depends on some kind of systematic integration or interpolation across a set of **viewer-centered representations** (see Tarr & Bülthoff, 1998, for a review). For example, starting with a representation of the image from a viewer-specific vantage point, the system may make a guess about what an object might be, compare that to stored representations of objects, measure the difference, and generate another hypothesis if the match is too poor. Notice that in these types of models, recognition of an object from a particular viewpoint depends heavily on comparison with stored descriptions in the brain (Riesenhuber & Poggio, 2000).

Several different kinds of evidence support some degree of viewpoint dependency in recognition. For example, behavioral studies demonstrate that although people are pretty good at recognizing objects from multiple viewpoints, their recognition tends to be faster and more accurate when they see the object from its most typical viewpoint, or the viewpoint that they have seen most often (e.g., Hayward & Tarr, 1997). In research with monkeys, one study found that during learning of new objects, cells became tuned to specific viewpoints of those objects (Logothetis & Pauls, 1995). In this study, monkeys were presented with novel objects seen from specific viewpoints. After training, monkeys saw those same objects in both the trained and untrained viewpoints. Recognition performance was best for the trained viewpoints and for views within about 40 degrees of rotation from the trained viewpoints. Nonetheless, monkeys could also interpolate to recognize the objects when presented with views that fell in between the viewpoints on which they had been trained. Further, individual cells in the ventral stream responded best to the objects presented in the trained viewpoints. These results suggest that cells become tuned to certain two-dimensional views of an object through experience, and that such viewpoint-specific cells may support some degree of recognition of alternative viewpoints.

Neuroimaging evidence using the adaptation method also offers some support for viewpoint-dependent recognition. In one application of this method, participants first became adapted to seeing an object from a particular viewpoint, and then later viewed the object from either the same or a different viewpoint (Andresen, Vinberg, & Grill-Spector, 2009). If the neural representations are viewpoint invariant, the adaptation will hold for different viewpoints of the same object; but if neural representations are viewpoint dependent, then adaptation to one viewpoint will not carry over to another viewpoint. The study found that the degree of cross-viewpoint adaptation depended on the specific region of the ventral stream. Generally, all the ventral stream regions that were studied showed some viewpoint dependence, though the viewpoint dependence was less pronounced for left fusiform cortex than for right fusiform or lateral occipital cortex.

Single-cell recording studies suggest that the brain uses both viewpoint-invariant and viewpoint-dependent codes in different subsets of cells. Some ventral stream cells respond to a favored object in a way that remains unchanged regardless of the viewpoint, whereas other cells' responses to an object change quite a lot depending on the orientation of the object (Booth & Rolls, 1998). One way to reconcile viewpoint-invariant and viewpoint-dependent models is to consider that different strategies may be used for different types of objects. For example, whereas a viewpoint-dependent approach may be well suited to recognizing familiar objects, a viewpoint-independent approach may be well suited for recognizing novel objects or objects in unusual orientations.

In sum, researchers are still trying to decode how the brain achieves the ability to recognize objects in an abstract way that does not depend on the particulars of how the image of that object falls on the retina. As the visual image is processed throughout the ventral stream, going from primary visual cortex to inferotemporal cortex, the image is re-represented in ways that become more abstracted from the actual retinal image, thus allowing complex objects to be differentiated and recognized (DiCarlo & Cox, 2007). Determining the precise mechanisms by which this happens will not only help solve the code of object recognition in the brain, but will help engineers in designing computer-based object recognition systems.

◼ Feature-Based versus Configural Coding of Objects

Although we recognize an object as one integrated entity, most objects are composed of parts. For example, a hand is composed of fingers, a thumb, and a palm; a cup is composed of a handle and a cylinder, and a car is composed of wheels, body, doors, and windows. To what extent is our recognition of objects influenced by the features of individual parts, and to what extent is our recognition of objects dependent on the way those parts fit together in certain configurations to make a whole?

Clearly, integrating parts into whole objects is an important function of the visual system. As you remember from earlier in the chapter, apperceptive agnosics are unable to integrate parts into wholes, and this radically changes their experience of visual objects. For example, a case study presented one agnosic patient with novel objects composed of two parts. The patient was able to tell correctly when one of the parts was replaced by a new part, but was unable to tell when the same two parts were presented together but in a different configuration

(Behrmann, Peterson, Moscovitch, & Suzuki, 2006). This evidence indicates that the integration of parts into wholes requires additional processing beyond that of recognizing individual parts.

What is the relative importance of features versus configural information in object recognition? In other words, do we tend to rely more on individual features or on the way those features are put together when we attempt to identify an object? One answer is that features and configural information matter differently to the two hemispheres. As discussed in Chapter 4, lesions disrupt the ability to perceive local, but not global, aspects of an item when the left hemisphere is affected (particularly in temporal lobe regions), whereas lesions of the right hemisphere have the opposite effect, disrupting the ability to perceive global, but not local, aspects of form (Delis, Robertson, & Efron, 1986; Robertson, Lamb, & Knight, 1988). Thus, there appear to be two distinct neural mechanisms involved in object recognition: one lateralized to the left ventral stream, important for analyzing the parts of objects; and another lateralized to the right ventral stream, important for analyzing whole forms.

Researchers have also discovered that configural information—that is, the overall relationship between different parts of an item—is especially important for object categories for which we have a lot of expertise. This is probably best illustrated by studies on face recognition examining what is known as the **inversion effect**. The basic logic is that if configural information is especially important for recognizing certain objects, then recognition ought to be substantially poorer when the objects are turned upside down (inverted), because inversion specifically disrupts configural relationships while leaving the local relationships between the parts intact. Indeed, inversion especially impairs the recognition of faces compared to other objects, such as houses and cars, suggesting that configural information is key (Yin, 1970). ● Figure 7.12 illustrates another way in which inverted stimuli can disrupt configural processing.

Studies also indicate that the configural processing tapped by the inversion effect is dependent on the right hemisphere. For example, Yin's classic study found that patients with right-hemisphere damage showed a reduced inversion effect for faces. Although these patients did as well as neurologically intact subjects at recognizing inverted faces, they were selectively poor at recognizing upright faces. These findings led Yin to suggest that the posterior section of the right hemisphere is specialized for the configural processing required for face recognition. This suggestion is consistent with a vast literature on face-recognition studies of neurologically intact people. Typically, a left visual field advantage is found for face recognition (e.g., Geffen, Bradshaw, & Wallace, 1971), but this effect diminishes when faces are presented in an inverted orientation (e.g., Leehey, Carey, Diamond, & Cahn, 1978).

● **FIGURE 7.12   Example of the importance of configural information for recognizing faces.** Examine the two faces and notice how from this vantage point they look similar. Now turn your book upside down so that the two faces are right-side up. You should immediately see a difference. This exercise, called the *Thompson illusion,* demonstrates the degree to which configural strategies are important for the processing of faces in the upright orientation and how they are minimized when the faces are inverted. *Source:* © Margaret Thatcher: A New Illusion, P. Thompson, 1980 Perception, Volume 9, pp. 483–484, Pion Limited, London.

Although faces are especially prone to such inversion effects, so are other stimuli for which the participants have expertise. For example, one group of investigators compared how well college students and judges of show dogs could distinguish between pictures of different dogs in a paradigm similar to that used by Yin (Diamond & Carey, 1986). As expected, the college students exhibited a much larger inversion effect for faces than for show dogs. In contrast, the show-dog judges displayed as large an inversion effect for show dogs as for faces, indicating that configural information processing played an important role in the experienced judges' identification of dogs (though see Robbins & McKone, 2007, for contradictory findings). Another study found inversion effects for fingerprints in people who were experts at recognizing fingerprint patterns (Busey & Vanderkolk, 2005). Other studies have found that face-inversion effects are most pronounced for same-race faces, with which participants typically have more experience. For example, Chinese individuals exhibit a greater inversion effect for Chinese faces than for European faces, whereas European individuals exhibit the opposite pattern (Rhodes, Tan, Brake, & Taylor, 1989). These results probably occur because we have more experience with the configural nature of the faces of individuals of our own race than with that of other races. When asked to differentiate among faces, we can do so more easily if they fit into a configuration with which we are familiar. Finally, developmental evidence indicates that children begin to

rely on configural, right-hemisphere strategies as they gain more experience with recognizing faces (Carey & Diamond, 1977; Levine, 1984). This change in strategy is accompanied by decreases, through the childhood and adolescent years, in the response of the right lateral fusiform gyrus to inverted faces (Passarotti, Smith, DeLano, & Huang, 2007).

Evidence from single-cell recordings in monkeys can also provide information about the relative importance of object features versus configurations as individuals learn about certain objects. Although there is some evidence that cells in the inferotemporal cortex may become tuned to specific features when learning to differentiate objects (Sigala & Logothetis, 2002), other research has discovered cells in inferotemporal cortex that are most responsive to combinations of features. In one study (Yamane, Tsunoda, Matsumoto, Phillips, & Tanifuji, 2006), researchers used optical imaging to identify regions of the cortex in the macaque monkey that were activated in response to configurations of features, such as a 2-D drawing of a cat, but were not responsive to individual elements of that drawing, such as just the cat's head or just the cat's body (● Figure 7.13A). The researchers then recorded from individual cells within these identified areas of cortex, and found cells that responded best when features of an object were arranged in a particular spatial configuration (● Figure 7.13B). These results indicate that individual cells can code for combinations of features in particular spatial configurations.

Another study found that when monkeys were trained to recognize novel two-part objects, cells in the inferotemporal cortex fired more vigorously when both features were present compared with what would be expected from the presence of either feature alone (Baker, Behrmann, & Olson, 2002). In other words, as the monkey learned to recognize these novel objects, cells in the inferotemporal cortex became especially sensitive to the conjunction of the two features that were part of the object. This cellular-level evidence suggests a possible mechanism for the shift from featural to configural encoding as we become more experienced with categories of objects.

■ Category Specificity: Are Some Types of Stimuli More Special than Others?

One of the most hotly debated topics in the study of object recognition is the question of whether specific neural modules within the ventral stream are specialized for recognizing specific categories of objects. Some evidence supports the notion of specialized modules. For example, one region, known as the **fusiform face area (FFA)**, exhibits a greater response to faces than to other objects (Kanwisher, McDermott, & Chun, 1997). Another region, known as the *parahippocampal place area,* appears to process information related to places in the local environment (Epstein, Harris, Stanley, & Kanwisher, 1999), while a third appears to respond preferentially to buildings (Aguirre, Zarahn, & D'Esposito, 1998). Finally, the **extrastriate body area** responds preferentially to human bodies and body parts, compared to various inanimate objects and object parts (Peelen & Downing, 2007). Several of these areas are shown in ● Figure 7.14. Such findings seem to suggest that the ventral visual-processing stream consists of a variety of regions each tuned to identify a specific class of objects.

Nowhere has the debate about category specificity raged more vigorously than over the question of a face-specific module, and we now turn our attention to that question. Without a doubt, face recognition is an ecologically important task, possibly one of the most important tasks for a primate. The ability to distinguish among people's faces is critical for many aspects of social interaction and communication. Moreover, these abilities have probably been honed over evolutionary time. Whereas humans as a species have known how to read and write for only the last 5,000 years, the ability to distinguish family, friends, and foes on the basis of facial features has been of great importance for the survival of humans and other primates for millions of years. So, does the brain indeed treat faces differently than other objects?

Evidence from Other Primates

Single-cell recordings in monkeys provide evidence for a specific neural substrate underlying face recognition. As mentioned earlier in this chapter, cells in the inferotemporal cortex can be tuned to highly specific

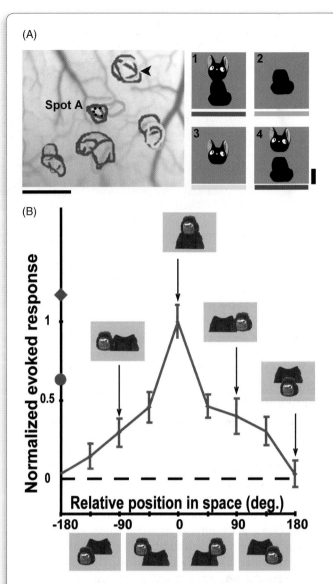

● **FIGURE 7.13   Cells in inferotemporal cortex that prefer configurations of parts.** (A) Results from an optical imaging study in monkeys that examined activity measured at the cortical surface in response to object parts and their configurations. Colored circles indicate the region of the brain that is responsive to the stimuli shown on the right (1-red; 2-green; 3-yellow, 4-blue). Area A showed activity only in response to the cat head and body together (stimuli 1 and 4). In contrast, the area indicated by the arrow was responsive to all cat heads (stimuli 1, 3, and 4), regardless of whether they occurred with bodies or not. (B) In the same study, researchers measured spike rates of individual neurons in brain areas such as Area A from part A of the figure. Individual neurons tended to have a preference for object parts arranged in a particular configuration. *Source:* Fig 4A and 6A from Yamane, Y., et al (2006). Representation of the spatial relationship among object parts by neurons in macaque inferotemporal cortex. Journal of Neurophysiology, 96, 3147–3156. Reprinted by permission of American Physiological Society. J Neurophysiol 96: 3147–3156, 2006. Yukako Yamane, Kazushige Tsunoda, Madoka Matsumoto, Adam N. Phillips and Manabu Tanifuji.

visual information. In some cases, the cells in this region are tuned to fire specifically in response to faces, regardless of whether the faces belong to monkeys or people (Gross, Bender, & Rocha-Miranda, 1969; Gross,

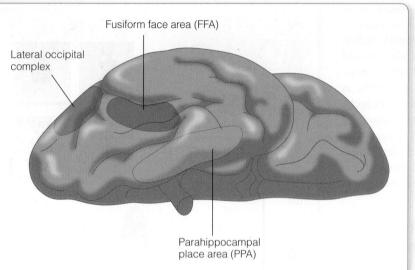

● **FIGURE 7.14   The relative locations of the fusiform face area, the parahippocampal place area, and the lateral occipital complex.** This view shows the ventral surface of the brain. © 2011 Cengage Learning

recording technique—with painstaking recording of individual cells in different places—makes it hard to tell if many such cells are clustered together into a specific region of the ventral stream. In recent years, researchers have applied fMRI to monkeys, and have found face-selective patches of cortex (Tsao, Freiwald, Knutsen, Mandeville, & Tootell, 2003). Within these patches, as many as 97% of the individual cells appear to be face-specific (Tsao, Freiwald, Tootell, & Livingstone, 2006) (● Figure 7.15). Using other imaging methods, researchers have found that face-specific cells in the monkey are distributed asymmetrically, with more such cells evident in the right hemisphere (Zangenehpour & Chaudhuri, 2005). These results fit nicely with data from humans indicating that areas of the ventral stream in the right hemisphere are especially important for face recognition.

Evidence from Prosopagnosia

Can evidence from brain-damaged patients help us to assess whether faces are special? Researchers have turned to the study of prosopagnosic patients to address this question. As discussed in Chapter 3, double dissociation is a particularly powerful method for demonstrating that two mental processes can proceed independently of one another, and that they rely on different neural substrates. Such a double dissociation has been observed for face and object recognition. As discussed earlier, prosopagnosia is a syndrome in which the identification of faces is impaired but the recognition of other objects is relatively normal. Originally it was thought that selective face-recognition deficits might just be due to the fact that

Rocha-Miranda, & Bender, 1972). These cells do not fire in response to other round objects, such as alarm clocks, or to other emotionally important stimuli, such as snakes. Even more specialized cells in the inferotemporal cortex fire only in response to specific aspects of faces or only in response to faces that have particular characteristics. For example, some fire only in response to certain facial features, such as eyes. Other cells fire in response to the components of monkeys' faces only if the components are correctly positioned but not if their positions are scrambled. In some cases, cells are selectively responsive to individual faces, such as that of the experimenter (for reviews, see Gross, 2005; Rolls, 2004).

Although it has long been known that individual inferotemporal cells could be face-specific, the single-cell

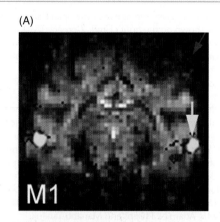
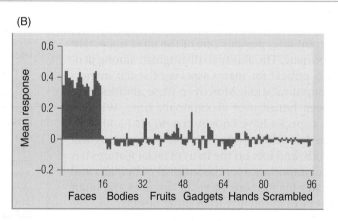

● **FIGURE 7.15   Face-selective patches in monkey visual cortex.** (A) fMRI was used to identify regions in macaque monkey brains that were responsive to faces. (B) Recordings from individual cells within these regions show stronger responses to faces than to other categories of objects. *Source:* Tsao, D.Y., Freiwald, W.A., Tootell, R.B.H., & Livingstone, M.S. (2006). A cortical region consisting entirely of face-selective cells. Science, 311, 670–674.

faces are harder to recognize than objects. However, there have been case reports of patients who exhibit the opposite syndrome compared to prosopagnosics: they can recognize faces but exhibit agnosia for objects (e.g., Feinberg, Schindler, Ochoa, Kwan, & Farah, 1994; Moscovitch, Winocur, & Behrmann, 1997) (● Figure 7.16). These cases appear to confirm that face recognition is dissociable from recognition of other objects, and therefore relies on a separate neural system. Further, prosopagnosia can result from damage limited to the right hemisphere (DeRenzi, Perani, Carlesimo, Silveri, & Fazio, 1994), consistent with other evidence that the right hemisphere is more important than the left for face recognition.

Some researchers have questioned whether prosopagnosia is really best defined as a deficit in face recognition, or whether it is more appropriately described as a deficit in within-category individuation. In other words, when we discuss face recognition, we are usually referring to the ability to tell apart the faces of two individuals (e.g., Susan vs. Maria), whereas when we discuss object recognition, we are usually referring to the ability to tell apart two different types of objects (apples vs. bananas) rather than two different instances of that type (apple #1 vs. apple #2). So, could prosopagnosics' deficits really reflect a problem in making individual distinctions within a particular category?

Some case reports suggest that prosopagnosics may also be deficient in the ability to distinguish among members of other (nonface) categories. In one case report, a farmer who became prosopagnosic could no longer distinguish among the cows in his herd (Bornstein, Sroka, & Munitz, 1969). In another case, a bird watcher could no longer individuate among birds of a given species (Bornstein, 1963). Yet in other case studies, these abilities dissociate. For example, some prosopagnosics appear to retain the ability to differentiate among cows (Bruyer et al., 1983) or to differentiate personal objects from other objects (e.g., DeRenzi, 1986). The existence of these dissociations in some (even if not all) cases serves as evidence that face-recognition can be disrupted independently of other within-category discrimination abilities.

Two case studies are of particular interest because they directly address the issue of expertise in making within-category distinctions. In one case, the individual with prosopagnosia was a car expert, possessing a set of more than 5,000 miniature cars. To test his ability to distinguish among cars, researchers showed him 210 pictures of cars and asked him to identify each car's make, model, and year of production (within two years). He identified all three aspects correctly for 172 of the pictures, and of the remaining 38, he correctly identified the company in 31 cases and the model in 22 cases (Sergent & Signoret, 1992). This individual retained his ability to individuate among cars even though he had lost the ability to do so for faces.

● **FIGURE 7.16   Picture used to test object and face recognition in patients with agnosia.** A patient was unable to recognize the fruits or vegetables in the pattern but could recognize the face. Together with prosopagnosics, who are unable to recognize faces while still recognizing objects such as fruits, the pattern of performance of this patient helps to demonstrate a double dissociation between object and face recognition.

© Lebrecht Music and Arts Photo Library / Alamy

In another case, a patient who became a gentleman farmer after becoming prosopagnosic was able to learn the individual faces of his flock of sheep (as well as sheep he had never seen before), even though he was unable to distinguish among human faces (McNeil & Warrington, 1993). Interestingly, this person's ability to identify sheep faces was superior to that of other new farmers. Such findings hint that he could use cues to recognize sheep faces unencumbered by the "human face schema" that the other farmers might have been imposing on sheep faces.

In sum, evidence from prosopagnosia generally supports the idea that faces are special. Face recognition is doubly dissociable from recognition of other objects, and can be disrupted even when the ability to make other fine within-category distinctions is still intact.

Evidence from Brain Imaging Studies

A variety of neuroimaging methods have been applied to assess the question of face specificity in the human ventral stream. Recordings of electrical potentials are one source of information about the neural substrates of face processing. In neurologically intact individuals, a particular negative-going brain wave occurring at about 170 ms poststimulus (i.e., an N_{170}) occurs with greater amplitude when individuals are asked to view faces compared to other categories of stimuli, such as cars, butterflies, or scrambled faces. Moreover, it tends to be greater over the right hemisphere than the left (Bentin, Allison, Puce, Perez, & McCarthy, 1996).

Recordings from the surface of the brains of patients about to undergo surgery for the relief of epilepsy provide confirmatory evidence and a bit more information on the brain region likely to be generating this potential (Allison, McCarthy, Nobre, Puce, & Belger, 1994). The source of this potential varies from patient to patient, but generally it is recorded bilaterally from fusiform and inferotemporal regions (● Figure 7.17A). In any given patient, however, the size of the region providing such a response is small, perhaps only 1 to 2 cm wide, suggesting a fair amount of anatomical variability with regard to the exact location of face-specific regions. Hemispheric differences have also been found in these

recordings, with the right hemisphere, but not the left, exhibiting different responses to upright faces than to inverted faces (● Figure 7.17B).

However, a recent study calls into question whether the "face-specific" N_{170} is really specific to faces (Thierry, Martin, Downing, & Pegna, 2007a). These researchers argued that the stimuli used in earlier studies that compared the N_{170} for faces, cars, and butterflies may have been plagued by a confound, namely that there was less perceptual variation among the examples of faces than among the examples in the other categories. When these researchers controlled the amount of perceptual variation within stimulus sets, the "face-specific" effect in the N_{170} disappeared, suggesting that the N_{170} may not be face-specific after all. While this debate is far from over (Bentin et al., 2007; Thierry, Martin, Downing, & Pegna, 2007b), it is a good reminder that it can be very challenging to demonstrate that a neural response is truly face-specific, and not driven by other, less interesting perceptual factors. One possibility is that the N_{170} response may index the degree to which configural

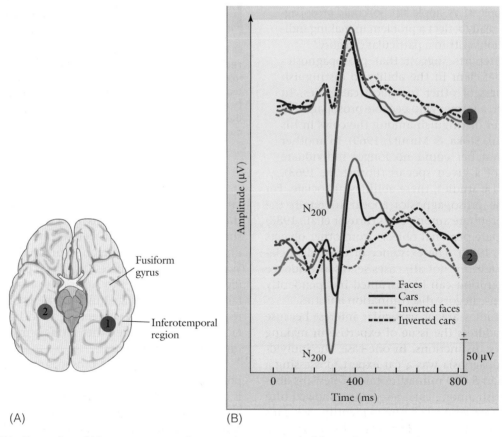

(A)   (B)

● **FIGURE 7.17   Examples of N_{200} responses to faces and cars recorded from the cortex of one individual about to undergo surgery for the control of epilepsy.** (A) The sites (labeled 1 and 2) in the fusiform gyrus at which the potentials were recorded. (B) The potentials recorded over the left hemisphere (top) and over the right hemisphere (bottom). Note that the N_{200} response is larger to faces than to cars. Also notice that the larger response over the right hemisphere to upright faces than to inverted faces (bottom) does not occur for the left hemisphere (top). The N_{200} peak recorded from intracranial electrodes corresponds to the N_{170} peak that is recorded from the scalp surface. © 2011 Cengage Learning processing is required to recognize an object, and, as such, the N_{170} response to faces is enhanced because faces require configural processing.

Despite these complications, the findings from these electrophysiological studies, seeming to indicate a specific response of ventral temporal regions to faces, mesh well with those of functional imaging studies of face processing. Early PET studies identified ventral regions of extrastriate cortex in the right hemisphere as critical for discriminating among the physical features of faces (Sergent, Ohta, & MacDonald, 1992). These regions are highly similar in location to the fusiform face area (FFA) described by Kanwisher and colleagues using fMRI (Kanwisher, McDermott, & Chun, 1997). Although this evidence points strongly to the involvement of the FFA in face identification, recent evidence also suggests that the organization within the FFA may not be uniform. Rather, some patches of cortex within the FFA are highly selective for faces whereas other patches are less so (Grill-Spector, Sayres, & Ress, 2006).

Subregions within the ventral stream seem to be especially important in distinguishing between different individuals, rather than simply being responsive to all faces compared to nonface objects. Anterior regions of the right fusiform gyrus and parahippocampal gyrus are active only during a face-identification task but not during a gender-identification task, suggesting that these regions of the right hemisphere may be specialized for determining facial identity (Sergent, Ohta, & MacDonald, 1992). Subsequent fMRI studies also suggest activation of this region when people have to retrieve biographical information associated with faces (Leveroni, Seidenberg, Mayer, Mead, Binder, & Rao, 2000), and damage to this region results in a selective impairment in semantic identification of famous faces (Tranel, Damasio, & Damasio, 1997).

There is yet one other area of the brain that appears to be involved in processing faces, the superior temporal sulcus (STS; look back at Figure 7.1). Single-cell recordings in monkeys have shown that cells in this region are sensitive to gaze and head direction, with most cells preferentially firing to full views of the face with eye contact and profile view of faces with averted gaze (Perrett et al., 1985). Such cells are also sensitive to facial gestures, especially those involving the mouth, such as a grimace, teeth chatter, or threat display (Perrett & Mistlin, 1990). In humans, attending to the eye-gaze direction causes greater activity in the STS than in the fusiform region, whereas paying attention to facial identity activates lateral fusiform areas more than superior temporal regions, suggesting a dissociation between these two areas (Hoffman & Haxby, 2000). Electrode recordings in individuals about to undergo surgery for epilepsy also indicate that certain cells within the STS show a specific response to mouth movement (Puce & Allison, 1999). This role of the STS in interpreting facial expression may be part of its larger role in interpreting movements that have social significance (Materna,

Dicke, & Their, 2008; Allison, Puce, & McCarthy, 2000). It may also be that superior temporal regions are important for the changeable aspects of the face, such as perception of eye gaze, expression, and lip movement, while the lateral fusiform area is important for processing those aspects of the face that are invariant and thus helpful for identifying individual people (Haxby, Hoffman, & Gobbini, 2000).

All these studies indicate that a broad range of areas within occipital and ventral temporal regions are involved in face processing, with the right hemisphere playing a predominant role. In general, posterior regions seem to be important for the perceptual processes that must be performed to create a configural representation of a face (as distinct from other objects) and to extract the invariants of the face that make it unique. In contrast, more anterior regions are involved in linking a particular facial representation to the pertinent biographical information about that person. Finally, regions of the STS are involved in processing those features of the face that change, such as eye gaze and expression, and thus provide critical information for social cues.

If Faces Are Special, Why Are They Special?

Converging evidence indicates that regions of the human and monkey brain are especially responsive to faces. But what makes faces special? Are primates hard-wired such that the FFA is innately programmed for this particular category of visual stimuli, because faces are so important evolutionarily? Can other stimuli activate the FFA, and if so, what does that tell us about the specialization of this brain region?

One possibility that may have already occurred to you is that we are highly experienced with faces, more so than with many objects. In particular, from early in life we learn to distinguish between the faces of many different individuals, whereas most of us do not learn to distinguish between hundreds of different trees, chairs, or cars. Could the FFA really just be an area that helps to make fine distinctions among objects within a category?

Neuroimaging studies support the idea that expertise with a particular category leads to increased activity in the FFA. In one study, 11 car experts and 8 bird experts, individuals who on average had 20 years of experience identifying such items, were asked to decide whether a previously seen item (car/bird) was the same as the present one. The car experts exhibited greater activity in the "face" region for cars than for other objects, while the bird experts exhibited greater activity in this region for birds than for other objects, as illustrated in ● Figure 7.18 (Gauthier, Skudlarski, Gore, & Anderson, 2000; though see Grill-Spector, Knouf, & Kanwisher, 2004).

Furthermore, activation in this "face" region increases as people become better trained to recognize novel objects. In one study, individuals were trained to become expert at recognizing novel objects, known as "greebles" (● Figure 7.19). Greeble experts but not greeble novices activated the right FFA when viewing the

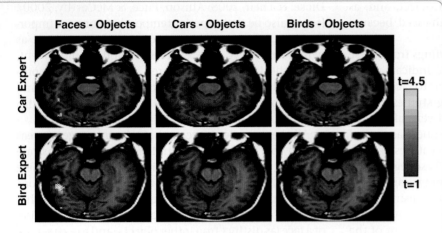

● FIGURE 7.18   The sensitivity of the right fusiform area to expertise in individuating members among a class of objects. Shown here are patterns of activation for faces, cars, and birds versus other objects in columns 1, 2, and 3, respectively. The top row shows data from a car expert and the bottom row shows data from a bird expert. (The brain slices are shown according to radiological convention in which the right side of the brain is on the left side of the image.) Notice that in the car expert, a similar region is activated for faces and cars, while for the bird expert, a similar region is activated for faces and birds. Adapted by permission from Macmillan Publishers, LTD: Gauthier, I., Skudlarski, P., Gore. J.C., Anderson, A.W. (2000). Expertise for cars and birds recruits brain areas involved in face recognition. Nature Neuroscience, 3(2), Figure 3, page 193.

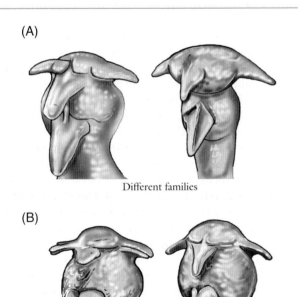

● FIGURE 7.19   Other objects that can activate the fusiform face area. Shown here are "greebles," somewhat facelike objects that can activate the fusiform face area after individuals gain expertise in individuating such objects. (A) Two greebles from different "families," which are differentiated by their large central part. (B) Two greebles from the same family. Their central portions are similar, but the smaller parts are different. As an indication of expertise, greeble experts can distinguish between two members of the same family as quickly as they can distinguish between two greebles from different families. © 2011 Cengage Learning

greebles. Furthermore, the activation in the right FFA for upright compared to inverted greebles increased with training (Gauthier, Tarr, Anderson, Skudlarski, & Gore, 1999). Remember that the inversion effect is taken as an index of configural processing. These findings have led some to suggest that the FFA is really a "flexible fusiform area" specialized for subordinate-level visual processing (i.e., differentiating individuals), which becomes automatic with expertise (Tarr & Gauthier, 2000; but see McKone, Kanwisher, & Duchaine, 2006, for a dissenting viewpoint).

What are we to make of the evidence that the FFA is sensitive to greebles in greeble experts, to birds in bird experts, and to cars in car experts? Does it mean that faces aren't special? Some critics have pointed out that the greebles, and possibly bird and car images as well, are somewhat face-like, in the sense that they have a configural structure (Kanwisher, 2000; though see Gauthier, Behrmann, & Tarr, 2004, and Xu, 2005, for refuting evidence). Therefore, perhaps the increasing involvement of the FFA with expertise in cars, birds, or greebles occurs because people rely on the innate face-processing module to individuate these other classes of objects.

So, is the basic specialization of the FFA really for configural processing (required for individuating objects) but masquerading as a "face" area simply because we have more experience with faces than other objects? Or is the FFA innately specialized for processing faces, but also relied upon for other stimulus categories when they become more and more face-like?

For a number of reasons, the latter interpretation is more likely to be correct (Kanwisher & Yovel, 2006). First, a brain imaging study showed that the FFA is no more activated by configural tasks than part-based tasks, while confirming that it is more activated by faces than other categories of objects (Yovel & Kanwisher, 2004). This evidence suggests that the selectivity of the FFA is for the stimulus category of faces, not for the process of recognition through configural processing. Second, evidence we've already reviewed from prosopagnosic patients suggests that the neural mechanism allowing us to differentiate among individual faces is independent from the mechanism allowing us to distinguish among individuals of other classes, such as cars or sheep. Finally, a case study suggests that the right-hemisphere specialization of this region for processing of faces is at least partially innate. A 16-year-old boy who sustained brain damage in occipital and occipital-temporal regions at one day of age has always been and remains prosopagnosic—profoundly impaired at recognizing faces but not other objects (Farah, Rabinowitz, Quinn, & Liu, 2000). Thus, it seems likely that FFA may be innately preprogrammed to carry out face recognition. Nevertheless, the fact that the FFA may also be used for perceiving other objects provides interesting clues about the flexibility of the inferotemporal cortex (Bukach, Gauthier, & Tarr, 2006).

Bodies May Be Special Too

Most research on category specificity in object recognition has focused on the study of faces as a special category. However, in recent years, investigators have also begun to understand how the visual system represents other parts of the body (Peelen & Downing, 2007). It should not come as a surprise that visual representations of the body are also of paramount significance in the brain—consider that throughout the history of art, representations of the human form are ubiquitous. For both humans and other primates, it is crucial to recognize and interpret information conveyed by the bodies of other members of one's species. This involves recognizing not just their facial identities and expressions, but also their bodily movements, postures, stances, and gestures.

Behavioral studies have shown that our perceptual processing of bodies may be similar in some ways to our processing of faces. For example, the recognition of bodies appears to be based on configural information, just like the recognition of faces. This claim is supported by evidence that inversion disrupts the recognition of bodies, just as it does for faces; in fact, the effects of inversion are similar for body postures as for faces, with both showing a larger effect than nonbiological categories such as houses (Reed, Stone, Bozova, & Tanaka, 2003; Reed, Stone, Grubb, & McGoldrick, 2006).

Research with other primate species has identified body-specific neural responses in regions of the temporal lobe. Single-cell recording studies dating back several decades demonstrated that individual cells in the monkey's temporal lobe are especially responsive to specific body parts, such as hands (Gross, Rocha-Miranda, & Bender, 1972). Confirming these results with fMRI in the macaque monkey, researchers found body-responsive areas in regions of the temporal cortex that are adjacent to face-responsive areas (Pinsk, DeSimone, Moore, Gross, & Kastner, 2005).

Converging evidence from human studies also supports the claim that certain regions are especially sensitive to visual images of bodies. For example, one study recorded electrical responses from the temporal lobe in the right hemisphere of a patient about to undergo surgery for epilepsy (Pourtois, Peelen, Spinelli, Seeck, & Vuilleumier, 2007). These researchers found a response to images of bodies that was greater than the response to other categories of images, such as faces, nonhuman mammals, and tools. Another study disrupted activity

in a subregion of the temporal lobe using TMS, and found that this interfered with the ability to distinguish between bodily forms, such as hand and leg postures (Urgesi, Candidi, Ionta, & Aglioti, 2007).

Human imaging studies using fMRI have provided more information about the location of body-sensitive regions within visual cortex. The current understanding is that there are two separable areas that are responsive to images of bodies (Peelen & Downing, 2007). One is called the *extrastriate body area,* and it is located in Brodmann area 18 in the occipitotemporal cortex (Downing, Jiang, Shuman, & Kanwisher, 2001). Interestingly, this area is near area MT, a region that is especially sensitive to motion; perhaps this adjacency reflects the importance of connecting the image of a bodily form with its motion. The other body-sensitive region is called the **fusiform body area**, and it is located in the fusiform gyrus just adjacent to the fusiform face area that we have already discussed. Initially some researchers thought that the fusiform's response to faceless body images challenged the face-specificity of the fusiform cortex (see Peelen & Downing, 2005). However, subsequent research using higher-resolution imaging methods demonstrated that face-sensitive and body-sensitive subregions of the fusiform gyrus can be distinguished from one another (Schwarzlose, Baker, & Kanwisher, 2005) (● Figure 7.20).

Research on the neural representation of bodily forms is exciting for several reasons. First, the perception of other people's bodies is crucial for social cognition. The ability to visually represent another person's posture and actions can give us insight into that person's state of mind and intentions toward us. Second, the perception of the body can be directly relevant to one's sense of self. A person's perception of her own body is constructed from multiple cues, such as somatosensory information about the position of the muscles and joints. Interestingly, activity in the extrastriate body area is influenced by a person's own motion, even when there is no visual feedback (Astafiev, Stanley, Shulman, & Corbetta, 2004). Although these results are preliminary, they imply that this region may play a role in representing information about a person's own body position, as well as representing the bodies of other people.

Object Recognition in Auditory and Tactile Modalities

As we have already noted, the study of human perception has been predominantly centered on understanding the visual modality, because vision is such a dominant sense in humans. However, we can also recognize objects by other senses, such as hearing and touch. For example, if you closed your eyes, you could still recognize the sound of an ambulance or the feel of your favorite coffee mug in your hand. In this section, we consider how

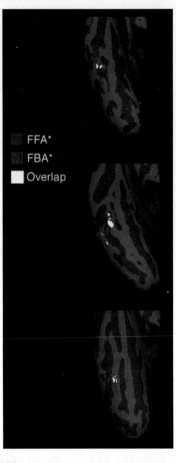

(A)

Faces	Headless Bodies	Body Parts	Cars	Assorted Objects

(B)

● **FIGURE 7.20   Separable regions of activation in the fusiform gyrus in response to faces and to faceless bodies.** Part (A) shows activity in the fusiform face area (FFA) and fusiform body area (FBA) for three different participants. The view is of the ventral surface of the posterior right hemisphere. Part (B) shows stimuli that were used in the experiment. The FFA was defined as the region in which activity was greater for faces than for cars and other objects. The FBA was defined as the region in which activity was greater for headless bodies or other body parts than for other objects. Areas labeled as "Overlap" in part (A) were activated by both faces and bodies more than by other kinds of objects. *Source:* Schwarzlose, R.F., Baker, C.I., & Kanwisher, N. (2005). Separate face and body selectivity on the fusiform gyrus. Journal of Neuroscience, 25, 11055–11059.

object recognition in other modalities can be disrupted, as well as current issues in understanding how object recognition may occur across different senses.

■ **Agnosias in Other Modalities**

We focused on visual agnosia in the first part of this chapter, but agnosias can occur in other modalities as well. For example, **auditory agnosia** is characterized by normal processing of basic auditory information but an inability to link that sensory information to meaning, despite the fact that other cognitive functions such as attention, memory, and language appear to be normal (see Bauer & McDonald, 2006, for review).

Individuals with auditory agnosia can perceive the occurrence of a pure tone (that is, a tone of a single frequency), and they do so at loudness thresholds generally equivalent to those of the average person without agnosia. However, when a person with auditory agnosia hears a complex sound, he cannot classify it.

Auditory agnosia usually manifests in one of three ways. In **verbal auditory agnosia** (also known as **pure-word deafness**), words cannot be understood, although the ability to attach meaning to nonverbal sounds is intact. The individual can read, write, and speak normally, an indication that this condition is not a disorder of linguistic processing. However, patients with this type of auditory agnosia complain that although they know a noise has occurred, speech sounds like "an undifferentiated continuous humming noise without any rhythm" or "like foreigners speaking in the distance."

Likewise, in **nonverbal auditory agnosia**, which is rarer than verbal auditory agnosia, the ability to attach meaning to words is intact, but the ability to do so for nonverbal sounds is disrupted. Such an individual knows that a sound has occurred but cannot categorize it, for example as a car horn, a dog bark, or a lawn mower. This difficulty can be quite a problem in real life. For example, if a car's driver is honking a horn as a warning for people to move out of the way, an individual with auditory agnosia would hear a noise but might not hurry across the street, because the sound was "unintelligible, sort of like how I remember crickets chirping or static on a telephone line." In **mixed auditory agnosia**, the ability to attach meaning to both verbal and nonverbal sounds is affected, although the patient can determine whether two sounds are identical or different and whether one sound is louder than the other. That is, in these patients the ability to *hear* the sounds is intact, and they are not deaf.

Agnosia can also occur for touch information. **Somatosensory agnosia**, or **tactile agnosia** (sometimes referred to as *astereognosia*), is a condition in which a person is unable to recognize an item by touch but can recognize the object in other modalities (e.g., Reed & Caselli, 1994; Reed, Caselli, & Farah, 1996). As with other agnosias, two types have been proposed, one in which the affected person has an inability to use tactile information to create a percept, and another in which the percept is more or less intact but cannot be associated with meaning. This latter agnosia is sometimes called **tactile asymbolia** because the tactile information cannot be linked to its symbolic meaning (e.g., a small metal object that is big at the top and thin at the bottom with a jagged edge cannot be linked to the concept of a key).

The existence of agnosia in the auditory and tactile modalities illustrates that deficits in recognition can occur even when visual recognition is intact. This, in turn, reminds us that recognition can occur independently through several different senses. Yet, in everyday life, we often receive parallel cues to recognition simultaneously from multiple modalities, such as when you see the face of your cat, hear her purr, and feel her soft fur. We next consider several approaches to understanding the relationship between recognition through visual, tactile, and auditory senses.

■ Multimodal Object Recognition

One perspective on multimodal object recognition emphasizes the commonalities in recognition through vision and touch. For example, studies have shown that people who are trained to recognize novel objects by touch show inversion effects, implying configural processing, just as seen for expertise in visual object recognition (Behrmann & Ewell, 2003). In addition, both touch and vision provide information about the three-dimensional shape of an object in a way that auditory information does not. To illustrate, imagine an alarm clock of a particular shape and size. You could either see or feel its shape and size, but just hearing the sound of the alarm clock's ring would not provide information about its shape and size. Vision and touch can also provide information about an object's texture, whereas hearing typically cannot.

Consistent with this connection between touch and vision, imaging studies have found that the lateral occipital complex is sensitive to tactile as well as visual information about objects. As we noted earlier, this region is known to be important in the visual perception of objects. More recently, researchers have found that a subregion of the LOC was activated when participants felt common objects with their hands, even though the participants could not see the objects (Amedi, Malach, Hendler, Peled, & Zohary, 2001). Interestingly, the lateral occipital region was not activated by feeling textures such as sandpaper and fur, indicating that the response was specific to objects rather than to any recognizable tactile sensations. Subsequent research showed that auditory stimulation, such as the sound of a hammer or a helicopter, did not activate this region (Amedi, Jacobson, Hendler, Malach, & Zohary, 2002). This result indicates that the region codes object properties that are shared between vision and touch but not audition.

Although vision and touch may have certain properties in common that hearing does not appear to share, hearing can also be used to recognize objects. As we learned in Chapter 6, higher-level areas of auditory cortex are crucial in auditory pattern recognition. For example, recognizable auditory sounds (water dripping, egg cracking, horse galloping) evoke greater activity in the middle temporal gyrus than do those same sounds played backward, which makes them unrecognizable (Lewis, Wightman, Brefczynski, Phinney, Binder, & DeYoe, 2004). Researchers have also examined whether certain categories of auditory objects activate different regions of auditory cortex. In one study, participants listened to two categories of sounds, animal vocalizations (e.g., bird song, horse whinny) and tool-related sounds (e.g., sound of a hammer, typewriter, stapler). Animal vocalizations activated the superior temporal gyrus bilaterally, whereas tool sounds activated numerous areas in the left hemisphere, including motor areas (Lewis, Brefczynski, Phinney, Janik, & DeYoe, 2005). Intuitively, it makes sense that tool sounds would activate motor areas, because the sound of a typewriter may prime the participant to think about the action of typing, whereas the sound of a bird would not necessarily prime any particular motor action.

Interestingly, one study found that the voices of familiar people activate the FFA more than the voices of unfamiliar people, even when no face is presented at

IN FOCUS: Visual Imagery: Seeing Objects with the Mind's Eye

Have you ever imagined yourself on a tropical island in the Caribbean? Can you see the long, white, sandy beach? The blending of the water's colors from pale green to jade to aquamarine to royal blue? The palm trees with their fronds waving in the breeze? And, to complete the picture, your latest romantic interest looking perfectly enticing in an ever-so-alluring bathing suit? If so, then even though our discussion of objects has centered on recognizing objects in the real world, you realize that we also have the ability to examine and manipulate objects in our mind's eye by mental imagery.

The nature of mental imagery has been the subject of a long-running debate, the resolution of which was based, in part, on data from cognitive neuroscience. The researcher Stephen Kosslyn proposed that mental imagery is much like visual processing, except in the mind's eye. Some support for this position came from studies in which he found that the time needed to "see" particular parts of an image was proportional to the distance that we would expect the mind's eye to have to move to get to that part. For example, participants were told to imagine an item (e.g., an airplane) and to focus on one end (e.g., the propeller). Then they were given the name of a particular feature to look for ("the tail") and instructed to press a button when they could see it. Kosslyn (1973) found that individuals took longer to press the button if the feature was located at the other end of the imagined item (e.g., the tail) than if it appeared in the middle (e.g., the wing).

In contrast, Zenon Pylyshyn (1973, 1981) argued that we don't actually draw mental images. Rather, he suggested, the results of Kosslyn's experiment could just as easily be explained by *propositional knowledge*. Propositional knowledge describes entities (e.g., a propeller, a wing), their relations (next to, behind), their properties (long, silver), and their logical relations (if). He argued that a person takes less time to decide about the wing than the tail because the individual must remember only that the wing is behind the propeller, which is fewer propositions than remembering that the tail is behind the wing, which in turn is behind the propeller.

The arguments for and against each theory were debated for more than another 10 years, until Kosslyn and Martha Farah turned to neuropsychological evidence, which played a large role in settling the matter (for a more detailed but readable account of this debate, see Kosslyn, 1990). These researchers reasoned that if imagery does rely on producing a picture in the mind's eye, it should require some of the same neuronal machinery required by vision (e.g., Farah, 1988). Alternatively, if imagery tasks can be performed simply by resorting to propositional knowledge about objects in the world, then the memory or semantic-processing areas of the brain should be active, but visual areas should not.

Studies of regional brain activation and of patients with brain damage, as well as "reversible lesions" caused by transcranial magnetic stimulation (TMS), all suggest that visual areas play a major role in imagery. For example, Kosslyn and colleagues (1993) reasoned that if imagery relies on the visual cortex, some relationship should exist between the size of the imagined object and the area of visual cortex that is activated. This finding would be expected because, as discussed in Chapter 6, visual space is mapped onto visual cortex in a retinotopic manner. Consistent with their hypothesis, these investigators found that when a person was imaging small letters in the center of the mind's eye, activation was greatest in posterior regions of the medial occipital lobes, which is the region that processes information from the fovea. In contrast, when a person was imaging larger letters, activation occurred over a larger area of visual cortex that included more

the same time (von Kriegstein, Kleinschmidt, Sterzer, & Giraud, 2005). The same study found that when listening to the voices of familiar people, activity in the FFA was coupled with activity in the superior temporal sulcus, which is known to be responsive to human voices (Belin, Zatorre, Lafaille, Ahad, & Pike, 2000). Does this mean that the familiar voice primes the mental image of a face, thus activating the FFA, or does the FFA represent more abstract information about specific person identities? Remember that prosopagnosic subjects are often able to recognize people by their voices but not by their faces, meaning that the damaged region in prosopagnosia is essential for face recognition but not voice recognition. This suggests that rather than representing abstract person identities, the FFA represents face identities. The activation of the FFA in response to familiar voices may then reflect priming of a face image by other regions that represent the sound of that person's voice.

Auditory and visual object recognition may also be synergistic. Evidence for visual-auditory interactions in object recognition comes from a study that asked participants to press a button as quickly as possible in response to a particular animal (dog, cow, etc.). The animal might be presented visually, through a sound (bark or moo), or through a combination of a visual image and sound. Participants were faster to recognize the animal when both visual and auditory cues were present; furthermore, the presence of the auditory cue enhanced the scalp-recorded early visual evoked potential, the N1, which occurs about 100–200 ms after the stimulus begins (Molholm, Ritter, Javitt, & Foxe, 2004). These results suggest that auditory and visual information about objects is combined very early during processing.

One commonality across all the different senses is that they must distinguish "what" and "where"—what

anterior regions, which is where more peripheral regions of visual space are processed (see also Slotnick, Thompson, & Kosslyn, 2005, for similar results).

In another creative experiment, researchers recorded brain activity using fMRI while participants either viewed an X or an O or imagined either of those two stimuli (Stokes, Thompson, Cusack, & Duncan, 2009). The researchers trained a computer program to classify each trial as an X or an O, based on the different patterns of brain activity in the lateral occipital complex during actual perception of the X versus the O. The computer program was then able to generalize its learning based on the actual perception trials and apply it to the imagery trials. In other words, the computer program could tell, at above-chance levels, if the participant was imagining an X or an O, based on the similarity of the brain activity to that shown when the participants was actually seeing the X or the O. These findings further indicate that perception and imagery share some common basis.

Additional evidence that imagery relies on visual cortex comes from an unusual case study in which an individual had elective surgery to remove the occipital lobe of one hemisphere because it was the source of intractable epileptic seizures (Farah, Soso, & Dasheiff, 1992). The researchers calculated the visual angle of the patient's mental image before and after the surgery (see the original article for details on how this was done). The researchers reasoned that if imagery relies on the visual cortex, after surgery the visual angle of images in the horizontal dimension should be half what it was previously, because the visual cortex of one hemisphere is responsible for processing information from one half of visual space. However, the visual angle of images should be unchanged in the vertical dimension, because the remaining intact occipital cortex would be able to process information from both the upper and lower halves of space. These investigators found, as expected, a reduction by approximately half of the visual angle of images in the horizontal dimension, but no change for the visual angle of images in the vertical dimension.

With the advent of TMS, it has been possible to disrupt processing of visual areas. If imagery relies on visual-processing regions of the brain, then disrupting those areas should also disrupt the ability to use imagery. To test this premise, Kosslyn and colleagues had participants memorize four sets of lines. Participants were given auditory information about which two sets of lines to compare and along what dimension (e.g., relative length, width, orientation or spacing between them). Compared to a control condition in which no imagery was required, the individuals exhibited activity in V1 (BA 17). They then applied TMS while the individuals were either performing the imagery task or a perceptual version of the task in which the stimuli were kept in front of the individual. TMS interfered with both perception and imagery, suggesting that primary visual areas are critical for this function (Kosslyn et al., 1999).

Does this mean that the regions of the brain involved in perception and imagery are identical? If so, then how would we ever be able to tell the difference between what we experience in a particularly vivid dream and our everyday perceptual experience? Although neuroimaging studies suggest a high degree of overlap, there are areas activated uniquely for each (Kosslyn, Thompson, & Alpert, 1997). Furthermore, there are case studies of individuals who have impaired object perception but intact imagery (Behrmann, Moscovitch, & Winocur, 1994), and also the converse, individuals with disrupted imagery but intact perception (Farah, Levine, & Calvanio, 1988). These findings suggest that at least some aspects of the neural control of imagery and perception must be separable, although in most situations they may rely on very similar brain structures (for a very readable and short review of this issue, see Behrmann, 2000).

an object's identity is and where it is located. As we have already learned, in the visual system there is a major dissociation between these functions, with the ventral stream primarily concerned with the "what" problem and the dorsal stream concerned with the "where" problem. We learned in Chapter 6 that some researchers have also proposed a "what versus where" distinction in the auditory system, although evidence for this dissociation is not as clear for audition as it is for vision. A dissociation between coding for object identity and location has also been reported for touch information. For example, when participants are required to mentally rotate a tactile object (a spatial task), the parietal lobe is activated, whereas when they must distinguish the identities of tactile objects, the lateral occipital complex is activated (Prather, Votaw, & Sathian, 2004; see also Reed, Klatzky, & Halgren, 2005). Thus, the distinction between "what" and "where" pathways in the brain seems to be a basic organizational feature that transcends any specific modality.

As we have seen in this chapter, the problems posed by object recognition in any modality are astounding—and yet our brains solve these problems, recognizing thousands of objects across many different viewing conditions, linking the sensory images of those objects to stored knowledge and meaning, and combining information across modalities to fully comprehend an object in an instant. While the convergence of human imaging, single-cell recording, and patient studies has led to progress in understanding the brain systems underlying object recognition, researchers are still far from fully unraveling the puzzle. Still, recognizing object identities is only one part of the problem that the brain has to solve. Another major challenge is representing where objects are located in the environment, and we explore issues of spatial representation in Chapter 8.

Summary

The "What" Ventral Visual System

- This brain system, which plays a major role in the ability to recognize objects, courses ventrally from the occipital regions toward the anterior pole of the temporal lobe.
- Single-cell recordings in monkeys indicate that cells located more anterior in the ventral visual-processing stream fire to specific forms, have a larger receptive field, and are sensitive to color, attributes that are all helpful to recognizing specific objects.

Deficits in Visual Object Recognition

- Apperceptive agnosia is an inability to process basic features of visual information that precludes perception of even the simplest forms (e.g., an "X").
- In associative agnosia, the basic perceptual properties of visual information can be processed but not to a high enough degree to allow for object recognition.
- Whereas apperceptive agnosia is associated with diffuse bilateral damage near and extending into occipital regions, associative agnosia is associated with bilateral damage near the occipitotemporal border.

Prosopagnosia: Agnosia for Faces

- Prosopagnosia is the inability to recognize faces but not other objects, and can occur after damage to certain areas of the ventral stream or, in rare cases, during development with no known brain injury. Some aspects of faces can be recognized implicitly, even though the person cannot identify or otherwise classify the face.

Category-Specific Deficits in Object Recognition

- Some disorders affect the ability to recognize items within certain categories (e.g., fruits and vegetables), but not other categories (e.g., items manufactured by humans).
- The most plausible explanation for these disorders is that we gain access to memory for different classes of items through different means. For example, damage to visual areas will impair recognition of items differentiated on the basis of visual forms, such as flowers and plants, whereas damage to motor areas will affect recognition of objects that we differentiate on the basis of how they are manipulated and used, such as tools.

Theoretical Issues in Object Recognition

- Although some cells in the ventral stream appear to have high selectivity for certain complex stimuli, objects are most likely coded by dynamic patterns of activity across populations of cells.
- One major problem the visual system must solve is recognizing objects despite variation in their size, position, lighting, and viewpoint. For example, researchers are still working to understand how viewpoint-invariant representations can be constructed from cells that mainly respond best to specific viewpoints.
- Both individual features and their holistic configuration are important in object recognition. The left hemisphere is specialized for featural recognition, whereas the right hemispheric is specialized for configural recognition. We tend to rely on configural information more for objects with which we have expertise.
- Evidence from brain-damaged individuals, neuroimaging, and electrophysiology indicate that faces are processed differently than other classes of objects. Recent evidence indicates that perception of other body parts may also take place in specialized regions.
- Determination of the physical characteristics of a face, linkage of that physical description to information about the person's identity, and recognition of facial features that can help convey social or emotional information each occur in distinct regions of the temporal lobe, mainly in the right hemisphere.
- Regions of the right hemisphere that are specialized for recognizing faces can be recruited to help recognize other classes of objects as one gains expertise with that class of objects.

Object Recognition in Other Modalities

- Auditory agnosia impairs the ability to recognize verbal sounds, nonverbal sounds, or both.
- Somatosensory, or tactile, agnosia, impairs the ability to recognize items by touch.
- The lateral occipital complex is involved in recognizing objects through touch as well as vision.
- Recognition of an object in one modality may prime a representation of that object in other modalities as well.

Key Terms

Book Companion Site at www.cengage.com/psychology/Banich

This website provides instructors and students with a wealth of free information and resources, including tutorial quizzes, flashcards, and the glossary.

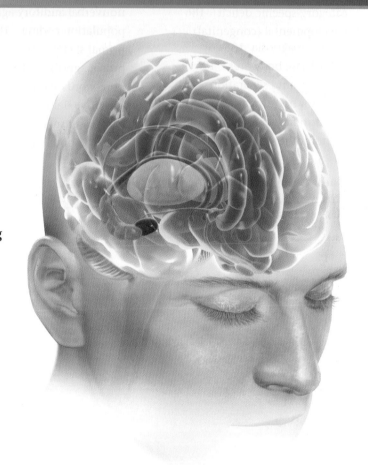

Spatial Cognition

A FUN-LOVING, middle-aged woman, C.J. had spent her entire adult life as an outdoor enthusiast. Then she suffered a mild stroke that damaged a small portion of the posterior section of her right hemisphere. She hated the confinement of the hospital and eagerly awaited her chance to spend some time outdoors again. Because her basic visual-processing abilities were intact (an indication that the lesion had spared primary and secondary visual areas), she didn't anticipate having any problems doing the things she loved: hiking, skiing, and backpacking.

A few weekends after being released from the rehabilitation unit, C.J., along with her friend Sarah, decided to take a day hike up to a mountain pass. They started up the trail on a beautiful, crisp autumn day, with great views of the valleys below unfolding before them. They hiked for about an hour, passing a number of turnoffs, until they entered a more forested area, where the trail became less well defined and had many switchbacks. The hiking was difficult, but C.J. was feeling like her old self again. Soon afterward, they came to a fork in the trail. They knew from the map that their cutoff should be nearby, but they weren't sure exactly where, so C.J. decided to pull out the map and compass. Once she had them out, though, she had difficulty determining how to align the map with reference to the compass. As she had previously had a strong sense of direction, C.J. was surprised to find herself confused as to which way was north, east, south, or west. At that point, Sarah called out, saying that she had found a trail marker indicating that they wanted the rightward fork. C.J. was relieved to realize that despite her trouble with the map and compass, she had no trouble correctly distinguishing the rightward fork of the trail from the leftward one.

They reached the top of the pass after a couple of hours and were rewarded with a spectacular view of mountains all around them. As was their usual routine, they pulled out their map and tried to identify the surrounding peaks. Even though both the compass and the position of the sun could be used for orienting their direction, C.J. once again found herself confused. She was unable to translate the fantastic vista in front of her to the representations on the map. Although she and Sarah usually disagreed about the position of at least one mountain (after which a lively discussion would ensue), this time C.J. just listened carefully, startled at her own confusion.

C.J. was subdued on the hike down. Usually fit, she was a bit out of shape from her hospital stay, and as with any trauma, her body had not yet fully recovered. Sarah asked C.J. whether she was feeling okay, and although C.J. said that she was just tired, her mind was elsewhere. She was wondering whether her stroke might have had some unexpected consequences that would interfere with one of her favorite pastimes.

THE STORY ABOUT C.J. helps to illustrate that spatial processing is not a simple cognitive function, but rather consists of many different abilities. Some of C.J.'s spatial abilities, such as understanding the relationship between the map and the surrounding terrain, and knowing geographical points of reference (north, south, east, and west), were compromised by her stroke—yet other abilities, such as determining left and right, were unaffected. In this chapter, we examine the many ways in which spatial relations among items can be computed and the brain systems that underlie and enable these computations.

We learned in Chapter 6 that the visual cortex provides a precise retinotopic map of space. However, a retinotopic map is inadequate for fully understanding the space around us. First, as we have already discussed in relation to object recognition, the retina only provides two-dimensional information about the three-dimensional world. Second, you need to create a mental map of space that is constant regardless of where your eyes are looking, where your head has turned, and which way your body is facing. For example, you need to know that the cup of coffee sitting on the table just to the left of your hand is the same cup of coffee, both when it is in the center of your retinotopic map (as when you are looking directly at it) and when it is slightly off center in your retinotopic map (as when you move your eyes to the piece of cake sitting next to it). Third, retinotopic maps provide information only about the scene as you are currently viewing it. Often, however, we need a mental representation of space that includes areas that we are not currently viewing. For example, when you turn your head away from the table to greet a friend who is joining you for coffee, you need to remember the position of that full cup of coffee so that you don't knock it over when you get up to shake hands. Finally, you also need spatial maps that extend to places that aren't within your field of view. To be able to get from your house to the coffee shop where you will meet your friend, you need a mental map of the larger world around you.

This chapter discusses several major issues related to the brain's processing of space. First, we consider how the brain is able to code for the three dimensions of space, including issues in coding for left and right and calculating depth. Second, we consider how the brain is able to consider spatial relations with respect to different reference frames. We also distinguish between different scales of space: small scales, such as understanding the spatial relations of objects on your dinner table; and large scales, such as navigating through the streets of Chicago. The perception of motion is also closely tied to spatial perception, because motion is inferred from the change in an object's spatial position over time. Finally, we consider the relationship between spatial understanding and action. After all, it's no good knowing where that cup of coffee is located unless you can reach out and grab it.

As we will see, many of these spatial functions depend on regions within the dorsal visual stream, located primarily in the parietal lobe. The parietal lobe within the right hemisphere seems to be especially important for many aspects of spatial perception, further illustrating cerebral asymmetry in the human brain (see Chapter 4). However, although these are valid generalizations, other brain regions also contribute to spatial processing, and the functions of the parietal lobes are not limited to spatial processing (Husain & Nachev, 2007). Therefore, while it is appropriate to associate the parietal lobe with spatial processing, it is important to recognize that the situation is, as always, somewhat more complex.

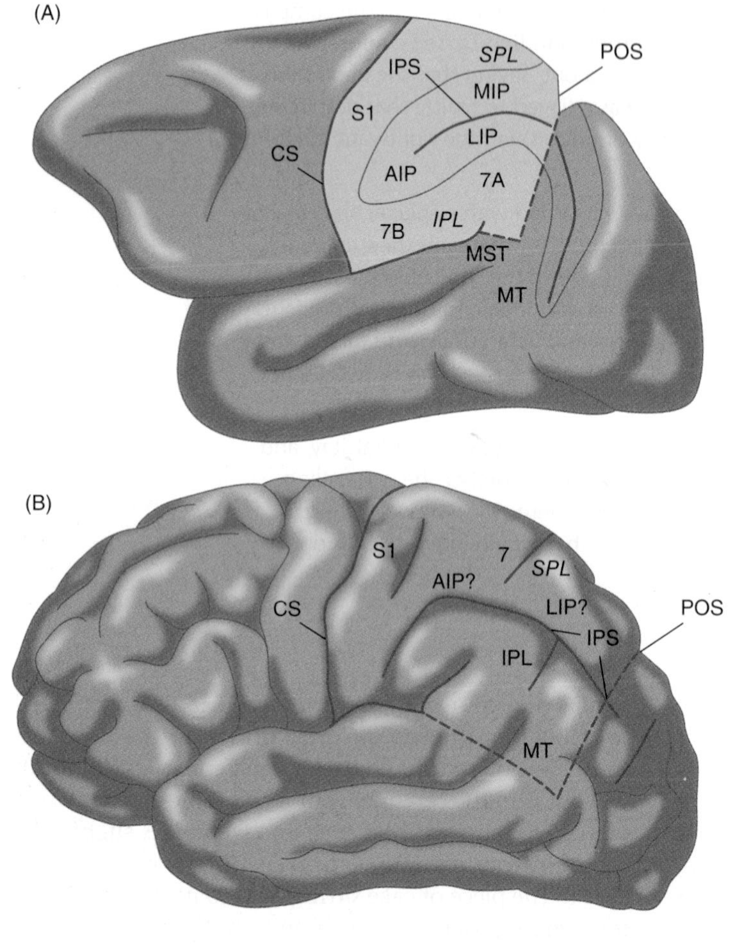

The Dorsal Visual System for Spatial Processing

In Chapter 7, we examined the functioning of the ventral visual-processing stream, which plays an important role in object recognition. In this chapter, we focus on the dorsal visual-processing stream. This processing stream projects from primary visual areas to parietal regions, and it supports many aspects of spatial processing. The main components of the dorsal stream are shown in ● Figure 8.1. As you can see, many key components of the dorsal stream are located in the parietal cortex, which has several subdivisions. The anterior parietal lobe (also known as the *postcentral gyrus*) is concerned primarily with somatosensory representations, and is not considered part of the dorsal stream proper. In contrast, the posterior parietal cortex (PPC) is multisensory and is crucial in many aspects of spatial cognition. Within the PPC, researchers often distinguish between the superior parietal lobule and the inferior parietal lobule, which are separated by the intraparietal sulcus. Even in cortex buried within the intraparietal sulcus, different subregions have been distinguished in the monkey brain, such as the anterior, lateral, and medial intraparietal areas. As we will learn later in this chapter, these subregions appear to be important for visual guidance of specific kinds of actions. In addition to these parietal areas, other cortical regions are also relevant to the dorsal stream. For example, areas MT and MST contribute to our understanding of motion.

● **FIGURE 8.1 Dorsal visual stream.** Major dorsal stream areas are shown in the macaque monkey (A) and human (B). The parietal lobe is separated from the frontal lobe by the central sulcus (CS) and from the occipital lobe by the parietal-occipital sulcus (POS). The primary somatosensory cortex, in the anterior parietal lobe, is represented as area S1 and is not part of the dorsal stream proper. The posterior parietal lobe is divided by the intraparietal sulcus (IPS) into the superior parietal lobule (SPL) and the inferior parietal lobule (IPL). In the macaque, subregions buried within the sulcal tissue (shown opened up) are the anterior intraparietal area (AIP), medial intraparietal area (MIP), and lateral intraparietal area (LIP). The analogous locations of these regions in the human are still under investigation. Finally, outside the parietal lobe, areas MT and MST are important for motion perception. *Source:* Culham, J.C. & Kanwisher, N.G. (2001). Neuroimaging of cognitive functions in human parietal cortex. Current Opinion in Neurobiology, 11, 157–163.

The dorsal stream is well positioned to subserve spatial functions. The dorsal stream receives visual information from the primary visual cortex, but it also receives input from the somatosensory cortex in the anterior parietal lobe and from the vestibular system, both of which provide information about the position of the body in space. This convergence of information from other senses allows regions of the parietal lobe to construct a multisensory representation of space in reference to the body's position. The parietal regions of the dorsal stream are also closely connected with frontal lobe regions that control the body's movement. These connections make sensory information about space available to the motor planning regions of the brain.

Just as the properties of cells in the ventral visual system make those cells well suited for the task of object recognition, so properties of cells in the dorsal stream make the cells well suited to process spatial information. Research with monkeys indicates that posterior parietal cells are sensitive to different attributes than cells in temporal regions. Unlike cells in the ventral processing stream, cells in parietal areas are not particularly sensitive to form or color, making them ill suited for detecting the visual properties from which shape can be derived. Furthermore, they are not particularly sensitive to items positioned in central vision, where acuity is the highest, a fact indicating that these cells do not play a large role in object recognition.

Cells in the posterior parietal cortex are most responsive to attributes of visual information that are useful for processing spatial relations. First, cells in this area appear to be responsive to a combination of the retinal location of the visual stimulus and the position of the animal's eyes or head (e.g., Andersen & Mountcastle, 1983), which allows the creation of a stable spatial map of the world. Second, the cells seem to fire in response to a specific direction of motion, either inward toward the center of the visual field or outward toward the periphery. Such sensitivity provides a means for objects to be tracked as they move across space. Third, the optimal velocity of movement for stimulating these cells to fire is about the speed at which the animal walks or runs (Motter & Mountcastle, 1981). Sensitivity to this range of speeds provides a way to update the spatial positions of items as the animal moves past them while locomoting. Finally, cells within the inferior parietal lobe often fire in close relationship with planned movements such as reaching or grasping, as well as in response to visual and tactile stimuli (e.g., Rozzi, Ferrari, Bonini, Rizzolatti, & Fogassi, 2008). These joint sensory-motor cells reflect the close relationship between spatial perception and action within the dorsal stream.

In sum, anatomical and cellular features of the dorsal stream indicate that it is well suited for spatial processing. In the following sections, we consider the complexities of spatial representation and the skills that the dorsal stream supports.

Coding for the Three Dimensions of Space

Space, as you know, is three-dimensional. This might seem like it is stating the obvious, but it is worth thinking about how the brain is able to code for the three dimensions of space: namely, the vertical (up-down) dimension, the horizontal (left-right) dimension, and the depth (near-far) dimension. As discussed in Chapter 6, the retinal images that the brain receives are two-dimensional, and the depth dimension must be computed in the cortex. We begin by discussing the coding of spatial dimensions that can be derived directly from the retinal image, and then turn to coding of depth.

■ Distinguishing Left from Right

As we learned in Chapter 6, the visual world is mapped in a retinotopic manner onto visual cortex, with the map reversed in relation to the visual world with respect to both the up-down and left-right dimensions. It would seem fairly easy to distinguish left from right based on this map-like organization within the brain's visual-processing stream. However, it is trickier to distinguish left from right than to distinguish up from down, the other dimension coded on the retina. Developmentally, children often confuse left and right long after they have a clear understanding of up and down. One study even found that a sizable minority of college professors report having some left-right confusion (Harris & Gitterman, 1978). What is so hard about telling left from right? Whereas up and down can be easily determined with respect to an absolute reference point (the earth), left and right are inherently relative terms. For example, if I am facing you, an object on my right side is on your left side, and vice versa.

A fascinating patient described by Michael McCloskey and colleagues (1995; McCloskey, 2009) demonstrated vividly how left-right understanding can go wrong. The patient, a college student with no known brain damage, had a history of trouble with reading, but her problems turned out to be more pervasive. Numerous tests showed that she often mistakenly perceived the spatial locations of items in a mirror-image fashion. ● Figure 8.2 dramatically illustrates what happened when the patient was asked to directly copy a complex figure. Notice how many of the figure's elements she places in the opposite location across the left-right midline. The researchers found that she also showed such mirror-reflections in a simple reaching task. A target would be placed in a particular position—say, 45 degrees to the left of midline—but the patient would initially reach for it in the location 45 degrees to the right of midline. The fact that the patient's reaching was not random, but rather mirror-reversed, suggests that she was able to represent some aspects of the object's spatial

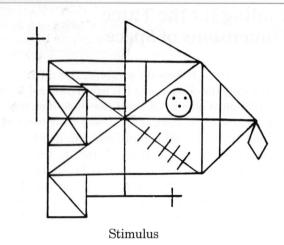

Stimulus

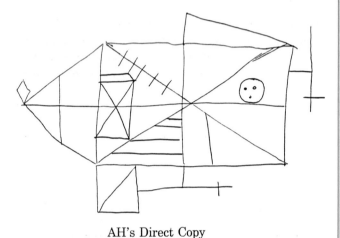

AH's Direct Copy

● **FIGURE 8.2   Evidence of left-right mirror reflection in a patient.** The patient's direct copy of the complex figure is shown at the bottom. *Source:* Figure 1 from McCloskey, M., et al. (1995). A developmental deficit in localizing objects from vision. Psychological Science, 6, 112–117. Reprinted by permission of Association for Psychological Science.

coordinates correctly. However, she consistently misrepresented the object's direction in the left-right dimension. Although the researchers have not identified any localized region of damage within this patient's brain, the fact that she was able to perform well on tests of object identity implies that processing in the ventral stream was intact.

Additional evidence from brain-damaged patients provides some intriguing clues about the spatial coding of right and left. Left-right confusion can be a symptom of damage to the dorsal stream of either hemisphere, but the way in which that left-right difficulty is expressed depends on which hemisphere is damaged. Traditionally, left-right confusion has most often been associated

with damage to the left parietal region (e.g., McFie & Zangwill, 1960). However, right parietal damage can disrupt left-right discriminations that require a spatial transformation, such as determining right from left on a person facing you (Benton, 1985).

■ Depth Perception

Depth perception helps us to localize items in the near-far plane. As discussed in Chapter 6, depth is not provided directly by the retinotopic map, but it can be computed in part by comparing the images from the two eyes. The amount of **binocular disparity**, or discrepancy between the images seen by the two eyes, is a cue to depth. Cells in primary visual cortex are sensitive to different amounts of binocular disparity, and provide important information about depth for use by the dorsal stream regions.

Depth perception is crucial to an understanding of space, and therefore we would expect the dorsal stream to code for depth information in some way. Studies with other primates have established that cells in various regions of the dorsal stream are sensitive to binocular disparity. Specific areas of the dorsal stream that appear to code for depth include the inferior parietal lobe, area 7a, and the lateral intraparietal area (Sakata, Taira, Kusunoki, Murata, & Tanaka, 1997) (see Figure 8.1). In these areas, different subsets of cells are most responsive when the eyes are fixated at different locations in depth, much the way that certain cells in the ventral visual stream seem to be tuned to specific objects. Most of these cells respond maximally when the eyes are fixated on locations in near space, but others prefer locations in far space. Another dorsal stream area that codes for depth information is area V5/MT, which we discuss in more detail later in the section on motion perception. In this region, cells are especially sensitive to movement or rotation in the plane of depth (Sakata et al., 1997).

These studies indicate that individual cells are sensitive to depth information, but how do we know that these cells actually are responsible for the perception of depth? One study addressed this issue by stimulating clusters of cells sensitive to binocular disparity within area MT and observing the effect on monkeys' perceptions (DeAngelis, Cumming, & Newsome, 1998). In the experiment, monkeys had to indicate the depth of a stimulus through either an up or down eye movement (up for far stimulus, down for near stimulus). The researchers found that when near-preferring cells in area MT were stimulated, the monkey's eye movements indicated that it was seeing the stimulus at a near depth location; likewise, when far-preferring cells were stimulated, the monkey's eye movements were biased toward far target locations. This study demonstrates that activity of MT cells influences the monkey's perception of depth.

Evidence from humans suggests that although damage to the parietal cortex in humans can impair depth perception (e.g., Holmes & Horax, 1919), there does not seem to be any syndrome in which perception of spatial depth is disrupted but all other spatial functions are intact. This finding tells us that coding for depth probably does not rely upon a single dedicated brain region whose function is to compute depth and nothing else. Rather, processing of depth probably occurs throughout various dorsal stream areas that represent space for a variety of purposes, such as providing a spatial framework for reaching and grasping motions and for understanding motion in the plane of depth. This idea is consistent with the finding that cells across many regions in the dorsal steam of monkeys show sensitivity to depth.

Spatial Frames of Reference

One important aspect of coding spatial information involves **frames of reference**. This concept refers to the idea that we can understand the spatial location of an object with respect to multiple reference points. For example, imagine that you are sitting in front of a table with a bowl of fruit in front of you. Your body is aligned with the bowl of fruit, but your head is tilted slightly to the left as you turn your eyes to the right to gaze at a person standing beside the table. Consider now the task of representing where that fruit bowl is located. First, consider where the bowl is in relation to your body midline; it is directly in front of the midline of the trunk of your body. However, because your head is tilted, the bowl is not neatly lined up with the midline of your head. Also, because your eyes are shifted rightward within your head, the bowl is not falling on the midline of your retina, either. In other words, because the trunk, head, and eyes can all move independently, an object's location relative to any one of these body parts must be coded independently. At the same time, these reference frames also have to be co-referenced to one another to provide a stable representation.

The frames of reference we just mentioned—body-centered, head-centered, and eye-centered—all belong to a category of reference frames known as **egocentric reference frames** because they all specify an object's location in relation to some aspect of the self. However, we can also think of spatial relations in ways that do not specifically refer to the self. For example, you could consider whether the fruit bowl is on top of or underneath a book, or you could specify how many inches the bowl is from the salt shaker. When you consider spatial relations of objects relative to one another, and independent of your own location, you are specifying the object locations in an **allocentric reference frame**.

Studies using single-cell recordings in monkeys have begun to reveal how these multiple frames of reference are coded by the brain. To address this issue, first consider how receptive fields are mapped at the level of primary visual cortex. As we learned in Chapter 6, individual cells in primary visual cortex have retinotopically defined receptive fields; that is, the cell will fire best when a particular location on the retina is stimulated with light. Now, consider a receptive field that is defined relative to the midline of the animal's head, regardless of where the eyes are looking. A cell with a head-centered receptive field would fire optimally when a visual stimulus appears a certain distance from the midline of the head, even if the animal's eyes are fixated off to the side rather than aligned with the midline of the head (● Figure 8.3). Cells with head-centered receptive fields code for space in a more complex manner than cells in primary visual cortex. Such cells must compute head-centered location based on combining two sources of information: the place on the retina that was stimulated and the position of the retina in relationship to the head midline.

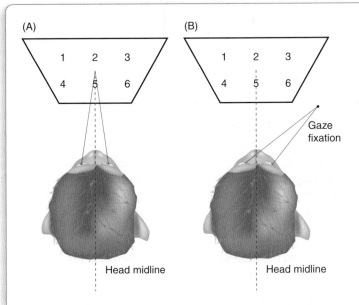

● **FIGURE 8.3   Illustration of head-centered coding of spatial location.** Head-centered cells have receptive fields that are defined in relation to the head midline. Imagine recording the activity of a single cell as a monkey views a screen on which a light could flash in one of six locations (numbered 1–6 in the figure). Consider a head-centered cell that fires strongly when the light flashes at location 1 in panel A, but does not respond when the light flashes at locations 2–6. When the monkey shifts its eyes rightward, as in panel B, this head-centered cell will continue to fire most strongly to light at location 1, even though that stimulus is now striking a different part of the retina. As long as the head remains in the same position, this head-centered cell will continue to fire to light in location 1. A cell that coded for space in allocentric terms would continue to fire to its preferred location (such as location 1) even if the monkey moved its head or body.

One study investigated whether cells in the lateral and medial intraparietal cortex are more sensitive to head-centered or eye-centered (retinotopic) spatial location (Mullette-Gillman, Cohen, & Groh, 2005). Approximately 33% of visually responsive cells in these regions seemed to code for location primarily in eye-centered (retinotopic) coordinates, about 18% of cells seemed to code primarily for head-centered coordinates, and the remainder of the cells (nearly half) could not be easily categorized as either solely head-centered or solely eye-centered. Thus, it seems that different kinds of egocentric representations (head-centered vs. eye-centered) are coded by overlapping populations of cells.

Another finding from single-cell studies is that egocentric and allocentric representations are coded in different subregions of the parietal lobe. Cells within the lateral intraparietal (LIP) region are sensitive to spatial location in egocentric coordinates but not sensitive to spatial location in allocentric coordinates, whereas cells in area 7a in the superior parietal lobe tend to be more sensitive to allocentric coordinates (Snyder, Grieve, Brotchie, & Andersen, 1998). The authors of this study suggest that these two reference frames may be important for different functions. Specifying an object's location in relationship to the eyes can be helpful in controlling gaze direction; for example, knowing how far to shift the eyes to look directly at that object. Consistent with that hypothesis, the LIP region is anatomically connected with brain regions that control eye movements, such as the frontal eye fields. In contrast, allocentric coding is more important for navigating through a spatial environment, in which it is important to understand how objects and landmarks are related to one another. Therefore, area 7a in the monkey, which has more allocentrically sensitive cells, projects to regions of the brain that are important in navigation, such as the parahippocampal gyrus. Even more fascinating, some cells in parietal cortex seem to use a kind of allocentric reference frame that specifies the location of an object part in relation to the whole object, not in relation to the head or eyes (Chafee, Averbeck, & Crowe, 2007). This is analogous to coding where an apple stem is located in relation to the rest of the apple, rather than where the stem is located in relationship to your head or eyes.

One puzzle is how the brain is able to compute such object-centered frames of reference, when the initial input coming into the dorsal stream is represented in a retinotopic (eye-centered) frame of reference. Evidence from single-cell recordings in monkeys has begun to unravel this mystery. One group of researchers had monkeys complete a construction task in which a target object was made up of several squares, and the monkey had to choose the correct location of a missing square to complete the object (Crowe, Averbeck, & Chafee, 2008). The researchers recorded the firing of 20–30 individual neurons in a region within the superior parietal lobe. During each trial of the task, this group of cells first

coded information about the missing square's location in retinotopic coordinates (relative to the monkey's fixation point), and then about 100 ms later the same group of cells represented the location of the missing piece in object-centered coordinates (relative to the center of the object, independent of where the monkey's gaze was fixated). Thus, this ensemble of cells seems able to compute the necessary transformation of spatial information from a retinotopic to an allocentric reference frame. Researchers are still attempting to understand exactly what inputs the cells use to engage in this computation and how they transform the information from one reference frame to another.

Adding to the complexity, the parietal cortex is also involved in creating representations of space that are multisensory; that is, based on senses such as touch and hearing as well as vision. However, information from touch and audition is not necessarily represented in the same frame of reference as visual information. For example, eye-centered representations are more likely for vision than for other senses, whereas head-centered coordinates are more likely for touch and audition. How, then, is spatial information from multiple senses integrated? One possibility is that regions of the parietal lobe manage to align maps constructed from different senses. For example, one fMRI study in humans found an area of superior parietal lobe that appears to align visual and touch information in head-centered coordinates (Sereno & Huang, 2006). Single-cell recording studies in monkeys suggest that in other areas of the parietal cortex, such as the ventral intraparietal area, tactile information is represented with respect to a head-centered reference frame, whereas visual information is often represented by the same cells in either head-centered or eye-centered reference frames (Avillac, Deneve, Olivier, Pouget, & Duhamel, 2005). As you can see, researchers are still far from understanding exactly how multiple reference frames from various senses are integrated.

Nonetheless, studies of brain-damaged patients indicate that reference frames can be independently disrupted by brain damage. That is, in a given patient, spatial understanding in one frame of reference may be affected while other frames of references are spared. The best evidence for this conclusion comes from studies of patients with hemineglect, in whom damage to the right hemisphere produces a failure to attend to the "left" side of space (see Chapter 11). Some hemineglect patients fail to attend to information on the left side of the body midline, whereas others fail to attend to information to the left of the eyes' fixation, and still others fail to attend to information on the left side of the head. Some patients may even neglect the left-hand side of an object regardless of where that object is placed in relation to the patient's body, indicating an allocentric form of neglect (see Halligan, Fink, Marshall, & Vallar, 2003, for a review). Recent evidence indicates that egocentric neglect is most often associated with damage to the supramarginal gyrus of the right parietal lobe, whereas object-centered neglect is most often seen in conjunction with damage to middle and inferior temporal lobe regions (Medina et al., 2009). These different patterns of breakdown across patients reinforce the idea that coding in these different reference frames is at least partly dissociable.

Evidence from patients with neglect also tells us that space can be divided into different realms or spheres based on distance relative to the body (Halligan et al., 2003) (● Figure 8.4). *Personal space* refers to spatial position on the body. For example, some neglect patients show left-sided neglect only with respect to their own bodies, such as failing to shave the left side of the face. Other neglect patients show neglect only for the left side of *peripersonal space*, which refers to the spatial realm within arm's reach, or near space. Finally, there are also neglect patients who seem to have the most trouble with information presented on the left side beyond arm's reach, in what is referred to as *extrapersonal space* or far space. Because patients' understanding of space can be independently disrupted in either the personal, peripersonal, or extrapersonal realms, it seems that these regions of space must be coded using somewhat different brain regions or processes.

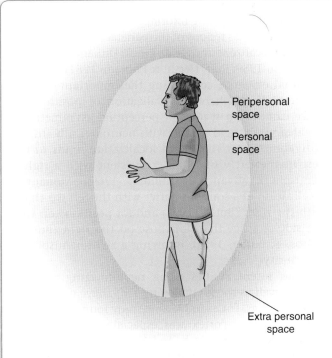

● **FIGURE 8.4   Illustration of personal, peripersonal, and extrapersonal realms of space.** Studies of patients with hemispatial neglect have found that coding for these different realms of space can be independently disrupted by brain damage.

Spatial Relations in Small-Scale Space

In this section, we consider some of the abilities involved in understanding the relationship between items in relatively small-scale space, such as a dinner table. In order for you to be able to eat your dinner, you need to know where your plate is located, and you also need to be able to find your fork, knife, and spoon, not to mention the food itself. These seemingly simple abilities rely on several component functions within the dorsal stream.

■ Localization of a Point in Space

Probably the most basic aspect of spatial processing is the ability to find a point in space. Back in 1918, Holmes noted that such an ability could be compromised by brain damage. He reported on patients who could recognize objects, like a fork, placed directly in front of them. But if the objects were placed somewhere else, such as on a table set for dinner, the patients would act as if blind, groping and misreaching for the item. Localization in all three dimensions of space was affected because patients would reach too near or too far, too much to the left or too much to the right, or too high or too low. Furthermore, these individuals were at just as much of a loss at determining relative position (e.g., determining which of two objects was farther left) as they were at determining absolute position (i.e., determining the precise point in space at which an object was located).

As you might imagine, such deficits greatly disrupted these patients' lives.

The syndrome that Holmes observed was not a specific deficit in spatial localization, because his patients exhibited various other disruptions in spatial processing as well. Nonetheless, the location of damage in these patients, which typically involved the parietal lobes of both hemispheres, hinted at the involvement of this region in spatial localization.

Since Holmes's time, the evidence has become clearer. Unilateral damage to superior regions of the parietal lobe can cause an inability to accurately reach for items on the contralateral side of space, regardless of the arm used, while leaving accuracy of localization for ipsilateral targets intact (e.g., Cole, Schutta, & Warrington, 1962; Ratcliff & Davies-Jones, 1972). Moreover, parietal damage can impair the ability to perceive the location of a point in space even when no reaching action is involved. Such investigation can be done in the laboratory in diverse ways—for example, by asking individuals to decide whether two dots, presented successively, appear in the same location, or by displaying a dot on the screen briefly and then asking the individual to locate its position among an array of dots. Although some variation occurs across studies, deficits on these tasks are most likely to be observed following damage to posterior regions of the right hemisphere (e.g., Hannay, Varney, & Benton, 1976; Warrington & James, 1988;

Warrington & Rabin, 1970). The parietal region also plays a role in localizing information in auditory as well as visual space, as lesions of the parietal lobe disrupt the ability to localize sounds (e.g., Pinek, Duhamel, Cave, & Brouchon, 1989; Ruff, Hersh, & Pribram, 1981).

Initial evidence confirming the important role of the right hemisphere in localization of position in space came from studies of perceptual asymmetries. Divided visual field studies with neurologically intact individuals show that point localization tends to be best in the left visual field, consistent with a right-hemisphere advantage (Kimura, 1969). Monaural localization of a sound is better with the left ear than with the right (Butler, 1994) and for positions on the left side of space than for those on the right (Burke, Letsos, & Butler, 1994), implying a right-hemisphere superiority.

More recent studies using neuroimaging techniques, as well as those employing TMS, have confirmed these findings. For example, one study found that right inferior parietal cortex was especially active during a sound localization task, and that higher activity in this region predicted better localization performance (Zatorre, Bouffard, Ahad, & Belin, 2002; see also De Santis, Clarke, & Murray, 2007; Maeder et al., 2001; Rämä et al., 2004). When people make judgments about whether a point represents the true midpoint of a line, right parietal cortex becomes activated (Fink et al., 2000), and disruption of right parietal activity through TMS leads to an inability to bisect a line in its true center (Fiero, Brighina, Piazza, Oliveri, & Bisiach, 2001). Studies using TMS have shown that such abilities rely critically on right inferior parietal cortex, as TMS over the anterior parietal lobe or superior temporal gyrus of the right hemisphere does not disrupt accurate line bisection (Oliveri & Vallar, 2009).

■ Relations between Points in Space

Consider a dinner table again. The ability to localize a specific point in space allows us to determine the exact point where an item, such as a bowl of mashed potatoes, is located. But it is also important to understand the relation between points in space. For example, if our friend is looking for the salt, we might tell her that "The salt is behind the bowl of mashed potatoes"; or we might notice that the salt is a couple of inches past her grasp and pass it to her. The spatial relationship described in the first example (the salt is behind the potatoes) is an example of **categorical spatial relations**, which specifies the position of one location relative to another in dichotomous categorical terms (e.g., above vs. below, top vs. bottom, front vs. back, left vs. right). The spatial relationship described in the second example (the salt is two inches beyond a person's grasp) is an example of **metric (coordinate) spatial relations**, which specifies the distance between two locations. Evidence suggests that the left hemisphere is specialized

for computing categorical spatial relations and that the right hemisphere is specialized for metric spatial relationships (Kosslyn, 1987, 2006; see Jager & Postma, 2003, for a review).

One important feature of this theory is that metric and categorical spatial relations are considered to be independent of one another, because describing relations between two points from a metric perspective provides no information about their relationship from a categorical perspective, and vice versa. For example, saying that the salt shaker is two inches beyond your friend's grasp provides no information about whether the salt shaker is to her right or left. Likewise, saying that the salt shaker is behind the mashed potatoes provides no information about whether it is an inch or two inches behind the mashed potatoes. Furthermore, computational models suggest that the ability to represent each of these types of information can be carried out better by two distinct subsystems than by one (Baker, Chabris, & Kosslyn, 1999; Kosslyn, Chabris, Marsolek, & Koenig, 1992).

Studies of brain-damaged patients support the distinction between categorical and metric processing (e.g., Laeng, 1994). As noted earlier, people with left-hemisphere damage often have difficulty distinguishing right from left, a task that involves categorical descriptions of spatial relations, whereas individuals with right-hemisphere damage have difficulty localizing items in space, which implies that they are unable to compute the distance of an item from some reference point within a spatial framework. Similarly, deactivation of the left hemisphere by sodium amobarbital in epilepsy patients produces more errors on a categorical task, whereas deactivation of the right hemisphere produces more errors on a coordinate spatial task, at least for difficult versions of the tasks (Slotnick, Moo, Tesoro, & Hart, 2001).

Studies with neurologically intact people also support this distinction. Under divided visual field conditions, neurologically intact people typically show a RVF (left-hemisphere) advantage for judgments about categorical spatial relations and an LVF (right-hemisphere) advantage for judgments about metric spatial relations (e.g., Kosslyn, Koenig, Barrett, Cave, Tang, & Gabrieli, 1989; Hellige & Michimata, 1989) (● Figure 8.5). Interestingly, this visual field difference is observed only when the situation makes it difficult to recode coordinate spatial relations in a categorical manner (e.g., Banich & Federmeier, 1999; van der Ham, van Wezel, Oleksiak, & Postma, 2007). For example, in a delayed matching task, researchers found an RVF advantage for categorical and LVF advantage for coordinate relations only when the delay between the two stimuli to be compared was relatively short (500 ms), but not with longer delays (van der Ham, van Wezel, Oleksiak, & Postma, 2007). This pattern could reflect the fact that as time passes, we tend to remember spatial information using a verbal strategy that lends itself better to categorical distinctions (e.g., above/below, left/right, etc.).

Brain imaging studies also confirm this hemispheric distinction. For example, in one study participants viewed abstract shapes with a dot placed some distance from the shape. Later, participants viewed the same shapes and had to make either categorical or coordinate judgments based on their memory of where the dot had been in relation to that shape. During memory retrieval, left prefrontal cortex was activated for categorical judgments, whereas right prefrontal cortex was activated for coordinate judgments (Slotnick & Moo, 2006; see also Kosslyn, Thompson, Gitelman, & Alpert, 1998). We discuss the role of the frontal lobes in spatial working memory in more detail in Chapter 10. In sum, the distinction between categorical and coordinate spatial processing has been upheld across a wide range of converging methods, though factors such as task difficulty and time for memory decay can influence the pattern of results.

Constructional Abilities

We have examined the ability to *perceive* spatial relations but have not yet discussed the ability to motorically produce or manipulate items so that they have a particular spatial relationship. These latter abilities are often referred to as **constructional praxis**. In everyday life, such abilities can be critical for tasks ranging from picking up a bowl of mashed potatoes so we can put some on our plate to manipulating a key so that it fits correctly into a lock.

In the laboratory and the clinic, constructional skills are examined by tasks that are relatively simpler than the real-life instances just discussed. Such tasks can include copying a complicated nonsense drawing, building a block world, and manipulating and arranging colored cubes to match a particular pattern. The Rey-Osterrieth Complex Figure shown in ● Figure 8.6A is often used to assess spatial-constructional skills and perceptual skills. For the most part, constructional abilities are disrupted by damage to the right hemisphere (e.g., Benton, 1967). The role of the right hemisphere in such tasks can be seen by looking at the copies of the Rey-Osterrieth figure drawn by three individuals who had strokes that damaged the temporoparietal region of the right hemisphere (● Figure 8.6B).

Although deficits in spatial-constructional skills are typically associated with right-hemisphere damage, such deficits can also occur following left hemisphere damage (e.g., Black & Strub, 1976; Trojano et al., 2004). Deficits following left-hemisphere damage probably occur for one of two reasons. First, although these tasks measure constructional abilities, they are likely to involve other subskills as well, such as fine motor control. Thus, performance may be disrupted as a result of damage to additional regions besides the one critical for

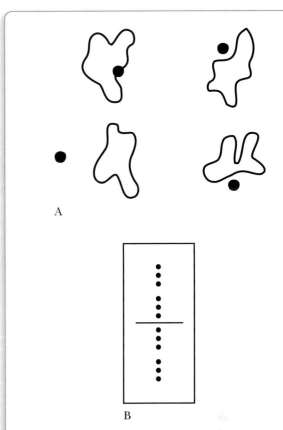

● **FIGURE 8.5   Examples of stimuli used to investigate the difference between categorical and metric spatial relations.**   (A) Each of these four stimuli is shown individually. In the categorical task, an individual is asked to decide whether the dot is on or off the blob. In the metric task, the person is asked to decide how far the dot is from the blob. (B) In this task, the bar and one dot are shown in each trial. The figure depicts 12 possible locations of dots. In the categorical task, subjects decide whether the dot is above or below the bar. In the metric task, they decide whether the line is near (within 0.79 in., or 2 cm) or far away (farther than 0.79 in., or 2 cm) from the dot. For both tasks, a RVF advantage is generally observed in the categorical task and a LVF advantage for the metric task. © 2011 Cengage Learning

the constructional component of the task. Second, it is likely that many of these tasks can be performed using verbal strategies. For example, ● Figure 8.7 shows a Block Design subtest that requires an individual to arrange blocks with colored sides so that the top of the blocks matches a template pattern (Figure 8.7A). One way to perform this task is to analyze the spatial relationships in a given template. Another approach is to use a verbal strategy to perform the task, such as saying, "I need a solid white block and must place that to the left of a block that has the black design at the bottom with the white part on top." Sometimes differences in strategy can be detected by qualitative differences in how individuals perform the test. For example, after right-hemisphere damage, patients tend to make errors that involve the overall arrangement of the blocks (Figure 8.7B), whereas

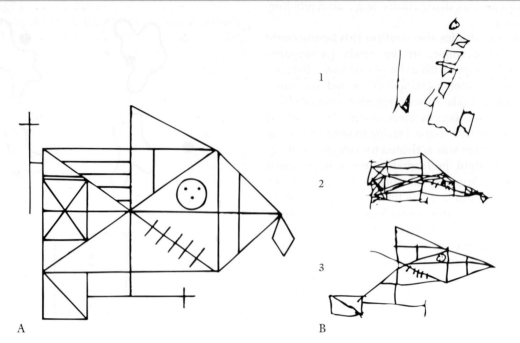

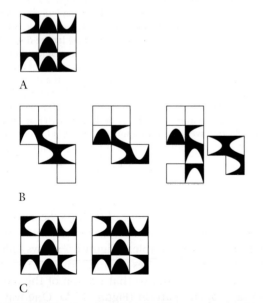

● **FIGURE 8.6   The testing of visuospatial drawing abilities.** (A) The Rey-Osterrieth Complex Figure.
(B) Examples of attempts to copy this figure by three individuals with damage to posterior sections of the right hemisphere.
From Neuropsychology Assessment (2nd ed. P. 396), by M.D. Lezak, 1983, Oxford, England: Oxford University Press;
B. Adapted with permission from "The Role of the Right Cerebral Hemisphere in Evaluating Configurations," by L.I. Benewitz,
S. Finkelstein, D.N. Levine, and K. Moya, as appeared in Brain Circuits and Functions of the Mind (p. 327), edited by
C. Trevarthen, Copyright 1990, Reprinted by permission of Cambridge University Press. © 2011 Cengage Learning

● **FIGURE 8.7   Constructional skills as measured by a Block Design subtest.** (A) A sample design that individuals must copy. (B) Three steps in an attempt to copy the design by an individual with right-hemisphere damage. The patient does not even recognize the basic square pattern of the design. (C) The first and second attempts to copy the same figure by an individual with left-hemisphere damage. The overall configuration is correct, but the details are incorrect. In the first attempt, the block in the upper left-hand corner is rotated 180 degrees from the correct position, whereas in the second attempt, the block in the lower right-hand corner is rotated 180 degrees. © 2011 Cengage Learning

errors by left-hemisphere-damaged patients tend to involve a specific piece of the pattern (Figure 8.7C).

Neuroimaging evidence also demonstrates that both left and right parietal lobes are involved in drawing, another kind of constructional ability. For example, one study used fMRI to compare brain activity in conditions in which neurologically normal people either named pictures, or named the pictures and then drew them with the right hand (Makuuchi, Kaminaga, & Sugishita, 2003). In the naming-plus-drawing condition compared to the naming-alone condition, activation was observed bilaterally in the parietal lobes, and in fact was greater on the left than the right in most of the participants. The left hemisphere is probably activated during drawing tasks because although the task is visuospatial, it also involves planning movements of the right hand, a function dominated by the left hemisphere.

Given the role of motor control in constructional tasks, you might wonder if such tasks really measure spatial representation skills at all, or whether they are simply measures of motor planning and coordination. Addressing this question, one study found that visuospatial abilities, such as judging line orientation, angle width, and geometric figures, significantly predicted performance on visuomotor copying tasks, and this pattern held true for both neurologically normal people as well as patients with right-hemisphere damage (Trojano et al., 2004).

Motion Perception

So far we have considered a spatial world in which spatial relations are static. But spatial relations can change with time; that is, they may involve motion. Motion perception is inherently tied to spatial perception, because perceiving motion involves perceiving changes in an object's spatial location over time. In addition, we must be able to represent our own motion through the world in order to fully understand where we are presently located.

■ Motion Perception as Distinct from Other Aspects of Spatial Processing

A clinical case study provides some initial evidence that the analysis of motion has a unique neural substrate, different from that which supports other spatial skills. The patient in this study lost her ability to perceive motion in all three dimensions, but her other basic visual and spatial functions were intact, including visual acuity, binocular vision, color discrimination, discrimination of visual objects and words, and localization of items in space (Zihl, Von Cramon, & Mai, 1983). As you might imagine, this disorder created much difficulty in her life. When pouring liquids, such as tea or coffee, the flowing stream would appear to this patient as a glacier or a snapshot, much the way such a stream does in magazine ads. Because she could not see the rising level of fluid in a container, it was impossible for her to determine when to stop pouring. Even more troublesome was her difficulty in judging the speed of cars (which she had no trouble recognizing). This impairment made crossing streets extremely dangerous. In describing her dilemma, she said, "When I'm looking at the car, first it seems far away. But then, when I want to cross the road, suddenly the car is very near" (Zihl et al., 1983, p. 315). Eventually, she learned to rely on auditory cues, such as the loudness of a car, to estimate how close or far away it was.

In this woman, damage occurred in a broad range of parietal regions in the right hemisphere and a more restricted area in the left hemisphere, as well as the middle and superior temporal gyri bilaterally (Hess, Baker, & Zihl, 1989). Another individual who also had difficulty perceiving motion (but in this case in only two, not all three, dimensions) sustained damage in a similar location, namely bilateral posterior temporoparietal areas (Vaina, Lemay, Bienfang, Choi, & Nakayama, 1990).

A vast amount of research in both monkeys and humans has more specifically identified the brain regions that are crucial to the ability to perceive and represent motion. The two most important regions are areas MT (also known as V5) and MST (see Figure 8.1). **Area MT** receives input from early visual areas like V1, V2, and V3, and it sends projections back to those areas as well as to higher-level areas like the ventral intraparietal cortex and area MST.

Single-cell studies in monkeys suggest that activity in area MT leads to the perception of motion. First, single cells in area MT respond best to a pattern that moves in a particular direction and with a particular speed, with different cells having different speed and directional preferences (Born & Bradley, 2005; Zeki, 1974). More importantly, researchers found that the firing rate of certain speed-preferring MT cells could actually predict a monkey's behavioral response in a task that required indicating which of two patterns was moving faster (Liu & Newsome, 2005). Perhaps the most impressive evidence has come from experiments in which experimenters stimulated different groups of MT cells, each of which has certain speed preferences. The researchers looked at the effect of such stimulation on a monkey's decision about the speed of a stimulus. Depending on the group of cells stimulated, the experimenter could actually shift the monkey's response, presumably by altering the monkey's perception of the stimulus speed (Liu & Newsome, 2005). Stimulation of specific direction-preferring cells in area MT can also shift a monkey's decision about the direction of movement of a stimulus (Nichols & Newsome, 2002).

Imaging studies have confirmed that MT and surrounding regions become very active when people are viewing moving patterns (e.g., Tootell et al., 1995; Zeki, Watson, Lueck, Friston, Kennard, & Frackowiak, 1991; see also Hesselmann, Kell, & Kleinschmidt, 2008). In addition, disruption of area MT, either due to brain lesions or due to TMS, affects the perception of motion and the ability to use motion cues to guide actions (e.g., Bosco, Carrozzo, & Lacquaniti, 2008; Newsome & Pare, 1988; Schenk, Ellison, Rice, & Milner, 2005; Whitney et al., 2007).

Area MST, like area MT, is sensitive to motion, but it seems to encode somewhat more complex patterns of motion. Specifically, cells in area MST respond to patterns that include optic flow (Britten, 2008). **Optic flow** refers to the pattern of movement of images on your retina as you move actively through an environment. For example, imagine that you are running through a field. As you run, the world is whipping past you; trees, shrubs, and fenceposts first appear before you, and then fly by as you pass them. The movement of these images on your retina forms a predictable pattern: the overall rate of movement will be determined by your running speed, and objects that are closer to you will appear to move past you faster than objects in the distance. In addition, objects get bigger as you approach them and then smaller after you run past them. Although these kinds of flow patterns occur naturally all the time as we move through our environments, they can also be created in lab settings and characterized with mathematical precision (e.g., Heuer & Britten, 2007). Numerous studies have found that cells in area MST are excited by optic flow bilaterally (in either visual field), whereas cells in area MT are most excited by simpler motion within the contralateral field only. We have here another example of the hierarchical nature of visual processing that we encountered in Chapter 6, as simple representations are built into more complex ones.

■ Incorporating Knowledge of Self-Motion

One problem that the brain must solve is distinguishing between the real movement of an object in the world and the movement of an object's image on the retina. The position of an object's image on the retina can change for two reasons: either the object moved while the retina remained in the same location, or the object remained stable while the retina moved because of an eye movement (● Figure 8.8). For example, as you move your eyes across a stationary object, such as your house, its image moves across your retina—yet you do not perceive your house to be moving. Why not? You can also think of the reverse situation, in which the image of a moving object remains stationary on your retina because your eyes are tracking it. For example, imagine that you are following a bird as it flies across the sky. If you are tracking it well, you will keep its image centered on your fovea, yet you still perceive it to be moving even though the retinal image is stable.

One way to illustrate the importance of distinguishing between object movement and retinal-image movement is to consider what happens when that ability is lost. Indeed, such a case has been reported in a patient with bilateral damage to extrastriate regions (Haarmeier, Thier, Repnow, & Petersen, 1997). The patient reported that when he moved his eyes across a stationary background pattern, the background pattern seemed to move. (Unfortunately, this led to a lot of vertigo in his daily life.) To measure this phenomenon, the researchers determined how much movement of the pattern was necessary for it to seem stationary to the patient as he moved his eyes across it. They found that the patient perceived the pattern as stationary only when it was moving at the same speed as his eyes, and therefore when its image was kept stationary on his retina. (This

is unlike the rest of us, who would perceive the pattern as stationary when it actually was stationary!) This patient had an impairment in incorporating information about his eye movements into his understanding of motion in the visual world.

How, then, can the brain distinguish real movement from movement of the image on the retina? The famous perceptual psychologist Hermann von Helmholtz proposed a solution to this problem back in 1910. Helmholtz understood that the only way to distinguish between real and retinal movement is if the movement-perception areas of the brain receive information about eye movements. That is, if eye movements are taken into account, the visual system can figure out if the retinal image is moving because the eyes are moving or because the object itself is moving in the world. If the movement of the retinal image matches that of the eye movement, then the brain can infer that the object is really stationary. In contrast, if the movement of the retinal image does not match the eye movement, then the object in the real world must really be moving.

There are two different sources that could provide the visual system with information about eye movements, so that these eye movements can be taken into account in understanding the movement of a retinal image. One possibility is that the motor regions of the brain let the visual system know when they are planning to move the eyes; this is the model that Helmholtz proposed. According to Helmholtz's hypothesis, motor-planning regions of the brain send a **corollary discharge**, which is a signal to visual areas about the upcoming eye movements. Although this hypothesis is plausible, there is currently no direct evidence either supporting or refuting it (though see Sommer & Wurtz, 2008, for a review of related issues).

Another possibility is that sensory receptors within the eye muscles provide ongoing feedback about changes in position of the eye. Supporting this possibility, cells within the somatosensory cortex of the monkey brain

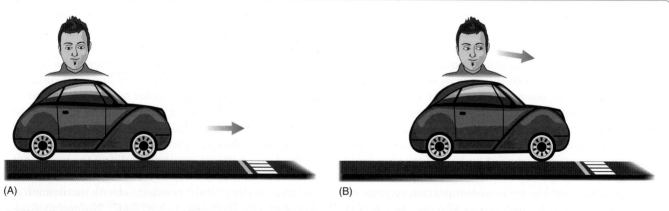

(A)   (B)

● **FIGURE 8.8   Two different conditions that can cause movement of a visual image on the retina.** (A) A person gazes straight out onto a street while a car drives by; the image of the car will move across the retina. (B) A person scans his eyes across a parked car. Here, the movement of his eyes will cause the image of the car to move across the retina. © 2011 Cengage Learning

can represent the position of the eyes (Wang, Zhang, Cohen, & Goldberg, 2007). These cells appear to depend on sensory cues from the eye itself, rather than on commands from the motor cortex, because the cells do not respond when the monkey attempts to move an eye that has been immobilized through anesthetization. A recent study using TMS in humans also found that the somatosensory cortex in the anterior parietal lobe encodes information about the position of the eyes. When the somatosensory cortex was transiently disrupted by TMS, participants were unable to correctly use cues from their eye positions to perceive what point was straight ahead of them (Balslev & Miall, 2008). Because somatosensory cortex cells can code for the orientation of the eyes, they can provide useful information for motion-perceiving areas of the dorsal stream, as well as for processes that involve aligning eye-centered and head-centered frames of reference.

Real-world motion perception is even more complex, because it is not only our eyes that can move, but our whole bodies. In fact, most of our perceptions probably occur while we are on the move, strolling through our neighborhoods or driving our cars around them. So, our motion-perception systems must have a way of taking into account the whole body's movement through space (whether running, walking, or sitting in a moving car), to accurately perceive whether objects around us are moving or stationary. Researchers are still determining how the brain performs this calculation. One clue is that area MST receives input from the body's vestibular system (Gu, DeAngelis, & Angelaki, 2007). The vestibular system provides sensory information from the inner ear about the body's movement (whether active or passive, as in a car) and the body's orientation with respect to gravitational forces. Area MST may then integrate information about the body's movement through space together with retinal-image information to infer the movement speed and direction of external objects.

■ Rotation

One final important ability in the arena of movement detection is the ability to understand rotation, which is a special class of movement. Rather than movement from one location in space to another, rotation is movement of an object around an axis. Single-cell recordings in monkeys have identified cells that are responsive to rotation (especially in a clockwise or counterclockwise manner) in the superior temporal and inferior parietal regions of the brain (e.g., Saito, Yukic, Tanaka, Hikosaka, Fukada, & Iwai, 1986; Sakata, Shibutani,

Kawano, & Harrington, 1985). Moreover, other cells respond to rotations in depth (e.g., front to back).

In humans, the ability to rotate objects mentally has been studied extensively by Shepard and colleagues (Shepard, 1988), who found that the greater the degree of mental rotation required to align two 3-D objects, the greater the time required to decide whether they are identical (● Figure 8.9). For example, a person will take longer to decide whether two items are identical when the items are positioned 180 degrees apart in rotation, compared to when they are only 60 degrees apart.

Many studies suggest that the parietal regions are responsible for rotational abilities. For example, increased blood flow to the right hemisphere is found during a rotation task similar to that depicted in Figure 8.9 (Deutsch, Bourbon, Papanicolaou, & Eisenberg, 1988). When simplified versions of the same stimuli are used, rotational abilities are more disrupted by right parietal lobe damage than by left parietal lobe damage (e.g., Ditunno & Mann, 1990). In addition, disruption of the right parietal region by TMS in neurologically intact people led to impaired performance on a mental rotation task (Harris & Miniussi, 2003).

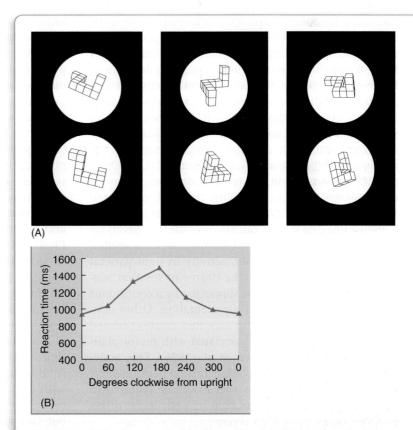

● **FIGURE 8.9 Classic paradigm for examining mental rotation.** (A) The type of three-dimensional stimulus often used to assess the ability to rotate objects in three dimensions. Whereas the left two pairs can be rotated to match each other—the first by an 80-degree rotation in depth and the second by an 80-degree rotation in the sideways plane—the final pair cannot, because the forms are mirror images. (B) Typical performance on such rotational tasks for a group of neurologically intact individuals. © 2011 Cengage Learning

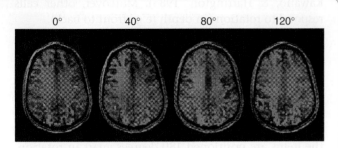

● **FIGURE 8.10   Increasing brain activation with increasing degree of mental rotation.** Shown here is a slice through the ventral portion of the superior parietal lobe, near the intraparietal sulcus. From left to right, the pictures depict the degree of activation associated with 0, 40, 80, and 120 degrees of rotation. Notice that the degree of activity increases as more rotation must be performed. From Carpenter, P.A., et al. (1999). Graded functional activation in the visuospatial system and the amount of task demand. *Journal of Cognitive Neuroscience*, 11 (1), p. 14.

Compelling evidence for right parietal involvement in mental rotation is provided by brain imaging studies that exploit the fact that increased reaction time is associated with an increased degree of rotation. Researchers reasoned that the brain region specifically involved in rotation should show a specific relationship between the degree of activity and the degree of rotation (e.g., Carpenter, Just, Keller, Eddy, & Thulborn, 1999); in contrast, other brain regions involved in the task (e.g., motor regions involved in responding) should exhibit activity, but that activity should not be proportional to the degree of rotation. As shown in ● Figure 8.10, activation associated with the mental rotation task is specifically localized to the superior parietal lobule, mainly in the right hemisphere but involving both hemispheres (e.g., Carpenter et al., 1999; see also Milivojevic, Hamm, & Corballis, 2008; Ng, Bullmore, de Zubicaray, Cooper, Suckling, & Williams, 2001; Podzebenko, Egan, & Watson, 2005; Richter et al., 2000).

Neuroimaging studies can also provide insights about the nature of computations that may underlie mental rotation. As discussed earlier, activity in right parietal cortex that increases with the degree of rotation suggests that mental rotation is supported by a continuous transformation of a spatial representation. Other neuroimaging studies have also reported rotation-related activity in frontal regions associated with motor planning and execution (Cohen et al., 1996). This activity suggests that mental rotation can be performed by thinking about the actions that would be required to manipulate the object to rotate it in a particular direction (see Zacks, 2008 for a review).

Space and Action

Perception of spatial dimensions, reference frames, spatial relations, and motion is important in being able to construct an accurate view of the spatial layout of the external world. However, we need to be able to do more than just represent the world in spatial terms; we need to be able to act upon the world. Therefore, one important function of the dorsal stream is to participate in sensory-motor translation—transforming sensory representations into action patterns. These sensory-motor transformations allow a monkey to reach for an overhead branch at the correct location and then to form its hand into the correct shape for grasping the branch. Similarly, to search the sky for a bird whose song you have just heard, your brain must link up a spatial map of the world with eye movement commands. For these reasons, some researchers prefer to think of the dorsal stream as a "how" pathway that contributes to planning action, rather than a "where" pathway that simply maps locations in space.

As you may remember from Chapter 5 on motor control, damage to the superior parietal lobe can result in motor deficits, implicating the dorsal stream in coding space for action. Patients with superior parietal lobe damage may exhibit **optic ataxia**, which refers to a failure in visually guided reaching (Perenin & Vighetto, 1988). Even when patients can verbally describe the location of targets, they misreach for them, indicating a problem in sensory-motor translation, not just a problem in sensory representation. Interestingly, such patients may also fail to take obstacles into account when reaching for an object. For example, imagine that you are reaching for your cup of tea, but the sugar bowl is in your path; you will direct your arm around the sugar bowl. In contrast, patients with optic ataxia do not do so (Schindler, Rice, McIntosh, Rossetti, Vighetto, & Milner, 2004). Other research has also found, somewhat counterintuitively, that the poor reaching performance of optic ataxics improves if there is a delay between the presentation of the target and the reaching movement, suggesting that the deficit is most profound for real-time integration of vision and motion (Milner, Dijkerman, McIntosh, Rossetti, & Pisella, 2003).

Moreover, a double dissociation in human brain-damaged patients suggests the independence of the dorsal "how" system from the "what" system in the ventral stream. In one case study, a patient with bilateral parietal damage could recognize line drawings of common objects but could not adjust the gap between her index finger and thumb to grasp these same objects (Jakobson, Archibald, Carey, & Goodale, 1991). In contrast, patients with damage to ventral extrastriate regions cannot recognize the size, shape, and orientation of visual objects, but can accurately guide both the hand and fingers to them (e.g., James, Culham, Humphrey, Milner, & Goodale, 2003).

Evidence from TMS also supports the critical role that these regions play in controlling the direction of action in space. Researchers used tasks in which the participants had to make online adjustments in reaching and grasping movements as the location and size of a target changed in space. Imagine that you are trying to catch a Frisbee that a friend has thrown to you. To know how to position yourself for the catch, you have to continually update the visual information about the location of the Frisbee as it approaches you—an especially tricky task if it is a windy day or if your friend threw the Frisbee in a wobbly manner. TMS over the parietal regions impairs the ability of neurologically intact individuals to make these kinds of online adjustments (Della-Maggiore, Malfait, Ostry, & Paus, 2004; Desmurget, Epstein, Turner, Prablanc, Alexander, & Grafton, 1999; Glover, Miall, & Rushworth, 2005; Tunik, Frey, & Grafton, 2005).

Research with monkeys has demonstrated that the cells in parietal cortex are well suited for sensory-motor integration (Scherberger & Andersen, 2004). For example, a monkey is given a task in which he first fixates his eyes on a center spot on the screen, then observes a target stimulus flashed somewhere else on the screen. After a delay, he must reach his arm to that particular location. Cells in the parietal cortex are active when the target appears in the cell's receptive field, during the delay, and also during the movement (Batista, Buneo, Snyder, & Andersen, 1999). The fact that the cell is active during the movement, even though the target is no longer present, suggests that the cell is not just coding sensory information about the location of an item.

Anti-saccade tasks have also been used to examine the role of parietal cells in sensory-motor transformations. In an anti-saccade task, a monkey sees a stimulus presented in a particular location, but must shift his eyes to a location away from the stimulus, rather than to the stimulus itself (● Figure 8.11). In this way, the anti-saccade task cleverly dissociates the location of sensory stimulation from the location of the intended movement. Cells in the lateral intraparietal cortex appear to code first for the location of the actual stimulus, but then, in less than one second, they change their firing to code instead for the location of the planned movement (the anti-saccade location) (Zhang & Barash, 2000). Likewise, an EEG study in humans found that in an anti-saccade task, gamma-frequency oscillations (indexing coordinated neural activity) are first evident over the parietal lobe contralateral to the stimulus location, but then shift to the parietal lobe contralateral to the intended movement location (Van Der Werf, Jensen, Fries, & Medendorp, 2008). This converging evidence from monkey and human studies suggests that parietal cells code for the spatial location of the intended movement even when it is different from the location of the sensory stimulus.

Different subareas within the parietal cortex appear to contribute to the sensory-motor transformations necessary for different kinds of movements. For example, in monkeys, two different parietal regions appear to be involved in coding for intended eye movements (lateral intraparietal cortex) versus intended arm-reaching movements (medial intraparietal cortex) (Snyder, Batista, & Andersen, 1997; see also Chang, Dickinson, &

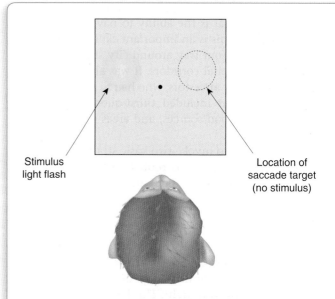

● **FIGURE 8.11   An anti-saccade task used to study sensory-motor translation.** In this task, a monkey sees a visual stimulus in one location, such as the left visual field, and must shift his gaze to the opposite location in order to receive a treat. Cells in parietal cortex code for the location of the intended movement, even though there is no visual stimulation in that location. *Source:* Janzen, G., & van Turennout, M. (2004). Selective neural representations of objects relevant for navigation. Nature Neuroscience, 7, 673–677.

Snyder, 2008). Human neuroimaging data also support this distinction (Iacoboni, 2006). For example, a task that involved planning eye movements activated a region on the lateral bank of the intraparietal sulcus, whereas a task that involved planning hand movements activated a more medial parietal region (Rushworth, Paus, & Sipila, 2001; see also Astafiev, Shulman, Stanley, Snyder, Van Essen, & Corbetta, 2003). Additionally, an anterior region of the parietal cortex is activated during tasks that involve grasping or manipulating objects (Binkofski, Buccino, Stephan, Rizzolatti, Seitz, & Freund, 1999; Frey, Vinton, Norlund, & Grafton, 2005). Therefore, there appears to be some segregation within parietal cortex such that different subregions assist in transforming spatial information into different kinds of actions.

Together, then, studies of both monkeys and humans indicate that the spatial representations coded by the parietal cortex play an important role in guiding limb and eye movements to specific spatial locations. Next we investigate a different kind of movement: navigation through a large-scale environment.

Spatial Navigation

Our discussion so far has focused on spatial understanding within a relatively small scale, such as the spatial relations among a set of items in one's immediate view.

In everyday life, though, there is another crucial spatial skill, and that is the ability to navigate around an environment. This is an important skill in modern life, as we must find our way around city streets, neighborhoods, and hospital corridors. It was also important to our evolutionary ancestors, who had to navigate around a landscape that included thirst-quenching watering holes, reliable food sources, and areas of either shelter or danger.

People seem to invoke two basic strategies for spatial navigation, referred to as route-based versus cognitive map strategies (Aguirre, 2003). In route-based strategies, the person's understanding is represented as a sequence of steps, often specified in terms of particular landmarks. You are familiar with this kind of navigation from the typical driving directions you receive from a friend: go two blocks on Market Street, turn right at the gas station, turn left at the next stop sign, and my house is the third one on your right. This kind of spatial navigation does not require a map-like understanding of how the neighborhood is laid out. Rather it just involves being able to follow directions, by responding to a particular cue (stop sign) with the correct action (turn left). It is also egocentrically oriented, in the sense that the instruction "turn left" means "left" in relationship to you. In contrast, a map-based strategy involves having an allocentric understanding of how all of the different parts of the landscape relate to one another. Such an understanding incorporates a mental map of the terrain to be traversed and one's position in that map at any given time. A person with map-like knowledge can still give and follow route-based directions, but this person is in better shape if she makes a wrong turn, because she understands enough about the spatial layout to create a new route to her goal.

Navigational skills can be assessed in a variety of ways. One task often used to assess route-finding is the stylus maze task, in which the individual must maneuver a stylus through an orderly array of identical bolt heads to reach a goal (● Figure 8.12). Another type of route-finding ability requires an individual to maneuver himself through a maze (rather than moving an object through a maze, as in the stylus maze task). In one such task, the locomotor maze, a series of nine dots is placed in a grid on the floor of a large room (Semmes, Weinstein, Ghent, & Teuber, 1955). The individual is given a map that designates a route, from start to finish, and the person has to walk that route as quickly and accurately as possible.

Both the stylus maze and locomotor maze tasks are performed poorly by patients with damage to the parietal lobe (Newcombe, 1969; Semmes, Weinstein, Ghent, & Teuber, 1963), yet they are also doubly dissociable (Ratcliff & Newcombe, 1973). Various factors may account for this dissociation. First, the stylus maze task is much smaller in scale. The individual can view the entire map in a bird's-eye fashion while maneuvering through it, unlike the locomotor maze. Second, in the stylus maze task, a person's orientation with regard to the maze remains constant, whereas in the locomotor maze task, even though the map direction stays static, the individual's orientation relative to the map constantly changes. Another difference is that in the stylus maze task the individual must remember the route, whereas in the locomotor maze task the route is given.

Further research with brain-damaged patients illustrates that spatial navigation can be disrupted in several different ways (Aguirre, 2003). The syndrome most closely tied to the dorsal stream pathways is **egocentric disorientation**, which involves the inability to represent the location of objects in relationship to the self. This syndrome is associated with damage to the posterior parietal region, either bilaterally or unilaterally in the right hemisphere. Patients with this disorder have difficulties with navigation (both route-based and map-based) because they are unable to represent spatial relations. Performance is typically poor on other tasks of spatial understanding as well, such as spatial working memory tasks and mental rotation. Descriptions of navigational routes by these patients are severely impaired. Patients with this type of serious disorientation are often unwilling to venture out alone.

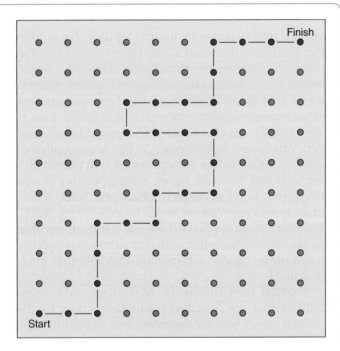

● **FIGURE 8.12   Example of a path that might have to be learned through the stylus maze.** The maze is an array of identical metal bolt heads, depicted here by circles. Although the path is shown in this diagram, it is not presented to the person being tested. Rather, each time the person touches an incorrect bolt head, a loud click occurs. Thus, the individual must discover the correct direction of movement at each choice point and remember information about previously discovered portions of the maze. © 2011 Cengage Learning

Navigational difficulties can also arise from problems elsewhere within the brain. For example, the syndrome called **landmark agnosia** is more like an object recognition deficit than a true spatial deficit, although it does disrupt way-finding ability. In this syndrome, patients lose the ability to recognize certain landmarks that are usually used for navigation. For example, a patient may fail to recognize his house or his bedroom. Such patients often perform well on other spatial tasks, and their deficits typically occur following damage to ventral stream areas rather than dorsal areas. The deficits tend to involve damage to the medial surface of the occipital lobe, including a region known as the lingual gyrus as well as the parahippocampal gyrus (Aguirre, 2003). Damage to the parahippocampal gyrus can also lead to **anterograde disorientation**, in which a patient is unable to construct new representations of environments, although she is still able to navigate successfully around previously known environments (Epstein, DeYoe, Press, Rosen, & Kanwisher, 2001).

Evidence from these latter two syndromes, landmark agnosia and anterograde disorientation, fits nicely with neuroimaging evidence indicating that the parahippocampal gyrus is especially activated by the perception of places (Epstein & Kanwisher, 1998); this is the so-called *parahippocampal place area* that we mentioned in Chapter 7. In one study (Janzen & van Turennout, 2004), participants learned to navigate around a novel environment presented on a computer screen. Some objects were encountered at "decision points" in the route through the novel environment. (These objects are analogous to the stop sign where your friend's directions tell you to turn left.) Objects associated with such decision points were more likely to activate parahippocampal regions compared to objects that were encountered but not relevant to a choice point in the route (● Figure 8.13). These findings support the idea that the parahippocampal region is especially involved in coding for landmarks that are important for navigation.

One currently debated issue in the study of spatial navigation is the role of the hippocampus. Studies over the last few decades have provided convincing evidence that the hippocampus and closely related regions are crucial in spatial navigation in rodents. For

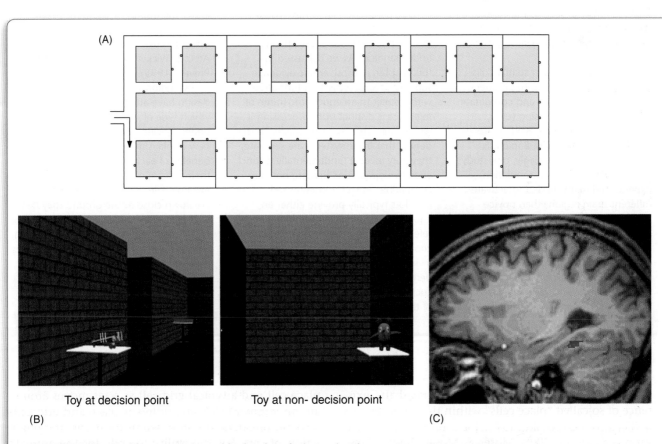

Toy at decision point   Toy at non- decision point

(B)   (C)

● **FIGURE 8.13 Brain areas activated by landmarks in navigation.** In this study (Janzen & van Turennout, 2004), participants navigated through a virtual maze, shown in panel A. Cartoon toys (see panel B) were placed in certain locations in the maze. Some toys were placed at decision points in the maze, where the participant had to decide which direction to go, and other toys were placed at nondecision points. Brain imaging data showed that the parahippocampal gyrus (see panel C) was more activated by pictures of toys that marked decision points than by toys that were present in the maze but did not mark a decision point. Adapted by permission from Macmillan Publishers, LTD: From figures 1 and 3 in Janzen, G., & van Turennout, M. (2004). Selective neural representations of objects relevant for navigation. Nature Neuroscience, 7, 673–677.

IN FOCUS: Spatial Abilities in Aviation

Rudimentary spatial abilities are essential in daily life for most people, but in some occupations, exceptionally strong spatial skills are paramount. When you get on an airplane, you probably hope that the pilot has pretty strong spatial skills. Successful piloting requires many skills, including the ability to divide attention and prioritize tasks, but spatial abilities are especially crucial (see Wickens, 2002, for a review). Unlike earthbound mortals, pilots must navigate in three dimensions. The pilot must consider the angle of the plane's pitch (that is, the degree to which the nose of the plane is pointing upward or downward), as well as the plane's degree of roll as it banks to the left or right. The pilot also has to be able understand the plane's altitude and its relationship to a specified flight path. Furthermore, he or she must navigate under conditions in which major landmarks, such as the earth and the horizon, are sometimes obscured from view by clouds, blizzards, and other obstructions.

Pilots tend to excel in spatial skills that depend on the right hemisphere, such as mental rotation and coordinate or metric spatial processing (Dror, Kosslyn, & Waag, 1993; Banich, Stokes, & Elledge, 1989; Stokes, Banich, & Elledge, 1991). Interestingly, one study found that during flight simulation, experienced pilots tended to activate different brain regions than novice pilots (Peres, Van De Moortele, Pierard, Lehericy, Le Bihan, & Guezennec, 2000). During a visual tracking task, novice pilots tended to engage more visual processing areas, including regions in the dorsal stream, whereas experts showed greater activity in frontal regions

involved in working memory and decision making. This might suggest that with expertise, spatial processing by dorsal stream regions becomes more streamlined. However, so far very few neuroimaging studies have examined simulated flight tasks, so there is still little known about how different brain systems are utilized in expert pilots.

Even experienced pilots can make spatial errors, and those errors can be costly. In fact, spatial disorientation is considered to be a major contributing cause of airplane crashes, affecting experienced commercial and military pilots as well as amateur pilots (Albery, 2007). For this reason, researchers in applied cognitive psychology have focused on understanding the challenges in spatial cognition that pilots face, and how those challenges might be most effectively met.

One pertinent issue is how visual displays of information should be designed to facilitate pilots' spatial understanding. As we discussed in this chapter, neuroscientific evidence suggests that processing information with respect to an egocentric frame of reference is distinct from processing it with respect to allocentric space. To the degree that these systems are separate, they may involve fundamentally distinct cognitive operations that are not very compatible. In fact, displays used by pilots typically provide either an egocentric or an allocentric frame of reference, but not both. One system, known as *track-up alignment*, provides a view of the world that is aligned perfectly with the world outside the cockpit window: What is straight ahead of the window is straight ahead on the

map. As the plane turns, the alignment of the display turns with it so that the pilot has an egocentric frame of reference (● Box Figure 8.1A). The other system, known as *north-up alignment*, provides a map of the world that remains static; north is always straight ahead regardless of the direction in which the plane is moving. This map provides an earth-based, or allocentric, frame of reference (● Box Figure 8.1B).

The advantage of the track-up map is the direct mapping between locations on the display and locations outside the cockpit window. Its disadvantage is that it hinders a pilot's ability to build a static mental map of the world, because the display constantly changes. In contrast, the north-up map, which provides an earth-centered frame of reference, aids in composing a cognitive map, but it requires the pilot to mentally rotate either the display or the view outside the cockpit so that both are aligned, an operation that takes time (Aretz, 1991; Aretz & Wickens, 1992; Wickens & Prevett, 1995).

Psychologists interested in cockpit design have attempted to determine which type of map is most advantageous under specific conditions or to invent new displays that will maximize the benefits of each system while reducing their costs (e.g., Aretz, 1991). For example, aircraft such as helicopters that are flown close to the ground may be best guided by track-up maps so that the map is continuously aligned with terrain, whereas aircraft flown at higher altitudes may be best guided by north-up maps (e.g., Harwood & Wickens, 1991).

Recent research in aviation psychology has also been concerned

example, studies in rats have demonstrated the existence of so-called "place cells" within the hippocampus (O'Keefe & Dostrovsky, 1971; for a review, see Moser, Kropff, & Moser, 2008; Moser & Moser, 2008). These cells are active when the animal is located in a particular place in its local environment. In addition, in the entorhinal cortex, which projects directly to the hippocampus, there exist "grid cells" that respond to multiple spatial locations in a grid-like fashion (e.g., Fyhn, Molden, Witter, Moser, & Moser, 2004; Sargolini et al., 2006). ● Figure 8.14 illustrates the response of a typical

place cell and a typical grid cell as a rat moves around an environment. Because different place and grid cells respond preferentially to different locations, the population of cells has the ability to code for the animal's location anywhere within an environment. Besides containing these two cell types, the hippocampal complex also includes head-direction cells, which fire when the animal is facing in a particular direction, and border cells, which fire when the animal is close to a border within its environment. Furthermore, damage to the hippocampal complex in rodents is known to produce

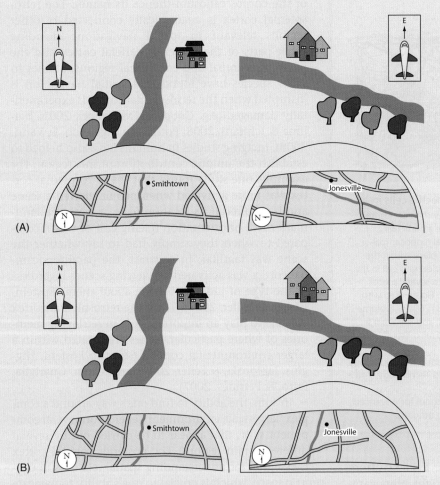

to roll too much to one side. Likewise, an audio system might change the volume of white noise being played to the left and right ears, depending on how steeply the plane is banking to the left or right. Researchers are also developing 3-D auditory devices, so that when a pilot listens to voices of the ground control, copilot, and flight engineer, those voices sound as if they are coming from different places, rather than all coming over one sound channel. By separating the perceived locations of these voices, it may be easier for the pilot to quickly identify and distinguish them. In many ways, these technological developments attempt to capitalize on the natural strengths of the brain's sensory systems, such as the ability to compare inputs from the two ears or to use spatial localization to separate different auditory streams.

Of course, as more sensory information is added to a pilot's input, the danger of "information overload" increases (Wickens, 2002). In Chapter 11, we consider how the brain's attention systems attempt to cope with large quantities of information. Interestingly, military aviation researchers are considering using EEG measures to monitor a pilot's brain states while he or she is flying (Albery, 2007; Russo, Stetz, & Thomas, 2005). In theory, such a system could be used to detect brain states such as drowsiness or hyperattentive states, and could adjust interactions with the pilot accordingly. Although there is still a lot to learn, knowledge gleaned from cognitive psychology and neuroscience could be used to make flying a safer experience for both pilots and their passengers.

● **BOX FIGURE 8.1   Two navigational systems that rely on different frames of reference.** (A) An example of track-up alignment: what is outside the cockpit window corresponds directly with the map. (B) An example of north-up alignment: the map always provides a constant view of the space; therefore, the pilot must mentally rotate it to align it with the view outside the cockpit window. In both A and B, the letter above the plane icon indicates the direction in which the plane is heading. The letter in the circle indicates the direction of north on the pilot's display. ©2011 Cengage Learning

with designing multisensory technology that can convey crucial spatial information to the pilot not only through vision, but also through sound and tactile sensations (Albery, 2007). For example, a pilot may wear a kind of jacket that is designed to vibrate in certain sections when the plane begins

severe problems in environmental navigation (Morris, 1981; Schenck & Morris, 1985; Sutherland, Whishaw, & Kolb, 1983). All of this evidence points strongly to the importance of the hippocampus, and regions closely linked to it, in spatial navigation. Yet, neuroimaging studies with humans have tended to focus on the role of the parahippocampal region in way-finding (Aguirre, Detre, Alsop, & D'Esposito, 1996; Maguire, Frith, Burgess, Donnett, & O'Keefe, 1998), while at the same time associating the hippocampus more generally with memory encoding.

Nonetheless, some studies with humans imply that the hippocampus is important for navigational abilities in people, just as for rodents. In one study, Maguire and colleagues (Maguire, Frackowiak, & Frith, 1997) recruited taxi drivers in London. These individuals made ideal participants because London taxi drivers are experts at knowing the topography of the city: they must train for approximately three years and pass a stringent test to obtain a license. The taxi drivers exhibited significantly more activation of the right hippocampus when asked to remember specific routes, compared to when

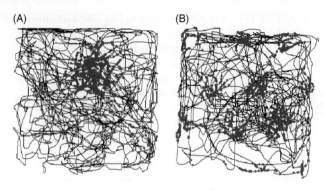

● FIGURE 8.14   Responses of location-specific cells in a rat. Dark lines show the rat's path as it runs around an enclosure. Superimposed red lines show locations that cause a particular cell to fire. Panel A shows the response of a typical hippocampal place cell, which fires when the rat is in a specific place within the environment. Panel B shows the response of a typical grid cell in the medial entorhinal cortex. The grid cell responds to several spatial locations that are organized in a grid-like pattern. Figure used with Permission: Annual Review of Neuroscience Vol. 31: 69–89 (Volume publication date July 2008) Place Cells, Grid Cells, and the Brain's Spatial Representation System. Edvard I. Moser,[1] Emilio Kropff,[1,2] and May-Britt Moser[1]

[1]Kavli Institute for Systems Neuroscience and Centre for the Biology of Memory, Norwegian University of Science and Technology, 7489 Trondheim, Norway.

[2]Cognitive Neuroscience Sector, International School for Advanced Studies, Trieste, Italy; email: edvard.moser@cbm.ntnu.no.

of the corpus callosum (hence its name). The retrosplenial cortex is anatomically connected to other regions relevant to spatial navigation, including other parts of the posterior parietal cortex and the parahippocampal and entorhinal regions. Studies in other species have found that spatial navigation is disrupted when the retrosplenial cortex is experimentally damaged (e.g. Cooper & Mizumori, 2001; Haijima & Ichitani, 2008; Pothuizen, Aggleton, & Vann, 2008). Imaging studies in humans have also helped to establish the unique contribution of this region. For example, one study found that the retrosplenial cortex was more activated when people viewed a scene and had to recall its location (east or west of a landmark road) or orientation (facing east or west), compared to when they simply had to say whether the scene was familiar; in contrast, the parahippocampal cortex was activated by viewing scenes regardless of the type of judgment made about them (Epstein, Parker, & Feiler, 2007). Thus, the retrosplenial cortex appears to play an important role in retrieving memories of where particular scenes are located within a larger environmental context (see also Epstein, Higgins, Jablonski, & Feiler, 2007; Iaria, Chen, Guariglia, Ptito, & Petrides, 2007).

In sum, the ability to find one's way around a complex, large-scale environment depends on several component skills that appear to be carried out by several different brain regions. The posterior parietal cortex is essential for understanding spatial relations in egocentric space, which is crucial to one's ability to navigate around the world. At the same time, the hippocampus and parahippocampal region appear to be important in coding for specific environmental locations and landmarks, respectively, while the retrosplenial cortex represents specific locations within a larger spatial context.

Challenges to the Dorsal-Ventral Stream Dichotomy

Throughout most of this chapter, we have emphasized the importance of dorsal stream regions in various aspects of spatial perception, in contrast to the ventral stream regions important in object recognition, as discussed in Chapter 7. The distinction between these two processing streams has provided a powerful way of organizing our understanding of the various complex visual tasks that the brain must perform. However, we must also be aware of the limitations of a simple model that divides processing so starkly between the dorsal and ventral streams (Husain & Nachev, 2007).

First, it is important to recognize that spatial functions are not completely segregated to the parietal region of the brain. Although the parietal lobes (particularly in the right hemisphere) are extremely important in spatial cognition, they are not the only brain regions involved. As we learned in this chapter, other

they just had to remember landmarks. Evidence from patient studies also indicate that the right hippocampus is important for remembering where objects are located within a scene. For example, individuals with right temporal lobe damage, especially if the damage impinged upon the hippocampus, were unable to detect changes in a scene when the locations of two objects were switched (Pigott & Milner, 1994).

Another study examined the role of the hippocampus using a different methodology. This study (Ekstrom et al., 2003) recorded from individual cells in the medial temporal lobe—including hippocampus and parahippocampal cortex—in epileptic patients who explored a novel "town" through a computer-based virtual reality system. The researchers found that hippocampal cells tended to respond best to specific spatial locations (as had been previously demonstrated with rodents) whereas parahippocampal cells tended to respond best to views of certain landmarks. This study helps to connect findings from the animal literature and the human imaging literature, suggesting that the hippocampus is more important for localization of places and the parahippocampal region is more important for landmark recognition.

Although the posterior parietal cortex, hippocampus, and parahippocampal gyrus have been most studied with respect to their roles in spatial navigation, another region called the *retrosplenial cortex* also appears to be implicated in navigation. This region is on the medial surface of the parietal cortex, posterior to the splenium

brain regions also play a role in certain aspects of spatial processing. Among these are the hippocampus and parahippocampal regions, important in long-term spatial memory and spatial navigation. Likewise, the parietal lobe is not solely dedicated to spatial functions. It also plays an important role in attention and vigilance, as we will learn in Chapter 11.

Remember also that some processes are important in both spatial understanding and object recognition. Therefore, some types of information are represented in both dorsal and ventral streams, but for different purposes. For example, the shape of an object is represented by cells in the lateral intraparietal area in a way that preserves information about the object's size and position; this representation is useful for guiding grasping movements (Janssen, Srivastava, Ombelet, & Orban, 2008). In contrast, cells in the ventral stream represent an object's shape in a size- and position-invariant manner, which is useful for recognizing the object's identity. Depth and movement cues are also important for both ventral and dorsal stream processes. Depth perception allows a three-dimensional understanding of an object, which is important in object recognition, as discussed in Chapter 7 (see Orban, Janssen, & Vogels, 2006; Parker, 2007). Motion perception can also be useful in recognizing an object. For example, you may be able to tell whether a dark form in the distance is a dog or a bear, depending on whether its motion is bounding or lumbering. Therefore, it should not be surprising that motion-processing area MT feeds into the ventral stream as well as being part of the dorsal stream. Spatial navigation provides another example: one way we work our way around space is by recognizing certain landmarks such as buildings and signs, a ventral stream process. These examples remind us that the functions carried out by the dorsal and ventral streams are related to one another, if still separable. In fact, much recent research is focused on elucidating how the dorsal and ventral processing streams interact (e.g., Himmelbach & Karnath, 2005).

Summary

The Dorsal Visual System for Spatial Processing

- The perception of spatial relations depends heavily on the parietal lobe, which is part of the dorsal, or "where," visual system.
- Single-cell recordings indicate that cells in the parietal region are sensitive to a combination of eye and head position, and are sensitive to motion in the range of speeds at which animals locomote—all of which make them well suited for processing spatial relations and constructing a map of external space.
- Monkeys with lesions to the parietal area cannot make decisions about the relative positions of items in space, but can recognize objects.

Coding for the Three Dimensions of Space

- Depth is coded by comparing inputs from the two eyes, and is useful for both spatial localization and object recognition. Cells in the dorsal stream are sensitive to the depth of a target and to motion in the plane of depth.
- Left-right confusion is associated with damage to the left parietal cortex, but right parietal cortex damage can also compromise the ability to determine left and right on another individual, as that involves a transformation of the frame of reference for left and right.

Spatial Frames of Reference

- Spatial positions can be coded with respect to some aspect of the self, known as an egocentric reference frame; or with respect to external references, known as an allocentric reference frame.
- Evidence from monkeys suggests that cells within the parietal cortex can code for spatial location in multiple reference frames, including head-centered, eye-centered, and object-centered.
- Evidence from brain-damaged patients indicates that different kinds of egocentric and allocentric coding can be independently disrupted, indicating that they rely on separable brain processes.

Spatial Relations in Small-Scale Space

- The ability to localize a point in space relies on superior regions of the right parietal lobe.
- The left hemisphere is specialized for determining categorical spatial relations, in which the relationship of two points is described according to categories of locations (above vs. below, to the left vs. to the right), whereas the right hemisphere is specialized for computing metric (coordinate) spatial relationships that specify the distance between two points.
- Constructional abilities, which are those required to make the correct motor movements to manipulate items into a particular spatial relation, are generally disrupted by right-hemisphere damage.

Motion Perception

- Studies of brain-damaged patients and neuroimaging studies indicate that a very specific region of the brain, area MT (V5) at the juncture of the parietal and temporal lobes, is critically important for perceiving motion.

- To accurately understand whether external objects are moving or stationary, the person must take into account the body's own motion. Parietal lobe regions receive input from the vestibular system and from areas controlling and sensing eye movements, so that the movement of external objects can be calculated in reference to the self.
- Neuroimaging studies suggest that perception of rotation is dependent on the superior parietal lobule.

Space and Action

- Cells in the parietal region are essential for translating a perceptual understanding of space into actions toward specific spatial locations. Different subregions of the parietal cortex are involved in coding for intended eye movements and arm movements toward targets.
- Optic ataxia is a disorder of visually guided reaching that illustrates the importance of the parietal lobe in integrating perception and action.

Spatial Navigation

- Navigating through large-scale space can rely upon either route-based or map-based representations.
- Egocentric disorientation is a condition associated with parietal lobe damage in which way-finding is severely disrupted by a deficit in the broader understanding of spatial relations.
- Landmark agnosia is a difficulty in recognizing landmarks used for navigation, and is typically associated with ventral stream damage.
- Anterograde disorientation is an inability to learn to navigate new environments, despite retention of previously learned navigational information. This deficit is typically associated with damage to the medial temporal lobe.
- Within the medial temporal lobe, the hippocampus appears to code for specific spatial locations within an environment, whereas the parahippocampal region appears to be especially important in recognizing navigational landmarks.

Key Terms

allocentric reference frame 213	constructional praxis 217	landmark agnosia 225
anterograde disorientation 225	corollary discharge 220	metric (coordinate) spatial relations 216
area MT 219	egocentric disorientation 224	
binocular disparity 212	egocentric reference frame 213	optic ataxia 222
categorical spatial relations 216	frames of reference 213	optic flow 219

Book Companion Site at www.cengage.com/psychology/Banich
This website provides instructors and students with a wealth of free information and resources, including tutorial quizzes, flashcards, and the glossary.

Language

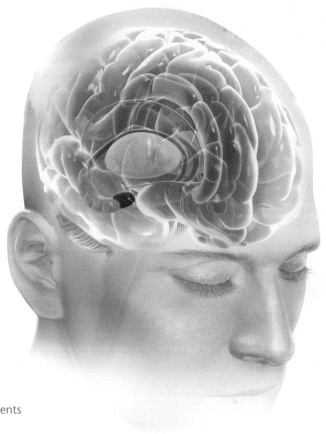

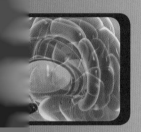

DR. SHEILA CHORPENNING, a neurologist, had just joined the staff of a hospital for U.S. Army veterans. In the large patient recreation room, she noticed two men sitting on a sofa, one middle-aged and one younger. The middle-aged man, Bill Rieger, had been a rising star in high school—academically talented and a top athlete. But then his mother died unexpectedly. Confused by her death, he turned down a scholarship to college and joined the army. During a combat mission, he was hit by shrapnel that damaged his left frontal lobe as well as parts of his parietal lobe. Dr. Chorpenning introduced herself and asked Bill to tell her about his history. He replied:

> "My un mother died . . . uh . . . me . . . uh fi'tenn. Uh, oh, I guess six month . . . my mother pass away. An'uh . . . an'en . . . un . . . ah . . . seventeen . . . seventeen . . . go . . . uh High School. An uh . . . Christmas . . . well, uh, I uh . . . Pitt'burgh" (Goodglass, 1976, p. 239).

He told the story with much effort, and the words seemed to explode as they came out of his mouth. His intonation was uneven, which made his speech difficult to follow initially, but with time Dr. Chorpenning found him easier to understand.

The younger man, who was in his late twenties, was named Jim Hurdle. He had had a carotid artery aneurysm (the ballooning, then breaking of the carotid artery), which had caused brain damage. As Dr. Chorpenning began to converse with him, he attempted to explain that he didn't live at the hospital but had just been brought there by his father to have some dental work performed:

> "Ah . . . Monday . . . ah, Dad and Jim Hurdle [referring to himself by his full name] and Dad . . . hospital. Two . . . ah, doctors . . . , and ah . . . thirty minutes . . . and yes . . . ah . . . hospital. And, er Wednesday . . . nine o'clock. And er Thursday, ten o'clock . . . doctors. Two doctors . . . and ah . . . teeth. Yeah, . . . fine" (Goodglass, 1976, p. 238).

Like the first man, Jim spoke in a slow, halting cadence, and his words were produced in a harsh and guttural manner.

Despite their difficulties in speaking, both men seemed to understand most of what Dr. Chorpenning said to them. When she mentioned that the weather was spring-like, Bill pointed to the open window through which a warm breeze was blowing. When she discussed what a relief the present weather was compared with the cold, hard winter that they had been experiencing, Jim pulled his sweater tightly around himself and imitated a shiver. Before she left, she thanked both men for chatting with her, realizing how frustrated they were with their inability to communicate.

LANGUAGE IS THE mental faculty that many people consider most uniquely human and that most distinctly separates us from the other species that inhabit the earth. Language is also a function that has long been studied by neuropsychologists and cognitive neuroscientists. Symptoms like those experienced by Bill Rieger and Jim Hurdle first led Paul Broca in the late 1800s to realize that the hemispheres have different functions, an event that heralded the advent of modern-day neuropsychology. Broca noticed that a lesion to a specific region of the left hemisphere causes a loss of fluent speech even though the person's speech comprehension is relatively spared. This syndrome, known as **Broca's aphasia**, has provided a window to understanding the neurological organization for language.

Aphasia is the loss of a language-processing ability after brain damage. In this chapter, we discuss a variety of aphasias, gleaning from each some lessons about the neurological organization for language. We consider the neural underpinnings of spoken and written language and examine the degree to which their neural substrates are both similar and distinct. Although most of our discussion focuses on the neural organization for Indo-European languages, such as English, we also consider the neural underpinnings of other languages, including those from Asia and languages created by people who are deaf. If some aspects of the neurological organization for language are universal, they should reveal themselves despite the different grammatical structures found across languages (e.g., Indo-European vs. Asian languages) and despite differences in the modality in which the information is conveyed (e.g., sound in English vs. hand movement in American Sign Language). We end the chapter by examining how the right hemisphere, which was initially thought to be relatively uninvolved in language, contributes to language comprehension.

The Left Hemisphere Plays a Leading Role in Language Processing

We know from individuals with aphasia and from patients with the split-brain syndrome (see Chapter 4) that the left hemisphere plays a leading role in speech production. This fact is supported by two methods used during surgery for epilepsy to isolate brain regions involved in language processing. One of these, the Wada technique, was discussed in Chapter 4. As a reminder, this procedure involves the injection of sodium amobarbital, a barbiturate, into one of the two carotid arteries, causing only one of the hemispheres to become anesthetized. After the drug takes effect, the test administrator asks the patient to name a series of items that the patient was able to name prior to injection. If the anesthetized hemisphere is responsible for speech output, the person will be unable to name the items after anesthetization. Typically the procedure is repeated the next day with the opposite hemisphere (Grote, Wierenga, & Smith, 1999). This second injection is necessary even if speech was disrupted by the first anesthetization, because in a relatively small percentage of cases speech output is controlled by both hemispheres.

Table 9.1 presents the percentages of left- and right-handed people who have left-hemisphere, right-hemisphere, and bihemispheric control of speech output as determined by the Wada test in a classic study (Rasmussen & Milner, 1977a). These percentages accord well with more recent data on lateralization for language inferred from speech arrest after the administration of TMS in neurologically intact individuals (Khedr, Hamed, Said, & Basahi, 2002) and data from fMRI in neurologically intact individuals (Springer et al., 1999). Due to this concordance between the Wada test and less invasive measures, the Wada technique may soon be replaced by methods such as fMRI (Baxendale, 2009; though see Paolicchi, 2008).

As you can see from Table 9.1, speech output is rarely controlled by the right hemisphere in right-handed people, and in no case is speech output controlled by both hemispheres in right-handers. This information is consistent with the clinical observation that **crossed aphasia**—that is, aphasia resulting from a right-hemisphere lesion in a right-hander—occurs with a frequency of 1% or less (Benson & Geschwind, 1972).

Language organization is more varied among left-handers than right-handers. Although left-handers, like right-handers, are most likely to have speech output controlled by the left hemisphere, in a significant proportion of left-handers the *right* hemisphere is specialized for speech output. Furthermore, in still other left-handed people, each hemisphere is capable of producing speech, a pattern rarely if ever observed in right-handers.

Another means of investigating the localization of language is to stimulate the brain electrically before or during surgery for the removal of epileptic tissue (see Hamberger, 2007, for a review). We previously discussed using stimulation to determine the location and extent of the motor and somatosensory regions (see Chapter 3); a similar stimulation method is used to map areas crucial for language. The stimulation method reveals that language is lateralized to the left hemisphere in nearly all right-handers, a finding consistent with the results of lesion studies and the Wada test (e.g., Wylie, Luders, & Murphy, 1990). Now we turn our attention to work that tells us more about how the left hemisphere is organized for different aspects of language function.

Neural Organization of Language as Inferred from Brain-Damaged Patients

At the beginning of this book, we discussed how the relationship between the brain and mental function can be examined from either of two vantage points: one emphasizing the neurological organization of the brain, and one emphasizing the psychological processes performed by the brain. These two vantage points are extremely well illustrated by the differing perspectives on language breakdown after brain trauma. The early classic advances in this field, made in the mid- to late 1800s, came squarely from a neurological, or medical, perspective in which physicians characterized the patterns of language impairment that accompany specific brain lesions. Because damage to particular regions of the cortex can each produce distinct language problems, the early *aphasiologists* (i.e., people who study aphasia) proposed that each region of the cortex had a specific role in language processing: one area was deemed critical for recognizing sound images of words, and another was supposed to be critical for producing

TABLE 9.1	Control of Speech Output in a Sample of Left- and Right-Handed Patients as Determined by the Wada Technique			
		Speech Representation (%)		
Handedness	No. of Cases	Left	Bilateral	Right
Right	140	96	0	4
Left	122	70	15	15

speech. According to these models, the brain processes language much as a factory manufactures products along a conveyor belt. Input is received at one region, then is packaged and sent to another region for output. From this perspective, these models have a "knee bone is connected to the thigh bone" feel to them.

Since the 1960s, psycholinguists have examined the neurological bases for language from a different perspective. In attempting to understand the effects of brain damage on language processing, these researchers have emphasized the organization of language rather than the organization of the brain. This approach has led them to ask very different questions about aphasia. For example, they have used aphasia to help test theories about the fundamental components of language.

In this chapter, we examine language processing from both perspectives, the neurological and the psychological. Because each can provide useful information, these views should be considered complementary rather than mutually exclusive ways to conceptualize brain organization for language. After discussing both perspectives, we determine the generalizations about language that can be made regardless of the viewpoint taken. In this section, we focus mainly on spoken language, saving our discussion of written language for later in the chapter.

■ Classical Neurological Conceptions

As we mentioned, the two men discussed in the opening vignette of the chapter, Bill and Jim, had a type of aphasia similar to that experienced by Broca's patients. If you reread what the two men said, you may be struck by certain characteristics. You may have noticed the paucity of speech output: people with Broca's aphasia have great difficulty producing words. Broca deduced that the deficit he observed in his patients was specifically linguistic in nature, because their difficulty with speech output was not accompanied by motoric problems of the vocal musculature, such as paralysis. The patients could utter sounds, albeit not linguistic ones, and were sometimes able to use the mouth and lips to perform orofacial movements, such as blowing out candles. Because the deficit appeared to be limited to the language domain, Broca conceptualized the region of the brain that now bears his name as the area that is critical for programming speech output.

Although difficulty in speech output is a glaring symptom of Broca's aphasia, you may have noticed other characteristics from Bill's and Jim's dialogue as well. For instance, the sentences do not fit a standard structure, but seem more like a telegram or text message (e.g., "Need help, send money"). This characteristic is often referred to as **telegraphic speech** because the words produced tend to be only content words, such as nouns and verbs. Function words and word endings are missing. Conjunctions (e.g., *but, and*) and prepositions (e.g., *around, behind, about*) are examples of function words that are missing from the speech of patients like Bill and Jim. Function words are important for speech

comprehension because they provide information about the relations among words. Word endings also convey meaning that is important for language comprehension. For example, -*ing* appended to the end of a word designates an action that is happening at the present time. We return to a discussion of these characteristics in the next section, when we discuss the psychological perspective on Broca's aphasia.

Until this point, we have not discussed the specific location of the lesion that causes Broca's aphasia other than to say that it is in the left hemisphere. However, the knowledge we have gained in the previous chapters should enable us to make a well-educated guess as to its general location. First, guess whether the lesion is located anterior or posterior to the central fissure. Here's a hint: Remember that the most prominent behavioral deficit in Broca's aphasia is a disruption of speech output with relatively spared comprehension. Given that hint, you can reason that the lesion causing Broca's aphasia is anterior to the central fissure, because anterior regions are specialized for motor output. Now, decide whether the lesion is mainly to the motor strip. You should conclude that it is not, because Broca's aphasia is not a result of facial or vocal muscle paralysis. Finally, consider whether the lesion causing Broca's aphasia is located ventrally or dorsally in the frontal lobe. This decision is more difficult, but if you remember the organization of the motor strip, you might be inclined to choose ventral, because the head and the face are represented at the inferior portion of the motor strip. In fact, the lesion that typically causes Broca's aphasia is in the frontal region, centered just anterior to the section of the motor strip that is responsible for control of the face (● Figure 9.1) (e.g., Damasio, 1991).

An intriguing anatomical neuroimaging analysis of two of the original patients seen by Broca has yielded additional clues about the role of subcortical and cortical regions involved in Broca's aphasia (Dronkers, Plaisant, Iba-Zizen, & Cabanis, 2007). Analysis of other patients suggested that when damage is limited to Broca's area alone, speech difficulties tend to be transient. Rather, the lesion that produces full-blown Broca's aphasia typically also involves surrounding white matter and subcortical connections (Mohr, Pessin, Finkelstein, Funkenstein, Duncan, & Davis, 1978). Because of these findings, researchers recently went back to the Musee Dupuytren in Paris, France, where the intact brains of two of Broca's patients have been stored for more than a century (● Figure 9.2). Researchers carefully took the brains and put them in an MR scanner to discern the exact extent of the lesions. This analysis revealed that the lesions involved not only Broca's area on the lateral surface of the brain, but also more medial regions, including nearby white matter (Dronkers et al., 2007). This paper also provides a fascinating discussion of the symptoms of these patients and Broca's original interpretation of his findings.

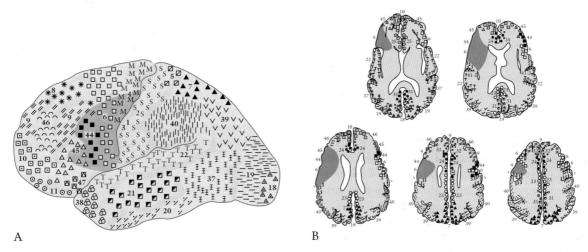

● FIGURE 9.1   Site of damage that causes Broca's aphasia. Shown here is the location of the lesion in one patient with Broca's aphasia, as viewed (A) laterally and (B) in oblique brain slices that go from the lowest region of the brain that is affected (top row, left-hand slice) to the highest region (bottom row, right-hand slice). The damage in this patient involves not only Broca's area proper (Brodmann areas 44 and 45), but also other areas that are often damaged, such as the motor and premotor areas (areas 4 and 6). © 2011 Cengage Learning

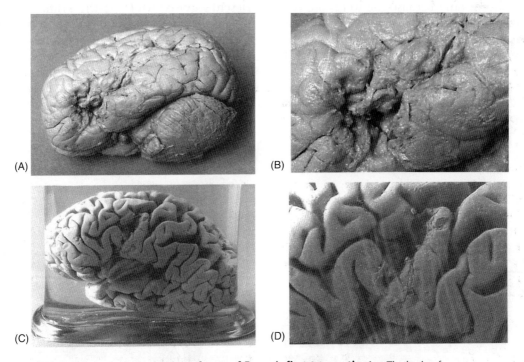

● FIGURE 9.2   A lateral view of the brains of two of Broca's first two patients. The brain of Broca's first patient, Leborgne, is shown in the top row (A, B); that of his second patient, Lelong, is shown in the bottom row (C, D). The left column shows the position of the lesion in the context of the whole brain (A, C), whereas the right-hand column shows the lesion in more detail (B, D). Notice that the lesion in Leborgne's brain encompassed not only Broca's area, but also surrounding tissue on the lateral surface. In contrast, the lesion in Lelong's brain was limited to the posterior section of Broca's area. Neuroimaging on these brains indicates that the lesion in both cases extended into adjacent medial areas, including the white matter. *Source:* Dronkers, N. F., Plaisant, O., Iba-Zizen, M. T. & Cabanis, E. A. (2007). Paul Broca's historic cases: high resolution MR imaging of the brain of Leborgne and Lelong. Brain, 130, Figure 3, pg. 1436. By permission of Oxford University Press.

About 20 years after Broca characterized his aphasia, Karl Wernicke described the converse syndrome—disrupted speech comprehension along with fluent (but nonsensical) speech output—which became known as **Wernicke's aphasia**. *Fluent* is the operative word in describing this syndrome, because speech output occurs without hesitation, sounds are well formed, and all parts of speech are present. Yet, what these individuals say makes little sense; their output is a jumble of words, often referred to as a *word salad*. In fact, the speech of a person with Wernicke's aphasia can be so disjointed that someone without proper training in a medically relevant field might be tempted to refer the individual to a psychiatrist rather than a neurologist.

Following is an example of speech from a 70-year-old man who acquired Wernicke's aphasia after blockage of part of his middle cerebral artery. Unlike the speech of individuals with Broca's aphasia, his speech was produced at a normal rate and rhythm and with an intonational pattern that was, if anything, exaggerated: "I feel very well. My hearing, writing been doing well, things that I couldn't hear from. In other words, I used to be able to work cigarettes I don't know how. . . . This year the last three years, or perhaps a little more, I didn't know how to do me any able to" (Goodglass, 1976, p. 239).

The speech of people with Wernicke's aphasia is hard to comprehend not only because the words are combined in a way that makes little sense, but also because of errors in producing specific words, known as **paraphasias**. Paraphasias manifest in numerous forms. In a **semantic paraphasia**, the substituted word has a meaning similar to that of the intended word (e.g., substitution of "barn" for "house"). In a **phonemic paraphasia**, the substituted word has a sound similar to

that of the intended word (e.g., "table" becomes "trable" or "fable"). On other occasions, persons with Wernicke's aphasia produce sounds known as **neologisms**, which are made-up words that follow the rules for combining sounds in the language, yet are not real words (e.g., "galump," "trebbin").

Despite the fluency of their output, individuals with Wernicke's aphasia generally have quite a lot of trouble understanding language. They may not even be able to understand enough to follow simple commands such as "Point to the blue square" or "Pick up the spoon." Wernicke originally postulated that these individuals cannot link the "sound images" of language to meaning.

From what we just learned about the behavioral manifestations of Wernicke's aphasia, you should be able to make an educated guess as to the location of the lesion that typically results in this disorder. Is the lesion anterior to or posterior to the central fissure? You should have guessed posterior, because those regions of the brain are involved in interpreting sensory information. But where in posterior cortex? Consider that Wernicke described this aphasia as an inability to link a sound image to meaning or stored information. What posterior brain regions might that bring to mind? Because we are discussing a sound image, you might consider regions in the superior temporal lobe near Heschl's gyrus, which is the primary auditory area. Because the retrieval of meaning is important, other regions of the temporal lobe might be considered plausible candidates. Finally, because translating a sensory input to meaning involves making linkages across representations, the parietal lobe might also be a viable candidate. As you can see in ● Figure 9.3, the lesion that typically causes Wernicke's aphasia is close to all

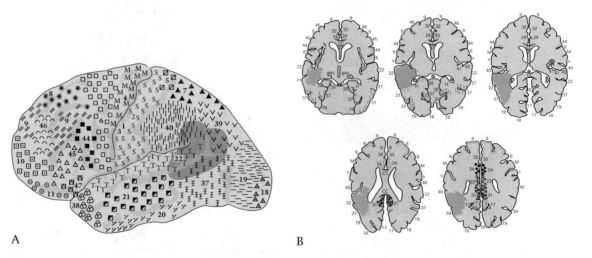

A   **B**

● **FIGURE 9.3   Site of damage that causes Wernicke's aphasia.** This diagram shows a composite of the lesions observed in patients with Wernicke's aphasia, as viewed (A) laterally and (B) in oblique brain slices that go from the lowest region of the brain that is affected (top row, left-hand slice) to the highest region (bottom row, right-hand slice). In general, not only is Wernicke's area (Brodmann area 22) affected, but so is primary auditory cortex (areas 41 and 42). The lesion sometimes extends into regions of the middle temporal gyrus (portions of areas 37 and 21) and the angular gyrus (area 39). © 2011 Cengage Learning

these areas; it is typically situated at the junction of the temporal lobe with parietal and occipital regions, near Heschl's gyrus.

It is important to note that the lesion that causes such difficulties is not limited to Wernicke's area, but rather includes Wernicke's area as well as surrounding tissue. Such a situation is similar to that in Broca's aphasia: to produce the disorder, the lesion must include Broca's area but also damage to surrounding areas, most notably the underlying white matter. Thus, although Broca's and Wernicke's areas are typically damaged in Broca's and Wernicke's aphasias, respectively, damage to these regions alone is not sufficient to cause the aphasic syndrome. Also, in at least some cases, an aphasic syndrome (e.g., Wernicke's aphasia) may be observed even if damage does not specifically include the region after which it is named (e.g., Wernicke's area) (Dronkers, 2000). Hence, the main distinction to be drawn is between aphasic symptoms that are observed after anterior lesions versus those observed after posterior lesions.

Not only did Wernicke discover the aphasia that bears his name, but he also postulated the existence of other aphasic syndromes, some of which were later documented. Wernicke assumed a basic blueprint for the neurological organization of language in which Broca's area is responsible for speech output and Wernicke's area is responsible for speech comprehension. He went on to suggest that damage severing the connection between these two areas should also result in yet another aphasic syndrome, one characterized by difficulty in repeating what was just heard. If the damage that severed the connection nevertheless spared both

Broca's and Wernicke's areas, both language comprehension and speech production would be intact, yet the person would not be able to repeat what was just heard, because sound images received by Wernicke's area could not be conducted forward to Broca's area to be produced. This syndrome has come to be known as **conduction aphasia**. When patients with conduction aphasia are asked to repeat words, they often make phonemic paraphasias, may substitute or omit words, or may be unable to say anything.

You may remember from Chapter 3 that syndromes caused by severed connections between intact brain regions are called *disconnection syndromes*. Conduction aphasia is a good example of a disconnection syndrome, because the behavioral dysfunction does not arise from damage to either the brain region that processes the sound image (Wernicke's area) or the region of the brain that produces the output (Broca's area); instead, the deficit arises from an inability to relay information from one intact area to another intact area. It is as if a communication cable between the two regions were broken. In fact, a large nerve-fiber tract, known as the *arcuate fasciculus,* connects these two regions, and part of this tract is typically damaged in conduction aphasia, along with surrounding tissue (● Figure 9.4).

Lichtheim and other aphasiologists of the late 1800s elaborated on Wernicke's model to include not only a brain region that is responsible for speech output and a brain region that processes sound images, but another region as well: the *concept center,* which was thought to be the place in the brain where meanings are stored and from whence they originate. This three-part model

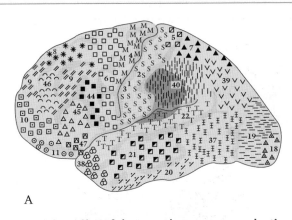

A

● **FIGURE 9.4   Site of damage that causes conduction aphasia.** This diagram shows a composite of the lesions observed in six patients with conduction aphasia, as viewed (A) laterally and (B) in oblique brain slices that go from the lowest regions of the brain that are affected (top row) to the highest region (bottom row, right). The lesion generally affects an area in the insula (the region tucked into the Sylvian fissure) that includes Brodmann areas 22, 41, and 42. More superior regions of the supramarginal gyrus (area 40) are often affected as well. Notice that the damaged area depicted here is located between those shown in Figures 9.1 and 9.3. © 2011 Cengage Learning

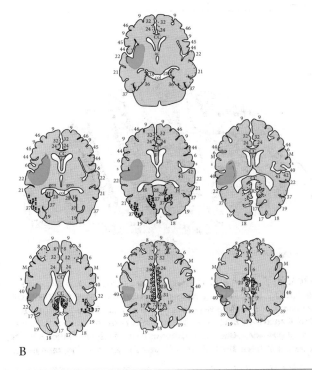

B

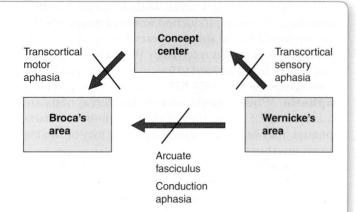

● **FIGURE 9.5   Lichtheim's model of language processing.** In Lichtheim's conception, Wernicke's area processes the sound images of words, and this information is then fed forward through a nerve-fiber tract, the arcuate fasciculus, to Broca's area, which is responsible for speech output. Damage to the region between Broca's area and Wernicke's area leads to conduction aphasia. Language disruption can also occur if either the input from Wernicke's area is disconnected from the concept center (which causes transcortical sensory aphasia), or the output from the concept center cannot reach Broca's area (which causes transcortical motor aphasia). © 2011 Cengage Learning

is shown in ● Figure 9.5. Although the model itself is flawed—because there is not a single "concept center" in the brain—it was used to predict the existence of certain aphasic syndromes that do occur regularly. We next discuss the characteristics of these syndromes.

Aphasiologists were interested in what difficulties would arise from a disconnection between the proposed concept center and the other components of the language-processing system. They reasoned that if the concept center were disconnected from the output

center (Broca's area), most of speech output would be disrupted, because ideas could not be translated into speech. However, if Broca's area itself was spared, at least some degree of output would be possible if access to this area could be gained by another route. As the model in Figure 9.5 shows, the sound image system, housed in Wernicke's area, is connected to the output center, Broca's area, not only via the meaning system, but also directly. The aphasiologists predicted that this intact direct route should enable the person to automatically feed-forward what was just heard for speech output, resulting in intact repetition. A syndrome with this behavioral profile has been observed, called **transcortical motor aphasia**. Symptomatically, these patients show the same deficits as those shown by patients with Broca's aphasia, except that they retain the ability to repeat. They often do so compulsively, a characteristic known as **echolalia**. The area of brain tissue typically damaged in this syndrome is shown in ● Figure 9.6.

The aphasiologists also considered the behavioral consequences of a disconnection between the region that processes sound images of words and the concept center. Such a disconnection, they reasoned, should prevent an individual from interpreting the meaning of words. Nevertheless, the remaining connection between the intact sound image and the output area would enable words to be repeated (refer back to Figure 9.5). A syndrome with this behavioral profile, called **transcortical sensory aphasia**, has also been observed. Patients with this syndrome have symptoms similar to those of patients with Wernicke's aphasia, except that they can repeat words and they exhibit echolalia. The damage typically associated with this syndrome is shown in ● Figure 9.7.

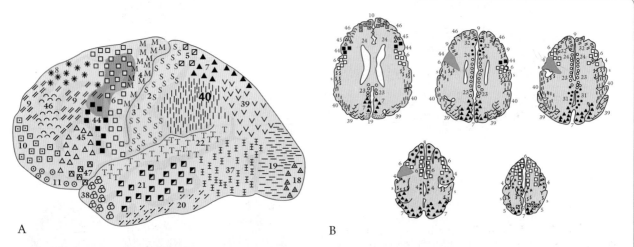

● **FIGURE 9.6   Site of damage in a typical case of transcortical motor aphasia.** Shown here is the damage as viewed (A) laterally and (B) in oblique slices that go from the lowest region of the brain affected (top row, left) to the highest region (bottom row, right). In general, the lesion is located outside Broca's area and is either more anterior or more superior. In this particular case, left premotor and motor cortices, just above Broca's area, are affected. © 2011 Cengage Learning

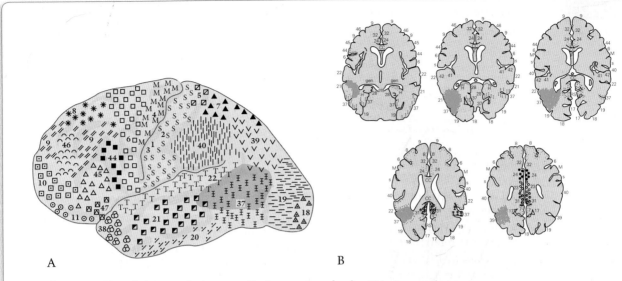

● **FIGURE 9.7   Site of damage in transcortical sensory aphasia.** This diagram shows a composite of the lesions observed in six cases of transcortical sensory aphasia, as viewed (A) laterally and (B) in oblique brain slices that go from the lowest region of the brain that is affected (top row, left) to the highest region (bottom row, right). In this type of aphasia, Wernicke's area (area 22) is never completely damaged, but more posterior regions of the temporal lobe (area 37) are always damaged. Sometimes the angular gyrus (area 39) and extrastriate regions (area 19) are also affected. © 2011 Cengage Learning

Finally, the aphasiologists speculated that people who had extensive damage to multiple parts of the system (e.g., the output center and the sound image center) would be left with neither the ability to comprehend language nor the ability to produce it. Behaviorally, such a syndrome has been observed, **global aphasia**. This syndrome is associated with extensive left-hemisphere damage that typically includes not only Wernicke's and Broca's areas, but the area between them as well (● Figure 9.8).

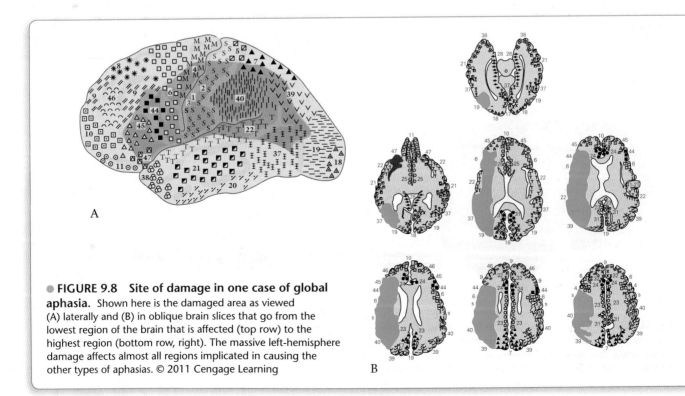

● **FIGURE 9.8   Site of damage in one case of global aphasia.** Shown here is the damaged area as viewed (A) laterally and (B) in oblique brain slices that go from the lowest region of the brain that is affected (top row) to the highest region (bottom row, right). The massive left-hemisphere damage affects almost all regions implicated in causing the other types of aphasias. © 2011 Cengage Learning

TABLE 9.2	Basic Characteristics of the Major Aphasic Syndromes				
Type of Aphasia	**Spontaneous Speech**	**Paraphasia**	**Comprehension**	**Repetition**	**Naming**
Broca's	Nonfluent	Uncommon	Good	Poor	Poor
Wernicke's	Fluent	Common (verbal)	Poor	Poor	Poor
Conduction	Fluent	Common (literal)	Good	Poor	Poor
Transcortical motor	Nonfluent	Uncommon	Good	Good (echolalia)	Poor
Transcortical sensory	Fluent	Common	Poor	Good (echolalia)	Poor
Global	Nonfluent	Variable	Poor	Poor	Poor

Table 9.2 lists the major aphasic syndromes observed clinically and their characteristics. Because different nomenclatures are used for these various syndromes, you may also find Broca's aphasia referred to as *nonfluent, agrammatic,* or *anterior aphasia,* whereas Wernicke's aphasia is also sometimes referred to as *fluent,* or *posterior, aphasia.* ● Figure 9.9 provides a summary schematic of the typical lesion locations for each type of aphasia discussed in Table 9.2. (For a recent review regarding the latest thinking about aphasia, see Hillis, 2007).

Although it provides a useful organizing framework, the three-part model of Lichtheim and other 19th-century aphasiologists does not adequately explain all the symptoms of aphasia. The primary difficulty with their model is that it presents an oversimplified view of language deficits following brain damage. For example, the model posits that Broca's aphasia is caused by damage to the language-output center. However, as we will see, the difficulties experienced by patients with Broca's aphasia are not limited to speech output. In the next section, we further explore the complexity of aphasic symptoms from a psycholinguistic perspective.

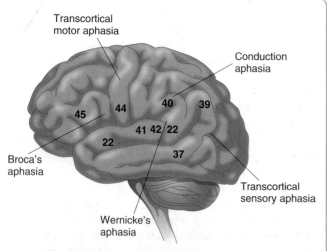

● **FIGURE 9.9   Composite diagram indicating the regions associated with the various major types of aphasias.** The numbers in this diagram refer to Brodmann areas. © 2011 Cengage Learning

■ Psycholinguistic Perspectives

Since the 1960s, interest in aphasia has been renewed by psychologists and psycholinguists using aphasic disorders as a window for uncovering the mental structure of language (Hillis, 2007). Psycholinguists have traditionally divided language into three main components: phonology, syntax, and semantics. Roughly speaking, **phonology** examines the sounds that compose a language and the rules that govern their combination, **syntax** is the rules of grammar, and **semantics** is the meaning of language. In the subsequent sections, we discuss each of these components of language and how they are affected by aphasic syndromes.

Phonology

As just mentioned, *phonology* refers to the rules governing the sounds of language. Linguists have conceptualized two ways of representing the sounds of speech: phonemically and phonetically. A *phoneme* is considered the smallest unit of sound that can signal meaning. For example, /b/ and /p/ mean nothing by themselves (/ / is used to symbolize a linguistic sound, allowing, for example, the sound /b/ to be differentiated from the letter *b*), but they nonetheless cause /bat/ and /pat/ to have different meanings. In contrast, the *phonetic* representation of a speech sound describes how it is produced on particular occasions or in particular contexts. For example, the /p/ in *pill* is aspirated (produced with a burst of air), whereas the /p/ in *spill* is not aspirated.

People with Broca's aphasia, and other persons with aphasia whose speech is nonfluent, have difficulty producing the correct variant of a phoneme (Blumstein, 1991), meaning that they cannot produce the correct *phonetic* representation of a speech sound. The production of different variants of the same phoneme requires precise control over the articulatory muscles, with each version varying in subtle but important ways, a precision lacking in individuals who have Broca's aphasia.

In contrast, patients with Wernicke's aphasia (and other fluent aphasias) do not have difficulty producing the correct variant of a given phoneme. However, they often have difficulty producing the correct phoneme. This dissociation suggests that the phonemic representation of a speech sound is distinct from its phonetic representation. Patients with Broca's aphasia appear to have difficulty producing both the correct phonetic and the correct phonemic representations of a speech sound, whereas those with Wernicke's aphasia have difficulty only with phonemic representations.

The disruption of the phonemic representation of a speech sound in aphasia occurs systematically and can be well explained by a psycholinguistic perspective that considers speech sounds as being composed of a set of distinctive features. According to linguistic theory, consonants vary in distinctive features, two of which are place of articulation and voicing. Both of these features describe the voyage of air from the lungs out through the vocal tract. **Place of articulation** describes the *location* in the vocal tract where airflow is obstructed. For example, /b/ and /p/ are known as *labial stops* because obstruction occurs at the lips; /d/ and /t/ are *alveolar stops* because the obstruction occurs from tongue placement at the alveolar ridge behind the front teeth; and /g/ and /k/ are *velar stops* because the air is obstructed at the velar, or soft, palate in the back of the mouth. Say these sounds to yourself right now and it will become obvious how the airflow is obstructed in different places. **Voicing** describes the timing between the release of the air for the stop consonant and the vibration of the vocal cords. When a consonant is voiced, the release of air and the vibration of the vocal cords coincide (/b/, /d/, /g/), whereas in an unvoiced consonant (/p/, /t/, /k/), the vocal cords do not begin to vibrate until after the release. The only difference between a /b/ and a /p/, which are both labial stops, is that vocal-cord vibration and air release are coincident in time for a /b/, whereas for a /p/ the air release precedes vocal-cord vibration by a mere 40 to 80 ms! (Perhaps you'll appreciate the precision of your brain a bit more the next time you utter or hear a sentence like "Pat, it's your turn to bat.")

The distinctive features of a phoneme have been found to influence the production errors of patients with aphasia, as well as some of their receptive difficulties. When making phonemic errors, people with aphasia (regardless of the type of aphasia) are much more likely to substitute a sound that differs in only one distinctive feature (e.g., /b/ for /p/, which differ only in voicing) rather than two (e.g., /b/ for /t/, which differ in both voicing and place of articulation) (Blumstein, 1991). Researchers have found that most persons with aphasia exhibit some problems in perceptually discerning these features as well as in producing them (e.g., Miceli, Gainotti, Caltagirone, & Masullo, 1980). Not all distinctive features have equal saliency, though, because some may be less resistant to confusion than others. For example, errors based on place of articulation (e.g., /pa/ vs. /ta/) are more common than errors based on voicing (e.g., /pa/ vs. /ba/) (e.g., Baker, Blumstein, & Goodglass, 1981).

Phonological theory describes not only the sounds of language, as we have just been discussing, but also the rules by which sounds can be combined. So, for example, in English a valid combination of sounds would be "casmeck," whereas an invalid combination would be "cnamzik." As you may remember from our earlier discussion, patients with aphasia, most notably Wernicke's aphasics, often construct novel series of sounds called *neologisms*. These neologisms *could* be words, because they follow the rules for combining sounds, but the particular combination used does not constitute an actual word in the language. In this sense, people with aphasia appear to respect the rules of phonology for the language that they speak.

In summary, phonologic processing can be disrupted in aphasia in two major ways. First, phonetic representations of phonemes are often disrupted in patients with nonfluent aphasias (but remain intact in patients with fluent aphasias). Second, phoneme substitution in production and difficulty in phoneme discrimination are common occurrences in both fluent and nonfluent aphasias and appear to be governed by the similarity of phonemes to each other along the dimensions of distinctive contrasts. Analysis of language breakdown in aphasia suggests that the phonetic and phonemic representations of sounds are distinct, in that the phonemic representation may be compromised even when the phonetic representation is intact. Despite these difficulties, the rules that govern the combination of specific phonemes are preserved in aphasic speech.

Syntax

The second fundamental component of language, *syntax*, describes the rules governing how words are put together in sentences. For example, in English we generally use a subject-verb-object (SVO) word order, as in the sentence "The cat chased a mouse," whereas in Turkish, for example, the standard word order is subject-object-verb (SOV). Within a language, various syntactic forms or frames are often allowed. SVO word order in English is considered the active voice, and OVS is considered the passive voice, as in the sentence "The robber [object] was chased [verb] by the police officer [subject]."

People with certain types of aphasia, most notably those with anterior lesions, often have specific difficulties with the syntactic aspects of language processing. In the opening vignette, function words and word endings are missing from the men's speech, and the words are not structured in a standard syntactic frame. Historically, researchers assumed that persons with anterior aphasia failed to produce function words and prepositions not because they had difficulties with syntax, but because they found it so hard to produce speech, so they carefully chose those words that would convey the most meaning for the least effort—that is, nouns and verbs. However, people with anterior aphasia have a compromised ability both to produce *and* to comprehend the grammatical aspects of language. Therefore, anterior aphasia is sometimes called **agrammatic aphasia**. For example, because of their relative insensitivity to syntactic markers, individuals with anterior aphasia assume an SVO word order for both the active sentence "The cat chased the kitten" and the passive sentence "The cat was chased by the kitten." They ignore the grammatical markers of the auxiliary verb *was* and the preposition *by* as signaling the nonstandard OVS (object-verb-subject) word order. As a result, when asked to select a picture representing the meaning of each sentence, these aphasics select the same picture for both sentences, one of an adult feline chasing an immature feline.

These difficulties in syntax are observed consistently even across different languages with varying grammatical markers. For example, in English, we have only one definite article, *the*, but in other languages, *the* for a noun that is the subject of the sentence may differ from *the* for a noun that is the object. In German, *the* for male nouns that are the subject of the sentence is *der*, whereas when a male noun is the object of a sentence, *the* becomes *den* and an *-n* is added to the end of the noun. The sentence "Der Junge küsste das Mädchen" means "The boy kissed the girl," whereas "Den Jungen küsste das Mädchen" means "The girl kissed the boy." The *den* and the *-n* at the end of *Junge* indicate that the boy is playing the role of the object. Given these two sentences, German-speaking people with anterior aphasia will have difficulty realizing that the boy is being kissed in the second sentence, because they are insensitive to the grammatical markers that signal the less typical grammatical construction (von Stockert & Bader, 1976).

Despite having problems differentiating between different syntactic constructions, patients with anterior aphasia have little trouble understanding sentences such as "The ice-cream cone was eaten by the boy," because their ability to understand the meaning of words (i.e., semantics) limits the interpretation of such sentences. A person with anterior aphasia knows that ice-cream cones cannot eat boys (except, perhaps, in some very bizarre horror movie) and therefore is not confused by the OVS word order.

Knowledge of syntax appears to be spared in persons with posterior aphasia, in contrast to those with anterior aphasia. As mentioned at the beginning of this chapter, speech in posterior aphasia is fluent and contains all the grammatical markers (e.g., verb endings, prepositions, auxiliary verbs) that would normally be found in intact speech production, although the sentences produced are largely devoid of meaning.

Semantics

The third fundamental component of language, *semantics*, is concerned with the meaning of words and word combinations. Sentences may have different syntactic structures yet have approximately the same meaning. For example, "The beaver appeared among the reeds on the far side of the lake from where I was standing" has the same basic meaning as "On the side of the lake opposite from where I was positioned, the beaver appeared among the reeds."

The ability to extract meaning from language or to use words to produce meaning is seriously com-

promised in patients with posterior aphasia. In severe cases, such patients may not understand even simple commands such as "Point to the blue circle" and "Point to the big red square," which are included in a quick screening device for aphasia known as the *Token Test* (DeRenzi, 1980). In less severe cases, the patients understand simple nouns but have difficulty comprehending more complicated linguistic material. Furthermore, this difficulty in comprehending the meaning of language is pervasive across modalities, extending to both auditory and written language. This finding indicates that the meaning system itself, rather than some modality-specific (e.g., auditory) access to that system, is disrupted. Posterior aphasics read and write no better than they can understand speech, and their speech output conveys no more meaning than they appear to extract from spoken language.

In contrast, patients with anterior aphasia appear to have intact semantic processing. They can usually follow simple commands with ease, although, as mentioned previously, they might exhibit minor problems in comprehension when syntax plays a large role in interpreting sentences. For example, if told, "Place the blue circle *on top of* the big red square," patients with anterior aphasia might react by putting the blue circle *next to* the big red square. Their problems with syntax hinder their ability to comprehend the prepositional phrase that describes the desired relationship between the two items.

■ Double Dissociations in Language Processing

We have conceptualized the difference between anterior and posterior aphasias in two distinct manners. On the one hand, we have viewed anterior areas as important for speech output and posterior areas as important for speech comprehension. On the other hand, we have suggested that anterior areas are important for syntactic processing and posterior areas are involved in semantic processing. Each of these models has some validity, but a melding of the two probably best characterizes the manner in which these brain areas actually process language.

Regardless of how the deficits in the two types of aphasias are distinguished (input-output or syntactic-semantic), these syndromes represent a double dissociation in language processing. On a theoretical level, this dissociation tells us that no *unitary* language center or language system exists in the brain. Rather, the system has specific components that can act more or less independently of one another. This knowledge is important both for more complete understanding of the neural control of language and for practical reasons. Because the input and output of auditory language are governed by different systems, therapies geared toward speech production are likely to have little effect on comprehension. Likewise, because the grammar and meaning of a language are under separate neural control, being tutored in the rules of grammar is unlikely to aid a person with aphasia who is having difficulty producing meaningful sentences.

In sum, the human brain appears to have two distinct and separable subsystems that play different roles in language functioning. Although the anterior and posterior systems are intimately linked and interact seamlessly in the normally functioning brain, their separability can be revealed by brain damage.

Neural Organization of Language as Inferred from Other Research Methods

Since the 1960s, there has been an explosion of research using neuroimaging and electrophysiological techniques to examine the organization of language processing in the brain. Some of this work corroborates ideas that were derived from studies of aphasic patients. In other cases, information from newer methods reveals the shortcomings of models based solely on aphasiology. In this section we discuss how neuroimaging evidence extends our understanding of the neural organization of language. At the end of this section, we propose a more integrative, system-based approach to the understanding of language processing in the human brain, as an alternative to the models proposed by aphasiologists.

■ Consistencies with Models Derived from Brain-Damaged Patients

With the advent of neuroimaging methods, researchers wanted to determine how well models derived from people with brain damage could explain processing in a neurologically intact brain. These studies provided converging evidence that anterior and posterior regions of the left hemisphere play different roles in language. For example, increased activity in the superior temporal regions of the left hemisphere, which Wernicke described as processing sound images of words, is observed when individuals must distinguish aurally presented words from aurally presented nonwords (e.g., Frith, Friston, Liddle, & Frackowiak, 1991). In contrast, Broca's area, which is implicated in speech production, becomes active when words must be repeated rather than just heard (Petersen, Fox, Posner, Mintun, & Raichle, 1988).

Brain imaging studies also support the idea that anterior regions of the left hemisphere are more involved in processing syntax and posterior regions are important for semantics. For example, there is more activation in Broca's area (BA 44) when people must process syntactically more complex sentences such as "The limerick that the boy recited appalled the priest," compared to those that are less complex, such as "The biographer omitted the story that insulted the queen." In the former case, a clause (i.e., "that the boy recited") separates the subject (i.e., "the limerick") from the verb phrase ("appalled the priest"), whereas in the latter case, the subject ("the biographer") and the verb phrase ("omitted the story") are adjacent (Stromswold, Caplan, Alpert, & Rauch, 1996). Furthermore, activation is observed in the left posterior temporoparietal cortex (BA 39), near Wernicke's area, when individuals make semantic decisions, such as deciding whether a word names a living or nonliving object (Price, Moore, Humphreys, & Wise, 1997). Greater activation is also observed in neighboring regions (BA 22) for sentences or stories as opposed to unrelated words or sentences (Price, 1998).

Research from electrophysiological techniques also supports the conclusion that the brain segregates syntactic from semantic processing. As you may remember from Chapter 3, a specific ERP component, the N_{400}, is elicited when a word, either visual or auditory, in a sentence violates semantic expectation, such as "He spread the warm bread with socks" or "The girl dropped the sky on the table." As shown in ● Figure 9.10A, this component tends to be large over posterior recording sites and tends to be larger over the left hemisphere than the right (Hagoort & Brown, 2000a). Recordings from patients with brain damage, intracranial recordings, and magnetoencephalographic data strongly suggest that this effect reflects activity in the left temporal lobe (Van Petten & Luka, 2006). This localization is consistent with the fact that Wernicke's aphasia, which affects left temporal regions, leads to difficulty in semantic processing.

In contrast, a different component is elicited when words occur that render a sentence ungrammatical, such as "The spoiled child *throw* the toys on the floor." This component, the P_{600} (also sometimes referred to as the SPS, for *syntactic positive shift*), is observed both over posterior and anterior recording sites, as shown in ● Figure 9.10B. Because it has been observed across a variety of languages, such as German, English, and Dutch, the P_{600} is known to be sensitive to syntax regardless of the particulars of a given language system (Friederici, Hahne, & Mecklinger, 1996; Osterhout & Holcomb, 1992; Hagoort & Brown, 2000b). Suggesting a dissociation between syntax and semantics, a P_{600} can also be found when the sentence makes no sense semantically but nonetheless has a grammatical violation, such as "The boiled watering-can *smoke* the telephone in the cat" (Hagoort & Brown, 1994). Thus, ERP studies provide converging evidence that the brain processes syntax and semantics in distinct manners (for a short review, see Osterhout, McLaughlin, & Bersick, 1997).

Although these studies provide converging evidence in support of basic components of language as identified by aphasiologists, more recent research has provided additional insights that underscore the need to step beyond traditional models of language processing in the brain. We turn next to that research.

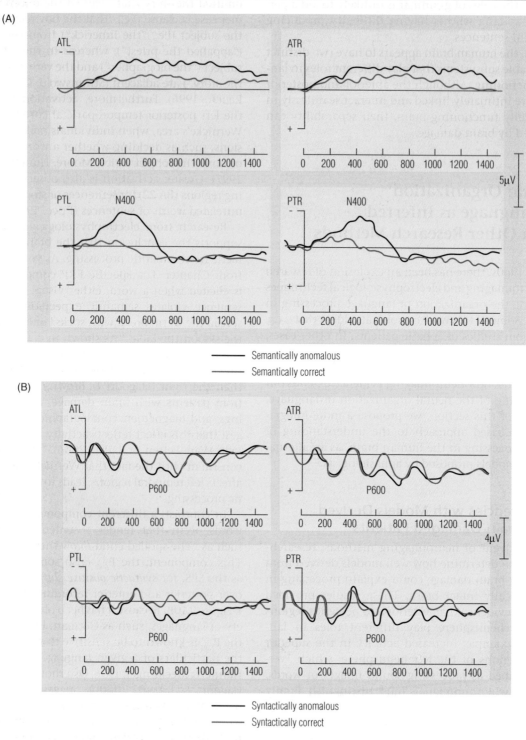

● **FIGURE 9.10   ERP components sensitive to aspects of language processing.** (A) Shown here is the N_{400} that occurs in response to semantically anomalous material in the auditory modality. Notice that it is larger over posterior regions of the brain (panels labeled PT) than anterior regions (panels labeled AT) and larger over the left hemisphere (panels labeled L) than the right (panels labeled R). (B) Shown here is the P_{600} that occurs in response to syntactically anomalous sentences. Notice that, unlike the N_{400}, it is observed over both anterior and posterior regions. © 2011 Cengage Learning

■ Additional Insights Beyond Traditional Conceptions

Three big insights about language have been provided by neuroimaging studies of language. The first has been to provide more specific information about the localization of brain tissue that performs specific language-related processing. The second insight is that the language subsystems are not as distinct as we initially supposed. Rather, somewhat distinct but overlapping networks appear to be involved in processing phonology, syntax, and semantics. The third important insight is that the activation of these networks can be modified under specific conditions or experience.

Brain imaging has refined our understanding of the neural structures underlying language processing (for a review, see Bookheimer, 2002). Results of imaging studies indicate that during language tasks, much larger regions of the left hemisphere are activated than those traditionally considered "language" areas (e.g., Broca's, Wernicke's). Many of these additional regions are in the temporal lobe outside Wernicke's area (Binder, Frost, Hammeke, Cox, Rao, & Pricto, 1997).

In addition, these studies have provided a more detailed map of the cortical anatomy underlying language processing. For example, the classical viewpoint was that posterior regions in the superior temporal gyrus processed only language-related sounds. Yet this does not seem to be the case, as at least one subdivision of the superior temporal gyrus appears to be equally activated by linguistic (words) and nonlinguistic stimuli (tones), suggesting that it is important for extracting parameters of acoustic information in general (Binder, Frost, Hammeke, Rao, & Cox, 1996) rather than acoustic parameters specifically related to language, as suggested by Wernicke. A more posterior but nearby region appears to be specifically involved in phonological analysis, but it is active regardless of whether the item is presented auditorily in speech (Zatorre, Meyer, Gjedde, & Evans, 1996) or visually (Pugh et al., 1996). This region is also more active when hearing words than when hearing pseudowords, suggesting that it is crucial for analyzing specific phonological patterns encountered in one's native tongue (Price, Wise, Watson, Patterson, Howard, & Frackowiak, 1994). Furthermore, this region is specifically responsive to phonological information, as it is not activated by tasks that involve the extraction of semantic information (e.g., deciding if a word represents a living or nonliving item).

Another surprising finding from the neuroimaging literature is the degree to which the left inferior prefrontal cortex plays a role in receptive language tasks, such as word reading (e.g., Kelley et al., 1998; Fiez & Petersen, 1998). The particular region of left inferior prefrontal cortex activated appears to depend on whether phonological or semantic processing is paramount. When an emphasis is placed on phonological processing, such as how a word sounds compared to how it looks (Fiez, Tallal,

Raichle, Miezin, Katz, & Petersen, 1995), when a specific phoneme must be detected (e.g., /pa/), or when a decision about the final consonant in a word is required, activation is observed in Broca's area in BA 44 (Zatorre, Meyer, Gjedde, & Evans, 1996). In contrast, activation is observed in more anterior portions of the inferior frontal lobe when semantic processing is emphasized (BA 45/47) (Wagner, 1999). This dissociation between the involvement of more caudal regions of the left inferior frontal region in phonology and more rostral regions in semantics is also supported by studies using TMS (Devlin & Watkins, 2007).

Haven't we mentioned many times in this chapter that the left frontal region is involved in speech production and syntax? So now what are we to make of the idea that these regions are involved in phonological and semantic aspects of receptive language tasks? Is the classical model all wrong? Probably not; it just needs some refinement. The consensus is that whereas long-term storage of phonological and semantic knowledge is dependent on posterior regions, frontal regions are involved in the effortful retrieval, short-term maintenance, and/or strategic control of phonological and semantic information. In fact, individuals with Broca's aphasia have been shown to have difficulty in processing certain aspects of phonology (Fiez, Tranel, Seager-Frerichs, & Damasio, 2006).

With regard to phonology, these left inferior regions appear to be involved in linking the sound-based linguistic representation to motor production. Remember that earlier in this chapter we discussed how phonological representations must be translated into phonetic descriptions so that the correct pronunciation is produced, and opined that these regions probably play a role in that translation process. Understanding why left frontal regions are involved in semantic processing may appear a bit more vexing, but their role appears to be related to executive processes (see Chapter 12). These regions may aid in accessing a particular word, such as when you are searching for just the right word to describe something, or they may serve as working memory buffers to hold language-related information online (Snyder, Feigenson, & Thompson-Schill, 2007). For example, nonaphasic people with bilateral prefrontal damage do as poorly as Alzheimer's patients when asked to name as many animals as possible in 15 seconds. Is their semantic knowledge gone? No, because when given a cue every 15 seconds (e.g., animals found on a farm, animals that live in water), they outperform the Alzheimer's patients and do as well as normal people (Randolph, Braun, Goldberg, & Chase, 1993).

Some evidence suggests that areas 45 and 47 of the left inferior prefrontal cortex may play slightly different roles in such processes (Badre & Wagner, 2007). One way to explain this distinction is to consider a situation in which you want to verbally describe another person. According to this model, area 47, which is the more anterior of the two regions, is involved in controlling the access to your semantic knowledge for the appropriate meaning. For example, this region would work to *retrieve* words that are related to the meaning that you wish to convey—for example, identifying semantically related words that you feel describe your friend, which might be "kind," "caring," "selfless," "warm," and "considerate." Then Area 45 would be involved in selecting which of the words that you have retrieved is most appropriate. For example, you might decide to describe your friend as "selfless" rather than "considerate" because she is more than considerate of other people's needs and does things for others even if it is not in her best interest.

Support for this idea comes from a study in which participants saw a cue word and then had to determine which of two words presented along with it were semantically related. Area 47 was more active when the semantic association between the cue and target word was somewhat weak (e.g., "candle"–"halo"), which presumably requires a bit more of a search through memory, than when the association was strong (e.g., "candle"–"flame"). In contrast, the activity in area 45 was greater when the decision was difficult because the incorrect response (e.g., the word "league" for the pair of "ivy"–"jade", both of which are green) had an association with the target ("ivy league") but not the appropriate one in this context, as compared to when the incorrect response had no such association and thus did not make it difficult to select the correct word (e.g., the word "coal" for the pair of "ivy"–"jade") (Badre, Poldrack, Pare-Blagoev, Insler, & Wagner, 2005).

Although we have treated syntax, semantics, and phonology as distinct and separable systems, they are much more likely to have some degree of overlap, and that may depend on the demands of a particular situation. According to classic psycholinguistic theory, one first builds a syntactic frame (e.g., subject–verb–object) and then drops the appropriate semantic values into that frame (e.g., "The dog bit the mailman"). Thus, not only are syntax and semantics separable, but syntax also precedes semantics, according to the traditional view. However, results from event-related potential studies of language processing suggest otherwise. Remember, as we discussed earlier, an N_{400} is elicited when a word in a sentence violates semantic expectation, whereas a P_{600} is elicited by words that render a sentence ungrammatical. If a syntactic frame is constructed and then words are dropped into it, we would expect that the following initial part of a sentence, "The hearty meal was devouring . . ." to elicit an N_{400}, because it is impossible for meals to eat anything, and not to elicit a P_{600}, as the grammatical structure of the noun phrase is perfectly reasonable (e.g., "The lion was devouring . . ."). Yet this sentence does not produce an N_{400}, but rather a large P_{600} (● Figure 9.11) (Kim & Osterhout, 2005), while the sentence, "The dusty tabletops were devouring . . ." does produce an N_{400}.

How are we to understand these results? One way is to assume that syntax does not always precede semantics and that the language system does a quick first pass for semantic associations. Under such conditions, the word "meal" and "devouring" are appropriately related and therefore do not elicit an N_{400}, whereas the lack of a semantic relationship between "tabletops" and "devouring" does. But when "meal" and "devouring" are detected as syntactically anomalous given the semantics of the sentence, a P_{600} is emitted. This has led some researchers to suggest that the P_{600} is not a

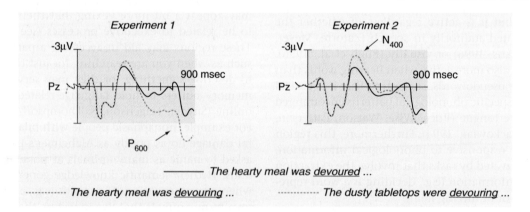

● FIGURE 9.11   ERP evidence of the interaction between syntactic and semantic processing.
(Left) Here the semantically anomalous phrase "The hearty meal was devouring" does not elicit an N_{400} but rather a P_{600}. (Right) In contrast, the semantic mismatch between "tabletops" and "devouring" elicits an N_{400}. These findings are inconsistent with the idea that a syntactic frame for a sentence is constructed and then words with the appropriate semantic value are dropped into that frame. If that were the case, the sentence on the left should have elicited an N_{400} just like the sentence on the right. *Source:* Kuperberg, G. R. (2007). Neural mechanisms of language comprehension: challenges to syntax. Brain Research, 1146, Figure 5A, page 30 adapted from "The independence of combinatory semantic processing: Evidence from event-related potentials" by Albert Kim and Lee Osterhout in Journal of Memory and Language, 52 (2005), 205–225.

marker for syntax per se, but rather for the combination of semantic and syntactic processing (Kuperberg, 2007), suggesting overlap between these two systems.

The idea that language involves overlapping rather than functionally independent systems is also supported by neuroimaging. For example, when a person listens to spoken words, not only does Wernicke's area show activity, but so do a variety of other regions as well. This has led researchers to think of language-processing regions in the left hemisphere in terms of networks, rather than discrete regions. In a recent meta-analysis of more than 129 neuroimaging studies, Vigneau et al. (2006) suggested that there are three distinct but overlapping systems. As shown in ● Figure 9.12, phonological processing is carried out in regions of the superior temporal gyrus involved in auditory processing as well as posterior areas of the premotor region, including area 44. This makes sense, because sound is processed in the temporal cortex and we often use motor commands to keep phonological information in our verbal working memory (such as repeating a telephone number over and over again until you dial it).

Semantic processing appears to involve two separable routes in the temporal lobe, a more dorsal route related to auditory material and a more ventral route related to visual aspects of language. Portions of both of these routes have at least one section that overlaps with the phonological system. In addition, both of these routes have connections with regions of the frontal lobe involved in semantics (which, as discussed earlier, are more anterior than those involved in phonology).

Finally, syntax, as already discussed, involves posterior frontal regions as well as dorsal temporal regions. Some models suggest a division in which more local and more global aspects of syntactic structure are processed in different subsystems (Grodzinsky & Friederici, 2006). According to this view, the local aspects, such as the construction of a noun phrase (determiner–adjective–noun, as in "the fluffy rabbit") depends on regions more ventral and medial to Broca's area, along with anterior regions of the superior temporal gyrus. In contrast, Broca's area (BA 44/45) processes syntax at a more global level across the entire sentence, along with posterior temporal regions.

As you can see, a number of regions are thought to be involved in more than one type of process (phonology, syntax, semantics). This makes sense if you consider

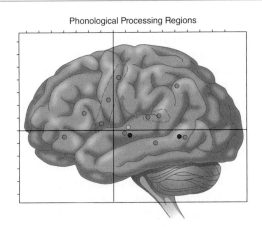

Phonological Processing Regions

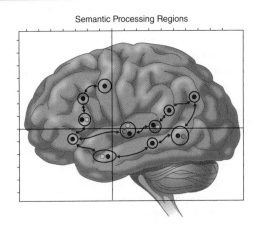

Semantic Processing Regions

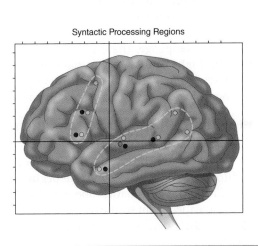

Syntactic Processing Regions

● **FIGURE 9.12 Main brain regions involved in semantic, syntactic, and phonological aspects of language processing.** In this diagram, regions involved in phonology are shown in blue, areas involved in semantics are shown in red, and areas involved in syntax are shown in yellow. Notice that anterior language areas, such as Broca's area, are involved in syntactic processing. They are also involved in effortful retrieval of phonological and semantic aspects of words. Posterior language areas are involved in semantic processing as well as phonological processing. However, it is clear that most aspects of language processing involve networks that span the anterior and posterior areas. *Source:* Vigneau et al. (2006) Meta-analyzing left hemisphere language areas: phonology, semantic, and sentence processing. Neuroimage, 30, Figure 2, pg. 1420, Figure 3, pg. 1420, Figure 4, page 1421.

that in most aspects of language processing we must join phonology, syntax, and semantics. What you also should have noticed is that smooth functioning of the language system requires integration between brain regions. Such integration was already noted in part by classical theorists who suggested that conduction aphasia results from a disconnection between posterior and anterior brain regions. Studies of comparative neuroanatomy indicate that the white-matter tracts that connect anterior and posterior brain regions are not observed in other primates, suggesting that they may serve as an important basis for language processing in the human brain (Rilling et al., 2008). Recent techniques, such as diffusion imaging tractography techniques that can identify white-matter tracts between brain regions, will likely help to expand our knowledge of how the neural highways between anterior and posterior language areas of the left hemisphere help them to work together (e.g., Friederici, 2009). There is also evidence of functional interactions between anterior and posterior brain regions, even when one might not suspect it. For example, a joint TMS–PET study shows that activity in Broca's area during *speech perception* predicts the size of the motor potentials observed at the lips in response to simultaneous TMS over primary motor cortex (Watkins & Paus, 2004). This finding suggests that posterior processing of speech may prime "motor" regions involved in language even during comprehension.

Finally, neuroimaging studies have illustrated that the patterns of activation across language-processing regions can vary depending on experience, practice, or development. In one of the first studies to show such an effect, researchers examined the brain regions that are involved in generating a verb in response to a noun (Raichle et al., 1994). When participants were naive to either the task or the particular set of stimuli used, activation occurred over the regions of the left hemisphere that when damaged typically cause Wernicke's aphasia. However, when the individuals were given a familiar and well-practiced set of stimuli, activation was more anterior, in an area typically associated with conduction aphasia (which, as you should remember, disrupts the ability to repeat sequences). More recent research has suggested that changes in the relative weighting of activity across the different nodes of the language-processing network occur as children become older and more fluent with language (e.g., Chou et al., 2006). Still other research has shown that changes in the relative pattern of activity across regions can predict the learning of new phonemic contrasts (e.g., speech sounds in Hindi for non-Hindi speakers). Increased learning was correlated with greater activity in temporal-parietal speech regions and less in frontal speech areas (Golestani & Zatorre, 2004). In part, one's brain morphology may influence how easy it is to acquire such new linguistic knowledge. In another study (Golestani, Molko, Deheane, Le Bihan, & Pallier, 2007), those individuals who had greater white matter in Heschl's gyrus before

training learned the phonemic contrasts the quickest! (For a longer discussion of how aspects of brain morphology are associated with an individual's degree of language skill, see Richardson & Price, 2009).

Thus far we have learned that in addition to lesion studies, various methods—such as electrical stimulation, Wada procedures, brain imaging, and electrophysiological studies—all provide evidence of left-hemisphere specialization for speech output, and for somewhat distinct neural systems for processing phonology, syntax, and semantics. Traditional models of language, based on patients who have suffered brain damage, suggest somewhat compartmentalized regions of brain tissue, each of which is involved in a specific aspect of language processing. However, newer neuroimaging and electrophysiological methods suggest a much more complicated and integrated language network spanning both anterior and posterior portions of the brain. Now we turn our attention to how the brain processes visual language, a system of communication that humans invented relatively recently in evolutionary time.

Neurological Bases for Visual Language Processing

Portions of the neurological system that support written language functions are distinct from those that support spoken language functions, although in right-handers both reside within the left hemisphere. We should not be surprised that the neural machinery for spoken and written language is somewhat distinct. First, these two types of language processing occur in different modalities. To the degree that they interact with different sensory regions of the brain, they might be presumed to differ in their neural organization. Second, although spoken language has existed for some time, written language is a relatively new invention. The organization of the brain is likely to have undergone evolutionary pressure for the development of spoken language; not enough time has passed for that to be the case for written language. Third, as we see in the following section, interpretation of written language does not always rely on using spoken language as an intermediary. To the degree that processing of visual words is independent of spoken language, these two types of language processing might be expected to have different neurological bases. We now turn to a more detailed discussion of the neurological bases for visual language.

■ Evidence from Studies of Patients with Brain Damage

As we did when discussing the neurological bases for auditory language processing, we begin this section by examining the information about written language that can be gleaned from studies of patients with brain damage. We then discuss converging evidence from other methods.

Alexia versus Agraphia

Just as the production of spoken language is distinct from the perception of spoken language, so too is the production of written language (writing) distinct from the perception of written words (reading). When the ability to read is lost as a consequence of brain damage, the ensuing syndrome is known as **alexia or acquired dyslexia** (to distinguish it from *developmental dyslexia,* in which an individual has great difficulty acquiring the ability to read during childhood; see Chapter 15). When instead the ability to write is lost, the deficit is known as **agraphia**. Although alexia and agraphia typically co-occur after damage to the angular gyrus (located in the ventral region of the parietal lobe above the Sylvian fissure), the two can dissociate. In some cases individuals have alexia without agraphia (e.g., Greenblatt, 1973), and in other cases agraphia without alexia (e.g., Hécaen & Kremin, 1976). These dissociations can lead to some strange situations. Although an individual who has alexia without agraphia can write a sentence with little difficulty, that person is unable to read sentences, including those that she or he previously wrote! Likewise, individuals who have agraphia without alexia are unable to write sentences, but can read without much difficulty.

As you should recognize by now, the syndromes of alexia without agraphia and agraphia without alexia are examples of a double dissociation. In this case, the double dissociation indicates that the neural control systems for reading and writing are separable to some extent and do not critically rely on each other. That is, we do not have a single module in the brain that is important for written language; instead, we have distinct systems, one for interpreting written language and one for producing it.

Reading

To better understand how the brain processes written language, we first examine the cognitive processes underlying written language. Here we use reading as an example, then later describe how these findings generalize to writing.

Phonological versus Direct Route to Meaning Researchers have proposed two distinct routes whereby information in a visual linguistic format can be linked to meaning (e.g., Coltheart, Rastle, Perry, Langdon, & Ziegler, 2001). The first route is known as the **phonological route** (or nonlexical route) **to reading** because sound is a mediator in the process of associating print with meaning. This route, which you likely used when learning to read, requires you to identify each letter (e.g., *c, a, t*), sound out each letter (/k/, /a/, /t/), and then blend the three sounds to produce a word ("cat"). Once you pronounce the word, you can recognize its meaning because you already associate this sound pattern with the concept that it represents ("a small, furry household pet with claws that is known for its taste

for tuna and mice and for an aloof and independent demeanor"). Thus, the auditory sounds were the intermediary allowing you to link print to meaning.

The rules whereby print is associated with sound are known as **grapheme-to-phoneme correspondence rules**. *Graphemes* are the smallest units of written language that are combined to make words. For example, the visual pattern "c" is a grapheme, and this grapheme can take many forms, such as "c," "*c,*" "C," and "**C**." Grapheme-to-phoneme correspondence rules let us know how each grapheme should sound (e.g., "c" is usually pronounced /ka/) and how graphemes should be combined. For example, these rules dictate that for most words ending in *vowel-consonant-"e"* (e.g., *lake, mike*), the first vowel is long and the final "e" is silent.

The second route is known as the **direct route** (or lexical route) **to reading** because print is directly associated with meaning, without the use of a phonological intermediary. For a certain proportion of words in the English language, the direct route *must* be used because these words, known as **irregular words**, do not follow grapheme-to-phoneme correspondence rules and so are impossible to sound out correctly. If grapheme-to-phoneme correspondence rules are used to pronounce *colonel,* for instance, the result will be the incorrect "koe-loe-nell," rather than "kur-nel." When the direct route is used, an association is made between a particular visual form of a word (e.g., *colonel*) and its meaning (e.g., "a high-ranking military officer whose rank is just below that of a general").

Neuropsychological Evidence for These Two Routes

Evidence from patients with brain damage has suggested that these two routes can be used independent of each other. To assess the integrity of the phonological route, researchers examine how well individuals can read words they have never seen before. For such new words, no prior linkages from the visual form to meaning would exist, making direct access impossible. Reading nonwords requires the phonological route because nonwords have no meaning. (For instance, until now, you probably never saw the nonword *glimay,* but you can read it using your knowledge of grapheme-to-phoneme correspondence rules.) Likewise, investigators assess the integrity of the direct route by determining how well people can read words that do not follow the grapheme-to-phoneme correspondence rules (i.e., common irregular words), such as *colonel* and *yacht.*

One set of patients, who have a syndrome known as **surface dyslexia** (or *surface alexia*), have a disruption in the direct route but not in the phonological route. Their syndrome is so named because these patients cannot link the surface information—that is, the visual form of a word—directly to meaning. Such patients cannot read irregular words correctly, but rather sound them out (using the phonological route) and hence misread them. They often confuse *homophones,* which are words that sound the same but have different meanings, such as

IN FOCUS: Brain Organization in Bilinguals

Understanding the psychological and neural mechanisms of a single language may seem like a nearly insurmountable task, but now consider that most of the world's population is fluent in more than one language. The phenomenon of bilingualism raises intriguing questions about language. How are two languages organized within the same brain? Do they rely upon separate or different neural systems? How does the brain shift between two or more language systems?

Traditionally, cognitive neuroscientists have tried to understand the bilingual brain by examining the pattern of disability following brain damage from stroke or other sources. In most cases, aphasia in bilinguals follows left-hemisphere damage, just like aphasia in monolinguals. However, there is an extremely wide variation in how left-hemisphere damage affects functioning in the two languages and how the two languages are recovered with rehabilitative therapy (Lorenzen & Murray, 2008). Some patients show aphasia in both languages, some show deficits in the native language but not a second language, and yet others show more severe deficits in the second language. In addition, some bilingual aphasics exhibit problems in translation, either because they lose the ability to translate from one language to another or because they constantly engage in translation and are unable to inhibit it. Clearly, the evidence from aphasic patients does not support a simple understanding of neural organization for two languages.

A similarly complicated picture is derived from studies of cortical stimulation of bilingual patients undergoing neurosurgery. A study of a series of patients in the United States concluded that the brain regions specific to a second language tend to be located in parietal and posterior temporal regions. Moreover, posterior regions responsive to a second language represented a subset of those regions responsive in monolinguals (Lucas, McKhann, & Ojemann, 2004). However, investigations in Europe, where bilingualism and multilingualism are more common, revealed second-language-specific sites not only in parietal and temporal language areas, but in frontal regions as well (Giussani, Roux, Lubrano, Gaini, & Bello, 2007) (● Box Figure 9.1).

Several variables complicate the seemingly simple question of understanding whether two languages rely upon the same brain system in bilinguals. First, bilingual people differ in the age at which they acquired their first and second languages (often referred to as L1 and L2, respectively). Some people are exposed to two languages from birth, whereas others learn L1 from birth but acquire L2 at a later age. Later-acquired languages are often learned through a different method, such as explicit schooling, rather than being learned implicitly from immersion within a specific language environment. In addition, bilingual people differ in their level of proficiency in L2; some reach a level of fluency that equals their fluency in their native tongue, whereas others are considerably less fluent in L2 than in L1. Bilinguals also differ in the specific languages they know. Spanish and French are more similar to one another than Mandarin and Arabic are. So, the answer to whether two languages are organized together in the brain could depend on the similarity of the languages. Finally, we need to consider which aspect of language is being examined. As you know from this chapter, language is not a single function; rather, it consists of many components, such as phonology, syntax, and semantics. Whether two languages share common neural substrates may depend on whether we are examining brain regions involved in grammar or vocabulary, for example.

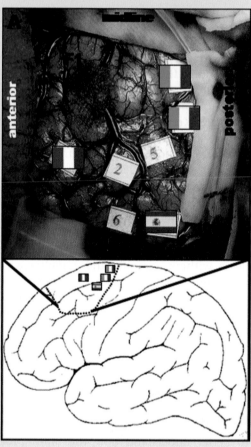

● **BOX FIGURE 9.1 Cortical stimulation evidence for the dissociation of language processing in bilinguals.** Shown here are areas that elicited a language-specific response in a native speaker of Italian who learned French and Spanish as an adult and used those languages daily at work. The region for each language is depicted by the flag of that country (red, white, green—Italy; red, white, blue—France; yellow, red, black—Spain). *Source:* Giussani C, Roux FE, Lubrano V, Gaini SM, Bello L (2007). Review of language organisation in bilingual patients: what can we learn from direct brain mapping? Acta neurochirurgica, 149, 1109–1116. Wien-New York: Springer, 2007.

beat and *beet*. Thus, when asked to define the word *pane*, these patients may say "to feel distress," or when asked to define *mown*, they may say "to complain." Their spelling errors also indicate their reliance on the phonological route because their spellings are often phonologically correct but graphemically incorrect (e.g., writing *whisk* as *wisque*, or *mayonnaise* as *mayenaze*) (e.g., Coltheart, 1982; Shallice, Warrington, & McCarthy, 1983). In contrast, they have no difficulty reading nonwords or regular words, because their phonological route is intact.

Brain imaging studies have attempted to address this basic question (whether two languages depend on the same brain systems), while taking into account some of the variables just discussed. Despite the complicating variables, a number of conclusions can be drawn. In general, brain activations in L1 and L2 seem to overlap to a large degree in most studies (Perani & Abutalebi, 2005), and this degree of overlap is higher when L2 is acquired early rather than late (Bloch et al., 2009). In other words, there is no evidence that radically different brain regions are used for L2 than for L1. However, the degree to which those regions are recruited during language processing may vary for monolinguals compared to bilinguals (Kovelman, Shalinksy, Berens, & Petitto, 2008), and it may vary depending on age of acquisition of the second language (Sakai et al., 2009). For example, one study found that Wernicke's area was similarly activated by both languages regardless of age of acquisition of L2, but activation in Broca's area overlapped only in those bilinguals who acquired both languages early in life. For those who acquired L2 later in life, distinct subregions of Broca's area were activated for L1 and L2 (● Box Figure 9.2) (Kim, Relkin, Lee, & Hirsch, 1997). Other research found that age of acquisition influences neural organization for grammatical aspects of language, but not semantic aspects; specifically, early L2 learners showed greater overlap in neural activity during grammatical tasks in the two languages, compared to late L2 learners (Wartenburger, Heekeren, Burchert, De Bleser, & Villringer, 2003). The same study found that proficiency in L2, rather than age of acquisition, affected brain activity for semantic tasks. (For other studies on the role of language proficiency, see also Chee, Hon, Lee, & Soon, 2001; Tatsuno & Sakai, 2005).

Learning a second language not only affects what areas of the brain activate during language tasks, but may also influence the actual anatomy of the brain. One study compared the density of gray matter and white matter in the cortex of bilingual and monolingual participants, and found greater gray-matter density among the bilinguals in left inferior parietal cortex (Mechelli et al., 2004). In a second sample, the researchers found that gray-matter density in this region was highly correlated with both proficiency and age of acquisition of L2; density was higher among those with greater proficiency and earlier age of acquisition. Such work is interesting in light of research discussed earlier in this chapter which suggests that the neuroanatomical substrate of the brain may influence how well one can acquire new language skills (e.g., Golestani et al., 2007). Because of the correlational nature of the studies, it is not clear whether structural changes in the brain occur as a result of bilingual language experience or whether individuals with particular preexisting brain anatomy are more likely to be able to acquire a second language.

A final issue involves how the bilingual brain manages to coordinate processing across two language systems. Some bilinguals may engage in "code-switching" several times within a single conversation, and others may switch between languages only when in different situations, such as at school versus at home. In both cases, though, the brain must be able to select a particular language and then overcome conflicts arising from the other language (e.g., Abutalebi, Brambati, Annoni, Moro, Cappa, & Perani, 2007). Such conflict seems to be inevitable, as fMRI and ERP studies indicate that when a word is read in one language it also becomes available in the other, suggesting simultaneous activation of both language systems (Martin, Dering, Thomas, & Thierry, 2009; van Heuven, Schriefers, Dijkstra, & Hagoort, 2008). Evidence suggests that brain regions involved in executive control (discussed in more detail in Chapter 12) are involved in the code-switching required to manage two languages within one brain (van Heuven, Schriefers, Dijkstra, & Hagoort, 2008). In fact, acquiring two languages may actually have the unanticipated side effect of increasing executive abilities (see Bialystok, Craik, Klein, & Viswanathan, 2004). There may be many good reasons to learn another language besides the opportunity to explore other cultures and travel abroad comfortably!

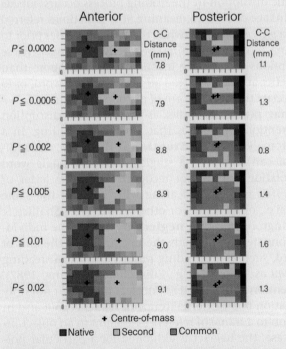

● BOX FIGURE 9.2   Regions activated by a native language as compared to one learned later in life. Although both languages lead to similar activation in Wernicke's area, there are distinct areas of activation in Broca's area. © 2011 Cengage Learning

Individuals with the contrasting syndrome, **phonological dyslexia** (or alexia), have a disrupted phonological route but an intact direct route. They have relatively little trouble reading previously learned words, because meaning can be extracted directly from the visual form regardless of whether the words are regular or irregular. Their disability becomes apparent only when they are asked to read nonwords or words with which they are unfamiliar. In these cases, the direct route does not suffice, because the person does not have an association between the visual form and meaning (e.g., Patterson, 1982). Without that association, the person must rely upon sounding out words through the phonological route, which is disrupted in phonological dyslexia.

There is a syndrome related to phonological alexia known as **deep dyslexia** (or deep alexia). Individuals with this disorder show many of the deficits exhibited by those with phonological alexia (such as the inability to read nonwords), but they also show additional difficulties. First, when reading, they often make **semantic paralexias**, which are reading errors in which a word is misread as a word with a related meaning. For example, *forest* may be read as "woods" and *tulip* as "crocus." Second, these individuals have more difficulty reading abstract words (e.g., *sympathy, faith*) than words that represent concrete entities in the physical world (e.g., *refrigerator, basket*). Third, these patients have difficulty reading small function words that serve as grammatical markers. Because of this constellation of symptoms and its similarity to the reading capabilities of the isolated right hemisphere of split-brain patients (Zaidel, 1990), the syndrome may represent reliance on the right hemisphere for reading (Coltheart, 2000). Supporting this claim, one study found that a patient with a developmental variant of the disorder exhibited right-hemisphere activation during reading (Pitchford, Funnell, De Haan, & Morgan, 2007).

The dissociations in patterns of deficits across disorders speaks to the fact that written language can either rely on phonology to access meaning or bypass phonology. Nevertheless, in everyday life both routes are probably used. In fact, researchers can predict overall reading ability by assessing the ability to read irregular words (tapping the direct route) and nonwords (tapping the phonological route), in young normal readers, in children with reading impairment (Coltheart et al., 2001; Castles, Bates, & Coltheart, 2006), and in individuals with acquired alexia (Rapczak, Henry, Teague, Carnahan, & Beeson, 2007).

Writing

Just as there are two routes to reading, studies of patients with unilateral brain damage suggest that two routes can transform thoughts into writing. One route goes from thought directly to writing, whereas the other uses phoneme-to-grapheme correspondence rules as an intermediary. In **phonological agraphia**, individuals can manually or orally spell regular and irregular words in dictation but perform poorly with nonwords (e.g., Shallice, 1981). In **lexical agraphia**, the opposite occurs: a reasonable spelling can be produced, both manually and orally, for virtually any regular word or nonword, but spelling of irregular words is poor (e.g., Beauvois & Derouesne, 1981). Just as with reading, writing seems to entail two routes, a direct one and a phonological one. Although you may have anticipated such a distinction on the basis of what we learned about

reading, this need not have been the case. Even though reading and writing are similar, the process of writing is not just reading in reverse order. For example, phoneme-to-grapheme rules are not the opposite of grapheme-to-phoneme rules. Consider the following case in point. Although /k/ is the most common sound for the grapheme "k," the most common grapheme for the sound /k/ is "c." Nevertheless, in both reading and writing, there appear to be both phonological and direct routes that associate the written form with meaning.

Other Components of Visual Language Processing

The syndromes we discussed so far are sometimes called *central* alexias or *central* agraphias because the problem arises in the linkage to meaning, which is considered to be "central." In contrast, the peripheral processes required for reading and writing, such as the ability to analyze letters visually or to produce the motor patterns for writing graphemes, are intact. Someone who is unable to recognize many types of visual forms would not be considered to have a specific problem in reading, yet if these difficulties were limited to processing visual forms of linguistic relevance, such as letters, we would be more inclined to categorize the problem as specific to reading. When a specific disruption in the reading process occurs outside the linkage of form to meaning, it is sometimes referred to as a *precentral* alexia (when the difficulty arises prior to gaining access to meaning) or a *peripheral* alexia. These disruptions include the inability to process more than one letter at a time, to read all the letters in a word, or to appreciate the overall form of a group of letters.

Some precentral dyslexias result from a disruption in attentional processes that affect only reading. In a syndrome known as **attentional dyslexia**, the individual can recognize a single letter or a single word in isolation but cannot recognize the same letter or word if it is presented along with items of the same kind (i.e., other letters or other words) (e.g., Shallice & Warrington, 1977). In **neglect dyslexia**, the individual consistently misreads the beginning or the end of a word, such as misreading *this* as "his" or misreading *discount* as "mount" (e.g., Ellis, Flude, & Young, 1987). As mentioned in Chapter 8, neglect may occur not only in relation to an external frame of reference, but also in relation to a frame of reference inherent to an object. In this case, the neglect is exhibited for a particular portion of a word regardless of its length or orientation (Caramazza & Hillis, 1990).

In another syndrome, known as **letter-by-letter reading** (sometimes referred to as *spelling dyslexia* or *pure alexia*), individual letters can be identified, but they cannot be integrated to form a word (e.g., Patterson & Kay, 1982; Warrington & Shallice, 1980). Individuals with this syndrome use oral spelling as a means to reading; they say each letter aloud and then use that information to deduce the word. Thus, a letter-by-letter reader sees the word *cat* and identifies it by saying "C, a, t, oh, that must be *cat*!"

In sum, studies of patients with neurological disorders demonstrate that difficulties in visual language can occur either in the linkage between the written form and meaning or in other processes specific to visual language skills (for a review of all of these acquired dyslexias/alexias, see Coslett, 2000).

■ Converging Evidence from Other Research Methods

In this section we discuss what converging methods can tell us about how the brain performs both the precentral (i.e., prior to meaning) and central (i.e., linking form to meaning) aspects of reading. We start by discussing how brain imaging studies, electrophysiologic studies, and behavioral studies of neurologically intact individuals provide insights into how the brain processes visual word forms.

Initial encoding of word forms is handled in different ways by the left and right hemispheres. The right-hemisphere system encodes words in their specific visual form, whereas the left-hemisphere system extracts an abstract representation of word form that is common across different instances of a word, such as variations in font or case. Evidence supporting this difference comes from priming studies of neurologically intact subjects. If a particular physical shape of a word (e.g., uppercase) is presented to the right hemisphere, subsequent processing of that word is facilitated to a greater degree when it appears in the same case (i.e., uppercase) than when it appears in a different case (i.e., lowercase). However, priming is equivalent in the left hemisphere regardless of the case of the prime (e.g., Burgund & Marsolek, 1997). This hemispheric difference is probably not specific to words, but represents hemispheric asymmetries in how visual information is processed in general.

The earliest stage of word processing that appears to be lateralized to the left hemisphere consists of mechanisms that are sensitive to the rules that govern how letters are combined, known as *orthography*. This process seems to occur around 200 milliseconds postpresentation, as at this point, ERPs in response to words also converge regardless of whether a word is presented in the RVF or the LVF, suggesting a common processing mechanism in the left hemisphere (Cohen et al., 2000). MEG recordings detect a similar process at about 150 milliseconds postpresentation and indicate that the source of this activity is inferior occipitotemporal regions of the left hemisphere (Tarkiainen, Helenius, Hansen, Cornelissen, & Salmelin, 1999). These findings are consistent with results from fMRI studies that indicate activity during reading near the occipital-temporal sulcus, bordering the fusiform gyrus (Brodmann area 37). This area has been dubbed the *visual word form area,* because it seems to activate regardless of the word's spatial position and is more active during tasks that require orthography (e.g., real words) as compared to those that do not (e.g., consonant strings) (Petersen, Fox, Snyder, & Raichle, 1990; Pugh et al., 1996; Cohen et al., 2000, 2002) (● Figure 9.13).

Although the visual word form area has been suggested to represent abstract orthography, Kronbichler et al. (2009) found that the visual word form area showed greater activation to case-deviant and letter-deviant forms as compared to familiar forms of the word (e.g., TaXi and Taksi vs. Taxi). Such a finding is consistent with some speculations that activity in this region may not be specific to orthography. Rather, like other regions of the fusiform gyrus that become active with perceptual expertise in classifying objects such as birds and cars (see Chapter 7), it becomes tuned to the recurring properties of a writing system of words (McCandliss, Cohen, & Dehaene, 2003). As such, it is important for reading because it allows the legal and common combinations of letters within a language to be easily identified.

Brain imaging studies of neurologically intact people have attempted to provide more information about the areas involved in the direct and phonological routes than can be gleaned from the relatively rare case studies of phonological or surface alexia. (Some neuroimaging studies of word reading have also been performed on these rare patients; see Price et al., 2003). To investigate the phonological route, researchers examine which brain regions are more active when the person has to read pseudowords, which critically rely on a translation of orthography to phonology, as compared to regular or irregular words. Alternatively, researchers may compare activity for word naming to picture naming, because naming either a picture or a word requires a linkage of phonology and semantics, but only in word naming will there also be a translation of orthography to phonology. To investigate the direct route, researchers examine which brain regions are more active when one

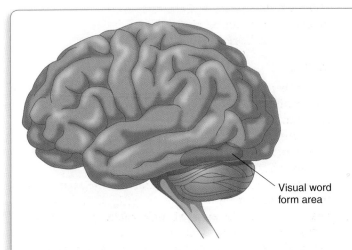

Visual word form area

● **FIGURE 9.13   The location of the visual word form area in the ventral visual-processing stream.** This area is thought to be responsible for identifying the invariant nature of written words regardless of their size, font, or position.
© 2011 Cengage Learning

has to read irregular words compared to regular words, because irregular words can only be recognized via the direct route. Alternatively, researchers attempt to find regions that are more active in response to real words, which can utilize a direct semantic route, as compared to nonwords, which cannot.

A meta-analysis across a large number of studies suggests that at least some brain regions are more involved in the phonological route than the direct route, and vice versa (Jobard, Crivello, & Tzourio-Mazoyer, 2003). Phonological analysis of words appears to activate three major regions. First is the superior and middle temporal gyrus, which is likely to be involved in accessing sounds related to letters. Second is supramarginal gyrus, in the inferior parietal lobe, which is likely to play a major role in symbol-to-sound transformation as is required in grapheme-to-phoneme conversions. Third is Broca's area (BA 44), which is likely to play a role in linking phonology to speech.

In contrast, the direct route appears to activate somewhat different regions. First it activates a ventral region of the inferior temporal gyrus. This region appears to sustain semantic processing of words and objects. The second area in the posterior portion of the middle temporal gyrus accords well with Wernicke's area, which we know is important for processing semantics. Finally, there is activity in area 45, which we discussed earlier is also involved in semantic processing (● Figure 9.14).

Even though these routes can be differentiated, are they truly separable systems in neurologically intact readers? One alternative suggested by computational models of word reading is that there are not two discrete and separate routes from orthography to meaning, but

just one system (e.g., Seidenberg & McClelland, 1989). In these models, pseudowords can be considered to be read "by analogy" to real words, and therefore do not activate a separate phoneme-to-grapheme route. Portions of words are linked to pronunciation units, and their degree of association is coded by the connection weights, which are modified with learning (e.g., Plaut, 2003). Damage to these computational models can, in fact, mimic some aspects of reading impairments resulting from brain damage (Patterson, Seidenberg, & McClelland, 1989).

This model provides an alternative way of thinking about language processing in the brain. Rather than having two discrete brain systems—the phonological route and the direct route—there would be one system with the connection weights between the nodes of the system varying depending on the type of reading demand. In fact, the neuroimaging data do make clear that although there may be some differences between patterns of activation observed when a phonological translation is required or when there is a more direct route to meaning, there is also a high degree of overlap (e.g., Rumsey, Horwitz, Donohue, Nace, Maisog, & Andreason, 1997).

Regardless of whether reading is controlled by one or two systems, it is very clear that the way in which reading is accomplished (the "how") varies depending on the task demands and the nature of the language. For example, during the reading of pseudowords (which would be more likely to require the phonological route), activity in the angular gyrus is most highly correlated with activity in other areas that are involved in phonological processing, such as superior temporal regions (BA 22) and Broca's area. In contrast, during the reading of real words, activity in the angular gyrus is more highly correlated

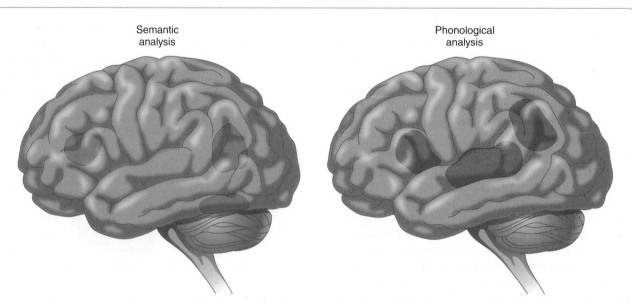

● **FIGURE 9.14   The brain regions involved in the direct and indirect routes to meaning.**
(Left) The regions involved in the direct route, in which print is translated directly to meaning, bypassing phonology. (Right) The regions involved in the indirect route, in which phonology is linked to meaning.
Source: Cohen, L. et al. 2002; Language-specific tuning of visual cortex? Functional properties of the Visual Word Form Area, Brain,125, Figure 2, pg. 1058.

with activity in regions in occipital and ventral temporal cortex, which are more often associated with the direct route (Rumsey et al., 1997). Similarly, statistical models of connectivity between brain regions suggests that input from posterior temporal regions to posterior frontal regions is greater during the reading of pseudowords than regular or irregular words, whereas input from anterior temporal regions to anterior frontal regions is greater during the reading of irregular words than pseudowords or regular words (Mechelli et al., 2005). These findings suggest that it may be the relative level of activity across each of a set of language-related brain regions, as well as their relative connectivity with other portions of the language network, that distinguishes the direct route from the phonological route to reading.

The relative reliance on each route may also depend on the nature of the language. For example, Italian orthography is referred to as consistent because there are reliable rules for the conversion of graphemes to phonemes that yield correct pronunciation of the word. Orthography in English, in contrast, is much less consistent. When reading real words, Italian people showed more activation in left superior temporal regions than English readers, consistent with a reliance on phonological processing when decoding written language. In contrast, when reading nonwords, English readers exhibited more activation in left inferior posterior temporal regions and anterior portions of the left inferior frontal gyrus compared to Italians (Paulesu et al., 2000). Because these regions of the brain are typically associated with the direct route, these results suggest that English readers, in part, may indeed read nonwords by using a strategy of reading them "by analogy" to real words.

How are we to understand the pattern of results across all of these studies of reading? As we have discussed, the set of regions involved in language is quite diverse and depends on what one is reading and the nature of the specific language (e.g., Italian vs. English). This diverse pattern probably reflects the fact that there has been little or no evolutionary pressure to sculpt brain organization for reading. Rather, during reading the brain appears to cobble together processing modules that are important for other cognitive domains. For example, the process of identifying the form of words appears to rely on neural machinery that is important for object recognition, and the phonological analysis of items appears to rely, in part, on frontal regions involved in motor production of those sounds.

Not only does reading rely on a diverse set of regions, but it also appears to rely on the coordination between regions. Consistent with many models of reading, MEG studies suggest that visual word form regions are first activated around 200 milliseconds after the presentation of a written word. Afterward, at about 400 milliseconds, activity is observed over both posterior regions (temporal, parietal) and frontal regions, including regions that support phonological processing as well as those that support semantic processing (Mainy et al., 2008). (For a detailed review of the ERP markers that may index the early stages of processing of each of these routes, see Dien, 2009). Moreover, MEG studies find that there is coupling in time of activity across these temporal and frontal regions (Salmelin & Kujala, 2006). These findings highlight the fact that reading relies not only on particular brain areas, but also on the coordination between them. As discussed earlier with regard to auditory language, coordination of these processes occurs via white-matter tracts. The importance of these tracts for the integrity of the reading process is a recent focus of investigation (Ben-Shachar, Dougherty, & Wandell, 2007). We return to this idea in Chapter 15, in which we discuss developmental dyslexia, a disorder in which children have difficulty learning to acquire the skill of reading.

All the evidence we have discussed so far has come from studies involving speakers and readers of Indo-European languages. We now turn our attention to other linguistic systems to provide more insight into the cognitive neuroscience of language.

Processing of Non-Indo-European Languages and Other Symbolic Systems

Many languages are used around the world, and some of these languages do not rely on the kind of phonological system that is used in English. By investigating the organization of the brain for other types of languages, we can determine the degree to which certain aspects of brain organization for language are universal.

■ Kana and Kanji

Because not all writing systems in the world use a phonetic alphabet based on phoneme-to-grapheme correspondences, as English does, cognitive neuroscientists can look to other language systems to investigate the distinction between phonological and direct routes to meaning. Japanese provides one such opportunity. It consists of two writing systems: one known as *kana*, which is syllabic and sound-based, and another, known as *kanji*, which is logographic and derived from Chinese (Paradis, Hagiwara, & Hildebrandt, 1985).

In a syllabic writing system such as kana, each symbol is linked to a whole syllable rather than to an individual phoneme. For example, a syllabically based language might have a symbol for the sound "tor," which would appear as the first of three symbols in a three-syllable word such as *torrential*, and the second of two symbols in the two-syllable word *motor*. Because syllabic systems are sound based, these words can be read using a phonological route. In contrast, in a logographic writing system, such as kanji, each symbol stands for a concept, and the visual form of the word has no systematic relationship to how the word is pronounced. Typically, thousands of basic logographs are used in such languages; the reader

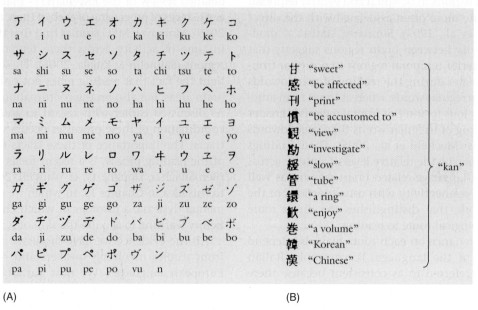

● **FIGURE 9.15   Examples of kana and kanji.** (A) Almost all of the 77 symbols in kana represent a consonant-vowel combination. (B) In kanji, the symbol has little relation to how the word is pronounced. Pictured here are various symbols, all of which are pronounced "kan" but each of which has a different meaning. *Source:* from Salmelin R, Kujala J (2006). Neural representation of language: activation versus long-range connectivity. Trends in cognitive sciences, 10, Figure 1c, pg. 520.

must be able to associate each different symbol with a different word. Logographic systems require a direct route because little or no information in the symbol provides hints as to its pronunciation. Some examples of kana and kanji characters are presented in ● Figure 9.15.

After brain damage, the ability to read words in kana can dissociate from the ability to read words in kanji, implying a distinction between direct and phonological routes to meaning. Sometimes individuals who lose the ability to read kanji retain the ability to read kana, whereas other individuals who retain the ability to read kanji lose the ability to read kana (Sasanuma, 1980). Furthermore, both case studies of patients with lesions (e.g., Kawamura, Hirayama, Hasegawa, Takahashi, & Yamaura, 1987; Kawahata, Nagata, & Shishido, 1988) and neuroimaging studies suggest that kana is primarily dependent on more dorsal regions of the left hemisphere, including the angular gyrus and temporoparietal junction, whereas the reading of kanji appears to rely more on inferior posterior temporal regions bordering on the occipital lobe (e.g., Sakurai, Momose, Iwata, Sudo, Ohtomo, & Kanazawa, 2000), consistent with reliance on the phonological route and the direct route, respectively. Although both scripts activate the visual word form area of the left hemisphere (Bolger, Perfetti, & Schneider, 2005), other evidence suggests that because the nature of the scripts differs, they are also processed somewhat differently in ventral visual-processing regions. Using direct electrical stimulation of the brain in patients with epilepsy, researchers have found that stimulation in different portions of the ventral visual-processing stream interrupts the ability to

read kana compared to kanji (Usui et al., 2009). Despite these differences, neuroimaging studies suggest a substantial overlap of brain regions involved when reading either script (e.g., Ino, Nakai, Azuma, Kimura, & Fukuyama, 2009). These findings provide converging evidence from a language other than English that access to meaning through a sound-based reading system can be independent of access to meaning through a visually based system.

■ American Sign Language

Other evidence about neurological organization of the brain for language can be derived from examining "spoken" language systems that are not aurally based but are instead completely visual. American Sign Language (ASL), the language used by most deaf individuals in the United States, is one such language.

Basic Structure of ASL

To evaluate the evidence that ASL provides about the neural organization of language, we first need a brief introduction to the structure of this language. Each noun in ASL is represented by a particular hand shape that is made in a particular way at a particular location in space with regard to the body. Just as distinctive contrasts exist among phonemes (e.g., voicing), distinctive contrasts can be seen among signs in ASL. One distinctive feature that can be used to distinguish among different words is hand shape itself; another such feature is where that hand shape is made relative to the face. An example of three words in ASL that differ only in place of articulation is presented in ● Figure 9.16.

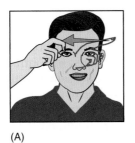
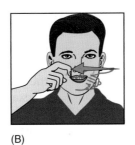

(A)   (B)   (C)

● **FIGURE 9.16   The distinctive contrast of place of articulation in American Sign Language.** The same hand shape has a different meaning depending on where the shape is produced. (A) If produced at eye level, this sign means "summer." (B) If produced at nose level, it means "ugly." (C) If produced at the chin, it means "dry." © 2011 Cengage Learning

Syntactic structure in ASL differs from that of spoken language. In ASL certain aspects of syntax are communicated through the position of the hands in space rather than through word order (e.g., SVO vs. OVS) or by the type of hand movement rather than by word endings (e.g., -*ly*). When a sentence is produced in ASL, a noun is placed within a frame, or theater of space, that is directly in front of the speaker's body. A speaker of ASL will make a hand shape for a noun and point to a particular location within this theater. Each noun in the sentence is given a different location in this theater. A sign designating a verb (e.g., "bit") is made from the location of noun acting as the subject (e.g., "dog") to the location of the noun acting as the object (e.g., cat). Thus, the syntactic distinction between subject and object is made spatially, by the direction of hand movement, as shown in ● Figure 9.17.

The type of hand movement also provides syntactic information, such as inflections of a verb, which in English are indicated by different word endings (e.g., -*ed*, -*ing*). For example, if a person wants to say that something occurred repeatedly, the hand movement is different than if the event happened only once, just as in English an ongoing action is indicated by an -*ing* ending. Examples of some of these distinctions are provided in ● Figure 9.18.

Dog index$_a$ Cat index$_b$ $_a$Bite$_b$

(A)

Dog index$_a$ Cat index$_b$ $_b$Bite$_a$

(B)

● **FIGURE 9.17   Spatial frame of reference in American Sign Language to make a syntactic distinction between subject and object.** (A) Here the individual is signing the sentence "The dog bit the cat." First, the speaker makes the sign for the word "dog" and notes a particular spatial location for this noun (left frame). Then he makes the sign for "cat" and notes a different spatial location to denote this noun (middle frame). He next makes the sign for "bit," moving his hand from the "dog" position to the "cat" position (right frame). (B) In this case, the individual is signing the sentence "The cat bit the dog." The procedure of signing this sentence is identical to that for the other sentence, except that the motion is made from the spatial position denoting "cat" to the one denoting "dog." © 2011 Cengage Learning

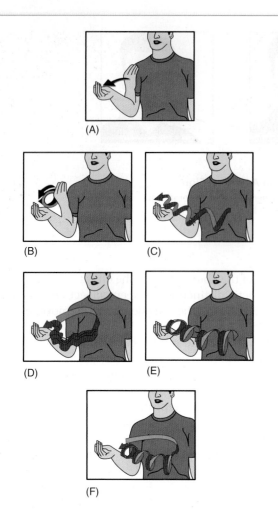

● **FIGURE 9.18   Examples of how variations in hand movement denote verb inflection in American Sign Language.** (A) The basic sign and hand movement for "give." (B–F) Variations indicating the duration of the action and to whom it is directed. The various signs mean (B) "give continuously"; (C) "give to each"; (D) "give to each, that action recurring with time"; (E) "give continuously to each in turn"; and (F) "give continuously to each in turn, that action recurring with time." © 2011 Cengage Learning

Brain Organization for ASL

Now that we know the basics about the structure of ASL, we can discuss the insights it provides into the brain's neural organization for language. First, even though ASL is a visual language in which spatial processing plays a large role in syntax, it appears to be dependent on the left hemisphere. The comprehension of signs is more disrupted by damage to the left hemisphere, especially left temporal regions, than by damage to the right hemisphere (Hickok, Love-Geffen, & Klima, 2002).

Second, case studies of native speakers of ASL who have become aphasic reveal that, as in spoken language, there is a distinction between anterior and posterior language systems (Poizner, Klima, & Bellugi, 1987). As seen with standard English, damage to either of these two systems has different effects on comprehension versus production, and syntax versus semantics. Those with

anterior damage exhibit a paucity of signs and a lack of fluency. Their production of ASL is agrammatic, with disruptions of hand movements that serve as syntactic markers and loss of the elaboration of hand movements that act as inflections. In contrast to these difficulties, the signs produced are semantically correct. Following is an example of one native speaker of ASL, who sustained a large lesion to her left frontal lobe, attempting to relate a story from her childhood. Notice that she had little difficulty comprehending the examiner's questions.

EXAMINER: What else happened?

GAIL D.: car . . . drive . . . brother . . . drive . . . I . . . S-T-A-D [attempts to gesture "stand up"]

EXAMINER: You stood up?

GAIL D.: Yes . . . I . . . drive . . . [attempts to gesture "wave good-bye"]

EXAMINER: Wave goodbye?

GAIL D.: Yes. . . brother . . . drive . . . dunno . . . [attempts to gesture "wave good-bye"]

EXAMINER: Your brother was driving?

GAIL D.: yes . . . back . . . drive . . . brother . . . man . . . mama . . . stay . . . brother . . . drive (Poizner, Klima, & Bellugi, 1987, p. 120).

Converging evidence for the role of Broca's area in speech production in ASL is provided by a case study of a deaf signer who produced errors in sign production when Broca's area was cortically stimulated (Corina, McBurney, Dodrill, Hinshaw, Brinkley, & Ojemann, 1999).

Another signer whose damage included anterior regions but also extended to posterior regions exhibited a linguistic profile that was more like that of a person with Wernicke's aphasia. His signing in ASL, as well as his writing, was fluent but did not have much meaning. Following is a translation of a sample of his signing in which he described the layout of his apartment, which had a glass-enclosed patio off the living room:

And there's one (way down at the end) [unintelligible]. The man walked over to see the (disconnected), an extension of the (earth) room. It's there for the man (can live) a roof and light with shades to (keep pulling down). And there's a glass wall with four different. . . . He hammered. The man (makes hands), makes mobiles, many on the wall. A wonderful (always brillianting) man (Poizner, Klima, & Bellugi, 1987, p. 98).

Evidence from ERPs also suggests a distinction between semantic and syntactic processing in ASL. When native deaf speakers are presented with signed sentences containing a syntactic error, a late positivity (i.e., P_{600}) is observed. When presented with sentences containing a semantic error, an N_{400} is elicited, similar to that observed for spoken languages (Capek et al., 2009).

Third, numerous neuroimaging studies demonstrate that organization of regions within the left hemisphere for language processing is highly similar for ASL and spoken language. For example, the same set of regions of the left hemisphere are activated in tasks such as the naming of single words in ASL (e.g., Emmorey et al., 2003; Horwitz et al., 2003; Kassubek, Hickok, & Erhard, 2004) or the production of narratives in ASL (Braun, Guillemin, Hosey, & Varga, 2001) as is observed when these tasks are performed for spoken language.

Nevertheless, not everything about the neural underpinnings of spoken language and sign language is identical. For example, when asked to name concrete objects, signers activate two regions of the left parietal role to a greater degree than hearing speakers. One of these is located in the supramarginal gyrus and may reflect phonological aspects of processing in ASL, such as the selection of distinctive features (e.g., hand configuration, place of articulation). The other is within the left superior parietal lobe and may reflect proprioceptive monitoring of the motoric output that is being produced (Emmorey, Mehta, & Grabowski, 2007). Moreover, there tends to be greater right-hemisphere activation in signers than in hearing individuals who utilize a spoken language. Because individuals who sign are usually deaf, it is impossible to know whether this activation results from deafness or from use of a sign language. To disentangle these two possibilities, researchers compared patterns of brain activation in deaf individuals who are native signers of ASL with patterns in hearing individuals who are bilingual from birth in spoken English and ASL (these individuals are typically born to deaf parents). This investigation found that native speakers, both hearing and deaf, not only activate classic language areas of the left hemisphere when processing language materials, but also activate homologous regions of the right hemisphere (Neville et al., 1998). One might think that this activation merely reflects the fact that this language is visual and spatial. However, activation of some regions of the right hemisphere, such as the angular gyrus, occurs only in native speakers, not in those who learn sign language after puberty (Newman, Bavelier, Corina, Jezzard, Neville, 2002). Accordingly, the activation in native speakers appears to indicate a recruitment of right-hemisphere regions for language processing. Supporting this idea are findings of changes in brain morphology—specifically, increased white matter in the insula of the right hemisphere—in both deaf and hearing native speakers of ASL as compared to individuals with no knowledge of ASL. This white matter may allow increased cross-modal sensory integration in signers (Allen, Emmorey, Bruss, & Damasio, 2008).

In addition, one can examine the pattern of activation across different sign languages. Just as English and Chinese are distinct languages, so are different sign languages. Knowing ASL will not help a person understand Chinese Sign Language. To look at the commonalities across sign languages, researchers have compared patterns of brain activation in speakers of ASL to patterns in speakers of Langue des Signes Québéçoise (LSQ), which is a sign language used in Quebec and other parts of French Canada (Petito, Zatorre, Gauna, Nikelski, Dostie, Evans, 2000). They found that the pattern of activation

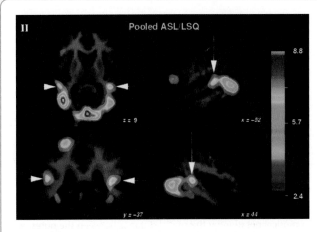

● **FIGURE 9.19 Activation of "auditory areas" in deaf individuals.** Shown by the arrows is activation in the superior temporal gyrus of speakers of American Sign Language (ASL) or the Sign Language of Quebec (SLQ) while they are reading words or legal nonwords in sign. Red shows the highest area of activity. *Source:* Petito et al., 2000. Speech-like cerebral activity in profoundly deaf people processing signed languages: Implications for the neural basis of human language. Proceedings of the National Academy of Sciences, USA, 97, p. 13964, fig. 1.1. Figure 1, pg. 13964. Copyright 2000 National Academy of Sciences, U.S.A.

does not vary significantly depending on the type of sign language used. More surprisingly, regions within the superior temporal gyrus that were considered dedicated to processing information in the auditory modality produced activation when deaf individuals processed sign nonwords! These results suggest that these regions are not specialized for auditory processing per se, but are dedicated to processing basic units of a complex pattern in rapid temporal sequence, an ability that could underlie either an auditory or a visual language (● Figure 9.19).

In sum, the evidence from speakers of sign language indicates that the left hemisphere plays a large role in language processing, regardless of the modality (speech, vision) in which that language is expressed. Moreover, the subcomponents of the network of regions involved in language processing are similar across spoken and signed languages. However, processing of sign language appears to recruit right-hemisphere regions to a greater degree than spoken language (see Campbell, MacSweeney, & Waters, 2007, for a recent review).

■ Music

Like language, music is an abstract symbolic system. Consequently, investigating how the brain processes music can provide insights into the basis of neural organization for language. If a region of the brain is active during language because it is specialized for processing an abstract representational system based on auditory information, such activation should be observed not only for language, but also for music. In contrast, if a brain region is truly specialized for language, then it should not be utilized when processing music. At present, the data suggest that there may be some truth in both viewpoints (for a review, see Peretz & Zatorre, 2005).

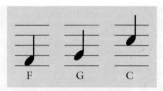

● FIGURE 9.20   Spatial aspects of musical notation. In musical notation, each note has a particular location on the musical staff (which comprises five lines); either between two lines (as in the case of the notes F and C) or intersecting a line (as in the case of the note G). The higher the location, the higher the pitch (e.g., F at 343 Hz is lower in pitch than G at 384 Hz, which in turn is lower than C at 512 Hz). The relationship between the pitch of two notes is depicted in musical notation by the spatial distance between the notes. Because G is only slightly higher in pitch than F, it is located just a little above F; because C is significantly higher in pitch than G, it is located substantially above G. © 2011 Cengage Learning

Case studies of patients show that *amusia*—a term used for acquired disorders of music perception, performance, and reading or writing following brain damage—can occur without the loss of language abilities. Conversely, aphasias can be exhibited without amusia (see Alossa & Castelli, 2009, for a recent discussion of amusia; and Stewart, von Kriegstein, Warren, & Griffiths, 2006, for a

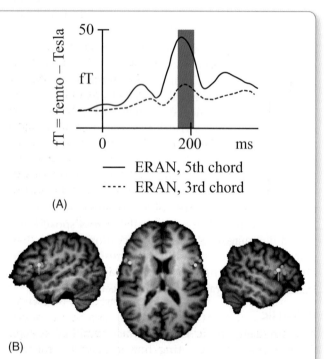

● FIGURE 9.21   Early right anterior negativity (ERAN) as recorded using MEG. (A) Notice that the negativity is greater to an anomalous chord, the Neapolitan fifth, as compared to a standard chord, the third. (B) The average source of the ERAN, shown in yellow. Note that it is located in Broca's area. The individual locations for each participant in the study are shown in blue. *Source:* Adapted by permission from Macmillan Publishers, LTD: Maess B, Koelsch S, Gunter TC, Friederici AD, Nat Neurosci. 2001 May;4(5):540-5. Figure 5, pg. 54.

longer discussion of disorders of musical listening). This double dissociation suggests that music and language are separable. In fact, melodic intonation therapy, which relies on using embedding speech within a melodic context, takes advantage of the fact that individuals with nonfluent aphasia are capable of singing words that they cannot speak (see Norton, Zipse, Marchina, & Schlaug, 2009, for a review).

Neuroimaging studies of brain activation during the performance of musical tasks suggest that for reading, at least, different brain regions are used for language than for music. An initial PET study examining activity when a person reads a musical score (compared to looking at dots) found activity centered in the left occipitoparietal junction, in a region dorsal to that activated during the reading of language (Sergent, Zuck, Terriah, & Macdonald, 1992). Subsequent studies have focused more narrowly on the specific processing of musical notation as examined to other potential systems for signifying musical notes. As shown in ● Figure 9.20, in musical notation, specific notes have particular spatial positions on the musical staff. The position of the note on the staff indicates how high or low its pitch is, and the distance between two notes indicates their difference in pitch. To determine which regions are specific to reading musical notation, the brain activity of trained musicians was examined when they had to play a note on a five-button keyboard based on musical notation of the note, as compared to a verbal label for the note or viewing the number of the finger that would be used to play that note. In this study, musical notation yielded greater activity (compared to the other two methods of identifying notes) in right occipitotemporal regions, which the authors suggested might be the right-hemisphere homologue of the visual word form area. They also observed more activity in the right supramarginal gyrus, which they suggested might be involved in translating a spatial notation to a motor pattern (Schön, Anton, Roth, & Besson, 2002). Thus, the spatial nature of musical notation appears to engage right-hemisphere mechanisms to a greater degree than written language (see Stewart, 2005, for a review).

In contrast to the separateness of brain regions required for reading language compared to reading music, there is some evidence that "syntax" processing in both language and music may rely on a similar neural substrate. As discussed earlier, Broca's area is important for detecting a violation of syntactic structure, such as when a word in a sentence makes it ungrammatical. Similarly, one can determine what brain region reacts when a chord is played out of sequence, as the expectation of typical sequences in music can be considered akin to the syntactic structure of language. As with language, MEG reveals a component elicited by a chord in an anomalous position. It occurs approximately 200 ms after presentation of the chord, with dipole modeling indicating a source located in Broca's area (● Figure 9.21; Maess, Koelsch, Gunter, & Friederici, 2001; see Fadiga, Craighero, & D'Ausilio, 2009, for a recent discussion).

Language and the Right Hemisphere

Since Broca, the role of the left hemisphere in language has been considered so central that this hemisphere is often referred to as the *verbal* hemisphere. However, more recently researchers have come to appreciate that the right hemisphere is not a silent partner in language processing. Thus, we next turn our attention to the ways in which the right hemisphere contributes to language processing (for recent reviews, see Lindell, 2006; Jung-Beeman, 2005).

■ Right-Hemisphere Contributions to Language Processing

As we discussed in this chapter and in Chapter 4, the right hemisphere of split-brain patients can comprehend written and auditory language, but its abilities are limited. It has a poor understanding of complicated syntax, cannot produce speech or use phoneme-to-grapheme correspondence rules, and has a vocabulary restricted mainly to concrete words as opposed to abstract words. Despite these limitations, the right hemisphere contributes to the extraction of meaning from linguistic material in two main ways. First, the right hemisphere is involved in processing certain aspects of **prosody**, which is the intonation pattern, or sound envelope, of an utterance. Second, the right hemisphere plays an important role in narrative and inference. **Narrative** refers to the ability to construct or understand a story line, whereas **inference** refers to the ability to "fill in the blanks" and make assumptions about material that is not explicitly stated (i.e., material that is implied). We now examine these two contributions of the right hemisphere in more detail. We then examine the role that the right hemisphere may play in the development of language abilities. We end our discussion by considering why the right hemisphere is not specialized for language processing.

Prosody

Prosody, the sound envelope around words, can be useful in providing information about interpretation of a statement. For example, in English, a declarative statement is usually accompanied by a decrease in the pitch of one's voice, whereas a question is usually accompanied by a rising intonation pattern. In some cases, intonation pattern may be the only cue allowing one to differentiate between two interpretations of an ambiguous sentence. Consider how prosody could differentiate the meaning of the four words "She did it again" as a response in the following dialogue:

LYNN: After all her injuries, you would think that Alice would be a bit more cautious. But yesterday, she followed me down a very steep ski run and took a bad tumble.

SARA: *She did it again.*

If said with a rising intonation, Sara is asking whether Alice hurt herself again. In contrast, if Sara said these same words emphatically with a falling pitch (e.g., "She did it again!"), the intonation would indicate that she is asserting what she already knows: Alice has managed to injure herself once more.

For the most part, the right hemisphere is superior to the left in its ability to interpret prosodic cues (e.g., whether a tone of voice is warm and friendly, sarcastic, condescending, or excited). Even though patients with severe aphasia (and hence left-hemisphere damage) can distinguish between questions and statements on the basis of prosodic cues (e.g., Heilman, Bowers, Speedie, & Coslett, 1984), evidence from patients with split-brain syndrome, individuals with epilepsy, individuals undergoing the Wada test, and dichotic listening studies suggests that the right hemisphere is extremely important in the perception of prosody (e.g., Benowitz, Bear, Rosenthal, Mesulam, Zaidel, & Sperry, 1983). A role for the right hemisphere in understanding prosody is not limited to situations in which prosody implies an emotional state (e.g., a brief high-frequency monotone might imply surprise) or a speaker's attitude (e.g., confidence, politeness) (Pell, 2006), but can also be found when prosodic information is emotionally neutral (i.e., rising and falling intonation contours) (e.g., Weintraub, Mesulam, & Kramer, 1981; Zatorre, Evans, Meyer, & Gjedde, 1992). We discuss the role of the right hemisphere in emotional prosody in greater detail in Chapter 13.

In contrast to the predominance of the right hemisphere in interpreting prosodic cues, both hemispheres seem to play a role in the production of prosody, but each makes a different contribution. Prosody consists of two classes of cues: those related to pitch or tone and those related to timing. Consistent with a right-hemisphere superiority for tonal processing, **aprosodic** speech, in which an individual speaks all at one pitch, is observed after damage to anterior regions of the right hemisphere (Behrens, 1988). After damage to the left hemisphere, speech is not so much aprosodic as **dysprosodic**, meaning that it has disordered intonation. The dysprosodia seems to result from the ill-timed prosodic cues consistent with a left-hemisphere superiority for temporal aspects of processing. For example, neurologically intact individuals tend to elongate the final word rather than the initial word of an utterance. In contrast, persons with Broca's aphasia do the opposite, elongating the first word rather than the last (e.g., Danly & Shapiro, 1982). Based on the results of patients with brain damage, the right hemisphere's organization for prosody appears to mimic that of the left hemisphere for language, with a distinction between anterior regions involved in production and posterior regions involved in perception (Ross & Monnot, 2008).

One more point is worth mentioning in relation to prosody: The production of prosody can be disrupted by damage to other regions of the brain besides the cerebral hemispheres. Prosody can be compromised by damage to the basal ganglia and cerebellum (e.g., Cancelliere & Kertesz, 1990; Kent & Rosenbek, 1982), but such damage simultaneously disrupts various other processes that depend on precise timing of motor control.

Inference and Narrative

Because the meaning of language is not always clear, readers and listeners use certain strategies to aid comprehension. For example, determining the theme of a story can help in interpreting ambiguous information, in making inferences about what has not been explicitly stated, and in anticipating what information will be presented next. To demonstrate this effect, read the following sentence: "With mosquitoes flying all about the room, she came across a small black bug that was being used to eavesdrop on her conversation." Because of the way the initial part of the sentence biased you, you probably did a double-take to reinterpret the meaning of *bug*. This sentence is an example of how we build upon previous information to make inferences about upcoming words. Individuals with right-hemisphere damage have difficulty with the types of tasks just discussed: following the thread of a story (e.g., Kaplan, Brownell, Jacobs, & Gardner, 1990), making inferences about what is being said (e.g., Beeman, 1993), and understanding nonliteral aspects of language such as metaphors (e.g., Brownell, 1988). These difficulties manifest themselves across spoken and written sentences, and in stories, dialogues, and paragraphs. We now examine these specific difficulties in more detail.

To comprehend language, we superimpose structure upon discourse. This structure allows us to organize information so that clauses within sentences, or episodes or events within stories, can be linked to one another, and so that material is presented in an orderly fashion, building upon that presented previously. Individuals with right-hemisphere damage have difficulty building such structures. They have difficulty ordering sentences so that they form a story (e.g., Delis, Wapner, Gardner, & Moses, 1983), ordering words so that they form a sentence (Cavalli, DeRenzi, Faglioni, & Vitale, 1981), and determining whether an utterance is relevant to a conversation (that is, determining whether it builds upon previously presented material) (e.g., Rehak, Kaplan, & Gardner, 1992). Individuals with right-hemisphere brain damage also have difficulty extracting the theme of a story (e.g., Moya, Benowitz, Levine, & Finklestein, 1986) or using information about a story's theme to help them in other tasks, such as arranging sentences into coherent paragraphs (e.g., Schneiderman, Murasugi, & Saddy, 1992). This role for the right hemisphere appears to occur even in visual languages, as case reports of deaf signers with right-hemisphere damage also indicate that they exhibit difficulties in discourse processing (Hickok, Wilson, Clark, Klima, Kritchevsky, & Bellugi, 1999).

Converging evidence for the role of the right hemisphere in these operations is provided by neuroimaging studies. Activation of the middle temporal gyrus of the right hemisphere is observed when people are told to pay attention to the general theme or moral of one of Aesop's fables, as compared to being asked specific information about an attribute of a fable character (Nichelli, Grafman, Pietrini, Clark, Lee, & Miletich, 1995). Likewise, this area is more activated when individuals read an untitled paragraph and have to deduce its main theme, compared to reading a paragraph when the title provides such information (St. George, Kutas, Martinez, & Sereno, 1999). Currently there exists a debate as to how much the left hemisphere also contributes to such processes. A recent meta-analysis of neuroimaging studies of text comprehension (not restricted to cases of inference) found consistent bilateral activation in anterior temporal regions (Ferstl, Neumann, Bogler, & von Cramon, 2008).

One interesting ramification of an inability to comprehend a coherent theme in stories is that it becomes difficult to comprehend jokes. Certain researchers have suggested that jokes are funny because most of a joke forms a coherent story, but then the punch line contains a surprise or twist that nevertheless coheres with the overall story. Given that individuals with right-hemisphere damage have difficulty following the thread of a story, it is not surprising that they have difficulty selecting the correct punch line for a joke. They are likely to pick a surprising ending but not one that is compatible with the previously presented material (e.g., Brownell, Michel, Powelson, & Gardner, 1983). However, neuroimaging studies reveal bilateral activation when comprehending either verbal jokes (Goel & Dolan, 2001) or jokes presented in nonverbal form, such as cartoons (e.g., Bartolo, Benuzzi, Nocetti, Baraldi, & Nichelli, 2006; Mobbs, Greicius, Abdel-Azim, Menon, & Reiss, 2003).

People with right-hemisphere brain damage also have difficulty with the nonliteral aspects of language such as metaphors and indirect requests. For example, individuals with such damage may be horrified to hear that someone was "crying her eyes out" because they interpret the sentence literally, and thus visualize a gruesome scene. When asked to point to a picture of someone who has a "heavy heart," an individual with right-hemisphere brain damage is likely to point to a picture of a large heart rather than to a picture of someone who looks sad (Winner & Gardner, 1977). When given a sentence such as "Can you open the door?," an individual with this type of brain damage might respond defensively, saying, "Of course I can open the door. Why do you ask? Do you think I'm such a weakling that I can't even open a door!?," when what was really meant was "Please open the door for me" (e.g., Foldi, 1987). Consistent with these findings, fMRI studies indicate that processing the metaphorical aspects of language leads to changes in activation in the right hemisphere, most notably the middle temporal gyrus and the frontal pole (e.g., Bottini et al., 1994).

In sum, the right hemisphere brings a richness to our understanding of language. Although damage to the right hemisphere will not so severely disrupt the ability to comprehend language and convey meaning, the aspects of language that we may find most appealing, such as a wonderful metaphor or an unexpected twist or turn of phrase, go unappreciated or are left unsaid.

■ Bihemispheric Models of Language Processing

How are we to integrate the findings that the left hemisphere plays a predominant role in language processing, but that the right hemisphere may contribute as well? Researchers have pondered this question and provided some frameworks for thinking about the relative processes that each hemisphere might bring to bear.

Some authorities have suggested that each hemisphere gains access to the meaning of words in a different manner than its partner. Experts have known for some time that when we hear or read a specific word, such as *nurse*, it primes our ability to process a network of words related in meaning, such as *doctor, hospital, needle,* and so forth. Divided visual field studies have demonstrated that the network of associated words that gets primed by a given word is more restricted in the left hemisphere than in the right. For example, whereas the right hemisphere retains activation of both meanings of an ambiguous word (e.g., *bank*) for about 1 second, the left hemisphere retains only the dominant meaning (e.g., "repository for money"), not the subordinate one (e.g., "side of a river") (e.g., Burgess & Simpson, 1988; Chiarello, 1991). Furthermore, weakly related words facilitate the processing of a word presented in the left visual field (LVF) but not a word presented in the right visual field (RVF) (e.g., Rodel, Cook, Regard, & Landis, 1992).

These results have been interpreted to suggest that there are parallel semantic processing systems in each hemisphere. Whereas fine semantic coding by the left hemisphere allows information occurring close together in a sentence to be integrated, the coarser and more diffuse semantic processing of the right hemisphere may play an important role in integrating information over larger linguistic expanses (Jung-Beeman, 2005). Supporting this idea, when an individual must generate a word to finish off a sentence that has many possible endings (e.g., "He went into the *house, garden, bank, office, store,* etc.), there is activation of the right temporal lobe relative to merely reading a sentence with one of those possible endings (Kircher, Brammer, Andreu, Steven, Williams, & McGuire, 2001).

A somewhat different but related conceptualization has been provided by ERP studies (e.g., Federmeier, 2007). This model suggests that when the left hemisphere accesses semantic meaning, it does so with a bias influenced by the context in which a word appears. Thus, the left hemisphere can rapidly generalize away from the specific input and biases the system toward an interpretation consistent with the larger context. In contrast, the right hemisphere processes words on a more stimulus-specific level, retaining the specific (rather than the generalized) meaning of a word. This ability is important when information must be reconsidered or reanalyzed, such as in garden-path sentences in which the meaning of the sentence initially appears to mean one thing but then actually means another. For example, when you read the sentence "The author wrote the novel was likely to be a best seller," you may have initially assumed that the author had written the novel. However, as you continue reading you must reinterpret the sentence to its correct meaning that the author had written *that* the novel was likely to be a best seller. The right hemisphere's retention of specific meaning may also hold for such reinterpretation (Federmeier, 2007). Regardless of which model turns out in the end to better describe the differences between the hemispheres, one point is clear: Like many other cognitive skills discussed in this book, the complete functioning of language skills relies on an entire brain, not just one hemisphere.

Summary

Neurological Bases for Auditory Language Processing

- A breakdown in language functioning after brain insult is known as aphasia.
- Anterior regions of the left hemisphere, more specifically Broca's area, are specialized for speech output.
- Posterior regions of the left hemisphere, most notably Wernicke's area, are specialized for speech comprehension.
- Phonology, which refers to the rules by which sounds in a language are formed and the rules by which they can be combined, is disrupted in both anterior and posterior aphasias.
- Syntax, which refers to the rules of grammar dictating the ways in which words are conjoined to form sentences, is disrupted in anterior aphasias.
- Semantics, which is the aspect of language that specifies meaning of words and sentences, is disrupted after damage to posterior regions of the left hemisphere.
- The Wada test, in which one hemisphere is anesthetized, provides evidence of left-hemisphere specialization for speech output in all but a fraction of right-handers.
- Brain imaging and electrophysiological studies also support the idea that anterior and posterior regions of the brain are specialized for syntax and semantics, respectively.

Neurological Bases for Visual Language Processing

- Alexia is the loss of reading ability as a result of a brain insult.
- Agraphia is the loss of the ability to write as a result of brain damage.
- The phonological route to meaning links the orthography (graphic form) of a word to its phonology (sound), which is then linked to meaning. This route is required for words one has never encountered and for nonwords (e.g., glimp) that could be real words but are not, and is lost in phonological alexia.
- The direct route links the orthography directly to the meaning. It is used to read irregular words, such as "colonel," that do not follow the typical grapheme-to-phoneme correspondence rules, and is lost in surface alexia.
- In phonological agraphia, individuals cannot spell using phoneme-to-grapheme correspondence rules.
- In lexical agraphia, individuals cannot spell using the direct route.
- The exact location of the left-hemisphere system that links word form directly to meaning is the subject of debate, but likely involves ventral regions of the temporal lobe as well as portions of the middle temporal gyrus.
- The location of the system that links phonology to meaning is thought to reside in regions of the supramarginal and angular gyri that border on the temporal lobe.

Processing of Non-Indo-European Languages and Other Symbolic Systems

- Kana is a syllable-based system in which each symbol is related to sound, much like the alphabetic system in English, and hence can rely on the phonological route.
- Kanji is a logographic system, in which the symbol for each word is unique, and relies on the direct route.
- Evidence from both brain-damaged patients and brain imaging suggests that these two systems are dissociable.
- In American Sign Language, information is conveyed visually by hand symbols rather than auditorally by sounds. Syntax is marked not only by word order, as in English, but also by the spatial location where a symbol is made and by the type of hand movement.
- ASL seems to rely on similar regions of the left hemisphere as spoken languages, although the right hemisphere may play a somewhat larger role.
- The reading of music and the reading of words rely on similar, but distinct, regions of the left hemisphere, suggesting that these activities are separable.

Language and the Right Hemisphere

- The perception of prosodic cues, which are the intonation contour and timing parameters of speech that help disambiguate the meaning of utterances, is performed mainly by the right hemisphere.
- The right hemisphere plays a major role in discourse by aiding a person in comprehending a story line, making inferences based on previously presented material, and extracting the main theme or moral of a story.
- By activating a more diffuse and remote set of semantic associations than the left hemisphere, the right hemisphere aids in the metaphorical and nonliteral use of language.

Key Terms

agrammatic aphasia 241
agraphia 249
alexia (acquired dyslexia) 249
aprosodic 261
attentional dyslexia 252
Broca's aphasia 232
conduction aphasia 237
crossed aphasia 233
deep dyslexia 252
direct route to reading 249
dysprosodic 261
echolalia 238
global aphasia 239
grapheme-to-phoneme
  correspondence rules 249

inference 261
irregular words 249
letter-by-letter reading 252
lexical agraphia 252
narrative 261
neglect dyslexia 252
neologisms 236
paraphasias 236
phonemic paraphasia 236
phonological agraphia 252
phonological dyslexia 251
phonological route to reading 249
phonology 240

place of articulation 241
prosody 261
semantic paralexias 252
semantic paraphasia 236
semantics 240
surface dyslexia 249
syntax 240
telegraphic speech 234
transcortical motor aphasia 238
transcortical sensory aphasia 238
voicing 241
Wernicke's aphasia 236

Book Companion Site at www.cengage.com/psychology/Banich
This website provides instructors and students with a wealth of free information and resources, including tutorial quizzes, flashcards, and the glossary.

Memory

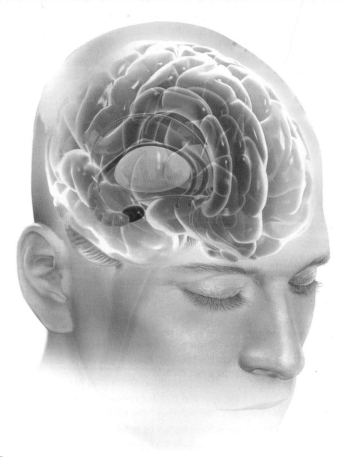

IN RESPONSE TO A SEIZURE DISORDER that could not be controlled effectively by anticonvulsant medications, in 1953 a young man underwent an experimental surgical procedure that removed medial temporal lobe structures that we now know are critical to memory. Although the surgery was successful in bringing the seizure disorder under control, it resulted in a profound deficit in memory. After the surgery, this man was unable to remember the events of his life or the people he met after the surgery, such as his physicians and other caregivers, or to learn new facts about the changing world around him. After the surgery he could not tell his age, the current date, or any aspect of his recent history (such as where he was living and how long he had lived there). In fact, on occasion in his later years, he misidentified a current picture of himself as a picture of his father. His memory was no better for people in the public eye or the public events in which they figured. Such deficits persisted until his death in 2008 at the age of 82.

Nevertheless, throughout his life, he still expressed a wide range of memory abilities. He could reason and solve problems, recognize objects, and perform voluntary and reflexive motor acts appropriate to all manner of objects and situations. These abilities, along with his full range of linguistic skills, demonstrated that he could access the considerable store of knowledge that he had acquired early in life before the surgery. His ability to remember the remote past prior to his surgery seemed largely intact, as was his ability to hold information in memory temporarily while working with it, as long as he was not interrupted.

Because of the mixture of memory loss and memory retention, his life had some surreal qualities. For example, he enjoyed solving crossword puzzles and could happily do the same crossword puzzle over and over again, because he didn't notice the repetition. Although he also enjoyed watching television shows, they were difficult for him to understand because the commercials interspersed throughout a show caused him to forget the story line. He could also hold a perfectly reasonable conversation, except that his conversation was devoid of current content; he could not tell you about recent weather conditions or the books that he had most recently read. If you avoided such topics in your conversation with him, you would be hard-pressed to notice any memory deficit at all. However, if you left for a short while, even for only a few minutes, upon returning you would find that he could not remember what you had been conversing about minutes earlier, and, most likely, he could not remember having ever met you!

What was nearly as striking as his near-total inability to recollect his experiences was his intact ability to be affected by his experiences. Remarkably, he was able to acquire and express a variety of new skills, such as learning how to read words backwards. He did so despite being unable to remember that he had ever been asked to read such words. Moreover, like neurologically normal individuals, his improvement in performance with practice was larger for the items he had previously seen than for new items presented for the first time. But the improved performance with repeated items occurred despite the fact that he was unable to judge which items were the repeated ones and which ones were new.

THE PATIENT in the opening vignette of this chapter is known in the scientific literature by his initials, H.M. After realizing the unintended effects of the operation, his surgeon, Dr. Henry Scoville, contacted Brenda Milner and her colleagues at McGill University in Montreal to unravel the mystery of his memory loss. Professor Milner discovered the divide in H.M.'s memory that we just discussed: the paradox that while certain aspects of memory were lost after removal of his medial temporal lobe, others were retained. This work was critical in demonstrating the existence of at least two separable systems that support our ability to remember. As noted by Eric Kandel, who won the Nobel Prize in Physiology and Medicine in 2000 for his work on the molecular mechanisms involved in memory formation, "[t]he study of H.M. by Brenda Milner stands as one of the great milestones in the history of modern neuroscience. It opened the way for the study of the two memory systems in the brain, and provided the bases for everything that came later." (Carey, 2008). (For a short review of how much we have learned about memory systems in the brain in the past 40 years, see Squire, 2009b).

H.M.'s contribution to our understanding of memory did not stop there (Squire, 2009a). Over the next five decades, H.M. graciously participated in scientific studies conducted by Prof. Milner, and also by her former student Prof. Suzanne Corkin at MIT. These studies exhaustively documented his impairments and the abilities that he retained (e.g., Scoville & Milner, 1957; Corkin, 1984; Milner, Corkin, & Teuber, 1968; see Corkin, 2002 for a timeline of the major scientific landmarks in the study of H.M.). H.M.'s memory loss is known as **amnesia**, which in his case was remarkably profound and pervasive (● Figure 10.1). Amnesia includes loss of memory for materials such as words, text, names, faces, spatial layout, routes, geometric shapes, nonsense patterns, tunes, tones, public events, and personal episodes. H.M.'s amnesia apparently affected all aspects of his life and caused him to forget the events of his daily life "as quickly as they occur[ed]" (Scoville & Milner, 1957, p. 15). It is an irony that although H.M. is undoubtedly the most famous and intensively studied patient in the annals of neurology, neuropsychology, and cognitive neuroscience, his memory impairment was so severe that he had no idea of his fame.

The disorder of memory seen in H.M. and in numerous other cases of amnesia, studied by various investigators in the field, tells us much about what memory is and how the brain manages to record our past experiences. Because memory can be compromised in apparent isolation from other cognitive abilities, amnesia demonstrates a basic functional independence of memory from other cognitive capacities. Because amnesia can be so selective, affecting only certain memory capacities while leaving other aspects of memory fully intact, it indicates that there are different kinds of memory. Like other functions we have discussed in this book, memory must be thought of as a collection of abilities supported by a set of brain and cognitive systems that operate cooperatively, each system making different functional contributions. Normal memory performance involves various systems, which ordinarily operate together so seamlessly that it is difficult to gain any intuitive appreciation of the separateness of the contributions made by the various systems. Only through careful and converging neuropsychological, neuroimaging, psychophysiological, and neurophysiological studies can we infer the distinct roles and contributions of the various brain and cognitive systems that collectively mediate memory. This chapter lays out our current understanding of the different systems and their functional roles.

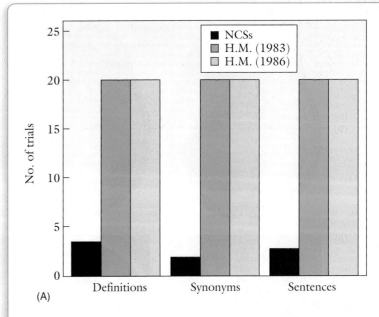

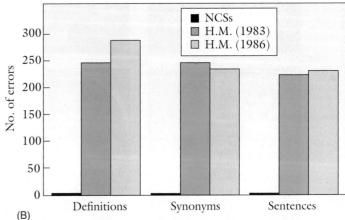

● **FIGURE 10.1 Illustration of profound inability of H.M., a patient who underwent bilateral removal of the temporal lobe, to acquire new information.** In this study (Gabrieli, Cohen, & Corkin, 1988), H.M. and neurologically intact control subjects (NCSs) were taught the definitions of vocabulary words that they did not previously know. (A) This graph depicts the number of trials required to meet the learning criterion. Note that when tested in both 1983 and 1986, H.M. received the maximum number of trials, 20, whereas the NCSs could learn the definitions, synonyms, and appropriate sentence frames for words in fewer than 5 trials. (B) In learning to select either the appropriate definition, the appropriate synonym, or the correct sentence frame for these vocabulary words, the NCSs showed almost no errors, whereas H.M. made more than 200 errors in each case, never learning any of the words. © 2011 Cengage Learning

What Is Memory?

We begin our examination of memory by posing the most basic question right from the start: What *is* memory? Perhaps the best answer to this question is that memory is the group of mechanisms or processes by which experience shapes us, changing our brains and our behavior. Tennessee Williams said, "Life is all memory except for the present moment that flies by so quickly we can hardly catch it going by." For our purposes, memory is the ability to capture each successive "present moment" within the nervous system so that we are forever changed by it. How and where memory is captured within the nervous system is what we need to understand.

We can also ask, what is memory *for*? To this question there are many answers: Memory is for holding onto the details of everyday life; remembering to take our keys, coat, or lunch; recalling where we parked the car,

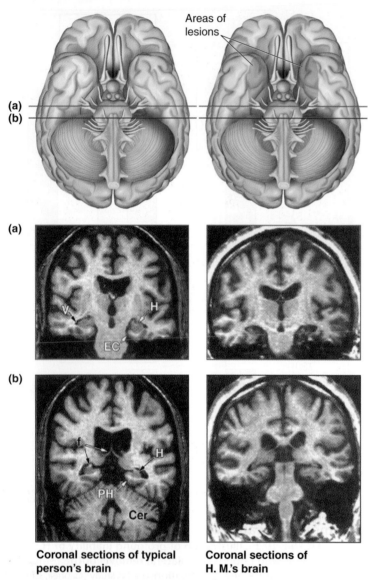

Coronal sections of typical person's brain

Coronal sections of H. M.'s brain

● **FIGURE 10.2   Brain structures removed during H.M.'s surgery.** To control life-threatening seizures, patient H.M underwent surgery that removed the hippocampus (H), entorhinal cortex (EC), parahippocampal gyrus (PH), and other portions of both medial temporal lobes. These MRI scans compare a typical control participant with patient H.M. Courtesy Dr. Suzanne Corkin, Massachusetts Institute of Technology. Permission conveyed through Copyright Clearance Center, Inc. *Source:* Suzanne Corkin, David G. Amaral, R. Gilberto González, Keith A. Johnson, and Bradley T. Hyman H. M.'s Medial Temporal Lobe Lesion: Findings from Magnetic Resonance Imaging J. Neurosci., May 1997; 17: 3964–3979.

interactions among them. Finally, memory is for capturing the regularities in the world—the correlations and patterns of co-occurrence (of the letter combinations we type, of sights and sounds of related objects, or of smells and tastes of common foods)—and adapting our brains and behavior in accordance. All of this, as we shall see later, occurs whether or not we are aware of those regularities and how we adapt to them.

However we look at it, memory encompasses a large collection of capabilities that share a common label. The brain, in accomplishing memory, must perform all these different capabilities. To do so requires a set of mechanisms supported by a set of brain systems. We turn now to identifying and characterizing those systems and the roles they play.

Amnesia: A Disorder of Long-Term Memory

Work on the cognitive neuroscience of memory has focused disproportionately on one particular form of memory disorder, namely amnesia. From the study of amnesia, scientists have learned about many fundamental aspects of how the brain supports memory processing. Because this work has been so influential, we begin our examination of memory in the brain by discussing amnesia. We will point out particular features of memory loss in amnesic syndromes and then consider how those pieces of data inform neural models of memory.

Although our discussion includes cases of amnesia resulting from varying etiologies, we will focus on the most famous case, that of H.M. Prior to the development of technology for CT or MRI scans of the brain, there was no way to clearly identify the structural damage to the brain in a given neuropsychological patient, so the fact that H.M.'s amnesia resulted from a surgical resection was crucial. It meant that researchers knew specifically which structures were lesioned. In addition, they knew exactly which aspects of memory were impaired by the lesion, because H.M. had been evaluated prior to the surgery that left him amnesic.

The case of H.M. was the first to indicate that amnesia results from extensive damage to the regions of the medial temporal lobe, including the hippocampus, dentate gyrus, subiculum, amygdala, and neighboring areas (the parahippocampal, entorhinal, and perirhinal cortices) (● Figure 10.2). Subsequent work with patients

left our backpack, or placed the groceries; remembering scheduled appointments, class assignments, or plans for the evening; and knowing the names, appearance, and defining characteristics of people we have met. But memory is also for holding information in mind for just a short time while we work on it, such as doing mental arithmetic or keeping the phone number of the pizza delivery place in mind while we place the call. Memory is also for remembering the events of our lives and the people who inhabit them, and for identifying, appreciating, and responding appropriately to various objects and situations and the

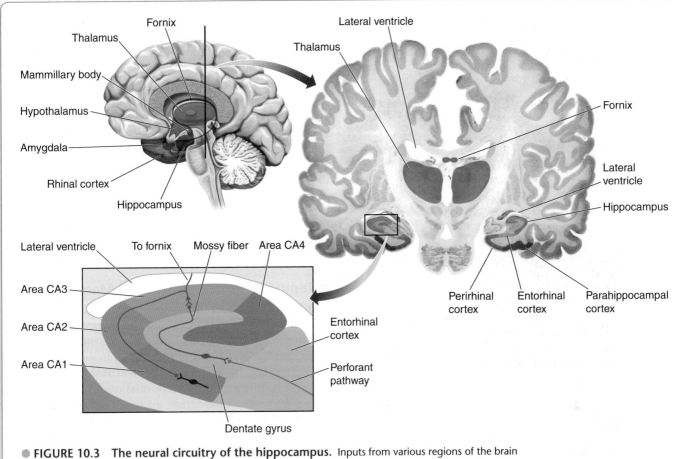

● **FIGURE 10.3   The neural circuitry of the hippocampus.** Inputs from various regions of the brain converge on the hippocampus via the perforant pathway from entorhinal cortex. Output to the brain from the hippocampus occurs via the fornix. © 2010 Cengage Learning

has confirmed that a critical structure involved in amnesia is the hippocampus, regardless of how that damage is sustained—whether by surgical resection, as with H.M., or any of a number of other etiologies, such as those involving loss of blood supply to the region, as in stroke or as a result of anoxia, or in certain disease processes that target this region, as in herpes simplex encephalitis. The hippocampus is aptly named from the Greek for "seahorse," because it is indeed shaped like one (● Figure 10.3). In addition, amnesia can also result from damage to the closely related **midline diencephalic region**, involving particularly the dorsomedial nucleus of the thalamus and the **mammillary bodies** of the hypothalamus. Damage to these regions can originate in a number of ways—for example, as occurs in Korsakoff's disease, following chronic alcohol abuse, or sometimes through an accident, as shown in ● Figure 10.4. Regardless of etiology, the fundamental nature of the deficit is an inability to form most new long-term memories.

■ Global Nature of the Deficit

One of the most fundamental aspects of amnesia is that it is global with regard to modality and material. For example, H.M.'s impairment was shown to affect memory of material presented in the visual, auditory,

somesthetic, and even olfactory modalities (see Corkin, 1984; Milner, Corkin, & Teuber, 1968). The deficit in amnesia also applies to many different kinds of material, affecting memory of both verbal and nonverbal material, spatial and nonspatial information, meaningful and nonsense stimuli, and so forth.

The modality- and material-generality of amnesia has been crucial in identifying the disorder as specifically one of *memory* functions rather than perceptual, linguistic, or other cognitive processing functions. Damage to the cortical brain systems critical for processing language, visual objects, or motor sequences can cause memory problems, but these are invariably modality- and/or material-specific. For example, in visual agnosia the patient fails to identify objects presented visually, but has no problem identifying the same objects by touch or sound (see Chapter 7). *Unilateral* damage to the **hippocampal system** can produce **material-specific memory disorders**. After left-hemisphere damage, memory is selectively impaired for verbal material, whereas after right-hemisphere damage, memory is impaired for nonverbal materials (e.g., Milner, 1971; see Chapter 4). When there is bilateral damage, as in the case of H.M., a general impairment across all types of materials occurs.

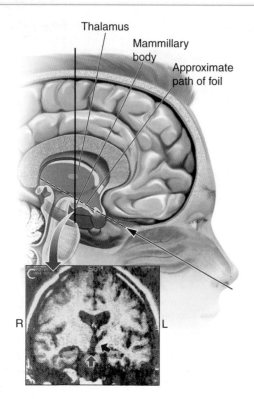

FIGURE 10.4   Damage to the midline diencephalic structures can also lead to amnesia. (Above) Shown here is the location of the mammillary body, one on each side of the brain's midline, relative to the thalamus. Damage to these regions occurs in Korsakoff's amnesia, but can also occur via accident. In the case of patient N.A., damage to these midline structures occurred via a fencing foil, the path of which is shown by the purple arrow. (Below) An MRI scan of N.A.'s brain. The red and blue arrows indicate areas damaged by the foil. The mammillary bodies are no longer visible, as they were obliterated by the accident. Courtesy L. R. Squire, University of California San Diego. © 2011 Cengage Learning

This modality- and material-general aspect of memory can be observed regardless of how memory is assessed. Consider a paradigm in which an amnesic is read a list of 15 words to remember (e.g., *motel, cathedral, broker, bowl, cyclone . . .* , etc.), and then is tested 30 minutes later. Memory deficits are observed regardless of whether the amnesic uses **free recall** (the individual is told, "Report all of the words on the study list"), **cued recall** (the individual is told, "Report all the words from the study list that were examples of buildings or that began with the letter 'b'"), or **recognition memory** (the individual is given 15 word pairs, each containing one item from the list and one novel item, and for each pair is asked, "Which of these two words ['cabin' or 'cathedral'] was on the study list?"). Any theory of memory must take into account the global nature of the deficit observed after damage to the hippocampus.

■ Temporal Profile of Affected Memories

A theory of memory must also account for the time span of memories that are affected by amnesia. Memory impairment can be divided into two distinct temporal phases: anterograde and retrograde amnesia. So far we have emphasized **anterograde amnesia**, which is the deficit in learning new information *after* the onset of amnesia. Yet, anterograde amnesia virtually always occurs in association with at least some retrograde amnesia. **Retrograde amnesia** is the impairment in memory for information that was acquired *prior* to the event that caused the amnesia—a deficit stretching back in time to some point before the onset of amnesia (● Figure 10.5; see Kapur, 1999, for a longer discussion). The temporal extent of retrograde amnesia varies greatly across patients, from a week to decades (e.g., Kapur & Brooks, 1999; Bayley, Hopkins, & Squire, 2006). This variability, as we will learn later in this chapter, has implications for models of memory.

Many instances of retrograde amnesia are **temporally limited**. For example, in *mild closed head injury* (associated with car accidents, falls, and sports-related activities), the retrograde amnesia extends back less than 60 minutes before the injury in about 95% of patients (Paniak, MacDonald, Toller-Lobe, Durand, & Nagy, 1998). Temporally limited retrograde amnesias are not always brief, however: they can extend to years, as in the case of the amnesia associated with bilateral electro-convulsive treatment (ECT) (for a review, see Fraser, O'Carroll, & Ebmeier, 2008). For example, when asked to remember information about television programs that had aired for just one season, patients who had received ECT were disproportionately impaired in recalling information about shows aired one to two years prior to the ECT treatment. They could not even remember the single most salient fact about such a show, including

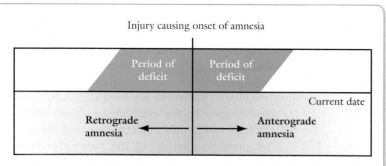

FIGURE 10.5   Timeline illustrating anterograde and retrograde components of amnesia. Any memory deficit that extends forward in time from the onset of amnesia and prevents the formation of new, enduring memories is known as *anterograde amnesia*. Any memory deficit that stretches backward in time from the onset of amnesia and prevents retrieval of information acquired prior to the onset of the amnesia is known as *retrograde amnesia*. © 2011 Cengage Learning

whether it was a sitcom or a cop show. However, they could remember much more, including even specific episodes, about shows that aired farther back in time (Squire & Cohen, 1979) (● Figure 10.6).

Temporally extensive retrograde amnesia that can span back decades is often seen in patients with progressive disorders like Korsakoff's, Alzheimer's, Parkinson's, or Huntington's disease (e.g., Reed & Squire, 1998; Kopelman, Stanhope, & Kingsley, 1999). For example, when asked to name the current U.S. president, these patients are likely to name someone whose presidency occurred during the patient's youth, such as Harry Truman or Dwight Eisenhower (whose terms ran from the mid-1940s through the late 1950s). Studies of individuals with localized damage suggest that these more extensive retrograde amnesias are associated with damage that extends beyond medial temporal regions into lateral regions (Bright, Buckman, Fradera, Yoshimasu, Colchester, & Kopelman, 2006).

Despite these deficits, as long as the damage is limited to the hippocampal system and does not involve extensive additional damage to neocortical brain regions, these individuals will have intact memory for the basic perceptual, motor, linguistic, and intellectual competencies they had before the onset of amnesia. They also retain information learned early in life about language, objects, and the world in general (Cipolotti & Bird, 2006). This dissociation—between the ability to retain such information and the inability to remember specific life events—plays an important role in theories of the neural underpinnings of memory, a point we will revisit later.

Having discussed the amount of time over which retrograde amnesias extend, we can ask whether the deficits are equal across that time period. Typically, there is greater compromise of more recent memories than more remote memories. This effect is often referred to as the **temporal gradient** of retrograde amnesia and is now known as **Ribot's Law**, after the 19th-century scientist, Theodule Ribot, who first noted it (Ribot, 1881/1882). The temporal gradient has been observed in patients in whom the retrograde amnesia extends back decades, such as patients with Korsakoff's disease and Alzheimer's disease (Kopelman, Stanhope, & Kingsley, 1999; Meeter, Eijsackers, & Mulder, 2006; Sadek et al., 2004). In one study, patients were asked to identify the faces of public figures who were famous across many decades (Albert, Butters, & Levin, 1979). Patients were more likely to correctly identify them in older photographs (such as Ronald Reagan as the 1930s- to 1950s-era actor) than in more contemporary photographs (Ronald Reagan as the 1970s- to 1980s-era American politician and president) (● Figure 10.7).

Not all forms of amnesia exhibit a temporal gradient, however. Instead, some are relatively uniform across time periods. Such "flat" gradients have been observed in patients with focal damage to midline diencephalic structures, and Huntington's disease (Kopelman, Stanhope, & Kingsley, 1999; Sadek et al., 2004) (see

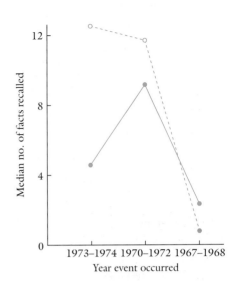

● **FIGURE 10.6 Evidence of temporally limited retrograde amnesia in patients who have undergone electroconvulsive treatment.** 20 individuals were asked to recall information about former television programs that aired for just one season. Shown here is a graph of the median number of facts recalled. Before ECT (dashed line), patients showed a normal forgetting curve; their best recall was for shows from the most recent time period, and their poorest recall was for shows from the most remote time period. After ECT (blue line), a selective impairment occurred in the recall of shows from the most recent time period. © 2011 Cengage Learning

Chapter 16), as well as in some etiologies of amnesia with hippocampal-system damage (e.g., Mayes et al., 1994; Noulhaine, Piolino, Hasboun, Clemenceau, Baulac, & Samson, 2007). Gradients of retrograde amnesia suggest that memory might undergo change during the time after learning. Thus, whether retrograde amnesia is temporally graded or "flat" affects how scientists conceptualize the role of the medial temporal lobe structures in memory, as we discuss in a later section of this chapter.

■ Spared Working Memory

Amnesic patients display a deficit of long-term memory, which is the ability to retain information for as long as a lifetime. In contrast, working memory is unaffected. *Working memory* is the ability to hold a limited amount of information online over the short term while it is being actively processed. A classic experiment illustrates this dissociation using a **digit span task**, in which H.M. had to report back a sequence of digits read one at a time by the experimenter (Drachman & Arbit, 1966). H.M.'s performance was within the normal range (7 +/− 2 items), indicating an intact working-memory span. However, once his working-memory span was exceeded, his

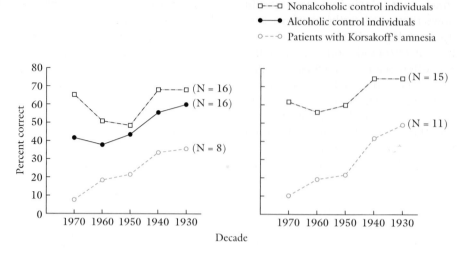

● **FIGURE 10.7** **Evidence of extensive retrograde amnesia in patients with Korsakoff's disease.** Alcoholic and nonalcoholic control individuals and patients with Korsakoff's disease were asked to identify photographs of public figures who became prominent during different decades from the 1930s through the 1970s. Across all decades, the performance of patients with Korsakoff's disease was impaired compared with that of the control individuals. (Left) Results of research by Cohen and Squire (1980). (Right) Results of research by Albert, Butters, and Levin (1979). © 2011 Cengage Learning

performance suffered. This deficit was demonstrated by an **extended digit span** task, in which the same digit string is presented on each trial but with an additional digit added to extend the span. For example, participants are repeatedly given a string of digits that surpasses their digit span by one digit (e.g., 2-7-9-1-3-4-8-6) until it can be correctly recalled. Then they are given multiple trials with the same initial string but with an additional digit at the end (e.g., 2-7-9-1-3-4-8-6-5) until it can be recalled, and so forth. Neurologically intact subjects can recall strings of at least 20 digits using this procedure, because they use long-term storage in addition to working memory to complete the task. H.M. could not recall even a single string that was one digit larger than his span, despite 25 repetitions of the same string. This suggests that his performance on the task was supported only by working memory, and that he was unable to use long-term memory to extend the list of digits beyond his working-memory span.

Because patients with amnesia have intact working memory, they perform normally when the delay between the exposure to information and the memory test is short, or when the amount of material to be remembered is small. Thus, they can comprehend episodes and events normally if those events unfold over a relatively short time, and they can engage in reasonable discourse if the conversation remains on topic. However, because their memory impairment emerges with longer delays, they are unable to retain this information for the long term. Consequently, these patients exhibit little cumulative learning across events or episodes. For example, you can comprehend this paragraph and then integrate

it not only with the knowledge acquired from the previous paragraphs in this chapter, but with information from the preceding chapters as well. Patients with amnesia, such as H.M., cannot do this. Indeed, patients with the most severe amnesias often comment on the difficulty that reading presents to them. As a result, they have great difficulty learning new facts and data about themselves or about the world.

The dissociation between a deficit in long-term memory and fully functional working memory is also seen in nonhuman primates with hippocampal damage. This effect is demonstrated in a variant of the **delayed nonmatch-to-sample task** (e.g., Gaffan, 1974; Mishkin & Delacour, 1975). On each trial in this task, an animal is exposed to one of a large set of objects. Following a delay, the object just viewed is presented again, this time together with another from the set of available objects. To receive a reward, the animal must select the object that was not previously presented (i.e., the nonmatch object). Following extensive hippocampal system damage, performance is markedly impaired for delays longer than about 10 seconds, but normal for shorter delays (e.g., Gaffan, 1977; Mishkin, 1978, 1982; Zola-Morgan & Squire, 1985). This dissociation between intact short-term memory abilities and disrupted long-term memory abilities points to the fact that these two types of memory processes rely on different neural structures.

■ Spared Skill Learning

Because H.M. was such a unique case, he has been studied extensively and intensively over decades. As we have just discussed, the aspect of his disorder that so impressed researchers was the profound and global nature of his long-term memory impairment. But in the course of all this testing, a funny thing happened. The researchers began to discover that in spite of this pervasive impairment, there were some tasks on which H.M. exhibited evidence of learning. Furthermore, even though H.M. exhibited such learning, he seemed to be unaware that he was learning anything! Rather, he would just comment "Huh, this is easier than I thought it would be."

Let's discuss some of the tasks on which H.M. and other amnesics show evidence of spared learning. In general, these tasks involve appreciating regularities in the environment that allow for increasingly improved performance. One main category of preserved learning is **skill learning**, which refers to the acquisition—usually gradually and incrementally through repetition—of motor, perceptual, or cognitive operations or procedures that aid performance.

One of the first examples of skill learning that scientists observed in H.M. was on a **mirror tracing task**, which involved tracing the outline of a figure (such as a star) by looking in a mirror (Milner, 1962; Corkin, 1968)

(● Figure 10.8). Across sessions, the number of times H.M.'s drawing fell outside the outline of the figure decreased, as did the time it took him to complete the task. Similar learning is demonstrated by amnesics on another perceptual-motor skill, that of **rotary pursuit**. In this task an individual has to track a circularly moving target. With practice, amnesics show an increase in the time spent on target (e.g., Brooks & Baddeley, 1976; Cermak, Lewis, Butters, & Goodglass, 1973).

Notice that in these tasks, the person is doing exactly the same task over and over again. Researchers wondered whether amnesics were learning the specific instances of these tasks (e.g., mirror drawing of a star) or a skill in general. To examine this question, they used a **mirror-reading task** (Cohen & Squire, 1980) to determine whether the skill would generalize to new exemplars, not just items seen before. For this task, word triplets are presented in mirror-image orientation, and the viewer reads them aloud as quickly and accurately as possible (● Figure 10.9A). Of critical importance, half of the word triplets are presented multiple times, appearing once in each block of trials (left panel of ● Figure 10.9B), and half are presented only once during the experiment (right

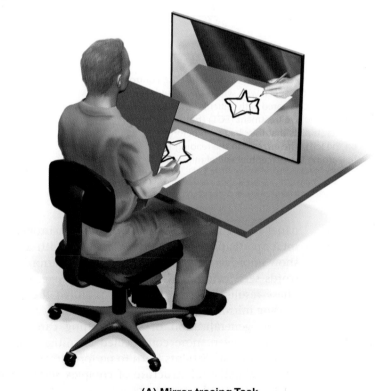

(A) Mirror-tracing Task

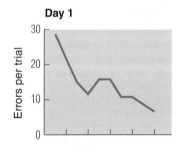
Day 1

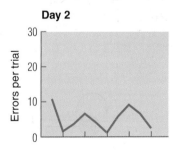
Day 2

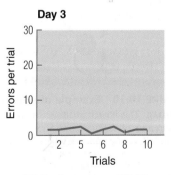
Day 3

(B) Performance of H. M.

● FIGURE 10.8 **The mirror-drawing task, which first provided evidence for new learning in the amnesic, H.M.** (A) In this task, one must trace between the lines of a star while looking in the mirror. (B) As shown here, the number of errors (going outside of the lines) exhibited by H.M. decreased with practice. His performance improved at about the same rate as observed in typical control participants. © 2010 Cengage Learning

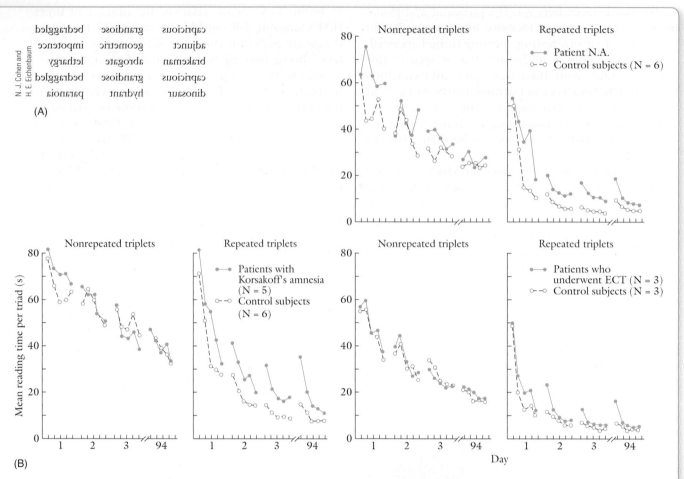

● FIGURE 10.9   Example of spared perceptual skill in patients with amnesia. (A) Examples of the mirror-image word triads used in a mirror-image reading task (Cohen & Squire, 1980). (B) Just like control individuals, patients who have amnesia from different causes increased the speed with which they could read the triads. Patient N.A., who has midline diencephalic damage (top) is compared with patients who have Korsakoff's amnesia (middle) and patients who underwent electroconvulsive treatment (ECT) (bottom). This increase in all these patients occurred not only for repeated triplets (triplets that they had seen before; graphs on the right), but also for new (nonrepeated) triads (graphs on the left). The increase in the reading times for novel triplets indicates that the patients with amnesia were learning the perceptual skill of mirror-image reading. © 2011 Cengage Learning

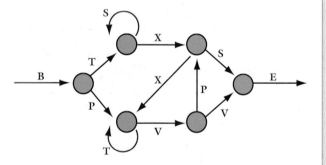

● FIGURE 10.10   Example of rules for an artificial grammar. This flowchart shows the rules for legal letter strings in an artificial grammar. Straight arrows indicate letters that can follow one another, whereas circular arrows indicate the ability for a letter to repeat. Hence, in this grammar "BTSSX" would be a legal string but "BPTTX" would not.
© 2011 Cengage Learning

panel of Figure 10.9B). With practice, neurologically intact participants as well as individuals with amnesia show improvements in reading both the mirror-imaged words seen before and the new mirror-imaged words. These results indicate they have acquired the skill of reading mirror-imaged text (Figure 10.9B).

This generalization of skill learning can also be found for even more complicated cognitive tasks, in which amnesic patients learn to perform in accordance with the statistical structure of complex sets of materials. For example, having been exposed to a series of letter strings generated by *artificial grammars* (made-up rules specifying which letters can follow which other letters), amnesics learned to classify as "grammatical" or "ungrammatical" new letter strings that do or do not follow the rules, even though they could not identify which items had been previously studied (Knowlton, Ramus, & Squire, 1992) (● Figure 10.10).

Another major category of preserved learning and memory in amnesia, and one that has been most extensively studied, is **repetition priming**, in which performance is enhanced, or biased, as a result of previous exposure to an item, even though the individuals are not directly or explicitly asked about the item. One of the earliest demonstrations of repetition priming in patients with amnesia used figures from the Gollin Incomplete Pictures task (Milner, Corkin, & Teuber, 1968; Warrington & Weiskrantz, 1968, 1970). In this task, patients are shown very degraded and incomplete line drawings of objects (bottom row of ● Figure 10.11), which they are to name. For those that cannot be named, somewhat less degraded drawings of the same objects are presented (row of figures just above the bottom row of Figure 10.11). This procedure is repeated with sets of increasingly complete drawings of the objects until the patient can correctly name all the objects, and the number of trials required to correctly name each object is recorded. After a delay, the procedure is repeated once more. All participants, including patients with amnesia, benefited from the previous exposure. They were able to identify the objects from more degraded, less complete versions than they could the first time.

What is even more remarkable is that this spared learning occurs even when the patients cannot recollect the training events during which the new skills were acquired, cannot recall or recognize the material on which the increasing skill is demonstrated, and have no insight into their improved performance. The dissociation in amnesia is probably best illustrated by the **word-stem completion task** (Graf, Squire, & Mandler, 1984). In this task, people are given a list of words to study. After a delay, memory for the words is then tested in two ways, both of which involve the presentation of three-letter stems (e.g., *mot, cyc*). In one condition, the cued-recall condition, participants are asked to recall the word from the study list that started with those same three letters. Not surprisingly, patients with amnesia perform poorly in this condition compared with neurologically intact control participants. In the other condition, the word-stem completion condition, individuals are to report "the first word that comes to mind" that completes each stem. The measure of performance was how much more often than chance the person completes the stem with a word from the study list, like *mot*el and *cyc*lone, as compared to a word not on the list with the same initial three letters, such as *mot*her or *cyc*le. Patients with amnesia performed normally on this task, being biased to complete the stems with items from the study list, just as were neurologically intact adults (● Figure 10.12).

So what have we learned about memory from amnesia? First, we have learned that medial temporal lobe structures appear to be critically important for the formation of new long-term memories. Second, it is clear that the neural systems for long-term memories

● **FIGURE 10.11   Example of visually degraded line drawings for which patients with amnesia show repetition priming.** Individuals are shown line drawings of three objects in different stages of completeness, ranging from very degraded (bottom row) to fully complete (top row), and the level of completeness at which an individual can first recognize the figures is determined. When shown the figures again after some delay, neurologically intact individuals recognize the objects at a less complete stage than initially, which indicates that prior exposure to the items influenced their performance. Individuals with amnesia show the same effect, which is indicative of repetition priming. *Source:* "Priming Effects in Picture Fragment Completion: Support for the Perceptual Closure Hypothesis," by J. G. Snodgrass and K. Feenan, 1990, Journal of Experimental Psychology: General, 119, p. 280. Copyright 1990 by the American Psychological Association. Reprinted with permission.

are in part separable from those for short-term memory. Third, the dissociation between skill learning and recognition memory suggests that these two types of memory may rely on different systems. We next examine

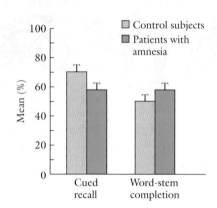

● **FIGURE 10.12   Evidence of a dissociation between disrupted cued recall and intact word-stem completion in patients with amnesia.** Patients with amnesia are impaired relative to control individuals on cued recall of words from a previously studied list (left). However, when asked to complete the word stems with the "first word that comes to mind," these individuals are just as biased as neurologically intact control individuals to report the word that they saw previously on the list (right). Hence, the prior exposure primes their behavior even though they cannot explicitly recall their experience. © 2011 Cengage Learning

what information about the organization of memory can be gleaned from the study of nonhuman animals.

■ Perspectives from Nonhuman Animals

The contribution of the hippocampal system to learning has also been clearly demonstrated in research with both rodents and nonhuman primates. Rats with damage to the hippocampal system exhibit marked deficits in learning and remembering spatial relations, such as required in the **Morris water maze** (Morris, 1981) (● Figure 10.13A). In this task, the rat is placed in a circular tank filled with an opaque liquid that obscures a slightly submerged platform. The platform is positioned at a constant location relative to various visual cues outside the maze (i.e., objects placed around the room, such as light fixtures, doors, and windows). From trial to trial, the animals are placed into the tank at different locations around the circumference of the pool. Across trials, normal animals learn the position of the platform in relation to the extra-maze cues, and thus the time it takes them to swim to the platform decreases rapidly (● Figure 10.13B). In contrast, a rat with hippocampal-system damage does not learn the relations among the cues (● Figure 10.13C) and must

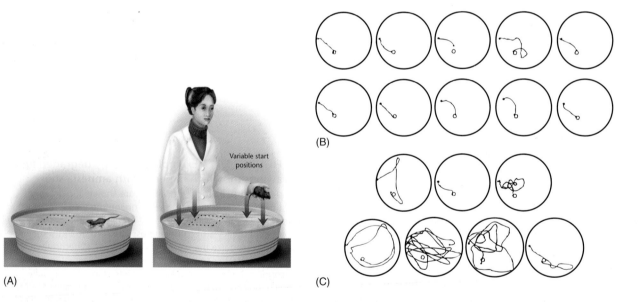

● **FIGURE 10.13   Morris water maze task used in animal models of amnesia.** (A) The rats are placed in a circular pool near the perimeter. Submerged in the pool is a platform on which the animal can rest, but which is hidden from view because the liquid in the pool is opaque. The position of this platform is constant relative to various objects around the room, but the animal is placed into the pool at various start locations across the different training trials. Hence, good performance on the task requires the animal to learn to associate the spatial relations between different landmarks and the platform. (B) The path (black line) from a specific starting point to the escape platform for each of 10 normal rats who had only sham lesions. Over a series of trials, normal animals can learn the location of the escape platform, which permits them to swim short, direct paths to the platforms. (C) The paths for seven animals with hippocampal-system damage. Because these animals fail to learn the location of the escape platform, they spend much time swimming around the pool. © 2009 Cengage Learning

search exhaustively each time for the platform's location, not reaching it any quicker from trial to trial (e.g., Schenck & Morris, 1985; Sutherland, Whishaw, & Kolb, 1983). However, if the platform is always in the same place relative to the start position, animals with hippocampal damage show no impairment (Eichenbaum, Stewart, & Morris, 1990; Whishaw, Cassel, & Jarrad, 1995). This spared ability is similar to what we observed in humans with hippocampal damage; they retain the ability to perform a well-practiced task in which the performance requirements do not change from episode to episode.

Animal research on the neuroanatomy and physiology of the hippocampal system indicates that this system possesses the anatomical connections and the neural mechanisms that allow the binding or association of disparate pieces of information together in memory. From an anatomical perspective, the hippocampal system receives inputs from the diverse cortical brain regions that perform different mental operations, such as object recognition and spatial processes, and from regions that process information of different modalities, such as vision and audition. This information arrives via the perforant pathway. The hippocampus thereby receives highly preprocessed input about the "items" encountered in the environment. In turn, the hippocampus projects back to these cortical processors via the fornix (refer back to Figure 10.3). Accordingly, it is in a position to receive, and bind together or associate, diverse sources of information, including that about the objects present in the environment, the spatial relations among them, the events in which they play roles, the temporal relations among those events, and the affective and behavioral responses they elicit.

Furthermore, electrical recordings in animal tissue indicate that the hippocampal system also has a neuronal mechanism that allows processing of the conjunctions or co-occurrences of inputs. It exhibits a phenomenon called **long-term potentiation (LTP)**, in which brief, patterned activation of particular pathways produces a stable increase in synaptic efficacy lasting for hours to weeks (see Raymond, 2007, for a review). LTP is mediated by a class of neurotransmitter receptors (*N*-methyl-D-aspartate [NMDA] receptors) that constitute superb conjunction detectors, being activated specifically by converging inputs arriving in close temporal contiguity (e.g., Wigstrom & Gustafsson, 1985). As you may remember from Chapter 2, NMDA receptors are a type of glutamate receptor.

Furthermore, the electrophysiological response of hippocampal neurons indicates that they are sensitive to various relationships among significant cues or objects in the environment. For example, as you may remember from Chapter 8, when rats are actively exploring the environment, their hippocampal neurons show **place fields**, meaning that they fire preferentially when the animal is in a particular "place" in the environment (O'Keefe & Dostrovsky, 1971). Notably, firing of these cells does not depend on any specific environmental stimulus, but rather on the relationships among them. If the relative positions of some of the relevant cues are shifted in some systematic way (e.g., rotated 90 degrees clockwise), the place fields often are correspondingly shifted (e.g., Shapiro, Heikki, & Eichenbaum, 1997). When the environment being explored (e.g., a cylindrical enclosure) is scaled up in size, the place fields may correspondingly scale up (Muller, Kubie, & Ranck, Jr., 1987). When the boundaries of the environment that is being explored are moved outward, the place fields may be stretched out in size (O'Keefe & Burgess, 1996). Thus, in all cases, the cells are responding not to an exact spatial location, but rather to the relative position between items (● Figure 10.14).

However, activity of hippocampal cells is not driven exclusively by relations of a spatial nature. In one study, hippocampal activity was recorded in rats during a task in which the relationship between the odors found at a particular location on the current and prior trial (match/nonmatch) indicated whether or not digging at the location would yield a food reward (Wood, Dudchenko, & Eichenbaum, 1999). Whereas some hippocampal neurons fired preferentially for one attribute (e.g., a particular spatial location, a particular odor), the activity of most neurons was associated with one or another of the conjunctions of odor, location, match versus nonmatch, and movement (digging or no digging) (Wood et al., 1999).

Activity of hippocampal neurons can also be driven by a variety of higher-order relationships between spatial location and the animal's behavioral activity (see Eichenbaum, Dudchenko, Wood, Shapiro, & Tanila 1999). Neuronal activity while the animal is in the place field depends heavily on the speed with which the animal is moving and the direction in which it is heading and turning. Furthermore, the same neurons have different firing properties depending on which behaviors are task-relevant at any given time. For example, these neurons can have a preference for one place in the behavioral apparatus when the animal is engaged in spatial navigation, but a preference for a different place in the same apparatus when the animal is engaged in an olfactory discrimination task.

Taken altogether, the study of memory, amnesia, and the hippocampal system in humans and animals implicates this brain system as being critical for the formation of new long-term memories of a particular type: those that depend on associating or relating disparate pieces of information so that they are bound together.

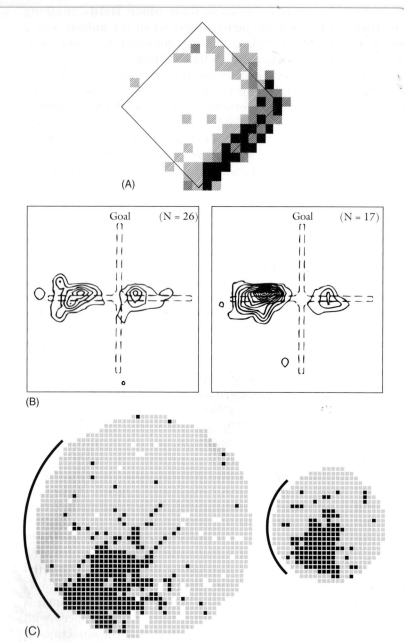

● **FIGURE 10.14   Examples of firing rates and patterns of rat hippocampal neurons with place fields as the rats explore their environment.** (A) This display indicates the rate of neuronal firing as a function of the animal's location in the environment. The darker the box, the higher the firing rate. Note that the neuron fired preferentially and at the highest rate when the animal was in one specific place in the environment: namely, along the lower right edge of the diamond-shaped environment. (B) Shown here is the firing pattern of a neuron whose place field (within the contour lines) caused it to fire preferentially when the rat was in two arms of the maze (dashed lines); the neuron fired more in response to one arm than in response to the other. A similar pattern occurred both when the animal could see the surroundings (perceptual condition, left) and when those cues were taken away after the animal had been oriented within the environment (memory condition, right). (C) These figures show the firing rate of a neuron (dark, high; light, low) when an animal was in a given location within an environment. When the animal was placed within a small circular environment (right), the cell fired preferentially to a location within that environment. When the animal explored the larger circular environment (left), the neuron's place field was "scaled up": The neuron still fired preferentially to the same quadrant of space even though that quadrant now encompassed more total area.
© 2011 Cengage Learning

Multiple Memory Systems

The striking dissociation between memory abilities that are impaired and spared in amnesia has led to the view that there are multiple long-term memory systems. As the evidence from amnesia suggests, one of these memory systems is thought to rely on the hippocampal system, whereas another does not. Although researchers agree on this point, they do not agree on exactly what dichotomy best describes the differences between these two systems. (e.g., Cohen & Squire, 1980; Eichenbaum, 1997; Eichenbaum & Cohen, 2001; Gabrieli, 1998; O'Keefe & Nadel, 1978; O'Reilly & Rudy, 2001; Schacter, 1987; Schacter & Tulving, 1994; Squire, 1987, 1992). A discussion of the nuances in the differences between these various models is beyond the scope of this textbook. Rather, we will try next to provide a general overview of at least some of the contrasts that have been proposed.

■ Conceptualizations of the Dichotomy

One influential dichotomy that has been proposed contrasts explicit and implicit memory. The memory system that is lost in amnesia has been called the **explicit memory system**, because it permits the conscious recollection of prior experiences and facts. The other system, the **implicit memory system**, allows prior experience to affect behavior without consciously retrieving the memory or even being aware of it (e.g., Schacter, 1987). Because amnesic patients cannot consciously engage in introspection about the contents of their knowledge, they are said to have "memory without awareness" (Jacoby, 1984; Moscovitch, 1994). Rarely, if ever, are neurologically intact individuals so devoid of familiarity with their previous experience, while nonetheless exhibiting memory for it. Therefore, some researchers see memory without awareness as a key aspect of amnesia.

Another contrast that has been proposed is between declarative and procedural memory. The memory system supported by the hippocampus is referred to as the **declarative memory system**, because people "know" particular information, and that information can be used flexibly and is not linked to the situation in which it was acquired (e.g., Cohen & Squire, 1980; Cohen, 1984). For example, you can "declare" that the capital of Italy is Rome in situations other than that in which you first learned that fact. Furthermore, you can link that knowledge with other facts about Rome, such as that it is referred to as "the eternal city." Being asked to provide information about what one did on a particular date or in a particular class are also examples of declarative memory. Much of the regular social interaction we have with friends and family is of this nature, where, in sharing the details of our lives, we consciously harken back to specific events and recount the things that happened.

The **procedural memory system**, in contrast, appears to support memory of "how" things should be done, allowing for the acquisition and expression of skill. Learning in this system is probabilistic, integrating information across events rather than storing each event separately. Typically, this memory is expressed in situations similar to that in which something was learned. One example of this type of memory is your ability to ride a bicycle. This ability is usually expressed in only one context—when you are on a bicycle—and typically one does not really have conscious knowledge of how such abilities are expressed. This system is unaffected in amnesia, and hence is independent of the hippocampal system.

Finally, other researchers have characterized the hippocampal system as one that supports **relational learning**, whether conscious or unconscious. Relational learning occurs in tasks or situations where performance depends on acquiring memory for the relations among items, especially items associated only arbitrarily or accidentally. One example is learning the names connected with particular people's faces or the addresses and telephone numbers that we learn to associate with them. These relations are arbitrary in that people's real names are rarely, if ever, derived from people's appearance (e.g., parents did *not* name their child Emily because they decided that she looked like a "Emily"); nor are telephone numbers and addresses in any way meaningfully related to people's names or appearance (e.g., the telephone company did *not* assign you with a particular number because it seemed an especially good match to your particular name or your particular face). Retrieving the name of the person whom you met yesterday and remembering her phone number cannot be accomplished by deriving such information from other knowledge about the person; rather, you must access a memorized relationship among the name, face, and number. This real-world relational memory task is a challenge for anyone, but it is particularly challenging for patients with amnesia. For example, H.M. never learned the face-name pairings of any of the people who saw him and tested him (e.g., Corkin, 1984). The relational system represents associations among the constituent elements of a given scene or event, such as the co-occurrences of people, places, and things, along with the spatial, temporal, and interactional relations among them, that constitute the event. It also represents relationships among various events, providing the larger record of one's experience over time.

Functional neuroimaging studies of humans using PET and fMRI provide converging evidence that the brain region damaged in amnesia, the hippocampal system, is associated with memory for relations. When tasks place a high demand on memory for the relations among items, disproportionate activation of the hippocampal system is observed (see the review by Cohen, Ryan, Hunt, Romine, Wszalek, & Nash, 1999). One demonstration comes from a PET study in which neurologically intact people viewed a series of pictures, each showing a person and a house (Henke, Buck, Weber, & Weiser, 1997). In one condition, participants had to make separate decisions about the person (*is it male or female?*) and the house (*is it an exterior or interior view?*). In the other condition, participants made subjective decisions about the relation between the person and the house (*is this person an inhabitant or just a visitor to this house?*). There was no right or wrong answer; participants were simply asked to make a decision based on the person's age and stereotypes they had about people and the types of houses they might live in. Although the stimuli were identical in the two conditions, greater hippocampal activation was found when the materials were encoded relationally than when they were encoded separately.

■ Memory and Consciousness

One issue that has generated much debate is whether recollective experience and consciousness are related to the nature of the deficit in amnesia and to hippocampal function (e.g., Gray, 1998; Moscovitch, 1994). As discussed earlier, some theories of memory suggest that the hippocampal system supports explicit or conscious memory, while other brain systems support implicit or unconscious memory. However, the issue of whether conscious recall is linked to hippocampal activity has been debated, with some researchers arguing that the criterion of consciousness is probably not the best way to differentiate between memory systems from the viewpoint of either brain function or computational modeling (Reder, Park, & Kieffaber, 2009).

It is important to note that the hippocampal system does not itself produce conscious awareness, nor is it critical for conscious awareness to be produced. Large lesions of the hippocampal region, resulting in profound memory impairments, have no demonstrable effect on consciousness in humans. Furthermore, the degree to which tests require conscious recollection does not seem to be the critical determinant of whether memory performance is impaired or spared. For example, there have been several demonstrations of amnesic patients failing to perform normally on indirect, implicit tests of memory when they had to learn relations among arbitrarily associated items.

Consider a vocabulary-learning experiment in which H.M. failed to learn the definitions of uncommon words, such as *tyro* and *cupidity* (Gabrieli, Cohen, & Corkin, 1988). In each of the three test phases of this experiment, an indirect, implicit test of memory was used. It was not necessary to make reference to or consciously recollect any specific learning experience in order to select from a list of choices the definition that "went best" with a word, the synonym that "went best" with it, or the sentence frame it would "best complete." Participants were not asked whether they remembered having previously seen or had conscious awareness of previous experience with any of the words, definitions, synonyms, or sentence frames. Although H.M. shows normal performance on any number of indirect, implicit tests of memory, in this task requiring memory for the relations between new words and their meanings H.M.'s performance was profoundly impaired.

This deficit in relational learning can also be observed in amnesics under conditions in which the specific contextual information—that is, the set of multiple cues that defines a particular episode—cannot be consciously recalled by neurologically intact individuals (Chun & Phelps, 1999). Furthermore, the deficit can be observed even without asking amnesic patients to explicitly recall their experiences. In one study, eye movements were recorded after people viewed images of real-world scenes two times each (Ryan, Althoff, Whitlow, & Cohen, 2000). On the third presentation, the participant viewed one of three scenes: a scene identical to the initial presentation (repeated scenes) (● Figure 10.15A), a scene in which a subtle but important manipulation of the relations among some of the elements of the scene were changed (manipulated scenes) (● Figure 10.15B), or an entirely new scene (novel scenes). Eye movements elicited by the different types of scenes revealed two distinct effects in neurologically intact people. One was a repetition effect, exhibited as reduced sampling of locations in previously viewed scenes versus novel scenes. Amnesic patients showed this repetition effect, indicating that they are affected by their prior experience with the material, much as is observed with repetition priming. The second effect observed in neurologically intact people was a *relational manipulation effect,* exhibited as increased viewing directed to the regions of change in the manipulated scenes relative to the original scene (● Figure 10.15C). This effect indicates sensitivity to the relations among the constituent elements of the originally studied scenes. Amnesics failed to show the relational manipulation effect, thereby revealing a selective deficit in memory for relations among items, even though it was tested implicitly without need for conscious awareness (but see Smith & Squire, 2008, for an alternative viewpoint regarding what type of memory is indexed by eye movements).

Rather than viewing the hippocampal system as mediating conscious recollection, it seems more reasonable that the hippocampal system provides the information about relations among people, places, objects, and actions on which conscious recollection and introspective reports can be based. This theory, in addition to accounting for the human amnesia data, permits us to include the animal work on hippocampal-dependent memory without having to address the thorny issue of the degree to which the "conscious recollection" of animals is or is not similar to that of humans. Damage to the hippocampal system in rodents and nonhuman primates produces a dissociation among memory capacities that is every bit as compelling as that seen in human amnesia. Such animals show impairments in learning and remembering spatial relations among environmental cues, configurations of multiple perceptually independent cues, contextual or conditional relations, and comparisons among temporally discontinuous events—all requiring a relational form of memory that associates different pieces of an experience or event. Yet, the same animals can show normal learning and remembering of a large variety of conditioning, discrimination, and skill tasks, none of which requires a relational form of memory but only gradual, incremental changes in bias or reactivity to individual items with repeated exposure. This dissociation parallels closely the dissociation observed in human amnesia.

In sum, conscious recollection and conscious awareness probably depend on many brain regions. These regions interact with the hippocampal system to mediate conscious recollection because the hippocampus provides information on the relational aspects of experience.

Nonhippocampal Regions Involved in Memory

The work with amnesics reveals a strong dissociation between at least two memory systems. So far we have concentrated our discussion on one of those systems, the one that is supported by the hippocampus. Now we turn our attention to the role that other regions of the brain play in memory.

■ Domain-Specific Neocortical Regions

Here we discuss evidence supporting the idea that memories are stored, in part, in the same brain regions that were originally involved in processing information for a given experience. For example, consider areas within the ventral visual-processing stream that support visual object recognition, such as inferotemporal cortex (area TE) in the monkey and the fusiform gyrus in humans. Anatomical, neurophysiological, neuropsychological, and neuroimaging data all indicate that this region of the brain both processes information

(A)

(B)

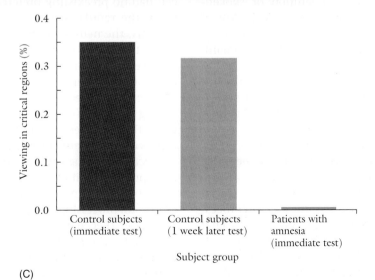

(C)

about visual objects and acts as the site of long-term storage of memory for those objects. As discussed in Chapter 7, this region is at the end of the "what" visual pathway, which in turn projects to the hippocampal system. Damage to this region results in visual agnosia, which prevents individuals from identifying previously known visual objects or learning the visual form of new objects. This association suggests that damage to this region affects both perception and memory of visual objects.

Evidence for a tight coupling of visual processing and visual memories comes from functional neuroimaging studies of neurologically intact humans. The same regions of the visual ventral stream, particularly the fusiform gyrus, become active when an individual reactivates or reimagines a visual form in the absence of the visual stimulus itself (e.g., Grady et al., 1992; Haxby, Horwitz, Ungerleider, Maisog, Pietrini, & Grady, 1994; Sergent, 1994). In one study, participants studied words that were paired with either a picture or a sound. At test time, the participants were presented with words individually and had to recall whether they had previously been associated with a visual form or with a sound. When participants were able to recall the pictures associated with the word, fusiform activation was similar to that observed during initial presentation of the picture (Wheeler, Petersen, & Buckner, 2000; for a similar finding, see Nyberg, Habib, McIntosh, & Tulving, 2000). When recalling the sounds associated with words, activation was observed in auditory regions of the superior temporal gyrus, similar to that observed when the word was initially presented (Wheeler, 2000). Taken together with the earlier results, we can see that the same regions are activated for the initial processing of perceptual information as well as for its recall, indicating that these neocortical sites are engaged in both perceptual and memory functions.

Finally, neuropsychological disorders that affect particular, circumscribed domains of world knowledge, such as impairment in face recognition or spoken-language comprehension, manifest both as the loss of previously acquired knowledge in that domain and as the inability to acquire new information in that domain. Each such type of knowledge deficit thus seems to reflect damage to the cortical substrate for both the initial processing and memory of that domain of knowledge. However, each of these domains represents only specific elements of memory.

In sum, as we experience the world, the various elements that make up a given specific experience are handled by different cortical processors—those involved in vision, audition, language, and spatial processing, to name a few. These same cortical processors also store the outcomes of their processing. That is, memory for visual elements of the experience is stored in visual-processing areas, memory for linguistic elements is stored in language-processing areas, and so forth.

Now that we understand that different portions of a given event are processed and stored in separate regions of the cortex, each of which is domain-specific, we are also in a better position to understand how the hippocampus may aid in storing memory for a particular event. The hippocampus is thought to be particularly important for binding together information *across* different cortical areas, rather than for the binding of information *within* a given area (Mayes, Montaldi, & Migo, 2007). That is, disparate aspects of an experience are bound together as a coherent event or episode because they are tied together by virtue of their interconnections with the hippocampal system. When such information is retrieved, the hippocampus is thought to provide an index that points to the locations within the brain where the various different pieces of a particular event or episode are stored (Tyler & DiScenna, 1986). However, the actual information about each piece of the memory is stored within the domain-specific cortical region that originally processed the information.

So far, we have discussed only situations in which memory for a specific event is to be stored and retrieved. But what if you are learning an association over time within a given domain or incrementally learning a skill? Evidence suggests that such learning occurs via alterations within a specific neocortical processor. Consider the following example from a study conducted with monkeys (Sakai & Miyashita, 1991). As we learned in Chapter 7, neurons in the inferotemporal area in the monkey are responsive to specific visual objects. The visual object that is preferred by a neuron—that is, the one that elicits maximal firing—differs from neuron to neuron. In this study, the researchers assessed the responsiveness of neurons to various visual forms, permitting the testers to determine which objects the cells preferred and which they did not. Then monkeys were trained to associate one preferred item with one for which the cell had no preexisting preference. After this training, when the monkeys were tested with the items individually, the neurons now fired robustly to the newly trained objects, the ones for which they had no previous preference. Presumably this occurred because the newly trained items were able to elicit cued recall of the preferred objects based on the associations formed during training (● Figure 10.16). This finding illustrates that experience can change the response of neurons within domain-specific processors.

Electrophysiological and anatomical studies in animals provide additional evidence showing how experience changes the networks involved in basic perceptual and motor processing areas. For example, Recanzone and colleagues (Recanzone, Schreiner, & Merzenich, 1993) found that training monkeys to discriminate among tones of certain frequencies resulted in a larger representational area for those frequencies in auditory cortex. Furthermore, this change correlated with increments in

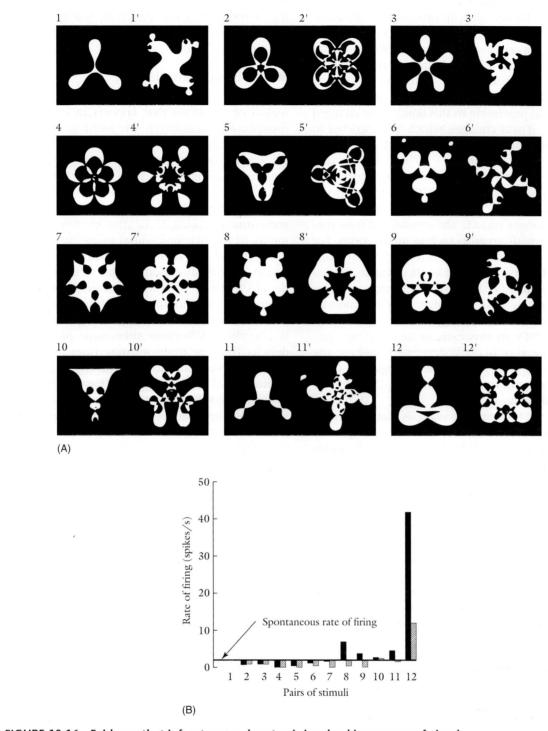

● **FIGURE 10.16   Evidence that inferotemporal cortex is involved in memory of visual objects.** (A) In the experiment of Sakai and Miyashita (1991), the monkey had to learn to associate specific pairs of these 24 visual shapes. (B) The response of a neuron to each item (shown in black) and the item with which it was arbitrarily paired during training (shown in grey). In this case, the cell was differentially sensitive to item 12 and during the course of learning also became sensitive to item 12′. *Source:* "Neural Organization for the Long-Term Memory of Paired Associates," by K. Sakai and Y. Miashita. Reprinted with permission from Nature (354, pp 152–155). Copyright 1991 by Macmillan Magazines Limited. © 2011 Cengage Learning

behavioral performance. Similar changes in the basic processing machinery of the brain as a function of experience are seen also in somatosensory and motor cortices. As a result of tactile discrimination training in monkeys, neurons representing the "trained" areas of the skin surface developed larger receptive fields (Merzenich, Recanzone, Jenkins, & Grajski, 1990; Recanzone, Merzenich, & Jenkins, 1992). Moreover, training on a task that emphasized skilled movements of the digits of the hand to pick up small objects increased the representation of the hand in primary motor cortex; likewise, training on a task that emphasized movement of the forearm to turn a key increased the representation of the forearm (Nudo, Milliken, Jenkins, & Merzenich, 1996). Clearly, the networks that support basic perceptual processing in this domain are changed by experience. These changes, which are restricted to domain-specific processors, are thought to support implicit/procedural memory.

Investigations with animals provide evidence that these changes within domain-specific processing occur via structural change—a rewiring of the brain, if you will. These changes include the creation of new synapses (synaptogenesis) in areas such as motor cortex. For example, rats that learned the acrobatic motor skills necessary to traverse an obstacle-filled course showed an increased number of synapses per neuron in motor cortex, an increase that correlated with the increase in performance (Kleim, Lussnig, Schwarz, Comery, & Greenough, 1996). In this case, as in the others just mentioned, the very brain systems necessary for the performance of a given task showed changes as a function of experience in that task, providing the substrate for procedural memory.

Evidence with humans also suggests that experience can alter the functioning of domain-specific processors. For example, in neuroimaging studies, the learning of specific finger-movement sequences resulted in changes in activation of various portions of the motor system critical for performance of that skill, including changes in the distribution of activation in motor cortex (Karni et al., 1995) and the cerebellum (Jenkins, Brooks, Nixon, Frackowiak, & Passingham, 1994). Research has also documented changes in motor cortex during the course of learning tasks whose performance is spared in amnesia, such as the rotary pursuit task (Grafton, Woods, & Tyszka, 1994), as well as in drawing or tracking tasks (Flament, Ellermann, Kim, Ugurbil, & Ebner, 1996).

Similarly, repetition priming effects for visual materials are linked to changes in activation across visual-processing regions. Remember that repetition priming is the form of learning in which items are responded to more quickly or accurately upon subsequent presentations than at initial presentation. Behavioral evidence of such learning is accompanied by changes in activation of the same extrastriate areas that are engaged in processing these visual materials (e.g., see Buckner, Koutstaal, Schacter, Wagner, & Rosen, 1998). This conclusion is also supported by neuropsychological findings in two single-case studies of individuals who had damage to extrastriate regions. Lesions of these regions in patient L.H. (Keane, Clarke, & Corkin, 1992) and patient M.S. (Gabrieli, Fleischman, Keane, Reminger, & Morrell, 1995) resulted in impaired perceptual priming for visual materials. This deficit was selective, as neither individual showed difficulty in explicit remembering of the same visual materials, nor did they exhibit deficits in priming in other sensory modalities, such as audition.

■ The Basal Ganglia

In addition to domain-specific processors, another region of the brain that appears to enable implicit/procedural processing is the basal ganglia. Much of this knowledge initially came from neuropsychological studies of patients with either Parkinson's disease or Huntington's disease. These patients appear to show a pattern of deficits opposite to that shown by patients with hippocampal damage—that is, they show intact explicit/declarative memory with impairments in implicit/procedural memory. As we learned in Chapter 5, Parkinson's and Huntington's diseases result from dysfunction of the striatum. Therefore, deficits in these patients implicate striatal regions as critical for implicit/procedural learning. Nonetheless, the assessment of skill learning in these patients is complicated because they have profound motor deficits that are quite separate from any deficits in learning and memory. In addition, drug treatments administered to these patients have cognitive consequences. However, results from neuroimaging studies and other approaches provide converging evidence that the basal ganglia are important for implicit/procedural memory.

Patients with Huntington's or Parkinson's diseases show deficits on many of the skill-learning tasks on which amnesics exhibit intact performance. One category of skill learning in which they are impaired is **habit learning**, which, while gradual and incremental, may *not* necessarily generalize to new exemplars. We were introduced to one task of this type earlier in the chapter: the rotary pursuit task, which involves tracking a target on a circularly moving platter with a handheld stylus. The striatal damage in patients with Parkinson's disease or Huntington's disease keeps them from having as large an increase in time on target as do neurologically intact people (Gabrieli, 1995). In neurologically intact people, changes in activation of the striatum correlate with learning on this task (Grafton et al., 1992).

Another example of the deficit in habit learning in these patients can be observed on the *serial reaction time (SRT) task*. In this task, one of a number of different locations on a computer screen is flashed on each trial, and the individual presses a button corresponding to that location. Unbeknownst to the individual, the locations are flashed in a particular repeating order. Learning in this task is shown in two ways: by a gradual decrease in reaction time across blocks in response to the repeating sequence, and by an increase in the degree to which performance is disrupted when individuals are switched to a block of trials in which stimuli are presented in random order. Such learning can be considered implicit because people get better on the task even though they are not aware of the repeating sequence. Several reports have indicated deficits in learning on this task in patients who have Parkinson's disease or Huntington's disease (Willingham & Koroshetz, 1993; Ferraro, Balota, & Connor, 1993; Pascual-Leone et al., 1993). Converging evidence comes from functional neuroimaging work, in which activity in the striatum is associated with learning on this task, as well as on similar tasks such as finger sequencing (Grafton, Hazeltine, & Ivry, 1995; Seitz & Roland, 1992).

At this point, you may have noticed that all the tasks discussed so far involve some sort of motor output, whether it be controlling one's limb to stay on a target in the rotary pursuit task or pushing a sequence of buttons in the serial reaction time task (for a review of motor-sequence difficulties in these patient groups, see Doyon, 2008). You might be wondering whether patients who have Parkinson's or Huntington's disease have difficulty on these tasks only because the basal ganglia play an important role in motor processing.

This is certainly a reasonable question, but other evidence suggests that the difficulties generalize to other learning tasks that do not require a motor output, and they also generalize across a range of exemplars in the trained domain (for reviews, see Gabrieli, 1995; Salmon & Butters, 1995; Knowlton et al., 1996). One example is a deficit in the mirror-reading task exhibited by patients with Huntington's disease (Martone, Butters, Payne, Becker, & Sax, 1984). Moreover, functional neuroimaging data indicate that learning to read mirror-reversed text is associated with activation of striatal and left prefrontal regions as well as temporal lobe and cerebellar regions (Poldrack, Desmond, Glover, & Gabrieli, 1998; Poldrack & Gabrieli, 2001).

In addition to the evidence provided by mirror reading, there is other evidence that the role of the striatum in implicit/procedural learning is not restricted to the motor domain. Patients with damage to the basal ganglia, including patients with Parkinson's disease (Knowlton, Mangels, & Squire, 1996; Shohamy et al. 2004) and Huntington's disease (Knowlton, et al., 1996), are impaired at *probabilistic learning tasks,* in which cues predict outcomes probabilistically, not in a one-to-one fashion. In one such task, the weather prediction task, individuals must predict which of two outcomes (*rain* or *shine*) follows from cues presented on cards. On each trial, one to three cards from a deck of four is presented. Each card is associated with the sunshine outcome only probabilistically: either 75%, 57%, 43%, or 25% of the time. The outcome with multiple cards is associated with the conjoint probabilities of the cards presented in any of 14 configurations. On each trial, the cards are presented, then the person chooses between rain and shine, after which he or she is given feedback. The probabilistic nature of the task makes it somewhat counterproductive for individuals to attempt to recall specific previous trials, because repetition of any particular configuration of the cues could lead to different outcomes. Instead, the most useful information to be learned concerns the probability associated with the mapping of outcomes with particular cues and combinations of cues—information acquired gradually across trials.

Over a block of 50 trials, neurologically intact people showed significant and gradual improvement in their weather prediction performance, but patients with Parkinson's disease failed to show significant learning. Moreover, individuals with amnesia due to damage to the hippocampal regions perform as well as neurologically intact individuals. Converging evidence for the role of the striatum in learning on such probabilistic tasks is provided by neuroimaging studies (e.g., Poldrack, Prabhakaran, Seger, & Gabrieli, 1999). Thus, a variety of evidence suggests that the striatum is fundamentally important for implicit/procedural learning, both in the motor and cognitive domains (for a review of evidence from both animals and humans, see Packard & Knowlton, 2002).

Given these findings, the question arises as to exactly *what* role the basal ganglia play in learning. Some theories suggest that the basal ganglia are important for learning associations between particular stimuli and the response to which they lead. The response may be of a motor nature, such as in some of the skill-learning tasks we have discussed; or it may be what response or outcome is expected, as in the weather prediction task. Other viewpoints argue that the basal ganglia modulate performance by helping to select among different response alternatives based on the stimulus inputs received from different portions of the cortex (Atallah, Frank, & O'Reilly, 2004).

Notice that the type of association made by the basal ganglia is distinct from associations made by the hippocampus. In general, associations made by the basal ganglia are between stimuli and responses, whereas the hippocampus makes associations across a variety of diverse neocortical processors. In the final section of this chapter, we consider other contrasts between the learning systems supported by the basal ganglia and those supported by the hippocampus.

■ The Amygdala: An Interface between Memory and Emotion

As we will discuss in more detail in Chapter 13, the amygdala plays a large role in the analysis of affective information and the expression of emotional output. Here we emphasize its role as an interface between memory and emotion. The initial evidence for this role of the amygdala came from the amnesic patient H.M. His surgery, which included bilateral removal of his amygdala, left him with a decreased ability to access information about his internal states. In a systematic study of his responsiveness to pain and hunger (Hebben, Corkin, Eichenbaum, & Shedlack, 1985), H.M. differed from other amnesic patients in whom the amygdala was intact, and from neurologically intact individuals, as he failed to identify pain stimuli as "painful" no matter how intense they were. He also failed to show changes in his ratings of hunger before and after meals. Indeed, on one occasion, he rated his hunger as 50 on a scale of 0–100 both before and after a full dinner. Afterward, he was engaged in conversation with the experimenters and then given another full dinner. He did not remember the earlier dinner, ate the second dinner at his usual pace, and when done, still rated his hunger as 50.

Since those initial studies, we have learned that the amygdala plays two distinct and critical roles in the interaction of emotion and memory (see Eichenbaum & Cohen, 2001). First, it mediates the learning and expression of emotional responses to stimuli whose emotional significance is not automatic but has been learned via association. Second, it allows emotional experience to modulate certain aspects of long-term memory. Each of these roles is discussed in turn.

The amygdala is critically involved in emotional memory and the learning of emotional responses. Perhaps the best-studied example of emotional memory involves the brain system that mediates Pavlovian **fear conditioning** (e.g., LeDoux, 1992, 1994; Davis, 1992, 1994), in which a stimulus comes to invoke fear because it is paired with an aversive event. For example, rats are placed in a chamber in which they are presented multiple times with a 10-second pure tone that is terminated with a brief electric shock through the floor of the cage. They come to exhibit conditioned fear to the subsequent presentation of just the tone, because it was paired with the shock. This fear is expressed by changes in autonomic responses, such as arterial blood pressure; in motor responses, such as stereotypic crouching or freezing behavior; and in suppression of the urge to drink sweetened water, which rats usually like.

● **FIGURE 10.17 • A radial arm maze used to test spatial memory in rats.** A rat that reenters one arm before trying the other arms has made an error.

Animals with selective lesions in the lateral amygdala show dramatically reduced conditioned autonomic and motor responses to the tone.

Intact animals also exhibit **contextual fear conditioning**, meaning that their fear response is selective to the context, or environment, in which conditioning occurs. When intact rats are again placed in the conditioning chamber after initial exposure, they begin to freeze even *before* the tone is presented. Their reactions have been conditioned both to the tone and to the environmental context in which tones and shock have been paired. If placed in a different environment, they do not freeze unless a tone is presented. Amygdala lesions block this contextual fear conditioning, just as they block Pavlovian fear conditioning. In contrast, damage to the hippocampus selectively blocks contextual fear conditioning because it requires memory for the relation between the conditioning and the specific context or environment.

A variety of other paradigms show that the amygdala is critical for learning stimulus-reward associations. One particularly nice example of this comes from a study by White and McDonald (1993) on radial arm maze performance of rats (● Figure 10.17). Animals with amygdala damage failed to develop a preference for the maze arm consistently associated with a food reward, compared to an arm in which they spent an equivalent amount of time but without a food reward. Yet, the same animals were fine in the standard "win-shift" variant of the radial maze task, in which they learned to sample each of the eight arms once before revisiting any of them; and they were fine in a "win-stay" variant of the task in which they learned to visit only arms that were illuminated by light and to avoid dark arms. Animals with hippocampal damage or damage to the striatum had no difficulty learning the place-preference task, but were impaired on the "win-stay" or the "win-shift" tasks, respectively. Thus, amygdala damage produced a selective impairment in learning the reward significance, or the stimulus-reward association, necessary to develop a preference for a single rewarded arm.

The second contribution of the amygdala to memory involves the modulation of memory by emotional experiences. Perhaps the best evidence for this comes from a paradigm developed by Cahill and colleagues for studying human memory (1995, 1996, 1999). Their test involves presentation of a single series of slides and two alternative narratives, one of which is emotionally charged (e.g., a story about a mother and son involved in a traumatic accident), and one of which is not (e.g., a story about a safety drill). In subsequent delayed-memory testing, neurologically intact individuals showed a selective enhancement of recall for the emotional component of the tragic story but not the analogous portion of the neutral story. Bilateral damage to the amygdala in a patient with Urbach-Wiethe syndrome selectively wiped out the enhancement of memory for the emotional part of the tragic story, but did not affect memory for the neutral components of the story. This damage also did not prevent such individuals from appreciating the emotional content of the tragic story.

The amygdala is thought to exert such an influence over memory through its interaction with many structures involved in memory processing that we have already discussed, such as the hippocampus and striatum, and other regions, such as frontal cortex, that we discuss in subsequent portions of this chapter (see LaBar & Cabeza, 2006, for a review). As we learn in more detail in Chapter 13, the amygdala is thought to respond to emotional situations that are highly arousing. When it becomes active, it in turn influences portions of the memory circuitry in the brain. Thus, at least a portion of the amygdala's action on memory can be thought of as modulating activity within the memory circuitry. Such a mechanism, as you might imagine, is quite adaptive. Highly arousing situations are often those that can be important for survival, such as when one encounters a serious threat. Having a mechanism that enhances memory for such situations is obviously advantageous.

■ Anterior Temporal Regions

To understand the role that anterior temporal regions play in memory, we need to consider that the explicit/declarative memory system can be divided into two subdivisions: semantic memory and episodic memory (Tulving, 1972). **Semantic memory** refers to knowledge that allows the formation and retention of facts, concepts, categories, and word meaning and retention of information about ourselves and the people we know, such as where they live, their occupations and interests, and their personality characteristics—all of which are expressed across many different contexts. In contrast, **episodic memory** refers to those autobiographical memories that are specific to our own particular experience that includes context about the time, space, etc. To make this distinction clearer, consider an example of an episodic memory, the memory of your first kiss. This memory includes information about the person whom you kissed, the place where it occurred, how you felt, and so forth. In contrast, your semantic memory about kisses includes information such as that they involve the placing of a person's lips on someone else or an object; are used to demonstrate ardor, affection, or appreciation; and are commonly given when people are meeting one another or when they are leaving. In this example, whereas information contained in semantic memory is about kisses in general, information contained in episodic memory is about a particular kiss. As such, episodic memory allows a reexperiencing of the event—providing the opportunity, in essence, to travel back in time (Tulving, 1985).

As we have discussed at many points in this chapter, people with damage to the medial temporal lobe lose the ability to form new memories about episodes in their lives, suggesting a disruption of episodic memory. However, after injury they can learn at least some new semantic information, suggesting that such semantic memories may not rely entirely on the medial temporal region (e.g., Bayley, O'Reilly, Curran, & Squire, 2008). One of the most dramatic examples of such learning comes from three case studies of children who sustained damage in childhood (at birth, age 4, and age 9) that included portions of the hippocampus (Vargha-Khadem et al., 1997). Despite having a pronounced amnesia for the everyday episodes that occurred in their lives, they were nonetheless able to attend mainstream school, at which they learned language skills (including the ability to read) and enough factual information to place their intelligence within the low average to average range! These findings suggest that semantic memory does not require the hippocampus.

At least some aspects of semantic memory may rely on domain-specific neocortical processors. For example, your memory of the feel of wool is likely to be retained in somatosensory regions, whereas your memory of the shape of sheep is stored by visual areas. But what about semantic information that is not linked to a particular modality? Anterior temporal lobe regions may play a role in retaining such information. Evidence for this viewpoint comes from a disorder called **semantic dementia**, in which patients progressively lose the ability to retain semantic information. For example, when traveling through the countryside to visit a friend, a patient with this disorder reminded his wife where to turn to reach their friend's house, but then looked at sheep in a field they were passing and asked her, "What are those things?" The most notable pathology in this disorder is degeneration of the anterior temporal regions. Converging evidence is provided by functional neuroimaging, which indicates activation in this region during tasks requiring semantic processing (for a review, see Patterson, Nestor, & Rogers, 2007).

Brain Systems That Contribute to Encoding, Consolidation and Storage, and Retrieval

So far we have spent some time discussing different types of memories: declarative memories, both episodic and semantic; implicit memories, including skills and habits; and emotional memories. Yet another way to understand memory is to break it down, not by the type of memory, but by the different processing stages that are involved in memory. First, memories have to be created—that is, information must be *encoded* into memory. Memories also must be *stored*, or maintained over time. While they are stored, they may undergo *consolidation,* or strengthening. Finally, for a memory to be useful we need to be able to access it; that is, we need to be able to *retrieve* it. In this section, we examine which regions of the brain make these processes possible.

Before we do so, however, it is important to realize that we needed converging evidence from various techniques to identify the critical brain regions for each of these processes. For example, consider the limitations of work done solely on patients with amnesia. Deficits in memory seen at some lengthy delay after learning could reflect impairment in any of these stages of memory. Impairment in the initial encoding of memories could prevent information from being fully processed or from being stored in a robust enough form to allow for later retrieval. Alternatively, impairment in the storage, maintenance, or consolidation of memories could cause information to decay abnormally rapidly over time, limiting the patient's ability to remember the information. Finally, impairment could occur in the retrieval of memories despite normal storage and maintenance of the information. No definitive answer about which of these stages is the locus of the impairment in amnesia can be provided by studies of these patients alone. Nevertheless, the results of these studies, taken together with newer methods in cognitive neuroscience, have provided a more complete answer in identifying the brain systems that exert their effects at multiple times in the lifetime of a memory: at encoding, during storage and consolidation, and at retrieval.

◾ Encoding

Two major brain regions play a role in encoding: the hippocampus and prefrontal cortex. Evidence for the participation of the hippocampal system at the time of encoding comes from ERP and functional neuroimaging studies. Numerous studies have indicated that the hippocampal system is activated during encoding of faces, words, scenes, or objects (e.g., Kelley et al., 1998; Martin, Harley, Smith, Hoyles, & Hynes, 1997; Brewer, Zhao, Desmond, Glover, & Gabrieli, 1998; Wagner, Desmond, Glover, & Gabrieli, 1998; Kirchhoff, Wagner, Maril, & Stern, 2000). Such studies have also shown that the left hippocampus is more involved for verbal materials, such as words, whereas the right is more involved for processing of nonverbal materials, such as faces (Powell et al., 2005).

However, these studies alone do not supply much information about whether hippocampal activation plays a central role in the successful encoding of an item. Stronger evidence for such a role is provided by studies of the **subsequent memory effect**: subsequently remembered items are associated with greater brain activity at encoding than items that are not subsequently remembered. This effect was first demonstrated using ERPs, in which activity recorded at the scalp at the time of encoding predicted subsequent memory performance (e.g., Paller, Kutas, & Mayes, 1987; Fabiani & Donchin, 1995). At the time this research was done, it was not possible to identify the particular brain systems that produced the effect. However, subsequent work using depth recordings in the hippocampus yielded the same ERP effect (Fernandez et al., 1999), suggesting that the hippocampus is the likely neural source of

such activity. Finally, fMRI studies have demonstrated that the amount of hippocampal activity at the time an item is first seen and encoded predicts how well that item will be remembered later on (Brewer et al., 1998; Wagner et al., 1998). Taken together, this work illustrates that the hippocampal system is active at the time information is encoded into memory, and that this activity is predictive of how well that information will be remembered.

Another region of the brain that neuroimaging studies have indicated is robustly and reliably active at the time of acquisition of information and encoding in various long-term memory tasks is ventrolateral prefrontal cortex (see Buckner, 1996; Buckner, Koutstaal, Schacter, Wagner, & Rosen, 1998). Like the hippocampal system, lateralization of activity is observed depending on the nature of the material being encoded (Poldrack & Gabrieli, 1998; Wagner et al., 1998). For example, when individuals are told to remember items, disproportionate activity is observed over the left prefrontal cortex for words, which are coded verbally, while disproportionate activity is observed over right prefrontal cortex for unfamiliar faces, which are coded spatially. Activity is distributed over both left and right prefrontal cortex for namable objects, which can be coded both verbally and spatially (Kelley et al., 1998). Ventrolateral prefrontal activity is seen whether individuals are purposefully trying to encode information, known as *intentional encoding,* or are just doing so passively, with *incidental encoding* (Buckner, Wheeler, & Sheridan, 2001). Importantly, as with the hippocampal system, this activity predicts subsequent memory performance. Items that are subsequently remembered elicit greater activation at the time of encoding than do items that are not subsequently remembered. Furthermore, neuroimaging studies suggest that it is posterior ventrolateral prefrontal regions (e.g., BA 44) that predict the subsequent memory effect.

More recent evidence suggests that dorsolateral prefrontal cortex, which is important for working memory, may also contribute to encoding. This region may aid encoding by holding together multiple pieces of information at the same time, which would then, in turn, enhance their ability to be bound and associated in long-term memory (see Blumenfeld & Ranganath, 2007, for a review of prefrontal contributions to encoding).

These findings point to the hippocampal system and ventrolateral prefrontal circuits each contributing to operations performed at encoding that enable the successful formation of memories. Because prefrontal regions are involved in planning, these prefrontal regions may play a role in strategically mediated aspects of memory. The prefrontal cortex might enable the focusing and organizing of such processes, perhaps by inhibiting irrelevant information and encoding information in such a way that it can later be easily retrieved. Interestingly, there is a reduction in prefrontal activation for recently processed items (Buckner et al., 1998, 2001), as if the operations required for encoding are already known and therefore less involvement of the prefrontal cortex is necessary. Furthermore, the contribution of the ventrolateral prefrontal cortex to encoding is distinct from that of the hippocampal system, as normal activation of the ventrolateral prefrontal cortex is seen even in patients with hippocampal-system damage, who exhibit severely impaired memory (Dupont et al., 2000). The hippocampus, in contrast, is critical for binding together the co-occurrence of different information that uniquely identifies a particular event so that the event can be encoded and subsequently retrieved.

■ Consolidation and Storage

At least some theories suggest that the hippocampus also plays a role in memory **consolidation**, the process by which memories are strengthened to allow for long-term retention. The notion that memories may undergo consolidation comes from investigations of retrograde amnesia. As you may remember, people who sustain an injury often show a retrograde amnesia in which they cannot remember events for some period

prior to the injury. Assuming that their hippocampal system was working perfectly fine prior to their injury, the memories for events prior to the injury should have been encoded normally. Yet, the ability to recall those memories is compromised, suggesting that the damaged structure must play an ongoing role in supporting those memories, even past the stage of initial encoding.

Even stronger support for a period of consolidation comes from the way retrograde amnesia typically manifests itself after a closed head injury. Generally, immediately after the injury, the retrograde amnesia covers a time period that extends further into the past than is observed hours or days after the injury (● Figure 10.18). It shrinks from an amnesia that includes the portions of the more remote past to one that covers only the most recent period (e.g., Guillery-Girard et al., 2004). For example, immediately after an injury a person may not remember what happened in the 20 minutes prior to the injury. However, after a couple of days, the retrograde amnesia may extend back in time only to 5 minutes prior to the injury, with memories

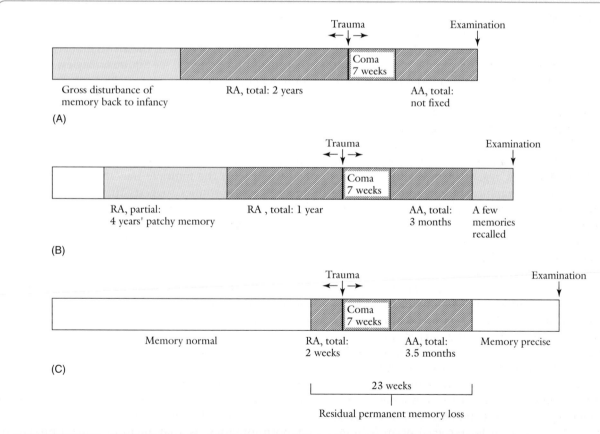

● **FIGURE 10.18   Illustration of the phenomenon of shrinking retrograde amnesia.** The memory status of a patient was assessed at three examination times: (A) 5 months, (B) 8 months, and (C) 16 months after closed head injury. The time of the head injury is indicated by the heavy vertical line in each timeline. The portion of time for which memory was impaired is depicted by diagonal lines, and times of patchy impairment are represented by lightly shaded areas. The portions of time affected to the right of the heavy vertical line indicate the extent of the anterograde amnesia (AA). The portions of time affected to the left of the heavy vertical line indicate the extent of the retrograde amnesia (RA). Across the three timelines, the retrograde amnesia shrinks from an initially extensive impairment encompassing years to a more limited amnesia affecting only weeks. © 2011 Cengage Learning from this time period never being recovered. (For this reason, people who have been involved in accidents that have caused head injury, even minor ones, invariably cannot say what caused the accident.)

One model, known as the *consolidation model,* argues that the hippocampal system is required not only to lay down memories, but also to consolidate them. In this consolidation process, the hippocampus aids in slowly binding together pieces of a memory trace in separate neocortical processors. Once they are bound in this way, they can be retrieved independently of the hippocampal system (Squire, Stark, & Clark, 2004). As an analogy, imagine that you introduce two friends to one another. At first, they might only see one another when the three of you get together. However, over time you help to establish a relationship between the two of them, so that eventually they can get together on their own without your help. In a similar way, the hippocampus may act over time to establish a relationship between different pieces of a memory that are stored in different cortical units. Once the relationship is established, the hippocampus can be removed from the picture without damaging the relationship.

This model explains the temporal gradient of retrograde amnesia, in which more recent memories are more affected than more remote memories. More recent memories were not fully consolidated prior to the insult, so damage to the hippocampus precludes full consolidation. In contrast, older memories have already been consolidated and are unaffected by hippocampal damage—they no longer require the hippocampus and essentially reside in other portions of the cortex (Squire & Alvarez, 1995). Furthermore, according to this model, such a consolidation process is proposed to occur for all explicit memories, regardless of whether they are of an episodic/autobiographical or semantic nature.

However, some evidence suggests that retrograde amnesia can be severe and of long duration after hippocampal damage, calling into question the notion that certain memories become independent of the hippocampus (Warrington & Sanders, 1971; Warrington, 1996). Moreover, the memories that seem to be most affected by such severe retrograde amnesia are those of an episodic or autobiographical nature (Kinsbourne & Wood, 1975). Another model, the *multiple trace theory* (Nadel & Moscovitch, 1997; Moscovitch et al., 2005), argues that the hippocampus is obliged to encode the different aspects of any experience and bind them together. The hippocampal stores a pointer to the various representations distributed across the cortex, and this pointer is critical for retrieval of an episode. According to this view, there is no prolonged consolidation period; rather, this process occurs in a matter of seconds or at the most days. Thus, the hippocampus is critical for episodic memory, and its involvement does not vary with the age of the memory.

This model argues that every time a memory is retrieved, a new trace, mediated by the hippocampus, is formed—hence the name "multiple trace" theory. In this manner, old memories will be represented by stronger hippocampal-neocortical traces than new ones. Thus, they are less susceptible to disruption from brain damage than memories that have been created more recently. According to this model, when these autobiographical or episodic traces are related (e.g., the time that you viewed a picture of Princess Diana dancing with John Travolta in a magazine tabloid, or watched her interview with the BBC confirming infidelities in her marriage), the relationship facilitates the extraction of information that is common among all of the traces of these events in neocortical regions (e.g., the characteristics that you came to associate with Princess Diana—her voice, her smile, her movements, etc.). According to this model, this information is then bound together with semantic knowledge (e.g., that Princess Diana was married to Prince Charles, that they had an unhappy marriage) to create memories that are independent of the hippocampus. The argument here is that the nature of the memory trace shifts, from one that is specific to the episode to one that is represented in a more semantic manner. It is this prolonged process of memories morphing from a more episodic to a more semantic nature that gives the impression of a prolonged consolidation process.

A discussion of the merits of these different models is beyond the scope of this textbook (for a relatively short recent discussion of each of these two models by one of their major proponents, see Squire & Bayley, 2007, and Moscovitch, Nadel, Winocur, Gilboa, & Rosenbaum, 2006, respectively). It is an active area of research. For example, research with some amnesic patients has suggested that all autobiographical memories are affected regardless of their remoteness (e.g., Noulhaine et al., 2007; Steinvorth, Levine, & Corkin, 2005), a finding consistent with the multiple trace theory; but a meta-analysis across studies suggests that the more typical pattern is a graded decrement (Brown, 2002). Likewise, whereas some neuroimaging studies show greater activation of medial temporal regions in older adults for recent as compared to remote memories (e.g., Haist, Bowden Gore, & Mao, 2001), consistent with the consolidation theory, others do not find variations with regard to the age of the memory (Maguire, Henson, Mummery, & Frith, 2001), consistent with the multiple trace theory.

These studies illustrate how complicated the issues regarding the neural bases of memory can be. One of the reasons why memories are so important in our daily life is that not only do we encode them, but we also retrieve them and connect them with the rest of our experience. What this means, and what is reflected in both theories, is that memories are unlikely to remain static. Rather, they are transformed over time by our subsequent experience and the new memories that we acquire.

■ Retrieval

As with encoding, both hippocampal and prefrontal regions are involved in the retrieval of memories. In addition, left parietal regions have also been implicated.

We discuss the contributions of each of these three regions in turn.

Hippocampus

Neuroimaging evidence indicates that activity in the hippocampal system occurs across a wide variety of retrieval conditions, including those requiring recall of episodic, semantic, and autobiographical information (Burianova, McIntosh, & Grady, 2010; Ryan, Cox, Hayes, & Nadel, 2008). The region of the hippocampus involved in retrieval, however, may be somewhat distinct from that involved in encoding. Meta-analyses across PET and fMRI studies suggest that more anterior regions of the hippocampus are engaged for encoding of episodic memories than for their retrieval (see Lepage, Habib, & Tulving, 1998; Schacter & Wagner, 1999; Spaniol et al., 2009). These findings suggest that different portions of the hippocampus may support encoding and retrieval.

The nature of the processes or operations being performed by the hippocampus at the time of retrieval are still somewhat of a mystery. One prominent theory suggests that the hippocampus may be participating in the reactivation of long-term memories. When some aspect or component of an event is experienced later in time, the interaction of the hippocampal system with neocortical storage sites may allow the rest of the information that was originally bound with that component to be retrieved. In this manner, the hippocampus can be seen as allowing for **pattern completion**—one piece can

be used to reconstitute the whole (see Halgren, 1984; Eichenbaum, 2000).

A variety of evidence suggests that the degree to which the hippocampus is involved in memory retrieval may vary depending on the manner in which information is retrieved. The processes involved in retrieving a memory have been an issue of investigation for psychologists for more than a century. Some researchers have argued that recall of an item, as well as the recognition that an item has been seen before, rely on the same fundamental processes, but that the confidence one has or the strength of information is greater for recall than recognition (e.g., Dunn, 2004). However, other psychologists have argued that two separate and distinct processes may occur in memory retrieval. These models, known as *dual-process models* (for a review, see Yonelinas, 2001), argue that recognition relies on the strength of undifferentiated information about the item or event, or, said more simply, a sense of familiarity. In contrast, recall involves remembering something specific about the item, such as the instance or episode in which the information was first learned. In memory studies, experimental psychologists often ask participants to differentiate the type of memory they have for an item by asking whether the person is familiar with and "knows" that he or she has seen the item before, as opposed to recalling the specific item and "remembering" that he or she has seen it before.

Electrophysiological studies, such as ● Figure 10.19, supply evidence that there are distinct neural signatures

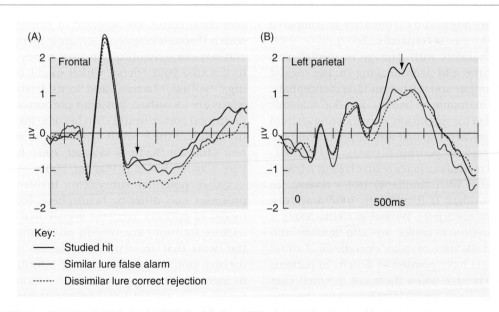

● **FIGURE 10.19 Event-related potentials that index different memory processes.** (A) The left frontal negativity indexes the process of familiarity. This component is greater for those items that the individual perceives as being new (dissimilar lure correct rejection) than for the item the individuals thinks he or she has seen before, regardless of whether the items are indeed old (studied hits) or not (similar lure false alarm). (B) In contrast, a left parietal component indexes the process of recognition. It is larger for items that individuals report as having seen previously (studied hit) than for items they have not seen, regardless of whether they report the item as being old (similar lure false alarm) or new (dissimilar lure correct rejection). *Source:* Rugg, MD and Curran, T, "Event-related potential and recognition memory," Trends in Cognitive Sciences, 11, Figure 2, page 253 (2007).

for each of these processes, suggesting that they are indeed separable. In a typical experiment, individuals see a list of items to remember. Afterward, they are given a list of items and must decide whether they have seen the word before or not. Included in the list are new words, known as *lures*. Some of the lures are very dissimilar to words on the initial list. Others, however, are quite similar (e.g., "trucks" as compared to "truck"). Not surprisingly, people often report having seen these similar lures before, resulting in a false alarm. One ERP component, recorded maximally over posterior regions of the brain at about 600 ms postpresentation as a positive deflection, is greater to correctly recognized item than to either similar lures that individuals claim they have seen before or dissimilar lures that they correctly identify as new. Notice that this component distinguishes items actually seen before from those not seen before, regardless of what the person reports that he or she has seen! This parietal component may index processes that are required when one really remembers an item, such as accessing information about the spatial and temporal context in which the item was learned. In contrast, a negative component, recorded over frontal leads at about 400 ms, is larger for correctly rejected new words than for items that the person thinks he or she has seen before, regardless of whether that is the case (e.g., studied items correctly identified as old and similar lures incorrectly identified as old) (Figure 10.19) (Curran, 2000; see Rugg & Curran, 2007, for a longer discussion of what ERPs can tell us about recognition memory). Converging evidence from neuroimaging studies and patients with circumscribed brain lesions also suggest that different neural systems are engaged by familiarity as compared to recollection (Skinner & Fernandes, 2007).

Results from patients with damage to medial temporal lobe structures and neuroimaging studies suggest that the hippocampus and related midline diencephalic structures (e.g., mammillary bodies, anterior thalamic nuclei) are required for specifically remembering an item or event within its larger spatial and temporal context. In contrast, the nearby perirhinal cortex and connections with dorsal medial nucleus are involved in retrieval processes associated with familiarity (for a review, see Eichenbaum, Yonelinas, & Ranganath, 2007; for a dissenting viewpoint, see Squire, Wixted, & Clark, 2007).

Regions of prefrontal cortex are also reliably and robustly active at the time of memory retrieval. A number of investigators have pointed to deficits in patients with prefrontal damage when there are minimal cues at test time to aid memory performance, as is the case for tests involving recall (e.g., Gershberg & Shimamura, 1995; Wheeler, Stuss, & Tulving, 1995). The prefrontal cortex is probably involved in organizing and monitoring memory retrieval, as patients with damage to this area tend to *confabulate,* generating narratives that include false memories (e.g., Moscovitch, 1995). In addition, they tend to show an increased proportion of false positives in recognition-memory tasks, saying

that they had viewed items that in actuality were not previously seen (Schacter, Curran, Galluccio, Milberg, & Bates, 1996).

Prefrontal Cortex

Regions of prefrontal cortex (PFC) are reliably activated during memory retrieval. Activity in posterior PFC at retrieval time is lateralized depending on whether the material being retrieved is verbal or nonverbal (McDermott, Buckner, Peterson, Kelley, & Sanders, 1999; Wagner et al., 1998). These laterality effects are similar to those we noted with regard to encoding. For example, left posterior PFC is activated by verbal tasks, including word generation, word classification, and word memorization.

Interestingly, at least some studies suggest that activity in posterior PFC is more related to retrieval attempt than to retrieval success (Buckner, et al. 1998; Konishi, Wheeler, Donaldson, & Buckner, 2000; Buckner, Wheeler, & Sheridan, 2001). That is, the amount of activation observed in this region is related to the effort required when retrieval is being attempted. When retrieval is more difficult, because encoding of the items was relatively poor, there is greater posterior prefrontal activation than when retrieval is less difficult because the items were well encoded. Moreover, the amount of activation is independent of whether the item is successfully remembered.

As you may recall from Chapter 9, evidence points to a differential role of anterior and posterior ventrolateral prefrontal regions in semantic retrieval. At least one model suggests that anterior regions of left ventrolateral prefrontal cortex are involved in helping to guide the search through long-term semantic memory to identify and retrieve semantically related words (such as words to describe your friend, which might be "kind," "caring," "selfless," "warm," and "considerate"). Once those words are identified, posterior portions of ventrolateral prefrontal cortex would then become involved in selecting which of these words is most appropriate in the current situation (Badre & Wagner, 2007; Badre, Poldrack, Pare-Blagoev, Insler, & Wagner, 2005).

Other potential subsystems involved in retrieval processes may differ by hemisphere. For example, one model of episodic retrieval argues that left prefrontal regions are more involved in producing or generating the items that are retrieved, whereas right prefrontal regions monitor whether or not information is stored in memory. The support for such a model comes from findings of greater left prefrontal activity for recall than for recognition tasks, and more right prefrontal activity for recognition than for recall tasks (Cabeza, Locantore, & Anderson, 2003).

The idea that specific prefrontal regions might play a role in recognition maps nicely onto the neuropsychological data, which emphasize that deficits in recall but not recognition are observed in patients with prefrontal damage. Although details must still be worked out, taken altogether, it appears that different portions of prefrontal cortex make contributions to strategic and executive aspects of memory. They appear to aid in the organization, selection, monitoring, and evaluation of processing that occurs at both encoding and retrieval.

Left Parietal Cortex

Like the prefrontal cortex, parietal regions also contribute to retrieval, even though damage to these regions does not lead to severe memory deficits. Rather, when asked to recall information about various autobiographical memories, regardless of the aspect of the memory (e.g., spatial, perceptual) patients with bilateral parietal damage report information in less detail and less vividly than controls. However, when asked specific questions about their lives, they can answer without difficulty, indicating that basic memory processes are intact (Berryhill, Phuong, Picasso, Cabeza, & Olson, 2007).

Recent neuroimaging evidence also suggests that the left parietal cortex plays a general role in memory retrieval, regardless of the nature of the content (e.g., verbal, nonverbal) or the modality (e.g. auditory, visual) of the memory (see Vilberg & Rugg, 2008). In fMRI studies of recognition memory, left parietal cortex exhibits more activation for studied items correctly identified as "old"—that is, correctly remembered—than novel items correctly identified as "new," regardless of the nature of the materials (Henson, Rugg, Shallice, Josephs, & Dolan, 1999; Konishi et al., 2000; Sanders, Wheeler, & Buckner, 2000). This result is congruent with those of other neuroimaging studies in which more left parietal lobe activity is found for old items than for new items (see Habib & Lepage, 2000), even when no recognition-memory decision is required (Donaldson, Petersen, & Buckner, 2001). Parallel studies run using fMRI and ERPs suggest that the distinct ERP effect over left parietal regions is indeed greater for correctly remembered old items than for new items (Curran, 2000), reflecting activity in parietal cortex (Vilberg & Rugg, 2009).

The exact operation being performed by left parietal cortex in retrieval remains unclear. A variety of models have been proposed (see Wagner, Shannon, Kahn, & Buckner, 2005; Cabeza, Ciaramelli, Olson, & Moscovitch, 2008, for reviews), although currently there is no definitive answer. These models range from ones suggesting that parietal regions play a role in helping to direct and maintain attention to internally generated information in memory, to others arguing that it plays a role in integrating information from different brain regions according to the strength of the memory. Notice that both of these models suggest that the operation performed by parietal cortex overlaps with operations performed in other domains. For example, the parietal cortex plays an important role in attention and in integrating information from various modalities. In these models, however, those operations are performed on internal representations, that is, those related to memory, rather than being performed on stimuli from the external world.

Working Memory

Prior sections of this chapter have explored the processes by which information is encoded, stored, and retrieved from long-term storage. In this section, we focus on a more short-term aspect of memory: namely, working memory. As we noted earlier in our discussion of H.M., *working memory* is the ability that allows us to retain limited amounts of information for a short amount of time while we are actively working on that information. We discuss evidence from patients who have a selective deficit in this type of memory, as well as the burgeoning evidence from other methodologies such as neuroimaging.

■ Evidence from Patients

As we have already discussed, although hippocampal damage impairs long-term memory, it leaves working memory intact. In contrast, there are patients who exhibit a selective impairment in verbal working memory, demonstrating a deficit in temporary maintenance in an active state of the information they are currently processing (see Shallice & Warrington, 1979; Vallar & Baddeley, 1984). Their working memory is so compromised as to preclude immediate verbatim recall of as few as two items (e.g., two digits). The first well-recognized patient with such a disorder was a man known as K.F., who had a lesion in the left temporoparietal area, and showed a profoundly reduced capacity to hold in working memory even short strings of words or digits (Shallice & Warrington, 1970). Nonetheless, he had intact long-term memory for word lists, paired associates, and the content of stories and discourse across significant delays.

The fact that a deficit in working memory does not also cause a deficit in long-term memory is in some ways surprising. Earlier theories of memory had suggested that working memory and long-term memory handled information in a strictly serial manner. Information was first held in a short-term store, which served as the gateway to the long-term store. The neuropsychological findings of a double dissociation between these syndromes indicate instead that working memory and long-term memory are systems that work somewhat in parallel. The working-memory system operates to maintain information in an active state to support online processing, whereas the long-term memory system works to create enduring records of experience for later use.

Deficits of working memory tend to be closely tied to individual information-processing systems, occurring for a narrow domain of processing. Thus, the best-known example of a working-memory deficit, as in the case of K.F., involves impairment of **auditory-verbal working memory**, or what is currently known as the

IN FOCUS: Does Sleep Help You to Remember?

Have you ever heard someone say, "I think I'll sleep on it"? The idea that the act of sleeping might help one's memory actually goes back to ancient times. Around the first century A.D., the Roman rhetorician Quintilian noted that "what could not be repeated at first is readily put together on the following day; and the very time which is generally thought to cause forgetfulness is found to strengthen the memory." But is there any truth to this idea?

Recently scientists have begun to examine whether sleep might indeed play a role in enhancing memory. In fact, a variety of research results in animals and humans suggest that getting a good night's sleep may help one to remember (see Stickgold, 2005; Marshall & Born, 2007, for reviews).

Research has found that both explicit/declarative and implicit/procedural memory are aided by sleep. Boosts in performance after sleep compared to wakefulness have been found for procedural tasks such as mirror tracing (Plihal & Born, 1997), motor sequencing (Fischer, Hallschmid, Elsner, & Born, 2002), and word-stem priming (Plihal

& Born, 1999). Also aided by sleep are tasks of associative memory, which are likely to rely on the hippocampus (Gais, Lucas, & Born, 2006; Talamini, Nieuwenhuis, Takashima, & Jensen, 2008).

In fact, sleep research provides additional evidence that declarative and procedural memories rely on different neural systems. Human sleep cycles are typically 90 minutes long and are defined by two distinct types of neural activity. The first half of the cycle is characterized by what is termed *slow-wave sleep*, because the activity tends to occur at less than 4 Hz (also referred to as *delta activity*, see Chapter 3). The second phase, known as *REM (rapid eye movement) sleep*, is characterized by faster theta activity (4–8 Hz). Non-REM sleep appears to aid declarative memories, whereas REM sleep appears to aid procedural memories. Thus, a quick daytime nap that does not allow enough time to reach the second phase of REM sleep, aids the ability to remember paired associates, but does not lead to improvement on a mirror-drawing task (Tucker et al., 2006).

What are the potential mechanisms by which sleep might aid memory? At present there is no agreement among researchers, but a number of distinct possibilities are being considered (see Axmacher, Draguhn, Elger & Fell, 2009; Ellenbogen, Payne, & Stickgold, 2006, for reviews). One interesting possibility is that sleep aids the consolidation process, and that such consolidation buffers old memories from interference by new ones. Evidence for this viewpoint comes from a study in which four groups of individuals were taught cue-target word pairs (e.g., blanket-village). Participants were then given the cue and asked to recall the target. The first two groups were simply tested for their recall, one group following 12 hours of wakefulness, and the other following 12 hours of sleep. The individuals who were tested after sleep had marginally better recall (94%) compared to those who remained awake (82%). In the other two groups, 12 minutes before testing of the original pairs, they were taught a new target to the same cue (e.g., blanket-rubber). Typically, learning a second target to the same cue interferes with recall for the

---

phonological store. This deficit consists of difficulty in repeating aloud and verbatim the contents of the immediately preceding verbal utterance, such as is required in the digit span task. Nevertheless, patients with working-memory deficits can retain and recover basic content of a verbal utterance and can even learn word lists. Importantly, their working memory for other processing domains, such as spatial processing or arithmetic, is perfectly intact.

Some researchers have reported further specificity among verbal working-memory deficits, such that different aspects of language processing, either comprehension or production, may be selectively affected (Caramazza, Miceli, Silveri, & Laudanna, 1985). They suggest that the **input phonological buffer** holds auditory-verbal information received by the listener online while an utterance is being parsed, whereas the **output phonological buffer** holds the phonological code online as a speaker is preparing his or her own utterance. Other patients have deficits in **visual-verbal working memory**, which involve difficulty in the ability to hold visual-verbal information online during reading. Still other deficits occur in what Baddeley (1986) refers to as the **visuospatial scratch pad**, which involves deficits in the ability to hold

nonverbal visual information while performing perceptual analyses of the stimulus array. Thus, each of these deficits is tied to a very specific processing domain, leaving working memory for other processing domains intact. This pattern has been interpreted to support the idea of multiple working-memory capacities, each intimately tied to the operation of specific information-processing systems in the brain.

■ Studies with Nonhuman Animals

Evidence from lesion and electrophysiological recording studies in animals has specifically implicated the dorsolateral prefrontal cortex (DLPFC) as playing a critical role in working memory. The role of frontal cortex in a short-term form of memory has been known since 1935, when Fulton first used the spatial delayed-response task with dogs. In each trial of this task, the experimenter put food in one of several food wells in view of the animal and then covered them. After a delay interval, the animal was given the opportunity to choose one of the food wells to obtain the food reward (● Figure 10.20). Following frontal lobe damage, the animal was unable to perform this task, even with delay intervals as short as 1 second. Subsequent work by various investigators has shown that the deficit in

first target. What was so interesting was that this effect was greatly increased for the group that had just had 12 hours of wakefulness (32%) versus the group that had had 12 hours of sleep (76%). This finding suggests that sleep allows the consolidation of episodic memories, so as to become more resistant to interference by subsequent learning (Ellenbogen, Hulbert, Stickgold, Dinges, & Thompson-Schill, 2006).

One neural process that may help to consolidate memories is the reactivation of already stored memories during the time after learning. Some interesting evidence ties such reactivation to activity in the hippocampus, neocortex, and prefrontal cortex during sleep that occurs after the learning event. For example, some researchers noted that hippocampal neurons active during an animal's exploration of the spatial parameters of an environment went on to fire at an elevated rate during subsequent slow-wave sleep (Pavlides & Winson, 1989). Other researchers (Wilson & McNaughton, 1994; Skaggs & McNaughton, 1996) found that sets of hippocampal cells with a high degree of co-activity when an animal was exploring particular locations in an environment also show a high co-activity during subsequent sleep. Furthermore, multicell recordings in hippocampus and visual cortex during maze learning indicate that these two regions exhibit synchronized spiking patterns that are organized into frames, or stepwise increases in the activity of neuronal populations. Such frames may represent specific episodes or experiences. Notably, these multicell firing sequences are replayed during sleep, raising the possibility that specific events are being re-remembered (Ji & Wilson, 2007).

A fascinating study with humans supports the idea that sleep affects the coordination of activity between the hippocampus and neocortex. Participants played a children's game known as concentration. In this game there is a matrix (e.g., 6 rows by 5 columns) of similarly colored cards. On the opposite side of each card is a figure. In the game, individuals turn the items over in pairs and over time learn where matching sets of figures are located. As such, it is an associative memory task. The individuals played the game on two different days, but on both days the researchers presented them with the scent of a rose during play. Then, on the night following each play day, the researcher waited until the participants had entered slow-wave sleep. On one night they presented the rose scent; on the other, they presented an inert substance instead. The next morning, the participants were tested regarding their memory for the specific pair locations they had learned the prior day. Their memory following the evenings during which they had been administered the rose smell was 97%, but after administration of the insert substance it was only 86%. These findings are consistent with the idea that the hippocampus serves as a mechanism from which memories can be reconstructed from partial information, allowing for pattern completion, and that such a process may occur during sleep.

What are the implications of these studies? They clearly indicate that if you want to memorize the facts about the brain that you are learning in this textbook, you should get a good night's sleep—and perhaps a nap after class might not be a bad idea, either! In fact, scientists have suggested that in certain business settings, employers might want to reconsider whether sleeping on the job is really a waste of time (Stickgold, 2009).

 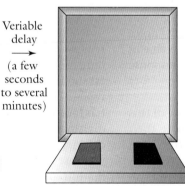 

(A)   Veriable delay
→
(a few seconds to several minutes)   (B)   (C)

● **FIGURE 10.20   The delayed-response paradigm, used with monkeys, that illustrates the importance of dorsolateral prefrontal areas for working memory.** (A) In the cue period, the animal sees food placed under an object. (B) Then a screen drops, preventing the monkey from viewing the bowls. (C) After a delay of 1 to 10 seconds, the screen is raised and the animal gets to choose one of the two covers, obtaining the food morsel if the correct choice is made (response phase). Monkeys with dorsolateral prefrontal damage cannot perform the task when the delay is longer than 1 second. © 2011 Cengage Learning

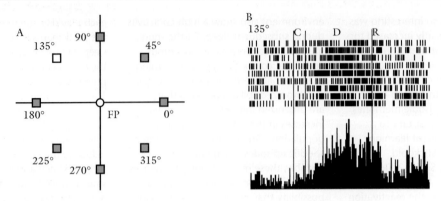

● **FIGURE 10.21   Activity in cells of dorsolateral prefrontal cortex in the monkey across a short time delay on the order of seconds.** (A) The task involves a display with a fixation point (FP) and eight possible cue locations. Whenever the light is on at fixation, the monkey's eyes must remain there. Three-quarters of a second after the onset of the light at fixation, one of the cue locations lights up for a second. Then there is a three-second delay, after which the fixation light goes off and the monkey must respond by moving its eyes to the location at which the cue was presented. (B) A recording of activity in a neuron in DLPFC. Notice that activity increases during the delay period (D) relative to the time period of the cue (C) and the response (R). Because of this increased activity during the delay period, it has been suggested that these neurons play an important role in working memory. © 2011 Cengage Learning

performing such tasks does not require damage to large portions of the frontal lobes, but can instead be limited to dorsolateral prefrontal cortex (DLPFC) (see Goldman-Rakic, 1988).

The way in which the DLPFC plays a critical role in working memory is powerfully illustrated by the work of Goldman-Rakic and colleagues with an oculomotor version of the delayed-response task in monkeys (e.g., see Funahashi, Bruce, & Goldman-Rakic, 1993; Goldman-Rakic, 1995). In this paradigm, the monkey maintains fixation on a central spot on a display. As the monkey is doing so, one of eight possible target locations is briefly lit. Afterward, there is a short delay period during which the monkey must continue to maintain fixation. When the light at the fixation point is turned off, the monkey must move its eyes to the location where the target was presented in order to obtain its reward. During this choice period, no information in the display provides a clue as to the correct location. Rather, the monkey's response must be guided by information held in working memory during the delay period (● Figure 10.21A).

Lesions to the DLPFC impair the performance of this task. The monkeys are unable to correctly guide their eye movements by memory—and the longer the delay, the greater the deficit. In contrast, eye movements guided by visual information are unaffected, indicating that the deficit is selective to memory-guided eye movements, leaving the control of eye movements in general intact.

Neurons in this region maintain firing during the delay period, when the animal must maintain the position of the target in memory. These cells fire for as long as the delay period lasts, whether for just a few or many seconds (● Figure 10.21B). Moreover, the

pattern of firing of these neurons is related to the animal's behavior. This firing is maintained only during the delay period for trials in which the monkey correctly remembers the target location; it is absent on trials in which errors are made. This activity has been interpreted to indicate that regions of the dorsolateral prefrontal cortex hold information online during the delay period, and therefore represent the site of storage for information in working memory (see Funahashi, 2006, for a review).

Single-cell recording studies in monkeys have shown that the exact region of the prefrontal cortex that holds information online depends on the nature of that information. Populations of cells in different regions of the PFC fire preferentially when locations must be remembered across the delay, as compared to when objects must be remembered, and both these regions differ from when motor responses must be remembered. Moreover, damage to the various prefrontal subdivisions in monkeys causes deficits in different types of delayed-response performance, either for spatial locations, objects, or movements. Each of the subdivisions of PFC involved in working memory receives distinct and nonoverlapping inputs from other brain regions. The region of the DLPFC that maintains information about location receives information from the inferior parietal gyrus, which is part of the dorsal visual-processing stream and is involved in spatial processing (see Chapter 8). The region of the PFC that maintains information about object identity receives information from the inferotemporal cortex, which, as we learned in Chapter 7, is part of the ventral visual-processing stream important for item identity (see Ungerleider, 1995; Goldman-Rakic, 1996). Motor projections go to yet a different subdivision of PFC. Thus, there appears to be an organization by which those regions of the brain that process a particular type of information (e.g., spatial information) are intimately connected with frontal regions that can hold that information online.

■ Studies with Neurologically Intact Individuals

More recent data, quite surprisingly, have begun to provide evidence that is inconsistent with the interpretation of data from single-cell recordings in animals: namely, that the dorsolateral prefrontal cortex is the region in which information is maintained in working memory. If this interpretation were correct, then one would expect working-memory deficits in patients with prefrontal lesions—but patients with prefrontal damage do not have significant impairments, whether they are asked to recall a series of digits or to maintain information across a delay period (D'Esposito, Cooney, Gazzaley, Gibbs, & Postle, 2006; Müller & Knight, 2006). In addition, rTMS over dorsolateral prefrontal cortex (DLPFC) does not interfere with performance on a task in which participants decide if the current item is the same as the previous one (Sandrini, Rossini, & Miniussi, 2008). Such findings do not indicate that prefrontal regions play a special role in holding information in working memory. If not, then where is such information held?

At least one hint is provided by the patients we discussed earlier, such as K.F., who after sustaining damage to the left temporoparietal region exhibited working-memory deficits. Consistent with the idea that posterior brain regions may play a role in working memory, neuroimaging studies have revealed that posterior regions of cortex that process the specific type of item being held online (e.g., fusiform cortex for faces) show sustained activity across the delay period (e.g., Postle, Druzgal & D'Esposito, 2003). Therefore, when information must be retained short-term, it may be reactivated in the region of cortex that is storing such information. If so, then what role does prefrontal cortex play in working memory?

To solve this mystery, we need to turn back to psychological models of working memory. Beginning principally with Baddeley (Baddeley & Hitch, 1974; Baddeley, 1986, 1992, 1996; Repov & Baddeley, 2006), some researchers have strongly advocated distinguishing storage, or maintenance, properties of working memory from control, or executive, processes of working memory. In Baddeley's model of working memory, specialized subsystems mediate the storage process, and a distinct **central executive** performs the mental work of controlling these slave subsystems and forming strategies for using the information they contain.

The distinction between the maintenance and manipulation portions of working memory helps to make clear at least one of the reasons that the term *working memory* is preferred to the term *short-term memory*. Working memory involves the important addition of

mental "work" that is performed by the central executive above and beyond the more passive retention capability of a short-term store. Sometimes all that is demanded of working memory is the maintenance portion, such as when we have to recall verbatim a phone number we have read in the phone book or heard from the operator just long enough to dial it. More often, though, working memory is required to do more, such as when we are preparing an ambitious meal or doing mental arithmetic.

The working-memory challenge used in many neuroimaging studies, the *N-back task*, typically involves both executive, or control, functions and maintenance functions. In this task, a series of items is presented one at a time and the task is to respond affirmatively when an item matches one that is *N* (either one, two, or three) items back. Whereas the one-back version of the task simply requires a comparison with the prior item, the two- and three-back versions require many more operations. For example, in a two-back task, if the sequence is 4-2-9-2-7-5-7, the person would begin answering after the third item, with the correct responses being "no, yes, no, no, yes." Thus, on each trial of a two-back condition, a person must maintain in working memory the current item as well the last two items. Then he must compare the current item to the earlier ones, responding affirmatively only if the current item matches the item that was shown two places back, not one or three back. After each trial, the contents of working memory must be updated to include the newest item, while the items that are more than two back must be discarded. Thus, the task requires maintaining, comparing, updating, and inhibiting, among other operations. This type of task reliably activates the prefrontal cortex (Wager & Smith, 2003), and a two-back version of this task is disrupted by rTMS over prefrontal regions (Sandrini, Rossini, & Miniussi, 2008).

Similarly, prefrontal regions are involved in working-memory tasks when an individual must select which type of information is currently important, rather than just holding online what information has recently been retained. For example, in one task, participants are shown four target items on a screen and then after a delay given a probe. Their task is to decide whether the probe was one of the four targets. On some trials, however, the probe is not one of the four targets on the current trial, but rather was a target on the prior trial. In this case, one must act to select the information that is currently relevant and disambiguate it from information that has recently been active. This task also activates prefrontal regions (Jonides, Smith, Marshuetz, Koeppe, & Reuter-Lorenz, 1998). Understanding that there is an executive, or information-manipulation, component of working memory helps to make sense of why working memory is so dependent upon prefrontal cortex. The prefrontal cortex plays an important role in various aspects of executive functions, including the planning, organizing, and monitoring of behavior, which we discuss in more detail in Chapter 12.

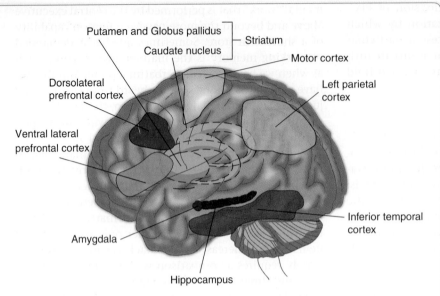

Putamen and Globus pallidus ⎤
Caudate nucleus ⎦ Striatum
Motor cortex
Dorsolateral prefrontal cortex
Left parietal cortex
Ventral lateral prefrontal cortex
Inferior temporal cortex
Amygdala
Hippocampus

● **FIGURE 10.22** **Network of structures underlying the ability to remember and learn.** Shown here are the major structures involved in memory. The hippocampal system (including the hippocampus and surrounding entorhinal cortex), shown in purple, plays a critical role in declarative and episodic memory. The amygdala, shown in deep blue, is important for emotional memory. The striatum, shown in green, has been implicated in procedural/implicit memory. Regions of the dorsolateral prefrontal cortex, shown in red, are involved in working memory, whereas ventromedial prefrontal regions, shown in orange, have been implicated in encoding and retrieval. The left parietal cortex, also shown in yellow, has been suggested to play a role in retrieval. Finally, memory for perceptual information relies on sensory cortices, such as inferior temporal regions, shown in brown, whereas motor memory relies on motor regions, such as primary motor cortex, shown in tan. © 2011 Cengage Learning

At this point we have considered all the major brain regions that are involved in memory processing. These include the hippocampal system (including the hippocampus and parahippocampal area), frontal lobes, left parietal cortex, amygdala, and the striatum, which are depicted in ● Figure 10.22. To conclude the chapter, we consider the relationship between different memory systems in the brain.

The Relationships between Memory Systems

In this section we consider why the brain might have a need for multiple memory systems and how such systems might interact with each other.

■ Computational Perspectives

One way to understand the need for such a complicated set of neural systems to support our memory capabilities is to consider what is required to remember and learn. Computational models have assumed that we need at least two types of learning systems. One system is used to generalize across different experiences via general statistical learning. Over many, many instances, general statistical features common across all experiences are extracted. For example, over many, many trips, you may have learned the best place to park your car relative to some specific locale, such as your favorite restaurant. Here your knowledge comes from many similar experiences—those surrounding similar trips to the same or similar locations in space. Because these experiences share many commonalities, the representations of them are highly overlapping. Furthermore, the learning rate of such a system is slow and incremental, as information is accumulated over many different instances.

Consider now the different requirements for a learning and memory system that is designed to help you remember where you parked your car *today*. Notice that the system we have just described is relatively useless for remembering such information. It only saves information about where you typically park your car. On this particular day, you may have indeed parked your car in a typical location. But maybe you got lucky and found a spot closer than usual, or, conversely, you decided to park further away so as to enjoy a longer walk in the sunshine. A system that is designed to store such information must learn quickly—on this very day you need to encode the information about where your car is parked—and you need it to encode all the specifics of the particular place where your car is located, not just more general information about the relative neighborhood in which your car is parked. Furthermore, you need this representation to be discrete and not overlap with other representations, so that you keep the memory of where you parked your car today separate from where you parked your car yesterday.

By now, you probably have realized that the first incremental learning system describes the type of learning that supports implicit and semantic aspects of memory; this is the type of learning that is thought to occur in specific neocortical processors, such as motor regions or visual-processing areas. In contrast, the system that encodes and stores specific instances of events by combining specific different pieces of information is the type of learning that occurs in the hippocampus (O'Reilly & Norman, 2002).

This perspective provides some insight into why we might have separate learning systems. The goals of these systems and how they need to store information are mutually incompatible. By having somewhat discrete and separable memory systems, our brains can retain information in more than one manner so it can be used to best suit a particular situation.

■ Empirical Findings

We can now ask how these two brain systems interact. Do they act in tandem, or in opposition, or do they interact in some other manner? At present, relatively little definitive information exists on this issue. Some evidence comes from fMRI studies using the weather prediction task (Poldrack & Gabrieli, 2001). As a reminder, the task involves predicting which of two outcomes (*rain* or *shine*) follows from cues presented on cards. The outcome is associated with the conjoint probabilities of the cards presented in any of 14 configurations. As discussed earlier in the chapter, it is possible to learn the task without involvement of the hippocampus, as evidenced by normal performance on this task by amnesics. However, that does not mean that in neurologically intact individuals the hippocampus plays no role in learning. In fact, at least one fMRI study suggests that the striatal- and hippocampal-dependent memory systems compete with each over the course of learning this task. Very early on in training, activation is observed in the hippocampal system, but that activity declines across trials and in fact decreases below initial levels. In contrast, striatal activation increases across time. This pattern suggests that participants at first tried to utilize a strategy that relied more on declarative memory (perhaps, for example, trying to remember specific card combinations). At this point, the striatal system would not have been of much use, because it learns gradually and incrementally. However, later in learning with more experience, the striatal system had learned the stimulus-response contingencies, and it could guide performance. Finally, the fact that the hippocampal activity decreased below baseline raises the possibility that activity in the striatal system is in opposition to that of the hippocampal system.

In another experiment, fMRI data were collected from people performing either a standard version of the weather task or a version that emphasized declarative memory in a **paired-associate learning** format. Whereas striatal regions were engaged by the standard version, hippocampal regions were engaged by the latter version. Furthermore, activity in one region was negatively correlated with that in the other: high activity in the striatum was associated with low activity in the hippocampus, and vice versa. The apparent competition between the learning of stimulus-response contingencies, dependent upon striatal circuits, and memory for relations, dependent on the hippocampal system, is also strongly supported by a variety of studies in rodents (Packard & McGaugh, 1996; White & McDonald, 1993) (for a review of this issue, see Poldrack & Packard, 2003).

Other studies have more directly examined the relationship between these two systems via pharmacological intervention. The advantage of such an approach is that one can examine performance in the same individuals when they are "on" the drug and when they are "off" it. These studies use midazolam, which is a sedative drug that inactivates the hippocampus, leading to profound deficits in explicit memory. (In fact, midazolam is often given to individuals prior to invasive medical procedures, such as minor surgery, so that they can be only mildly sedated and yet have no memory of the procedure.) However, skill learning, as assessed by the mirror-reading task, is unaffected by the drug (Thomas-Antérion, Koenig, Navez, & Laurent, 1999). In one study, people were given midazolam, and their performance on a task thought to rely on the implicit/procedural memory system was actually superior to when they were off midazolam (Frank, O'Reilly, & Curran, 2006). This finding suggests that the explicit/declarative learning system and the implicit/procedural systems indeed may be somewhat in competition.

These results should not be overinterpreted, however, to suggest that these two systems work in a totally antagonistic manner, such that learning in one system precludes learning in the other. Rather, as discussed earlier, each system provides a different way of storing information. It may be that the relative activation of these two systems varies by task requirements, across learning, and across individuals. As just one example, researchers gave people a task in which they had to learn the location of a single target relative to a small set of landmarks (Baumann, Chan, & Mattingley, 2009). Neuroimaging revealed that greater activity within the right hippocampus and the parahippocampal gyrus during the encoding of information predicted more accurate navigation in the retrieval stage, suggesting that the explicit/declarative system was important for initial learning. However, during retrieval, those people who performed better showed greater striatal activity than poor learners, suggesting that the good learners ended up performing the task via the use of a more implicit/procedural strategy. Thus, there has to be a mechanism whereby information in one system can be transferred or transformed to the other. In contrast, the poor learners showed greater left hippocampal activity than good learners, suggesting that they may have learned the task via a less effective verbal strategy.

In sum, memory, by its very nature, is a system that allows us to relate what we have experienced in the past to what is occurring in the present. As such, memories are not static entities. Moreover, we need memories that are specific to a time and place, such as the episodes bound together by the medial temporal regions, as well as memories that fuse the present with the past, such as occurs in the statistical learning typical of skill learning. In addition, we need memories that are independent of a context so that they can be accessed across a variety of situations, such as occurs in semantic memory. It makes sense that there are different brain systems and processes to meet these disparate needs.

Summary

What Is Memory?

- Memory is the group of mechanisms or processes by which experience shapes us, changing our brains and our behavior.

Amnesia: A Disorder of Long-Term Memory

- Amnesia occurs after damage to the hippocampal region, or to midline diencephalic structures, such as the dorsomedial nucleus of the thalamus and the mammillary bodies of the hypothalamus.
- Anterograde amnesia is the deficit in new learning, resulting in impairment in memory of information acquired after the onset of amnesia.
- Retrograde amnesia is the impairment in memory of information that was acquired normally *prior* to the onset of amnesia, a deficit stretching back in time from amnesia onset.
- Amnesia occurs for information regardless of the sensory modality or the nature of the material (e.g., verbal, nonverbal), and regardless of the mode of testing, such as free as compared to cued recall.
- Amnesia selectively disrupts the process of developing new long-term memories, particularly of the relations among the elements of a scene or event, while leaving intact the ability to form short-term memories.
- Amnesics retain the ability to learn new skills and habits, and can exhibit priming, in that their performance is speeded or aided by prior exposure to the materials.
- Although amnesics exhibit a deficit in explicit tests of memory, being unable to recollect a particular study episode or learning event, they typically exhibit intact performance on implicit tests of memory, as their performance can be influenced by past experience when the learning event need not be recalled.
- Animals also exhibit memory deficits following damage to the hippocampal system, being unable to remember the relations between different aspects of an experience.
- Two characteristics of cells in the hippocampus of animals—their ability to exhibit long-term potentiation and their ability to act as place fields—provides evidence that this brain region has attributes that enable it to play an important role in the formation of new long-term memories.

Multiple Memory Systems

- The dissociations between the affected and spared abilities in amnesia suggest that the brain contains multiple memory systems.
- One prominent viewpoint suggests that the hippocampal system is critical for explicit, conscious recall of information, whereas nonhippocampal regions support memory of an implicit, unconscious nature.
- Another prominent viewpoint suggests that the declarative memory system, which depends critically on hippocampal regions, allows one to remember the relations between the different pieces of an experience or event, whereas the procedural memory system, independent of the hippocampus, allows one to acquire and express skill through gradual incremental learning.
- Although the hippocampal system is involved in conscious recollection of a learning situation, consciousness does not rely on the hippocampus.

Nonhippocampal Regions Involved in Memory

- Memory relies in part on reactivation of those same domain-specific regions of the cortex that were activated when an event was experienced.
- Changes in patterns of activity in the domain-specific neural processors are involved in skill learning, such as motor regions involved in learning of a finger-sequencing task.
- The basal ganglia plays a role in implicit/procedural learning, which usually occurs gradually and incrementally through repetition of motor, perceptual, or cognitive operations, and which leads to improved performance. The basal ganglia most likely do so by aiding in the linkage of sensory information to the motor outputs, actions, or choices required to exhibit such learning.
- The amygdala plays an important role in fear conditioning, linking events and stimuli to a fearful experience. It also plays a role in learning stimulus-reward associations, and in the modulation of memory by emotional experiences.
- Anterior temporal regions play a role in semantic memory, which is the portion of memory that reflects our general knowledge about the world, such as facts, concepts, and categories that cut across many different contexts and are not modality- or domain-specific. In contrast, episodic memory, which is memory for a specific episode or event, appears to rely on hippocampal regions.

Brain Systems That Contribute to Encoding, Consolidation and Storage, and Retrieval

- Both the hippocampus and prefrontal regions contribute to the encoding of new memories, as activity in these regions at the time of encoding predicts subsequent memory for an item. The hippocampus binds together the different attributes of an event, whereas prefrontal regions likely aid in focusing and organizing the encoding processes.

- For at least some length of time, the hippocampus is involved in storing information or indexing where in neocortical processors discrete aspects of an event (e.g., sights, sounds, feelings) are stored.
- The index stored in the hippocampus allows memory retrieval via pattern completion of information stored in neocortical areas.
- Prefrontal regions assist in retrieval by aiding in the search process for relevant information stored in memory, as well as selecting the most appropriate information for the current context after the relevant options have been retrieved.
- Left parietal regions are implicated in recognition memory and in judging the familiarity of information retrieved from memory.

Working Memory

- Some patients exhibit a specific deficit in working memory while retaining their long-term memory.
- The double dissociation between these patients and amnesic patients indicates that working memory and long-term memory are supported by distinct neural systems.
- Impairments of working memory are closely tied to domain-specific processing systems, such as auditory-verbal working memory or visuospatial working memory.
- Single-cell studies in animals indicate that cells in the dorsolateral prefrontal cortex fire during a delay when information must be held online, suggesting a role for prefrontal cortex in working memory.
- Studies with human suggest that prefrontal regions are involved in executive processes that act on information in working memory, such as selecting the most relevant contents of working memory or manipulating information in working memory.

The Relationships between Memory Systems

- Computational models suggest the need for two memory systems because they learn in fundamentally different manners. One of these permits generalization of knowledge through slow and incremental learning over many different instances and through the use of highly overlapping representations. The other system enables the fast learning of specific episodes and events via discrete and nonoverlapping representations.
- Initial evidence suggests that learning in these two systems may be somewhat incompatible and/or that they are preferentially engaged at different stages of learning.

Key Terms

amnesia 267
anterograde amnesia 270
auditory-verbal working memory 293
central executive 297
consolidation 289
contextual fear conditioning 286
cued recall 270
declarative memory system 278
delayed nonmatch-to-sample task 272
digit span task 271
episodic memory 287
explicit memory system 278
extended digit span 272
fear conditioning 286
free recall 270

habit learning 284
hippocampal system 269
implicit memory system 278
input phonological buffer 294
long-term potentiation (LTP) 277
mammillary bodies 269
material-specific memory disorders 269
midline diencephalic region 269
mirror-reading task 273
mirror tracing task 273
Morris water maze 276
output phonological buffer 294
paired-associate learning 299
pattern completion 291
place fields 277
procedural memory system 279

recognition memory 270
relational learning 279
repetition priming 275
retrograde amnesia 270
Ribot's Law 271
rotary pursuit 273
semantic dementia 287
semantic memory 287
skill learning 273
subsequent memory effect 288
temporal gradient 271
temporally limited 270
visual-verbal working memory 294
visuospatial scratch pad 294
word-stem completion task 275

Book Companion Site at www.cengage.com/psychology/Banich
This website provides instructors and students with a wealth of free information and resources, including tutorial quizzes, flashcards, and the glossary.

Attention

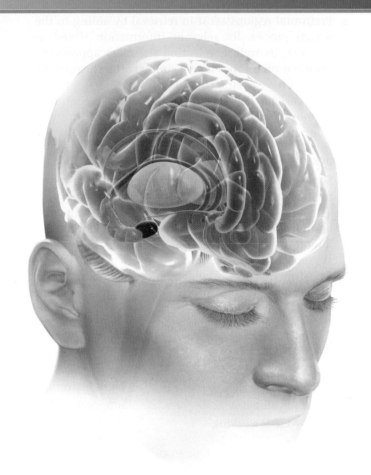

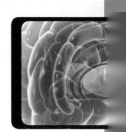

AS HE DID EVERY MORNING AFTER WAKING, Bill went into the bathroom to begin his morning ritual. After squeezing toothpaste onto his toothbrush, he looked into the mirror and began to brush his teeth. Although he brushed the teeth on the right side of his mouth quite vigorously, for the most part he ignored those on the left side. Then he stepped into the shower and began rubbing a bar of soap to produce a frothy lather. After generously distributing the suds over the right side of his body, he began to rinse off without lathering the left side of his body.

After getting dressed, Bill went to his favorite local diner for breakfast. He ordered the daily special of two eggs, toast, bacon, and hash browns; the last two items were his favorites. When his order arrived, the waitress placed the plate in front of him with the fried eggs and the toast toward the right, and the bacon and hash browns to the left. He took one bite each of bacon and of hash browns, and then turned to the eggs and toast. Strangely, once he started eating the eggs and toast, he never took another bite of hash browns or bacon. While Bill was sipping his coffee, a busboy, walking to the kitchen off to Bill's left, dropped a stack of dirty dishes, creating a commotion. Bill, like everyone else in the diner, watched the rattled busboy clean up the mess. Afterward, Bill resumed eating his breakfast and now heartily consumed the hash browns and bacon he had previously ignored.

When Bill asked for the check, the waitress placed it on the left side of the table. After a few minutes, he waved the waitress over and complained, saying, "I asked for my tab five minutes ago. What's taking so long?"

She looked at him quizzically, pointed to the bill on the table, and replied, "But sir, it's right here. I put it there a while ago."

With that, Bill rose to leave, and the waitress, still bemused by the whole encounter, watched him bump into the left-hand part of the door frame as he walked out into the street. As she turned to clean the table, she saw that Bill had left a generous tip. Shrugging, she said softly to herself, "I guess the customer is always right."

THE SEEMINGLY BIZARRE behavior displayed by the gentleman in this story can be attributed to a syndrome known as **hemineglect**, or **hemi-inattention**. Despite having intact sensory and motor functioning, people with hemineglect ignore, or do not pay attention to, one side of space. Hemineglect is considered to be mainly a spatial phenomenon, because the neglect of information occurs with reference to a spatial frame (i.e., information contralateral to the lesion is ignored) and because all types of information, regardless of modality, on the neglected side of space are ignored. Given what you learned in Chapter 8 about the important role that the parietal lobe plays in spatial processes, it should not surprise you that hemineglect is most typically observed after a right parietal lobe lesion.

Because attention is a multifaceted process that has been conceptualized in different ways, we begin this chapter by briefly discussing what attention is and how it influences behavior. Next, we identify and discuss the many brain systems that play a role in different aspects of attention. Even more than other mental abilities we have discussed so far in this book, aspects of attention are controlled by a large and distributed network of brain structures. The first half of this chapter surveys how this network of brain structures underlies attention. The latter half of the chapter presents a detailed discussion of hemineglect. This syndrome has received much attention (no pun intended), not only because

the pattern of deficits is so bizarre and intriguing, but also because it can provide further insight into how the brain is wired to help us to pay attention.

What Is "Attention"?

Attention is a concept often invoked by psychologists, but one that does not have a standard, universally accepted definition. Nonetheless, most psychologists agree that the brain has inherent limitations to the amount of information it can process at any one time. Therefore, our brains can function effectively only if there is a means to select specific information for further processing. This selective process is known as **attention**. Just as we learned that *memory* is an umbrella term that covers many different types of memory, so there are also different types of attention.

Alertness and arousal represent the most basic levels of attention; without them a person is unable to extract information from the environment or to select a particular response. Alertness and arousal are low when you are tired or sleepy, which is why at these times you may miss important information or have trouble choosing the correct action. In some extreme cases, such as coma, alertness and arousal are so disrupted that the person is almost totally unresponsive to the outside world and has no control over his or her responses.

A closely related category of attention is **vigilance**, which is also known as *sustained attention*. Vigilance is the ability to maintain alertness continuously over time. In common parlance, we often say that someone has a "short attention span" when he or she cannot maintain consistent attention for long periods. Vigilance is important when a task must be performed in a nonstop manner—when "tuning in" and "tuning out" would be disadvantageous. Your ability to sustain attention is especially challenged whenever you try to listen to every word of a lecture for an entire class period. (And if the lecturer is particularly boring, your ability to remain alert and aroused may be taxed as well!).

A third general category of attention is **selective attention**, which involves the selection of information essential to a task. Selective attention is often conceptualized as a filtering process that allows us to hone in on critical information from the vast amount of information available. This selection process can be performed on incoming sensory information, on information that we are keeping "in mind," or on the set of possible responses. For example, as you read this page and try to understand what is written on it, you cannot simultaneously listen to a song on the radio and monitor the movements of people around you. Selective attention is the cognitive mechanism that allows you to select—from all the possibilities before you—the words on the page and the task of comprehension as the most salient aspects of processing that must be accomplished at this time.

A fourth general category of attention is known as **divided attention**, which is the kind of attention that we use to split our attention across tasks. A central concept in divided attention is that of the **resource**, or effort, that is required to process information. The brain is thought to have limited resources, which is why dividing attention between tasks is difficult. Originally, these resources were thought to be undifferentiated; that is, they were assumed to be interchangeable. When multiple tasks or a multifaceted task had to be performed, these resources would be doled out for different component processes until none were left (e.g., Kahneman, 1973), much like a stack of U.S. dollar bills. You can use some of them to buy breakfast, another to buy a magazine, some more to buy a bus ticket. It doesn't matter which particular bills you use for any of these purchases. However, **multiple-resource theory** suggests that a limited set of distinct resource pools may exist, each of which can be applied only to certain types of processes, much as only U.S. dollars can be spent in the United States, only euros can be spent in Europe, and only yen can be spent in Japan. For example, spatial and verbal processes appear to rely on different resources, as do auditory and visual processes. The brain's processing capacity is larger when tasks draw from different resource pools than from the same one (e.g., Wickens, 1980). Thus, it is easier to perform an auditory and a visual task simultaneously than it is to perform two visual tasks at the same time. We now discuss what cognitive neuroscience can tell us about the neural systems that support these different aspects of attention.

Brain Structures Involved in Attention

As you may have deduced already, attention is somewhat different from the other cognitive abilities we have discussed so far. It does not provide the ability to process a certain or specific type of information, such as programming a movement, distinguishing between different visual forms, speaking a sentence aloud, or remembering a name. Rather, attention serves to *modulate* or modify ongoing processing across all domains of function. Given this role, it should not surprise you that attentional control occurs via circuits that span many brain regions, as would be required to modulate processing broadly. In this section, we introduce the different neural systems that enable the various types of attentional abilities discussed in the preceding section: arousal, vigilance, selective attention, and divided attention.

■ Arousal

At the most basic level, the ability to pay attention requires the nervous system to be receptive to stimulation. The brain system responsible for overall arousal is the **reticular activating system (RAS)**. As might be expected of a system that causes arousal of the brain, it relies on the neurotransmitter glutamate, an excitatory neurotransmitter (see Chapter 2). Not surprisingly, this system is also responsible for controlling sleep-wake cycles. The cell bodies of the RAS are located in the reticular formation of the brainstem. The RAS has an ascending portion that connects diffusely to most regions of the cortex (● Figure 11.1), allowing it to modulate the arousal of the entire cortex. (A descending branch of the RAS, which we do not discuss here, projects to the spinal cord.) These connections to the cortex occur via two routes: a dorsal system that travels to the cortex via the thalamus, and a ventral route that travels from the hypothalamus to the basal forebrain and then on to the cortex.

The RAS is so critical to alertness that coma results when it is damaged or disrupted. People in a state of **coma** remain with their eyes closed and are seemingly unresponsive to and unaware of the outside world. In severe cases, they may not even exhibit defensive movements to noxious or painful stimuli. Coma occurs either after bilateral lesions to the RAS or because of diffuse problems that interfere with RAS functioning. In some instances, the factor causing coma affects the brain but not the body, as in the case of meningitis, a tumor, hemorrhage, head trauma, or seizures. In other cases, the causative factor affects other regions of the body as well, as in the case of a metabolic disorder, an abnormal gas in the blood (e.g., carbon monoxide), lack of a certain vitamin (e.g., thiamine), or the presence of a toxin (e.g., alcohol or heavy metals) (Young, 2009). Coma and related states are discussed further in Chapter 16.

Two other neurotransmitter systems have been implicated in overall arousal, the cholinergic and noradrenergic systems (see Chapter 2). One branch of the cholinergic system, whose cell bodies are located in the brainstem, forms a pathway parallel to the ascending RAS. These neurons similarly project to the thalamus and basal forebrain. Stimulation of these neurons leads to cortical activation (Jones, 2003).

The noradrenergic system, whose cell bodies are located within the locus coeruleus of the brainstem, also plays a prominent role in arousal (see Sara, 2009, and Berridge, 2008, for reviews). Neurons in the noradrenergic system project diffusely throughout the brain. Single-cell recordings reveal that cells in the locus coeruleus fire at a regular slow rate (about 1 Hz), but increase their firing in response to arousing stimuli and decrease their firing during periods of drowsiness and sleep. In fact, activity in the locus coeruleus appears to prevent sleep. Moreover, lesions to this region lead to deficits in cognitive tasks in rats and monkeys, especially under conditions of high arousal or high task demand. The noradrenergic system appears to be involved in stress-related aspects of arousal and has been implicated in psychiatric disorders, such as posttraumatic stress syndrome, that are characterized by hyperaroused states (see Chapter 14; Krystal & Neumeister, 2009).

Because these brainstem nuclei project to the thalamus, it should not surprise you that the thalamus also helps to keep us alert and awake by modulating the level of arousal of the cortex. The portions of the thalamus that are specifically implicated in this function are the **medial dorsal**, **intralaminar**, and **reticular nuclei** (● Figure 11.2). Damage restricted to these thalamic nuclei is enough to result in coma (Schiff, 2008). A dramatic example of the role this region plays in arousal is provided by a case study of a patient who had been in a minimally conscious state for six years following a traumatic brain injury. In a minimally conscious state, the person shows only intermittent evidence of awareness of the environment and the self. Researchers placed stimulating electrodes in the intralaminar nucleus and adjacent paralaminar regions of the thalamus, and compared the patient's behavior

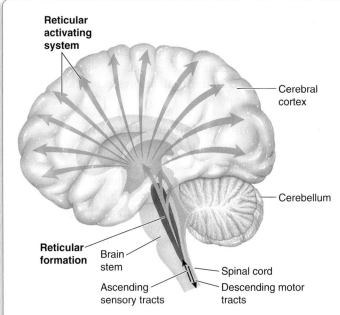

● **FIGURE 11.1   The reticular activating system is involved in overall arousal.** The reticular formation is a widespread network of neurons within the brainstem (in red). The ascending portion of the RAS (in blue) projects to many different regions of the cerebral cortex. This input serves to arouse and activate the cerebral cortex. © 2010 Cengage Learning

when the stimulation was turned on versus when it was off. Longer periods of eye opening, increased responsiveness to commands, and the ability to control the limbs were observed when thalamic stimulation was

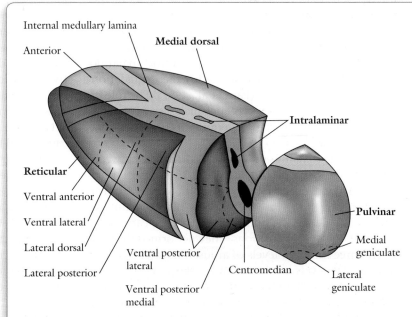

● **FIGURE 11.2   The nuclei of the thalamus thought to be involved in attention.** The reticular, intralaminar, and medial dorsal nuclei have been implicated in arousal and vigilance; the pulvinar has been implicated in selective attention. © 2011 Cengage Learning

on (Shiff et al., 2007). Neuroimaging studies have also found that the intralaminar nucleus is activated when a person must make a quick response to a visual or somatosensory stimulus (Kinomura, Larsson, Gulyas, & Roland, 1996). Together, these pieces of evidence confirm the important role of thalamic regions in alertness and arousal.

■ Vigilance and Sustained Attention

Two of the neurotransmitter systems we have just discussed, the cholinergic and noradrenergic systems, also play a role in vigilance and sustained attention. As noted, cells from the reticular activating system and the brainstem cholinergic system project to the basal forebrain (including the septal nuclei, diagonal band of Broca, and nucleus basalis). Residing here are the cell bodies of another branch of the cholinergic system, which appears to play an important role in sustained attention and vigilance. In rats, targeted chemical lesions that destroy cholinergic paths in this region lead to a loss of sustained attention (McGaughey, Kaiser, & Sarter, 1996). Furthermore, animal studies indicate that the higher the demands in a sustained attention task, the greater the release of acetylcholine (Sarter, Givens, & Bruno, 2001).

The noradrenergic system appears to be important for alerting the brain that it should get ready to receive information or make a response. For example, modulating the noradrenergic system pharmacologically in humans affects their ability to make use of a cue that provides information about the upcoming task (Coull, Nobre, & Frith, 2001).

Neurons from the basal forebrain and the noradrenergic system project to the midline nuclei of the thalamus, which are important for vigilance (in addition to being important for arousal, as discussed in the preceding section). For example, during a 60-minute auditory vigilance task, activity in midline thalamic regions decreased systematically with the degradation in performance over time (Paus et al., 1997). The role of arousal-related regions in vigilance makes sense: to sustain a constant attentive state requires a constant, tonic level of arousal.

In fact, the thalamus may act as an interface between arousal and other aspects of attention, such as sustained attention. Evidence for this viewpoint comes from a neuroimaging study in which people had to maintain attention to detect the numeral "7" that appeared randomly in one of four positions. They performed the task under three different levels of arousal: normal levels of arousal, low levels of arousal (after sleep deprivation), and high levels of arousal (after being given caffeine). Cortical regions (discussed in subsequent sections of this chapter) showed activation during the task, but cortical activation did not change as a function of arousal level. In contrast, activity in ventrolateral regions of the thalamus was greatest under conditions of low arousal, when the cortex required stimulation to counter the effects of sleep deprivation, and lowest under conditions of high arousal, when no such additional boost to the cortex was required (Portas, Rees, Howseman, Josephs, Turner, & Frith, 1998).

Cortical regions are also involved in arousal and vigilance, and converging evidence suggests that the right hemisphere plays a predominant role. For example, although brain damage almost always slows responses to stimuli, damage to the right hemisphere causes the greatest decrement in performance, regardless of whether stimuli are auditory or visual (Coslett, Bowers, & Heilman, 1987; Howes & Boller, 1975). Heart-rate responses to warning signals are also disrupted by right-hemisphere damage (Yokoyama, Jennings, Ackles, Hood, & Boller, 1987), and passive-vigilance tasks are performed more poorly by the isolated right hemisphere than the isolated left hemisphere in patients with split-brain syndrome (e.g., Dimond & Beaumont, 1973).

Converging evidence for the special role of the right hemisphere in vigilance comes from studies of brain activation in neurologically normal people. Activation in the right hemisphere is observed in vigilance tasks in which individuals must wait for a stimulus and respond rapidly (e.g., Sturm et al., 1999; Sturm et al., 2004). The regions that become activated during vigilance tasks include frontal and inferior parietal regions of the right hemisphere as well as thalamic and brainstem regions. Moreover, electrophysiological recordings also suggest a right lateralized system for sustained attention (e.g., Arruda, Walker, Weiler, & Valentino, 1999).

■ Selective Attention

Paying attention requires more than simply being alert and awake; we must also have a means of directing attention to prioritize certain types or pieces of information for processing over others. In fact, selective attention is probably the most intensely studied aspect of attention. Although there are many different models of selective attention, most make a distinction between what are referred to as bottom-up versus top-down aspects of attentional selection. In **bottom-up attentional selection**, some intrinsic aspect of the stimulus itself causes it to be attended or to receive priority in processing. For example, an item might grab attention because it is brighter than others or because it has emotional significance.

In contrast, in **top-down attentional selection**, a person determines how to direct his or her attention. Attention can be directed according to any number of different features. For example, while on a hike, you could decide to direct attention to a particular location in space, such as a point 90 degrees to your right; or you could direct your attention to particular objects, such as flowers. Furthermore, you might direct your attention based on certain physical characteristics of those flowers, such as flowers with a specific color or a particular form (e.g., variegated leaves). Alternatively, you can decide to direct attention to a particular task or goal, such as following the trail map to reach a lake. In this chapter we mainly discuss how attention is directed on the basis of physical attributes of the world (such as spatial location or color). We consider directing attention to goals and more abstract processes when we discuss executive functions in Chapter 12.

The Time Course of Attentional Selection

Before we discuss the brain regions involved in selective attention, it is important to realize that attention does not just happen at one point in time. Rather, attention may act from the time a sensory stimulus is processed until a response to that stimulus is emitted. Keeping this point in mind will help you understand why so many different brain regions are involved in selective attention: they act during different time frames of stimulus processing. Rather than thinking of attention as a single filter, it is better to think of it as a series of filters that act to enhance different aspects of information that may be relevant as the information is processed from input to output.

Although researchers now appreciate this point, it was not always well understood that attention can act at multiple points in time. Years ago, one of the major debates that engaged psychologists studying attention was the question of exactly *when* attentional selection occurs. Does it occur relatively soon after the receipt of sensory information, or later? There were two schools of thought. The **early-selection viewpoint** suggested that attentional selection occurs at an early stage of processing, before items are identified (e.g., Broadbent, 1958). The **late-selection viewpoint** argued that selection occurs only after sensory processing is complete and items have been identified and categorized (e.g., Deutsch & Deutsch, 1963).

The debate raged on, in part, because the measures of standard cognitive psychology experiments (i.e., recording accuracy and reaction time) could not provide the critical information needed to distinguish between these two possibilities. Event-related potential (ERP) studies, though, are perfectly suited to answer this question, because they provide information about when processes occur. ERP investigations have demonstrated that the answer to the question of when attention occurs is not an either/or proposition. Instead, attentional selection can occur both earlier and later in processing.

ERP and MEG studies indicate that at least some relatively automatic filtering or *gating* of sensory information occurs very soon after the receipt of a stimulus. To measure sensory gating, an auditory stimulus is presented, followed 500 ms later by the same auditory stimulus. The measure of gating is the degree to which the response is diminished on the second presentation compared to the first (Smith, Boutrous, & Schwarzkopf, 1994). This gating is adaptive, because the brain is registering that it has already processed the information and need not pay much attention to it again. A diminished response to the second stimulus is reflected in an ERP component known as the P_{50}, which occurs 35–85 ms after receipt of auditory information.

The effects of directing attention are observed a bit later, usually about 80–100 ms after stimulus presentation. Such effects are demonstrated by comparing two conditions: one in which a stimulus receives attention, and another in which the identical stimulus is presented but does not receive attention. Any difference in the ERP response to the two conditions must be attributable to the attentional manipulation. In a classic example of this type of experiment, participants are instructed to count the number of target tones, such as long tones, interspersed within more frequent nontargets, such as short tones. They are told, however, to attend only to information in one ear (e.g., the left). Responses are compared for targets when they are attended (e.g., left-ear targets when attention is directed to the left ear) versus when they are unattended (e.g., left-ear targets when attention is directed to the right ear). Researchers can obtain an estimate of when attention begins to exert its influence by noticing the point in time when the amplitude of the ERP to the attended stimulus begins to diverge from that of the unattended stimulus. In this case, the ERP in the attended condition begins to become more negative in amplitude (compared to the nonattended condition) approximately 80 ms after stimulus presentation, a difference that may continue for some time (Hillyard, Hink, Schwent, & Picton, 1973). This increased negative shift for the attended stimulus is often called the N_d *(negative difference) component* and is shown in ● Figure 11.3.

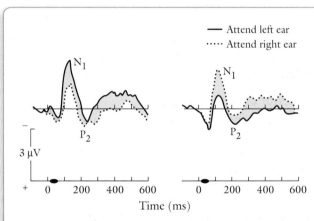

● **FIGURE 11.3 Modulation of early ERP components by attention.** The response to the stimulus is enhanced when it is presented in the attended location as compared with when it is not. (Left) For example, the amplitude of the N_1 is greater to a left-ear tone when the individual is attending to the left ear (solid line) than when the same tone is heard but the individual is attending to the right ear (dotted line). (Right) Likewise, the response to a right-ear tone is greater when the right ear is attended (dotted line) than when the left is attended (solid line). The difference between these two waveforms (shaded area) is the N_d component. This effect begins relatively soon after stimulus presentation, within the first 100 ms. © 2011 Cengage Learning

Although we used auditory stimuli in this example, a similar negative electrical shift can be observed for visual (Van Voorhis & Hillyard, 1977) and somatosensory (Desmedt & Robertson, 1977) information. These findings suggest that the early negativity in the ERP reflects a general attentional process that is not modality specific. Because the onset of the N_d occurs as soon as 80 ms after stimulus presentation, the brain systems that direct selective attention must exert their influence relatively early in the stream of processing, though not immediately after receipt of information by the cortex.

Attention can act at later stages as well, as demonstrated by the effect of attentional manipulations on later ERP components. The N_{2pc} component, which occurs approximately 180–280 ms after stimulus presentation, is thought to reflect the focusing of attention on potential target items in a display in order to prioritize processing of these items over distractors (e.g., Luck & Hillyard, 1994). It is labeled "pc" because it is recorded maximally over *parietal* areas *contralateral* to the position of the target. The P_{300} (which occurs at least 300 ms postpresentation) is found only when a person is paying attention and monitoring the sensory world for a target (e.g., Donchin, 1981). This component is thought to index the degree to which an attended item is task-relevant, the degree to which working memory must be updated, or the amount of attention paid to a task (e.g., Wickens, Kramer, Vanasse, & Donchin, 1983).

Given these findings, it should be clear that various brain regions involved in attention may not only perform different roles in the selection process, but they may also do so at different times. That is, selection does not occur in one brain region or at one specific time. Rather, selection occurs across different portions of the brain and on different time scales. We now turn to the different brain regions involved in selective attention.

Superior Colliculus

To flexibly allocate attention, you must be able to move your focus of attention from one position or object to another. The midbrain structure that has been implicated in this process, at least for visual stimuli, is the **superior colliculus** (refer back to Chapters 1 and 6). Although your focus of attention need not necessarily be the same place as where your eyes are fixed, it often is. The superior colliculus aids in shifting attention to new locations or objects by controlling the eye movements responsible for bringing peripheral stimuli quickly into foveal vision. This process is accomplished by a **saccade**, an eye movement in which the eyes jump from one position to the next with no processing of the intervening visual information, rather than moving smoothly across space. Saccades come in two varieties: express saccades and regular saccades. *Express saccades*, which take about 120 ms, tend to be reflexive and are triggered by the appearance of a novel visual stimulus in the periphery. Research with monkeys indicates that express saccades are programmed by the

superior colliculus, because when this structure is damaged, such saccades are extinguished.

In contrast, *regular saccades* are under voluntary control and take longer, about 200 to 300 ms (Schiller, Sandell, & Maunsell, 1987). They are not affected by damage to the superior colliculus, but are instead disrupted by damage to the frontal eye fields, which we discussed in Chapter 5 (Guitton, Buchtel, & Douglas, 1985). From an anatomical perspective, the superior colliculus is well situated for controlling reflexive eye movements. The portions of it that receive sensory and motor information are tightly coupled to the oculomotor regions of the brainstem that serve as the final common pathway for control of eye movements (Wurtz & Goldberg, 1972).

Evidence from single-cell recordings suggests that the superior colliculus aids in bottom-up aspects of attention. Cells in the superior colliculus are relatively unselective for any particular visual feature (e.g., a specific line orientation, a particular direction of motion). Rather, they appear to be sensitive to the overall salience of visual items regardless of what feature makes the item salient. As such, they help to detect visual information that is perceptually salient and then aid in moving gaze to the spatial position of that information (Shipp, 2004).

Understanding of the role of the superior colliculus in attention has also been aided by the study of patients with *supranuclear palsy,* which is characterized by degeneration of parts of the basal ganglia as well as specific degeneration of the superior colliculus. In everyday life, these patients often behave as if blind. Researchers have noted, "They often fail to turn towards those who approach them, to maintain eye contact during conversation, or to look at their plates when eating, even though they may still be able to do so on command" (Rafal, Posner, Friedman, Inhoff, & Bernstein, 1988, p. 268). In the laboratory, these patients exhibit difficulty in moving attention from one point in space to another.

Before we leave our discussion of the superior colliculus, it is important to note that the inferior colliculus is believed to play a similar role in attention for auditory information. Nevertheless, one should not think of these regions as completely specific to the visual and auditory modalities, respectively. For example, activity of the superior colliculus is increased when attention is directed to a location that is relevant to the integration of information across modalities (e.g., the location of lips that are producing words being heard) (Fairhall & Macaluso, 2009). In this manner, the superior colliculus can aid in directing attention to the location of the most salient sensory information.

Thalamus

Regions of the thalamus appear to play a role in gating, or filtering, the barrage of sensory information that constantly impinges upon the brain. As mentioned in Chapter 1, information from sensory receptors is relayed to the cortex through the thalamus. These thalamic relay stations may serve as gating mechanisms.

For visual information, the thalamic relay point is the lateral geniculate nucleus, which receives input from the eyes. As you may remember from Chapter 6, the organization of the geniculate is such that information from each visual field projects to the contralateral portion of the lateral geniculate. When attention is directed to one visual field, increased activity is seen in the contralateral geniculate, suggesting that attention can act to modulate information that will reach the cortex. Therefore, one may think of the geniculate as playing the role of a "gatekeeper" to the cortex, enhancing relevant information and suppressing irrelevant information (Kastner & Pinsk, 2004).

Another thalamic structure, the **pulvinar**, also plays a role in attention (refer back to Figure 11.2). When the pulvinar is chemically deactivated in monkeys, the animals have difficulty filtering out distracting information (Desimone, Wessinger, Thomas, & Schneider, 1990). In humans, damage to the pulvinar interferes with the ability to engage attention to a particular location while filtering out information at other locations (Rafal & Posner, 1987); pulvinar damage also leads to difficulty in discriminating the orientation of a target in the presence of distractors (Snow, Allen, Rafal, & Humphreys, 2009). Positron emission tomography (PET) studies indicate that the pulvinar is more engaged when filtering of information is required. For example, it exhibits greater activation when an item must be detected in the midst of eight other items, compared to when it is seen alone (LaBerge & Buchsbaum, 1990).

At present it is not clear exactly how the pulvinar acts to exert attentional control. One theory, based on anatomical connectivity, argues that because the pulvinar receives major input from several portions of the ventral visual-processing stream (e.g., V3, inferotemporal cortex), it serves to modulate information about a given visual item across each of the different portions of the ventral stream representing that item (Shipp, 2004). Currently also a mystery is how the modulation performed by the pulvinar may be distinct from that of thalamic relay stations, such as the lateral geniculate nucleus.

Parietal Lobe

Although initial aspects of attentional control are exerted by subcortical regions, parietal areas provide the ability to control attentional selection more precisely as well as enabling the overall allocation of attentional resources to a particular stimulus or task. We will discuss each of these functions in turn. Before we do so, however, we should note one way in which the parietal lobe exerts more precise control of attention is through top-down control; that is, attention directed by the person rather than being driven entirely by stimuli in the environment. For example, if you are to meet your friend outside your favorite restaurant, the parietal lobe will play a role in directing attention to the location of that particular restaurant as compared to the location of other restaurants or storefronts on that street.

Single-cell recordings in monkeys provide strong evidence for a role of the parietal region in visual attention. For example, the firing rate of cells in this region is enhanced any time attention is directed to a visual object. This increase cannot be attributed to motor actions toward a stimulus, because it is independent of eye or arm movements to the stimulus (e.g., Wurtz & Goldberg, 1988). Single-cell recordings have also indicated that a portion of the parietal lobe, the lateral intraparietal region, is important for the representation of attended or salient spatial locations (Colby, Duhamel, & Goldberg, 1996). Cells in this region respond to an attended location regardless of whether the information about location is auditory or visual and whether or not the monkey makes a motor response to the location.

Firing rates of cells in the lateral intraparietal area are influenced by both top-down and bottom-up factors. This dual influence was demonstrated by single-cell recordings while monkeys performed a visual search task, in which a target must be found among a set of distractors (Gottlieb, Balan, Oristaglio, & Suzuki, 2009). Indicating a sensitivity to bottom-up factors, the cell's firing rate varied with the number of distractors, which influence the physical saliency of the target (targets are more salient when presented with fewer distractors). In addition, cells are also sensitive to top-down influences; for example, a cell's firing rate was increased when a cue indicated the likely location of an upcoming target, compared to when the cue was not informative of the target's location.

In humans, the intraparietal sulcus, shown in Figure 11.4, appears to be critically involved in selecting

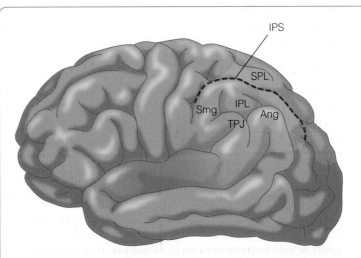

● **FIGURE 11.4 Parietal regions bordering the intraparietal sulcus play an important role in attention.** The intraparietal sulcus (IPS), shown by the dashed line, divides the superior parietal lobe (SPL) from the inferior parietal lobe (IPL), which is made up of the more anterior supramarginal gyrus (Smg) and the more posterior angular gyrus (Ang). Below the inferior parietal lobe is the temporal parietal junction (TPJ). *Source:* Husain, M., & Nachev, P. (2007). Space and the parietal cortex. Trends in Cognitive Sciences, 11, Portion of Figure 1, pg. 31.

among competing visual stimuli. This conclusion is supported by evidence from both functional neuroimaging studies and studies mapping the location of lesions in patients with attentional deficits (Vandenberghe & Gillebert, 2009). Increased activation in the intraparietal sulcus is observed across a variety of tasks that involve increased visual attention, including tasks directing attention to spatial locations, those directing attention toward objects, and those requiring attention to the co-occurrence of visual attributes. However, this region is not activated by tasks that are demanding but do not involve selection. For example, no increased activation is seen for a more difficult language task (semantic categorization) compared to a simpler one (characterizing the height of letters) (e.g., Wojciulik & Kanwisher, 1999). Some evidence hints at hemispheric specialization in this region: Whereas the right parietal cortex plays a role in visual attention, regions of the left parietal cortex appear to be associated with orienting attention to specific moments in time (see Coull, 2004, for a review).

Directing attention to a particular point in space may aid the identification of target items among distractors because it allows the features of the target, such as color and orientation, to be bound together. Prominent theories of attention suggest that such binding allows us to select information for further processing. According to this viewpoint, "attention" is the glue that lets you know that a particular item is at a particular location. Before we review the evidence for the role of the parietal lobe in such a function, we need to discuss this theory in a bit more detail.

According to *feature integration theory* (Treisman & Gelade, 1980), basic visual features, such as color (e.g., green) and form (e.g., X), are detected relatively automatically. However, we cannot know whether these features co-occur in a given item unless we direct our attention to the location where that item is situated (see also Wolfe's 1994 guided search model). Thus, attention binds those features together to form the percept of an item, such as a green X. A classic illustration is provided by experiments in which a person must find a target item in a visual display that contains many nontargets. When a target can be differentiated from all the nontarget stimuli on the basis of a simple visual attribute, the time required to find the target tends *not* to vary with the number of nontarget items. For instance, a target such as a red X will "pop out" of a field of nontargets, such as green Xs, no matter how many green Xs there are in the display. Similarly, a red X will pop out of a field of red Os. In such situations, processing is said to be "preattentive," which means that attention need not be implemented to find the target. In contrast, when a target item, such as a red X, must be identified on the basis of a conjunction of basic visual attributes (e.g., both shape and color) from among a mixture of nontargets, such as red Os (which share the same color as the target) and green Xs (which share the same shape as the target), the time required to find the target increases with the number of nontargets.

This increase in the time necessary to detect the target occurs because attention can be directed to only one location at a time. The more items in the display, the more locations must be sampled before the target is located. The important concept for purposes of the present discussion is that directing attention to a point in space allows the features at that location to be bound together so that an item can be identified (Treisman & Gelade, 1980). If items are located at unattended locations, their features become "free-floating" and can be combined in illusory manners. For example, if a red X and a green O are at unattended locations, an individual may report having seen a red O, incorrectly combining one item's color with another item's shape (Treisman & Schmidt, 1982).

The parietal region is thought to play a critical role in this binding process, as bilateral damage to parietal regions disrupts the ability to bind features together. Patients with such deficits cannot detect conjunction of features, whereas their ability to detect a single attribute remains intact (e.g., Friedman-Hill, Robertson, & Treisman, 1995). In addition, transcranial magnetic stimulation (TMS) applied to the right parietal cortex of neurologically intact adults increases the time for conjunction searches but not simple feature searches (Ashbridge, Walsh, & Cowey, 1997). More specifically, it appears that a portion of the right inferior parietal lobe, the angular gyrus, is critical, as TMS over this region disrupts the ability to perform conjunction searches (Muggleton, Cowey, & Walsh, 2008; though see Ellison, Rushworth, & Walsh, 2003, for a different view).

A distinct region of the parietal lobe, the superior parietal region, has been implicated across a number of different neuroimaging studies in which the participant must make shifts in spatial attention (e.g., Nobre et al., 1997; Yantis et al., 2002). Shifting attention requires at least two steps. First, attention must be disengaged from its current location, and then it must be shifted to a new location, which is peripheral to the current point of fixation. Recent research suggests that the regions of the superior parietal lobe involved in disengaging attention from fixation may be different from those involved in shifting attention to a new location in the periphery (Kelley, Serences, Giesbrecht, & Yantis, 2008). Interestingly, the superior parietal lobe appears to allow shifts of attention in general, not only shifts in attention to different spatial locations. For example, this region is also activated when one must switch attention between a male voice or a female voice (Shomstein & Yantis, 2006), or when one must shift between attending to a face and a house, when the pictures of each are overlapping (Serences, Schwarzback, Courtney, Golay, & Yantis, 2004).

In contrast to more dorsal regions of the parietal lobe, which appear to be involved in top-down aspects of attentional control, inferior parietal regions of the right hemisphere appear to be involved in more bottom-up aspects of attention control. For example, these regions do not show increased activity when a cue provides information about an upcoming target, suggesting that they are relatively uninvolved in exerting top-down control. Moreover, portions of the supramarginal gyrus and superior temporal gyrus (often referred to as the temporal-parietal junction) become very active during detection of a target when that target is at an unattended location and an individual reorients to that location. This region also becomes active in response to infrequent changes in a stimulus stream or a feature of a stimulus, regardless of the modality of that stimulus (for example, a change from blue to red or from a sound of a croaking frog to that of running water). Taking all these findings together, we may hypothesize that this region is involved in detecting unattended or low-frequency events (see Corbetta & Shulman, 2002, for a longer discussion). The pattern of deficits observed in patients with hemineglect, which is associated with inferior parietal lesions, is consistent with this idea (Vallar & Perani, 1986). When these patients are oriented to the contralateral side of space by a cue (that is, when top-down information is provided), they are able to detect stimuli on their neglected side. However, if no cue is provided, they do not detect the stimulus (Posner, Walker, Friedrich, & Rafal, 1984), indicating a reduced sensitivity to unattended information.

The parietal lobe has also been implicated in the overall allocation of attentional resources. Evidence for this proposition comes from a variety of sources. First, as discussed earlier in this chapter, right parietal regions are involved in sustained attention. Obviously, attentional resources must be allocated if one is to maintain attention across a period of time.

Second, although different types of attention activate different regions of parietal cortex, common regions are activated in right inferior parietal cortex regardless of whether attention is directed to particular regions of space or particular periods of time (Coull & Nobre, 1998) or to spatial locations or objects (e.g., Fink, Dolan, Halligan, Marshall, & Frith, 1997). For example, spatial orienting of attention relies more on regions within the right inferior parietal lobe, whereas temporal orienting of attention relies more on regions of the left intraparietal sulcus. Nevertheless, other areas of the inferior parietal lobe and intraparietal sulcus show common activation for both tasks.

Third, damage to the temporal-parietal junction, but not other regions such as the frontal lobe, eliminates the P_{300} (Knight, Scabini, Woods, & Clayworth, 1989). This finding is significant because the amplitude of the P_{300} has been found to index the degree of attentional resources that are voluntarily allocated to a particular stimulus or task. For example, when trying to perform two tasks simultaneously, attention can be divided equally between the tasks (50% to Task A, 50% to Task B) or unequally (e.g., 80% to Task A, 20% to Task B, or 20% to Task A, 80% to Task B). The more attention a person allocates to a given task, the greater the P_{300} is for that task. So, for example, if 80% of attention is directed to Task A and only 20% to Task B, a larger P_{300} is elicited by Task A than by Task B (Kramer, Wickens, & Donchin, 1985). Because the P_{300} indexes allocation of attentional resources, and because the P_{300} is disrupted by damage to the temporal-parietal junction, we can infer that this region is important in the allocation of attention.

Medial Prefrontal Cortex

Thus far, we have discussed how the brain becomes alert and aroused, how it orients toward previously unattended information, how it performs early gating of sensory information, and then how it performs more fine-grained selection of sensory information. Once the brain has accomplished all these processes, it then needs to select from a variety of possible responses. The region of the brain that is responsible for doing so is the medial portion of the prefrontal cortex, including the anterior cingulate cortex and supplementary motor area.

It has long been known that frontal regions are involved in selection of actions. For example, frontal lesions cause a motor neglect that exhibits itself as an inability to make motor movements toward the neglected side of space (e.g., Damasio, Damasio, & Chui, 1980). This deficit is attentional in nature, in that there is no motor paralysis that would preclude making such movements. Moreover, it is distinct from the neglect of sensory information, which is typically associated with parietal lobe damage (e.g., Bisiach, Geminiani, Berti, & Rusconi, 1990).

Recent research using a variety of methods has provided a much richer understanding of the role of medial prefrontal regions in selection of action. For example, in one study, cells within rostral areas of the cingulate motor area in the monkey brain increased their firing in response to cues that signal the motor parameters of a given trial (e.g., whether to hold or release a bar in response to the target; Isomura, Ito, Akazawa, Nambu, & Takada, 2003). Notice that the activity here is tied to the selection of a context-appropriate action.

Similarly, intracranial EEG recordings in patients about to undergo surgery for epilepsy indicate that beta-wave activity in dorsal regions of the cingulate (and portions of the SMA) are altered just prior to and immediately after a response. In contrast, theta-wave activity, which is altered in other portions of the frontal regions after a response is given, remains static (Cohen, Ridderinkhof, Haupt, Elger, & Fell, 2008). These findings fit with results from monkeys suggesting a role of medial prefrontal cortex in response selection.

Findings from human neuroimaging studies also support this conclusion, as well as indicating that the anterior cingulate cortex may be particularly important when selection of the correct action is difficult. You may remember that in Chapter 5, we discussed a

PET study in which the anterior cingulate cortex was found to be particularly active when a new or novel response had to be emitted (e.g., responding "L" to "A" and "M" to "B" rather than responding "B" to "A" and "M" to "L") (Paus, Petrides, Evans, & Meyer, 1993). This task requires attentional control over response selection because the person must use effort to inhibit a typical and automatic response to produce an appropriate action. As we also discussed in Chapter 5, the incongruent condition of the Stroop task is another situation in which a fair amount of control must be exerted to inhibit an automatic, but incorrect, response. As a reminder, in this condition, a person must identify the color of ink in which a word is printed (e.g., blue) when the word itself spells a conflicting color name (e.g., red). Because reading is so automatic, the individual usually wants to identify the color as red and must use attention to suppress this response and produce the correct one (e.g., "blue"). A specific portion of the cingulate exhibits activity when the word names a conflicting response (e.g., the word "blue" in green ink, when the possible responses are blue, green, and yellow), but not when the word is incongruent in meaning but does not

name a conflicting response (e.g., the word "purple" in green ink, when the possible responses are blue, green, and yellow) (Milham et al., 2001).

Cingulate activity is also observed in neuroimaging studies when selection of the correct response is demanding or complicated. For example, the cingulate is active when there are multiple possible responses, such as when a person is given a noun (e.g., *wood*) and must choose one verb from a larger set of verbs with which that noun is associated (e.g., *chop*) (Petersen, Fox, Posner, Mintun, & Raichle, 1988), or when distracting information suggests an alternative response (Bunge, Hazeltine, Scanlon, Rosen, & Gabrieli, 2002). Notably, TMS over regions of the medial frontal cortex increases errors only when information is present that suggests an alternative response, but not when such information is absent, again indicating the importance of this region for selecting between alternative responses (Taylor, Nobre, & Rushworth, 2007). Greater cingulate activity is also found when choosing the correct response relies on multiple attributes of a stimulus (e.g., color, form, speed) rather than a single one (e.g., color) (Corbetta, Miezin, Dobmeyer, Shulman, & Petersen, 1991), or when selecting a response is difficult because highly similar stimuli must be distinguished to select the correct response, compared to when response selection is simpler because each stimulus is more clearly mapped to a distinct response (Liu, Banich, Jacobson, & Tanabe, 2006) (● Figure 11.5).

Our discussion so far has centered mainly on studies in which the motor response is manual, but of course actions can be made with other parts of the body as well. Other prefrontal regions play a similar role in selecting nonmanual responses. For example, research with monkeys implicates the supplemental eye fields (see Chapter 5) in selection of the direction of gaze under conditions of response conflict (Schall & Boucher, 2007) or when a reflexive eye movement must be inhibited or overridden (Paus et al. 1991), On the other hand, as you previously learned, the frontal eye fields are important for voluntarily rather than reflexively directing the eyes to a particular point in space. We can better understand the different roles of these regions by considering how one must direct attention while driving a car. The frontal eye fields enable one to direct one's gaze to the road, whereas the medial regions keep your attention from being drawn away from the road in front of you every time a car on the other side of the median passes you!

As discussed earlier in this chapter, directing attention to a particular location in space is usually accompanied by moving the eyes

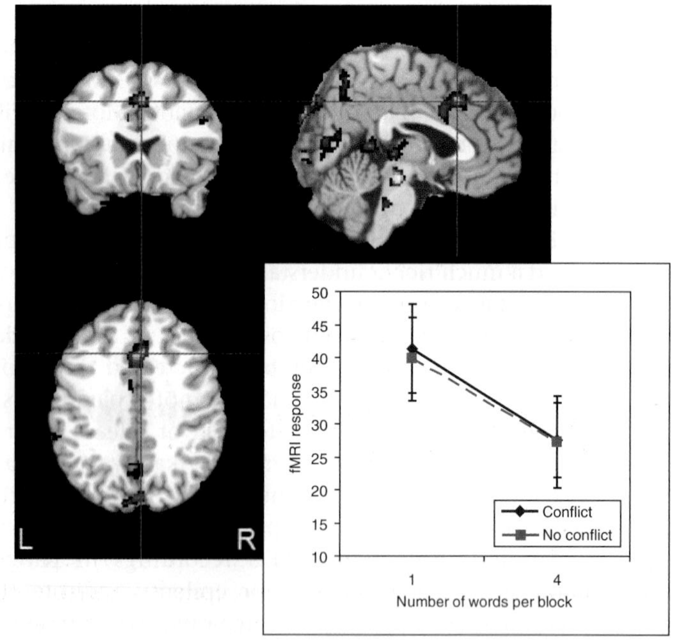

● **FIGURE 11.5 Medial regions of prefrontal cortex involved in response selection.** This region of the anterior cingulate cortex is more active when response selection is hard (left) because one stimulus is linked to four different responses, than when response selection is easier (right) because each stimulus is uniquely linked to a response. Notice that this pattern is unaffected by other aspects of selection, such as whether or not the stimulus itself contains conflicting perceptual or semantic information. *Source:* Liu X, Banich MT, Jacobson BL, Tanabe JL (2006). Functional dissociation of attentional selection within PFC: response and non-response related aspects of attentional selection as ascertained by fMRI. Cerebral Cortex, 16, Fig. 2, p. 832.

there. You may be wondering how scientists know that brain regions are involved in attentional control rather than in eye movements per se. Some evidence that directing attention does not require eye movements comes from research with monkeys that could not possibly be performed with humans (Wardak, Ibos, Duhamel, & Olivier, 2006). In this study, monkeys were trained to perform two tasks. In one task (saccade task), the monkey maintained fixation at a central point, which then disappeared. After a short delay, a target item appeared in the periphery and the animal was required to make a visual saccade to the target. In the other task (attention task), the animal had to maintain fixation on the central point throughout the trial. A number of items appeared in the periphery, and the animal had to press a lever if one of the items was a target and to refrain from pressing the lever if there was no target item within the display. The targets were defined by a conjunction of shape and color, so that attention was required to identify them. Notice that no eye movements occur in the attention task. Rather, attention must be directed *covertly* to each stimulus location to search for the target rather than overtly through eye movements. The researchers then injected muscimol, a GABA agonist, into the frontal eye field of one hemisphere. Not surprisingly, the ability to make saccades to the contralateral visual field was compromised in the saccade task, confirming that indeed the injection had disabled the frontal eye fields (FEF). Importantly, though, the injection also disrupted performance in the attention task, despite the fact that no eye movements were involved. This finding suggests that the FEF play a role in directing visual attention and not just eye movements.

Lateral Prefrontal Cortex

As discussed in Chapter 1, the prefrontal cortex plays a predominant role in processes that guide behavior. It plays a similar role in attention, setting the goal of what should be attended. Rather than selecting what stimulus should be attended or what motor response should be selected, this region guides our attention based on more abstract characteristics. For example, prefrontal regions play a role in guiding the category of information to which one should attend. In the Stroop task, for instance, prefrontal regions enable one to direct attention to the ink color and not the meaning of the word. Because these attentional functions performed by the frontal lobe are often are considered executive processes, we save most of the discussion of them for Chapter 12.

Here, however, we briefly discuss a distinction that is often made when discussing the roles that different brain regions play in attention. Theorists have distinguished between two types of role. One role is referred to as a *source of attentional control*. Regions with this role are thought to send a signal to other brain regions, and, in so doing, bias processing toward particular

information. Prefrontal regions are thought to act as a source of attentional control. In contrast, a *site of attentional control* is a brain region at which processing is modulated to enhance attention to a specific attribute, location, item, or other salient dimension.

To illustrate this distinction, let's consider the results from one neuroimaging study in which participants had to detect a target under two conditions (Kastner, Pinsk, De Weerd, Desimone, & Ungerleider, 1999). In one condition, they maintained attention on a central fixation point. In the other, which required greater attentional control, participants were given a cue indicating where in the periphery they should direct their attention. In this condition during the time period after the cue but before the target, a large increase in activity was observed in frontal regions and in the superior parietal lobe. With the onset of the visual stimuli, however, little additional increase in activity was observed in these regions, regardless of whether detecting the target was more demanding (because it was embedded among distractors) or less demanding (because it appeared by itself). Because these fronto-parietal regions became active after the cue but before the actual display of the stimulus, they appear to serve as sources of attentional control, setting the bias for subsequent processing. However, they do not appear to be as involved when selection must actually occur, which is after onset of the visual display, because their activity was not affected by the difficulty of the actual selection process. In contrast, activity of posterior visual regions (e.g., V4) also increased after the cue, but to a much smaller degree than that of frontal and superior parietal regions. It is as if these posterior visual areas are put "on alert" by biasing signals from frontal and parietal regions. After the target appeared, however, their activity increased substantially, suggesting that these regions are actively involved in the selection process and thus acted as sites of attentional control (● Figure 11.6).

Modulation of Activity in Specific Cortical Regions by Selective Attention

As we have just discussed, top-down signals appear to bias processing in other brain regions. Let's explore this concept in a bit more detail. Our visual world is made up of locations in space as well as the objects that inhabit those spaces. In the past, there was a debate about whether top-down signals cause attention to be directed on the basis of locations in space, the **space-based viewpoint of attention**; or whether it is directed on the basis of particular objects, the **object-based viewpoint of attention**. To make the distinction between space-based and object-based attention more concrete, let's assume that you have arranged to pick up your friend on a specific corner outside a train station. When you arrive and begin to look for your friend, you may direct your attention in a space-based manner to that particular corner and not other locations at the train station. Alternatively,

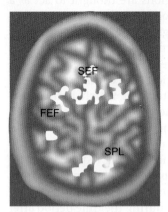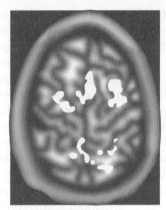

(A)   Visual Stimuli   (B)   Attention without
       and Attention   Visual Stimuli

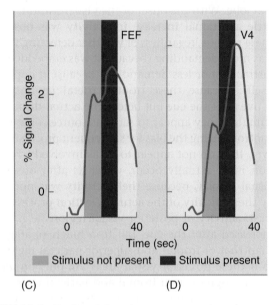

(C)   (D)

● **FIGURE 11.6   Prefrontal regions serve as a top-down source of attentional control that modulates activity in posterior brain regions.** Regions of the frontal lobe, including the supplementary eye fields (SEF) and frontal eye fields, become active when an individual is directing attention to a location—both (A) when a stimulus is present and (B) even when it is not yet present but expected. (C) Shown here is activity in the FEF as measured by fMRI. There is an increase in activity when attention is directed to the target location prior to the onset of the stimulus (green bar), which then increases only slightly when the stimulus actually appears (blue bar). (D) In contrast, for regions in visual cortex, there is a small increase of activity before the item appears (green bar), but a substantial increase in activity once the item is present (blue bar). *Source:* Kastner, S. & Pinsk, M. A. (2004). Visual attention as a multilevel selection process. Cognitive, affective, and behavioral neuroscience, 4, Figure 6, pg. 494, Figure 11.6 A and B.

basis of spatial location, on the basis of item attributes (e.g., color, form), and finally on the basis of whole objects. We now discuss each of these pieces of evidence in turn.

Neuroimaging studies indicate that regions of visual cortex are the site at which space-based attentional effects occur. As you may remember from our discussion of the visual system, the mapping of the visual world in early visual-processing areas (V1–V4) is retinotopic, so that each specific region of space is processed by a specific region of visual cortex. Of most importance for the current discussion, information in one visual field is processed by the contralateral visual cortex. Attending to information in one visual field increases activation over extrastriate (V2–V4) regions of the opposite hemisphere (Heinze et al., 1994), indicating that attention has space-based properties. ERP studies demonstrate that this space-based attentional modulation occurs relatively early in processing, approximately 100 ms after stimulus presentation. The amplitude of the P_1 component to a visual target is enhanced when the item appears in the attended location as compared to the unattended one (Heinze, Luck, Mangun, & Hillyard, 1990). Both PET and dipole modeling (Heinze et al., 1994), as well as functional MRI (Mangun, Buonocore, Girelli, & Jha, 1998), suggest that this component is generated by activity in secondary (i.e., extrastriate) visual cortex (● Figure 11.7). While extrastriate regions are the site of space-based attentional modulation, the parietal cortex plays a role in space-based selection by acting as the source of attentional control, as discussed earlier in this chapter.

Other evidence indicates that information can be selected on the basis of item features. In one classic neuroimaging study, participants decided whether two successive displays of moving colored shapes were identical or not (Corbetta et al., 1991). They were told to base their decision on one of the features (e.g., color) and to ignore the others (e.g., speed and shape). Thus, the perceptual information was equivalent across conditions, with variations only in what feature should be attended. When the person was attending to color, ventral visual regions sensitive to color, such as V4, were most active. When the person was attending to shape, greater activation was found in portions of the ventral visual-processing stream. When the person was attending to speed, activation was greatest in area MT, the portion of the dorsal processing stream that is sensitive to motion.

ERP data had suggested that selection on the basis of stimulus features (such as color and shape) occurs about

you may direct your attention in an object-based manner if you know that your friend will be wearing her long, oversized wool coat. As you look for your friend, you can selectively pay attention only to particular objects—long, oversized wool coats—while ignoring other objects such as ski jackets, short coats, and parkas.

Studies using a cognitive neuroscience approach have provided evidence that selection can occur on the

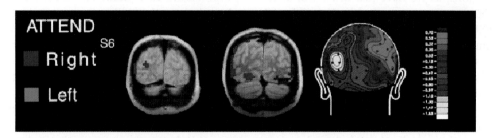

● **FIGURE 11.7   Contralateral control of spatial attention as shown by fMRI and ERPs.** The two figures on the left show activation in extrastriate cortex as measured by fMRI. Areas shown in red (or yellow) are those activated when the individual attended to the right side of space. Notice that activity is restricted to the left hemisphere. In contrast, the areas shown in blue are those activated when the individual attended to the left side of space. Notice that these regions are restricted to the right hemisphere. The drawing to the right shows the ERP component that occurs 100–140 ms after stimulus onset. Red and yellow indicate increased activity when attention is directed to the right side of space. Mangun et al., 1998. ERP and fMRI measures of visual spatial selection attention. Human Brain Mapping, 6, p.386, fig.1. By permission of John Wiley & Sons, Inc.

250–300 ms after stimulus presentation (Anilo-Vento, Luck, & Hillyard, 1998), a bit later than selection on the basis of spatial location. However, more recent evidence suggests that color-based attention can act as early as 100 ms after the stimulus is presented. In these studies, participants viewed a mixed display of red and green dots in one half of the visual field, and were instructed to attend to one color (e.g., red) within that half-field. The other visual field contained an array of single-colored dots, and they were to be ignored. These dots could either be all of the attended color (e.g., red) or all of the distractor color (e.g., green). The amplitude of the P_1 response was larger when the color at the unattended location was the attended color (e.g., red) compared to when it was the distractor color (e.g., green) (Zhang & Luck, 2009). Because the effects differed based on the color at the unattended location, we know that the effect cannot be due to spatially selective attention. Rather, the results reflect that the brain is biased to attend to a specific feature, regardless of where in the display that feature might occur.

Attentional selection can also be object-based (for a review, see Yantis & Serences, 2003). To demonstrate object-based attention, one needs a paradigm in which the spatial location of objects is held constant, so that selection based on location can be ruled out. Typically, paradigms used to assess object-based attention involve overlapping figures; the participant is instructed to pay attention to one object and ignore the other. In one study, displays included both faces and houses. When attention was directed to faces, activity increased in the fusiform face area. In contrast, when attention was directed to houses, activity increased in the parahippocampal place area (O'Craven, Downing, & Kanwisher, 1999). This modulation of attention appears to occur relatively early in processing, when visual features are first recognized as forming a particular object. As you may remember from Chapter 7, there is a specific ERP

component, the N_{170} that is elicited specifically by faces compared to other objects. The amplitude of the equivalent magnetoencephalographic component, the M_{170}, also reflects the effects of object-based attention. When a display contains overlapping faces and houses, the amplitude of the M_{170} is greater when individuals attend to faces than when they attend to houses (Downing, Liu, & Kanwisher, 2001). Therefore, attentional selection for objects can occur as soon as 170 ms after presentation of the display.

This evidence suggests that attention can act to select information in a variety of manners: on the basis of spatial location, on the basis of item attributes, or on the basis of objects. The neural bases of these effects exhibit an interesting pattern. When selection is based on a particular characteristic, activation is increased in the brain region specialized for processing that characteristic. For example, if selection occurs on the basis of space, increased activation is observed in sensory areas that are organized with regard to space, such as early visual-processing areas, and regions that provide a spatial map of the world, such as parietal regions. When attention is directed to an object, increased activation is observed in areas that process objects, such as the ventral visual-processing stream. If attention is directed to a certain characteristic, such as motion, increased activation is observed in the region of the brain most sensitive to motion, MT. Thus, it is clear that attention does not reside in one particular region of the brain. Rather, it acts to influence the processing of distinct brain modules, ramping up their activity if they are processing information that is attentionally relevant. Given this, we can consider attention to be a modulatory process.

You may have noticed that we have discussed a number of general neural mechanisms that enable selective attention. One mechanism is to increase activity of those brain systems that are actively processing the information that should be attended. That can be done at the level of brain regions, as we have just discussed, at the level of populations of neurons (Reddy, Kanwisher, & Vanrullen, 2009), or at the level of single cells (e.g., Moran & Desimone, 1985). Another mechanism is to increase the baseline rate of activity even before the stimulus appears, such as occurs in V4 in response to a cue indicating that a stimulus will appear. In both cases, neuronal firing is modulated for cells representing the attended or relevant information.

There is yet another mechanism that we have not considered, which is that attention can also reduce the influence of distracting information. This is illustrated by single-cell recordings in monkeys. In these studies, the scientist first records the cell's response to a set of visual items, each shown individually as the only item located within the cell's receptive field. Then the researcher adds another item within the receptive field. For the sake of this example, let's say that item A (shown alone) makes the cell fire at a moderate rate, and item B (shown alone) makes it fire at a slow rate. If the cell is responding to the additive effect of all items within the receptive field (i.e., response to A plus response to B), then when both items are shown together, the firing rate of the cell should be greater than observed for either item alone. In actuality, when both items are within the receptive field, the cell's response is an average of the responses to each item. The presence of item B, which doesn't drive the cell's response very well, actually suppresses the response of the cell to item A (e.g., Reynolds, Chelazzi, & Desimone, 1999). Thus, there is competitive interaction between the items within the receptive field. Most importantly, directing spatial attention to an item's location can reduce the suppressive effects of the other items in the visual field (● Figure 11.8). Similar mechanisms have been observed in humans: directing spatial attention to a particular location eliminates the suppressive effects of other items in the visual field (Kastner, De Weerd, Desimone, & Ungerleider, 1998). As such, attention may work by reducing the impact of distracting information.

According to one theory (Lavie & Tsal, 1994; Lavie, 1995), this suppressive mechanism is most likely to occur when overall attentional demands are high. When attentional demand is high, there are few resources left to process the distractors, and so they are suppressed; in contrast, when attentional demands are low, there are enough resources left over to allow for the processing of distracting information. Evidence for this viewpoint comes from a study in which participants were asked to perform one of two linguistic tasks that varied in difficulty (Rees, Frith, & Lavie, 1997). In the easier condition, participants just had to indicate whether a

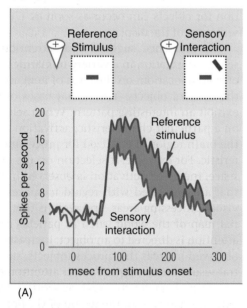

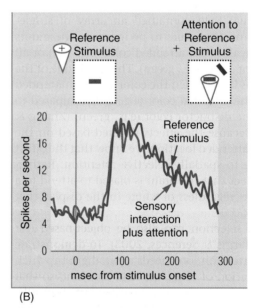

(A)   (B)

● **FIGURE 11.8 Neuronal activity that is modified by attention.** Shown here is the activity of a cell in V4 under different conditions. The cell's receptive field is indicated by the dotted square and the focus of the monkey's attention is indicated by the cone. In all cases, the blue bar represents an effective stimulus that by itself will cause the cell to fire and the red bar indicates an ineffective stimulus that by itself will not cause the cell to fire. (A) In this case, attention is being directed to a fixation point outside of the receptive field of the cell. (Left) The reference stimulus effectively produces a robust response, but (right) when an ineffective stimulus also appears within the visual field, the activity of the cell is substantially reduced (as shown by the green area between the curves). (B) This suppressive effect of the ineffective stimulus is negated when attention is directed at the position of the effective stimulus (right), as shown by the absence of a reduction in the cell's firing rate. *Source:* Pessoa, L., Kastner, S., & Ungerleider, L. G. (2003) Neuroimaging studies of attention from modulation of sensory processing to top-down control. The journal of Neuroscience, 10, Figure 1A and 1B, pg. 3992.

word was presented in uppercase. In the more difficult condition, they had to determine whether the word was bisyllabic. Surrounding the central words were dots moving radially toward the edge of the screen, which induces a strong sense of movement and is known to activate area MT. These dots were to be ignored; that is, they were not relevant to the task. Researchers used the degree of activity in area MT as an index of how much the unattended stimuli (moving dots) were being processed. The researchers observed that under the easier condition, there was increased activity in MT (compared to when no motion was present), indicating that area MT was processing the distracting motion information. In contrast, when the task was difficult, activity in area MT was actually reduced compared to the no-motion condition. These results indicate that attention can effectively suppress the processing of irrelevant information under attentionally demanding conditions.

Both the increased processing of attended information and the suppression of unattended information can be explained by a theory of attention known as the *biased-competition model* (Desimone & Duncan, 1995). This model states that attention works by biasing ongoing neural activity. Such a bias can be induced in a top-down manner by directing attention to a specific spatial location or by biasing attention toward items relevant for a task—for example, you may direct your attention toward locating a spoon rather than a fork if your goal is to eat soup. However, not all biases need be top-down. For example, a bottom-up influence that would bias the competition would be stimulus intensity—a brighter stimulus is more likely to capture attention than a dimmer one.

Computational models of attention have instantiated this idea of competition from both a bottom-up and a top-down perspective. For example, computational models of visual selective attention have been implemented in winner-take-all networks. In such networks, the winner, by virtue of having the highest level of activation, stands out above the rest (i.e., distractors) and is selected for additional processing. The activation level of each unit in such models can be influenced both by perceptual salience, a bottom-up factor, and by directed spatial attention, a top-down factor (e.g., Mozer & Sitton, 1998). Similarly, competition also plays a role in top-down models of attentional control. For example, computational models of the Stroop effect argue that because word reading is so automatic relative to ink-color identification, the competition between these two processes is biased toward reading the word. Top-down control from prefrontal cortex must modify this intrinsic bias so that attention is directed to the process of ink-color identification rather than word reading (O'Reilly & Munakata, 2000; Cohen, Braver, & O'Reilly, 1996). This bias from prefrontal regions, a source of attentional control, will in turn modulate activity in posterior regions involved in processing ink color (such as V4) and word reading (such as the angular gyrus).

In fact, computational models of the Stroop effect that incorporate these notions of prefrontal biasing signal can predict patterns of activity in the brain as measured with fMRI during performance of the Stroop task (Herd, Banich, & O'Reilly, 2006).

The idea of attention acting as a biasing mechanism is a powerful concept, a concept that has also been used to explain some of the deficits observed in hemineglect, as we discuss in a later portion of this chapter.

■ Divided Attention

Divided attention is the last category of attention that we consider. As discussed earlier, divided attention occurs when you must split your attention between different sources of information or different tasks. Sometimes attention must be divided between two sources of information, which can be either in the same sensory modality or in different modalities. An example within a single modality is when you are trying to decide which movie to attend with two friends, one who is speaking to you on the phone, and the other of whom is sitting next to you. If they both insist on talking to you at the same time, you must try to divide your attention between the two sources of auditory information so you can comprehend what they are both saying. In other cases, you may want to divide your attention across modalities, such as when you are conversing with someone while driving a car. In this case, you wish to focus your visual attention on the road while at the same time directing your auditory attention to your passenger's conversation.

Currently, there is no consensus on whether divided attention engages neural regions above and beyond those engaged by each task itself. Some research points to the idea that activity increases within prefrontal regions when attention must be divided between two tasks in different modalities (Loose, Kaufmann, Auder, & Lange, 2003; Vohn et al., 2007). In one study, rTMS over dorsolateral prefrontal regions (but not other regions) disrupted the ability to divide attention between two simultaneously presented auditory and visual tasks (Johnson, Strafella, & Zatorre, 2007). Moreover, some of the individuals who underwent rTMS had previously performed the divided-attention task while fMRI data were obtained (Johnson & Zatorre, 2006). The more an individual recruited dorsolateral prefrontal cortex during the divided-attention condition, the more his or her performance was disrupted by rTMS over this region. Thus, dorsolateral prefrontal region may provide top-down control or guidance for the distribution of attentional resources between tasks.

However, other researchers have argued that the engagement of prefrontal regions comes not because attention is divided per se, but rather because the overall demands on the brain are greater under divided compared to single-task conditions. To examine this hypothesis, they compared activation for a single-task condition matched in difficulty to the dual-task condition. They observed that the neural systems activated, including prefrontal cortex, were highly overlapping (Nebel, Wiese, Stude, de Greiff, Diener, & Keidel, 2005; Hahn et al., 2008). Thus, the degree to which divided attention requires prefrontal regions remains an open question.

Network Models of Attentional Control

Because attention can be defined in numerous ways and involves multiple brain regions, we need theoretical models to help organize our understanding of the complexity of attention. These models provide a way to conceptualize how various regions might interact and coordinate their processing to allow for attentional control. Here we briefly introduce three models of attentional control that organize the structures we have discussed above into different subsets or subsystems.

■ A Distributed but Overlapping Network

One classic model of the neural systems underlying attention, proposed by Mesulam (1981), was designed to help explain the clinical phenomenon of hemi-neglect. It views directed attention as controlled by a diffuse cortical network that is simultaneously specialized and redundant. In this model, each region in the network has some specialization because the role it plays is not exactly like that of any other region. However, this specialization is not absolute, in that lesions to different areas of the network can have similar effects. Thus, this model takes neither a strict localizationist approach nor one of mass action.

According to this model, each of four major brain regions plays a prominent, but not necessarily exclusive, role in controlling a certain aspect of attention. The main role of the reticular activating system is to maintain vigilance and arousal; the main role of the cingulate cortex is to impart motivational significance to information; the main role of the posterior parietal region is to provide a sensory map of the world; and the main role of frontal regions is to provide the motor programs for moving the attentional focus around the world by exploring, scanning, reaching, and fixating (● Figure 11.9A).

Because this model views attention as being supported by an interconnected neural network, it has three important implications for understanding how brain damage may affect attention. First, it implies that a lesion confined to a single brain region may affect not only attentional behaviors, but other behaviors as well. For example, although frontal regions are part of the attentional network, they are also involved in executive functions. Second, because the model is not a strict localizationist model, the same complex function can be impaired as a result of lesions in different locations. For example, as we discuss in more detail shortly,

hemineglect has been reported after lesions to many different regions of the brain. Third, the most severe disruption of a complex function will be observed after damage to more than one region in the network. Thus, neglect would be more severe if damage occurred to both frontal and parietal regions rather than just parietal regions.

■ Altering, Orienting, and Executive Attention

Another prominent model argues that attention can be divided into three somewhat separable systems that are involved, respectively, in alerting, orienting, and executive attention (● Figure 11.9B) (Posner & Rothbart, 2007). According to this model, one subsystem is responsible for alerting, which involves achieving and maintaining a state of high sensitivity to incoming information. This subsystem allows the brain to maintain a tonic alert state and to respond phasically to signals that warn of upcoming events. The alerting system relies on the locus coeruleus, parietal cortex, and right frontal regions, and has been conceptualized as being linked to the neurotransmitter norepinephrine. A second subsystem, the orienting subsystem, aligns attention with the source of sensory signals and selects among multiple sensory inputs. This second subsystem, according to the model, relies on the superior colliculus, the superior parietal region, the temporal-parietal junction, and the frontal eye fields, and is linked to the neurotransmitter acetylcholine. The third subsystem, one that supports executive attention, controls how attention is directed according to an individual's goals or desires, including detecting and resolving conflict. This system is composed of the basal ganglia, lateral ventral prefrontal regions, and the anterior cingulate, and is thought to rely on dopamine.

At least some recent evidence suggests that these systems may not be entirely separable; rather, aspects of processing in one system may affect the other systems. For example, when a cue directs attention to an incorrect location of a subsequent target, a process supported by the orienting system, it is harder for participants to resolve interference from conflicting information, a process supported (according to this model) by the executive system (Fan et al., 2009). If the two systems were totally separate, the processes being implemented by one system should be independent of the processes in another. Thus, we see that even models that attempt to segregate attentional functions to different brain regions ultimately must account for their interdependence.

■ Selection of Goals versus Detection of Behaviorally Relevant Stimuli

Another model posits two partially segregated networks that carry out different attentional functions (Corbetta & Shulman, 2002). The dorsal subsystem

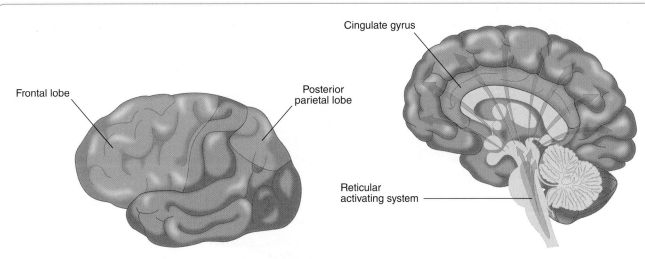

FIGURE 11.9A   Network models of attentional control. According to the model by Mesulam (1981), a reticular component provides the underlying level of arousal and vigilance; the posterior parietal lobe provides a sensory map of the world; the cingulate gyrus regulates the spatial distribution of attention with regard to motivational value; and a frontal component coordinates the motor programs for exploration, scanning, reaching, and fixating. This network requires at least three complementary and interacting representations of extrapersonal space: a sensory representation in posterior parietal cortex, a schema for distributing exploratory movements in frontal cortex, and a motivational map in the cingulate cortex.

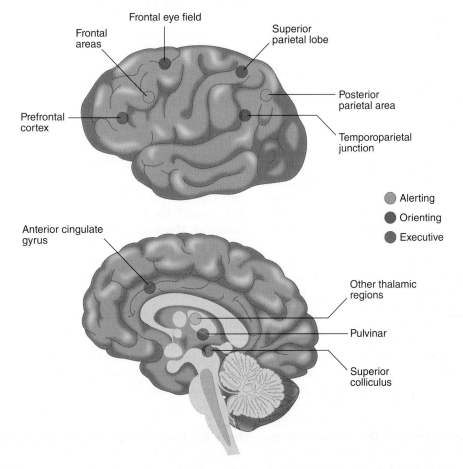

FIGURE 11.9B   According to the model by Posner and colleagues (Posner & Rothbart, 2007), there are three main attentional networks in the brain. The one for *alerting*, which is shown in green, is involved in achieving and maintaining a high state of sensitivity to incoming stimuli. Another, primarily associated with *orienting* and shown in purple, is involved in aligning attention to the source of a sensory signal. The third, shown in red, is involved in *executive aspects of attention*, which directs how attention is directed according to an individual's goals or desires. These systems are hypothesized to be modulated by the neurotransmitters norepinephrine, acetylcholine, and dopamine, respectively. *Source:* Posner, M. I. & Rothbart, M. K., (2007). Research on attention networks as a model for the integration of psychological science. Annual review of Psychology, 58, Figure 2, pg. 6.

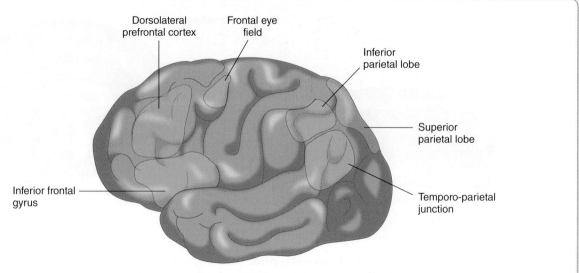

● **FIGURE 11.9C** According to Corbetta and Shulman (2002), visual attention is controlled by two networks. One network, shown in green, is a dorsal frontoparietal network involved in goal-directed aspects of attentional control. The other, shown in gold, is a ventral system, mainly in the right hemisphere, that is composed of inferior frontal and temporoparietal regions. It is specialized for the detection of behaviorally relevant stimuli. *Source:* Corbetta, M. & Shulman, G. L. (2002). Control of goal-directed and stimulus driven attention in the brain. Nature reviews Neuroscience, 3, left—Figure 3c (righthand portion) pg. 203, right—Figure 6d page 210.

is composed of portions of the intraparietal cortex and superior frontal cortex. This system prepares and applies goal-directed (top-down) selection for stimuli and responses. A ventral subsystem includes the temporoparietal cortex and inferior frontal cortex, mainly lateralized to the right hemisphere. This subsystem is specialized for the detection of behaviorally relevant stimuli, particularly when the stimuli are salient or unexpected. In this model, the dorsal system is more involved in top-down attentional control and the ventral system is more involved in bottom-up aspects of attention (● Figure 11.9C).

Why have two such systems? If we could direct our attention only to goals, places, or objects that we had selected in a top-down manner, we would likely miss salient environmental effects that we hadn't anticipated. In other words, the ventral frontoparietal network works as a "circuit breaker" for the dorsal system, "resetting" attention when important new events occur. The locus coeruleus may drive the ventral attentional system, implicating noradrenaline in the reset process. For example, when people were shown faces subliminally so that they could not consciously detect them, increased activity was observed in the superior colliculus, pulvinar, locus coeruleus, and amygdala when the faces had a fearful expression rather than a neutral one. The authors proposed that the colliculo-pulvinar pathway to the amygdala allows a subliminal fear signal to be processed, which in turn activates the locus coeruleus to act as a circuit breaker (Liddell et al., 2005). This study illustrates how the ventral system could play

an important role in redirecting attention so that we do not end up with tunnel vision based on current goals and objectives.

■ The Default Network: The Lack of Attention?

What occurs when we have lapses of attention? Is it just that the structures we discussed are offline or taking a nap? For many years, that is what researchers assumed. However, a recent proposal argues that there is a brain system that works in opposition to the brain regions engaged by attentional demand (Raichle, 2001). This system has been referred to as the "default network," presumably because it is activated when the brain is in "default mode" rather than being attentionally engaged.

According to this model, the default network consists of the regions shown in ● Figure 11.10, including medial orbitofrontal regions, posterior cingulate cortex, and specific portions of the inferior parietal lobe. Activity in this network decreases at the same time that activity increases in many of the regions we have discussed in this chapter, including the dorsolateral prefrontal cortex, SMA, other portions of the inferior parietal region, frontal eye fields, and the intraparietal sulcus (Fox, Snyder, Vincent, Corbetta, Van Essen, & Raichle, 2005). In other words, activity in the default network seems to have a reciprocal relationship with activity in brain structures involved in attentional control.

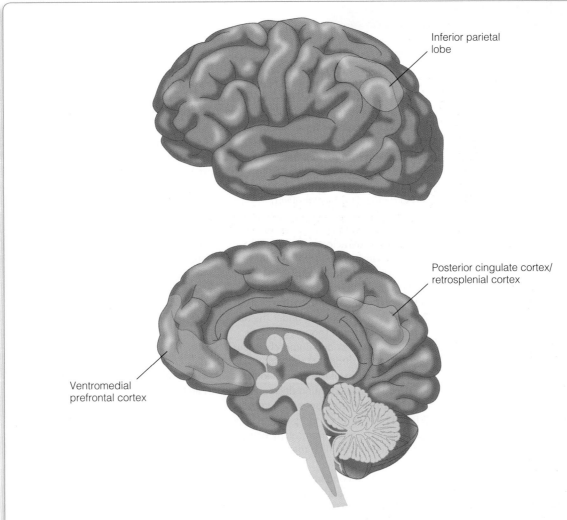

Inferior parietal lobe

Posterior cingulate cortex/ retrosplenial cortex

Ventromedial prefrontal cortex

● **FIGURE 11.10   The main regions involved in the so-called "default network."** This network is active when people are doing relatively little cognitive processing of external stimuli. The greater the activity within regions involved in attentional control, the more activity within this default network is reduced.

Further evidence comes from the study of attentional lapses. When people have lapses in attention (indicated by longer reaction times and higher error rates on specific trials), there is less deactivation (more activation) of the default network than when they appear to be attentive (Weissman, Roberts, Visscher, & Woldorff, 2006). Thus, the ability to pay attention seems to rely not only on engagement of attentional systems, but also on disengagement of the default-mode network.

Currently, the default network is the subject of much research, and researchers do not agree on exactly what function it serves. Whereas some scientists argue that activity in this network indexes the lack of attention, others have suggested that it reflects the degree to which attention is directed to internal states and thoughts rather than the external environment

(Buckner, Andrews-Hanna, & Schachter, 2008). Future research will have to distinguish between alternative interpretations of the function of this network.

Hemineglect: Clinical Aspects

We spend the rest of this chapter investigating hemineglect, the syndrome described in the opening vignette of the chapter. Hemineglect is one of the syndromes that is prominently and commonly associated with attentional dysfunction. First we describe the clinical aspects of neglect and then we discuss how this syndrome has increased our understanding of the cognitive neuroscience of attention (for good short reviews, see Adair & Barrett, 2008; Milner & McIntosh, 2005).

IN FOCUS: Pay Attention to the Road!

Although we often do not think about it, driving a car requires a good degree of attentional ability. That demand is reflected in phrases that a passenger may say to a driver, such as "Pay attention to the road!" This phrase may mean that the driver is not sufficiently alert and vigilant, such as during a late-night drive after too little sleep and no cups of coffee. Or, the driver may not be focusing attention in the correct spatial location; for example, he may be paying more attention to the scenery alongside the road or to the back seat of the car where the children are fighting. The driver may not be focusing enough attention on the task of driving in comparison to some other task, such as eating a sandwich or reading directions. Driving requires many of the different aspects of attention we have discussed— vigilance and sustained attention, selective attention, and divided attention.

The concept of divided attention is highly relevant to a current debate about the use of cell phones while driving, both in the United States and abroad. Various regulations, or the absence thereof, across states and countries reflect the current lack of consensus about the safety of using cell phones while driving. In general, many people tend to think that speaking on a cell phone while driving is relatively benign. However, research in driving simulators indicates that people who talk on a cell phone while driving show as much impairment, as measured by decrement in braking speed and frequency of traffic accidents, as people who are legally drunk. Furthermore, this pattern occurs regardless of whether the driver is using a handheld or hands-free phone (Strayer, Drews, & Crouch, 2006). This finding may surprise you, given that many states and municipalities within the United States have adopted a ban on handheld but not hands-free cell phone usage. However, the important factor may be that the person who is speaking to the driver over the cell phone cannot perceive when the driver is entering difficult driving conditions. Therefore, such speakers do not adjust their rate of speaking in response to the driver's current demands, as do actual passengers in the car (Charlton, 2009). Furthermore, giving people practice in dividing their attention

between a conversation and driving does not appear to reduce the frequency of accidents in a simulator. Nor do individuals who report more frequent experience with conversing and driving in the real world have fewer accidents than those who tend not to converse while driving (Cooper & Strayer, 2008).

A few studies have attempted to provide insights into why such situations are so demanding by examining patterns of brain activity associated with concurrent driving and conversation. In one study, participants performed a simulated driving task, either undisturbed or while listening to spoken sentences, while fMRI was used to measure brain activation (Just, Keller, & Cynkar, 2008). Performance deteriorated under the dual-task condition, even though driving is mainly a visual task and comprehending sentences is an auditory task. Moreover, activity in regions of the parietal lobe involved in visual attention decreased by 37% when participants concurrently listened to a sentence compared to when they did not! This finding clearly points out the degree to which the resources that could be directed to visual attention are limited by a concurrent conversation.

Another study addressed this question with a paradigm in which participants had to respond to a red light presented unpredictably to the left or below a driving video, either while responding to nonemotional questions, such as "What is your birthdate?" or to no questions at all (Hsieh et al., 2009). The concurrent auditory task led to increased activity in language-related regions and also in many of the right-hemisphere regions involved in visual attention, such as the right superior parietal lobe and the right intraparietal sulcus. This finding suggests that the conversation substantially increased attentional demand in the visual modality. A similar study with MEG showed that these effects appear to influence relatively early aspects of attention, as indicated by reduced activity over the right parietal region at 200–300 ms after presentation of a visual target in the conversation condition compared to the nonconversation condition (Bowyer et al., 2009). Thus, the additional resources required for a conversation seem to tax attentional brain regions, a fact also reflected in longer reaction times under the dual-task conditions.

Another important issue related to attention and driving is the issue of whether older drivers are still capable of driving safely. Although elderly adults are routinely screened to ensure that their visual function is intact (Kotecha, Spratt, & Viswanathan, 2008), researchers are now examining whether attentional measures may be a better predictor of future involvement in a motor vehicle collision in which an elderly driver is at fault. One test that appears to predict collisions is known as the *useful field of view test* (Ball et al., 2006). This test examines the ability to identify a central target while simultaneously detecting a peripheral target, requiring divided attention. Another test designed to examine different subcomponents of attentional control, including alerting, orienting, and executive function, also predicts performance on a simulated driving task (Weaver, Bédard, McAuliffe, & Parkkari, 2009).

A recent study examined changes in brain activation for older adults who had undergone training to improve their useful field of view, compared to those who had received no such training. The researchers were interested in this question because training on useful field of view might improve actual driving safety (Roenker, Cissell, Ball, Wadley, & Edwards, 2003). The training regimen was found to be effective, as the ability to detect peripheral targets increased in those individuals who received training, compared to the no-training group. Of interest, increased activity was observed in the right inferior frontal gyrus for the trained group compared to the untrained group. Furthermore, for the group that received training, the increased activation in this region predicted the improvement in their performance. Because the right inferior frontal gyrus has been implicated in the orientation of attention, the researchers suggested that the training particularly facilitated this aspect of attentional control (Scalf et al., 2007). By identifying the underlying neural systems that are affected in elderly drivers, new and more targeted training methods may be designed. Not only may such interventions allow elderly individuals to retain their ability to drive—and thus their independence—for a longer periods of time, but they are also likely to make the roads safer for all.

■ Clinical Features

In this section we discuss the clinical features of neglect, first by describing the typical way in which this disorder is manifested. We then examine the features in a bit more detail to illustrate that the disorder cannot be explained merely as a consequence of sensory deficits, but rather reflects a disruption in attention.

Typical Manifestation

As mentioned previously, hemineglect is a syndrome in which patients ignore, or do not pay attention to, the side of space contralateral to their lesion. The ignored side of space is usually defined with reference to body midline, but neglect may occur with regard to other spatial reference frames as well (e.g., information to the left of the head's midline when the head is not at body midline). This inattention is manifested regardless of the modality in which information is presented. Depending on the severity of hemineglect, patients might fail to eat food on the left side of the plate, draw the left side of objects, read the left side of words, or use the left side of the body. In severe cases, individuals may even deny that the left side of the body belongs to them.

Symptoms of neglect may vary depending on the time since the brain damage. The degree of neglect is usually severe at first: all items on the neglected side of space are ignored. Within weeks to months, this profound neglect usually dissipates, such that a single item on the neglected side of space can be detected. However, neglect rarely, if ever, disappears completely (Heilman, Watson, & Valenstein, 1985). If there is competing information, such as when identical stimuli are presented at the same time in both visual fields (a condition known as **double simultaneous stimulation**), the patient tends to neglect the stimulus on the left. This phenomenon is often called **hemi-extinction** or **extinction** because the information on the neglected side of space is extinguished from consciousness. This phenomenon reinforces the idea that competition plays an important role in how attention is directed.

Although neglect usually occurs after damage to the posterior right hemisphere, there is debate about the most critical brain region. Neglect is usually observed after vascular damage to the supramarginal gyrus of the parietal region, which extends into subcortical regions (e.g., Vallar & Perani, 1986; Heilman, Watson, & Valenstein, 1985) (● Figure 11.11). Other research, however, argues that the critical location is somewhat more inferior in the right superior temporal cortex (Karnath, Fruhmann Berger, Küker, & Rorden, 2004). TMS over the right inferior parietal region induces hemi-extinction (Dambeck et al., 2006), as does TMS over the temporal-parietal junction, an effect not observed with TMS over the right temporal gyrus (Meister et al., 2006). As you can see, the location critical in causing neglect is not clear, although (as we discuss later) different types of neglect may be produced by lesions at each of these locations.

Neglect is observed more commonly and more severely after right- than left-hemisphere lesions (e.g., Albert, 1973; Ogden, 1985). In other words, neglect is observed more often for the left than for the right side of space. Although occurring most commonly after damage to the right parietal lobe, neglect can also occur after damage to other brain regions, including the frontal lobe (e.g., Heilman & Valenstein, 1972), basal ganglia (e.g., Damasio, Damasio, & Chui, 1980), and thalamus (e.g., Watson, Valenstein, & Heilman, 1981).

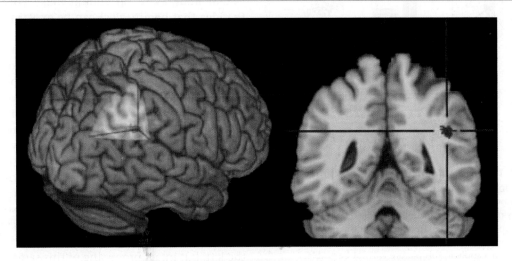

● **FIGURE 11.11   The region of the inferior parietal lobe that is classically considered to be associated with neglect.** In general, most individuals with hemineglect have sustained damage to this portion of inferior parietal lobe just superior to the temporal-parietal junction. *Source:* Mort, D.J., Malhotra, P., Mannan, S.K., Rorden, C., Pambakian, A., Kennard, C., & Husain, M. (2003). The anatomy of visual neglect. Brain, 126, Fig. 2, pg. 1990. By permission of Oxford University Press.

Not Due to Sensory Deficits

So far we have presented the neglect syndrome as a deficit in attentional processing, but we have not directly presented the evidence to support this assertion. In this section, we discuss findings demonstrating that neglect cannot be attributed to deficits in sensory processing. In the subsequent section, we review evidence showing that neglect is modulated by attentional factors.

To evaluate the possibility that neglect could result solely from deficits in sensory processing, let us reconsider the opening vignette of this chapter. Initially you may have thought that the gentleman's odd behavior might be explained by right-hemisphere damage that interfered with receipt of sensory information from the left side of space and motor control on the left side of his body. On closer investigation, though, you can see that this explanation is not plausible. He could perform motor acts competently, as demonstrated by his ability to shave, shower, dress, and eat. Despite such competence, however, motor acts were confined mainly to the right side of his body. Thus, the motor acts themselves were probably not disrupted. Rather, the ability to direct these acts to the left side of body was impaired.

Is it possible that a sensory deficit in the visual modality could explain his behavior? You might hypothesize that he had a dense hemianopsia of the left visual field (LVF) that left him functionally blind for all information to the left of fixation. Yet this explanation cannot account for a general inattention to visual information to the left of body midline, because patients with hemianopsia can process visual information on the left side of space. They do so simply by moving the center of their gaze to the far left.

For a fuller appreciation of this point, look at ● Figure 11.12A. Assume that you have left hemianopsia, are sitting at the center of the table, and want to make sure that the candle you lit on the left side of the table is not dripping wax. If your gaze is fixed straight ahead, you will be blind to all information to the left of body midline, including the candle. However, simply turning your head and fixating your gaze on the left edge of the table, as shown in ● Figure 11.12B, will enable you to see the candle because it now falls entirely within your right visual field (RVF). Thus, even though the candle remains to the left of body midline, it can be perceived merely by changing the point of visual fixation. Therefore, visual deficits cannot account for the fact that patients with hemineglect ignore what is on the left side of space.

Our analysis so far should make you skeptical of the idea that hemineglect can be explained by sensory loss in the visual modality. Is it possible, however, that patients with hemineglect are relatively insensitive to *all* sensory material received by the damaged hemisphere? We now entertain this hypothesis just long enough to disprove it!

If this hypothesis were true, then the severity of neglect would be predicted by the degree to which information in a given modality is processed by the contralateral hemisphere. For the purposes of this discussion, let us assume that the person is ignoring information on the left as the result of a right-hemisphere lesion. Because only the right hemisphere receives visual and somatosensory information from the left, this hypothesis would predict neglect of visual and somatosensory information from the left, but intact processing of this same type of material from the right. In the auditory modality, inattention to material on the left would be less severe because some information from the left ear projects ipsilaterally to the intact left hemisphere. In addition, some neglect of auditory information on the right would be expected

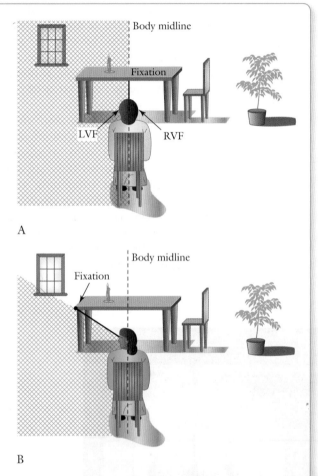

● **FIGURE 11.12   The influence of head position on the information that falls in each visual field.**
(A) When someone is looking straight ahead, information to the left of body midline falls in the left visual field (LVF) and information to the right of body midline falls in the right visual field (RVF). If the individual has hemianopsia for the LVF (green crosshatching), the candle in this picture will not be visible. (B) However, the individual can view the candle by simply turning her head so that the candle now falls within the good visual field, the RVF. Because patients with hemineglect ignore the left side of space, they fail to use such a strategy. © 2011 Cengage Learning

because the right hemisphere would be unable to proficiently process information from the right ear that is received through ipsilateral pathways. Finally, because the left nostril projects to the left hemisphere and the right nostril to the right hemisphere, no neglect would be observed for smells on the left, but neglect would be evident for smells on the right.

● **FIGURE 11.13   Typical example of line bisection by an individual with hemineglect.** Because the person with hemineglect ignores the left half of space, the line is bisected far to the right, as if the line extended only from its midpoint to its right endpoint. © 2011 Cengage Learning

In other words, if the neglect resulted from an inability of the right hemisphere to process sensory information, it would be exhibited by an extreme insensitivity to visual information in the LVF and tactile information from the left side of the body, less extreme neglect for auditory information on the left side of space, and no neglect for olfactory information on the left side of space. But such variations in the degree of neglect across modalities are not observed in cases of hemineglect. Instead, information from the contralateral side of space is generally ignored regardless of whether it is presented in the visual, tactile, auditory, or olfactory modality. Moreover, the severity of neglect in one modality, such as the visual modality, correlates with the severity of neglect in another modality, such as the auditory modality (for a review, see Pavani, Ládavas, & Driver, 2003). These pieces of evidence demonstrate that neglect does not appear to have a sensory basis.

Modulated by Attentional Factors

Because we know that hemineglect is not the result of sensory malfunction or damage, we now examine the evidence demonstrating that it arises specifically from a disruption in attentional processing. Let's return to the scenario at the beginning of this chapter. One odd aspect of the gentleman's behavior was that information on the left side of space that was ignored on one occasion was not ignored on others. So, although he initially ignored his hash browns and bacon, he eventually ate them, but only after his *attention* had been drawn leftward by the sound of the crashing dishes.

As this scenario suggests, neglect can be moderated by attentional factors. According to anecdotal reports, particularly salient or emotional information in the neglected half of space (such as a long needle in the hands of a nurse) will not be ignored. Even in experimental situations, neglect can be diminished by the manipulation of attention. For example, a classic sign of hemineglect is the inability to bisect a line correctly (● Figure 11.13). Patients with hemineglect most often place the "halfway" point about one-quarter of the way from the line's right end and three-quarters of the way from the left end (e.g., Reuter-Lorenz & Posner, 1990). They act as if the line extends only from the middle to the right and has no left side. However, line bisection can be improved (although it is still not totally accurate) if attention is first drawn to the left side of space by

placing a salient marker, such as a digit or letter that must be named, at the left edge of the line (e.g., Riddoch & Humphreys, 1983).

Furthermore, if information on the neglected side of space is critical for the understanding or comprehension of material, it tends to receive attention. For example, if a patient with hemineglect for the left side of space sees the word *antiballistic* centered on the page, he or she is much more likely to read the word as *ballistic,* even though the letters to the right of midline are only *llistic.* Thus, patients with hemineglect attend to information from the left side of space to the degree that it is needed to devise a reasonable interpretation of the available sensory information.

Finally, motivational factors can also mitigate the degree to which attention is allocated to the left. In one case study, a patient with hemineglect was asked to perform a letter-cancellation task that required crossing out every A on a page full of letters. On the first occasion, he was simply told to perform the task; on the second occasion, he was promised a certain amount of money for every A correctly detected. When he was provided with a motivation to direct attention to the left side of space, his neglect was reduced, as indicated by his ability to detect more As on the second occasion than on the first (Mesulam, 1985).

Thus, we know that neglect can be decreased by manipulations drawing attention to the left. These manipulations include external factors, such as the presence of particularly salient items or emotionally charged information. Attention to the left can also be increased by internal factors, such as a pressing motivation to process the left side of space or the need to do so to make sense of the world.

■ Theories Regarding the Underlying Deficit

One of the most striking aspects of hemineglect is that affected individuals seem to have little awareness that they are ignoring one side of space. To better appreciate this phenomenon, consider, as an analogy, how you usually conceptualize the area of space behind your head. Because your attention is focused on the world in front of you, generally you give little thought to the region behind you. Even if instructed to pay attention to what is behind you, you might start out by looking over your shoulder every few seconds, but would soon stop doing so. However, you'd probably do it for a longer period if you were paid a certain amount of money every time you reported on an event that occurred behind you. You might also pay attention to the world behind you if some extremely significant information were coming from that region, such as the sound of quickly approaching footsteps when you were walking down a dark street alone at night. The patient with hemineglect treats one side of space the way you normally treat the space behind your back.

Researchers have tried to discover why this profound neglect occurs. One suggestion is that these patients lack an internal mental representation of the neglected side of space. According to this view, that side of space doesn't even exist for these patients! This idea is nicely illustrated by a particularly ingenious study conducted by Bisiach and Luzzatti (1978), involving two patients from Milan, Italy, who had hemineglect for the left side of space. While the patients were in their hospital rooms, the researchers asked them to imagine in their mind's eye an extremely famous plaza, known to almost all inhabitants of Milan, that contains a variety of buildings, including the city's renowned

and ornate cathedral. First, the patients were asked to imagine standing at the end of the plaza opposite its imposing cathedral and to describe what they saw. The landmarks that the patients mentioned are designated by black circles on the map of the square shown in ● Figure 11.14A.

Notice that the patients could aptly describe the major landmarks on the right but not those on the left. Why not? Perhaps in their mind's eye, they were exhibiting neglect of information on the left. But there was an alternative explanation—their memory for the buildings situated in that part of the plaza was poor. To distinguish between these two possibilities, the researchers next asked the patients to imagine being at the opposite end of the plaza—standing on the steps of the cathedral with their backs toward it—and then to describe the plaza. As shown in ● Figure 11.14B, they described a whole new set of landmarks: those that were previously to the left but were now to the right.

We can draw a number of conclusions from this study. First, clearly the patients' memory for the entire plaza was fine, as all aspects of it were described across

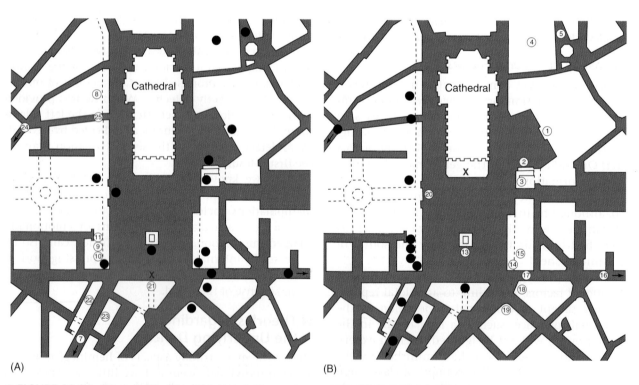

(A)   (B)

● **FIGURE 11.14   Maps indicating which structures were reported by patients with hemineglect when they imagined standing in the Piazza del Duomo in Milan, Italy.** The position in the plaza where the individual imagined himself or herself to be standing is marked with an X. The landmarks that the patients described are designated by filled circles. (A) The landmarks mentioned by patients when they imagined themselves facing the cathedral. These landmarks are situated mainly on the right. (B) The landmarks mentioned when the patients imagined themselves standing on the steps of the cathedral and facing away from it. Once again, mainly the landmarks on the right are mentioned. These individuals' memory for the square is intact because they mention most of the square's major landmarks across the two imagined positions. © 2011 Cengage Learning

their first and second imaginings of the plaza. Second, the patients were missing the conception of one side of space, in this case the left, because from either mental vantage point, they failed to report information on the left. Third, the attentional disruptions observed in hemineglect need not be driven by external stimuli. In this case, the patients were in their hospital rooms, not the plaza, imagining the square. These findings imply that patients with hemineglect fail to represent one side of space or fail to pay attention to one side of their mental representations of the world.

We can then ask whether there is a complete and total failure to represent the left side of space, or whether that representation is distorted in some systematic manner. One prominent theory argues that there is a gradient of attentional neglect, such that the further into the contralateral field an item is located, the greater the neglect (Kinsbourne, 1987) (● Figure 11.15A). Another theory, known as the *anisometry hypothesis,* argues that the representation of space is distorted such that the representation of space toward the periphery is more and more compacted (● Figure 11.15B) (Bisiach, Neppi-Modona, & Ricci, 2002).

Other theories of hemineglect do not focus on the representation or attention paid to the contralateral side of space, but rather consider hemineglect from the perspective of competition between the hemispheres. This viewpoint suggests that the problem is not so much that the left side of space is distorted for these individuals, but rather that the pull of sensory stimuli on the non-neglected side of space is so salient as to prevent these patients from attending to the information on the neglected side.

Consistent with this idea are a number of pieces of evidence. First, patients with parietal lesions often have difficulty disengaging attention from the non-neglected field. This phenomenon can be illustrated by the cueing paradigm in ● Figure 11.16. In this task, a cue identifies with a high degree of probability where the subsequent target will appear. When presented with a cue in the neglected field, patients with neglect do not have much difficulty detecting the subsequent target. In this condition, there is no competing information in the non-neglected field from which attention must be disengaged. However, if the cue is presented to the non-neglected field followed by a target in the neglected field, there is a large increase in reaction time, above and beyond that typically observed for neurologically normal individuals. These patients appear to have particular difficulty in disengaging their attention from the competing information in the non-neglected field (Posner, Walker, Friedrich, & Rafal, 1984). Likewise, we discussed how the long-lasting deficits in hemineglect are likely to occur under conditions of double simultaneous stimulation, once again a condition in which there is competing information in the non-neglected field.

An interesting demonstration of the degree to which information in the non-neglected field influences performance was provided by a study in which patients with unilateral neglect performed two versions of a cancellation task often used to assess hemineglect (Mark, Kooistra, & Heilman, 1988). In this task, a series of lines are randomly distributed across the page, and the person must "cancel" as many as possible. In one version, individuals canceled the targets on a dry-erase board by writing over them in darker-color ink. In this way, the lines remained even after they were canceled. In the second version, individuals were given an eraser and canceled the lines by erasing them. The neglect for left-side stimuli was less severe in the second condition than in the first. Because cancellation of the lines by erasure decreased the number of items in right hemispace, there were fewer items from which

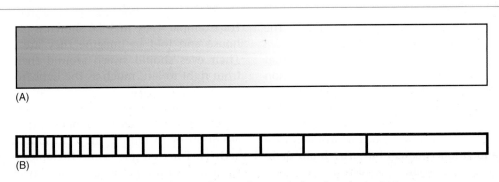

(A)

(B)

● **FIGURE 11.15   Proposed distortions of attention and space in hemineglect.** (A) In some models of neglect, attention is not disrupted equally across all portions of space contralateral to the lesion. Rather, neglect is thought to be more severe for the far portion of contralateral space as compared to the near portion. This attentional gradient is depicted by the darkness of the bar, with white indicating normal attention and blue indicating severe neglect. (B) In other models, the internal representation of space itself is thought to be distorted, such that the representation of information contralateral to the lesion of space is reduced and condensed.

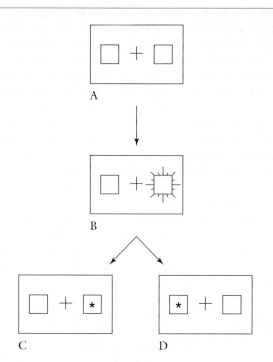

● FIGURE 11.16   A classic paradigm for measuring spatial attention that reveals deficits in individuals with hemineglect. (A) The individual is told to fixate on a central location (the cross) for the duration of the trial. (B) At some point, a cue occurs, in this case the brightening of a peripheral box. This cue predicts with a high degree of accuracy the location of the subsequent target. The target to which the individual must respond (an asterisk) appears after a variable time interval. Two types of trials are given: those in which the cue correctly predicts the location of the subsequent target, *valid trials* (C); and those in which the cue incorrectly predicts the location of the subsequent target, *invalid trials* (D). Responses to invalid trials take longer because the individual must move attention from the cued location to the actual location of the target. Individuals with hemineglect have specific difficulty on invalid trials when the cue is presented in the non-neglected field. © 2011 Cengage Learning

attention needed to be disengaged, and hence the neglect was less severe.

These data can also be interpreted to suggest that hemineglect results from an uneven competition between the hemispheres for controlling the direction of attention. As we learned earlier in this chapter, the notion of competition is fundamental to many models of attentional control. When both hemispheres are intact, the competition is equal, but after brain damage, the competition becomes lopsided and hemineglect is observed. Some of the most compelling data for this explanation of hemineglect come from studies of patients with unilateral brain damage who suffer from neglect and were administered TMS. The researchers reasoned that if neglect occurs because of an imbalance between the hemispheres, then giving TMS to disrupt

processing of the intact hemisphere should restore such a balance, and reduce neglect. In fact, that was exactly what they found (Oliveri et al., 2001).

Corroborative evidence of an imbalance between the hemispheres is provided by using TMS with neurologically intact individuals. When TMS is applied over the parietal region to deactivate this region, extinction is observed for information in the contralateral space (see Oliveri & Caltagirone, 2006, for review). Conversely, giving TMS to facilitate brain activity increases attention to the contralateral field (Kim, Min, Ko, Park, Jang, & Lee, 2005).

■ Treatment

As we mentioned earlier, although hemineglect may dissipate with time, it rarely (if ever) disappears completely. Hemineglect can be vexing because it interferes significantly with everyday life. For example, think about how having hemineglect would make it dangerous or even impossible to drive a car or cross the street! Finding an effective means of reducing neglect, therefore, is of great clinical interest. In fact, some researchers have attempted to train neglect patients in street-crossing in a virtual reality environment in which the costs of not noticing a passing car are clearly less severe than in real life (Katz, Ring, Naveh, Kizony, Feintuch, & Weiss, 2005).

Because attention can be modulated by both top-down factors and bottom-up factors, treatments designed to reduce neglect can attempt to ameliorate the disorder from either a top-down or a bottom-up perspective (see Marshall, 2009, for a review). Top-down approaches try to teach patients to guide their attention with aid from a therapist. In contrast, bottom-up approaches use sensory input or stimulation to bring attention to the neglected side. One therapy that is top-down in nature is visual scanning training. In this therapy, patients are prompted verbally by a therapist (or family member) to look to the left, leveraging the typically intact verbal abilities of individuals with neglect. Sometimes a metaphor is used to help patients think about how they should be controlling their attention. For example, they may be shown a picture of a lighthouse and told to imagine they are the lighthouse. Their eyes should sweep around their environment, from right to left, much as the light from a lighthouse sweeps across space.

Bottom-up approaches involve manipulating sensory input to the brain, either to increase overall arousal and attention or to redress the hemispheric imbalance in activity. For example, some therapies require patients to "drive" a car on a screen as quickly as possible while avoiding obstacles, with one key serving as the gas pedal and another as the brake, attempting to keep the person alert and aroused. Brain imaging with patients who have undergone this therapy show increased activity in right-hemisphere regions involved in attentional control, including the angular gyrus, cingulate cortex, and frontal regions, as well as increased activity in the homologous regions of the left hemisphere (Thimm, Fink, Küst, Karbe, & Strum, 2006).

Other approaches attempt to redress the hemispheric imbalance in arousal through sensory stimulation (see Kerkhoff, 2003, for a review). One simple method for reducing neglect is to either actively or passively move the limb on the neglected side of space within the neglected hemispace (e.g., Frassinetti, Rossi, & Ládavas, 2001). Another neglect-reducing technique, known as **caloric stimulation**, introduces water at least 7°C colder than body temperature into the ear canal, which induces motion in the semicircular canals of the vestibular system (Bisiach, Rusconi, & Vallar, 1991; Rode, Charles, Perenin, Vighetto, Trillet, & Aimard, 1992). Various studies have found that vibration of the left neck muscles (often referred to as *neck-proprioceptive stimulation*) reduces neglect (e.g., Johannsen, Ackermann, & Karnath, 2003), as does optokinetic stimulation (e.g., Vallar, Guariglia, Nico, & Pizzamiglio, 1997; Kerkhoff, Keller, Ritter, & Marquardt, 2006). In this latter technique, hemineglect patients view randomly distributed colored squares that move in a coherent pattern, and are taught to follow these items from right to left with their eyes without moving the head. This therapy increases activity in frontal and parietal brain regions associated with attention, although it tends to increase activity more in posterior regions than the sustained attention driving task we discussed earlier (Thimm, Fink, Küst, Karbe, Willmes, & Sturm, 2009). Finally, prism adaptation has been used over multiple sessions. In this method, patients are trained, while wearing prisms that move the visual world 10 degrees to the right, to point to target items near midline. When the prisms are removed, individuals now point closer to midline than they did before training, as the rightward shift induced by the prisms trained them to orient further leftward (Rossetti et al., 1998; Serino, Barbiani, Rinaldesi, & Ládavas, 2009).

At present, the more specific mechanism by which these types of therapies reduce neglect remains an issue of debate. Unilateral vestibular stimulation increases brain activation (as measured by regional blood flow) in the temporoparietal region of the brain (Freiberg, Olsen, Roland, Paulson, & Lassen, 1985), which in turn may reduce neglect. Because both caloric and neck-proprioceptive stimulation result in an illusion that straight ahead is shifted to the left (Karnath, Sievering, & Fetter, 1994), they may cause a shift in the person's spatial frame of reference, moving midline of the body toward the left (e.g., Vallar, Guariglia, & Rusconi, 1997). Consistent with this idea, these types of stimulation reduce neglect not only in the sensory and motor realms, but also with regard to mental representations (Cappa, Sterzi, Vallar, & Bisiach, 1987; Rubens, 1985; Vallar, Sterai, Bottini, Cappa, & Rusconi, 1990). Prism adaptation may also work by shifting an individual's frame of reference toward the left (Serino, Angeli, Frassinetti, & Ládavas, 2006).

Finally, as we discussed earlier, a most dramatic way to reduce neglect is to attempt to redress the imbalance in activity across the hemispheres through the use of TMS over the left hemisphere (see Fierro, Brighina, & Bisiach, 2006, for a review). Initial reports indicated that the reduction in neglect was only transient (Oliveri et al., 2001) or limited to about two weeks of effective time (Brighina et al., 2003), but other recent evidence suggests that, at least in some cases, the effects can be longer-lasting (Shindo, Sugiyama, Huabao, Nishjima, Kondo, & Izumi, 2006). Although controversy exists about the effectiveness of these different methods (see Marshall, 2009, for a discussion), research will continue in the hopes of finding improved treatments to address the core deficits in neglect.

Hemineglect: Implications for Understanding Brain-Behavior Relationships

Now that we have discussed the clinical aspects of hemineglect, we turn our attention to a number of issues regarding brain-behavior relationships that can be illuminated by this syndrome. As already discussed in Chapter 8, evidence from hemineglect patients allows us to understand that the brain encodes space according to multiple reference frames, since different patients may have neglect to the left of the different midlines (e.g., midline of body or midline of objects). In this section, we explore how hemineglect provides additional evidence for object-based attention, how it expands our understanding of hemispheric asymmetries in attention, and how it provides insights into the degree to which the nervous system processes unattended stimuli. Where relevant, we present converging evidence from other techniques used in cognitive neuroscience.

■ Attention Based on Objects

Most of our discussion of neglect so far has assumed a spatial framework defined in terms of the body midline. That is, neglect is assumed to occur for information to the left of the body midline. This assumes a conception of space that is centered around the body itself. However, patients can also show neglect for the left half of objects, regardless of where the objects are located in relation to the body. As you remember, earlier in this chapter we discussed how attention can be directed either to certain regions of space or to certain stimuli, such as objects. In this section, we consider how information from neglect patients can inform our understanding of object-based attention.

Indeed, neglect for certain portions of an object provides further evidence for an object-based form of attention. A number of case studies of **object-based neglect** have been reported both for nonverbal material (e.g., Young, DeHaan, Newcombe, & Hay, 1990; Young, Hellawell, & Welch, 1992; Behrmann & Moscovitch,

1994; Driver, Baylis, Goodrich, & Rafal, 1994) and verbal material (e.g., Caramazza & Hillis, 1990; Hillis & Caramazza, 1991). In these cases, the individual neglects the left half of the stimulus (typically an object or word) regardless of the position of the stimulus in space. Furthermore, no neglect is exhibited for the left half of space on standard measures, such as an item-cancellation test. To appreciate this form of neglect, take a look at ● Figure 11.17. Individuals with hemineglect are asked to put an X next to all items that are missing a segment and to circle all items without a missing segment. Notice that one patient neglects all items on the left side of the page, but manages to circle all items on the right side of the page that have a segment missing, even when that segment is on the left (Figure 11.17A). This individual is demonstrating neglect with regard to the spatial position of the item. In contrast, the other patient circles items across the entire page, but does not place an X next to items with a missing segment on the left, showing neglect that is linked to the objects themselves rather than to their spatial position (Figure 11.17B) (Ota, Fujii, Suzuki, Fukatsu, & Yamadori, 2001).

In some cases, whether space-based or object-based neglect is observed may depend on the orientation of the object. For example, when words were rotated 180 degrees (i.e., upside down), one patient exhibited neglect with respect to space, but when the words were mirror-reversed, the patient was more likely to show object-based neglect (Savazzi, 2003). In other cases, neglect may vary depending on the reference frame to which the tested individuals are told to attend, such as whether they are told to look across all of space on a computer monitor or to look at particular shapes on the monitor (Baylis, Baylis, & Gore, 2004). Thus, the type of environment in which information is embedded and how individuals search for the item may affect what type of neglect is exhibited.

Other evidence suggests that the type of neglect exhibited may also depend on the location of the lesion. Recent evidence suggests that hypoperfusion of tissue (that is, lack of a blood supply to neural tissue) in the angular gyrus predicts the severity of viewer-centered neglect, whereas hypoperfusion of the superior temporal cortex predicts the severity of object-based neglect. Hence, different regions of brain tissue may underlie neglect for each of these frames of reference (Shirani et al., 2009). This finding may explain, in part, the controversy over which region is critical in causing neglect—it may vary depending on the frame of reference that is most likely to be affected.

Before we leave our discussion of object-based neglect, we should point out that some researchers make a distinction between **stimulus-centered neglect** and object-centered neglect. In **object-centered neglect**, the individual ignores the left half of the object regardless of how that object is displayed. For example, an individual with a leftward

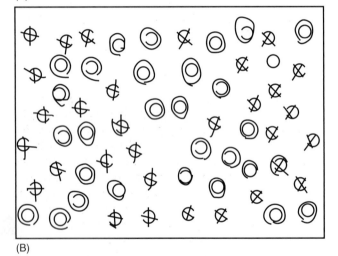

(A)

(B)

● **FIGURE 11.17   Space-based vs. object-based neglect.** In this task, individuals are told to circle all the items on the paper that are complete, and to put an X next to (or through) any item that is missing a part. (A) The behavior of one patient whose neglect is space-based. Notice that all items on the left side of the page are ignored. For those items on the attended (i.e., right) side of space, incomplete items are circled regardless of whether the missing information is on the left or right, indicating that there is no object-based neglect. (B) The behavior of another patient whose neglect is object-based. Notice that items are circled across both sides of space, indicating that he does not display space-based neglect. However, this patient fails to put an X next to circles that are missing a portion of their left side, circling them as if they were complete. However, he correctly detects the missing portion of the right side of the circle, putting an X next to those items. As such, he is exhibiting object-based neglect. *Source:* Ota, H. Fujii, Suzuki, K., Fukatsu, R. & Yamadori, A. (2001) Dissociation of body-centered and stimulus-centered representations of unilateral neglect. Neurology, 57, A) Figure 3, pg. 2066, B) Figure 4, page 2067.

stimulus-centered neglect, if shown the word "feet" in its normal orientation, might read the word as "meet," but if shown the word mirror-reversed, might read it as "feel." In both cases, what is on the left side of the stimulus is ignored. However, in object-based neglect, the individual ignores the left side of the object regardless of its position. Individuals who exhibit object-based neglect might misread "feet" as "meet" regardless of whether it was shown in its normal orientation or mirror-reversed, because "fe" is always on the left side of the canonical representation of the item regardless of how it is oriented (e.g., Hillis & Caramazza, 1991). Because few objects, except maybe words, have a canonical left and right, these frames of reference are often hard to distinguish. Nonetheless, researchers have shown that if you teach neglect patients to perceive particular nonverbal stimuli as having a canonical representation through repeated training, object-based centering can be demonstrated for such material as well (Savazzi, Mancini, Veronesi, & Posteraro, 2009).

■ Hemispheric Differences in Attentional Control

One of the most striking aspects of the hemineglect syndrome is that it is much more prominent and severe after right-hemisphere damage than after left-hemisphere damage (e.g., Denes, Semenza, Stoppa, & Lis, 1982). Theorists have wondered why this is so. Here we discuss some possible explanations.

Some theorists have proposed that the hemineglect exhibited after right-hemisphere damage reflects the effects of two distinct factors: an attentional bias of each hemisphere for information on the opposite side of space and a larger role of the right hemisphere in overall attention and arousal. We now consider each of these two factors and then examine how they might combine to cause the effects observed in hemineglect.

As we discussed earlier in this chapter, each hemisphere exhibits an attentional bias for information located in the contralateral space. To review, when individuals direct attention to one visual field, such as the LVF, the ERP recorded over the occipital lead on the contralateral hemisphere is larger than that over the ipsilateral hemisphere (e.g., Mangun & Hillyard, 1988). When attention has to be shifted among various locations, all of which are restricted to one visual field, activation measured by PET is greatest over left superior parietal and left superior frontal cortex for RVF locations, and over right superior parietal and right superior frontal cortex for LVF locations (Corbetta, Miezin, Shulman, & Petersen, 1993). Moreover, when task demands activate one hemisphere, it induces an attentional bias to the contralateral side of space, enhancing the processing of material in that location (Kinsbourne, 1974).

Such attentional biases for one side of space can be observed even when items are presented in free vision. Look at ● Figure 11.18. Which of the two faces looks happier to you? If you are right-handed, you are likely

A   B

● **FIGURE 11.18 Examples of chimeric faces that demonstrate attentional biases to one side of space.** Although these faces are identical except for being mirror images, most right-handed individuals perceive the face in (A), which has the smile on the left, as happier than the face in (B), which has the smile on the right. Experts think that the left half-face is perceived as more expressive because the right hemisphere is more adept at processing emotional and facial information, which causes an attentional bias toward the left side of space. Hence, information located on the left is perceived as more salient. I: "Asymmetry of Perception in Free Viewing of Chimeric Faces," by J. Levy, W. Heller, M. T. Banich, and L. A. Burton, 1983, Brain and Cognition, 2, p. 406. With permission from Elsevier.

to have said A. Because the right hemisphere of right-handers is better at the processing of faces and the interpretation of emotional expression, it becomes more activated. This leads to a bias for the contralateral side of space, in this case the left, making the half-face located there more salient and hence judged as happier. Notice that this bias is completely induced by the brain, as the two pictures are mirror images, which means that on the basis of perceptual factors, there is no reason to perceive one as happier than the other (Levy, Heller, Banich, & Burton, 1983). On the basis of evidence of this nature, as well as other study findings (e.g., Reuter-Lorenz, Kinsbourne, & Moscovitch, 1990), each hemisphere appears to have an attentional bias for the contralateral side of space.

Earlier in this chapter we discussed evidence that the right hemisphere plays a role in overall attention and arousal. Linking this factor more specifically to neglect, patients with hemineglect syndrome often have difficulty with sustained attention, especially in the spatial domain (Malhotra, Coulthard, & Husain, 2009). Moreover, the inability to sustain attention predicts the severity of neglect (Samuelsson, Hjelmquist, Jensen, Ekholm, & Blomstrand, 1998).

The manner in which these two factors might combine to produce neglect was demonstrated in a study in which an item-detection task was given to three groups

TABLE 11.1	Number of Items Missed in the Visual Search Task Used by Weintraub and Mesulam (1987)	
	Average No. of Items Missed	
Group	Left Side	Right Side
Patients with left-hemisphere lesions	1.25	2.38
Patients with right-hemisphere lesions	17.13	8.00
Neurologically intact control subjects	0.56	0.30

Patients with unilateral lesions miss more items on the side of space contralateral to the lesion than on the ipsilateral side. Overall, the patients with right-hemisphere damage miss many more targets than do those with left-hemisphere damage.

of individuals: patients with right-hemisphere damage, patients with left-hemisphere damage, and neurologically intact individuals (Weintraub & Mesulam, 1987). These individuals were asked to circle as many target items as they could find within a visual display; the results are presented in Table 11.1. As expected, the neurologically intact individuals missed practically no targets on either side of space. The results for patients with brain damage yielded two important findings. First, regardless of whether patients had right- or left-hemisphere damage, they missed more targets on the side of space contralateral, rather than ipsilateral, to the lesion. These results provide additional evidence that each hemisphere is primarily responsible for attention to information in the contralateral hemispace. Second, as you can see in Table 11.1, the overall performance of patients with right-hemisphere damage was worse than the overall performance of patients with left-hemisphere damage; that is, they missed more items overall on both the left *and* right sides of space. In fact, patients with right-hemisphere damage missed more items in their *non-neglected* hemispace (i.e., right hemispace) than patients with left-hemisphere damage missed in their *neglected* hemispace (i.e., right hemispace)! This piece of evidence, along with the others cited previously, suggests that the right hemisphere may exert more influence over overall attention and arousal than the left. (For a discussion of how both lateralized and nonlateralized aspects of attentional control could contribute to neglect, see Husain & Rorden, 2003).

Another potential reason for the greater severity of hemineglect after right-hemisphere lesions is that the gradient of attentional allocation that we discussed earlier in this chapter differs between the hemispheres (Kinsbourne, 1993). According to this model, the left hemisphere has a steep gradient, with a very strong bias for the far (i.e., right-hand) portion of space relative to ipsilateral regions of space. In contrast, the right hemisphere's gradient of attention (i.e., the difference in attentional allocation from contralateral to ipsilateral) may not be as drastic. Evidence consistent

with the idea of hemispheric differences in the gradient of attention comes from a variety of sources. As discussed earlier, rTMS that facilitates (rather than disrupts) processing will increase attention and performance for information in right hemispace—but it concomitantly increases errors for items in left hemispace. This finding illustrates that the left hemisphere has a strong attentional bias to the right and in fact, when activated, may even lead to a disruption of attention to left hemispace. In contrast, while rTMS over the right hemisphere increases performance for items in left hemispace, it does not increase errors in right hemispace, suggesting that its gradient of attention is not as severe (Kim et al., 2005). In addition, when attention must be distributed bilaterally (compared to only one half of space), increased activity is observed over the right but not the left inferior parietal, suggesting that the right hemisphere can distribute attention in a more bilateral manner than the left (Çiçek, Gitelman, Hurley, Nobre, & Mesulam, 2007).

■ Processing of Unattended Stimuli

Thus far, we have presented attention as a mechanism whereby the brain can choose what it wants to process from the vast array of information available. But what is the fate of unattended stimuli? Do they fall into a black hole of mental consciousness, leaving not even a trace of their existence, or are they processed but to a much lesser degree than attended stimuli? In Chapter 7, we discussed the fact that patients with prosopagnosia appear to be able to extract some information about faces that they cannot recognize. Such findings provide evidence that information may be processed to some degree even if it doesn't reach consciousness. Next, we examine evidence that although patients with hemineglect appear to ignore all information on the unattended side of space, under certain conditions this information can nonetheless influence their behavior.

One of the first hints that patients with hemineglect might process information in their unattended half of space came from the case of a patient with left-sided hemineglect who was shown drawings of two houses that were identical except for flames coming out of the left side of one (Marshall & Halligan, 1988). Although the patient claimed to detect no difference between the houses, when asked which house she would prefer to live in, she picked the one without flames. Although subsequent studies failed to replicate this particular finding (e.g., Bisiach & Rusconi, 1990), priming studies have demonstrated that information on the left, which cannot be explicitly recognized, nonetheless influences performance. In one study, researchers determined the speed with which neglect patients could categorize a picture in the RVF (their non-neglected field) as an animal or fruit. The important factor in this study was that, 400 ms earlier, a picture from either the same category or a different category was presented in the neglected field (i.e., the LVF). Responses to information in the RVF were faster when a related rather than an unrelated item was presented in the neglected field. This finding suggests that information in the neglected field was being processed to some degree, because it could influence processing of material in the nonneglected field (Berti & Rizzolatti, 1992). In contrast to patients with neglect, patients with hemianopsia for the LVF do not show such priming effects, as they are truly blind to information in that portion of space (McGlinchey-Berroth, Milberg, Verfaellie, Alexander, & Kilduff, 1993; for a review of such priming studies, see Driver & Vuilleumier, 2001).

Studies with fMRI have provided some insight into how brain regions might support such priming effects. These studies suggest that residual or low-level activation of brain regions allows priming but precludes conscious recognition. One case study demonstrating such a phenomenon reported a man who exhibited hemi-inattention after a right inferior parietal lobe infarction (Rees, Wojciulik, Clarke, Husain, Frith, & Driver, 2000). When shown items singly, he could identify them in each hemifield with better than 95% accuracy, yet under conditions of bilateral simultaneous stimulation he identified only 2 trials as having information on both sides and said that the remaining 58 contained just a single item in the RVF. The researchers compared brain activation for the bilateral condition in which he reported seeing only the RVF item to those trials in which he truly saw only a single item in the RVF. The patient's response was the same in these two conditions even though the stimuli were distinct (bilateral as compared to unilateral). The researchers focused on activation in the visual cortex of the right hemisphere (contralateral to the neglected left field). On the trials in which the patient reported not seeing anything in the LVF, there was activation in the contralateral visual cortex, albeit somewhat reduced as compared to that observed when an item was presented solely in the LVF (and could be correctly detected by the patient) (● Figure 11.19) (for follow-up, see Rees, Wojciulik, Clarke, Husain, Frith, & Driver, 2002).

ERPs provide evidence regarding the time point at which processing of neglected and non-neglected

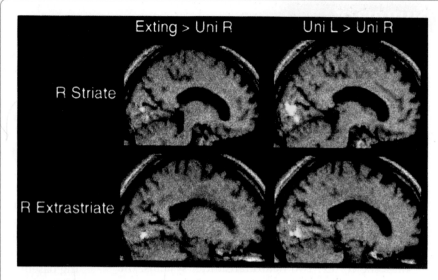

● **FIGURE 11.19** **Overlap between brain regions activated when there is conscious versus unconscious perception of an item.** In this study, the individual did not consciously perceive items in the LVF under conditions of bilateral stimulation. Shown on the right side of the figure are those brain regions in striate (top row) and extrastriate (bottom row) cortex that exhibited more activity on unilateral LVF trials than RVF trials. On the left side of the figure are those brain regions in striate and extrastriate cortex that exhibited more activity to extinguished stimuli in the LVF as compared with the RVF. Notice that although they were not consciously perceived, the extinguished stimuli evoked activity in similar regions as when they were consciously perceived, although to a smaller degree. *Source:* Rees et al., 2000. Unconscious activation of visual cortex in the damaged right hemisphere of a parietal patient with extinction, Brain, 123, p. 1629, fig. 2. By permission of Oxford University Press.

stimuli diverge. For example, a normal N_{170} is recorded to faces that are neglected under conditions of bilateral simultaneous stimulation (Vuilleumier et al., 2001). Similarly, in response to simple visual stimuli, visual evoked potentials for the neglected hemifield were intact up to approximately 130 ms from stimulus onset (Di Russo, Aprille, Spitoni, & Spinelli, 2008). In both cases, though, components that index activation in higher-order visual areas were absent. Because neglected stimuli are processed at early stages of the visual system, they can influence performance in subtle ways, causing the effects observed in priming studies. However, because they do not gain access to higher-order visual processing areas, they are not perceived consciously.

These studies reinforce the idea that attention serves to modulate the processing of information: Attended information is processed more fully, whereas unattended information is processed to a lesser degree. Our survey of attention has shown that this modulation occurs at many different points in time and involves many diverse regions of the cortex. This chapter has focused mainly on the modulation of activity that involves posterior regions of the brain. In Chapter 12, we examine the involvement of prefrontal regions in executive aspects of attentional control, as well as other aspects of executive function.

Summary

What Is "Attention"?

- Attention is the cognitive ability that allows us to deal with the inherent processing limitations of the human brain by selecting information for further processing.
- Psychologists often sort attention into four general categories: arousal, vigilance and sustained attention, selective attention, and divided attention.

Brain Structures Involved in Attention

- Alertness and arousal involve a number of brain regions. The reticular activating system, the cell bodies of which reside in the brainstem, diffusely activates the cortex. Two neurotransmitter systems, the cell bodies of which also reside in the brainstem, the noradrenergic and brainstem cholinergic systems, also aid in arousal. Finally, midline thalamic structures serve to activate the cortex.
- Vigilance and sustained attention are supported by the noradrenergic and cholinergic systems as well as the thalamus. In addition, posterior regions of the right hemisphere play a role in maintaining vigilance.
- Selective attention serves to prioritize information for additional processing and can act at various points in time, from relatively soon after stimulus input to the selection of a response.
- The superior colliculus, located in the midbrain, plays an important role in automatically orienting attention to particular locations in space.
- Portions of the thalamus act as a gating mechanism for selecting or filtering incoming information.
- The posterior parietal lobe provides a spatial frame of reference for attentional processing. It binds together features, such as color and form, so that items can be uniquely identified, and is likely involved in allocating overall resources needed to meet attentional demands.
- Medial prefrontal cortex is involved in the selection of the appropriate motor response, especially when tasks are attentionally demanding.
- Lateral prefrontal regions are important for top-down attentional control, providing the abstract category or goal that should guide attention.
- Some brain regions act as the source of attentional control, sending top-down signals about how attention should be directed. These signals are received at brain regions that act as sites of attentional control, and the activity of those regions is modified depending on how attention is allocated.
- Selective attention can be directed to a particular position in space; to a particular item attribute, such as color; or to a particular object.
- In general, attention acts to increase processing in brain regions that are responsible for processing the type of information to which attention is directed.

- Divided attention, which is the ability to split one's attention between different sources of information or different tasks, may rely more on prefrontal regions to allocate task resources than when attention is not divided.

Selective Attention

- Attention appears to work by biasing processing toward specific information, and serves to resolve competition between items.
- It can do so by increasing activation of neural tissue processing attended information, by suppressing activation of unattended information, or by increasing baseline activity.

Network Models of Attentional Control

- Conceptually, attention is thought to be supported by a network of brain structures. One theoretical model proposes that the reticular activating system maintains vigilance and arousal, the cingulate imparts motivational significance to information, the posterior parietal region provides a sensory map of the world, and frontal regions provide motor programs for moving the focus of attention.
- Another model argues for three subsystems. The first, involving the locus coeruleus, parietal cortex, and right frontal regions, supports alertness. The second, involving the superior colliculus, superior parietal region, temporal-parietal junction, and frontal eye fields, allows attention to be oriented to sensory signals to select among them. The third subsystem, involving the basal ganglia, lateral ventral prefrontal region, and the anterior cingulate cortex, supports executive aspects of attention.
- Still other models distinguish between a dorsal frontoparietal subsystem, involved in executive aspects of attention, and a ventral subsystem, consisting of temporoparietal cortex and inferior frontal cortex of the right hemisphere, which allows attention to be directed to salient stimuli in the environment.
- Recently researchers have identified a network, known as the default network, whose activity is decreased when individuals are engaged in an attentionally demanding task. Preliminary evidence suggests that if activity in this network is not reduced during demanding tasks, poor performance will result.

Hemineglect: Clinical Aspects

- In hemineglect, which is most often observed after vascular damage to the posterior parietal region, an individual ignores information on the side of space contralateral to a brain lesion.
- The neglect is not due to sensory deficits, as the severity of neglect for the contralateral side of space does

not vary with sensory modality, and individuals with a severe sensory deficit for the contralateral side of space do not exhibit neglect for that side of space.

- Neglect can be modulated by factors that draw attention to information on the neglected side of space, such as high emotional saliency, motivational factors, and a need to process such information to gain understanding or comprehension of material.

- Theories regarding the main underlying deficit in neglect include one suggesting that patients lose the mental conception of the neglected side of space, and another suggesting an uneven competition between the attentional biases of each hemisphere to the opposite side of space.

- Treatments for neglect include guided therapy, such as visual scanning therapy to change the individual's allocation of attention; sensory stimulation of the body parts located on the neglected side of space, to make that side of space more salient; and transcranial

magnetic stimulation to al
ity between the hemisphe

Hemineglect: Implicatio
Brain-Behavior Relation

- Neglect illustrates that att
based or object-based.

- The fact that neglect is
severe after right-hemisp
the right hemisphere is more important for overall arousal and attention, and/or that the attentional gradient for the contralateral versus the ipsilateral side of space is steeper for the left hemisphere than the right.

- Material in the neglected field that cannot be identified by patients with hemineglect can nonetheless influence performance by priming certain responses, and appears to undergo early stages of processing that allow unconscious but not conscious access.

Key Terms

alertness and arousal 303

attention 303

caloric stimulation 329

bottom-up attentional selection 306

coma 304

divided attention 304

double simultaneous stimulation 323

early-selection viewpoint 307

(hemi)-extinction 323

hemi-inattention 303

hemineglect 303

intralaminar nucleus 305

late-selection viewpoint 307

medial dorsal nucleus 305

multiple-resource theory 304

object-based neglect 330

object-based viewpoint of attention 313

object-centered neglect 330

pulvinar (of the thalamus) 309

resource 304

reticular activating system (RAS) 304

reticular nucleus 305

saccade 308

selective attention 304

space-based viewpoint of attention 313

stimulus-centered neglect 330

superior colliculus 308

top-down attentional selection 306

vigilance 304

Book Companion Site at www.cengage.com/psychology/Banich
This website provides instructors and students with a wealth of free information and resources, including tutorial quizzes, flashcards, and the glossary.

Executive Function

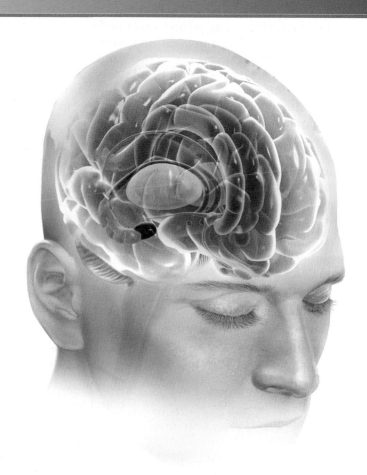

DR. P WAS A SUCCESSFUL, middle-aged surgeon who used the financial rewards of his practice to pursue his passion for traveling and playing sports. Tragically, while he was undergoing minor facial surgery, complications caused his brain to be deprived of oxygen for a short period. The ensuing brain damage had profoundly negative consequences for his mental functioning, compromising his ability to plan, to adapt to change, and to act independently.

After the surgical mishap, standard IQ tests revealed Dr. P's intelligence to be, for the most part, in the superior range. Nonetheless, he could not handle many simple day-to-day activities and was unable to appreciate the nature of his deficits. His dysfunction was so severe that returning to work as a surgeon was impossible for him, and his brother had to be appointed Dr. P's legal guardian. As a surgeon, Dr. P had skillfully juggled many competing demands and had flexibly adjusted to master changing situations. Now, however, he was unable to carry out any but the most basic routines, and then only in a rigid, routinized manner. Furthermore, he had lost his ability to initiate actions and to plan for the future. For example, his sister-in-law had to tell him to change his clothes, and only after years of explicit rule-setting did he learn to do so on his own. He managed to work as a delivery truck driver for his brother's business, but only because his brother could structure the deliveries so that they involved minimal planning. Dr. P could not be provided with an itinerary for the deliveries of the day because he was incapable of advance planning. Rather, his brother gave him information about one delivery at a time. After each delivery, Dr. P would call in for directions to the next stop.

Dr. P appeared to be totally unaware of his situation. He seemed unconcerned and uninterested in how he was provided with the basic necessities of life, such as clothes, food, and lodging, and was utterly complacent about being a ward of his brother and sister-in-law. Formerly an outgoing man, he now spoke in a monotone and expressed little emotion. He did not initiate any activities or ask questions about his existence, being content to spend his free time watching television.

THE CASE OF DR. P illustrates how brain damage can cause deficits in **executive functions**—which include the ability to plan actions to reach a goal, to use information flexibly, to think abstractly, and to make inferences. As illustrated by the preceding case study, difficulties in executive function can arise despite normal functioning in other domains of intellectual processing, such as those generally measured by IQ tests (e.g., retention of knowledge, vocabulary, spatial-processing abilities, and so forth).

As we will learn in this chapter, the term *executive function* covers many abilities, and thus it is a difficult concept to define precisely. To better understand the types of abilities that we discuss in this chapter, let's consider, by analogy, the skills and attributes required of a company executive. First, an executive must have a master plan, or a general conception of how the company should work. For example, the executive's goal may be to increase customer satisfaction, diversify markets, or raise production. He or she must be able to translate that general goal into specific actions, whether by increasing quality control, expanding the sales force, or automating factories. Second, the executive must be able to assimilate new information and use it to modify plans as the need arises; that is, the executive must be flexible and responsive to change. For example, fluctuations in the stock market or political changes in foreign governments may necessitate a modification of plans or adoption of a new course of action. Such planning

ability and flexibility are not usually required of assembly-line workers, who in many cases are directed what task to perform, how to do it, and when to do it. Third, an executive must keep track of multiple tasks simultaneously and understand the relationships among them, knowing which should come first and which should come second. As a result, the executive must often prioritize both decisions and actions. For example, if limited cash flow does not allow for a simultaneous increase in the sales force *and* the automation of factories, priorities must be set. In a related vein, the executive must be able to assess the effect of each decision and to estimate its relative worth. Finally, an executive must be a person who projects the company image and serves as its spokesperson. As such, this job requirement calls for a certain amount of social skill and political savvy, as well as a general ability to get along with other people.

These abilities—to create a plan and follow through with it, to adapt flexibly, to sequence and prioritize, to make reasonable judgments, and to interact in a socially astute manner—are multifaceted and share many characteristics. For example, the ability to prioritize often requires creating a plan and being flexible. When prioritizing, you must have an overall plan so that you can determine which actions will best help you reach your goal. Furthermore, you must be flexible because you need to consider a variety of paths toward your goal (rather than following a rigid rule). Because of the multifaceted nature of these executive functions, more than one function usually contributes to performance of many of the complex tasks discussed in this chapter. Consequently, for executive functions, it is difficult to link one particular type of function to a specific brain region, as we did in some of the previous chapters.

Even though *executive function* describes a family of related abilities, the concept has been useful to cognitive neuroscientists and neuropsychologists because it provides a way to understand a constellation of deficits. Although these deficits can occur after posterior brain damage (e.g., Anderson, Damasio, Jones, & Tranel, 1991; Grafman, Jones, & Salazar, 1990), they are most commonly observed after damage to prefrontal regions. Such damage is commonly observed, along with diffuse axonal damage, after closed head injury associated with vehicular accidents or falls (Stuss, 1987). In this chapter, we discuss classic work on individuals with brain damage that has linked the frontal lobe with executive function. This discussion is complemented by the rapidly expanding knowledge in this area that has been provided by neuroimaging techniques.

Theoretical Perspectives

Some theorists have discussed executive function in almost philosophical terms, speaking of the frontal lobes as playing an important role in an individual's ability to exert his or her will. Others have conceptualized the frontal lobe as a controller that aids in the selection of choices to produce a particular behavior, much as a controller on an assembly line might select different components to add to a car to produce the particular custom model desired by the customer. Regardless of how the issue is framed, it is clear that the guidance or control of behavior toward a goal is probably a signature aspect of executive function, and it is equally clear that such abilities rely heavily on the frontal lobe. Although we use the term *executive function* throughout the chapter, such processes are sometimes referred to as **cognitive control**, a term indicating a process in which one is guiding or controlling one's thoughts and actions. As you will see, the concept of control appears prominently throughout the chapter and is a central idea in executive function. To begin this chapter, we consider a number of proposed models of executive function, its critical elements, and its potential subcomponents.

■ Role of Controlled versus Automatic Processes

Two classic theories (Shallice, 1982; Stuss & Benson, 1986) view the frontal lobes as playing an important role in executive function because they are critical for controlled processing compared to automatic processing. Shallice (1982) suggested that a two-component system influences the choice of behavior. One part, **contention scheduling**, is a cognitive system that enables relatively automatic processing, which has

developed over time through learning. Stimuli or situations become linked to actions, routines, or processing schemes, and then groups of these routines become linked to one another. In this manner, a single stimulus may result in a relatively automatic string of actions, referred to as a *schema*. For example, seeing a red light when you are driving automatically causes a series of actions: taking your foot off the gas, depressing the brake pedal, determining how hard the pedal must be pushed to stop in time, deciding where to stop, and so forth. Once any action is initiated by this system, it continues to be active until inhibited by a mutually incompatible process.

The other part, the **supervisory attentional system**, is the cognitive system required to effortfully direct attention and guide action through decision processes. It is active only in certain situations: when no preexisting processing schemes are available, as occurs in novel situations; when the task is technically difficult; when problem solving is required; and when certain typical response tendencies must be overridden. Although the supervisory attentional system was initially thought of as a unitary system, more recent models assume that it has some subcomponents, such as those that activate certain schemas, inhibit others, and monitor the levels of activity across schemas (for more discussion of this model, see Shallice & Burgess, 1996).

According to this theory, frontal lobe damage disables the supervisory attentional system and thereby leaves actions to be governed totally by contention scheduling, a situation that has a number of implications. First, it implies that people with frontal lobe damage will show few deficits, if any, in fairly routine situations in which the appropriate response is evoked by a stimulus in a simple and obvious way. So, for example, their performance is the same as that of neurologically intact people on many tests administered in a standard IQ battery, because these tasks, such as providing a definition of a word, are often familiar and well practiced. However, when a situation is novel or requires flexibility, people with frontal lobe damage fail to respond appropriately, because no schema is available in contention scheduling.

Second, these patients will appear to act impulsively because their behavior is triggered by stimuli in the environment. For example, upon seeing a pen on a desk, they may pick it up and begin to write. This action occurs because over time one learns that a desk with writing implements is linked to certain actions—picking up the implements and using them to write—and when the supervisory attentional system is lost, the typical schemes of contention scheduling are invoked automatically. Some theorists have referred this behavior as an **environmental dependency syndrome** (e.g., Lhermitte, 1983; Lhermitte, Pillon, & Serdaru, 1986). It is as if these actions are impelled or obligated by the physical and social environment (see some examples of such behaviors in ● Figure 12.1). Notably, this environmental

● **FIGURE 12.1   Two examples of the environmental dependence syndrome exhibited by patients with frontal lobe damage when they visited their physician's home.** (A) The man, upon seeing two pictures lying on the floor, picked up a hammer and nails and hung the pictures on the wall. (B) The woman, upon seeing the dishes in the kitchen, began to wash them. *Source:* "Human Autonomy and the Frontal Lobes; Part II. Patient Behavior in Complex and Social Situations. The 'Environmental Dependency Syndrome'" by F. Lhermitte, 1986. Annals of Neurology, 19 (4), pp. 339, 340. By permission of John Wiley & Sons, Inc.

dependency syndrome will often be expressed in different forms depending on an individual's personal history prior to injury. Consider the following cases of two patients with executive dysfunction, each of whom was attending the same buffet dinner (Lhermitte, 1986). One patient, a man from an upper-class background, behaved like a guest expecting to be served. In contrast, the other patient, a woman who had been a modest housekeeper for most of her life, immediately began serving the other guests. The types of behavior that they had learned and that had become automatic, and thus controlled by contention scheduling, differed for these two people because of their different life experiences.

Third, this theory explains why individuals with frontal lobe damage often exhibit **perseveration**, which is the behavior of repeating the same action (or thought) over and over again. Once a strong trigger activates a scheme or an action, this process will continue to be invoked until some incompatible process is activated. Without the supervisory attentional system, iterative actions triggered by contention scheduling are difficult to interrupt, resulting in perseveration.

Like Shallice's theory, the theory of Stuss and Benson (1986) suggests that the frontal lobes are especially important in regulating behavior in nonroutine situations or in situations in which behavior must be carefully constrained. Their model links the degree of control to particular neural substrates in a hierarchical manner. At the lowest level, sensory information and simple tasks are processed by posterior regions of the brain in a relatively automatic manner that varies little from day to day. Processing of such information is thought to be difficult to control consciously. The next level of control is associated with the executive, or supervisory, functions of the frontal lobe. At this level, lower-level sensory information is adjusted so that behavior can be guided toward a goal. Control of behavior is effortful and slow and requires conscious control. The highest level of control involves self-reflection and meta-cognition. *Self-reflection* allows a person to have self-awareness and to understand the relationship of the self to the environment; **metacognition** is the ability to reflect upon a cognitive process. Such a level of control permits one to develop an abstract mental representation of the world and the way one chooses to act in the world. This process is considered to be under the control of the prefrontal cortex.

This model explains deficits in executive function by arguing that the organization of behavior is one of the main functions of frontal regions. It explains deficits in dealing with novelty and lack of cognitive flexibility because the frontal lobes are assumed to be important for nonautomatic behavior. The inability to guide behavior and the undue influence of the environment occur because without the frontal lobe, responses to sensory stimuli are automatic. Finally, the inability to self-criticize or self-monitor could be explained by this model as resulting from prefrontal region damage, which would leave patients devoid of any ability to reflect upon themselves or the processes in which they become engaged.

Other approaches to understanding the role of frontal regions in executive control also emphasize the role that these regions play in guiding behavior toward a goal, but take a perspective influenced by the fields of artificial intelligence and machine learning. One version of this class of theories suggests that a person has a list of task requirements or goals that she or he wants to achieve—a *goal list*. Typically, a variety of behaviors or strategies can be used to reach a goal, and each must be evaluated as to how well or how efficiently it will enable the goal to be met. According to this theory, frontal lobe damage disrupts the ability to form a goal list. Because this list is so fundamental to guiding behavior, loss of the list should lead to difficulties across a large variety of domains. Indeed, people with frontal lobe damage have difficulty in many arenas, including abstract thinking, perceptual analysis, verbal output, and so forth. The loss of a goal list would also imply that an affected individual would have difficulty staying on task (because the goal that would guide behavior is missing), would be unduly influenced by environmental stimuli (because no internal goal would be guiding behavior), and would have difficulty organizing actions toward a goal—all symptoms actually exhibited by people with frontal lobe damage (Duncan, 1986).

Yet another model argues that prefrontal cortex represents goals and the means to achieve them (Miller &

Cohen, 2001). Prefrontal cortex provides bias signals to the rest of the cortex, involving systems ranging from sensory processing to memory, emotion, and response output to meet these goals. As an analogy, you can consider the role of frontal cortex as akin to setting switches on a series of railroad tracks to ensure that a train arrives at the correct destination. The correct destination, however, will vary depending on the context. For example, a person might usually cook oatmeal in a pot of boiling water for breakfast in the morning, but if the goal is to make oatmeal cookies, cooking oatmeal in this manner would be inappropriate, and doing so would derail the train and keep it from reaching its destination. This model also emphasizes the need for sustained maintenance of the goal while the task is being performed, to aid in guiding the train to the correct destination. Remembering that the goal is to make cookies will preclude dropping the oatmeal into boiling water. Without sensitivity to context and the ability to modulate behavior based on goals, individuals will perseverate and engage in routine acts that may not be suited for the particular task at hand. Furthermore, their behavior will appear disorganized and off the mark. What is common to all these models is that they emphasize the role of the frontal lobe in executive function, although they may describe executive functions in somewhat different manners.

Theorists have debated whether the system that enables executive function is unitary or whether it has subcomponents. Some theorists have argued that the frontal lobes might support executive function in a relatively undifferentiated manner because the same set of brain regions becomes activated across a wide variety of executive tasks (Duncan & Owen, 2000). From this perspective, the frontal lobes and especially lateral frontal regions are viewed as supporting intelligent behavior in general rather than executive function specifically (Duncan et al., 2000).

However, studies that have examined the pattern of behavioral performance across a variety of executive function tasks suggest that it may be comprised of specific subcomponents. For example, in one study (Miyake et al., 2000), neurologically normal people were given a large battery of tasks on which patients with frontal lobe damage often have difficulty. Based on the patterns of correlations across tasks (using a mathematical technique known as latent variable analysis) researchers determined that performance could be explained by three underlying factors: the ability to shift mental set (for example, from one task to another), the inhibition or override of responses, and the updating of information in working memory. Moreover, follow-up research (Friedman, Miyake, Corley, Young, Defries, & Hewitt, 2006) suggested that response inhibition and mental-set shifting are not highly correlated with intelligence. This distinction between intelligence and executive function is consistent with the pattern often observed in patients with frontal lobe damage, such as we saw in the opening vignette of this chapter. Dr. P had serious impairments in executive function despite superior levels of intelligence as measured by IQ tests.

Other research also suggests that executive functions may be grouped into certain categories. Based on patterns of performance impairment in patients with brain damage, Stuss and Alexander (2007) suggested three basic subprocesses of executive function. One subprocess drives initiating and sustaining a response, especially when behavior is not triggered or driven by environmental stimuli. It is posited to rely on medial frontal regions. A second subprocess is that of task-setting, which enables a task to be chosen and provides the steps required to perform the task. It is thought to rely on lateral regions of the left frontal lobe. The final subprocess is monitoring, which involves checking behavior over time to ensure that it is being produced correctly and making any necessary adjustment of behavior. This subprocess is thought to rely on lateral regions of right frontal cortex.

Regardless of the model invoked, what we can derive from these models is that executive function is a process that allows behavior to be effortfully guided to a goal, especially in nonroutine behaviors (Banich, 2009). Furthermore, this ability may potentially be broken down into meaningful subcomponents. Because goal-directed behavior is such a critical aspect of executive function, in the next section we consider in more detail a variety of subprocesses that are invoked when working toward a goal. Some, such as the ability to inhibit behavior or to monitor behavior, have already been mentioned. However, there may be other subprocesses that aid goal-directed behavior, such as creating an attentional set, and we consider them as well.

Goal-Directed Behaviors

The ability to guide behavior toward a goal is not one simple task, but rather is multifaceted. As we will learn shortly, the loss of any facet of goal-oriented behavior can cause the entire plan to be derailed. Consider the multiple aspects of the "simple" task of making yourself a peanut butter and jelly sandwich. First, the ultimate goal must be kept in mind throughout the procedure. For example, even though you are in the kitchen, which contains many other foods, you need to keep focused on the peanut butter and jelly. You must also keep this goal in mind even though subgoals must be met along the way. For example, although locating the bread may be the first step in making the sandwich, after attaining that subgoal, you must remember the ultimate goal and switch to finding the peanut butter or the jelly. Second, attaining the goal requires flexibility and adaptability. If you remember that the jelly is on the top shelf of the refrigerator but do not find it there, you must devise an alternative strategy, such as searching the other shelves or looking among the racks on the door. Third,

for you to reach the ultimate goal, the completed portions of the task must be distinguished from those yet to be attained. Thus, after locating the jelly, you must remember not to turn your attention to finding some pieces of bread (because you already completed that part of the task). Fourth, you must evaluate the actions that will best help you to reach the goal. For example, you must realize that although a fork is in front of you, it is not the utensil best suited for making your sandwich. Instead, you must decide that the best course of action is to search through the silverware drawer for a knife. Finally, actions must be sequenced toward the goal. Only after you find the ingredients—the bread, the peanut butter, and the jelly—as well as the necessary utensil, the knife, do you proceed to make the sandwich. Although you probably do not think about it much when you go to the kitchen to fix yourself a sandwich, you can now appreciate how complicated that action really is!

In describing the construction of a peanut butter and jelly sandwich, we listed a number of skills: staying on task; sequencing, or planning, actions; modifying strategies; using knowledge in your plans; and monitoring your actions. We now examine these various subprocesses involved in goal-oriented behavior and the neural structures that support these functions. At the outset, we should point out that these functions are not likely to rely on only one particular region of the frontal lobe. This fact is reflected in the organization of this chapter—we organize it by subprocesses and not by brain region. While reading this chapter, you may want to refer to ● Figure 12.2 to help you stay oriented to the different regions under discussion. Moreover, as we learned in Chapter 11, the frontal regions are a source of control over activity in other brain regions. This means that executive function is likely to be supported not only by the pattern of activity within portions of the frontal lobe, but also by the degree to which frontal cortex influences or interacts with other regions of the brain. This point will come up numerous times in our further discussion.

■ Initiation of Behavior

One difficulty often observed in patients with executive dysfunction is what Luria (1966) and Lezak (1983) classically have referred to as **psychological inertia**. In physics, *inertia* is the tendency of a body at rest to stay at rest or a body in motion to stay in motion unless acted upon by an outside force; it is resistance or disinclination to motion, action, or change. Patients with executive dysfunction are poor at starting an action or a behavior, but once engaged in it, they have great difficulty stopping it. Here we focus on the initiation of behaviors; later in this section we discuss the interruption or cessation of behavior.

As illustrated by the vignette at the beginning of this chapter, difficulties in overcoming psychological inertia can permeate much of the existence of people with

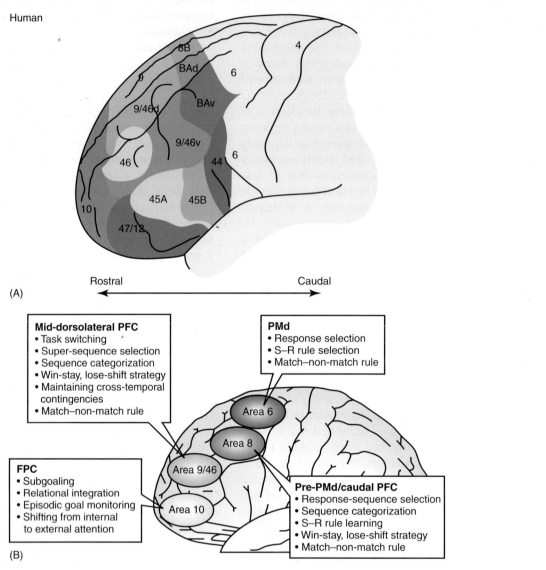

Human

8B

BAd

9

6

9/46d

BAv

9/46v

46

44

6

10

45A   45B

47/12

Rostral   Caudal

(A)

Mid-dorsolateral PFC
• Task switching
• Super-sequence selection
• Sequence categorization
• Win-stay, lose-shift strategy
• Maintaining cross-temporal
  contingencies
• Match–non-match rule

PMd
• Response selection
• S–R rule selection
• Match–non-match rule

Area 6

Area 8

Area 9/46

FPC
• Subgoaling
• Relational integration
• Episodic goal monitoring
• Shifting from internal
  to external attention

Area 10

Pre-PMd/caudal PFC
• Response-sequence selection
• Sequence categorization
• S–R rule learning
• Win-stay, lose-shift strategy
• Match–non-match rule

(B)

● **FIGURE 12.2   The human lateral prefrontal cortex.** (A) Brodmann regions of the lateral prefrontal cortex. (v = ventral, d = dorsal) (B) Different tasks or processes, as noted in each box, that have been found to be supported by somewhat distinct prefrontal regions. *Source:* Badre, D., & D'Esposito, M. (2009). Is the rostro-caudal axis of the frontal lobe hierarchical? Nature reviews neuroscience, 10, a) Fig. 1 lefthand portion, pg. 660, b) Fig. 2a, pg. 663.

prefrontal damage. Dr. P took no initiative in terms of his personal hygiene or his day-to-day activities, did not inquire about either the state of events in his life or those in the world, and tended not to speak unless spoken to. In fact, patients with left frontal lobe damage often exhibit a marked reduction in spontaneous speech (Milner, 1971). Yet the difficulties go beyond that. A waitress, explaining why she had lost her job after frontal lobe surgery, said, "You have to have a 'push' to wait on several tables at once, and I just didn't have it anymore" (Malmo, 1948, p. 542, cited in Duncan, 1986).

As mentioned earlier, one of the three major subcomponents of executive function proposed by Stuss and Alexander (2007) is the ability to initiate and sustain

responding. They have observed that individuals with damage to medial frontal regions, including the supplemental motor area and anterior cingulate, exhibit elongated simple reaction time, which is measured by determining how quickly a person can respond to a stimulus (e.g., a letter). Patients with medial frontal damage are also slow to respond in choice-reaction-time paradigms that require responding to the presence of one stimulus (e.g., an A) but not others (e.g., B, C, or D). This pattern is not observed in individuals with damage to other portions of the frontal lobe.

Difficulties in initiating behavior and overcoming psychological inertia can be observed on various neuropsychological tests that are commonly used to assess executive function. One such class of tests evaluates fluency, either verbal (Thurstone & Thurstone, 1943) or nonverbal (Jones-Gotman & Milner, 1977). These tests do not assess how well-formed an output is, as one might want to assess in the speech of an aphasic patient, but rather how easily, fluidly, and imaginatively a person can draw upon knowledge to produce an output. In these tests of fluency, an individual must, within a limited amount of time (e.g., four minutes) generate as many items as possible that meet certain criteria or constraints. For example, in the case of letter fluency, a person might be asked to think of words beginning with the letter *s* or to name as many words as they can from a specific category, such as animals. In the case of nonverbal fluency, the person might be asked to create as many figures as possible that can be constructed solely from four straight lines. Classic studies using this task have found that damage to the left frontal lobe is associated with poor verbal fluency (Milner, 1964) whereas right frontal lobe damage is associated with poor nonverbal fluency (Jones-Gotman & Milner, 1977). When told to start the task, neurologically intact individuals launch into the task immediately and continue to produce items during the entire time period. In contrast, individuals with executive dysfunction typically appear to mull over the possibilities, seeming to deliberate as they slowly begin to start the task. For example, whereas a neurologically intact person might reel off, "snail . . . snake . . . soil . . . shark . . . stem . . . stuck . . . stencil . . . storage . . . sullen," a person with executive dysfunction might generate just a few items such as "snake . . . . stand . . . . stall," and then continue with " . . . . snake . . . . snow . . . . snaked." Few words are produced, and many are likely to be identical or similar to those already mentioned.

More recent studies analyzing lesion location have found that damage to medial frontal regions yields a pattern of performance similar to controls in the types of words produced, but with far fewer words produced (Reverberi, Laiacona, & Capitani, 2006). This finding is consistent with the idea that medial prefrontal regions are important for initiating or activating responses. In contrast, patients with damage to lateral regions appear to have a deficiency in searching through semantic memory, consistent with findings discussed in Chapters 9 and 10. Whereas controls tend to produce a series of words in which each word is semantically related to the words preceding and following it (e.g., orange—lemon—lime), this type of relationship was observed less frequently in the patients with lateral damage.

So far in this textbook, we have provided converging evidence from different approaches to substantiate our support for the neural underpinnings of different mental processes. However, when we turn to the results of neuroimaging studies using the fluency task, we find that medial prefrontal regions are not implicated in the verbal fluency task. Rather, the common loci of activity for verbal fluency across neuroimaging studies, as

determined by a meta-analysis, are located primarily in the left inferior frontal cortex (Costafreda, Fu, Lee, Everitt, Brammer, & David, 2006).

This lack of consensus illustrates in part why executive function and the frontal lobes remain somewhat of an enigma in cognitive neuroscience. It also illustrates why it is sometimes hard to bridge the gap between research with patients who have brain damage and research with neurologically normal people. In the current case, studies with individuals who have sustained a lesion suggest that medial prefrontal regions may be involved in the initiation of behavior. Such findings are consistent with the research discussed in Chapter 5 on the role of the supplementary motor area in motor planning, and with our discussion in Chapter 11 about models of neglect in which the anterior cingulate, a medial prefrontal structure, is thought to play a role in motivation. If one has difficulty planning behavior and is not motivated to do so, what descriptively seems like psychological inertia will result.

However, in neurologically normal people, these intact regions permit the initiation of behavior during the performance of both the verbal fluency task and the baseline task to which verbal fluency results are often compared, which is word repetition. Because initiation is required for both tasks, the comparison between the two conditions does not yield a significant area of activity in regions involved in initiation. At the same time, in the neuroimaging studies, the fluency task is likely to yield more activation of left inferior frontal regions than the baseline task, because verbal fluency requires additional phonological and/or semantic processing that is not required by the word repetition task. This example demonstrates that it is sometimes challenging for scientists to integrate findings across methods, especially when they yield different results. Such discrepancies are more likely when the tasks and abilities explored are multifaceted and complicated, as are aspects of executive function, because it is difficult to construct task and baseline conditions that differ in only the specific function under investigation. Nonetheless, despite the lack of precise overlap between studies with patients and neuroimaging studies with neurologically intact individuals, the evidence as a whole suggests that medial prefrontal regions play a role in the initiation of behaviors.

■ Creation and Maintenance of a Goal or Task Set

Probably one of the most basic prerequisites for meeting a goal is the ability to stay on task. Individuals with frontal lobe damage are notorious for "wandering off task." For example, if asked to draw a square, persons with frontal lobe damage may start drawing a square but then begin to incorporate words from a nearby conversation into the drawing without seeming to realize or care that such actions are incompatible with (and irrelevant to) what they set out to do (Luria, 1966). This behavior contrasts with behavior of patients with non-frontal lesions in similar situations. For example, a person whose visuospatial abilities have been compromised by a right posterior lesion will have difficulty drawing the square, but will nonetheless continue in the attempt rather than engaging in some irrelevant activity. In fact, task-setting is considered one of the core subcomponents of executive function, according to some models (e.g., Stuss & Alexander, 2007).

Neuroimaging data suggest that dorsolateral prefrontal regions may aid in creating and maintaining an **attentional set**, which can be thought of as the process that designates which information is relevant to a task. One way to identify the relevant neural structures is to determine which regions become active in response to a cue that designates the attentional set that should be employed. For example, in one study using the Stroop task, a cue appearing 1.5 seconds before the actual stimulus indicated whether the individual should identify the ink color named by the word or the ink color in which the word was printed. Activation was observed in lateral prefrontal cortex during the cue

period. In addition, the greater the degree of activation after receiving the color-naming instruction, the smaller was the degree to which a competing color name slowed responses, suggesting that this region helps to impose the correct attentional or task set (MacDonald, Cohen, Stenger, & Carter, 2000). Of note, these lateral prefrontal regions are only activated when imposing an attentional set is difficult and not routine, such as when one must identify the ink color in which a word is printed while ignoring what the word means. This task is challenging because we read words automatically (Banich, et al., 2000). If, on the other hand, attention should be paid to the word rather than the color, no increased lateral prefrontal activation is observed because word reading is a well-rehearsed and practiced task.

Other experimental approaches also implicate lateral prefrontal regions in imposing an attentional set. Researchers have found that activity in these regions depends on how large the change in attentional set must be from one trial to the other. As shown in ● Figure 12.3, lateral regions of prefrontal cortex (as well as some medial regions) are active during a cue

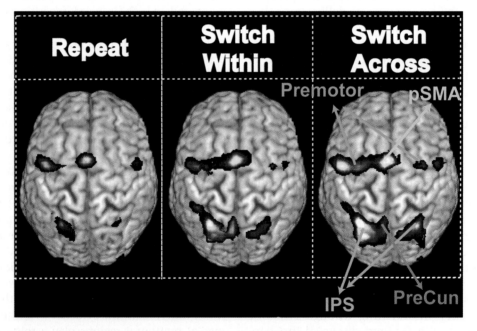

● **FIGURE 12.3   Evidence that prefrontal areas are involved in creating an attentional set for the task to be performed.**   Shown here is activity during a cue period (before any stimulus is presented on the screen) when individuals had to make a decision about the orientation of one of two rectangles. The cue identified the attribute of the rectangle on which a response should be based. In the repeat trials, the critical dimension was the same as for the previous trial (e.g., respond to the blue rectangle). In the switch within trials, the critical dimension was a different specific attribute (e.g., yellow) but within the same category (color). Finally, in the switch across trials, the attribute switched to a new category (e.g., location, left or right). Two important findings are shown above. First, during the cue period, there is activity in posterior regions of prefrontal cortex, including portions of the premotor area and pre-SMA, indicating that these regions are involved in creating a top-down attentional set for the task-relevant feature (i.e., color or location). Second, the greater the reconfiguration of this task set from one trial to another (greatest on switch across, intermediate on switch within, and least on repeat trials), the greater the activity within these regions. *Source:* Slagter, H. A., Weissman, D. H., Giesbrecht, B., Kenemans, J. L., Mangun, G. R., Kok, A., & Woldorff, M. G. (2006). Brain regions activated by endogenous preparatory set shifting as revealed by fMRI. Cognitive, affective and behavioral neuroscience, 6, portion of Fig. 2, pg. 179.

period indicating what dimension should be used to guide responses. Moreover, activity in these regions increases with a greater difference between a new task set and the task set needed on the prior trial (Slagter et al., 2006).

Another intriguing approach that demonstrates the role of lateral prefrontal regions in imposing an attention set compares brain activity when individuals decide what task they will perform (that is, when they must choose the task set), compared to when they are instructed what task to perform. To index the creation and maintenance of a task set rather than the implementation of the task, activity is examined for a delay period between the time that a cue appears (indicating either what task is to be performed or that a task must be chosen) and the presentation of the stimulus on which the task must be performed. More activity is observed in dorsolateral prefrontal cortex (DLPFC) when individuals make the selection themselves (Bengtsson, Haynes, Sakai, Buckley, & Passingham, 2009). Differences between these conditions have also been reported in portions of the anterior cingulate cortex (e.g., Forstmann, Brass, Koch, & von Cramon, 2006), which may reflect the creation of an attentional set for the selection of responses appropriate for a given task (e.g., get ready to select the response linked to the ink color) (Ruge, Braver, & Meiran, 2009). Fascinating research, in fact, suggests that by recording and analyzing the pattern of activity over each of these two regions, lateral prefrontal cortex and the anterior cingulate, scientists can actually predict which task the individual is about to perform (Haynes, Sakai, Rees, Gilbert, Frith, & Passingham, 2007)!

What happens if one needs to maintain more than one task set at a time? For example, you might be fixing dinner when the telephone rings. Here you need to keep both tasks—making dinner and answering the phone—in mind while performing the components of each. Research has implicated frontopolar cortex (BA 10) in such behaviors. According to one view, this area integrates the outputs of processing for two or more separate operations in service of a higher goal (for a review, see Ramnani & Owen, 2004). One good example of this type of coordination is provided by a task in which participants see a series of words. One goal of the task is to classify each word as being concrete or abstract. A second goal is to respond to any concrete word that follows an abstract one, but not to respond to abstract-abstract, concrete-concrete, or concrete-abstract sequences. Thus, this second higher goal must be kept in mind while performing the other task. When these two goals had to be organized, activity was greater in BA 10 compared to a condition in which the individual just had to decide whether a word was concrete or abstract (Braver & Bongiolatti, 2002).

Corroborating such findings, individuals with damage to frontopolar cortex have difficulty in managing subgoals, with a greater extent of damage predicting

greater impairment in the management of multiple goals (Dreher, Koechlin, Tierney, & Grafman, 2008). This region may serve as a controller that coordinates activity in other brain regions. Supporting this idea, patients with damage to rostral prefrontal cortex exhibit less ability to maintain coordinated activity across brain regions after a cue indicating what task set should be employed than do controls, even though the brain-damaged individuals seem to activate the more posterior prefrontal regions normally in response to presentation of the cue (Rowe et al., 2007).

In summary, regions of dorsolateral prefrontal cortex appear to be important in creating and maintaining an attentional set for the task to be performed, medial regions may aid in creating an attentional set for the appropriate group of potential responses, and frontopolar cortex is likely to organize and manage subgoals.

◼ Sequencing

One of the basic processes involved in reaching a goal is determining what steps to take to attain the goal, and the order or sequence in which those steps must be taken; that is, **sequencing**. Little in life can be accomplished in just one step, and even the most basic functions, such as feeding oneself, require multiple steps. In this section, we review evidence that sequencing and planning abilities rely mainly on frontal regions. As discussed in Chapter 5, anterior regions of the brain are important for sequencing movements. Here we learn that they are important for the sequencing of mental thoughts as well.

A basic ability required for sequencing behavior is to know what comes before and what comes after. Compared with patients who have brain damage in other cortical regions, patients with frontal lobe damage have difficulty in this arena (Milner, 1982). In one task, individuals view an inspection series of items, such as line drawings, one by one. They are then shown cards on which two items appear. If the task is to determine which of the two items was presented in the inspection series, individuals with frontal lobe have no difficulty. However, they do have difficulty if the task is to choose which of the two items came first in the series.

In the study just described, the participants passively watched a sequence of events whose order was controlled by the experimenter. We might want to consider the possibility that these patients' performance would be better if *they* controlled the order of events. However, this is not the case. In a paradigm known as the **self-ordered pointing task**, individuals are shown an array of items, anywhere from six to twelve, all of which are from the same category (e.g., abstract designs or high-imagery words) (● Figure 12.4). Assume for the moment that we are using a six-item array. On each trial, the participant views six sheets of paper presented sequentially. Although each sheet contains all six items (arranged in a two-by-three matrix), the position of each item in the array varies from sheet to sheet. On each sheet, the participant must point to an item that was not previously chosen. Because a given item appears in a different location on each page, the participant must keep track of which items were previously selected (Petrides & Milner, 1982). Deficits on this task are observed after frontal lobe damage.

Neuroimaging has provided evidence that mid-dorsolateral prefrontal cortex (BA 9/46) is critical for performance of these types of tasks. In the magnet environment, a slightly modified version of the task was employed. Participants saw four abstract black and white stimuli sequentially (one after the other) on the screen. Then two of four items were shown. In a recency

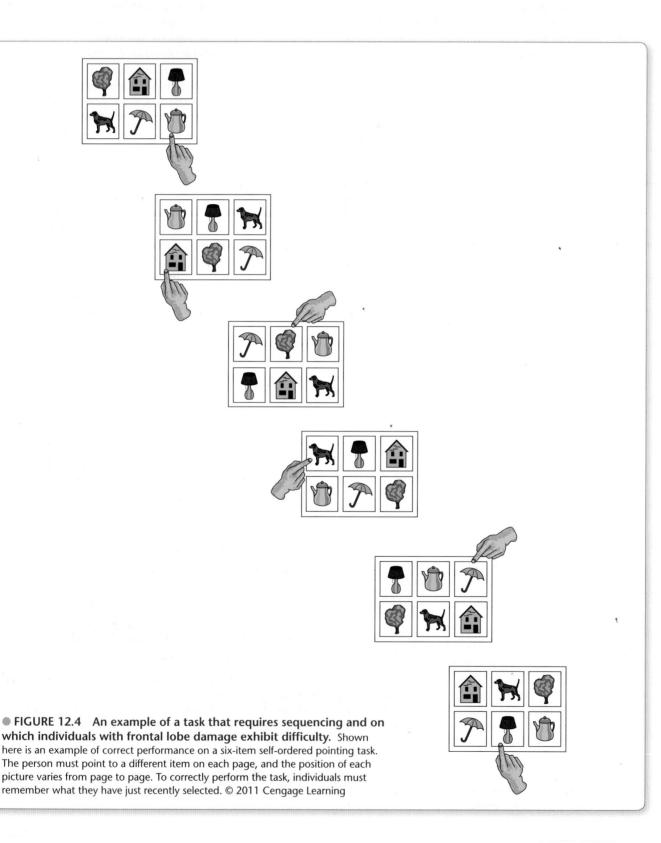

● **FIGURE 12.4   An example of a task that requires sequencing and on which individuals with frontal lobe damage exhibit difficulty.** Shown here is an example of correct performance on a six-item self-ordered pointing task. The person must point to a different item on each page, and the position of each picture varies from page to page. To correctly perform the task, individuals must remember what they have just recently selected. © 2011 Cengage Learning

task, the participant indicated which of the two items occurred first in the sequence. The control task, in contrast, was a recognition memory task, which merely required the participant to indicate which of the two items had actually been part of the sequence. More activity was observed in dorsolateral prefrontal cortex for the sequencing task than for the recognition memory task (Amiez & Petrides, 2007).

The frontal lobes may contribute to these tasks because they require working memory. As we have learned previously, working memory is used to keep information online to control behavior and as a sort of mental scratch pad during everyday actions. Working memory is important in the self-ordered pointing task because the person must keep track of which items have already been pointed to and which remain to be selected. Likewise, the recency judgment task requires a person to keep information on line in working memory so as to maintain information about the order in which events occurred. In fact, damage to lateral regions of the frontal lobe, which has been implicated in working memory, disrupts recency judgments more than damage to other regions of the frontal cortex (Milner, Corsi, & Leonard, 1991).

Thus far, we have discussed sequencing abilities from two perspectives: being able to appreciate the sequence in which events occur and being able to generate sequential behavior. Another important aspect of sequencing behavior is the ability to choose which sequence or strategy best allows a goal to be attained. Compared to patients who have damage to other brain regions, patients with frontal lobe damage are less likely to report that they use strategies, and when they do use a strategy, it tends to be ill defined or invoked inconsistently.

One task designed specifically to examine the ability to use strategies to sequence action is the **Tower of London task** (Shallice, 1982), shown in ● Figure 12.5. The apparatus for the task consists of three prongs of varying height and three colored balls with holes that allow them to be placed on the prongs. The first prong can hold three balls, the second can hold two, and the last can hold only one. The task requires the individual to move the balls, one at a time, from an initial position to a target configuration in as few moves as possible while keeping in mind the constraints imposed by the height of each prong. The puzzles range in difficulty: some can be solved in just a few moves (e.g., 3) and others take more moves (e.g., 7). Individuals with frontal lobe damage, most notably in the left hemisphere,

are both inefficient and ineffective at performing this task (e.g., Shallice, 1982; Carlin, Bonerba, Phipps, Alexander, Shapiro, & Grafman, 2000). They are inefficient because they take many moves to reach the end position and are ineffective because they engage in behaviors that are aimless rather than directed toward the goal. Researchers have attempted to determine whether performance on the Tower of London task can be predicted by basic underlying abilities, such as verbal or spatial working memory or general intelligence. In fact, performance on the more difficult puzzles cannot be predicted by any of these factors, suggesting that the task is a reasonably specific test of planning and sequencing (Unterrainer et al., 2004).

The first study to examine the neural underpinnings of the Tower of London task in neurologically intact people used single photon emission computed tomography (SPECT) to measure regional blood flow while participants performed a computerized touch-screen version of the task (Morris, Ahmed, Syed, & Toone, 1993). Once again, the task had to be modified to make it more appropriate for a neuroimaging environment. To explicitly examine the planning-sequencing aspect, the researchers asked participants to perform two versions of the task that were identical in sensorimotor requirements but differed in the degree of planning required. In the first, or control, version, the person was passively guided by the computer to solve the puzzle. An X marked

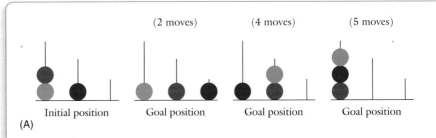

(A)

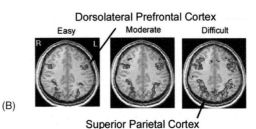

(B)

● **FIGURE 12.5 The Tower of London task, which is used to examine planning and sequencing abilities.** (A) In this task, individuals are shown an initial position and a goal position to which the balls must be moved, one at a time, in as few moves as possible. The minimum number of moves required to reach each goal is noted. (B) Increasing activation of prefrontal regions as task complexity increases in the Tower of London task. *Source:* Newman, S.D., Carpenter, P.A., Varma, S. & Just, M.A. (2003).Frontal and parietal participation in problem solving in the Tower of London: fMRI and computational modeling of planning and high-level perception. Neuropsychologia,Fig. 4, pg. 1673, Figure 12.5b. © 2011 Cengage Learning

each disk that should be moved, and after the person touched the disk, the computer moved the disk to the correct position. When the person then touched that position, an X appeared over the next disk to be moved. In the experimental condition, the person saw the same displays and made the same movements, except that he or she had to plan the sequence of the moves rather than being guided by the computer. Greater activation was observed in left prefrontal regions when participants had to actively plan the moves than when they were passively guided. Furthermore, the *degree* of activation of these regions in the experimental condition relative to the control condition predicted how well an individual performed the task. The participants who solved the puzzle in fewer moves exhibited greater activation of left prefrontal areas than did the participants who used more moves. Thus, this study provides converging evidence for the role of frontal regions in planning sequential behavior.

Subsequent studies revealed activity differences in DLPFC when using PET or fMRI to contrast performance between this task and a control condition (Lazeron et al., 2000; Owen, Doyon, Petrides, & Evans, 1996). In addition, other studies have found that activity in the DLPFC increases with the difficulty of the puzzles (van den Heuvel, Groenewegen, Barkhof, Lazeron, van Dyck, & Veltman, 2003). Increasing problem difficulty is also associated with increasing activity in rostrolateral prefrontal cortex (BA 10) (Wagner, Koch, Reichenbach, Sauer, & Schlösser, 2006). These findings are consistent with the work we described earlier, which suggests that rostrolateral prefrontal cortex is required when one must process information within a hierarchy or on the basis of contingencies. As the number of moves required for a correct solution on the Tower of London task increases, so does the hierarchy and contingencies of the moves required to reach that solution.

A final piece of evidence suggesting that DLPFC is critical for performance on the Tower of London task comes from a technique called *transcranial direct current stimulation (tDCS)*, in which electrical activity can be used to enhance brain activity. In this study, tDCS or sham activation was given over the dorsolateral prefrontal cortex just prior to and during performance of an initial set of trial blocks. Better performance, as measured both by accuracy and RT, was observed after tDCS compared to sham stimulation (Dockery, Hueckel-Weng, Birbaumer, & Plewnia, 2009). In sum, dorsolateral prefrontal cortex and frontopolar cortex appear to play an important role in sequencing behaviors.

■ Shifting Set and Modifying Strategies

So far we have presumed that attaining a goal simply requires determining what steps to take and then performing them. However, as we all know, the path to a goal is not always a simple linear progression; we often encounter some unexpected twists and turns. Such a situation arose in the example of preparing a peanut butter and jelly sandwich. The plan called for retrieving the jelly from the top shelf of the refrigerator, but, alas, the jelly was not there. At this point, a modification of strategy, or a deviation from a previously invoked plan, became necessary. This modification requires a shifting of one's attentional set, and as discussed earlier, is considered by some to be one of the three basic, underlying subprocesses supporting executive function.

The classic neuropsychological test used to examine task switching is the **Wisconsin Card Sorting Test (WCST)**. An example of the WCST procedure is shown in ● Figure 12.6. In this test, four cards are laid on the table in front of the participant. Each card is distinct from all the others on the basis of three attributes: the number of items on the card (one, two, three, or four), the shape of the items on the card (circle, triangle, cross, or star), and the color of the items on the card (red, green, yellow, or blue). For example, one card might have three yellow

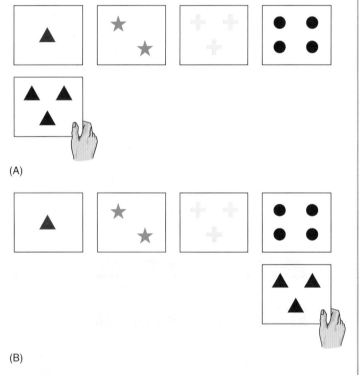

(A)

(B)

● **FIGURE 12.6   Two examples of sorting behavior on the Wisconsin Card Sorting Test.** For this particular series of trials, the individual must sort the cards on the basis of their color. (A) An example of an incorrect sort; the individual matched the card on the basis of shape instead. (B) An example of a correct sort; the individual matched the card on the basis of color rather than shape or number. © 2011 Cengage Learning

crosses, whereas another might have two green stars. The person is then given a stack of cards and told to sort them into four piles below the four cards already on the table. However, no explicit criteria for sorting are given. Rather, as the participant places each card onto one of the four piles, the experimenter indicates only whether the response is correct or incorrect. From the experimenter's feedback, the person must deduce the dimension on which the card should be sorted (e.g., color).

After the participant correctly sorts 10 cards on the basis of one particular attribute (such as color), the experimenter, without explicitly telling the person, changes the criterion for sorting the cards (e.g., to shape). Neurologically intact people quickly realize that although their behavior previously led to a correct response, it no longer does so. Therefore, they adjust their responses accordingly. In contrast, people with executive dysfunction perseverate, continuing to sort the cards by the same attribute despite the negative feedback. A noteworthy aspect of the lack of control of action exhibited by these patients is that it can occur even when the person appears to "know" how to act. Individuals with executive dysfunction will persist in sorting on the basis of a previously correct but now incorrect category even as they state that they *know* their action is wrong (e.g., Milner, 1963).

Classically, this test was considered very sensitive to frontal lobe damage (Milner, 1963), although patients with damage to other regions of the brain may also perform poorly on the task (see Nyhus & Barceló, 2009, for discussion). Nonetheless, a review of studies using this task finds that patients with frontal lobe damage tend to do worse than those with posterior damage, and those with damage to the dorsolateral prefrontal area tend to perform the most poorly (Demakis, 2003).

A large number of neuroimaging studies have used this card-sorting task to examine executive functions. Most common across these studies is activation of DLPFC along with ventrolateral prefrontal activation. In addition, activity in the inferior parietal lobe, temporoparietal association cortex, and the basal ganglia is often observed (see Nyhus & Barceló, 2009, for a review). These results highlight the fact that the WCST is a complex, multifaceted task, as are many tasks originally designed with the intent of detecting brain damage. What is required of the participant is not only the ability to switch categories, but also the abilities to create a rule that will guide sorting, to keep in mind (in working memory) the outcomes of prior trials, and to use deductive reasoning. We discuss these other processes, such as rule generation and deduction, in a later section of this chapter. Here we focus on set-shifting.

One of the main components of the WCST is task- or set-switching. Evidence from neurologically intact people suggests that switching between two tasks is not easy for anyone. It is easier to keep doing what you are doing than to switch from one task to another. Moreover, task-switching is likely to be directed by an executive control system that is independent of the systems that actually perform each task (see Monsell, 2003, for review).

Psychological research has shown that there is a cost to switching between tasks, a cost that is difficult if not impossible to eliminate. In a typical task-switching study, participants are asked to view a stimulus, such as a colored letter. Prior to the trial, a cue indicates the attribute that should be used to make a decision. For example, the person may have to indicate whether the letter is printed in green or red, or whether the letter is a vowel or a consonant. On some trials, which are referred to as *repeat trials,* the person performs the same task as on the prior trial (e.g., "determine color" followed by "determine color"). On other trials, which are referred to as *switch trials,* the person performs a different task than on the prior trial (e.g., "determine color" followed by "determine consonant/vowel"). Typically, responses are slower for switch trials than for repeat trials, and the slower responses are thought to reflect the requirement to switch or change the current task set. A typical manipulation in such studies is to vary the time between when the cue is given and the stimulus appears. Increasing the cue-stimulus interval reduces the **switch cost**, presumably because the person has additional time to configure the new task set before that task set must be applied to the stimulus. However, even with long delays, it is impossible to completely erase or eliminate the switch cost, suggesting that task-switching involves additional operations beyond just reinvoking the task set previously used.

Patients with left frontal lobe damage have a deficit in task-switching, especially when there are no strong or obvious cues indicating which task should be performed when (Rogers, Sahakian, Hodges, Polkey, Kennard & Robbins, 1998). Moreover, they have difficulty regardless of whether the switch involves a conceptual set (e.g., switching from sorting animals by where they live, land or water, to sorting by their degree of ferocity, domestic or dangerous; Delis, Squire, Bihrle, & Massman, 1992) or a perceptual set (e.g., switching from sorting based on color to sorting based on shape). The nature of this difficulty in task-switching may be influenced by other factors, depending on the side of the lesion. In patients with right inferior damage, an inability to exert inhibitory control (which we discuss in one of the following sections) may make task-switching even more difficult, whereas an inability to maintain a task set may exacerbate difficulty in task-switching in patients with damage to left dorsolateral prefrontal regions (Aron, Monsell, Sahakian, & Robbins, 2004).

The important role of prefrontal regions in task-switching is corroborated by brain imaging studies. These studies point to a large and extended network that enables such switches, including dorsal, inferior, and medial prefrontal regions, as well as parietal cortex (e.g., Wager, Jonides, Smith, & Nichols, 2005). This evidence, as well as studies with brain-damaged patients, suggests that there is not one particular region of the brain that metaphorically flicks the switch from task A to task B. Instead, the critical brain region may vary depending on the specific aspects of the task switch, such as the similarity between the task sets or the abstractness of the task sets.

To illuminate the idea of task-set similarity, look at the task illustrated in ● Figure 12.7, which was originally designed for use with animals. Participants are first taught to discriminate between two items (e.g., two black shapes) and to respond to only one of them. Then another dimension is added to the items (e.g., a simple white line pattern), and this dimension is to be ignored (Figure 12.7A). At this point, new stimuli consisting of novel shapes and novel white line patterns are introduced. In one test condition, the intradimensional shift condition, the discrimination is to be made solely on the basis of the same dimension used previously (e.g., on the basis of the black shapes, while ignoring the white line pattern) (Figure 12.7B). The shift is intradimensional because the identity of the target item

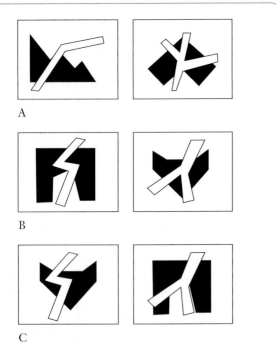

A

B

C

● **FIGURE 12.7   Intradimensional vs. extradimensional shifts.** (A) Individuals are first taught to respond to one of two black shapes and to ignore the white shapes on top of them. (B) In an intradimensional shift, individuals must learn to discriminate between two new black shapes while continuing to ignore the white shapes. (C) In an extradimensional shift, individuals must now discriminate between the two white shapes, which is the feature that was previously ignored. Individuals with frontal lobe damage have difficulty with this extradimensional shift. © 2011 Cengage Learning

shifts but the same dimension of the stimulus remains relevant. In the other, the extradimensional shift condition, the participants must respond to the dimension that was previously ignored (e.g., the white line patterns) (Figure 12.7C).

Compared with patients who have temporal lobe lesions and with neurologically intact individuals, patients with frontal lobe damage are deficient at the extradimensional shift but not at the intradimensional shift (Owen, Roberts, Polkey, Sahakian, & Robbins, 1991). Both PET (Rogers, Andrews, Grasby, Brooks, & Robbins, 2000) and fMRI (Nagahama et al., 2001) studies suggest greater activity in prefrontal cortex, including left anterior polar frontal cortex and right DLPFC, for extradimensional as compared to intradimensional shifts. Thought of differently, if a new strategy is similar enough to the old one, the frontal lobe is not required. But if a shift to a new set is needed, having a functional frontal lobe helps!

The frontal cortex may also be involved in set-shifting when the shift must occur between relatively abstract task sets. For example, neuroimaging studies indicate greater activation of the frontal cortex when one must shift between sets of rules (e.g., if the item is an "x," press the left button and if it is a "y," press the right button vs. if the item is a diamond, press the left button and if it is a square press the right button), whereas the parietal lobe may play a more important role when one must shift between sets of perceptual features (e.g., press the button based on an item's shape vs. press the button based on an item's color) (Ravizza & Carter, 2008). Other studies corroborate the role of dorsolateral regions in abstract rule switches, but also suggest that the basal ganglia may aid switches in response to specific objects (Cools, Clark, & Robbins, 2004).

Brain regions involved in task- or set-shifting may vary depending on what aspect of the switching is most important. For example, dorsolateral prefrontal regions may be more involved in task-switching by tackling the interference in working memory from the prior task set, whereas the anterior cingulate cortex may be more involved in reconfiguring which response set should be utilized (Hyafil, Summerfield, & Koechlin, 2009). Complicating the situation, meta-analyses across studies indicate that the inferior frontal junction, which resides at the base of dorsolateral prefrontal cortex and inferior frontal cortex, may play a prominent role as well (Derrfuss, Brass, Neumann, & von Cramon, 2005), by updating the representations most relevant to the task at hand.

If at this point you feel like most of the brain is involved in task-switching, you may not be far off. Our short review here makes an important point: task-switching is likely enabled by a large network of brain regions, with certain components playing a more prominent role than others, depending on the situation. The idea that task-switching is supported by a network is reinforced by findings that task-switching also depends on factors that affect connectivity between brain regions. For example, reduced white matter in the elderly is associated with poor performance in task-switching (Gratton, Wee, Rykhlevskaia, Leaver, & Fabiani, 2009). Also, providing a drink deficient in the amino acids that are precursors to dopamine appears to alter the prefronto-striatal connectivity that facilitates faster response times to a shift (Nagano-Saito, Leyton, Monchi, Goldberg, He, & Dagher, 2008). Thus, connectivity between regions, especially those that involve frontal regions, may play as important a role as the regions themselves in supporting set-shifting.

■ Self-Monitoring and Evaluation

Another skill that is important for attaining a goal is the ability to evaluate whether your performance is actually bringing you closer to your goal. Stated more simply, it is the ability to accurately answer the question, "How am I doing?" Individuals with executive dysfunction have difficulty evaluating or monitoring their performance. For example, given cards that must be rearranged in a sequence, patients with executive dysfunction may simply move a card or two and then declare themselves done. One might suspect that lack of motivation or concern about their performance level accounts for some of these difficulties, especially considering the changes in emotional processing that accompany frontal lobe damage (which we discuss in Chapter 13). Lack of motivation, however, is unlikely to be the sole explanation for these difficulties because, as discussed earlier, in some situations patients verbally declare that they should do something but then fail to follow through. The verbal declarations provide some evidence that the person is actually engaged by the task and has a degree of interest in reaching the goal. However, the ability to monitor performance or to specifically translate that idea into action is disrupted.

The issue of how people monitor their performance and detect when they have erred has received much investigation within the past decade. The results of this body of research indicate that we have a particular set of brain mechanisms that helps to monitor our performance and detect errors (see Taylor, Stern, & Gehring, 2007, for a review). Evidence for one such mechanism comes from an ERP signal known as the **error-related negativity (ERN)**. This component occurs approximately 100 ms after an error has been made (Falkenstein et al., 1991; Gehring, Goss, Coles, Meyer, & Donehin, 1993) (● Figure 12.8). It has been specifically linked to error monitoring because its amplitude increases under conditions in which accuracy of response is emphasized versus speed, and because larger errors (e.g., pushing the button with the wrong hand as well as the wrong finger) produce larger amplitudes of the ERN. When scientists discuss this component in less scientific terms, they refer to it as the "blunder blip."

The ERN component arises from rostral regions of the anterior cingulate, located on the medial portion of the frontal lobe, according to studies using dipole modeling of ERPs (e.g., Dehaene, Posner, & Tucker, 1994); fMRI (Kiehl, Liddle, & Hopfinger, 2000), or simultaneously recorded EEG and fMRI (Debener, Ullsperger, Siegel, Fiehler, von Cramon, & Engel, 2005). It remains unclear whether this region of the cingulate involved in error detection is distinct from the region involved in inhibiting responses or selecting among responses (discussed earlier).

The exact role of the anterior cingulate with regard to self-monitoring and evaluation is currently a matter

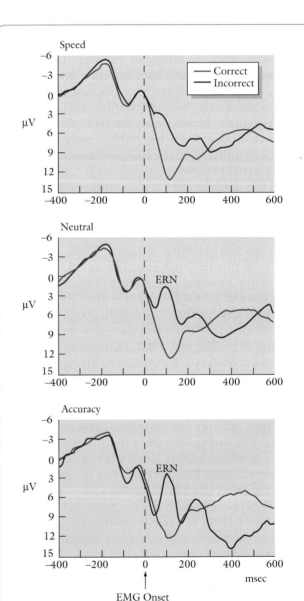

● **FIGURE 12.8   The error-related negativity (ERN).** In these graphs, negative electrical potentials are plotted on the upper portions of the graphs and positive potentials on the lower portions. Notice that the response to errors (shown in blue) peaks about 100 milliseconds after the beginning of the muscles' movement (as denoted by EMG onset). Also notice that the size of the ERN is much greater when accuracy is stressed (bottom panel) rather than speed (top panel). © 2011 Cengage Learning

of debate. One initial suggestion was that the cingulate actually detects errors (e.g., Scheffers, Coles, Bernstein, Gehring, Donchin, 1996). However, more recent evidence suggests that when a person is not consciously aware of his or her error, an ERN can be still be detected (Nieuwenhuis, Ridderinkhof, Blom, Band, & Kok, 2001), as can medial prefrontal activity in the region thought to produce the ERN (Hester, Foxe, Molholm, Shpaner, & Garavan, 2005). Instead, awareness of an error seems to be indexed by another component, the **error positivity (Pe)** (e.g., Davies, Segalowitz, Dywan, & Pailing, 2001), which typically follows the ERN by about 200–300 ms. At present, the neural source of this latter component remains unclear.

Another theory is that the anterior cingulate monitors for conflict. According to this view, the anterior cingulate is active during error detection because errors usually occur when there is conflicting information (e.g., Carter, Braver, Barch, Botvinick, Noll, & Cohen, 1998; Botvinick, Braver, Barch, Carter, & Cohen, 2001; Botvinick, Cohen, & Carter, 2004). Another feature of this theory is that when the cingulate detects conflict, it sends a signal to dorsolateral prefrontal cortex to ramp up the top-down control it is exerting, so as to reduce conflict and errors in subsequent behavior.

Still another viewpoint argues that the cingulate is particularly sensitive to negative outcomes or the loss of rewards (Holroyd & Coles, 2002). This viewpoint conceptualizes the cingulate as calculating the value of the outcomes of recent behaviors and using that history to guide subsequent actions and responses (Holroyd & Coles, 2008; Rushworth, 2008). Consistent with this idea, the ERN is also elicited by monetary loss (Gehring & Willoughby, 2002) or the unexpected lack of a reward (Holroyd, Nieuwenhuis, Yeung, & Cohen, 2003). From this viewpoint, the ERN may, in part, reflect the subjective evaluation of performance ("Oh damn, I just messed up and didn't get what I wanted"), rather than whether one did indeed make an error. Support for this viewpoint comes from findings that the amplitude of the ERN is larger when a person makes an error that leads to a monetary loss as compared to a monetary gain (Taylor et al., 2006).

As we have emphasized at many points in this chapter, there is unlikely to be a one-to-one mapping between a particular piece of frontal cortex and a specific function such as task-switching or self-evaluation. This point is reinforced by data from patients with circumscribed lesions to specific regions of the frontal lobe. At least some abilities relating to evaluation and monitoring are intact in patients with damage to the anterior cingulate cortex (Fellows & Farah, 2005), indicating that the anterior cingulate is not the "error detector" of the brain. Patients with cingulate damage are able to report errors. Moreover, they exhibit a behavior typically observed after errors, known as **post-error slowing**, which refers to responding more slowly on the next trial after an error. However, although these patients could correct

their errors, they did so very slowly, suggesting a deficiency in online aspects of error detection.

Conversely, damage to other brain regions, including lateral prefrontal cortex, can compromise certain aspects of monitoring and evaluation. Often, a person who realizes that he or she has made an error engages in self-corrective action, such as pressing the correct button. Furthermore, the force of a person's response is usually less on error trials, as if the system were detecting conflict and "holding back" a bit. Patients with damage to lateral PFC exhibit neither of these traits when making errors. Moreover, these patients show as large an ERN to correct trials as they do to incorrect trials (Gehring & Knight, 2000). These findings suggest that there is not a single region of prefrontal cortex that is important for the monitoring of action and detection of errors. Rather, this system is likely to involve a number of regions, including the anterior cingulate cortex and lateral prefrontal regions, as well as their interaction.

■ Inhibition

One last, critical aspect of goal-directed behavior is the ability to override or interrupt processing. The ability to stop, interrupt, or abort inappropriate responses, often referred to as **response inhibition**, is considered by some models to be a major subcomponent of executive function. As we have discussed, perseveration is one of the hallmarks of executive dysfunction, and it is easy to see how a disruption in inhibitory control could lead to such behaviors. If one cannot override inappropriate responses, perseveration will result.

Response inhibition has been investigated in neurologically intact people using a number of paradigms. One commonly used task is the **Go/No-Go task**. In this task, participants respond by pushing a button when certain visual stimuli appear (Go trials) and withhold response to other stimuli (No-Go). Response inhibition can be quite difficult if the No-Go trials are relatively rare. When Go responses are frequent and expected, they are said to be *prepotent,* meaning that the system is biased to produce them. Withholding a response on No-Go trials has consistently been found to engage a right-sided network of regions, including the right middle and inferior frontal cortex, the pre-SMA, and parietal cortex (see Simmonds, Pekar, & Mostofsky, 2008, for a meta-analysis).

Another task used to examine the inhibition of responses is the stop-signal task. In this task, the participant must respond as quickly as possible to a stimulus that appears on the screen. However, on a minority of trials, very shortly (e.g., one-quarter of a second) after the stimulus is presented, another signal (e.g., an auditory tone) occurs, indicating that the response should be aborted. This task is somewhat different from the Go/No-Go task: rather than overriding the tendency to produce a prepotent response, here the person must actually cancel an ongoing response. The stop-signal task activates a large network of brain regions, very similar to that observed for the Go/No-Go task.

Which of these various regions are critical for response inhibition, and which play an auxiliary role, is not clear. Some scientists have suggested that certain portions of this network, such as right inferior frontal cortex, may be specifically involved in response selection and override, whereas activity of dorsolateral prefrontal cortex may reflect a more general mechanism that is invoked when extra control is needed, such as when the No-Go trials are quite rare (Nee, Wager, & Jonides, 2007). Evidence that right inferior frontal regions are critical for response inhibition is suggested by the fact that performance on the stop-signal task is compromised by damage to this region and the degree of damage predicts performance (Aron, Fletcher, Bullmore, Sahakian, & Robbins, 2003). In addition, activity in right inferior prefrontal regions is greater on No-Go trials, in which a trial must be inhibited, than on Go trials; in contrast, activity of medial prefrontal regions, such as the anterior cingulate and SMA, show equivalent activity on Go and No-Go trials when the trials are equally probable (50/50), suggesting that these regions may be more involved in the initiation and monitoring of responses (Liddle, Kiehl, & Smith, 2001; Garavan, Ross, & Stein, 1999).

Other researchers, however, suggest the opposite, proposing that medial frontal and premotor regions are responsible for the actual inhibition of a response (Li, Huang, Constable, & Sinha, 2006). According to still other perspectives, the right inferior frontal gyrus is active in these tasks because its job is to detect salient or task-relevant cues that signal the need to interrupt behavior, consistent with its role in the ventral sensory-based attention stream discussed in Chapter 11 (Hampshire, Chamberlain, Monti, Duncan, & Owen, 2010). As you can see from these somewhat contradictory viewpoints, the issue of what role different subregions play in response inhibition remains to be resolved, despite general agreement that right inferior prefrontal and medial prefrontal regions likely play an important role.

Before we leave our discussion of response inhibition, it is worth noting that some researchers think that response inhibition may be a specific example of a more general function, that of **interference resolution**, which is the ability to resolve conflict between competing information or distracting information that might interfere with performing a task. A nonmotoric example of a task requiring interference resolution is the Stroop task, in which, on incongruent trials (e.g., the word "red" in blue ink) one must resolve the interference between the ink color of the item itself and the color named by the word. Both motoric and nonmotoric tasks that require interference resolution activate the dorsolateral prefrontal cortex, anterior cingulate cortex, inferior frontal regions, and posterior parietal cortex (Nee, Wager, & Jonides, 2007). Thus, the regions identified as involved in interference resolution

essentially are highly overlapping with the dorsal frontoparietal network involved in the goal-directed behavior introduced in Chapter 11. In fact, most of the abilities required for goal-directed behavior rely on some, or all, of the subcomponents of this system.

Higher-Order Thinking

So far in this chapter we have considered executive function mainly from the perspective of guided behaviors that enable us to reach a goal. However, executive function is often thought to include a set of abilities known as **higher-order thinking**. This term is broadly used to describe those more complicated aspects of thought, such as being able to think in an abstract and conceptual rather than concrete manner, the ability to deduce rules or regularity, and the ability to be flexible and respond to novelty. These abilities also appear to require the frontal lobes, as we discuss next.

■ Abstract and Conceptual Thinking

One deficit exhibited by patients with executive dysfunction is an inability to process material in an abstract rather than a concrete manner. As we discussed earlier, the more abstract the conceptual task set that must be imposed, the more difficult it may be for patients to do so.

An avenue for examining abstract thought is to identify the neural systems activated when individuals process metaphorical as compared to literal meaning. In Chapter 9, we emphasized the role of the right hemisphere in nonliteral language. Here we consider more carefully the role of frontal regions. In one neuroimaging study exemplifying this approach, participants were given three types of sentences: ones that had a literal meaning, ones that had a metaphorical meaning, or ones that were anomalous and did not make any sense. The person's task was to indicate whether he or she understood the meaning of each sentence. When reading metaphorical sentences, greater activity was observed in many areas of prefrontal cortex, including medial prefrontal cortex (BA 10), dorsolateral prefrontal cortex, and inferior frontal cortex, compared to reading literal sentences (Shibata, Abe, Terao, & Miyamoto, 2007).

Another way to examine the issue of abstract thinking is to examine analogical reasoning. Analogies require a person to integrate relational information at a more abstract than concrete level. One neuroimaging study nicely illustrates this point. In this study, researchers asked people to perform two similar tasks that differed only in the type of reasoning they required (Green, Fugelsang, Kraemer, Shamosh, & Dunbar, 2006). Both tasks involved the presentation of pairs of words. In the analogy task, participants viewed pairs of words such as "PLANET:SUN + ELECTRON: NUCLEUS" and had to decide whether or not the two word pairs constituted a valid analogy. The example given here is indeed a

IN FOCUS: Can You Repress a Memory?

In this chapter we have been talking about inhibition mainly from the perspective of inhibiting or suppressing an overt response, such as a button-press. However, within the field of psychology there is a long history, going back to Freud, of considering whether memories and thoughts can be inhibited. Freud proposed that one mechanism by which we protect ourselves from unwanted thoughts or desires is to repress them. He viewed repression as an unconscious process rather than one that is effortfully controlled, but central to his idea is that a person is able to control access to a memory, and in effect, to inhibit or suppress it. This idea has been very controversial; in fact, it has been referred to as "a clinical myth in search of a scientific explanation." (Kihlstrom, 2002). Moreover, the issue of whether memories that have supposedly been repressed can then be brought back into consciousness has been hotly debated; there is strong contention about whether "repressed" memories actually exist or whether they are in fact false and/or induced memories (Loftus, 2003).

As you might imagine, it is quite difficult to investigate whether such an inhibitory process exists. To determine in principle whether a memory could be inhibited, two conditions would need to be met. First, one would need to know that the memory existed in the first place. Second, one would need to have some indication that it had been inhibited. Recent neuroimaging work has provided evidence for both of these two conditions.

To address these two issues, researchers used a paradigm designed to investigate the inhibition of memories, called the Think/No-Think task (Anderson & Green, 2001). This task was based on the Go/No-Go paradigm used to study response inhibition. In the Think/No-Think task, participants are taught cue-item pairs that are random associates (such as the word pair "roach-ideal") during a training phase. They are trained on the pairs so that when given the cue, they can produce or identify the target item with a high degree of accuracy, confirming that the memory has been established. Notice that because these pairs are random associations, they will likely require activation of the hippocampus if they are to be encoded into memory (see Chapter 10). In the next phase, the experimental phase, participants are presented with just the cue. For some cues, there is a designation (e.g., a green box around the cue) indicating that the person should try to remember the target associated with that cue. These are known as *Think trials*. For other cues, the designation (e.g., a red box around the cue) indicates that the person should try to inhibit the associated item from coming to consciousness. These are known as *No-Think trials*. Moreover, a cue appears multiple times during this phase of the experiment, so that participants have multiple chances to try to retrieve the memory (in the case of Think trials) or to inhibit the memory (in the case of No-Think trials). Importantly,

in this phase of the study the participants never see the target item again. Rather, they are asked to exert control over the *memory* of that item. In the final phase, the test phase, participants are again given the cue and now they must produce the item that went with it.

In such experiments, recall of items is typically better for Think trials relative to baseline items (a set of items for which the cue is not shown in the second phase of the experiment). Conversely, recall of No-Think items relative to the baseline is reduced. These two findings indicate that control can be exerted over the memory. Moreover, neuroimaging studies reveal that regions of the dorsoparietal network are more active for the No-Think than Think trials during the experimental phase, suggesting engagement of control regions (Anderson et al., 2004). This finding is consistent with the idea that more control is being exerted over memories in the No-Think condition than in the Think condition.

Unfortunately, none of these studies definitively tells us whether the memory has indeed been inhibited. For example, poorer performance on No-Think trials might result from individuals conjuring up a new item to associate with the cue, rather than specifically repressing the original target (Hertel & Calcaterra, 2005). In a study performed by one of the co-authors of this book (Depue, Curran, & Banich, 2007), we provided evidence that inhibition of memory can indeed occur. To do so, we took advantage of what we know about the

valid analogy, as planets revolve around the sun and an electron revolves around the nucleus of an atom. In the control condition, participants decided whether the relationship between the two words within each pair was valid, and responded true if both relationships were valid. For example, in a valid trial they might see "DUCK:WATER + COW:MILK." Notice that although the semantic categories of each word in the pair are similar—both of the first items are farm animals and both of the second items are liquids—they do not represent an analogy since ducks live in water whereas cows produce milk. The researchers observed greater activity in the analogy task in the left dorsolateral prefrontal cortex, which is implicated in working memory and may hold online the different potential relationships

between items, and frontopolar cortex (BA 10), which (as discussed earlier) has been implicated in higher-order relational processing.

Not surprisingly, ERP evidence suggests that analogical reasoning takes time, with differences between easy and difficult analogies yielding differences only in late positive waveforms between 600 and 1,000 ms post-presentation. Source localization for these components agrees nicely with that from neuroimaging studies implicating medial portions of frontal polar cortex (BA 10) as well as lateral prefrontal cortex (Qiu, Li, Chen, & Zhang, 2008). Thus, current research with neurologically intact individuals implicates dorsolateral and frontopolar portions of prefrontal cortex in higher-order abstract thinking.

organization of the human brain and the power of neuroimaging. We used the Think/No-Think task in our study, but with face-picture pairs, in which the picture represented a scene or otherwise negative emotional picture (e.g., a car crash, a disfigured limb). We imaged participants' brains during the experimental phase as they were attempting to exert influence over their memories. We know that processing of complex visual information requires portions of the ventral visual-processing stream. Therefore, rather than asking someone if they are re-remembering or inhibiting a memory (which is obviously problematic), we could use activity in ventral visual-processing regions as a proxy for what their minds were doing. When people were thinking about an item, we should observe an increase in activity in regions representing that item, compared to a baseline (in this case, just a simple fixation cross on the screen); when they were not thinking about the item, we should observe a decrease in activity below baseline in these regions. In fact, this is what we found: ventral visual areas were more active when an item was being consciously remembered, and less active than baseline when an item was being consciously suppressed.

Notice that the decrease in activity for the No-Think items rules out an alternative explanation for the poorer recall of these items—that people are not actually inhibiting the No-Think item, but rather they are replacing it in the mind's eye with some other picture. If that were the case, then increased activity would have been observed in ventral visual-processing regions, because participants would be thinking about visual information on the No-Think trials, just as on the Think trials. However, this is not what we found; activity in visual areas was decreased in the No-Think condition, not increased. This example shows how cognitive neuroscience evidence can help researchers decide between two possible explanations that would be equally plausible based on performance data alone.

The study also examined activity in the hippocampus during the No-Think condition. As we learned in Chapter 10, the hippocampus plays an important role in memory retrieval. Therefore, if people are really inhibiting the memory in the No-Think condition, we should also observe decreases in activity in the hippocampus below the fixation baseline for these trials, whereas activity should be above baseline for Think trials. This expectation was also confirmed in the study. These results fit with the view that memories can indeed be inhibited.

The final issue investigated in this study was which regions are responsible for such inhibition. As you remember from Chapter 11, researchers distinguish between the *source* of attentional control and the *site* of attentional control. To identify the source of attentional control in the No-Think condition, we determined which brain regions exhibited *more* activity for No-Think trials than for Think trials. A series of regions spanning the right middle and inferior frontal gyrus showed this pattern. These findings are consistent with the role of the right inferior frontal gyrus in inhibitory processes and the right middle (i.e., dorsolateral prefrontal) cortex in top-down control processes. Moreover, individual participants who exhibited higher the activity in these regions in the No-Think condition showed lower activity in the ventral visual areas and hippocampus. These results imply that the prefrontal regions serve as the source of attentional control that modulates processing at the sites of attentional control (i.e., the hippocampus and ventral visual-processing stream). In this way, an executive system in the frontal lobes is important for controlling access to memory.

This experiment is just one example of how cognitive neuroscience can be used to investigate issues that have fascinated clinicians and scientists for quite some time. Of course, one difference between this study and the clinical question of repression is that the images used in the study did not necessarily have the same emotional significance as deeply traumatic experiences from people's lives. Nevertheless, the results may have implications for psychiatric disorders in which recurrent memories or images are a problem, such as posttraumatic stress disorder and obsessive-compulsive disorder. For example, these disorders may be characterized by deficiencies in prefrontal control, and therapies that target these regions may turn out to be of some use.

■ Rules and Inference

Another form of abstract thinking is the ability to deduce or invoke a rule. Here we consider results from both patients with frontal damage and neurologically intact individuals. Think back to the WCST, a task of set-shifting that we discussed earlier in the chapter. Although some patients with frontal lobe damage exhibit only perseverative tendencies on the WCST, others cannot even figure out the criterion by which the cards should be sorted. Because they are not given concrete instructions (e.g., sort the cards into piles based on the color of the items), they cannot determine how to perform the task.

These difficulties in conceptualization are well revealed by a modification of the standard WCST (Delis, Squire, Bihrle, & Massman, 1992). In this test, the participant is given a set of six cards that must be sorted into two equal piles. Each card contains an animal's name and a triangle placed against a background of lines. The cards are constructed so that eight possible dimensions can be used for sorting the cards into piles. For example, cards can be divided on the basis of whether the animal lives on land or in the water, whether the triangle is black or white, or whether the position of the animal's name is above or below the triangle. The difficulty that patients with frontal lobe damage have on this task reveals the underlying problem in abstract conceptualization. The patients are often deficient at describing the rule by which they sort. For example, they are unable to state something to the effect of "The animals on the cards I am putting in this pile live in water, whereas the animals on the cards in this pile live on land." Even when the examiner sorts the cards into piles, the patients cannot identify the rule used to sort the items. They also have difficulty sorting the cards into meaningful groups when given abstract cues, such as "It has to do with how these animals behave around people," or even more concrete ones such as "These animals are ferocious or tame."

Intriguing research with children suggests that inability to form abstract categories may have implications for some of the other executive abilities we discussed earlier, such as task-switching. In one study, children were given a developmentally appropriate version of the WCST in which they were shown trucks and flowers that could be either red or blue. On one set of trials, they were to told to play one game, such as the color game which required them to sort the items into two different piles—one for red items and the other for blue. On the next set of trials they were told to switch to a different game, such as the shape game and sort the items based on whether they were flowers or trucks. Based on their performance on the second set of trials, the researchers categorized the children into two groups: perseverators who continued to sort by the original rule and switchers who successfully made the switch to the new rule. Next they gave

children novel cards to sort (e.g., green houses and yellow apples) and told the children "You are doing great! Just keep doing what you are doing!" The researchers reasoned that if children had been using an abstract rule to guide their behavior, such as sorting on the basis of shape, then the children would generalize that rule and sort the new items by shape (e.g., into piles of houses versus apples). In contrast, if the rule the children were using was more concrete, such sorting on the basis of trucks versus flowers, then they should be poor at sorting the novel items in a systematic manner. In fact, children who perseverated were at chance at sorting the novel items in a systematic manner, whereas those who had been able to switch categories were above chance at using the second category as a sorting rule for the novel item. This finding suggests that the ability to conceptualize abstract categories (e.g., shape) as compared to processing items as specific exemplars (flowers and trucks) may aid the ability to switch task sets (Kharitonova, Chien, Colunga, & Munakata, 2009) (● Figure 12.9).

Variants of the WCST modified for use in a neuroimaging environment with adults have provided insights into the neural substrates of abstract rule-governed behavior in neurologically intact individuals. Some studies have compared a condition in which a person is told what rule should govern his or her behavior to a condition in which that rule must be deduced. For example, in one study, the participant decided whether there was a match between two nonsense symbols, presented sequentially about two seconds apart (Sprecht, Lie, Shah, & Fink, 2009). In one condition, the person was told the dimension on which to base the decision (color, shape, or position), whereas on other trials they had to deduce the rule. Both tasks activated a wide-ranging set of brain regions. However, much more activation was observed in dorsolateral and ventrolateral prefrontal cortex, as well as the angular gyrus, when participants had to figure out the rule by themselves rather than having it given to them.

Other research has attempted to distinguish between the ability to deduce a rule and the ability to implement a rule. In this study, researchers compared brain activity on trials in which the participant was in the process of discovering what the rule was, with trials in which participants were just implementing a rule they had previously discovered (Konishi et al., 2008). More activity was observed in left superior frontal regions during rule discovery than during rule implementation.

Yet another way to examine rule-governed behavior and the ability to deduce rules is shown in ● Figure 12.10. In this task, participants determined whether the relationship between two items is a valid inference based on the relationship shown for two other pairs of items. In this task, researchers compared inferences that could be deduced directly (e.g., deciding whether A>C

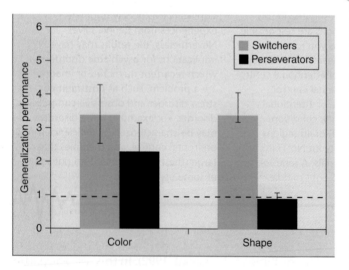

● **FIGURE 12.9   Evidence from children suggests that flexibility in task-switching is linked to the ability to maintain abstract representations of categories.** Two groups of children were identified, those who could switch task sets (from shape to color or vice versa) and those who perseverated. Performance of the first group is represented by the green bars, whereas performance of the latter group is represented by the blue bars. Children were then shown cards that could be sorted on the basis of either color or form. Switchers were more likely to generalize their sorting rule to the novel cards than were children who perseverated, suggesting they were being guided in their behavior by an abstract category. Only switchers performed better than chance, which is indicated by the horizontal line. *Source:* Karitonova, M., Chien, S., Colunga, E. & Munakata, Y. (2009). More than a matter of getting "unstuck": flexible thinkers use more abstract representations than perseverators. Developmental science, 12, Fig. 2 pg. 665.

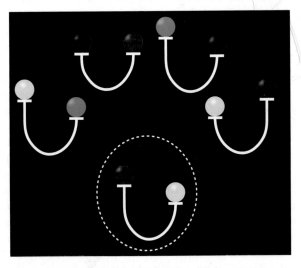 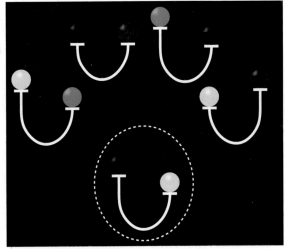

● **FIGURE 12.10** **Stimuli used to demonstrate the role of prefrontal cortex in a nonverbal inference task.** Individuals decided whether the figure shown in the dashed circle represented a valid conclusion based on the figures above. Here the height of each ball represents its value compared to another. For example, the value of yellow is greater than that of green, but the value of blue equals that of red. (Left) On these trials, no inference is required, as the conclusion can be reached directly from the examples above. (Right) Here one must make a transitive inference. Because blue equals red and red is greater than yellow, one can infer that blue is indeed greater than yellow.

when one of the other pairs depicts C>A) or by using transitive inference (e.g., deciding whether A>C when one of the pairs depicted A>B and the other pair depicted B>C). The right lateral prefrontal cortex exhibited more activity when transitive inference was required as compared to when it was not (Wendelken & Bunge, 2009).

How can these findings be integrated? One model argues that a number of prefrontal regions, along with their interactions with posterior cortex, are required when one uses rules to guide actions. According to this model, ventrolateral prefrontal cortex, by virtue of its connections to regions of the middle temporal gyrus, plays a role in retrieving stored knowledge that allows the retrieval of rules. This suggestion is consistent with information that we learned earlier in this book implicating ventral regions of prefrontal cortex as important in the retrieval of semantic information and temporal regions as important in the storage of amodal semantic information. By this model, DLPFC is more involved in selecting or influencing how rules should be used to guide responding than in actually selecting the rules (Bunge, 2004). Other viewpoints argue that DLPFC is important because it plays a direct role in abstracting the rules (Rougier, Noelle, Braver, Cohen, & O'Reilly, 2005), while still others argue that DLPFC simply holds rules in working memory (for a review of research on monkeys relevant to this issue, see Baxter, 2009).

However, evidence from a study with patients suggests that the left lateral cortex may indeed play a critical role in rule generation. In this study, patients were tested on two different tasks: a rule-generation task

and a rule-recognition task. In the rule-generation task, participants saw two rows of 6 circles numbered 1–12. They were instructed to touch the circles in a manner of their own choosing, but which was governed by a systematic rule. For example, they might decide to touch odd-numbered circles in ascending order. For the rule-recognition test, they saw a series of circles, one of which was blue. In a training phase, they had been taught seven different rules defining how the blue circle could move in a sequence. During the test phase, they had to predict where the next location of the item would be; correct performance of this task would indicate that the person recognized and understood the rule. Individuals with damage to the left lateral frontal region as well as the medial frontal region were impaired on the rule-generation test but not the rule-recognition test, suggesting a role for frontal regions in abstracting and generating rules (Reverberi, D'Agostini, Skrap, & Shallice, 2005). We therefore know that the ability to create and generate rules relies on a variety of regions, with the dorsolateral prefrontal cortex playing a prominent role.

Here we have mainly discussed problem solving from the perspective of learning a rule. Sometimes, though, we don't deduce the answer to a problem in a linear manner. Have you ever spent time spinning your wheels trying to logically solve a problem in a step-by-step manner, only at some time in your confusion to have an "Ah-ha!" moment? This type of problem solving has been referred to as *insight,* and it is characterized by an obviously correct solution suddenly popping into mind. Studying this process is not easy, but researchers have done so by examining the neural signatures of problems that people self-report as being either with insight or without insight. Interestingly, the state of brain activity *preceding* presentation of the problem appears to predict the type of problem solving that individuals report as occurring. Both EEG and fMRI data indicate that prior to presentation of problems reported as solved by insight, there is greater activity over medial frontal regions, as well as temporal areas associated with semantic processing. In contrast, for problems solved reported to be solved without insight, activity is increased in posterior regions, including those involved in visual selective attention (Kounios et al., 2006).

Before we leave our discussion of prefrontal cortex and rules, it is worth noting some theorists' suggestion that under certain situations we may be better off without our frontal cortex! Their argument is that when control by frontal cortex is limited or absent, we are freed from the restrictions provided by the rule-based behavior, which may allow for or enhance creativity. In addition, because the frontal lobes are poorly developed in children (see Chapter 15), this lack of executive control may also have implications for certain developmental learning processes (Thompson-Schill, Ramscar, & Chrysikou, 2009). One such dramatic example of how *not* having good frontal function may help in certain situations comes from a study in which people were given the matchstick problem (Knoblich, Ohlsson, Haider, & Rhenius, 1999). In this problem, the individual's job is to examine an arithmetic equation composed of Roman numerals "written" in matchsticks and to move only one matchstick to make the equation true. An easy problem is one such as the following, "II = III + I", which can be made correct simply by moving a matchstick on the right of the equal sign to the left (i.e., "III = II + I"). A more difficult problem is one in which individuals have to let go of focus on the numbers and focus instead on changing the operators of the equation. For example, the equation "IV = III − I" can be made legal by moving one of the matchsticks from the equal sign to the minus sign, to yield "IV − III = I." In the most difficult problems, a matchstick in the operator not only has to be moved, but it must also be rotated (e.g., "VI = VI + VI" becomes "VI = VI = VI"). Amazingly, although 43% of the controls could not solve the most difficult problem, 82% of those with lateral frontal lesions did so (Reverberi, Toraldo, D'Agostini, & Skrap, 2005)!

■ Response to Novelty and Cognitive Flexibility

Novelty, of course, is a relative concept, but we define it here as an event, a situation, or an action that has a low probability of occurring given a particular context. Flexibility is required not only in novel situations, but also when a new reaction must be made to an old situation.

In fact, electrophysiological studies emphasize the importance of frontal regions when a novel stimulus captures attention. As discussed in Chapters 3 and 11, an oddball stimulus that must be attended causes a P_{300} that is maximal over parietal regions (this P_{300} is sometimes referred to as the P_{3b}). A similar component, known as the P_{3a}, occurs when a novel or unexpected stimulus captures attention. This component is maximal at frontocentral leads, with an occurrence 20–50 ms earlier than the P_{3b} (● Figure 12.11). For example, the P_{3b} is elicited if a person must count or attend to the rare boops interspersed within a series of frequent beeps. If a totally unexpected or novel item, such as a dog bark, is inserted into the series of beeps and boops, a P_{3a} is elicited (Knight, 1984). We can be relatively certain that frontal regions of the brain contribute to the generation of this potential because (1) the P_{3a} decreases in amplitude after lesions to prefrontal cortex (Yamaguchi & Knight, 1991); (2) the amplitude of the P_{3a} is correlated with the volume of gray matter in the frontal lobes in neurologically intact men (Ford, Sullivan, Marsh, White, Lim, & Pfefferbaum, 1994); and (3) high-density electrode arrays suggest a frontal source (Spencer, Dien, & Donchin, 1999) (for a review, see Friedman, Cycowicz, & Gaeta, 2001). Neuroimaging studies provide converging evidence that greater activity occurs in prefrontal region in response to novel than to familiar stimuli (e.g., Kiehl, Laurens, Duty, Forster & Liddle, 2001; Friedman, Goldman, Stern, & Brown, 2009).

Not only must the brain detect novelty, but it also must be able to respond in new and flexible ways. Patients with executive dysfunction have trouble being cognitively flexible—that is, looking at situations from a multiplicity of vantage points and/or producing a variety of behaviors (Fuster, 1985). For example, patients with frontal lobe damage cannot generate alternative plans of action. Rather, they become "locked" into one way of dealing with information, which precludes the discovery of alternative responses. On a variant of a sorting task, an individual must discover the rule for solution of a problem on the basis of the examiner's feedback as to whether each choice is correct or incorrect. Patients with frontal lobe damage will continue to act in accord with an incorrect hypothesis even though enough information has accrued to eliminate it as a viable hypothesis (Cicerone, Lazar, & Shapiro, 1983).

The tendency of patients with frontal lobe damage to start down a particular path and not consider alternative solutions is demonstrated by another task in which a series of items, such as words or pictures, must be ordered (Della Malva, Stuss, D'Alton, & Willmer, 1993). This task involves two types of trials. In both types of trials, two target items that form a strong association (e.g., full moon; coffee cup) are presented in succession within a series of words that must be rearranged to create a meaningful sentence. For one type of trial, the target items need not be separated to form a valid sentence. An example is "sky/the/lit/*full*/*moon*/a," which should be ordered to read "A *full moon* lit the sky." In the other type of trial, the associated items must be separated, as in the set "of/full/the/was/*coffee*/*cup*," in which *coffee* and *cup* must be moved apart to correctly order the sentence to read "The *cup* was full of *coffee*." Patients with frontal lobe damage have no trouble ordering the sentence when the associated words need not be separated, but they are unable to successfully generating a valid sentence when the words must be separated, suggesting that they have difficulty overcoming the strong association between the target words.

Research across many species, including rats (Ragozzino, 2007), monkeys (Petrides, 2007), and humans, implicates the orbitofrontal cortex with aiding in flexible behavior. Orbitofrontal damage impedes the ability to exhibit normal **reversal learning**, in which an individual reverses a previous response. For example, after learning to press the right-hand key when a blue light appears and the left-hand key when a yellow light appears, in the reversal condition one would have to press the right-hand key when the *yellow* light appears and the left-hand key when the *blue* light appears. In neurologically intact individuals orbitofrontal activity is increased during reversal learning but not during the initial acquisition of the learning rule. Dorsal anterior cingulate cortex and right inferior frontal gyrus also become activated in reversal learning, each of which may play a role in overriding previously learned responses or response patterns (Ghahremani, Monterosso, Jentsch, Bilder, & Poldrack, 2009). Moreover, evidence from a complicated learning paradigm (which is too detailed to describe here) shows that the frontopolar cortex tracks the relative advantage over trials of sticking to the current choice versus switching to an alternative response option (Boorman, Behrens, Woolrich, & Rushworth, 2009). In sum, orbitofrontal and frontopolar cortex are likely to play a large role in the control of flexible behavior.

■ Judgment and Decision Making

Almost any clinician who treats or works with patients who have executive dysfunction will invariably tell you that the judgment and decision-making abilities of such people are compromised. Remember that the knowledge base of these patients usually remains relatively unaffected; that is, they can retain information such as the year of Canada's independence or the name of Henry VIII's second wife. In some cases, such knowledge can be used effectively. These patients are as competent as patients with temporal lobe damage or neurologically intact people at judging how many clues they will need to solve a puzzle (although they don't let such information guide their responses). Also, their estimates for judging how well they perform on concrete tasks, such as preparing meals, dressing themselves, and caring for

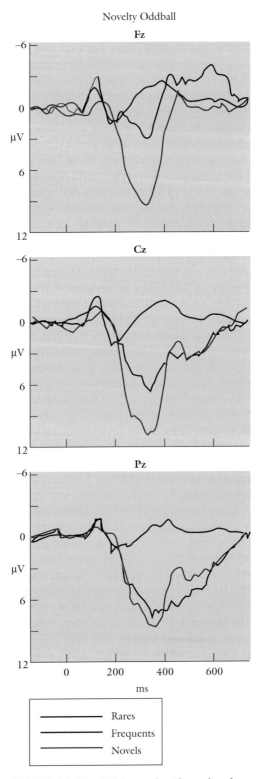

● **FIGURE 12.11 Evidence for the role of prefrontal regions in novelty.** Shown here are the ERP responses to rare, frequent and truly novel (i.e., unique) stimuli. Notice that the difference in the response to novel as compared to rare events is greatest over frontal leads (Fz) and practically indistinguishable over posterior leads (Pz), with an intermediate pattern over central leads (Cz). © 2011 Cengage Learning

personal hygiene, concur well with their relatives' estimates (Prigatano, Altman, & O'Brien, 1990).

However, if the task becomes a bit more abstract, they begin to exhibit difficulties. For example, patients with frontal lobe damage have difficulty estimating the length of the spine of an average woman. This type of information is not usually stored in memory nor easily obtained from reference materials, such as an encyclopedia or Wikipedia. Instead, making a realistic estimate requires the use of other knowledge, such as knowing that the average woman is about 5 feet 6 inches tall (168 cm), and that the spine runs about one-third to one-half the length of the body, yielding an estimated spine length of 22 to 33 inches (56–84 cm). Patients with frontal lobe damage have difficulty making such estimates, and often state absurd or outrageous values (Shallice & Evans, 1978). Likewise, patients with frontal lobe damage are poor at estimating the price of items, such as cars and washing machines, when shown a miniature replica (which is a somewhat abstract representation of the item). In fact, they provide bizarre estimates on 25% of all responses (e.g., 10 cents for a washing machine) (Smith & Milner, 1984). Their ability to estimate more abstract aspects of their own daily performance is also compromised. For example, in comparison with the ratings provided by relatives, patients with anterior lesions (coupled with diffuse axonal injury) grossly overestimate how capable they are of performing tasks such as scheduling their daily activities, fending off depression, or preventing their emotions from affecting daily activities (Prigatano, Altman, & O'Brien, 1990).

Some interesting research suggests that in neurologically intact people, portions of the frontal lobe are involved in abstract judgments and decision making, such as those required in making moral judgments. Consider the following types of decisions that researchers posed to their study participants. (As you read along, it might be helpful for you to consider what you would do.) The first scenario is as follows. "You are standing next to the train track. You see a runaway train that, if it maintains its current course, will run over five people. Your choice is either to let the train continue on its way, or to throw a switch that will send the train veering onto another track. Unfortunately, that action will cause a person standing on the other track to be killed." The second scenario is similar to the first but slightly different: "You are standing on a footbridge above a train track. You see a runaway train that, if it maintains its current course, will run over five people. Standing next to you is a person. Your choice is either to let the train continue on its way, or to throw the person off the bridge, which will cause the train to veer onto another track, but will unfortunately lead to the person's death." What did you decide in each of these cases? Most individuals claim that the first decision is relatively easy: they would pull the switch. In contrast, most people find the second task more difficult. Notice that in both cases, the outcome is the same: one action

will lead to five deaths whereas the other will lead to only one death. Despite similar outcomes, the second decision engages regions of DLPFC and frontopolar cortex (BA 10) to a larger degree (Greene, Sommerville, Nystrom, Darley, & Cohen, 2001; Greene, Nystrom, Engell, Darley, & Cohen, 2004), suggesting that these regions become more important as decisions become more difficult and conflict-laden.

At this point we have surveyed the neural underpinnings of a broad array of executive abilities. As should be clear, they involve a large and diverse set of frontal cortex regions. We next turn to a consideration of whether we can fruitfully conceptualize some of these regions as forming coherent, organized systems that work in a coordinated manner to exert executive control.

Organization of the Frontal Lobe for Executive Function

As you should be able to tell from the discussion in this chapter, the organization of the frontal lobe for executive function is quite complicated. As we mentioned at the outset of the chapter, there is unlikely to be a strict subregion-to-function mapping; rather, overlapping regions are involved in most of the functions we have described. Nonetheless, researchers have attempted to derive some principles or general trends concerning how prefrontal cortex might be organized for executive function. We discuss a number of these in turn.

One model argues that there is a nested hierarchy of control from caudal to rostral portions of frontal cortex, with the most posterior regions being influenced by the most immediate aspects of a situation and more anterior regions affected by the larger context (Koechlin & Summerfield, 2007) (● Figure 12.12A). This model can best be explained using an example, such as person's response to a phone ringing. Over time, you may have learned a simple behavior: when a phone rings, you pick it up quickly. Here a sensory stimulus, the phone ringing, leads to a motoric response, picking it up quickly. In this model, at the lowest level of the hierarchy, premotor regions guide behavior based on sensory information. For example, when the phone rings, you may decide to wait to pick it only after there have been five rings. If responding is not constrained by sensory information, then control must be implemented at the next level by posterior lateral prefrontal cortex, which uses contextual information to guide action. For example, if a phone rings but the context is your friend's house, you don't pick up the phone. If responding is not constrained by contextual information, then control must be implemented at the next level by anterior regions of lateral prefrontal cortex, which use particular episodes to guide action. For example, if your friend asks you to pick up the phone before she leaves the room (a specific episode), you will do so. Finally, if responding is not constrained by episodic information, then control must be implemented at the highest level by the frontopolar cortex, which is thought to integrate information with regard to sub-goals or specific conditions. This region helps you to revert back to the behavior of not answering the phone once your friend walks back into the room.

Another model also argues for a hierarchy of processing from posterior to anterior lateral fron-tal regions, but, unlike the prior model, posits that these regions implement control based on the level of abstraction at which the conflict occurs or the level at which control must be exerted (Badre, 2008) (● Figure 12.12B). Let's return to our example of a ring-ing phone. According to this model, posterior regions of lateral prefrontal cortex are involved in selecting information based on concrete stimulus-response rules. So this region might select one response, such as answering your cell phone when the unique ringtone identifies the caller as your best friend, but not answer-ing the phone when the ringtone identifies the call as coming from your parent's home phone. Regions a bit more anterior select control on the basis of stimulus features. For example, here a certain response, such as not answering the phone, might be implemented for all ringtones regardless of their sound, whereas a different response, checking your phone, would be implemented for all sounds indicating the receipt of a text message. Regions more anterior to those select on the basis of a still more abstract stimulus dimen-sion; for example, these regions might implement the response of answering the phone if the tone identi-fies the caller as known to you, but not answering the phone if the ringtone identifies the caller as someone unknown to you. Finally, the most anterior regions exert control with regard to the context. For example, this region might select an action of answering the phone when it rings but not looking at text messages when you are alone, but not answering the phone and reading text messages when you are with friends. What these two models have in common is that they view control as following a gradient from posterior to anterior regions of lateral prefrontal cortex.

Another viewpoint of prefrontal function is that selection or control processes involve prefrontal regions that exert control at different times, from task prepa-ration to stimulus processing to response output and then response evaluation. This model views control as implemented in a cascade involving lateral and medial prefrontal regions (Banich, 2009) (● Figure 12.13). According to this model, posterior regions of dorsolat-eral prefrontal cortex send a top-down signal to bias activity toward those regions of posterior cortex that will be needed to process task-relevant information, essentially imposing an attentional set. This can be imposed before a stimulus is even received. For exam-ple, in the Stroop task, posterior regions of DLPFC work to bias processing toward color identification and away from word reading. More anterior regions of DLPFC help in biasing processing toward items or item attributes

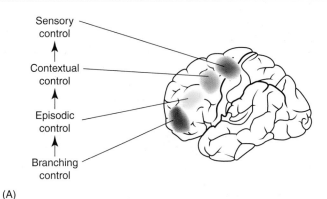

(A)

(B)

● **FIGURE 12.12   Different conceptual models of how lateral prefrontal cortex is organized for executive function.** (A) One model posits a nested hierarchy of control processes within prefrontal cortex. According to this model, there is a gradient from posterior to anterior, with more posterior regions selecting sensory information, then regions that select with regard to the context in which that sensory information occurs, then regions that select information with regard to the current episode or event, and finally regions that select with regard to the context of prior episodes or events. (B) Another model argues that selection of material occurs in posterior regions of prefrontal cortex on the basis of more concrete dimensions, and that the representations used for selection become more abstract as one moves in an anterior direction. *Source:* Badre, D. (2008). Cognitive control, hierarchy, and the rostro-caudal organization of the frontal lobes. Trends in cognitive sciences, 12, Figure 2, pg. 195.

that are most task-relevant, such as biasing processing toward processing the information contained in the ink color of that item rather than the color named by the word. Next, posterior regions of the dorsal anterior cingulate help to bias processing toward use of certain information, in this case ink color, for the selection of a response. Finally, more anterior regions evaluate the appropriateness of the response. Importantly, control in this model is viewed as a cascade. If control is not well implemented at a prior "waystation," more control will be required at the next point in the circuit. For example, if posterior dorsolateral prefrontal cortex does a poor job of imposing a top-down attention set, more ante-rior regions of the dorsolateral prefrontal cortex and the anterior cingulate will have to work harder to impose control. Future research will determine which of these models, or which portions of them, best explain how the frontal cortex actually exerts cognitive control.

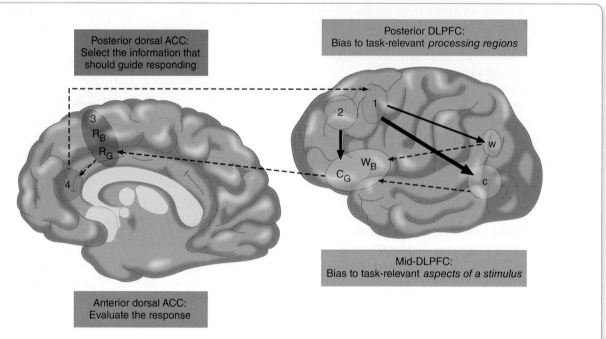

Posterior dorsal ACC:
Select the information that
should guide responding

Posterior DLPFC:
Bias to task-relevant *processing regions*

Mid-DLPFC:
Bias to task-relevant *aspects of a stimulus*

Anterior dorsal ACC:
Evaluate the response

● **FIGURE 12.13   A conceptualization of how lateral and medial prefrontal regions exert executive control, from stimulus input to response output, via a cascade of control, using the Stroop task as an example.** Consider here the case of the word "blue" written in green ink. According to this model, the first step in the cascade occurs when posterior regions of DLPFC (represented by a 1) bias activity toward posterior regions of cortex involved in the processing of color (represented by the circle with a c) and away from word reading (represented by the circle with a w). Next, middle regions of DLPFC (represented by a 2) bias processing to the representations that are most task-relevant, such as a specific color (e.g., green, denoted by C_G) rather than a specific word (e.g., blue, denoted by W_B). Posterior regions of the dorsal anterior cingulate cortex (ACC) (denoted by 3) aid in selecting which information should guide the responses; in this case, the response linked to green (R_G) rather than the response linked to blue (R_B). Because all conflict must be resolved before a response is emitted, this region becomes more highly activated if control has not been effectively exerted by the DLPFC. Finally, more anterior regions of the dorsal ACC (denoted by 4) are involved in helping to evaluate whether a response was correct. If the response was not correct, it sends a signal back to DLPFC to increase control. *Source:* Banich, M. T. (2009). Executive Function: The search for an integrated account. Current Directions in Psychological Science, 18, Fig. 2, pg. 92.

A Central Role for Working Memory in Executive Function

Before we leave our discussion of executive function, we should reiterate that much research views dorsolateral prefrontal cortex as playing a predominant role in many different aspects of executive function. That point should have become obvious to you as you read this chapter. But why is that? Researchers have argued that DLPFC may play a central role in executive function because it supports working memory. This is not to say that executive function is synonymous with working memory, but rather, as outlined in psychological theories, that working memory plays a central, prominent role in executive function.

To better understand the link between working memory and executive function, let's briefly review some of the characteristics of working memory. As you may remember from Chapter 10, working memory is a limited-capacity system that keeps information online

for use in performing a task. How might difficulties in working memory account for some of the deficits in executive functioning? If one cannot maintain information in working memory, one may not be able to keep a goal in mind; thus, this deficit interferes with a person's ability to direct behavior toward a goal or to formulate a strategy for attaining the goal. In addition, difficulty in keeping information online may disrupt a person's understanding of temporal relations between items and events. If what has just happened cannot be kept online, its relation to subsequent events will be lost. In such cases, sequencing would be quite difficult. Moreover, if one is not able to retain multiple pieces of information simultaneously in working memory, there may be difficulty in creating or following rules, in making inferences, and in understanding the relations between items in the world. As you may remember, psychological models suggest that both the ability to hold information online and the ability to update working memory are very important for executive function. If a person is unable to clear out what is held in working memory, perseveration will result. Accordingly, difficulties in working memory may account for a number of the problems observed in cases of executive dysfunction (for a computational model demonstrating how working memory supports executive function, see Hazy, Frank, & O'Reilly, 2006).

In consideration of these facts, we can see that the line between two processes we have treated as distinct in previous chapters—working memory and goal-directed aspects of attentional control—is really quite blurred. If you think about it, you can see that these functions clearly are related. Working memory allows you to keep in mind your ultimate goal, as well as the type of information to which you should be attending. For example, working memory allows you to keep in mind that the goal of your foray to the shopping mall is to buy a present for your friend, *and* that she needs a scarf, *and* that purple is her favorite color.

Likewise, executive aspects of attentional control are required to determine what information is selected to be maintained in working memory, and which of the contents of working memory are most relevant for current task demands (Milham et al., 2002). Suppose you are at an airport listening to the announcements. Working memory allows you to keep what you've just heard in mind. However, you need to select only that information associated with your flight number or your destination. Furthermore, when the announcement comes indicating the gate at which your flight number is embarking, you need to select the gate number but not your destination to be maintained in working memory. Thus, we can synthesize many of the perspectives presented in this chapter by suggesting that it is the interrelationship between regions of prefrontal cortex, and the interrelationship between working memory and selection processes, that lies at the heart of executive functioning.

Summary

Theoretical Perspectives

- Executive functions are a series of abilities that are required to guide or control behavior toward a goal; these abilities rely heavily on the frontal lobe.
- Executive control must also be exerted in novel situations when no preexisting schemas for how to act are available to use, and when typical responses must be overridden or inhibited.
- Some models view executive control as a unitary system, whereas others conceptualize it as having subcomponents. One set of proposed subcomponents consists of initiating and sustaining a response, setting tasks, and monitoring. Another proposed set consists of response inhibition, task-switching, and the updating of working memory.

Goal-Directed Behaviors

- Goal-directed behavior consists of many subcomponents, including the initiation of behavior; the creation and maintenance of a goal, plan, or set; sequencing; set-shifting; self-monitoring; and evaluation and inhibition.
- The initiation of behavior is often compromised in individuals who have frontal lobe brain damage. Behavior initiation appears to be relatively more reliant on medial prefrontal regions.
- The creation and maintenance of a goal or plan relies on many regions of prefrontal cortex, dorsolateral prefrontal cortex being prominent among them.
- The ability to sequence items also appears to rely on dorsolateral prefrontal regions.
- Set-shifting is supported by a large number of regions, including dorsolateral, inferior, and medial prefrontal regions. The regions that support this ability may vary based on task demands. For example, inferior frontal regions may play a prominent role when former task sets must be overridden, whereas dorsal regions may be more involved when shifts are made between rule-based task sets.
- The brain has a neural system that is active in self-monitoring and evaluation of actions. This involves the medial portions of the frontal lobe and is indexed by an ERP component known as the error-related negativity.
- Inhibition of responses involves the right inferior frontal cortex, which plays a role in overriding or inhibiting responses (especially when they are well learned), as well as in aborting or terminating responses.

Higher-Order Thinking

- The frontal lobes play a role in abstract and conceptual thinking, such as that required to understand metaphor or analogy.
- Implementing rules and making inferences require coordination between frontal regions and posterior brain regions where previously learned knowledge is stored.
- Frontal regions, especially the orbitofrontal cortex and frontopolar cortex, are required to flexibly exert behavior, such as changing from previously invoked plans or courses of action.
- Judgments and decisions, including those about moral dilemmas, require a contribution from frontal cortex.

Organization of the Frontal Lobe for Executive Function

■ Executive function requires the coordinated activity of different portions of the frontal lobe, although certain regions may play a more important role in certain aspects of control than others.

■ One prominent model argues that there is a nested hierarchy of control from caudal to rostral portions of frontal cortex, with the most posterior regions being influenced by the most immediate aspects of a situation and more anterior regions by the larger context.

■ Another model also argues for a hierarchy of processing from posterior to anterior lateral frontal regions, but holds that these regions implement control based on the level of abstraction at which the conflict occurs or the level at which control must be exerted.

■ Another view of prefrontal function is that selection or control processes involve prefrontal regions that exert control at different times, from task preparation to stimulus processing to response output and evaluation. This model posits a cascade of control involving lateral and medial prefrontal regions.

A Central Role for Working Memory in Executive Function

■ Dorsolateral regions play a prominent role in many aspects of executive function. This association may occur because this region supports working memory, which is required for many executive functions.

Key Terms

attentional set   344

cognitive control   338

contention scheduling   338

environmental dependency syndrome   338

error positivity (Pe)   352

error-related negativity (ERN)   351

executive functions   337

Go/No-Go task   352

higher-order thinking   353

interference resolution   353

metacognition   340

perseveration   339

post-error slowing   352

psychological inertia   341

response inhibition   352

reversal learning   359

self-ordered pointing task   345

sequencing   345

supervisory attentional system   338

switch cost   349

Tower of London task   347

Wisconsin Card Sorting Test (WCST)   348

Book Companion Site at www.cengage.com/psychology/Banich
This website provides instructors and students with a wealth of free information and resources, including tutorial quizzes, flashcards, and the glossary.

Emotion and Social Cognition

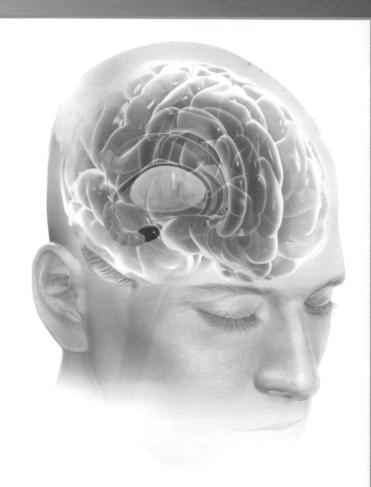

Subcortical Contributions to Emotion

Fight-or-Flight Response

Fear and Emotional Learning

Reward and Motivation

Cortical Contributions to Emotion

Representing Bodily Cues of Emotion

Monitoring for Emotionally Salient Events

Incorporating Emotion into Decision Making

Regulating Emotion

Communicating Emotion
 Facial Expression
 Prosody

Emotional Experience
 Approach-Withdrawal Models
 Valence-Arousal Models

From Emotion to Social Cognition

Understanding the Mental States of Others

IN FOCUS: The Pain of Rejection

Cognitive Neuroscience Approaches to Prejudice

Summary

Key Terms

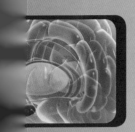

BY MARCH 30, 1981, James Brady had been serving for several months as the press secretary for U.S. President Ronald Reagan. Brady was known and liked by the White House press corps for his wit and energy. For example, during a lunch with reporters, he described a particular government bureaucrat as sleeping "in the closet hanging upside down with his wings over his eyes" (Bumiller, 1982). But March 30 was a terrible day for Jim Brady and all those who knew him. During a gunman's attempt to assassinate President Reagan, Brady took a bullet in the head.

The injury was very severe—in fact, at one point that evening, CBS anchorman Dan Rather mistakenly reported that Brady had died (Bumiller, 1982). Eventually surgeons were able to reduce the swelling and bleeding in his brain so that Brady survived. However, because of the bullet's trajectory, he suffered extensive brain damage to his right frontal lobe (Cytowic, 1981).

Many of the symptoms that Brady experienced are predictable from what we have already learned about the frontal lobes. Brady suffered paralysis of the left arm and leg, consistent with damage to the motor regions in the right frontal lobe. He also displayed cognitive symptoms of frontal lobe damage, such as difficulties with initiating action and a tendency to perseverate in his thought.

But the gunshot wound did not just affect Brady's cognitive functions—it affected his emotional regulation and emotional state as well. In an essay, his wife Sarah Brady wrote: "[S]trong feelings of any kind could bring on what we called a 'wail'—a very unnerving noise somewhere between crying and laughing. As his brain healed, he was increasingly able to control it, and in later years, he would wail only during extremely emotional moments—sad or happy—such as the singing of the national anthem. But in those early days, it happened all the time: He would start to say something, and suddenly his voice would just wail off." At other times, though, Brady was described as speaking in a "slow, measured cadence" (De Witt, 1990) that lacked the emotional inflections of normal speech.

After his injury, Brady also tended to be a bit more brutally honest than people in the political sphere are generally inclined to be. For example, he made highly unflattering remarks about some of his former colleagues in the White House, sometimes making those around him a bit uncomfortable (Bumiller, 1982). Although these tendencies may simply reflect the change in outlook that accompanies a brush with death, they may also reflect a failure of his damaged frontal lobes to inhibit socially inappropriate behavior.

Despite his tragic circumstances, Brady continued to maintain his trademark wit; about John Hinckley, the man whose bullet hit him but missed President Reagan, Brady said, "I think that guy was an awfully bad shot." He and Sarah Brady have dedicated themselves to advocating against gun violence and for the recognition of people with traumatic brain injuries. While James Brady can teach us about the emotional consequences of right frontal lobe damage, he also teaches us a lesson about emotional resilience in the face of tragedy.

IMAGINE A DAY without emotion. According to the psychologist and philosopher William James, living without emotion would require a person to "drag out an existence of merely cognitive or intellectual form." James thought this rather undesirable, arguing that "[s]uch an existence, although it seems to have been the ideal of the ancient sages, is too apathetic to be keenly sought after by those born after the revival of the worship of sensibility" (James, 1884, p. 194). Though emotions can be destructive, they also bring vitality to our lives; they permeate nearly all aspects of our thoughts, decisions, and interactions with other people.

This chapter surveys different components of emotion and the brain systems that are important in implementing them. First, though, we must be able to answer a basic question: What is an emotion? It has been said that everyone knows what an emotion is until they are asked to define it (LeDoux, 1996). The *American Heritage Dictionary of the American Language* defines *emotion* as "1. Agitation of the passions or sensibilities often involving physiological changes. 2. Any strong feeling, as of joy, sorrow, reverence, hate, or love, arising subjectively rather than through conscious mental effort." At first glance, this description seems to capture our everyday sense of the concept of emotion. However, when we examine this definition more closely, we begin to appreciate the complexity of trying to understand emotion.

This definition assumes some things about emotion that still arouse heated debate in the scientific literature. For instance, what does it mean for a feeling to arise "subjectively rather than through conscious mental effort"? Indeed, much of the processing that is associated with emotion seems to occur outside conscious awareness. We may know how to describe a feeling we are experiencing, but we are often unaware of how that feeling was generated. Nevertheless, most of us would recognize that conscious mental effort can play a role in generating or maintaining emotions. Imagine, for example, the jealous lover who dwells on thoughts of his beloved in someone else's arms, making himself more miserable in the process.

Another contentious issue is whether physiological changes in the periphery of the body play an important role in emotion. Emotional experience is associated with changes in heart rate, blood pressure, skin temperature, and electrodermal response (the degree to which the skin conducts electricity depending on the amount of perspiration). For example, imagine the emotion of fear: you probably associate it with bodily sensations such as a racing heart and sweaty palms. But are these bodily changes just a side effect of consciously experiencing an emotion, or do they in fact bring about the conscious experience? This issue has been debated ever since William James posed the question more than 100 years ago (James, 1884).

A final thorny problem involves the relationship between cognition and emotion; that is, between "thinking" and "feeling." People often assume that cognition and emotion are independent and even mutually exclusive—that rational thought runs counter to emotional impulses, or that more thinking involves less feeling and vice versa. But when we consider the many aspects of emotion and the neural systems that implement emotion, we will see that it is often difficult to draw sharp boundaries between cognition and emotion. For example, when we recognize a person's facial expression of happiness, are we using a cognitive system that decodes visual patterns, or are we using an emotional system that categorizes stimuli as pleasant or unpleasant? Does making adaptive choices in life depend upon elaborate rational thought, or upon instinctive understanding of the dangers and rewards of different choices? When a person's attention is captured by the sound of a scream in the distance, is that an emotional or a cognitive process? Although we will learn that certain brain systems are deeply involved in emotional functions, the brain does not divide neatly into two categories of "emotional" and "cognitive" regions, just as our psychological functions cannot be sharply divided into these two categories.

When you think of all the complexities subsumed in the term *emotion*, it should not surprise you to learn that there is no single brain region that serves as the emotion center. Rather, many different brain regions contribute to the experiences that we call emotion, which is sometimes also referred to as *affect* or *affective experience*. Some of these brain regions are concerned with specific emotions, such as fear or pleasure; others are concerned with specific processes, such as recognizing emotion in facial expressions or integrating emotion with cognitive processing. Our challenge is to work toward an understanding of how all these different brain regions work in concert to allow the full range of emotional experiences and abilities that we enjoy. This chapter focuses primarily on the emotions that most people feel every day, and it also lays the groundwork for Chapter 14, which examines disorders of emotion.

Subcortical Contributions to Emotion

Many emotions are uncomfortable to experience. However, their survival value is obvious. When a person is threatened, the body needs to mobilize its resources and take some kind of protective action: withdrawal (flight), perhaps, or aggression (fight). Furthermore, these responses often must be made quickly. As a result, they are often made before a person has time to perform any elaborate, conscious, cognitive assessments of the situation. In our survey of the brain regions involved in emotion, we begin by discussing the subcortical regions that implement these more automatic or subconscious aspects of emotion.

As long ago as 1937, James W. Papez (rhymes with "grapes") described a subcortical brain circuit involved in emotion that included the hypothalamus, hippocampus, anterior thalamus, and cingulate cortex. Paul MacLean (1949, 1952) later proposed that these structures are part of what was termed the **limbic system** (meaning "border" or "belt"), which consists of a series of structures that sit below the neocortex (● Figure 13.1). Although investigators agree that emotions depend on

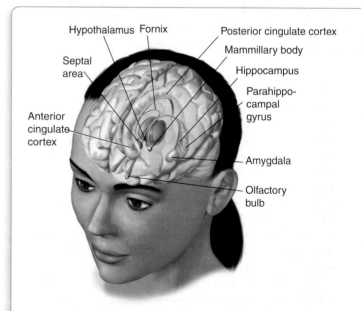

● **FIGURE 13.1 The major structures of the limbic system.** The limbic system forms a belt sitting below the neocortex, consisting of a wide variety of structures that have been implicated in emotional processing. © 2010 Cengage Learning

the limbic system, scientists' ideas about exactly which structures constitute this system have changed over time (Brodal, 1998). For example, the hippocampus, once thought to be the hub of the limbic system, plays an important role in memory functions. In contrast, the amygdala, which in the past was not identified as a key component of the limbic system, has received a great deal of attention from neuroscientists who study emotion (LeDoux, 1996). In this section, we consider what is currently known about the role of subcortical structures in crucial emotional functions.

■ Fight-or-Flight Response

As we have already discussed, emotional experiences often include bodily changes, such as an increased heart rate or sweaty palms. The body's fight-or-flight response depends upon the autonomic nervous system (● Figure 13.2), which consists of nerves that contact body organs such as the heart, the lungs, and the sweat glands. The hypothalamus governs the level of activity in the autonomic system, determining the extent to which the fight-or-flight response is activated. Activation of the sympathetic branch of the autonomic system causes increases in heart rate, blood pressure, respiration, and sweat secretion.

The hypothalamus also controls the hormonal systems of the body. For example, through its interactions with the pituitary gland, the hypothalamus influences the level of stress hormones in the body (● Figure 13.3). When stimulated by the hypothalamus, the pituitary gland releases hormones into the bloodstream. These pituitary hormones can affect target organs such as the adrenal glands, which in turn produce stress hormones like adrenaline and cortisol. Therefore, because the hypothalamus governs both the autonomic and hormonal systems of the body, it serves as an important gateway through which the brain can influence the state of the body.

So, how does the hypothalamus know when to kick the body's fight-or-flight response into high gear? How does it determine when a threatening event is present, for example? Such decisions appear to be determined by the amygdala, another subcortical limbic region that sends its outputs to the hypothalamus. We consider the role of the amygdala in fear and other emotions in the next section.

■ Fear and Emotional Learning

The amygdala plays an important role in early detection of emotional information and in learning the emotional significance of information. ● Figure 13.4 shows the location and subdivisions of the amygdala. Although it is a small structure, the amygdala consists of several identifiable and interacting nuclei. Some researchers refer to this region as the *amygdalar complex*, a phrase intended to capture the complicated nature of the region. A somewhat simplified description of this region notes that the basolateral nuclei project to the

hippocampus and prefrontal cortex, as well as brain regions involved in reward and punishment, allowing the amygdala to influence learning and memory. The central nucleus and corticomedial nuclei connect to the hypothalamus and other brain regions involved in autonomic and hormonal responses, enabling emotional modulation of these responses (see Freese & Amaral, 2009, for more detailed anatomy).

Scientists first became aware of the role of the amygdala when it was discovered that large temporal-lobe lesions in monkeys resulted in a set of behavioral changes known as *Klüver-Bucy syndrome*. These monkeys showed extremely abnormal reactions to the environment. They stopped being afraid of things they had feared in the past, attempted to engage in sexual behaviors with other species, and tried to ingest objects indiscriminately, including feces and rocks. Klüver and Bucy (1937) used the term **psychic blindness** to describe the disconnection between the animals' ability to process the sensory properties of objects and their understanding of the affective properties of these same objects. These initial studies involved the removal of the entire temporal lobes, including both the cortex and the subcortical areas such as the amygdala, but subsequent research found that amygdala damage alone could produce many of these behavioral changes (e.g., Emery, Capitanio, Mason, Machado, Mendoza, & Amaral, 2001; Machado, Kazama, & Bachevalier, 2009).

Lesions of the amygdala in humans also interfere with the processing of emotional information, though the effects are not as dramatic as with Klüver and Bucy's monkeys. Case studies of people with amygdala damage indicate that they lose the ability to detect aversive emotional cues embedded in visual and auditory stimuli. They have difficulty identifying fearful facial expressions as well as fearful or angry sounds (Aggleton & Young, 2000); they even have trouble recognizing scary music (Gosselin, Peretz, Johnsen, & Adolphs, 2007). When such patients are asked to judge faces for trustworthiness and approachability, they rate unfamiliar photographs as more trustworthy and approachable than neurologically intact individuals do (Adolphs, Tranel, & Damasio, 1998).

Neuroimaging studies provide converging evidence about the amygdala's role in responding to emotionally salient information. Activity in the human amygdala is increased in response to fearful compared to neutral faces (e.g., Dolan & Morris, 2000). Not surprisingly, the amygdala is also activated in people with phobias when they are exposed to their feared object (e.g., spiders or snakes) (Larson, Schaefer, Siegle, Jackson, Anderle, & Davidson, 2006; Phan, Fitzgerald, Nathan, & Tancer, 2006). Currently there is debate about whether the amygdala responds to fearful images even when those images are presented outside of conscious awareness. Some researchers have found that the amygdala does respond to subconsciously presented images (Whalen,

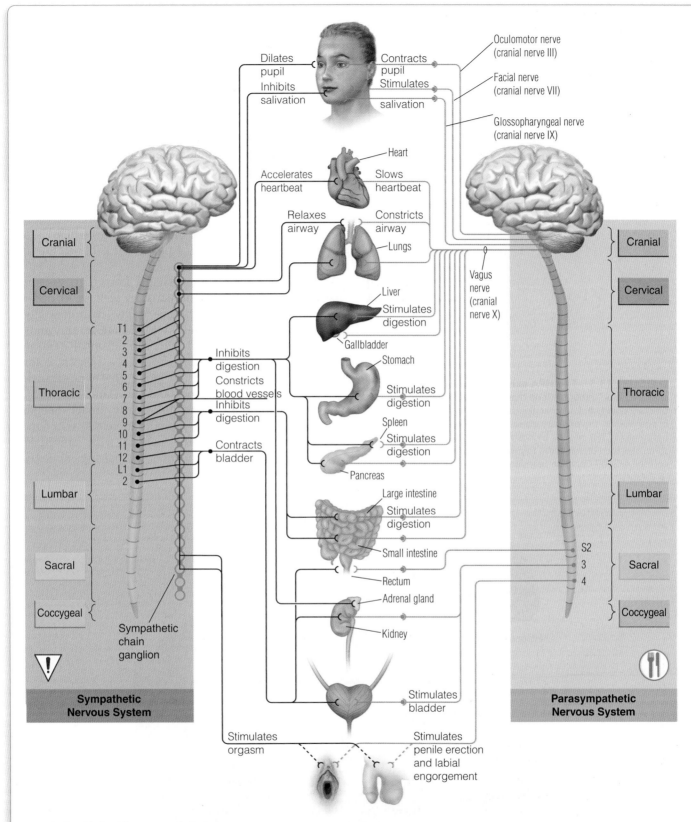

● **FIGURE 13.2   The autonomic nervous system.** Activation of the sympathetic branch of the autonomic nervous system is important in many bodily expressions of emotion, such as changes in heart rate, respiration, and sweat secretion. In contrast, the parasympathetic branch is activated under resting conditions. © 2010 Cengage Learning

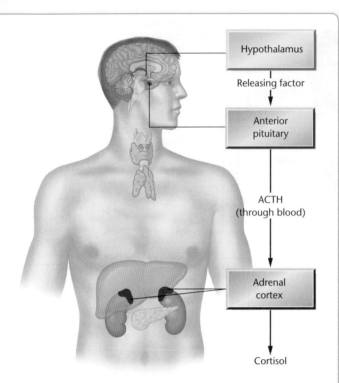

● **FIGURE 13.3** **The HPA axis.** The brain controls the body's stress response through a loop that connects the hypothalamus, pituitary gland, and adrenal glands. When stimulated by the hypothalamus, the pituitary gland secretes adrenocorticotropic hormone (ACTH) into the bloodstream, and this hormone stimulates the adrenal gland to produce the stress hormone cortisol. © 2009 Cengage Learning

Rauch, Etcoff, McInerney, Lee, & Jenike, 1998; Whalen et al., 2004), but others question such claims (Pessoa, Japee, Sturman, & Ungerleider, 2006).

The amygdala is especially involved in emotional learning, as demonstrated repeatedly in studies of fear conditioning. As discussed in Chapter 10, in fear conditioning paradigms a neutral stimulus develops a negative emotional connotation by virtue of its association with an aversive stimulus (● Figure 13.5). After pairing a neutral image with a very unpleasant noise, for example, people will eventually respond to the previously neutral image as if it were inherently aversive. This emotional response is reflected in physiological responses such as heart rate, skin conductance, and the *startle response*, which is a blink that occurs when a puff of air is blown into a person's eye.

Damage to the amygdala is known to disrupt fear conditioning in humans, as well as in other mammalian species. In one study, neurologically intact people, a patient with bilateral amygdala damage, and a patient with hippocampal damage were shown repeated pairings of a specific color slide with an unpleasant noise (Bechara, Tranel, Damasio, Adolphs, Rockland, & Damasio, 1995). After conditioning, neurologically intact people reacted to the slide by showing increased skin conductance. Although the patient with amygdala damage was able to remember the pairing explicitly

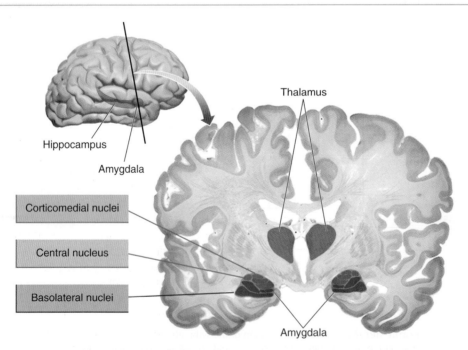

● **FIGURE 13.4** **The amygdaloid complex.** The amygdala is made up of several interrelated nuclei. The basolateral nuclei project to the hippocampus and prefrontal cortex, as well as regions involved in reward and punishment (including the caudate nucleus and nucleus accumbens), allowing the amygdala to influence learning and memory. The basolateral nuclei also project to the central nucleus and corticomedial nuclei, which have a different pattern of connections. They connect to the hypothalamus and other brain regions involved in autonomic and hormonal responses, allowing the amygdala to perform emotional modulation of these responses. © 2010 Cengage Learning

(e.g., "I know that the blue slide is the one with the shock"), she did not show the expected autonomic conditioned response. In contrast, the patient with hippocampal damage showed normal conditioned skin-conductance responses, but was unable to explicitly remember that the blue slide led to the shock! This is an example of a classic double dissociation, linking the amygdala with acquired fear responses and the hippocampus with explicit memory.

The amygdala is also important in learning fear through words rather than just through direct experience of an aversive consequence. For example, if you brought your hand very close to an electrical socket, you would probably show an elevated skin-conductance response, indicating activation of the sympathetic nervous system. To learn that response, you didn't need to actually stick your finger in the socket and experience the shock. Instead, you probably developed the response through verbal learning: when you were young, your parents told you not to stick your fingers in sockets. Recently, studies have demonstrated that this kind of verbal learning depends on the amygdala. In one experiment, participants were shown different colored squares and simply told that one specific color could be associated with a shock (although no shock actually occurred). When participants viewed that specific color, the left amygdala became activated (Phelps, O'Connor, Gatenby, Gore, Grillon, & Davis, 2001). Another study found that damage to the left (but not the right) amygdala disrupted verbal learning of fear (Olsson & Phelps, 2007). These studies indicate that the left amygdala is especially important in verbal learning of fear responses, which fits in well with other evidence of the left hemisphere's involvement in language.

Because fear learning is so easily studied in many species, for some time scientists tended to focus on fear learning as a model for understanding emotion more generally. However, subsequent research has found that damage to the amygdala disrupts not only fear learning, but also certain types of reward-based learning in rodents and primates (Baxter & Murray, 2002; Murray, 2007). Several neuroimaging studies have also found that the amygdala is more responsive to happy faces than to neutral faces, indicating that positive emotional images can activate this structure as well (e.g., Breiter et al., 1996; Williams, Morris, McGlone, Abbott, & Mattingley, 2004). However, the response of the amygdala to positive stimuli may be somewhat less reliable than its response to negative stimuli (see Zald, 2003, for a review).

One factor driving this difference in response to positive and negative stimuli is the arousal level of the stimuli. Negative stimuli, such as pictures of angry faces, snakes, or spiders, tend to be rated as more highly arousing than positive stimuli, such as pictures of happy faces or puppies. Studies using olfactory stimuli (pleasant and unpleasant odors) found that amygdala activity increased as the intensity level

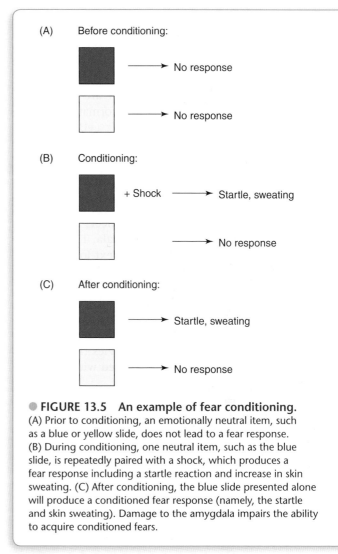

FIGURE 13.5   An example of fear conditioning.
(A) Prior to conditioning, an emotionally neutral item, such as a blue or yellow slide, does not lead to a fear response. (B) During conditioning, one neutral item, such as the blue slide, is repeatedly paired with a shock, which produces a fear response including a startle reaction and increase in skin sweating. (C) After conditioning, the blue slide presented alone will produce a conditioned fear response (namely, the startle and skin sweating). Damage to the amygdala impairs the ability to acquire conditioned fears.

of the stimulus increased, regardless of whether it was pleasant or unpleasant (Anderson et al., 2003; see also Small, Gregory, Mak, Gitelman, Mesulam, & Parrish, 2003, for similar results with pleasant and unpleasant tastes). However, researchers are still debating whether the amygdala's response is better explained by the valence of the stimulus—how pleasant or unpleasant it is—or by its emotional intensity level. For example, one study using pleasant and unpleasant pictures and sounds found that valence was a stronger determinant of amygdala response than arousal level (Anders, Eippert, Weiskopf, & Veit, 2008), inconsistent with the results from studies of odors and tastes. In another study, patients with damage to the amygdala rated the arousal level of negative pictures lower than did control participants, although they did not differ from controls in arousal ratings of positive pictures (Berntson, Bechara, Damasio, Tranel, & Cacioppo, 2007). While there is still much to be learned about the dimensions of emotional meaning that the amygdala encodes, it is clear that both emotional valence and intensity level are important factors in driving its response.

Given the amygdala's role in emotional learning, the brain must have some way in which sensory information from the outside world can be sent to the amygdala to enable such learning. In fact, there are two distinct pathways that convey sensory information to the amygdala (● Figure 13.6) (Armony & LeDoux, 2000). One pathway, which is important for quick, instinctive emotional responses, projects straight from the anterior thalamus to the amygdala. For example, this pathway allows a jogger to leap away from a shape on the road before the conscious mind has time to think, "That might be a snake." Another pathway connects the sensory areas of the neocortex to the amygdala. This pathway provides a more comprehensive context for processing emotional information. For example, after leaping to safety, the jogger might study the shape more carefully and realize that it is only a stick, not something to be feared. Thus, the amygdala appears to receive a progressively more complete image of the same information, much like a fade-in shot in the movies that becomes progressively clearer and more focused with time. The

thalamo-amygdaloid pathway carries a crude, preliminary sketch of some basic properties of the stimulus—not enough to clearly identify the object, but enough, perhaps, to ready or initiate a response. In contrast, the cortico-amygdaloid pathway, which is slower because it involves more synapses, delivers enough information to give rise to an affective reaction that takes into account the complexity and details of the situation.

This model emphasizes how incoming sensory information can influence the amygdala. When the amygdala registers something fearful or frightening, though, it is also important for that information to be taken into account by other brain regions. This is accomplished by additional connections running in the opposite direction from the amygdala to the cortex. These back-projecting fibers are thought to allow the amygdala to influence how attention is directed to different aspects of sensory information as they are processed by the cortex. Once the amygdala identifies an image as threatening or otherwise emotionally urgent, it can tell the cortex to pay more attention to that image. In neurologically intact people, attention tends to be captured by emotional stimuli (for reviews, see Compton, 2003;

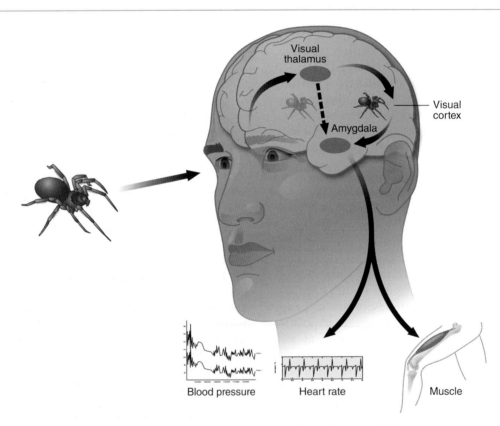

● **FIGURE 13.6 Two pathways by which sensory information reaches the amygdala.** One pathway from the thalamus to the amygdala provides basic sensory information very quickly, whereas the longer route involving the cortex provides more highly processed and detailed information. Output from the amygdala can then influence autonomic and hormonal responses. Although not depicted here, the amygdala can also influence how incoming sensory information is processed through backward projections from the amygdala to cortical regions. *Source:* LeDoux, J. (2002) Emotion, memory, and the brain. Scientific American, special issue on The Hidden Mind.

Vuilleumier, 2005), but patients with amygdala damage do not show such attentional effects (Anderson & Phelps, 2001).

The amygdala also interacts very closely with another important subcortical structure, the hippocampus. As we reviewed in Chapter 10, the hippocampus is crucial in encoding new information into long-term memory storage and in consolidating that information in memory over time. Close bidirectional interactions between the hippocampus and the amygdala allow them to influence one another's activity in several ways (see Phelps, 2004, for a review). For example, input from the amygdala to the hippocampus can allow the emotional meaning of a stimulus (coded by the amygdala) to influence the encoding and subsequent consolidation of that information by the hippocampus.

Indeed, the amygdala plays an important role in remembering events that are emotionally charged (LaBar & Cabeza, 2006). Normally, the greater the emotional intensity associated with an event or experience, the better it is remembered, a phenomenon known as the *memory enhancement effect.* Amygdala damage interferes with this memory enhancement effect (Adolphs, Cahill, Schul, & Babinsky, 1997; Cahill, Babinsky, Markowitsch, & McGaugh, 1995). Using PET to investigate this pattern further, researchers found that better memory for emotional versus neutral film clips was correlated with higher glucose metabolism in the right amygdala (Cahill et al., 1996; see also Dolcos, LaBar, & Cabeza, 2004). Furthermore, a pharmacological manipulation that reduced connectivity between the amygdala and hippocampus led to a reduction in the memory enhancement effect (Alkire, Gruver, Miller, McReynolds, Hahn, & Cahill, 2008).

In sum, while it is clear that the amygdala plays an important role in responding to salient emotional events and in emotional learning, we also know that it does not work in isolation. Rather, the amygdala's unique role in emotional functions comes about by virtue of its interactions with interconnected brain regions. These brain regions include higher-level areas involved in perception and memory, such as the sensory cortices and hippocampus, as well as lower-level areas that implement the fight-or-flight response, such as the hypothalamus.

■ Reward and Motivation

Although positive emotions have sometimes been neglected by scientists interested in emotion, there is a research tradition focused on pleasure and its close cousin, motivation for rewards. In the 1950s, Olds and Milner carried out experiments demonstrating that electrical stimulation to certain parts of the brain was "rewarding" for a rat. But what do we mean when we say the rats found the stimulation "rewarding"? Olds and Milner (1954) found that the rats would press a lever hundreds and hundreds of times to activate a current in certain brain regions. Because the rats would work

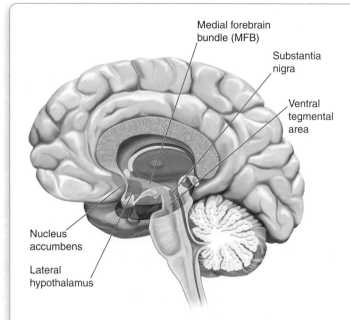

● **FIGURE 13.7   The location of the nucleus accumbens.** The nucleus accumbens receives ascending dopaminergic input from the ventral tegmental area. © 2010 Cengage Learning

so hard for this stimulation, the researchers inferred that it was rewarding. The areas where stimulation is most rewarding are the dopaminergic pathways stretching from the ventral tegmental area of the midbrain to a cluster of cells in the basal forebrain known as the **nucleus accumbens** (● Figure 13.7). This region is also referred to as the *ventral striatum,* because it is the ventral part of the basal ganglia (striatum).

It is tempting to refer to the reward pathway as the "pleasure center" of the brain, but caution is required here. Just because an animal presses a lever repeatedly for stimulation, does that mean the animal gets pleasure from it? Researchers have argued that "wanting" and "liking" can be dissociated. An analogy might be a cocaine addict who goes to great lengths to obtain the drug (i.e., wanting), but no longer experiences pleasure once she takes it (i.e., liking). Some researchers have proposed that the dopaminergic path leading to the core of the nucleus accumbens is not responsible for pleasure itself, but for the "wanting" aspects of reward-related behavior—those aspects that propel an animal toward desired goals (Berridge & Robinson, 1998, 2003). In contrast, only a certain part of the nucleus accumbens—specifically, a layer of cells surrounding the accumbens and referred to as the *nucleus accumbens shell*—is thought to underlie the sensation of consummatory pleasure upon achieving a desired goal; that is, the "liking" (● Figure 13.8) (Berridge, 2003).

Many studies of the reward pathways have focused on nonhuman animals, but neuroimaging studies have also examined the conditions under which the nucleus accumbens is activated in humans. (Note that because

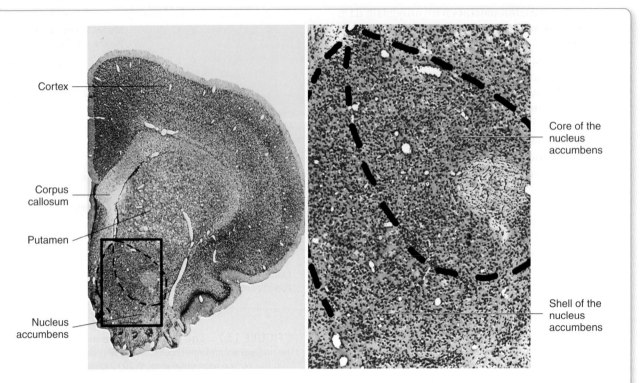

● **FIGURE 13.8   The nucleus accumbens core and shell regions in the rat brain.** The core of the nucleus accumbens is thought to play a role in wanting or desire incentive, whereas the shell is thought to play a role in consummatory pleasure. Courtesy of Harold Prüss

of limitations in the spatial resolution of imaging techniques, most studies of humans are not able to distinguish between the core and the shell of the accumbens.) Interestingly, the accumbens becomes activated in people when they receive a reward, especially when the rewards are unexpected (Berns, McClure, Pagnoni, & Montague, 2001). As you may remember from Chapter 2, dopaminergic responses in the accumbens are largest under such conditions. In contrast, in situations with predictable rewards, the accumbens is activated when the person anticipates the reward before actually receiving it (Knutson, Adams, Fong, & Hommer, 2001). These results suggest that the accumbens is initially sensitive to unexpected rewards; however, as a pattern of rewards emerges, the accumbens begins to anticipate the reward (for similar results in single-cell studies with monkeys, see Fiorillo, Tobler, & Schultz, 2003; Hollerman & Schultz, 1998).

The nucleus accumbens is activated by many stimuli that could be considered rewarding, such as sweet juice (Berns et al., 2001), money (Knutson, Westdorp, Kaiser, & Hommer, 2000), and attractive faces (e.g., Aharon, Etcoff, Ariely, Chabris, O'Connor, & Breiter, 2001; Kampe, Frith, Dolan, & Frith, 2001). This region is also activated by rewarding items that are addictive. For

example, smokers show greater accumbens responses to smoking-related imagery than do nonsmokers (David et al., 2005). For obvious reasons, clinically oriented research on the ventral striatum has centered on its role in addiction, to which we will return in Chapter 14.

Cortical Contributions to Emotion

Having just examined the roles that subcortical regions play in emotion, we now turn our attention to the functions of cortical regions. The cerebral cortex is crucial for emotional functions such as deciding whether a particular behavior is likely to lead to a positive outcome, inferring the feelings of others based on facial expression, and using the correct tone of voice to convey to others how we are feeling. Cortical regions are also important in representing bodily signals of emotion, as we will soon learn.

■ Representing Bodily Cues of Emotion

More than 100 years ago, the pioneering psychologist William James argued that conscious experience of an emotion depends upon the ability to mentally represent the state of the body. According to James, bodily signals provide the brain with information about the emotion that the body is experiencing, and therefore give rise to conscious emotional feelings. The finer points of James's theory have long been debated (see Ellsworth, 1994). Although researchers disagree about whether it is absolutely necessary for the brain to receive information from the rest of the body before a person can feel an emotion, it is true that our minds are able to represent our bodily states in some way. For example, you might be able to tell that you are anxious because you can perceive that your heart is beating very fast.

It is important to distinguish between the *control* of bodily states of emotion and the ability to *represent* those states mentally. As already discussed in an earlier section, the hypothalamus is involved in regulating autonomic functions (for example, controlling whether heart rate is high or low). However, the ability to perceive the internal state of the body, a function known as **interoception**, appears to depend upon another region, the *insular cortex* (or *insula*) (Craig, 2002, 2009; Verhagen, 2007). The insula is tucked deep inside the Sylvian fissure (● Figure 13.9), and its anterior region has extensive connections to other structures involved in emotion, including the amygdala and orbitofrontal cortex.

One study of the insula's role in interoception examined participants' ability to detect their own heartbeats (Critchley, Rotshtein, Öhman, & Dolan, 2004).

The researchers found that activation was enhanced in the insula during this task, compared to a control condition that involved detecting external stimuli (● Figure 13.10). In addition, people who were more accurate at detecting their own heartbeats had a right insula that was both bigger and more active compared to people with poor accuracy at the task. These data imply that the insula plays an important role in encoding interoceptive cues.

Whereas some research indicates that the insula is important in representing a variety of internal bodily cues of emotion, other research emphasizes its special role in the emotion of disgust. Interestingly, research with nonhuman primates indicates that part of the insula serves as the primary gustatory (taste) area. What does taste have to do with emotion? One clue is provided by the term *disgust,* which literally means "bad taste." Though disgust is a sensation that we associate with rotten food or foul odors, the term has broader significance as well. As Charles Darwin noted, the facial expressions we make in situations of moral repulsion are the same as those we make when recoiling from disgusting food (Darwin, 1873). Researchers have confirmed Darwin's observation by demonstrating that the same facial expression muscles (levator labii muscles) were activated when people tasted unpleasant liquids, viewed photographs of contaminants such as feces or insects, or experienced unfair treatment in a social game (Chapman, Kim, Susskind, & Anderson, 2009).

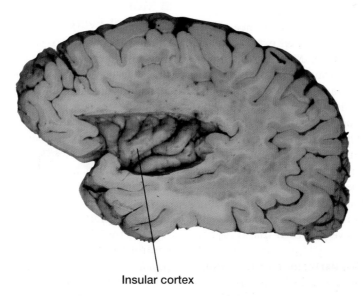

Insular cortex

● **FIGURE 13.9   Location of the insula.** The insula is a cortical region tucked between the frontal and temporal lobes. Here, a lateral section of the brain has been dissected away to reveal the insula.
Source: Adapted by permission from Macmillan Publishers, LTD. Fig 1 from Craig, A. D. 2009). How do you feel now? The anterior insula and human awareness. Nature Reviews Neuroscience, 10, 59–70.

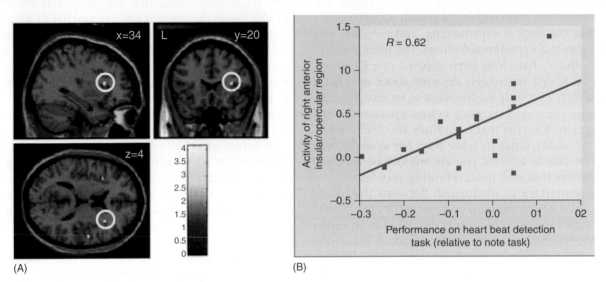

● **FIGURE 13.10   Activation of the insula during an interoceptive judgment task.** Participants had to determine whether a series of tones matched their own heartbeat. Those who performed better at the task (compared to performance on a control task involving detection of notes) had more activity in the right insula. Panel A shows the right insula region (in white circle) and panel B shows the correlation between activity in that region and performance. Adapted by permission from Macmillan Publishers, LTD: Fig 3 (a and b) from Critchley, H. D., Rotshtein, P., Ohman, A., & Dolan, R. J. (2004). Neural systems supporting interoceptive awareness. Nature Neuroscience, 7, 189–195. Figure 13.10a & b.

Several lines of research link the insula to disgust. Early studies performed during brain surgery found that stimulation of the insula in humans elicited sensations of unpleasant taste and nausea (Penfield & Faulk, 1955). Neuroimaging studies show that this area is sensitive to processes related to feeding, such as odor, taste, tongue stimulation, swallowing, thirst, and hunger (Small, Zatorre, Dagher, Evans, & Jones-Gotman, 2001). Damage to the insula interferes with both the experience of disgust and the ability to recognize facial expressions of disgust in others (Calder, Keane, Manes, Antoun, & Young, 2000). Likewise, neuroimaging studies have demonstrated activity in the anterior insula when the participant tastes bitter liquids, imagines disgusting scenarios, or sees another person expressing disgust (Jabbi, Bastiaansen, & Keysers, 2008). Additional neuroimaging studies have shown that activity in the insula is correlated with subjective ratings of disgust (e.g., Schienle, Schafer, & Vaitl, 2008; Stark et al., 2007).

How should we integrate these different findings about the insula? The human insula is anatomically complex, and researchers have proposed that posterior regions represent primary sensory representations (such as taste) and more anterior insular regions integrate these sensations with awareness (Craig, 2009; see also Taylor, Seminowicz, & Davis, 2009). A related possibility is that the insula originated as an area that represented taste, but then expanded to represent other bodily signals of emotion, such as heart rate, temperature changes, pain, and visceral sensations. In humans, this region may play a role in even more complex and abstract emotions. For example, one study found that the insula was active when participants imagined a personal event involving the most guilt they had ever experienced (Shin et al., 2000). Although there is clearly not a "guilt center" in the brain, feelings of guilt may involve some of the same interoceptive cues as sensations of disgust, nausea, or other bodily displeasure.

■ Monitoring for Emotionally Salient Events

From an evolutionary standpoint, it is crucial to be on the lookout for events in the world that could be either advantageous or disadvantageous—the appearance of a dangerous predator or the sight of a juicy fruit. As we have already learned, certain subcortical regions play a role in these basic motivations. That is, the amygdala is especially involved in responding to emotionally arousing stimuli, and the reward pathways are crucial in responding to positive incentives. In addition, another brain structure, the cingulate cortex, appears to be crucial in monitoring for events that have emotional significance and in integrating motivational aspects of behavior.

The cingulate cortex has been viewed as a component of the limbic system since Broca first described *le grande lobe limbique* in 1878 (for a review, see Allman, Hakeen, Erwin, Nimchinsky, & Hof, 2001). The cingulate wraps around the corpus callosum like a collar, or *cingulum* (● Figure 13.11). Traditionally, it is divided into two regions: the anterior cingulate cortex, forward of the central gyrus, and the posterior cingulate cortex, behind the central gyrus.

Because the cingulate is located on the medial surface of the brain, it is rarely damaged in isolation. As a result,

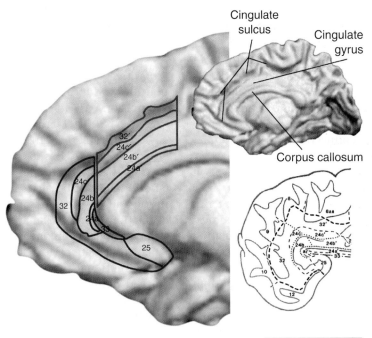

trends in Cognitive Sciences

● **FIGURE 13.11   Cingulate cortex is involved in cognition and emotion.** The cingulate lies directly above the corpus callosum. The anterior cingulate cortex has two main parts, a dorsal part (shown in red) and a rostral/ventral part (shown in blue). The rostral portion is more consistently implicated in emotional functions. *Source:* Fig 1 from Bush, G., Luu, P., & Posner, M. I. (2000). Cognitive and emotional influences in anterior cingulate cortex. Trends in cognitive sciences, 4, 215–222. Reprinted by permission of Elsevier.

for many years its organization was a relative mystery. More current research suggests that it has an intricate organization with as many as nine or more distinct subregions (Beckmann, Johansen-Berg, & Rushworth, 2009), the functions of which are still being hotly debated. Despite these debates, a good generalization is that the cingulate is a region where emotion, cognition, and motor control interface (see Paus, 2001, for a review). For example, one theoretical view is that the anterior cingulate cortex is involved in selecting motor actions, considering both the cost and effort entailed in those actions, and weighing how much reward has been gained by taking those actions previously (Rushworth, Buckley, Behrens, Walton, & Bannerman, 2007).

What is clear, however, is that lesions of the anterior cingulate cortex can result in a variety of emotional sequelae, including apathy, inattention, emotional lability, and changes in personality and social interaction (Bush, Luu, & Posner, 2000; Hadland, Rushworth, Gaffan, & Passingham, 2003). In addition, the cingulate is also involved in pain (Tracey, 2005), receiving input from subcortical structures that have neurons specialized to respond to noxious stimuli. Patients who received small cingulate lesions as a treatment for pain reported that the pain still existed but no longer bothered them as much (Cohen et al., 1999). Some

portions of the anterior cingulate appear to discriminate between the presence or absence of a painful stimulus but are not sensitive to pain intensity, whereas other portions appear to code the intensity of a painful stimulus (Büchel, Bornhövd, Qunate, Glauche, Bromm, & Weiler, 2002). Fascinating biofeedback research has shown that, in at least some situations, people can use information regarding the activity of their own anterior cingulate to control the intensity of the pain they experience. Whether such a biofeedback technique can be used more commonly in clinical practice remains an open question, but this research provides a potential new means of helping people who experience chronic pain (deCharms et al., 2005).

Certain portions of the cingulate appear to have distinct roles. In particular, researchers have made a distinction between the dorsal and rostral portions of the anterior cingulate cortex (see Figure 13.11) (Bush, Luu, & Posner, 2000). The rostral portion is also sometimes called the *subgenual portion,* because it sits underneath the genu or knee of the callosum. The rostral portion of the anterior cingulate appears to be more intimately involved in emotional functions than the dorsal portion. Anatomically, the rostral cingulate is connected to many other emotion-related areas, including the amygdala, the hypothalamus, the insula, and the orbitofrontal cortex. Imaging studies suggest that the rostral region is especially activated by tasks that have an emotional component (Bush, Luu, & Posner, 2000; Mohanty et al., 2007). Activity in this region is also correlated with changes in the autonomic nervous system (e.g., Critchley, Tang, Glaser, Butterworth, & Dolan, 2005; Matthews, Paulus, Simmons, Nelesen, & Dimsdale, 2004), and has been linked to depression, as we will learn in Chapter 14. In contrast, the dorsal portion of the cingulate has connections with lateral prefrontal cortex, parietal cortex, and motor areas. As we learned in Chapter 12, this region is more involved in cognitive function, especially executive function.

The dorsal and rostral subdivisions of the anterior cingulate may relate to one another in a reciprocal fashion at times. During cognitive task performance, activity often decreases in the rostral division while increasing in the dorsal division; during emotional conditions, activity often increases in the rostral division while decreasing in the dorsal division (Drevets & Raichle, 1998). These results suggest that there may be a reciprocal dynamic between emotion and cognition, with strong emotion functioning to shut down certain cognitive systems and vice versa. This notion seems intuitively appealing, as many of us have experienced for ourselves how an emotional state can interfere with paying attention to a nonemotional task. Conversely, many of us have also had occasion to "lose ourselves in our work" for the purpose of coping with an emotional stress or trauma.

These findings should not be taken, however, to suggest a strict and rigid dichotomy between the functions of the two cingulate subregions, as other evidence suggests that cognition and emotion may not be so easily separable (Compton et al., 2003; Davis et al., 2005; Phan, Wager, Taylor, & Liberzon, 2002). Indeed, it is probably no coincidence that the rostral and dorsal regions are highly interconnected with one another. That is, it may be adaptive for the rostral region, which responds to the emotional salience of events, to influence the dorsal region, which is involved in governing executive attention. After all, it could make sense to allocate attention depending on the emotional significance of the information at hand.

Studies of the error-related negativity (ERN), which is generated by the cingulate cortex, illustrate the complexity of teasing apart cognitive and emotional functions in the cingulate cortex. As discussed in Chapter 12, the ERN is an electrical response that occurs when a person detects that he or she has made an error, or when a person receives negative feedback about performance. Influential theories describe the ERN as part of a system of cognitive control, a signal that indicates when outcomes are worse than expected (Holroyd & Coles, 2002). Because an error is usually an unpleasant outcome, we could think of the error signal as an emotional signal. In this sense, the fact that the ERN is generated by the cingulate cortex fits with the idea that the cingulate is involved in monitoring for emotionally salient events. At the same time, an error signal also indicates the need for a change in attention or behavior, so as to avoid repeated mistakes. Some source-localization studies suggest that the ERN is generated by the dorsal or "cognitive" subdivision of the cingulate, while others point toward localization in the rostral or "emotional" subdivision (e.g., Herrmann, Römmler, Ehlis, Heidrich, & Fallgatter, 2004; Mathalon, Whitfield, & Ford, 2003; Taylor et al., 2006; van Veen & Carter, 2002). In the end, it may be useless to try to pigeonhole phenomena such as the ERN as either strictly cognitive or strictly emotional, both because the boundaries between cognition and emotion are somewhat artificial and because evaluation of one's behavior involves both cognitive and emotional components.

The cingulate cortex clearly acts as a central hub for both emotional and cognitive processing, but other cortical brain regions are important in specific functions that involve both cognition and emotion. These functions include the influence of emotion on decision making, the top-down regulation of emotion, and the communication of emotion through facial and vocal cues. We discuss each of these functions in turn in the next few sections.

■ Incorporating Emotion into Decision Making

Common sense tells us that emotions affect decision making. When deciding how to spend your Saturday evening, your choices will be affected by memories of activities that you found to be either pleasant or unpleasant in the past. When choosing to vote for a political candidate, your decision may be influenced in part by the candidate's emotional appeals. Although the influence of emotion on decision making is sometimes considered troublesome because it is "irrational," some researchers argue that emotional signals are actually important cues that effectively guide us toward outcomes that benefit us and away from outcomes that harm us (e.g., Damasio, 1994).

The brain region most implicated in integrating emotion and decision making is the **orbitofrontal cortex (OFC)**. A recent review described the OFC as "among the least understood regions of the human brain" (Kringelbach, 2005, p. 691), partly because of differences in this region across species and notable variation in its anatomical structure from one person to the next. In addition, the OFC includes several different subareas whose functional distinctions are not yet clear. Here we use the term *OFC* to include both regions that directly overlie the eye orbits and areas that extend into the medial wall of the frontal lobes, an area that is sometimes referred to as the *ventromedial prefrontal cortex* (● Figure 13.12). Anatomical connections imply that the OFC is important in emotion, as this region is reciprocally interconnected with many other emotion-related structures such as the hypothalamus, amygdala, insula, and cingulate cortex. Although the over-arching function of the OFC is still in dispute, current research implies that this region plays a role in understanding rewards and punishments and using that understanding to guide adaptive behavior.

Case studies have shown that people with damage to the OFC exhibit disinhibited behaviors (e.g., grabbing things they want from others), socially inappropriate behaviors (e.g., blurting out tasteless remarks), and irresponsibility. They seem to have difficulty anticipating the consequences of their actions, they make poor decisions that result in negative outcomes, and they do not seem to learn from their mistakes (Bechara, Damasio, Damasio, & Anderson, 1994; Rolls, Hornak, Wade, & McGrath, 1994). Bechara and colleagues (1994) have termed this behavior "myopia for the future." These behaviors are especially remarkable because the patients show no deficits in intellectual ability as measured with standard IQ tests. Some researchers have even suggested that the OFC may provide the substrate for the development of moral behavior, comparing people with OFC damage to those with the psychiatric disorder of psychopathy, a failure of empathy often seen in violent criminals (Anderson, Bechara, Damasio, Tranel, & Damasio, 1999).

People with damage to the OFC perform especially poorly on tasks in which past losses and gains must be considered in order to make appropriate choices in the present. Such deficits have been empirically demonstrated using gambling tasks, in which the participant must choose a particular stimulus that results in either winning or losing money (Bechara, Damasio, & Damasio, 2000; O'Doherty, Kringelbach, Rolls, Hornak, & Andrews, 2001). These tasks are designed so that people cannot simply associate one stimulus with one outcome; rather, the tasks are designed to work probabilistically, so that over time some choices tend to be better than others. In a gambling task, a person might win big by choosing a particular item, but continuing to choose that item over time results in a series of small losses, thus making this choice less profitable than an alternative choice. People with damage to the OFC tend stick with the "big win" stimulus even though it leads to greater losses over time. This behavior resembles that of a child who cannot resist the impulse to eat a huge piece of cake despite knowing that later on it will lead to an upset stomach. As we discuss in more detail in Chapter 14, similar impairments in decision making are also evident in substance abuse, in which people often make decisions on the basis of immediate gratification while ignoring the long-term consequences.

The OFC is especially important for learning in situations that require the individual to respond to changing patterns of reward and punishment. Researchers often study this phenomenon by varying what is called the **reinforcement contingency**, which simply refers to the degree to which a reward or punishment is associated

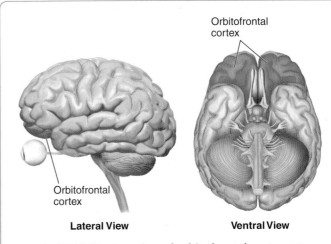

Orbitofrontal cortex

Orbitofrontal cortex

Lateral View   **Ventral View**

● **FIGURE 13.12   Location of orbitofrontal cortex.** The orbitofrontal cortex is so named because it lies directly above the eye sockets, or orbits. Sometimes the medial portion of the orbitofrontal cortex is referred to as *ventromedial prefrontal cortex.*
© 2010 Cengage Learning

with a particular stimulus or action. Single-cell recording studies in nonhuman primates show that neurons in the OFC respond to the rewarding value of taste, smell, and visual stimuli, and that some neurons respond only when the reinforcement contingencies change (Rolls, 1999). People with OFC damage are impaired in the ability to change their behavior when the contingencies change. One example of such contingency change is referred to as **reversal learning**. For example, let's say you were first rewarded for pressing the left button in response to a red light and the right button in response to a green light. In reversal learning, you are now rewarded for pressing the left button for the green light and the right button for the red light. Reversal learning is deficient following OFC damage in humans and other primates (Roberts, 2006). Neuroimaging studies also support the idea that the OFC tracks the changing reward value of a particular stimulus. For example, food becomes less rewarding as a person becomes satiated (full). Correspondingly, OFC activity decreases as the food becomes less desirable with satiation (Kringelbach, O'Doherty, Rolls, & Andrews, 2003).

Recent studies suggest that different subregions of the OFC respond to rewards versus punishments, an organization that may help the OFC to keep track of changing contingencies (Kringelbach, 2005). The lateral area of the OFC is activated following a punishing outcome in a gambling task, whereas the medial area is activated following a rewarding outcome (O'Doherty et al., 2001). These two regions appear to act in a reciprocal manner: the medial region increases activation to reward and decreases activation to punishment, whereas the lateral orbitofrontal region exhibits the opposite pattern. Furthermore, the larger the reward or punishment delivered, the greater the brain activation. An intact OFC therefore allows us to represent the costs and benefits associated with any choice, leading to more informed and effective decision making.

The OFC is also crucial for evaluating the consequences of our choices. One of the ways that we think about the consequences of our own decision making is to consider what might have happened if we had made a different choice. Would I have been happier if I had bought the Honda rather than the Chevy? When we discover that we made the "wrong" choice, we often feel regret. Interestingly, patients with OFC damage do not appear to feel regret (Camille, Coricelli, Sallet, Pradat-Diehl, Duhamel, & Sirigu, 2004). Neuroimaging research with neurologically intact people has also found that the OFC is active in situations of regret. For example, the OFC becomes activated when participants learn that a choice they rejected would have led to a greater benefit (● Figure 13.13) (Coricelli, Critchley, Joffily, O'Doherty, Sirigu, & Dolan, 2005). OFC activity is especially tied to situations in which participants felt agency (responsibility) for the choice, rather than instances in which the undesired outcome was simply a matter of chance. When participants in this study were faced with similar choices again, the OFC became reactivated in anticipation of the choice, presumably as participants reconsidered the regrettable consequences of their previous actions.

■ Regulating Emotion

An important aspect of emotion is being able to control it. If you've ever cheered yourself up after a bad day, suppressed your anger after a friend made an unfair or callous remark, or practiced meditation to help relieve stress, you've engaged in some form of emotion regulation. Although the term is conceived rather broadly, **emotion regulation** generally refers to attempts to manage the emotions that one experiences, so that they are socially appropriate and do not spiral out of control. Emotion regulation may be disrupted in certain clinical conditions, such as mood disorders. Although many strategies for emotion regulation are conscious, voluntary efforts, emotion regulation may take place at an unconscious level as well.

Studies using ERP methods have shown that emotion regulation strategies can influence how the brain responds to emotional information. Several of these studies have investigated the effect of reappraising

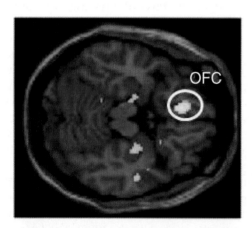

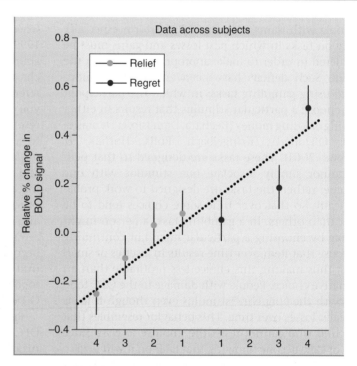

● FIGURE 13.13   Orbitofrontal cortex responds to degrees of regret in a decision-making task. Levels of regret (1–4) are defined by the discrepancy between what a participant earned from a particular choice and what she might have earned had she made a different choice. For example, level 4 of regret represents a condition in which the participant discovered that she lost 200 points when she could have gained 200 points if she had picked the other option. Level 1 of regret represents a condition in which the participant lost 50 points but could have earned 50 points. Levels of relief represent conditions in which the participant learned that she made the right choice, such as by earning 200 points when she could have lost 200 points (level 4 of relief) or by earning 50 points when she could have lost 50 points (level 1 of relief). Activity in the orbitofrontal cortex tracks the value of the actual choice relative to the value of the path not taken. Adapted by permission from Macmillan Publishers, LTD: Coricelli, G., Critchley, H. D., Joffily, M., O'Doherty, J. P., Sirigu, A., & Dolan, R. J., (2005). Regret and its avoidance: A neuroimaging study of choice behavior. Nature Neuroscience, 8, 1255–1262. Figure 13.13.

emotional pictures in less emotional ways. For example, participants might see a picture of a snarling dog with teeth bared; however, instead of thinking about how frightening it would be to run into such an animal, they would be instructed to try to view the picture in a more positive way, such as by imagining that the dog was protecting them from an intruder. Negative pictures usually produce a significantly larger P_{300} response in the ERP waveform, compared to neutral pictures, but engaging in reappraisal lessened this effect (Hajcak & Nieuwenhuis, 2006; see also Foti & Hajcak, 2008). Follow-up research demonstrated that the P_{300} response to positive pictures could also be lessened by reappraisal strategies, paralleling the effects shown with negative pictures (Krompinger, Moser, & Simons, 2008). Because the P_{300} is thought to reflect allocation of attention, these studies imply that less attention was allocated to the pictures when participants attempted to view them in a less emotional manner.

According to several studies, when people try to control their emotional responses, activity increases in frontal-lobe regions and decreases in subcortical regions that would normally process that emotion. For example, one study showed sexually provocative pictures to men and instructed them to suppress their sexual arousal responses to the pictures. In this suppression condition, brain activity increased in the right superior frontal gyrus and decreased in the hypothalamus and amygdala, compared to a simple viewing condition (Beauregard, Levesque, & Bourgouin, 2001) (● Figure 13.14). Likewise, when participants were instructed to reevaluate disturbing pictures in a way that would reduce their negative feelings, frontal-lobe activity increased and amygdala activity decreased (Ochsner, Bunge, Gross, & Gabrieli, 2002). Other investigators found that when participants were required to suppress emotional memories, the right inferior and middle frontal gyrus regions became more active, and hippocampal and amygdalar regions less active (Depue, Curran, & Banich, 2007).

Some studies have attempted to distinguish between brain regions that serve as the source of signals to regulate emotional responsiveness and brain regions that serve as targets over which such control is exerted. For example, imagine a situation in which you are about to experience a painful medical procedure. You may try to reduce your anxiety by mentally detaching yourself (for example, by imagining that you are lying on a cozy blanket in a lovely field of flowers with warm sunshine beaming down on you). Such strategies tend to lessen perceived pain. What brain regions are involved in generating the "detachment" experience (the source of emotional control), and how do those brain regions affect the regions that would normally code for pain (the target of control)?

In a study addressing this issue, Kalisch and colleagues (2005) instructed participants to imagine being in a "special place" while knowing that a painful shock might soon be delivered. During the period of anticipation, right lateral prefrontal cortex activity was increased when participants imagined the "special place," compared to control conditions in which no emotion regulation was encouraged; thus, this region was inferred to be the source of emotion regulation. In turn, when pain was actually administered, activity in the anterior cingulate region (which normally responds to pain) was lessened if the participant had used the emotional regulation strategy, indicating that this region was the target of emotion regulation.

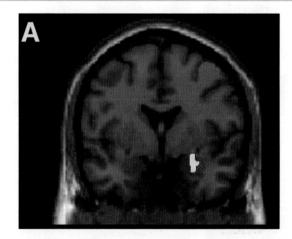
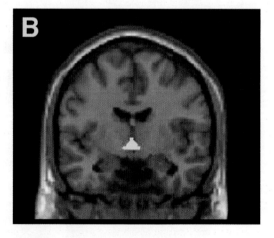

● **FIGURE 13.14   Influence of emotion regulation on subcortical regions.** The amygdala (panel A) and hypothalamus (panel B) were activated when men viewed sexually provocative pictures. Those same regions showed no activity when the men were asked to inhibit their arousal responses. Fig 1a and 1c from Beauregard, M., Levesque, J., & Bourgouin, P. (2001). Neural correlates of conscious self-regulation of emotion. Journal of Neuroscience, 21, RC165 (1–6). Permission conveyed through Copyright Clearance Center, Inc.
Source: Fig 1a and 1c from Beauregard, M., Levesque, J., & Bourgouin, P. (2001). Neural correlates of conscious self-regulation of emotion. Journal of Neuroscience, 21, RC165 (1–6). Permission conveyed through Copyright Clearance Center, Inc.

Most research on emotion regulation has focused on suppressing unwanted emotional responses, but future research may also help us to understand how positive and negative responses can be intentionally amplified (see Kim & Hamann, 2007; Ochsner et al., 2004). Though much remains to be learned about emotion regulation, these studies so far tell us that when people adopt voluntary strategies of emotional control, they change how their brains respond to emotional situations.

■ Communicating Emotion

Our emotions are not just felt internally; they are also conveyed to other people. Although we tend to think of language as the dominant means of communication in our species, nonverbal signals of emotion communicate important information among members of a social group. If you meet a friend and notice that her facial expression is angry, you will interact with her differently than if her face bears a happy expression. Likewise, a phrase such as "Susan and Bill have just eloped" can convey very different sorts of information depending on whether it is spoken in an excited, surprised, sad, or angry tone of voice. In the next two sections, we consider the neural systems involved in both perceiving and producing expressions of emotion.

Facial Expressions

The ability to produce and recognize facial expressions of emotion is nearly universal. Cross-cultural studies have found that similar facial expressions are used across a wide range of cultures to convey basic emotions such as happiness, sadness, anger, fear, surprise, and disgust (● Figure 13.15) (e.g., Ekman, Sorenson, & Friesen, 1969; Elfenbein & Ambady, 2002), although there are some differences across cultures in the exact way that expressions are formed and the social contexts in which they are considered appropriate (e.g., Marsh, Elfenbein, & Ambady, 2003; Matsumoto, Yoo, Hirayama, & Petrova, 2005). Nonetheless, the strong similarity of basic expressions across cultures implies that these expressions are rooted in our species' common biological heritage, as recognized by Charles Darwin more than a century ago (Darwin, 1873). So, what do we know about the neural mechanisms that recognize and produce expressions?

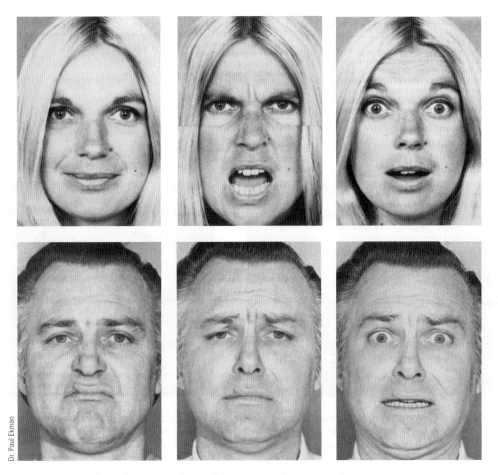

Dr. Paul Ekman

● **FIGURE 13.15   Facial expressions that are universally recognized.** From left to right, the top row shows expressions of happiness, anger, and surprise, and the bottom row shows disgust, sadness, and fear.

One of the most reliable findings in cognitive neuroscience is the right-hemisphere specialization for both recognizing and producing facial expressions of emotion. Right-hemisphere damage, particularly to temporal and parietal regions of the brain, disrupts the ability to recognize faces much more than does comparable left-hemisphere damage. Borod and coworkers (1998) found that patients with right-hemisphere damage were more impaired than left-hemisphere-damaged patients in tasks that required the patient to name or point to the correct label for an emotional expression depicted on a slide (see also Cicone, Wapner, & Gardner, 1980; DeKosky, Heilman, Bowers, & Valenstein, 1980). The most severe impairments in emotion recognition have been attributed to damage of the right parietal cortex. However, right anterior temporal lobectomy, a treatment for medically intractable epilepsy, has also been shown to cause impairments in processing emotional information, especially negative emotion in faces (see Adolphs, Tranel, & Damasio, 2001). Consistent with these findings from brain-damaged patients, divided visual field studies typically find that people recognize facial expressions of emotion better when the faces are presented to the left visual field (right hemisphere) than to the right visual field (left hemisphere) (e.g., Ladavas, Umilta, & Ricci-Bitti, 1980; Strauss & Moscovitch, 1981).

One important question is whether the perception of emotional expressions relies upon the same neural mechanisms as the perception of facial identity. As you remember from Chapter 7, patients with prosopagnosia (due to occipitotemporal-lobe damage) are unable to recognize the identities of individuals by their faces, but they are sometimes able to recognize emotional expressions (e.g., Tranel, Damasio, & Damasio, 1988). Conversely, some patients have trouble recognizing emotional expressions, but can recognize individuals' identities from their faces (e.g., Young, Newcombe, de Haan, Small, & Hay, 1993). This double dissociation implies that recognition of facial expression and recognition of facial identity rely upon partly separable mechanisms. Of course, both expression and identity recognition are likely to involve some similar steps in visual processing, such as constructing a coherent visual representation of the face structure. For this reason, it is not surprising that viewing emotionally expressive faces leads to activation in the fusiform gyrus of the right hemisphere, the region that is known to be more important for processing faces compared to other visual objects (e.g., Blair, Morris, Frith, Perrett, & Dolan, 1999; Kesler-West et al., 2001). However, the double dissociation tells us that beyond the stage of perceiving the visual image as a face, somewhat different brain regions are implicated in linking that face image with emotional information versus identification information.

Although there is a fair degree of overlap among brain systems that process the six main facial expressions—fear, disgust, anger, surprise, happiness, and sadness—it appears that not all emotional expression are treated equally by the brain (Hennenlotter & Schroeder, 2006). Fear is the expression for which there is the most evidence of a distinct neural substrate. For example, patients with damage to the amygdala are impaired in recognizing facial expressions, but these deficits seem to be most pronounced for fearful faces (Adolphs et al., 1999; Calder, Young, Rowland, Perrett, Hodges, & Etcoff, 1996). Some of the difficulty in recognizing facial expression may arise from the fact that amygdala-damaged patients do not seem to direct their eyes to the most emotionally informative parts of the face, such as the eyes (● Figure 13.16) (Adolphs et al., 2005). In fact, neuroimaging evidence shows that in neurologically intact people, the amygdala is responsive to specific facial features that indicate fear, such as enlarged whites of the eyes (Whalen et al., 2004). Thus, in amygdala-damaged patients, an inability to detect these specific

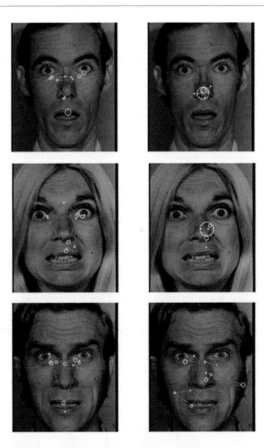

● **FIGURE 13.16   Patients with amygdala damage look at faces differently than neurologically intact individuals do.** The column on the left shows the eye-movement patterns of a normal participant; the column on the right shows the patterns of an amygdala-damaged patient when viewing fearful faces. Notice that the gaze of the normal participant is centered on examining the eyes and mouth, whereas the individual with amygdala damage tends to focus on the nose. Adapted by permission from Macmillan Publishers, LTD: Fig 2 in Adolphs, R., Gosselin, F., Buchanan, T. W., Tranel, D., Schyns, P., & Damasio, A. R. (2005). A mechanism for impaired fear recognition after amygdala damage. *Nature, 433,* 68–72.

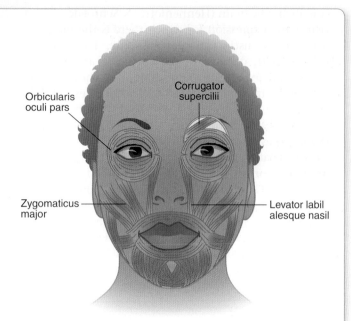

● **FIGURE 13.17   Muscles of the face that are used to make facial expressions.** The corrugator muscle is used to furrow the brow, as in anger or fear; the orbicularis and zygomaticus muscles are used in smiling, and the levator labii muscles are used to wrinkle the nose in disgust. *Source:* Fig 3 in Niedenthal, P. M. (2007). Embodying emotion. Science, 316, 1002–1005.

cues may lead to the deficit in recognizing fear expressions. While the amygdala clearly contributes to recognition of emotional expressions, the fact that its role is predominantly related to fear expressions indicates that additional brain regions must be important for recognizing other facial emotions.

These studies have focused on perceiving facial expressions in other people; but what about producing emotional expressions in your own face? Several muscles in the face seem to have evolved for the sole purpose of forming emotional expressions (● Figure 13.17). Facial muscles move when they receive input from cranial nerves that are controlled by the brain's various motor systems (see Chapter 5). There are at least two systems for control of facial expressions: a system centered in the basal ganglia that controls spontaneous facial expressions, and a system centered in the motor cortex that controls voluntary facial expressions. Thus, a patient with damage to the basal ganglia (such as a patient with Parkinson's disease) may not make any facial expressions in spontaneous conversation, contributing to a mask-like appearance, but he or she may be able to make posed facial expressions with voluntary effort.

Just like the perception of facial expressions, the production of facial expressions appears to be primarily under the control of the right hemisphere. In one research approach, the facial expressions of patients with left- or right-hemisphere brain damage are photographed or videotaped while the patients are talking, watching emotional films, or doing other tasks. The photographs or videotapes are then rated, either subjectively by judges or by using coding schemes to identify the muscle movements in the face. Typically, patients with right-hemisphere damage are found to be less expressive than those with left-hemisphere damage (e.g., Montreys & Borod, 1998).

In another approach, typically used with neurologically intact individuals, the emotional expression appearing on the left side of the face is compared with that appearing on the right. Often, we can observe facial asymmetries merely by looking at a face, as shown in ● Figure 13.18. However, one way to quantitatively evaluate facial asymmetry is to cut a picture of a person's face in half and to splice each half-face together with its mirror image to create a composite. The result is two chimeras, one consisting of two left half-faces and the other of two right half-faces. When this is done, we can instantly see large differences in the appearance of the two sides of the face (● Figure 13.19). People typically rate left-face composites as more expressive than right-face composites (Sackeim, Gur, & Saucy, 1978). Nonhuman primates, such as macaque monkeys and chimpanzees, also

(A)   (B)   (C)   (D)

● **FIGURE 13.18   Striking asymmetries in facial expression of emotion.** Although we think of people's faces as symmetrical, asymmetries can be seen. Note the asymmetrical expressions on some well-known faces: (A) the Mona Lisa, (B) Marilyn Monroe, (C) Elvis Presley, and (D) John Wayne.

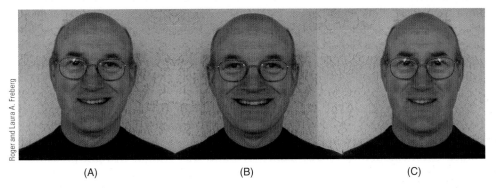

Roger and Laura A. Freberg

(A)   (B)   (C)

● **FIGURE 13.19   One method of demonstrating asymmetry of emotional facial expression.** An original photograph of the face, shown here in A, is bisected. Then, each half-face is spliced together with its mirror image to create a composite. Note the difference between the two composites depicted in B and C. Which one looks more emotionally intense to you? Usually, individuals choose the composite composed of two left half-faces, depicted in B, as more intense than the composite composed of two right half-faces, depicted in C. This result suggests that the right hemisphere, which controls the lower left half of the face, has a larger role in producing facial emotional expression.

exhibit more dramatic expressions on the left side of the face (Fernandez-Carriba, Loeches, Morcillo, & Hopkins, 2002; Hauser, 1993).

If you've carefully followed our discussion of hemispheric differences in perception and expression of emotion in the face, you may have noticed an odd paradox. Remember that, because of right-hemisphere specialization for emotional expression and perception, emotion is most strongly expressed on the left side of a poser's face (due to right-hemisphere specialization in the poser), and that people are best at understanding emotional expressions seen in the left visual field or left side of space (due to right-hemisphere specialization in the viewer). This means that for two people directly facing each other in a communication context, the most expressive side of the poser's face will fall into the least sensitive half field of the viewer! (Look at ● Figure 13.20 if you are having some left-right confusion.) This doesn't seem to be optimally adaptive for the purpose of communication. Interestingly, some research has shown that when people wish to communicate emotional information, they turn slightly to show more of the left side of

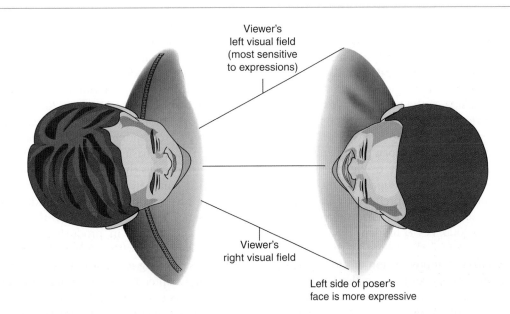

Viewer's left visual field (most sensitive to expressions)

Viewer's right visual field

Left side of poser's face is more expressive

● **FIGURE 13.20   Expressive asymmetry meets perceptual asymmetry.** When two participants interact in face-to-face conversation, the more expressive left side of one person's face is projected onto the less-sensitive right visual field of the other person. This illustrates the paradoxical outcome when both participants have right-hemisphere specialization for emotional expression and perception. However, people tend to adapt to this phenomenon in real life by turning the head to show more of the left side of the face.

the face. Analyses of portraits throughout history reflect a bias toward showing more of the left portion of the face, unless the portraits were made of scientists, who presumably put less emphasis on emotional expressivity (McManus & Humphrey, 1973; Nicholls, Clode, Wood, & Wood, 1999). When participants are asked to pose for a photograph in which they are encouraged to show their emotions, they are more likely to show the left cheek than if asked to pose for an "impassive" photo (Nicholls et al., 1999). This turning bias in portraiture illustrates how cerebral asymmetries for emotion can subtly manifest themselves in everyday life.

Prosody

The tone of voice in which a phrase is uttered is **prosody**. Monrad-Krohn (1947) first coined the term to describe vocal cues such as pitch or frequency, stress, intensity, and timing. Two types of prosody have been described. **Affective prosody** communicates the emotional context or tone of an utterance; for example, "My mother is coming to dinner" could be stated in a way that expresses elation or in a way that expresses dismay. **Propositional prosody** communicates lexical or semantic information—for example, "What's that in the road ahead?" versus "What's that in the road, a head?" Although prosody has been less well studied than facial expression as a means of conveying emotion, there is no question that prosodic cues are important in social interaction. For example, when you talk with a friend on the phone, you have no information about his facial expression, but you can use affective prosodic cues to deduce his emotional state or intent.

Clinical studies have suggested that patients with right-hemisphere lesions are significantly impaired in comprehending prosody, compared to patients with left-hemisphere lesions (e.g., Borod et al., 1998; Ross, 2006). Deficits in comprehension of prosody as a result of brain damage are referred to as **aprosodia**, and tend to be associated with damage to the region around the Sylvian fissure on the right side of the brain (Ross, 2006). This localization makes logical sense, serving as a complement to the role played by left-hemisphere Sylvian regions, which are involved in the auditory processing of language and language comprehension. Right-hemisphere lateralization for prosody is also supported by evidence of a left-ear advantage for comprehending prosody in neurologically intact people (e.g., Grimshaw, Kwasny, Covell, & Johnson, 2003; Ley & Bryden, 1982).

Nonetheless, there is some debate in the literature about how lateralized comprehension of prosody really is, because left-hemisphere damage can also lead to difficulties in interpreting prosody (Pell, 2006; Van Lancker & Sidtis, 1992). Some researchers have suggested that the right hemisphere is important for comprehending affective prosody (e.g., determining the emotional state of a speaker) and the left hemisphere for comprehending propositional prosody (e.g., distinguishing questions from statements based on tone of voice) (Walker, Daigle, &

Buzzard, 2002). Other researchers have argued that left-hemisphere contributions to prosody may involve incorporating prosodic cues, which were initially decoded by the right hemisphere, into the overall semantic understanding of language that is dominated by the left hemisphere (Pell, 2006).

Neuroimaging studies have also implicated the right hemisphere in perceiving affective prosody, although different studies point to different regions within the right hemisphere. Several neuroimaging studies have found that regions in right prefrontal cortex are activated during detection of affective prosody (George et al., 1996; Imaizumi et al., 1997), though other studies have found bilateral activation (Kotz, Meyer, Alter, Besson, von Cramon, & Friederici, 2003). One study compared a condition in which participants had to distinguish the emotional tone of a voice (e.g., angry vs. happy) to another condition in which they had to distinguish different phonemes (e.g., power vs. tower) (Buchanan et al., 2000). Both tasks activated both hemispheres, but the activation was greater in right inferior prefrontal cortex for the emotion task and in the left inferior prefrontal cortex for the phoneme task. This study also found significant activity in the right auditory cortex for the emotional condition. Taken together, the lesion and imaging data indicate that the right hemisphere is more involved in the perception of prosody, but it remains to be seen exactly which regions of that hemisphere are most important.

The production of prosody is also heavily dependent on the right hemisphere (Ross, 2006). For example, some studies have presented brain-damaged patients with neutral sentences and asked them to repeat the sentence in different tones of voice (e.g., happy, sad, angry, or indifferent). Typically, individuals with right-hemisphere damage speak in more of a monotone (e.g., Tucker, Watson, & Heilman, 1977). As you might expect, deficits in producing prosody tend to be associated more with anterior rather than posterior regions within the right hemisphere (● Figure 13.21) (Ross, 2006). Some work with clinical populations has focused on examining whether more specific components of the production of prosody, such as the basic frequency at which an utterance is made (known as the *fundamental frequency*), intensity, and timing parameters, may be differentially lateralized. Evidence suggests that deficits in producing fundamental frequency may be associated with right-hemisphere damage, and deficits in producing timing parameters may be associated with left-hemisphere damage (Pell, 1999). This finding is consistent with some of what we learned in Chapter 4: that the right hemisphere processes global aspects of a stimulus (such as a fundamental frequency that is relatively constant over the entire utterance) and that the left hemisphere processes details such as the changes in timing across an utterance.

In sum, communication of emotion, whether through facial expression or through tone of voice, tends to be dominated by the right hemisphere. This division of

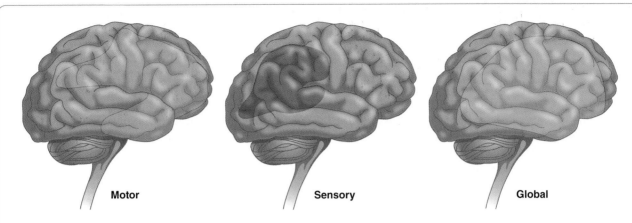

● **FIGURE 13.21   Areas of the right hemisphere that, when damaged, lead to difficulties in perceiving or producing emotional prosody.** The nomenclature used to name these disorders is parallel to that used for aphasia (see Chapter 9). Frontal-lobe damage is associated with poor production but intact comprehension (motor aprosodia), temporoparietal damage is associated with intact production but poor comprehension (sensory aprosodia), and widespread damage to the right hemisphere is associated with deficits in both spontaneous production and comprehension of prosody (global aprosodia).
Source: Fig 21-1 in Ross, E. D. (2006). The aprosodias. In M. J. Farah & T. E. Feinberg (Eds.) Patient-Based Approaches to Cognitive Neuroscience, 2nd ed. MIT Press.

labor between the hemispheres is very efficient, because during a communicative interaction the left hemisphere can take the lead in comprehending and producing appropriate syntax and vocabulary, while the right hemisphere can take the lead in comprehending and producing nonverbal cues. Further, consistent with the basic division of the cortex into anterior motor regions and posterior perceptual regions, production of emotional expressions tends to rely upon frontal regions, while perception of those expressions tends to rely upon posterior regions such as the temporal and parietal cortices.

■ **Emotional Experience**

Thus far we have considered the role of various cortical brain regions in representing bodily states of emotion, integrating emotion and cognition, regulating emotion, and communicating emotion through facial and vocal expressions. A final emotional function that we will discuss is the experiential aspect of emotion. When a person experiences a particular emotional state, such as sadness or happiness, what brain regions represent or reflect that experience? This question is difficult to address, because it involves reliably assessing the subjective experience of another person.

Despite the challenges of assessing subjective states of emotion, psychologists have developed models of the basic dimensions of emotional experience. These models attempt to describe emotional experience as existing along several basic dimensions. One type of model assumes that the basic dimensions of emotional experience can be described in terms of approach and withdrawal motivations. For example, happy states involve a tendency to approach and engage with the world, whereas sad states involve a tendency to withdraw from it. Another type of

model argues that the basic dimensions of emotion are *valence* (positive versus negative emotions) and *arousal* (low versus high emotional intensity). As we discuss in this section, each of these dimensional models has been related to activity in certain cortical regions.

Approach-Withdrawal Models

The first model that we examine posits that there are distinct brain systems for approach and withdrawal emotions. According to this model, initially proposed by Davidson and colleagues, approach and withdrawal are the most basic and rudimentary actions that organisms take in responding adaptively to the environment (Davidson, 1995; for reviews, see Davidson, 2004; Sutton, 2002). As emotions evolved, they became associated with already established approach or withdrawal action systems. Proponents of this model propose that the left frontal region houses a system involved in approach behaviors. Therefore, increased activity of the left frontal area is associated with emotions that tend to be accompanied by approach behaviors, including most positive emotions. In contrast, the right frontal region is posited to house a system involved in withdrawal behaviors. Increased activity of the right frontal area is associated with emotions, such as fear, disgust, and depression, that are accompanied by withdrawal behaviors.

Much of the evidence supporting the **approach-withdrawal model** is based on EEG measures of activity in right or left frontal regions, which vary from person to person depending on the individual's typical outlook or disposition. For example, EEG measures reveal that people differ in the degree to which they show more right versus left prefrontal activity during a resting baseline condition (Coan & Allen, 2004; Davidson, 1995). These asymmetries predict a person's disposition, with more left frontal activity associated with a more optimistic or positive outlook and more right frontal activity associated with a greater reactivity to negative stimuli. These patterns were replicated in 10-month-old infants, who were more likely to cry when separated from their mothers if they had more right than left prefrontal activation (Davidson & Fox, 1989; see also Buss, Schumacher, Dolski, Kalin, Goldsmith, & Davidson, 2003). Similar patterns of asymmetry exist in rhesus monkeys, who show higher levels of stress hormones if they have more right than left prefrontal activation (● Figure 13.22) (Kalin, Larson, Shelton, & Davidson, 1998; Kalin, Shelton, & Davidson, 2000). Such asymmetries are also associated with transient changes in mood. Increased left frontal activity is observed when people view happy film clips (Davidson, Ekman, Saron, Senulis, & Friesen, 1990) or when infants receive sweet-tasting sugar water (Fox & Davidson, 1986).

A similar relationship between hemisphere of activation and mood state has been observed in clinical populations with affective disorders. For example, during a resting condition, individuals with depression showed more activity in the right prefrontal region than in the left, whereas nondepressed individuals showed the opposite pattern (Schaffer, Davidson, & Saron, 1983; see also Reid, Duke, & Allen, 1998; Shankman, Klein, Tenke, & Bruder, 2007; Thibodeau, Jorgensen, & Kim, 2006). In fact, greater right than left EEG activity in the frontal-lobe regions may reflect a risk factor for depression, as discussed further in Chapter 14.

The approach-withdrawal model is also consistent with studies of the emotional consequences of damage to the left or right hemisphere. Studies of patients with unilateral brain damage found that 60% of the patients with left frontal lobe lesions exhibited symptoms of depression. The more anterior the lesion in the left hemisphere, the more severe the depressive symptoms (e.g., Robinson & Szetela, 1981; Morris, Robinson, Raphael, & Hopwood, 1996). These data fit with the approach-withdrawal model if we assume that damage to the left frontal region impairs the approach motivational system. That is, damage to the approach system (while leaving the withdrawal system intact) may lead to the classic depressive symptoms of apathy, helplessness, and inability to feel pleasure.

Approach and withdrawal might seem synonymous with positive and negative emotions, respectively. However, there is one emotion that does not quite fit this picture: anger. Anger is certainly a negative emotion, but it can be expressed either by "approach" behaviors, such as lashing out, or by withdrawal behaviors, such as giving someone the cold shoulder. For this reason, anger presents a unique test case for the approach-withdrawal model. If the model is correct, then people who tend to act out when angry should exhibit more left frontal activity. Studies have yielded results generally consistent with this prediction, supporting the approach-withdrawal model (Harmon-Jones, 2004, 2007; Harmon-Jones & Sigelman, 2001).

Valence-Arousal Models

Another cognitive neuroscience model of emotional experience (Heller, 1993; Heller & Nitschke, 1998) is based on psychological models arguing that emotions are best described by two fundamental dimensions: valence (pleasant vs. unpleasant) and arousal (high vs. low intensity) (e.g., Feldman-Barrett & Russell, 1999). According to the valence-arousal model, frontal regions are asymmetrically involved in the valence aspect of emotion, whereas the posterior right hemisphere is involved in the arousal aspect (● Figure 13.23).

How does the valence-arousal model differ from the approach-withdrawal model? The two models are very similar in their predictions for frontal regions. According to the valence-arousal model, the left frontal region is specialized for positive emotions and the right for negative emotions. In the previous section, we reviewed evidence that ties approach (typically positive) emotions to the left frontal region, and withdrawal (typically negative) emotions to the right frontal region. This evidence fits with both models.

However, the valence-arousal model also posits that arousal, or emotional intensity, is reflected in activity of posterior sections of the right hemisphere. Studies examining perceptual asymmetries have shown that emotional stimuli have a greater influence on heart rate, blood pressure, and the release of stress hormones when they are presented to the right hemisphere rather than the left (Wittling, 1990; Wittling & Pflüger, 1990; Wittling,

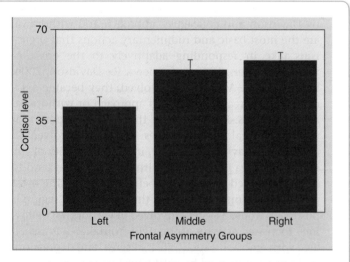

● **FIGURE 13.22** **Relationship between frontal-lobe activation asymmetry and stress hormones.** Rhesus monkeys with greater left than right frontal lobe activity (left bar) have lower levels of the stress hormone cortisol than monkeys with greater right than left frontal activity (right bar) or those with balanced asymmetry (middle bar). *Source:* Fig. 4 in Kalin, N. H., Larson, C., Shelton, S. E., & Davison, R. J. (1998). Asymmetric frontal brain activity, cortisol, and behavior associated with fearful temperament in rhesus monkeys. Behavioral Neuroscience, 112, 286–292.

Block, Schweiger, & Genzel, 1998). Further, directing participants' attention toward the left visual field, presumably activating the right hemisphere, leads to greater changes in self-reported arousal than directing attention to the right visual field (Compton, 1999). Also, the higher a person's self-reported level of energy or arousal, the larger his or her leftward perceptual bias on a face perception task (Heller, Nitschke, & Lindsay, 1997).

The valence-arousal model of emotion has been particularly helpful in differentiating the patterns of brain activity that characterize depression and anxiety (Heller, Koven, & Miller, 2003). Although both depression and anxiety are certainly unpleasant rather than pleasant mood states, they differ in the arousal dimension. Depression is typically a low-arousal state, whereas anxiety is often a high-arousal state, and therefore they are likely to differentially involve the right hemisphere's posterior regions. We consider the brain regions involved in anxiety and depression in more detail in Chapter 14.

As you may have noticed, neither the approach-withdrawal model nor the valence-arousal model is very specific about exactly which portions of the frontal or parietal lobe are involved in the experience of emotion. Rather, both emphasize a more general pattern of activity that is involved in emotional experience. This likely reflects the limitation of some of the methodologies used to examine the effect of mood. For example, EEG measures are not ideal for determining precisely where in the brain activity is occurring. It also likely reflects an important conceptual point: that there may be no single "mood" center in the brain. Instead, changes in mood are associated with modulation of activity across a wide range of brain areas, which affect not only the subjective feeling that one experiences, but also how one processes perceptual information, pays attention, values reward, and makes decisions.

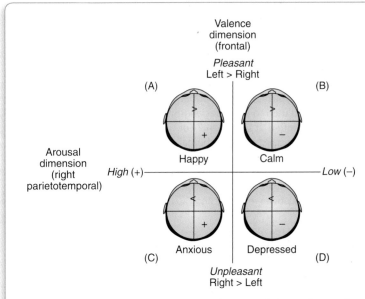

● FIGURE 13.23   **Model of regional brain activity and mood proposed by Heller (1993).** This model posits that the valence dimension of mood (positive or pleasant vs. negative or unpleasant; *y* axis) is mainly affected by activation of frontal regions of the brain, whereas the arousal dimension (high vs. low; *x* axis) is mainly affected by activation of the right posterior region. Depicted here are the patterns of brain activation for four mood states. (A) When activation of left frontal regions is greater than that of right frontal regions (which leads to pleasant emotion) and the right posterior region is highly activated (which leads to arousal), the individual is happy. (B) The pattern of activation is identical over frontal regions for a calm state, but the activity over the right posterior region is reduced, which leads to a lower level of arousal for a calm state than for happiness. (C) In anxiety, higher right than left frontal activation leads to a negative valence, and high activity in the right posterior region leads to increased arousal. (D) Finally, the brain activation in depression is similar to that in anxiety, in that higher right than left frontal activation leads to a negative valence. However, the low activity in the right posterior region causes the decreased arousal that differentiates depression from anxiety. © 2011 Cengage Learning

From Emotion to Social Cognition

The study of emotion is closely tied to the study of social behavior, particularly in social species such as humans and other primates. If you think back over the material covered in this chapter, you can see that many of our examples of emotional processing involved social stimuli or situations. For example, facial expressions and emotional prosody are necessarily social, because they take place in a situation in which two or more people are communicating with one another. We've also considered how patients with orbitofrontal damage are unable to inhibit socially inappropriate behavior, which reminds us that normally people have an internal understanding of how to control their behavior to meet social norms and expectations. As another example, we've noted that social stimuli, such as attractive faces, can engage the subcortical reward systems, much as very tasty food can.

Research on emotion has long involved social aspects, but in recent years there has been growing interest in applying the methods of cognitive neuroscience to understand social phenomena more broadly (Cacioppo, Visser, & Pickett, 2006; Lieberman, 2007). Here, we discuss two lines of research to illustrate the growing subfield of social cognitive neuroscience. First, we consider theories about how our minds are able to represent the mental states of other people. Second, we consider studies that attempt to apply cognitive neuroscience approaches to the topic of prejudice and discrimination.

■ Understanding the Mental States of Others

People are constantly trying to infer what other people are thinking about. You may wonder whether your roommate likes you, whether your boss intends to fire

IN FOCUS: The Pain of Rejection

There is nothing quite so bad as feeling excluded. Think back to junior high school: remember when the popular kids shunned you? Or think about any time that you tried to join a social group and were rebuffed. It hurt, right? For members of social species like humans, inclusion in a social group is thought to be part of the road to happiness and well-being, while exclusion is associated with a loss of power, esteem, and resources.

Scientists have spent years elucidating the neural underpinnings of physical pain, but recently affective neuroscientists have considered the underpinnings of social pain (see MacDonald & Leary, 2005, for a review). Does the pain of rejection "hurt" in the same places in the brain that physical pain does?

One influential study suggests that it does (Eisenberger, Lieberman, & Williams, 2003). In this study, participants played a virtual ball-tossing game with two other participants, depicted as cartoon characters on a computer screen. (Actually, the other "participants" were just a rigged computer program.) First the participant

watched the two others toss the virtual ball back and forth. Then, the participant was drawn into the game, and all three players tossed the ball around. In the third portion of the game, suddenly the other two "players" stopped tossing the ball to the participant. Not surprisingly, participants tended to say that they felt ignored and excluded. At the same time, they showed increased activity in the anterior cingulate cortex and right ventral prefrontal cortex compared to earlier when they had been participating in tossing the ball. Because the anterior cingulate is also activated by physical pain, these results could be interpreted as indicating that social exclusion "hurts" because it activates the same area in the brain as does physical pain.

However, as other researchers pointed out, the exclusion condition probably differed from the inclusion condition in another way: namely, that the exclusion condition violated expectations (Somerville, Heatherton, & Kelley, 2006). That is, the participant was probably surprised when the others stopped throwing the ball to him or her. Was the cingulate cortex activated because of the perceived social pain, or simply because

of the violated expectation? Other studies have shown that the cingulate cortex is activated by unexpected outcomes and other cognitive conflicts even in situations that do not involve pain of any sort. To differentiate between these two possibilities, Somerville and colleagues developed an experiment that included two different kinds of conditions: one that involved a violation of expectations and another that involved social feedback (indicating whether another "participant" reported liking the actual participant or not). They found that social rejection activated a different region of the cingulate cortex than did expectancy violation, indicating that these two processes are not one and the same, but rather are separable. Bolstering the idea that physical and social pain are connected, researchers have shown that participants who are more sensitive to social rejection in the ball-tossing game also tend to have lower thresholds for physical pain (Eisenberger, Jarcho, Lieberman, & Naliboff, 2006). This finding implies that physical pain and the pain of social rejection may indeed share a common basis.

---

you, or whether your study partner really understands the course material he or she is explaining to you. All of these examples involve attempting to understand what is going on in the mind of another person.

There are two main theories of how we understand others' thoughts and feelings. One theory, sometimes called **theory of mind**, assumes that we have a cognitive representation of other people's mental states, including their feelings and their knowledge. Through these cognitive representations, we are able to hold in mind two different sets of beliefs: what we know, believe, or feel, and what we think another person knows, believes, or feels. For example, a teacher might know how action potentials propagate in a neuron, while at the same time knowing that her students do not yet know this on the first day of class. (This can go even one step farther: imagine a student who has already learned about action potentials, thinking "The teacher doesn't know that I know this already!") Because of the high level of cognitive sophistication required for this kind of theorizing about another's knowledge,

this ability is not thought to develop until the late pre-school years (Flavell, 2004). Some argue that the ability to represent the mental states of others in this way is unique to humans and possibly great apes, though this topic is much disputed (e.g., Povinelli & Vonk, 2003; Tomasello, Call, & Hare, 2003; see also Brüne & Brüne-Cohrs, 2006).

Another theory suggests that we understand the mental states of others through simulation. In the simplest sense, **simulation** just means acting like another person. For example, if you see another person crying, you might understand his mental state by starting to tear up yourself. By mimicking that other person's actions and expressions, you feel as he does, and therefore you comprehend his mental state. This means of understanding another person is closely related to the concept of empathy.

It should be obvious that these two ways of understanding other people—theory of mind and simulation—are not mutually exclusive. For example, the theory-of-mind approach can more easily explain how we represent mental states that do not have an obvious outward expression, such as beliefs and knowledge. In contrast, simulation can best explain emotional behaviors and motor actions that can be easily mimicked. It can also explain how emotions (and behaviors like laughing) can be "contagious" even among small children and less cognitively sophisticated animals. At the same time, if we only used simulation to understand other people, it could be difficult to separate our own feelings from those of others. Therefore, it is likely that we rely on both means of representing others' mental states, though perhaps in different circumstances.

So, what do we know about the neural processes underlying these skills? As you might expect, it is not easy to localize theorizing about another person's internal knowledge to a particular brain region, because it is so abstract and probably involves several component operations. However, some studies have examined brain activity when people are required to make inferences about the beliefs of other people. Such studies have found activity in a network of areas, including medial prefrontal cortex, temporal poles, superior temporal sulcus, and the temporoparietal junction (Frith & Frith, 2003; Saxe, Carey, & Kanwisher, 2004). However, the precise operation carried out by each of these regions in the network has yet to be fully understood. There are some potential reasons that each of these regions might play a role. For example, the superior temporal sulcus plays a role in coding for the gaze direction of other people (Hoffman & Haxby, 2000; Jellema, Baker, Wicker, & Perrett, 2000; Pelphrey, Singerman, Allison, & McCarthy, 2003), which may be related to inferring their mental states. For example, if someone turns her gaze away from you, you may infer that she is bored or bothered by you.

The simulation notion of understanding others is easier to relate to brain processes. Remember that in Chapter 5, we learned about mirror neurons, which fire when an animal carries out an action or observes another carrying out the same action. Following the initial discovery of mirror neurons in motor regions of the brain, researchers began to consider the concept of *neural mirroring* more broadly. Indeed, in many situations the same brain regions seem to be activated when a person experiences a particular state as when he or she observes another person experiencing that same state. Motor areas are activated when we see another person perform actions (e.g., van Schie, Mars, Coles, & Bekkering, 2004), pain areas of the brain are activated when we see another person in pain (e.g., Jackson, Meltzoff, & Decety, 2005; Singer, Seymour, O'Doherty, Kaube, Dolan, & Frith, 2004), and disgust-related areas of the brain (the insula) are activated both when we smell foul odors and when we see another person smelling them (Wicker, Keysers, Plailly, Royet, Gallese, & Rizzolatti, 2003). In these examples, activation of

sensory, motor, and emotional systems by observation of another's experience may help us to simulate, and therefore understand, that experience.

Interestingly, the degree to which we simulate another's experiences may depend on social factors, such as how much we like that person or whether we see ourselves as similar to that person. One study found that the ventral striatum (nucleus accumbens) was activated when participants viewed someone else receiving a large reward, but the activity was greater when the reward recipient was deemed to be socially desirable, likeable, and similar to the actual participant (Mobbs et al., 2009). Likewise, in a study in which participants watched a confederate perform a simple computer task, the neural response to errors made by the confederate was influenced by the participant's judgment about the similarity between himself and the confederate (Carp, Halenar, Quandt, Sklar, & Compton, 2009). These studies suggest that although we have the capability to mirror other people's states, we may do so preferentially for others whom we see as similar to ourselves.

■ Cognitive Neuroscience Approaches to Prejudice

Prejudice and discrimination against other people, particularly against minority "out-groups," is a pervasive issue in all societies. The problems of prejudice and discrimination have been at the core of modern social psychology since its founding. Why do people engage in prejudice and discriminatory behavior, and what mechanisms sustain it? Clearly, dealing with the full scope of this problem would involve understanding behavior at the level of the group, inequalities in social structure and power, and how cultural norms and values are taught and learned. It would be naïve to think that we can fully understand prejudice by looking deep within the brain. But can cognitive neuroscience contribute anything to knowledge in this important area?

One thing we have learned from cognitive neuroscience approaches is that the brain distinguishes between in-group and out-group categories fairly rapidly. In one study, researchers measured ERPs in response to faces that belonged to different racial categories (Ito, Thompson, & Cacioppo, 2004). Some early ERP peaks appeared to respond equally to all faces, regardless of their racial category. For example, the face-specific N_{170} peak, which occurs about 170 ms after the presentation of a face, was bigger for faces than for other pictures, but did not differ for faces of different racial categories. However, at around 250 ms, the ERP response was larger in response to faces of in-group members than to faces of out-group members. Thus, within about a quarter of a second, people's brains distinguish between in-group and out-group members. Although early research was limited to white participants, subsequent studies confirmed the same basic pattern—early neural differentiation of in-group and out-group—in both white and black participants (Dickter & Bartholow, 2007).

People often seem to feel afraid or uncertain when interacting with those of other races. Could their brains be interpreting out-group members as threats? Some research has found that people acquire a conditioned fear to other-race faces more quickly than to faces of their own race (Olsson, Ebert, Banaji, & Phelps, 2005). In a neuroimaging study, researchers showed that unconscious racial bias was correlated with activity in the amygdala (Phelps et al., 2000). Unconscious bias was measured using a behavioral method that quantifies the speed of association between pictures of other-race faces and negative words (compared to other-race faces and positive words). The researchers found that the higher the measure of unconscious racial bias, the more the amygdala, particularly on the left, became activated. Of course, this does not tell us why some people exhibit stronger unconscious racial biases than others; it just tells us that those who do are activating the amygdalar circuitry of the brain when viewing other-race faces. Interestingly, patients with amygdala damage still show unconscious racial biases (Phelps, Cannistraci, & Cunningham, 2003), indicating that this brain structure is not solely responsible for sustaining racial prejudice.

Although these studies have focused on in-groups and out-groups based on race—a very salient category in our society—social psychologists have long known that in-groups and out-groups can be formed very easily based on virtually any kind of distinction between people. When people are randomly assigned to groups, even through a coin toss, they later show evidence of favoring their own group (Tajfel, 1970). In one neuroimaging study (Van Bavel, Packer, & Cunningham, 2008), participants were randomly assigned to belong to either the "Leopards" or the "Tigers" team, and they were encouraged to learn which other participants belonged to their team versus the other team, supposedly for a later phase of the study. Brain imaging results showed increased activity in a number of regions, including amygdala, orbitofrontal cortex, and fusiform gyrus, when participants viewed their own team members versus members of the other team. In addition, orbitofrontal cortex activity predicted how much the participants favored their in-group when asked to rate how much they liked each face. The difference between the response to in-groups versus out-groups in this study could not be accounted for by prior experience with the group, because the participants did not know each other before the study and the researchers controlled how long participants viewed each face. These results show that even the simplest kinds of social categorization, established within a single experimental session, can affect how the brain responds to other people.

In this day and age, most people know that overt racial bias is socially unacceptable, and are uncomfortable with the thought that they might act or think in a racist way. One study focused on this phenomenon by studying people's responses to their own errors that might imply they harbored a racial bias (Amodio, Harmon-Jones, Devine, Curtin, Hartley, & Covert, 2004). In this study, people had to quickly press a button to indicate whether a picture was a gun or a tool. Just before the picture, participants were primed with a picture of an African-American or Caucasian person. Overall, participants tend to be more likely to mistakenly press "gun" when primed with an African-American face than when primed with a Caucasian face, indicating an implicit biased association between African-Americans and guns. Researchers examined the error-related negativity (ERN) evoked when participants made errors in this task, and found that the ERN was significantly higher when participants made racially charged errors (e.g., mistakenly pressing the button for "gun" rather than "tool" when primed by an African-American face), compared to errors that would not imply racial bias (● Figure 13.24) (Amodio et al., 2004; Amodio, Kubota, Harmon-Jones, & Devine, 2006). Participants with a larger ERN to racially charged errors were more likely to slow down and become more accurate on the next trial, suggesting that they were trying to compensate to avoid such errors in the future. Based on what we know about the source of the ERN, we can assume that this cognitive control process involves the anterior cingulate cortex and related frontal-lobe regions.

Other findings by this same research group have tied feelings of guilt about racial prejudice to EEG asymmetries in the frontal lobe (Amodio, Devine, & Harmon-Jones, 2007). In this study, participants were given false feedback indicating that they had responded in a racially prejudiced way. The feedback altered patterns of frontal-lobe EEG asymmetry, toward less left-sided activity. According to the approach-withdrawal model, this is consistent with reduced approach motivation; perhaps the sense of guilt at being prejudiced made people want to pull back. However, participants who reported more guilt were also subsequently more interested in reading articles about prejudice reduction, which in turn was associated with an increase in approach-related left-frontal activation. In other words, the feeling of guilt was first associated with withdrawal-related EEG asymmetries, but taking advantage of the opportunity to make amends was associated with approach-related EEG asymmetries.

Once again, these results do not really tell us why some people are more or less prone to racial prejudice. However, they do give clues about what is going on in the brain when people perceive racial cues and try to regulate their own responses to those cues. Clearly, brain structures involved in emotion and emotion regulation play an important role in these social processes.

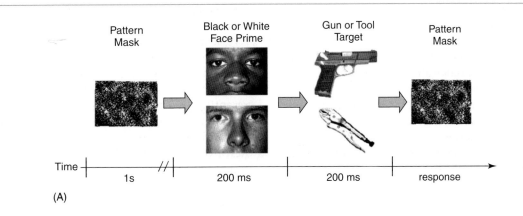

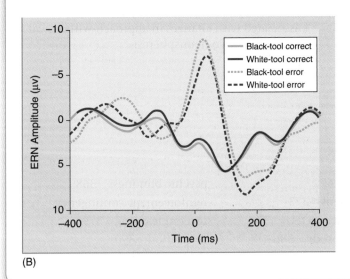

(B)

● **FIGURE 13.24   Error-related brain processes are influenced by racial meaning.** Panel A illustrates a task in which participants had to decide if a visual image was a gun or a tool. The image was preceded by the quick presentation of an African-American or Caucasian face. In Panel B, the error-related negativity was greater when participants made black-tool errors (that is, mistakenly calling a tool a gun after being primed with an African-American face), compared to white-tool errors or correct responses. These data indicate that errors reflecting racial bias elicit a stronger neural response than other errors. *Source:* Fig 1 from Amodio, D. M., Harmon-Jones, E., Devine, P. G., Curtin, J. J., Hartley, S. L., & Covert, A. E. (2004). Neural signals for the detection of unintentional race bias. Psychological Science, 15, 88–93 and Fig. 3a from Amodio, D. M., Harmon-Jones, E., Devine, P. G., Curtin, J. J., Hartley, S. L., & Covert, A. E. (2004). Neural signals for the detection of unintentional race bias. Psychological Science, 15, 88–93. Reprinted by permission of John Wiley.

Summary

Subcortical Contributions to Emotion

- The hypothalamus mediates some of the physiological phenomena associated with emotional states, such as changes in autonomic nervous system and endocrine function that are associated with fleeing or fighting.
- The amygdala is involved in learning the emotional significance of information and in producing a quick, instinctive, emotional response. The amygdala can also influence how attention is directed to emotionally significant events.
- The ventral striatum, or nucleus accumbens, is important in reward-seeking behavior. It is especially responsive to unpredicted rewards and becomes active when a person is anticipating a reward.

Cortical Contributions to Emotion

- The insula is involved in coding for unpleasant tastes, and also plays a role in the experience and perception of disgust. It is important in representing internal body states that are relevant to emotion.
- The rostral region of the anterior cingulate is involved in monitoring for emotionally salient events.
- Orbitofrontal cortex is involved in evaluating reward and punishment contingencies and in responding adaptively to changes in these relationships. Damage to the orbitofrontal cortex can lead to deficits in controlling behavior and emotion in a socially appropriate manner.
- Control of emotions depends upon interactions among cortical and subcortical brain regions.

Suppressing an emotion appears to involve top-down control over subcortical systems such as the amygdala and hypothalamus.

- Temporoparietal regions of the right hemisphere are important for comprehending emotional information expressed in tone of voice or facial expression.
- The right hemisphere plays a predominant role in producing prosody that is related to emotional affect and in governing the expression of emotion on the face.
- Positive affect is associated with more activity over the left than the right prefrontal cortex, whereas negative affect is associated with the reverse pattern (greater right prefrontal than left prefrontal activity).
- States of high arousal appear to differentially involve the right hemisphere, particularly in posterior regions.

From Emotion to Social Cognition

- Many aspects of social behavior are closely related to emotional processes.

- Two main theories address how we understand the mental states of others. "Theory of mind" is a cognitive representation of others' knowledge or beliefs, and involves a network of regions including medial prefrontal cortex, superior temporal sulcus, and the temporoparietal junction. "Simulation" refers to representing the mental states of others by activating the same brain regions as the other person is likely to be activating.
- Researchers have examined neural correlates of prejudice. The amygdala is activated by faces of other races, suggesting that those faces may be coded as threatening. People are especially sensitive to mistakes that might reflect racial bias, and try to correct themselves. Guilt associated with racial prejudice is associated with changes in approach-withdrawal systems in the two hemispheres.

Key Terms

affective prosody   386

approach-withdrawal model   387

aprosodia   386

emotion regulation   380

interoception   375

limbic system   367

nucleus accumbens   373

orbitofrontal cortex (OFC)   378

propositional prosody   386

prosody   386

psychic blindness   368

reinforcement contingency   379

reversal learning   379

simulation   390

theory of mind   390

Book Companion Site at www.cengage.com/psychology/Banich
This website provides instructors and students with a wealth of free information and resources, including tutorial quizzes, flashcards, and the glossary.

Psychopathology

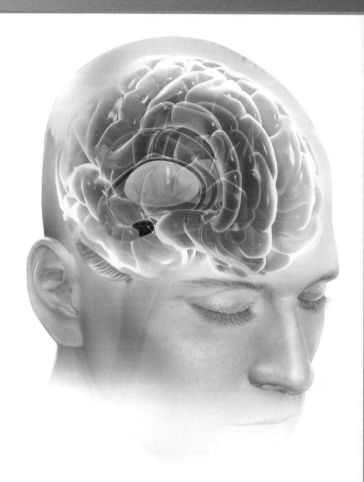

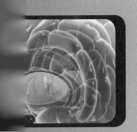

JOE GRAY JOINED OUR FAMILY when I was 15 and he was 60. He and my mother had grown up on neighboring ranches in southern New Mexico. After my father's death, he came to Philadelphia to support her. Although my brothers and I had never met him before, he became a friend, mentor, and guide. Joe lived with us until he ended his life at 72.

Although some of Joe's past is shrouded in mystery, there were certain facts of his life about which we were sure. We see him in photos as a young man astride a horse, handsome and confident. He knew how to ride and shoot and handle animals. He was a scholar and a man of intense curiosity who read widely in many disciplines. Educated at Princeton University, he studied the Spanish language. We knew that he had spent time as an undercover agent for the United States during the Cold War in South America, allowing him to combine his sense of adventure and his intellectual pursuit of Spanish, among other things, but he never told us any of the details. We also knew that he became an alcoholic and was a member of Alcoholics Anonymous for many years. When Joe came to live with us, he had retired and had been living in Albuquerque, New Mexico. But his zest for life continued—whether going to listen to bluegrass and folk music, training a puppy, repairing a faucet, or teaching us to drive.

Joe had his first stroke when I was in graduate school. I was home for the holidays. One day we noticed that although Joe, ever talkative, was speaking, what he was saying was incoherent. Even so, he did seem to follow, more or less, what we were saying. I had enough training by then to realize that it was a symptom of a brain injury, most likely Broca's aphasia. Indeed, a neurological exam confirmed that Joe was suffering the consequences of a left-hemisphere stroke. Joe worked hard in therapy to regain his spoken-language abilities, and took comfort that reading, one of the pursuits he enjoyed most in life, was not lost. His progress was quite good—until he had a second stroke. After that, he couldn't read, or drive, or find the right words to converse. It was then that his demeanor also changed.

Although often cantankerous, Joe had always been upbeat about life, retaining his sense that life was an adventure. After the second stroke, though, his moods could be positively dark, and the energy he had once had for life noticeably ebbed. He began to threaten suicide. He tried several times. He took an overdose of pills one night but woke up eventually, in mid-afternoon, and was groggy for a day or two. He drank a fifth of scotch, after having not touched alcohol for 20 years, but passed out on the kitchen floor before any major damage was done. I convinced him to see a psychiatrist, who got him so angry that he forgot to be depressed for a while. We tried to cheer him up, telling him how important he was to our family, taking him to his favorite places, and buying him a brand-new pair of western cowboy boots.

Finally, he decided to hang himself, and this time he succeeded in his suicidal intent. My mother came home from work on a Friday afternoon to find cardboard taped to the front door window so that no one could see inside, and Joe, having somehow fallen from the noose, lying dead on the floor in the hallway. He was wearing his new boots.

Perhaps it will come as no surprise to the reader that much of my research since graduate school has focused on the role of brain mechanisms in depression.

—Wendy Heller, clinical neuroscientist

AS IN OTHER AREAS of cognitive neuroscience, much of what we know about the brain and mental illness has been based on observations of people with damage to the brain. The depression that led Joe Gray to suicide was most likely due to more than his inability to accept his impairments, although no doubt the loss of independence and reduced intellectual capacity contributed to his despair. Research has shown that damage to parts of the left hemisphere, especially frontal regions, often leads to clinical depression. Findings such as these underscore the importance of particular brain regions in contributing to psychiatric disorders.

Fully understanding mental illness, or *psychopathology*, involves much more than understanding the brain. Psychopathology can be fruitfully approached from many different psychological perspectives, including not only the biological but also cognitive, social, and cross-cultural levels. For example, a condition like clinical depression may be correlated with certain biological variables, such as deactivation of the left frontal lobe, but it can also be described as involving changes in ways of thinking and making meaning from life; it can affect and be affected by interpersonal relationships; and its appearance and manifestation can be influenced by cultural values and norms. Although the focus in this chapter is on cognitive neuroscience approaches, you should be aware that a more complete understanding of psychopathology must also include these additional perspectives (see Nolen-Hoeksema, 2007).

Here our goal is to understand what unique information cognitive neuroscience can bring to understanding the complexities of mental illness. We focus on four major categories of disorders—schizophrenia, depression, anxiety disorders, and substance use disorders—because they are among the most common and devastating of mental afflictions. Psychiatric conditions associated with development (e.g., autism, attention deficit disorder) and aging (e.g., Alzheimer's disease) are covered in Chapters 15 and 16, respectively.

Before we discuss these disorders in more detail, it is important to raise a significant ethical concern. You will notice throughout this chapter that, in some studies that aim to extend the understanding of mental disorders, people may be placed in situations that are somewhat provocative or difficult. For example, we will discuss studies in which depressed people are asked to listen to sad stories, people with phobias are shown things that scare them, and people with posttraumatic stress disorder are asked to think about the situation that traumatized them. The design of these studies does not mean that cognitive neuroscientists are a mean or cold-hearted bunch. Rather, their goal is to understand these disorders so that, ultimately, treatment options can be expanded and improved. Like all cognitive neuroscience studies, studies involving participants with clinical conditions must be approved by a review board. These boards ensure that the provocation is not enough to cause the individuals more distress than they would ordinarily encounter in daily life as a result of their disorder. Typically participants are also "debriefed" so that any residual distress can be detected and eliminated, and they are informed about resources available to them should any ill effects occur in the future. It is a testimony to the good-heartedness and generosity of these research participants that they are willing to be involved in such experiments. Although participating in studies may not directly help their affliction, and might even be painful, they participate anyway, in the hope that it may help other people in the future with similar afflictions.

Schizophrenia

It is generally accepted that schizophrenia results from a disease of the brain, although researchers are still far from having a complete understanding of this condition. Schizophrenia is considered a chronic condition that is managed but never really cured. It often strikes first in late adolescence or early adulthood, and requires clinical intervention and management from that point forward. Because of its chronic nature, schizophrenia accounts for half of all admissions to psychiatric hospitals, and it is one of the top ten causes of years lost to disability worldwide (Mueser & McGurk, 2004). Moreover, the disorder is relatively common, with approximately 1 in 200 people affected at any given time (World Health Organization, 2001). These numbers give some sense of the magnitude of schizophrenia as a problem for individuals, families, and society at large. As we will see next, the variety and complexity of symptoms have made it impossible to pin down one single brain region or system as the focal point of this disorder.

■ Symptoms and Features

The diagnosis of schizophrenia, like that of other psychiatric conditions, is currently based on observable behavioral and psychological features, not on biological markers. In other words, there is no blood test or other biological indicator that can diagnose a person as having schizophrenia. Rather, the diagnosis is made by a trained clinician who interviews the patient and family members to ascertain the presence of certain key features that are thought to define the disorder. These include at least two of the following symptoms, which have lasted for at least one month in duration: hallucinations, delusions, disorganized speech, grossly disorganized or catatonic behavior, and negative symptoms, which we describe in this section (American Psychiatric Association, 2000 [hereinafter *DSM-IV-TR*, 2000]).

Many researchers group symptoms of schizophrenia into two main categories: positive and negative symptoms. **Positive symptoms** refer to excesses or distortions in normal behavior, whereas **negative symptoms** refer to the absence of normal behavior. Positive symptoms include the presence of hallucinations, delusions, and disorganized thought and behavior that can seem strange and irrational to an outside observer. Hallucinations consist of perceiving things that are not really there, such as hearing voices in one's head. Hallucinations in schizophrenia can occur in any sensory modality, but auditory hallucinations are most typical. *Delusions* are irrational beliefs, like thinking that the FBI is tapping your phones (paranoid delusion) or believing that you are the messiah (delusion of grandeur). Negative symptoms include apathy (lack of motivation), flattened affect (lack of emotional responsiveness), and failures of volition or self-directed behavior. Much research has focused on positive symptoms, probably because they are the most florid and obviously disruptive. However, negative symptoms can also greatly interfere with the person's ability to function normally. Negative symptoms are associated with a poorer prognosis and are less easily treated by antipsychotic medications (e.g., Gasquet, Haro, Novick, Edgell, Kennedy, & Lepine, 2005).

Regardless of diagnostic type, patients tend to show a combination of symptoms from a set of eight categories that are listed in Table 14.1. As you can see, these symptoms cross several domains of functioning, including motor functions, perception, emotion, motivation, and executive function. Therefore, it should not be surprising that multiple brain systems are affected in this disorder.

TABLE 14.1	Symptom Categories in Schizophrenia
Category	**Symptom(s)**
Content of thought	A delusion or false belief.
Form of thought	A formal thought disorder involving abnormalities in the way a person's thought processes are organized. "Loose association," in which ideas shift from one unrelated topic to another, is a common example of this type of symptom.
Perception	Hallucinations or the reporting of experiences for which no observable eliciting stimuli appear to exist.
Affect	Disturbed emotions. Most common are emotions that are blunted, flat, or inappropriate to the situation.
Sense of self	Confusion about self-identity. The person may feel unreal or controlled by outside forces.
Volition	Reduced motivation and interest in pursuing almost any sort of goal. These symptoms interfere severely with a person's ability to work.
Relationship to the external world	Withdrawal from the external world and preoccupation with internal fantasies and odd ideas.
Psychomotor behavior	Abnormalities of movement, including rocking, pacing, stereotyped actions, and bizarre behavioral rituals. Some patients diagnosed with schizophrenia become almost totally immobile; others take on a disheveled look or dress oddly, against social norms.

One of the first-noted and most reliable pieces of evidence of neural dysfunction in schizophrenia is enlargement of the lateral and third ventricles (Shenton, Dickey, Frumin, & McCarley, 2001). **Ventricular enlargement**, depicted in ● Figure 14.1, results from atrophy of brain tissue across many regions of the brain. As such, it is not an indicator of abnormalities in specific brain regions. Recent evidence suggests that the brain may continue to atrophy for up to 20 years after the person is first diagnosed, leading some to suggest that schizophrenia may be associated with a continuous pathophysiological process (Pol & Kahn, 2008).

To pinpoint more specific brain regions that may be implicated in schizophrenia, researchers have taken two main approaches. The first involves comparing cognitive deficits in schizophrenia to deficits in patients with known brain damage. A second approach is to use neuroimaging and other measurements of brain functioning to identify areas of difference in brain anatomy and function between schizophrenics and control groups. Both of these approaches have pointed to the frontal and temporal lobes as especially involved in schizophrenia.

■ Frontal Lobe

There are many indications that the functioning of the frontal lobes is compromised in schizophrenia. Many of the cognitive functions that are most disrupted in

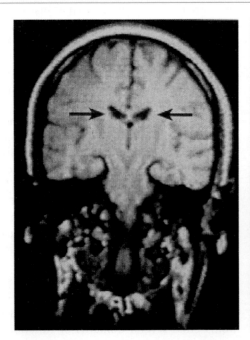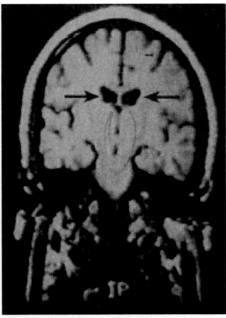

● **FIGURE 14.1** **Enlargement of the ventricles in schizophrenia.** These MRIs show the brain of an individual with schizophrenia (right) and his identical twin who is not affected by the disorder (left). Notice the discrepancy in the size of the ventricles (see arrows). Courtesy Dr. Weinberger, NIMH, St. Elizabeth's Hospital.

schizophrenia are dependent upon the frontal lobe, including working memory, self-monitoring, attention, cognitive control, and behavioral flexibility (for reviews, see Barch, 2005; Berman & Meyer-Lindenberg, 2004; Mitchell, Elliott, & Woodruff, 2001). For example, schizophrenic patients are impaired on tests of planning, such as the Tower of London test, and tests of mental flexibility, such as the Wisconsin Card Sort Test (see Chapter 12 for description of these tasks) (Goldberg, Saint-Cyr, & Weinberger, 1990; Parellada, Catarineu, Catafau, Bernardo, & Lomeña, 2000). Not surprisingly, dozens of functional imaging studies have demonstrated hypoactivation (reduced activation) of frontal regions in individuals with schizophrenia compared to controls (Figure 14.2). **Hypofrontality** (frontal hypoactivation) is evident in schizophrenia both when the person is quietly resting and when he or she is engaged in tasks that normally activate the frontal lobe (Berman & Meyer-Lindenberg, 2004).

A variety of different neurophysiological methods provide strong evidence that frontal lobe mechanisms involved in inhibiting behavior are disrupted in people with schizophrenia (see Campanella & Guerit, 2009, for a review). One example comes from a smooth-pursuit eye-movement task in which a person must track a continuously moving target across a screen (Braff, 2004). Because these eye movements are voluntary rather than involving the automatic orientation of attention, they require involvement of the frontal eye fields as well as other frontal regions (Tanabe, Tregellas, Miller, Ross, & Freedman, 2002). Successful performance of this task

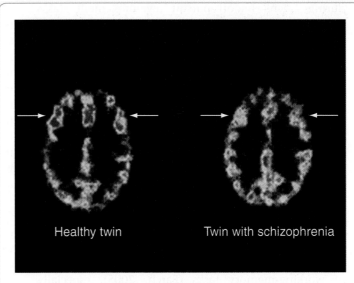

● **FIGURE 14.2   Hypofrontality in schizophrenia.** Areas of the frontal lobe (white arrows) show reduced activity in patients with schizophrenia compared with control participants, such as an identical twin who does not have the disorder. Areas with the most activity are shown in red, followed by regions shown in orange, and yellow.
Source: Daniel Weinberger, M. D., E. Fuller Torrey, M. D. (formerly of NIMH), Karen Berman, M. D. NIMH Clinical brain Disorders Branc Division of Intramural Research Progress, NIMH 1990.

requires activating the frontal systems responsible for smooth eye movements, while simultaneously inhibiting the saccadic system that would move the eye ahead of the target. Individuals with schizophrenia tend to show a bumpy eye-movement trajectory, jumping ahead of the target (Ross, Olincy, Harris, Radant, Adler, & Freedman, 1998), as depicted in ● Figure 14.3. In addition, they fail to activate the frontal eye fields as much as controls

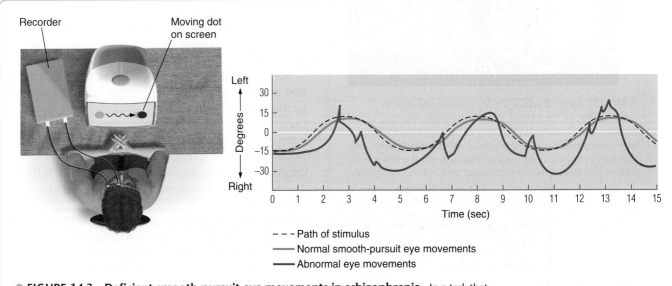

● **FIGURE 14.3   Deficient smooth-pursuit eye movements in schizophrenia.** In a task that requires the subject to visually track the path of a moving target across a screen, people with schizophrenia show an abnormal eye-movement trajectory, jumping from position to position. © 2010 Cengage Learning

during such smooth-pursuit eye-movement tasks (Tregellas, Tanabe, Miller, Ross, Olincy, & Freedman, 2004). Schizophrenic patients also have difficulties with anti-saccade tasks, in which a stimulus appears in one location but the participant must inhibit looking at the stimulus and instead shift her gaze to the location on the opposite side of the screen (Barch, 2005; Braff, 2004). Deficiencies on this task also indicate a problem in inhibition.

As we learned in Chapters 10 and 12, working memory is known to depend heavily on lateral regions of the frontal lobe, and may contribute to performance on many other tasks of executive function. Working memory is disrupted in individuals with schizophrenia. Numerous studies have found that people with schizophrenia show abnormal activity in the dorsolateral prefrontal cortex (DLPFC) during the performance of working-memory tasks (Barch, 2005), especially tasks that require the manipulation of information being held in working memory. For example, reduced activity in the DLPFC is evident when schizophrenic patients complete the N-back task of working memory, which requires holding in mind information from several previous trials in order to compare that information to the information in the current trial (Barch, Csernansky, Conturo, & Snyder, 2002; Perlstein, Carter, Noll, & Cohen, 2001; Perlstein, Dixit, Carter, Noll, & Cohen, 2003). As discussed in Chapter 12, disruptions in working-memory ability can compromise executive

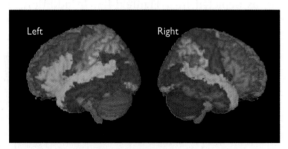

● FIGURE 14.4 Reduced gray-matter volume in schizophrenia. This figure shows areas of gray matter that were found, in numerous studies, to be reduced in individuals with schizophrenia compared to those without the disorder. Areas shown in yellow show the most consistent findings across studies, followed by areas shown in orange and dark red. Notice how the regions that most reliably exhibit volume reductions across many studies are the superior temporal gyrus in both hemispheres and the inferior frontal areas of the left hemisphere. Also notice that much of the frontal lobe is depicted in orange, indicating that studies also find reduced gray matter in these areas, but not as reliably across different studies. *Source:* From "Regional deficits in brain volume in schizophrenia: A meta-analysis of voxel based morphometry studies," by R. Honea, T. J. Crow, D. Passingham, and C. E. Mackay, American Journal of Psychiatry, 162, 2005. Reprinted with permission from the American Journal of Psychiatry, Copyright (2005) American Psychiatric Association.

function because of reduced ability to keep a goal in mind, prioritize information to be held in memory, and sequence behavior toward a goal.

There is also evidence for dysfunction of medial regions of the frontal lobe, especially those associated with monitoring and evaluating one's behavior. As noted in Chapter 12, one method of studying self-monitoring is through the error-related negativity (ERN), the brain potential that is normally evoked immediately following an error in performance. People with schizophrenia do not show normal ERN responses to errors, indicating a failure to effectively evaluate their own performance (Mathalon, Fedor, Faustman, Gray, Askari, & Ford, 2002). Likewise, fMRI has revealed reduced responsiveness of the anterior cingulate cortex following errors in schizophrenic participants (Kerns et al., 2005), providing further evidence of deficient self-monitoring in schizophrenia. These findings fit well with other studies demonstrating abnormalities in the structure and function of the anterior cingulate cortex in schizophrenia (e.g., Nordahl et al., 2001; Wang et al., 2007). In sum, alterations of function of various regions of the frontal lobe in individuals with schizophrenia are related to their poor executive ability, including aspects of inhibitory control, goal-oriented behavior, and self-evaluation.

■ Temporal Lobe

Although many studies have focused on the frontal lobes, other evidence indicates that posterior regions of the brain are also abnormal in schizophrenia. Intuitively, this should make sense if you think about the symptoms of schizophrenia. For example, hallucinations are usually auditory in nature, and auditory processing is performed by the temporal lobes. In addition, the loose and disorganized language production by schizophrenics is often described as similar to the "word salad" style characteristic of people with Wernicke's aphasia, who typically have damage to posterior regions of the temporal lobe (see Chapter 9).

Some of the evidence for dysfunction of temporal and posterior brain regions comes from anatomy. For example, even in individuals who have just experienced their first episode of schizophrenic behavior, there is a reduced volume of gray matter in the left and right middle temporal gyrus, left posterior superior temporal gyrus, and left angular gyrus (● Figure 14.4) (Kuroki et al., 2006; Nierenberg, Salisbury, Levitt, David, McCarley, & Shenton, 2005). Some of this gray-matter loss worsens during the course of the disease. For example, after the first episode of schizophrenic behavior, gray-matter volume in the left Heschl's gyrus and left planum temporale decreases over a period of 1.5 years (Kasai et al., 2003).

These anatomical differences have been linked to functional deficits measured using ERP and MEG methods. For example, people with schizophrenia filter incoming information in the auditory modality in a different manner than controls. Normally, when two successive auditory tones or clicks are presented, the neural response to the second one is less than the response to the first, a response known as **sensory gating**. It makes sense that our brain gates information in this way, because it allows the brain to attend to new information rather than becoming stuck on information it has already registered. Imagine what life would be like if you couldn't do such gating. For example, when you noticed a clock ticking in the background, each tick would capture your attention in the same way as the first, and you'd never become accustomed to the ticking. Sensory gating can be measured through an early event-related potential, the P_{50}, which occurs within 50 ms following an auditory stimulus like a click. The reduced P_{50} response to the second stimulus in a paired sequence is thought to represent an inhibitory process that allows very early attentional selection within the auditory system (● Figure 14.5).

Many studies have demonstrated that this inhibition effect is absent in schizophrenics, indicating a disturbance in sensory gating (e.g., Clementz, Geyer, & Braff, 1997; Yee, Nuechterlein, Morris, & White, 1998). Using MEG methods, researchers have linked the P_{50} deficit in sensory gating in schizophrenia to the superior temporal gyrus (Thoma et al., 2003). The size of the sensory gating deficit, as measured over the right temporal gyrus with MEG (the M_{50}), predicts the severity of negative symptoms in schizophrenia (Thoma et al. 2005). This finding connects the sensory gating deficit to the clinical symptoms of the disorder.

Another electrophysiological abnormality that has been clearly demonstrated in schizophrenia is a reduced P_{300} response to stimuli, particularly in the auditory

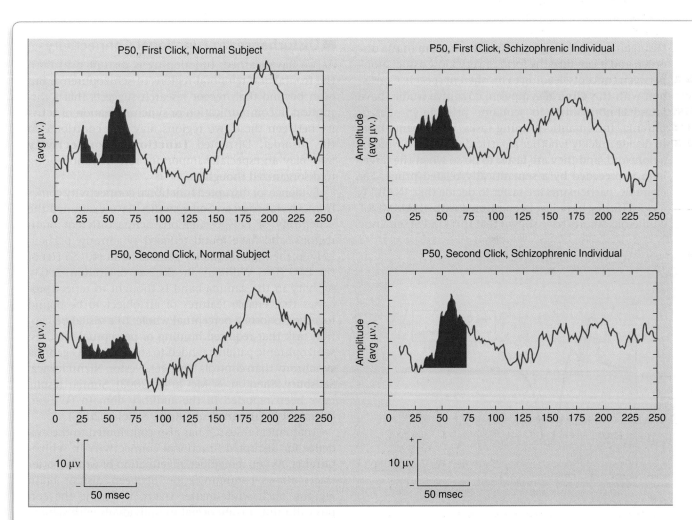

● **FIGURE 14.5   Deficits in sensory gating in schizophrenia.** In normal people (left panels), the neural response evoked by the second click (bottom row) in a pair of auditory clicks is reduced, compared to the response to the first click (top row). This reduction in response is not observed in people with schizophrenia (right panel), indicating deficient gating of sensory information. *Source:* Braff, D. L. (2004). Psychophysiological and information processing approaches to schizophrenia. In D. S. Charney & E. J. Nestler (Eds.), Neurobiology of Mental Illness, 2nd Ed. (pp. 324–338). Oxford: Oxford University Press.

domain (Ford, 1999). ● Figure 14.6 depicts this phenomenon. As discussed in Chapter 3, the P_{300} is an event-related potential that is elicited when a person must pay attention in order to detect a specific task-relevant stimulus within a stream of stimuli. It is thought to represent a process related to the updating of information in working memory. Schizophrenic patients tend to have a reduced P_{300} over many brain regions, but particularly over the left temporal lobe (Salisbury et al., 1998). This functional deficit may result from less gray matter in the region that generates the P_{300} response, as patients with a relatively smaller left planum temporale tend to also exhibit a relatively smaller left-sided P_{300} response to auditory stimuli (McCarley et al., 2002). Notably, a smaller P_{300} response over the left superior temporal gyrus predicts more severe positive and negative symptoms (Kawasaki, Sumiyoshi, Higuchi, Ito, Takeuchi, & Kurachi, 2007). These results imply that the reduced P_{300} and the reduced left-sided volumetric findings may reflect a common pathology that contributes to the clinical presentation of the disorder.

Electrophysiological measures have also been useful in studying semantic associations in schizophrenia. Disorganized thinking is a clinical symptom of the disorder, and it can take the form of very loose associations between concepts, leading to incoherent speech. Consistent with this clinical symptom, cognitive studies have found abnormalities in semantic priming in schizophrenia. In semantic priming tasks, participants have to decide quickly whether a particular item is a word or a nonword, and they are faster to do so when the target item is preceded by a semantically related prime. For example, participants are faster to decide that "NAIL" is a word if they have just been primed with "HAMMER." Numerous studies have shown that this kind of semantic

priming is abnormal in schizophrenia. Particularly when there is a delay between the prime and the target, people with schizophrenia tend to show reduced priming (Minzenberg, Ober, & Vinogradov, 2002; but see also Pomarol-Clotet, Oh, Laws, & McKenna, 2008). ERP studies of the N_{400} peak during semantic priming tasks have shown that in control participants, the amplitude of this peak tracks semantic relatedness (being largest for unrelated prime-target pairs, and smallest for related prime-target pairs); however, people with schizophrenia do not show this pattern (Kiang, Kutas, Light, & Braff, 2008). In other words, the brains of the patients are not differentiating as well between concepts that are highly related and those that are unrelated. Moreover, neuroimaging studies indicate that people with schizophrenia show abnormally increased activity in both the temporal cortex and inferior frontal cortex during priming tasks (Kuperberg, Deckersbach, Holt, Goff, & West, 2007), implicating these regions as a possible neural substrate of the loose and disjointed thinking that is often characteristic of schizophrenia.

■ Disturbances in Functional Connectivity

As we have learned, functioning is disrupted in both the frontal and temporal regions in schizophrenia. But even beyond that, recent research suggests that a disruption in communication or synchronization of activity between these two regions may also contribute to the disorder. Disrupted **functional connectivity** may play an especially important role in contributing to disorganized thought.

Evidence for disrupted functional connectivity comes from several sources. Some studies have examined the synchrony of EEG oscillations across different brain regions, and have found reduced synchrony, particularly in the high-frequency gamma band (40–55 Hz) of the EEG (Lee, Williams, Breakspear, & Gordon, 2003). Activity in the gamma band is thought to reflect processes that enable features of an object to be bound together to form a perceptual whole. In a visual perception task that required binding of perceptual features, schizophrenic patients tended to show less EEG gamma synchrony than controls (Spencer, Nestor, Niznikiewicz, Salisbury, Shenton, & McCarley, 2003). Similar results have been reported in the auditory domain (Wilson, Hernandez, Asherin, Teale, Reite, & Rojas, 2008).

Anatomical research has also contributed to the evidence for disrupted functional connectivity in schizophrenia. As you remember, myelination of white-matter tracts allows communication between distant brain regions. Such white-matter tracts, including the corpus callosum, are abnormal in individuals with schizophrenia compared to neurologically normal individuals (e.g., Brambilla et al., 2005; Buchsbaum et al., 2006; Narr, Thompson, Sharma, Moussai, Cannestra, & Toga, 2000). These effects may arise from abnormal expression of genes that contribute to myelination (Walterfang, Wood, Velakoulis, & Pantelis, 2006).

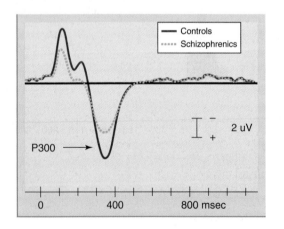

● **FIGURE 14.6 Reduced P_{300} component in schizophrenia.** Stimuli that normally produce a large P_{300} peak in the ERP waveform do not do so in people with schizophrenia. *Source:* Fig. 3 in Ford, J. M. (1999). Schizophrenia: The broken P300 and beyond. Psychophysiology, 36, 667–682.

One fascinating hypothesis suggests that disruptions in the connectivity between frontal and temporal regions may contribute to the experience of hallucinations. People with schizophrenia exhibit increased activity in Broca's area when they are having auditory hallucinations compared to when they are not (McGuire, Shah, & Murray, 1993). Imagine what might happen if these frontal regions, which generate speech, communicate poorly with the temporal lobes, which perceive speech. A person with this disconnection may lack a mechanism to differentiate internal speech—the kind of "talking to myself" thoughts that we all have constantly—from actual speech. Instead, the person may perceive the voice as coming from someplace else, as is typical of schizophrenic hallucinations.

Some evidence for this view comes from a study that examined EEG synchrony while people either talked aloud or listened to speech (Ford, Mathalon, Whitfield, Faustman, & Roth, 2002). In control participants, synchrony between frontal and temporal sites was increased during talking compared to listening, presumably because talking engages both speech generation mechanisms in the frontal lobes and speech perception mechanisms in the temporal lobes. However, individuals with schizophrenia—especially those prone to auditory hallucinations—did not show this increase in frontal-temporal synchrony during talking. A functional MRI study also found that during a task that required a word to be internally generated, activity in left frontal and temporal regions was less

tightly correlated among participants with a greater severity of hallucinations (Lawrie, Buechel, Whalley, Frith, Firston, & Johnstone, 2002). This functional disconnection may result from altered anatomical connections. In particular, the arcuate fasciculus, a white-matter tract that connects frontal and posterior language regions, is atypical in patients who tend to hallucinate (Hubl et al., 2004). These studies imply that anatomical changes may lead to functional disconnections that underlie certain symptoms of schizophrenia, such as hallucinations. Alternatively, certain kinds of symptoms may lead to decreased utilization of certain anatomical pathways, which in turn affects the development of those pathways.

What Causes Schizophrenia?

One of the most pressing questions about any mental illness is its *etiology*, that is, its cause (or causes). So far we have described numerous neurocognitive dysfunctions in schizophrenia—but what causes those dysfunctions in the first place? What factors operating during development lead to the profile of cognitive and neural function that we have just described?

As with many disease conditions, it is likely that genes play an important role in the development of schizophrenia. Data indicate that the risk of developing schizophrenia is increased if a first-degree relative (particularly an identical twin) has the disorder (Gottesman, 1991; McDonald & Murphy, 2003). Figure 14.7 illustrates the increasing risk of the disease

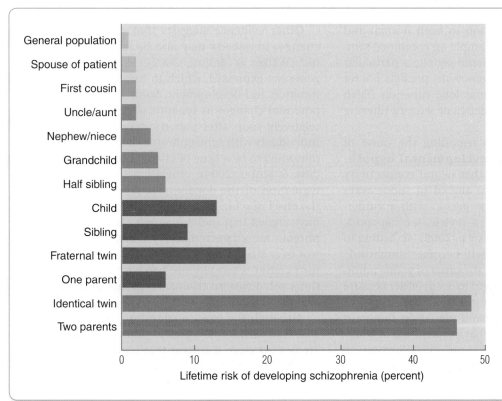

● **FIGURE 14.7   Risk of developing schizophrenia depends on relatedness to someone with the disorder.** Notice, for example, that the risk of developing schizophrenia is much higher if one has an identical twin with schizophrenia, compared to if one has a sibling with the disorder. Identical twins share all their genes, whereas siblings share only half of their genes, on average. © 2010 Cengage Learning

Lifetime risk of developing schizophrenia (percent)

with increasing biological relatedness to someone who suffers from it.

Interestingly, many of the neurocognitive characteristics of schizophrenia can also be observed to some degree in the first-degree relatives of those afflicted with schizophrenia, even when those relatives do not have a diagnosis of schizophrenia themselves (Fusar-Poli et al., 2007). Compared to control groups, individuals with a close relative who suffers from schizophrenia show reduced prefrontal gray-matter volume (e.g., Borgwardt et al., 2007; Pantelis et al., 2003) and altered frontal activity during cognitive tasks (e.g., Callicott et al., 2003; Seidman et al., 2006). However, such effects are generally not as large as observed in schizophrenic individuals. These findings suggest that shared risk factors contribute to a continuum of schizophrenia-like traits among relatives, rather than determining schizophrenia as an "all or none" phenomenon.

Most researchers agree that a disorder as complex as schizophrenia is unlikely to be explained by a single gene, or even a small number of genes. Genetic linkage studies have identified several chromosomal regions that seem to vary between individuals with schizophrenia and those without, though results have not been highly reliable across studies (Chen, Riley, & Kendler, 2009; Wong & Van Tol, 2003). Many of the genes that have been linked to schizophrenia are related to dopaminergic transmission, including genes that code for catechol-O-methyltransferase (COMT) and dopamine beta-hydroxylase; as we discuss later, dopaminergic drugs are often used to treat schizophrenia. Some studies suggest that individual differences in the COMT gene, which influences dopamine metabolism, may contribute to cognitive function in both normal and schizophrenic patients. For example, in combined samples of normal and schizophrenic people, a particular COMT gene variant, the val genotype, predicts poorer performance on tasks of frontal lobe function (Egan et al., 2001), as well as more deficient sensory filtering (Lu et al., 2007).

Another major hypothesis regarding the cause of schizophrenia is the **neurodevelopmental hypothesis**. This hypothesis argues that neural connectivity and biochemical function are altered in subtle ways from an early age, leaving the person with a vulnerable neural organization (for a review, see Rapoport, Addington, Frangou, & MRC Psych, 2005). According to this hypothesis, the disorder will become "unmasked" later in life, after puberty or at the onset of young adulthood. The unmasking is thought to occur either because of adverse or stressful environmental conditions or because of the increased demand placed on the brain by the broader repertoire of behaviors required in adulthood (e.g., Weinberger, 1987; Bloom, 1993). Supporting this hypothesis, studies have found that individuals with schizophrenia have minor physical anomalies

(associated with atypical prenatal development), cognitive and neurologic deficits that precede the first psychotic episode, a family history of difficult births, exposure to viruses in utero, and anatomical brain abnormalities in both the formation of brain structure and cellular organization (Rapoport et al., 2005). All of these findings implicate an abnormal developmental process that precedes the first onset of schizophrenic symptoms.

One particularly imaginative study demonstrated the early developmental signs of schizophrenia by obtaining childhood home movies from adults with schizophrenia and their nonschizophrenic siblings. The researchers had doctors rate the number of abnormalities in neuromotor behavior of the children seen in the home movies; crucially, the doctors did not know whether the child was later diagnosed with schizophrenia. The neuromotor behavior of children who later developed schizophrenia was rated as more abnormal than that of their nonschizophrenic siblings, even though the movies were taken long before the identifiable onset of schizophrenic symptoms (Walker, Savoie, & Davis, 1994). However, early neuromotor abnormalities cannot predict with certainty who will develop schizophrenia, because such abnormalities are sometimes seen in children who do not develop schizophrenia. In other words, these early behaviors are not diagnostic of schizophrenia. As an analogy, pneumonia is usually accompanied by a cough, but having a cough does not mean that a person has pneumonia. Likewise, people with schizophrenia usually have neurodevelopmental abnormalities, but such abnormalities are not specific to schizophrenia.

Other evidence suggests that neurodevelopmental changes in puberty may also be related to schizophrenia (Walker & Bollini, 2002). Hormones affect how genes are expressed, which in turn can affect neuronal function and development. Some theories suggest that potential changes in synaptic connectivity or pruning relatively soon after puberty may occur atypically in individuals with schizophrenia. Because adolescence is presumed to be a time of changes in dopamine activity (Sisk & Foster, 2004), others have suggested that dysregulation of the dopamine system is associated with the onset of schizophrenic symptoms. Some researchers have argued that individuals who later develop schizophrenia are characterized by reduced prefrontal control over striatal dopaminergic transmission, which in turn causes schizophrenic behavior such as hallucinations and delusions (Heinz, Romero, Gallinat, Juckel, & Weinberger, 2003).

Although the exact anatomical and neural changes that lead to the first onset of schizophrenic symptoms are not yet clear, it is clear that schizophrenia is associated with brain changes during development. For example, as shown in ● Figure 14.8, children and adolescents who show schizophrenic symptoms at an early age have already suffered gray-matter loss. This gray-matter loss occurs throughout the cortex, with the greatest loss beginning with posterior regions and then moving forward to encompass the frontal lobes (Thompson et al., 2001). These findings fit well with other research demonstrating abnormalities in several cortical regions in adults with schizophrenia.

■ Implications for Treatment

One of the biggest challenges for researchers is to translate basic scientific findings into more effective treatments for mental disorders. Because various pieces of evidence point to disruption of the dopaminergic system, the most common form of treatment for schizophrenia is the administration of antipsychotic drugs that affect the dopamine systems of the brain, particularly the D_2 dopamine receptor (see Chapter 2) (Tamminga, 2009). These drugs are effective in reducing the positive symptoms of schizophrenia, but they are relatively ineffective at reducing the negative symptoms. In contrast, reduced functioning of D_1 receptors may be linked to the presence of negative symptoms

and frontal lobe dysfunction. Traditional drug treatment for schizophrenia upregulates D_2 receptors over a long period of time, which has the unfortunate and counterproductive effect of further reducing the functioning of D_1 receptors (Lidow, Williams, & Goldman-Rakic, 1998). Thus, the search continues for a drug regimen that will affect both types of receptors in a way that reduces both the positive and negative symptoms of schizophrenia.

What role can cognitive neuroscience play in guiding the search for new treatments? One implication of cognitive neuroscience research is that cognitive deficits should be targeted for treatment in schizophrenia (Braff & Light, 2004; Gold, 2004). This is particularly crucial because severe cognitive deficits measured in the laboratory are correlated with poor real-life functional outcomes and poor quality of life in schizophrenia (Green, Kern, & Heaton, 2004; Ritsner, 2007). In recent years, researchers have examined the possibility that cognitive training can be an effective intervention for schizophrenia (see McGurk, Twamley, Sitzer, McHugo, & Mueser, 2007, for a review and meta-analysis). For example, one cognitive training study focused specifically on training in speech perception and other aspects of

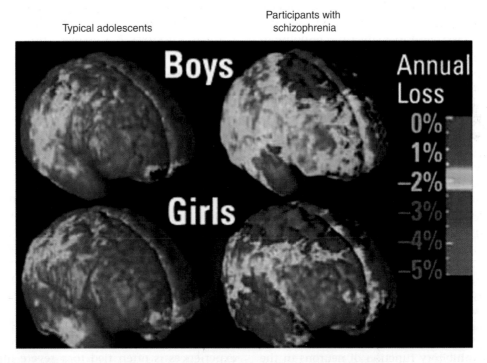

● **FIGURE 14.8 Gray-matter volume loss in schizophrenic and nonschizophrenic children and adolescents.** A longitudinal study followed participants from 13 to 18 years of age, collecting MRI scans at two-year intervals. Results showed that the loss of gray matter (measured here as % loss per year) across widespread cortical regions was pronounced in adolescents with schizophrenia compared to typical adolescents. *Source:* CNS Spectr. 2007;12(3 suppl 4):1–16. Copyright CNS Spectrums LLC.

auditory processing (Fisher, Holland, Merzenich, & Vinogradov, 2009). Patients with schizophrenia were randomly assigned to the auditory training or to a control group that played computer games for an equivalent amount of time. After 10 weeks of training, participants in the training group showed improved performance on measures of verbal learning, memory, and cognitive control (see also Fisher, Holland, Subramaniam, & Vinogradov, 2009).

Further research will be needed to discover whether such cognitive interventions only affect cognitive performance, or whether they can also lead to a decrease in clinical symptoms. Additional research will also be necessary to determine how such training affects the structure and function of brain regions. For example, auditory skills depend on temporal lobe regions that are known to be deficient in schizophrenia, so future research will likely focus on how this region of cortex is influenced in a beneficial way by auditory training.

Another implication of cognitive neuroscience research is that when researchers are evaluating whether a new biological treatment (such as a new drug) is effective in treating schizophrenia, they should assess whether it improves cognitive functioning. One test of whether a drug "works" in treating schizophrenia is whether it affects not only classic positive and negative symptoms, but also specific cognitive functions compromised in schizophrenia, such as attentional filtering or working memory. For example, an effective drug should improve performance on anti-saccade and working-memory tasks, lead to a larger P_{300} response to stimuli, and normalize the P_{50} inhibition effect (Braff & Light, 2004). These cognitive and neural markers provide quantifiable measures for researchers to use when evaluating whether a drug is successful in offsetting some of the deficits observed in schizophrenia.

As a good example of the development of possible new treatments, research has found that nicotine may have beneficial effects on some cognitive symptoms of schizophrenia. As you may know if you smoke, nicotine has the ability to heighten attention (a benefit that, of course, does not outweigh the negative effects of smoking). Astute clinicians observed that more than 90% of individuals with schizophrenia smoke tobacco, a potent source of nicotine. This led them to consider whether people with schizophrenia might have abnormal functioning of a nicotinic receptor (see Chapter 2). Smoking, they reasoned, might be self-medicating. Further research indicated that the alpha-7 nicotinic receptor and variations in its gene expression are linked to the effectiveness of inhibitory function of neurons in the hippocampus. Disruption of this inhibitory function has been linked to the sensory gating deficits (P_{50}) discussed earlier in this section. Interestingly, the P_{50} sensory gating deficit is reduced in schizophrenics who are given nicotine, suggesting a possible avenue for a novel treatment approach that is currently undergoing evaluation (Martin, Kern, & Freedman, 2004).

Cognitive neuroscience findings also point to relevant systems to study in animal models of schizophrenia (Carter, 2005; Carter & Barch, 2007). Novel pharmaceutical treatments are usually first tested on other animals before they are tested on humans. One obvious problem with animal models of schizophrenia is that it is hard to know what a hallucination or delusion might look like in a mouse. However, some of the cognitive deficits that we have discussed, such as working-memory or attentional deficits, can be modeled in other species. Likewise, neural regions that are implicated in schizophrenia, such as the frontal and temporal regions, exist in other species (although not always in the same form as humans). Therefore, when trying to ascertain whether a new drug might work to treat schizophrenia in humans, researchers can first see whether animal studies show that the drug affects cognitive and neural systems similar to those implicated in schizophrenia in humans.

Finally, cognitive neuroscience findings may suggest interventions that target specific brain regions. Because schizophrenia is known to affect several specific regions of the brain (i.e., frontal and temporal lobes), the ideal treatment should target those regions specifically. One avenue for treatment that is currently being explored is TMS, which involves magnetic stimulation of localized brain regions (see Chapter 3). Initial studies of TMS applied over frontal regions have shown mixed effectiveness in treating schizophrenic symptoms (Mogg et al., 2007; Prikryl, Kasparek, Skotakova, Ustohal, Kucerova, & Ceskova, 2007; Stanford, Sharif, Corcoran, Urban, Malaspina, & Lisanby, 2008). Further research will be necessary to determine whether interventions that affect localized brain regions hold promise for treating schizophrenia.

Depression

Depression is one of the most common mental illnesses. It afflicts approximately 1 in 10 adults within any given 12-month period, with a rate that is approximately twice as high for women as for men (Kessler, Chiu, Demler, Merikangas, & Walters, 2005). Some public health studies suggest that the cost of depression rivals that of heart disease, and depression often worsens other health conditions (Andrews & Titov, 2007; Moussavi, Chatterji, Verdes, Tandon, Patel, & Ustun, 2007). The first episode of depression that a person experiences is often tied to a severe life stress, such as bereavement or job loss, but subsequent depressive episodes may appear to be decoupled from discrete life stressors (Hammen, 2005); in many cases, then, depression can be considered a chronic disease (Andrews, 2001). In this section we consider the major characteristics of depression, and how cognitive neuroscience can shed light on this disorder.

Symptoms and Features

One issue that complicates research on depression is the vast array of symptoms, subtypes, and variations. Generally speaking, *depression* is a mood disorder characterized by chronic feelings of sadness and hopelessness and loss of interest or pleasure in activities that once were enjoyed. Other typical symptoms include poor appetite or overeating, insomnia (difficulty falling asleep or early-morning awakening) or hypersomnia (too much sleeping), low energy, slowed thinking and actions, low self-esteem, poor concentration and difficulty making decisions, and suicidal thoughts (*DSM-IV-TR, 2000*). As you can see, these symptoms encompass many domains of functioning, including affect, motivation, cognition, and regulation of the body's homeostatic systems.

While these features describe major depression, variations are also possible. A milder state of chronic depression lasting at least two years has been termed **dysthymia**. Depression can be seasonal, with a typical onset during mid-fall as the days quickly grow shorter and relief in the spring as the days quickly grow longer. Depression can also be interspersed between periods of mania. During manic episodes, the person often experiences euphoria, rushes of energy, reckless impulses to engage excessively in pleasurable activities such as sex and shopping, irritability, racing thoughts, and a sense of grandiose power (*DSM-IV-TR, 2000*). When mania occurs, either alternating with a depressive episode or occurring alone, a person is described as having **bipolar disorder**, formerly termed *manic-depressive illness*. At this point, it is unclear whether all of these variations of depression share similar neurocognitive characteristics, or whether each should be considered a unique entity. For present purposes, our discussion will focus primarily on major depressive disorder, the defining features of which include a profound negative mood, lack of interest in pleasurable activities, and feelings of helplessness and hopelessness.

Cognitive characteristics of depression have been well studied, and offer some clues to possible neural systems that may be disrupted. People with depression often perform poorly on standard tasks of executive functions (Elliott, 1998; Levin, Heller, Mohanty, Herrington, & Miller, 2007). Likewise, depressed people tend to recover poorly from mistakes and have difficulty with negative feedback, for example, showing increasingly poor performance after making errors (Compton, Lin, Vargas, Carp, Fineman, & Quandt, 2008; Murphy, Michael, Robbins, & Sahakian, 2003; Steele, Kumar, & Ebmeier, 2007). Depression is also associated with poor memory performance, and these deficits may be more evident when effortful encoding strategies are required (Hertel, 2000). (An example of effortful encoding is when you are at a party and you make a conscious attempt to remember that the name of the woman in the red jacket is Mary.) In addition, memory and attention are biased toward negative events and interpretations (Mineka, Rafaeli, &

Yovel, 2003). Finally, depressed individuals exhibit relatively poor performance on tasks that depend on the right hemisphere, such as judgment of line orientation, three-dimensional constructional skills, face recognition, spatial association learning, and performance with the nondominant hand on the Tactual Performance Test (Levin et al., 2007).

As you can see, multiple domains of cognition are affected by depression, implicating multiple brain regions. The most important regions to be affected are the frontal and parietal lobes, as well as limbic structures. In the next subsections, we review what is currently known about the functioning of these regions in depression.

Frontal Lobe

Many subregions of the frontal lobe have been implicated as functioning atypically in depression, including regions involved in emotional aspects of processing, such as the subgenual region of the cingulate cortex (i.e., regions below the genu or curve in the anterior part of the corpus callosum), as well as regions involved in cognitive control, such as the dorsolateral prefrontal cortex and dorsal regions of the anterior cingulate cortex (see Gotlib & Hamilton, 2008, for a review).

One region implicated in depression is the subgenual region of the anterior cingulate cortex (BA 25), which may be overactive in depression (for a review, see Ressler & Mayberg, 2007). This region, illustrated in ● Figure 14.9, shows increased activity during sad

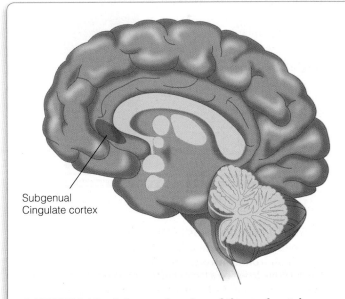

Subgenual
Cingulate cortex

● **FIGURE 14.9 Subgenual region of the prefrontal cortex that is implicated in depression.** This region shows increased activity in depressed compared to nondepressed people. Furthermore, activity in this region decreases when therapeutic interventions, such as antidepressant drugs or electroconvulsive therapy, are effective.

compared to neutral moods in nondepressed participants (Mayberg et al., 1999), and its activity is higher among depressed than nondepressed participants (Kennedy et al., 2001). Notably, activity in this region is modulated by a number of different therapeutic approaches to depression. For example, activity in the subgenual region decreases following treatment with antidepressant drugs and electroconvulsive therapy (Ressler & Mayberg, 2007). However, researchers are still attempting to understand exactly how the functions of the subgenual cingulate cortex contribute to depression. This region is highly interconnected with other regions involved in emotion, such as the hypothalamus, which controls the body's stress responses, and the insula, which represents bodily states. Therefore, dysregulation in the subgenual cingulate cortex may be related to the somatic and vegetative symptoms of depression (Levin et al., 2007).

Some cognitive features of depression that we reviewed in the previous section point to impaired functioning of the executive control systems of the frontal lobe. For example, depressed people have trouble shifting mental sets—they often get stuck in maladaptive ways of thinking. Likewise, such patients can have difficulty in changing strategies when they make errors or receive negative feedback. As we learned in Chapter 12, the dorsolateral prefrontal and dorsal anterior cingulate

cortex are especially important for these functions. Not surprisingly, brain imaging studies have found reduced activity in these regions in people who are depressed (Davidson, Pizzagalli, Nitschke, & Putnam, 2002; Levin et al., 2007). Activity in both DLPFC and dorsal cingulate cortex tends to increase or normalize following successful antidepressant treatment (Kennedy et al., 2001).

A recent study shows how dysfunctions in the cognitive control systems of the frontal lobe may contribute to poor performance in people with depression. In this study, depressed and nondepressed people completed a Stroop task while EEG activity was recorded (Holmes & Pizzagalli, 2008). The researchers examined the brain's response to performance errors during the task. As we reviewed in Chapter 12, the anterior cingulate cortex is involved in detecting errors, and it then alerts DLPFC regions so that the DLPFC can exert more top-down control over behavior. Consistent with that framework, this study found that among nondepressed participants, cingulate activity after mistakes was highly correlated with subsequent activity in the DLPFC. Depressed patients in this study showed a pronounced response to errors in the cingulate cortex, but this response was not correlated with activity in the DLPFC in the same way as in control participants. In other words, although the system that normally detects errors was intact, its connection with regions that would permit subsequent adaptive changes in behavior was disrupted. This disruption in the functional connectivity between cingulate and DLPFC regions may explain why depressed people are unable to respond adaptively to performance errors or negative feedback, even when they are able to process the feedback itself.

As we discussed briefly in Chapter 13, one aspect of frontal lobe functioning that has been consistently related to depression involves hemispheric asymmetries of brain activation. Using EEG methods that measure activity in resting states, numerous studies have demonstrated greater right than left frontal activity among depressed participants (for reviews, see Davidson et al., 2002; Thibodeau, Jorgensen, & Kim, 2006). Moreover, right-greater-than-left frontal activity is consistently observed among individuals who are at risk for a depressive episode: adolescents with a family history of depression (● Figure 14.10) (Tomarken, Dichter, Garber, & Simien, 2004), infants of depressed mothers (Dawson et al., 2001; Diego, Field, Hernandez-Reif, Cullen, Schanberg, & Kuhn, 2004), and formerly depressed people whose depression is in remission (Henriques & Davidson, 1990). These findings indicate that asymmetric activation of frontal regions, as measured with EEG, may be a marker of susceptibility to depression.

As you remember from Chapter 13, left frontal activation is associated with approach behaviors, whereas right frontal activation is associated with withdrawal behaviors. Therefore, the fact that the balance of activity in depressed patients favors the right hemisphere is consistent with their lack of engagement in pleasurable

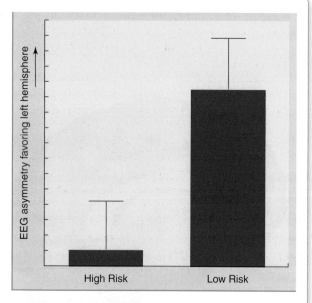

● **FIGURE 14.10 Patterns of left-right EEG asymmetry differentiate adolescents at risk for depression from controls.** Participants who are at high risk for depression, based on a family history of depression, show less asymmetry in EEG over frontal regions than do low-risk controls. The controls show a pattern of EEG activity that favors the left frontal lobe over the right, indicating greater activity in approach-related brain regions, a pattern not observed in high-risk participants. *Source:* Tomarken, A. J., & Keener, A. (1998). Frontal brain asymmetry and depression: A self-regulatory perspective. Cognition & Emotion, 12, 387–420.

activities. This connection is clearly illustrated by one study that examined asymmetry of EEG activity over frontal regions while participants anticipated receiving a reward in a gambling task (Shankman, Klein, Tenke, & Bruder, 2007). Consistent with the approach-withdrawal model, nondepressed participants displayed increased left frontal activity during the reward condition compared to a condition with no reward incentive. However, participants with depression failed to show an increase in left frontal activity while anticipating the reward, implying a failure to engage the approach system.

Increased activity in right frontal regions is also associated with the tendency of depressed individuals to focus disproportionately on sad or negative information. For example, while performing a task that involved sad words, activity in right dorsolateral prefrontal cortex was increased in depressed participants compared to controls (Elliott, Rubinsztein, Sahakian, & Dolan, 2002). In another study, the degree of right frontal activity while listening to a sad story predicted better memory for that story among depressed than nondepressed participants (Nitschke, Heller, Etienne, & Miller, 2004). Therefore, asymmetries in frontal lobe activity are clearly associated with sadness-focused memory biases in depression.

At present, it is not clear what specific subregions of the frontal lobe are critically important for generating these frontal lobe asymmetries in activity. As we learned in Chapter 3, EEG cannot localize brain activity with the specificity of fMRI. Surprisingly, depression-related asymmetries that are so widely replicated with EEG have not been replicated often in fMRI studies (though see Grimm et al., 2008). This discrepancy is likely due to different analysis techniques used in EEG versus fMRI studies (Herrington et al., 2005). New methodological approaches are attempting to link fMRI and EEG data more closely, and these approaches will likely help us to understand better which prefrontal regions show the asymmetric activity associated with depression.

■ Posterior Cortical Regions

In addition to the frontal lobes, posterior parts of the cortex, especially in the right hemisphere, are affected by depression (Levin et al., 2007). As already mentioned earlier in this chapter, cognitive deficits in depression include difficulties on tasks of spatial function, implicating the right hemisphere. In addition, reduced activity in the posterior right hemisphere could contribute to the lethargy and fatigue seen in depression, as this region is thought to play a role in maintaining levels of arousal and vigilance (Heller, Koven, & Miller, 2003).

Evidence of reduced activation of right posterior areas in people with depression comes from several sources. Behavioral studies have shown that depressed people tend to show less of a leftward perceptual bias, indicating reduced right-hemisphere activity, during visual tasks than control participants (e.g., Keller et al., 2000).

Further, EEG studies indicate that activity over the right parietal region is reduced in depressed participants during a resting baseline state (Bruder et al., 1997; Kentgen, Tenke, Pine, Fong, Klein, & Bruder, 2000) and while performing visuospatial activities such as dot localization and line orientation tasks (Henriques & Davidson, 1997; Rabe, Debener, Brocke, & Beauducel, 2005). Recent multigenerational studies have also demonstrated reduced right parietal activity in individuals who are at risk for depression based upon a history of depression among their parents and grandparents (Bruder et al., 2005; Bruder, Tenke, Warner, & Weissman, 2007). These latter studies imply that lower activity in this region may reflect a vulnerability factor that predicts susceptibility to depression. Finally, studies using event-related potentials have demonstrated that the N_{170} response to faces was reduced in depressed patients compared to controls; the group difference was especially evident over the right parietal region and for happy faces (Deldin, Keller, Gergen, & Miller, 2000). Altered perception or memory for happy faces could contribute to the difficulties in interpersonal interaction that characterize depression (Deveney & Deldin, 2004).

In summary, the disruption of activity in right posterior regions in depression not only affects arousal and attention, but also compromises additional cognitive functions supported by these brain regions. The cognitive consequences are sometimes not considered in clinical practice, but are nonetheless important. For example, when treating someone with depression who is a forklift operator, it would be important for the individual to know that his or her spatial abilities might be compromised.

■ Subcortical Regions

Although many cognitive neuroscience studies of depression have focused on the frontal and posterior cortical regions, other studies have pinpointed abnormalities in subcortical systems as well. In particular, the amygdala appears to be overactive in depression, particularly in response to negative information, whereas subcortical reward pathways are underactive in response to positive information. In addition, some evidence points to alterations in the hippocampal system as well. Next we review evidence implicating each of these structures in depression.

As we have learned, the amygdala is involved in the processing of negative or threatening information as well as in learning the emotional significance of information. Thus, it should not surprise you that the amygdala might be affected in depressed people, who tend to see the world in a more negative light. The amygdala is more active among depressed individuals compared to control groups, even when activity is assessed during resting states (Davidson et al., 2002; Phillips, Drevets, Rauch, & Lane, 2003). Moreover, once amygdala activity is stimulated, the activity level does not subside as quickly in depressed people as in controls. For example, after presentation of a negative word, the amygdala stays active for longer in depressed people compared to controls (Siegle, Steinhauer, Thase, Stenger, & Carter, 2002; Siegle, Thompson, Carter, Steinhauer, & Thase, 2007). Moreover, amygdala activity is especially heightened in depressed people during the encoding of negative information into memory, which may account for the persistence of negative memories in depression (Hamilton & Gotlib, 2008). These findings are consistent with other evidence that depressed people have difficulty disengaging attention from negative information, which then reinforces their negative mood state.

Because depression is characterized by an inability to find any pleasure in life—a characteristic termed **anhedonia**—you might expect that people with depression would have reduced activity in the subcortical reward pathways of the brain, such as the nucleus accumbens and related regions of the ventral striatum (Nestler & Carlezon, 2006). Related dopaminergic motor systems, such as the basal ganglia, may also be implicated in the psychomotor slowing that is characteristic of depressed people. Animal models support the possible involvement of these brain systems in depression; for example, rats exhibiting helpless behavior tend to show decreased metabolism in the basal ganglia and structures of the reward pathway (Shumake & Gonzalez-Lima, 2003; see also Lavi-Avnon et al., 2008).

Several studies have examined activity in the reward system in people diagnosed with depression. One study found that among depressed people with higher levels of anhedonia, the ventral striatum was less active while viewing happy faces and generating memories of positive events (Keedwell, Andrew, Williams, Brammer, & Phillips, 2005). Likewise, depressed participants showed reduced activity in the ventral striatum in response to positive words, compared to nondepressed controls; those who showed more pronounced reductions in activity also reported less interest or pleasure in life activities (Epstein et al., 2006). Similar results have been reported in a sample of children and adolescents at risk for depression based on a family history of depression (Monk et al., 2008; see also Forbes et al., 2006, 2009; Forbes, Shaw, & Dahl, 2007). Because the reward pathway is one of the brain's major motivational systems, failure to activate this pathway could contribute to the apathy and lack of motivation seen in people who are depressed or at risk for developing depression.

Another limbic region that has been associated with depression is the hippocampus. You might be surprised that this structure is implicated in depression, because the hippocampus is often associated with memory. However, as we learned in Chapter 13, the hippocampus works in conjunction with the amygdala to provide the context for learning emotional associations (Phelps, 2004). Further, stress hormones are often elevated in depression (Arborelius, Owens, Plotsky, & Nemeroff, 1999), and these hormones are known to have a detrimental effect on the structure and function

of the hippocampus (McEwen, 2009). Indeed, several anatomical studies indicate that the size of the hippocampus is reduced in people with depression (e.g., Videbech & Ravnkilde, 2004). Interest in the role of the hippocampus in depression also increased when researchers discovered that the hippocampus is a major site for neurogenesis, the generation of new nerve cells, in adulthood (Eriksson et al., 1998; Lledo, Alonso, & Grubb, 2006) (we will cover this topic in more detail in Chapter 15). Some researchers argue that the inability to generate new cells in the hippocampus may contribute to the origin or maintenance of depression (Duman, 2004; Jacobs, 2004), although this hypothesis remains controversial (Kempermann & Kronenberg, 2003; Sapolsky, 2004).

■ Therapeutic Interventions

Treatment for depression typically involves intervention at either the cognitive or the biological level, or both in combination. Cognitive therapy consists of identifying self-defeating and pessimistic thought patterns in depression and trying to alter those ways of thinking. Biologically based interventions often involve treatment with medication. Both cognitive therapy and antidepressant medication are relatively effective in treating depression in many people (Ebmeier, Donaghey, & Steele, 2006). In the following sections, we review what is known about the neural mechanisms involved in the treatment of depression and consider novel treatments that have been developed based on cognitive neuroscience findings.

How Standard Treatments for Depression Affect the Brain

Depression is often treated with drugs that affect the monoamine neurotransmitter systems of the brain (see Chapter 2). Typical drug treatments include serotonin-selective reuptake inhibitors (SSRIs), such as fluoxetine (Prozac) and paroxetine (Paxil), which target the serotonin systems that are spread throughout the brain. Some other antidepressant drugs affect other monoamine neurotransmitter systems, such as the norepinephrine and dopamine systems (Berman, Sporn, Charney, & Mathew, 2009; Dunlop, Garlow, & Nemeroff, 2009). Although these drugs are well characterized at the molecular level—meaning that their immediate effects on the synapse are well understood—it is not yet clear exactly how or why they make depressive symptoms better. One possibility is that they restore a normal balance of neurotransmitter function through long-term changes in receptor sensitivity (e.g., Duman, 2009; Elhwuegi, 2004). Another proposal is that these drugs may produce their therapeutic action by stimulating neurogenesis or other aspects of nerve cell growth (e.g., David et al., 2009; Santarelli et al., 2003). Still, these must be considered only partial explanations, because they do not explain how such biochemical changes produce changes in the cognitive and emotional symptoms of depression.

Brain imaging studies may help to bridge the gap between biochemical and psychological models of depression, because we have at least a preliminary understanding of how different regions of the brain relate to psychological functions. Therefore, examining how drug treatments affect regional brain activity can give some clues about how those drugs affect mental function. For example, one PET study found that successful treatment with the antidepressant paroxetine was correlated with increased activity in several frontal lobe regions, including dorsolateral, ventral, and dorsal anterior cingulate regions (Kennedy et al., 2001; see also Anand et al., 2005). These results fit well with other cognitive and neuroimaging findings of deficits in frontally mediated executive functions in depression. Likewise, researchers have also found that cognitive therapy, which leads to symptom improvement, is accompanied by changes in patterns of brain activation (for a review, see Roffman, Marci, Glick, Dougherty, & Rauch, 2005). For example, a PET study found that successful treatment with cognitive behavioral therapy was associated with increases in activity in the hippocampus and dorsal cingulate cortex, as well as decreases in activity in medial and ventral frontal lobe regions (Goldapple et al., 2004). Therefore, both drugs and psychotherapy may work to alleviate symptoms, in part, because they give a "boost" to the regions of the brain that are important in cognitive control and executive function.

Other studies have used brain imaging to identify participants who are more or less likely to respond well to drug treatment. These studies typically assess brain activity before patients begin the drug treatment regimen, and then follow up to see which patients show the most improvement in symptoms after they have been taking the drugs for a number of weeks. One study using this kind of design examined brain activity during a task of inhibitory control, and found that depressed participants who showed greater activation in inferior prefrontal, cingulate, and subcortical limbic regions were more likely to show improved symptoms over 10 weeks of antidepressant treatment, compared to patients who showed less activity in these regions (Langenecker et al., 2007; see also Chen et al., 2007). Other studies using similar designs found that improvement in mood symptoms was predicted by higher activity in the rostral cingulate cortex during the unmedicated state (e.g., Mayberg et al., 1999; Pizzagalli et al., 2001). Interestingly, the brain activity that predicts improvement with cognitive therapy is somewhat different from the pattern of activity that predicts improvement with drug treatment. Lower activity in the ventral cingulate cortex and higher activity in the amygdala during an emotional processing task predicted better response to cognitive behavioral therapy (Siegle, Carter, & Thase, 2006). In the long run, the knowledge gleaned from such studies could help to select treatments that will be most likely to succeed for particular patients, based on each patient's pattern of brain activity (Mayberg, 2003).

However, our knowledge is still too incomplete for that to be an immediate reality.

Despite the fact that medication and cognitive therapy can be effective treatments, as many as 50% of people with depression do not show significant symptom improvement with these treatments (Berton & Nestler, 2006). Given the high prevalence of depression, the large number of people who do not respond to standard treatments, and the high risk of suicide among those who are not successfully treated, there has been great pressure to develop new treatments. Next we discuss three experimental treatments that attempt to intervene on the neurological level. These include repetitive transcranial magnetic stimulation (rTMS), deep brain stimulation, and vagus nerve stimulation. These procedures are illustrated in ● Figure 14.11.

Repetitive Transcranial Magnetic Stimulation

Among these three experimental treatments, **repetitive transcranial magnetic stimulation (rTMS)** is the least invasive and most well researched. In the United States, rTMS was approved by the FDA for treatment of depression in 2008. The procedure involves applying repetitive magnetic pulses to the brain from a generator that is held outside the scalp (Figure 14.11A; see Chapter 3 for a review of the TMS method). rTMS is conceptually similar to electroconvulsive therapy (ECT), in which electrical current is used to stimulate the brain. However, unlike ECT, rTMS does not induce seizures. As we've already noted, activity in the left prefrontal cortex appears to be underactive in depressed people; therefore, rTMS has been targeted to stimulate this region in most of the studies carried out so far.

Several studies have found that rTMS is effective for treating depression (e.g., Avery et al., 2006; Fitzgerald, Brown, Marston, Daskalakis, de Castella, & Kulkarni, 2003; Rumi et al., 2005). For example, in one study (Avery et al., 2006), people whose depression could not be treated successfully with medication were randomly assigned to receive either rTMS or a sham procedure. The rTMS protocol involved 15 sessions spread over a 4-week period. Participants in the active treatment group received stimulation over the left dorsolateral prefrontal cortex in each session. Those in the sham control group attended the same number of sessions and also had the magnetic coil positioned over the left frontal cortex; however, the coil was positioned at an angle that would not actually stimulate the brain. After the 15 sessions, researchers found that about 30% of the rTMS-treated participants showed significant symptom reduction (symptoms reduced by at least half) on a rating scale, whereas only 5% of the sham-treated group showed such improvement. Other research suggests that rTMS treatment combined with the use of antidepressant drugs may improve the effectiveness of the drug treatment (Rumi et al., 2005).

Although these results are promising, not all studies have yielded successful treatment effects using rTMS

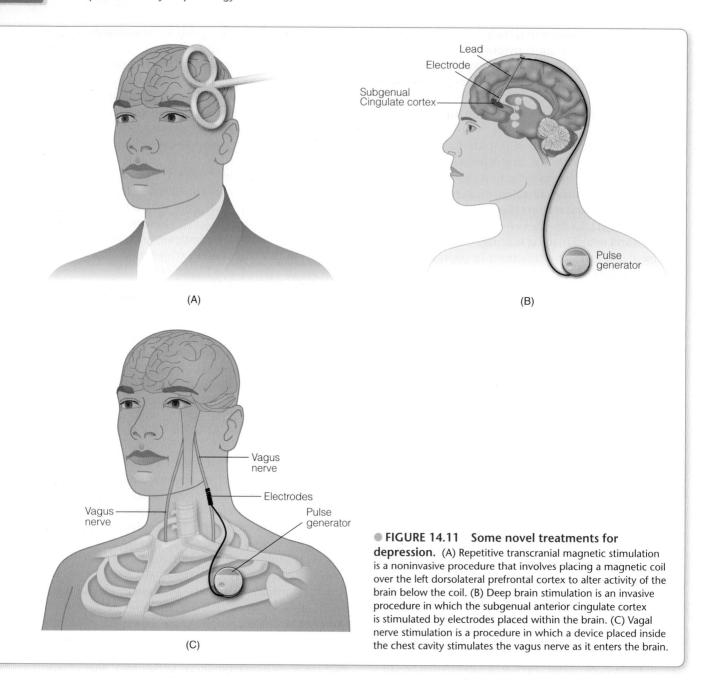

(A)

(B)

(C)

Vagus nerve

Vagus nerve

Electrodes

Pulse generator

Lead

Electrode

Subgenual Cingulate cortex

Pulse generator

● **FIGURE 14.11   Some novel treatments for depression.** (A) Repetitive transcranial magnetic stimulation is a noninvasive procedure that involves placing a magnetic coil over the left dorsolateral prefrontal cortex to alter activity of the brain below the coil. (B) Deep brain stimulation is an invasive procedure in which the subgenual anterior cingulate cortex is stimulated by electrodes placed within the brain. (C) Vagal nerve stimulation is a procedure in which a device placed inside the chest cavity stimulates the vagus nerve as it enters the brain.

(Couturier, 2005; Ebmeier, Donaghey, & Steele, 2006). The reasons for the discrepancies between results of different studies are not clear, but methodological factors may be important. There is no agreed-upon protocol that is consistently followed when using rTMS to treat depression. Furthermore, the groups receiving treatment in different studies may have differed in the nature of their symptoms, the severity of those symptoms, and the presence or absence of other disorders. Nonetheless, an analysis that integrated the results of all double-blind studies (in which neither the experimenter nor the participant knows whether rTMS or a sham procedure is given) found that rTMS over the left dorsolateral prefrontal cortex is just as effective as antidepressant medication (Schutter, 2009).

So, what is the possible mechanism that explains how TMS might work to treat depression? TMS is assumed to affect the activity of underlying brain tissue, though it can do so either by interfering with processing by that brain region or by stimulating processing in that brain region. High-frequency TMS is thought to increase brain activity, whereas low-frequency TMS decreases it (Speer et al., 2000). Thus, the underactivation of left compared to right prefrontal regions in depression could be ameliorated either by boosting the activity of left prefrontal regions or by reducing the activity of right prefrontal regions. High-frequency rTMS over the left dorsolateral prefrontal cortex (which most studies have used) increases activity in the dorsolateral prefrontal cortex and anterior cingulate regions (Kito, Fujita, &

Koga, 2008) and increases the release of the neurotransmitter dopamine in the caudate nucleus (Strafella, Paus, Barrett, & Dagher, 2001). Other researchers have attempted to decrease activity in right prefrontal regions by applying low- (rather than high-) frequency rTMS over the right frontal cortex, an approach that has also been found to be effective (Fitzgerald, Huntsman, Gunewardene, Kulkarmi, & Daskalskis, 2006). Nevertheless, the exact mechanism by which TMS affects depression is still uncertain (Paus & Barrett, 2004).

Although it might seem surprising that doctors would use a treatment without fully understanding why it works, this situation is not unusual in psychiatry (or medicine more generally). For example, you have probably taken an aspirin for fever or for pain relief, yet the mechanism by which it relieves pain is not well understood; similarly, the mechanism by which rTMS can influence mental functioning is also not fully understood. The overwhelming complexity of the brain, coupled with the pressing need for effective treatments, means that use of treatments often precedes complete knowledge of their mechanisms of action.

Deep Brain Stimulation

A more invasive experimental treatment for severe depression is **deep brain stimulation (DBS)**. This treatment involves the implantation of electrodes deep within the brain. Electrical current is then administered to modulate activity in the targeted brain region (see Figure 14.11B). DBS has been used with some regularity to treat Parkinson's disease, a movement disorder (Hardesty & Sackeim, 2007; see Chapter 5). Driven by the finding that depression involves dysfunction of subgenual regions of the cingulate cortex, researchers hypothesized that DBS targeted to this region might alleviate depression.

The initial study addressing this hypothesis focused on six patients with severe treatment-resistant depression (Mayberg et al., 2005). After DBS, the symptoms of four of these patients improved. These improvements were accompanied by decreases in activity of subgenual regions of the cingulate cortex. Although the number of participants was small, the study generated interest in the potential promise of this treatment. A follow-up study examined a larger sample of 20 patients (including the 6 patients from the prior study) (Lozano, Mayberg, Giacobbe, Hamani, Craddock, & Kennedy, 2008). Approximately a year after the DBS procedure, 55% of the patients met criteria for "response," which was defined as a 50% decrease in rated symptoms of depression.

Needless to say, implanting electrodes inside the brain is a risky procedure. Risks include complications from the surgery itself and the potential for seizures induced by the electrical current. For these reasons, it is likely that DBS will only be a treatment of last resort for patients with severe depression who have already exhausted other options. Furthermore, knowledge of the effectiveness of the procedure is still preliminary. No studies to date have included control groups, in which patients are randomly assigned to placebo or sham-operated conditions instead of the active treatment condition. There are good reasons for not including such controls in initial tests of the intervention; for example, it is ethically questionable to administer a sham surgery. However, full evaluation of the success of the procedure will ultimately require the comparison of treatment groups with adequate control groups. Further research is also needed to test the regional specificity of the effects; that is, the extent to which similar results can be obtained by stimulating brain regions other than the subgenual cingulate cortex (e.g., Malone et al., 2009; Schlaepfer et al., 2008).

Vagus Nerve Stimulation

Like DBS, **vagus nerve stimulation (VNS)** involves stimulation of the nervous system, but in this case the stimulated structure is the vagus nerve. This nerve carries sensory information from the internal organs—stomach, intestines, heart—into the brain, as well as carrying motor information from the brain to these organs. Just as DBS was adapted from treatments used for Parkinson's disease, VNS was adapted from treatments used for epilepsy. In the VNS procedure, a device containing stimulating electrodes is implanted in the upper chest, near the collarbone, where it can stimulate the vagus nerve before it enters the brain (see Figure 14.11C). This implantation is less invasive than DBS because the implantation does not penetrate the brain itself, but VNS still involves a surgical procedure and the presence of a foreign device inside the body.

Researchers using VNS to treat epilepsy noticed improvements in the mood of their patients. Building upon this finding, VNS became an experimental treatment for depression (see Groves & Brown, 2005, for review). Initial studies found significant improvements in depressive symptoms over time in people treated with VNS (e.g., Marangell et al., 2002; Rush et al., 2000). However, these studies did not directly compare VNS-treated people to untreated or sham-treated controls. Recent studies have shown more mixed and ambiguous evidence for the efficacy of VNS in treating depression (George et al., 2005; Rush, Marangell et al., 2005; Rush, Sackeim et al., 2005).

How might VNS work to treat depression? At the moment it is not entirely clear (Groves & Brown, 2005). The vagus nerve, coming from the chest cavity, terminates in a brainstem structure known as the nucleus of the solitary tract. The nucleus of the solitary tract projects to the locus coeruleus (also in the brainstem), which is the major source of noradrenergic projections throughout the brain (refer back to Figure 2.10). Therefore, stimulation of the vagus nerve can influence the activity of noradrenaline, a neurotransmitter associated with arousal and alertness (see Chapter 2). In

IN FOCUS: Can Your Genes Make You Unhappy?

Researchers have long been interested in the question of whether some people's genetic makeup predisposes them to be melancholy, pessimistic, or prone to worry or fear. Though results from twin studies imply that nearly every psychological trait, including personality traits and psychopathology, has a heritable component, twin studies cannot tell us which specific genes might play a role in mood disorders. With the recent advent of molecular genetics, such questions can now be addressed. Individual genotypes can be assessed from a simple cheek swab, in which cells from the inside of the cheek are collected with a cotton swab and DNA is extracted from the cells. Researchers can then try to determine whether possession of a particular variant of a gene is associated with certain psychological traits.

One of the best-studied genes related to emotion and mood disorders is the **serotonin transporter gene**. This gene codes for the serotonin reuptake protein, which takes the neurotransmitter serotonin from the synapse back up into the presynaptic cell (● Box Figure 14.1). Because we know that the serotonin system is implicated in depression—most antidepressant drugs are known to affect serotonin neurotransmission—it makes sense that individual differences in this particular gene could be relevant to mood disorders. There are two main variants of this gene, the so-called long allele (L) and the short allele (S). Because every person gets one copy (allele) of a gene from his or her father and one copy from his or her mother, any person can have one of three possible genotypes: L/L, S/S, or S/L. These genotypes are all fairly common in human populations; that is, they are all normal variations. Variations in this gene have been related in a surprising number of ways to psychological traits, cognition, and brain activity (Canli & Lesch, 2007; Hariri & Holmes, 2006).

Initial studies linked individual differences in the serotonin transporter gene with self-reported measures of anxiety and mood, finding that those with one or two S alleles tended to report higher levels of neuroticism, anxiety, hostility, depression, worry, and pessimism on paper-and-pencil questionnaires (e.g., Greenberg et al., 2000; Lesch et al., 1996). But researchers were interested in predicting more than self-report. Do these genotypes influence aspects of emotional learning and cognition? Subsequent research showed that people with at least one S allele were faster to acquire fear responses in a classical conditioning paradigm in which a previously neutral image, like a picture of a circle or triangle, was repeatedly paired with a mild shock (Garpenstrand, Annas, Ekblom, Oreland, & Fredrikson, 2001). People with this genotype also show different patterns of attention to emotional information. Whereas those with the L/L genotype tend to shift their attention away from emotionally threatening words, those with the S/S or S/L genotype tend to shift their attention toward emotionally threatening words (Beevers, Gibb, McGeary, & Miller, 2007). These studies show that genotype influences emotional learning and

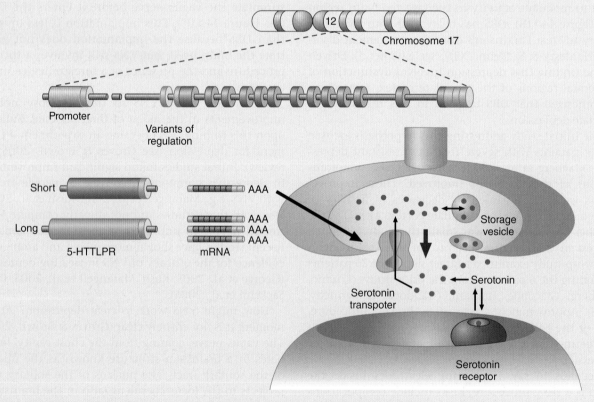

● **BOX FIGURE 14.1   Individual differences in the gene that codes for the serotonin transporter molecule.** This gene is located on chromosome 17, and a specific subregion of the gene, the promoter region, comes in either a "short" or a "long" variant. Compared to a long (L) variant, a short (S) variant results in less of the serotonin transporter molecule in the synapse and is associated with increased fear and anxiety. *Source:* Fig. 1 in Canli, T., & Lesch, K.P. (2007). Long story short: The serotonin transporter in emotion regulation and social cognition. NATURE NEUROSCIENCE, 10, 1103–1109.

attention, as well as correlating with self-reported personality traits.

Does the brain process information differently in people depending on their genotype? Given that people with an S allele seem to acquire fears faster, we would expect them to show heightened activity in the amygdala, which is responsible for fear learning. Indeed, researchers have found greater amygdala activity in response to fear stimuli relative to neutral stimuli among those with an S allele (S/S or S/L genotype) compared to those with the L/L genotype (Hariri et al., 2002; see also Canli, Omura, Haas, Fallgatter, Constable, & Lesch, 2005; Heinz et al., 2007). Another study found evidence that the amygdala may be more poorly regulated by the frontal lobes in those with an S allele (Pezawas et al., 2005). In this study, people with the L/L genotype tended to have a pattern of brain activity in which higher activity in the anterior cingulate was strongly associated with lower activity in the amygdala. This relationship was weakened in those with an S allele, implying that the cingulate had less tight control over the amygdala in individuals with the S allele. At the same time, a related study found increased coupling between amygdala and ventromedial prefrontal activity among those with the S allele (Heinz et al., 2005). Thus, in those with the S allele, the amygdala's activity may be more driven by the emotion-related ventromedial frontal cortex and, at the same time, be less influenced by cognitive control structures of the frontal lobe (● Box Figure 14.2).

Given all of these findings, it stands to reason that individuals with an S allele might be more prone to develop clinical depression or an anxiety disorder than those with the L/L genotype (Hoefgen et al., 2005). However, there is a wrinkle: Evidence indicates that it is not the mere presence of one of these genotypes alone that best predicts clinical symptoms, but rather the interaction of these genotypes with life stressors. In a landmark study, researchers collected both genotype information and measures of life stressors over a six-year period, and used those variables to predict depressive symptoms at the end of the six years (Caspi et al., 2003). Results revealed that those individuals who had the combination of a high number of life stressors and the S/S genotype were most likely to show high levels of depressive symptoms. The presence of an S/S genotype in a person with low levels of stress was not associated with depression. These results are an excellent demonstration of **gene-environment interactions**. A particular outcome—in this case, depression—can be predicted only when both genetic and environmental factors are taken into account.

Although these gene-environment results are promising and have been replicated by some other studies (e.g., Kaufman et al., 2004; Taylor, Way, Welch, Hilmert, Lehman, & Eisenberger, 2006), a recent meta-analysis called into question the reliability of the findings across all the studies that have tried to replicate them (Risch et al., 2009). The meta-analysis found that although depression is clearly associated with the presence of life stressors, the role of the 5HTT genotype in predicting the impact of those life stressors on the development of depression is not consistent across studies. Differences in results across studies may be due to different samples, different ways of measuring life stressors, or different clinical indices. Nevertheless, future research is likely to continue to consider how life experiences interact with specific genetic factors to predict mental health outcomes.

Thus, the answer to the question "Can your genes make you unhappy?" may be a partial "yes." People with the S allele of the serotonin transporter gene appear to be more reactive to negative emotional information and are perhaps more likely to develop depression in response to serious life stressors, compared to people with L/L genotypes. However, there are important caveats. First, many people have a copy of the S allele—as much as 20% of the population has the S/S genotype, and roughly 50% of the population has the S/L genotype. Clearly, not all of these people are clinically depressed! So, while a single gene may provide some predictive information about a person's likelihood of responding negatively to stress, it is clearly not the sole determinant. Other genes and life experiences also interact in complex and as-yet-unknown ways to influence a person's resilience to the slings and arrows of life.

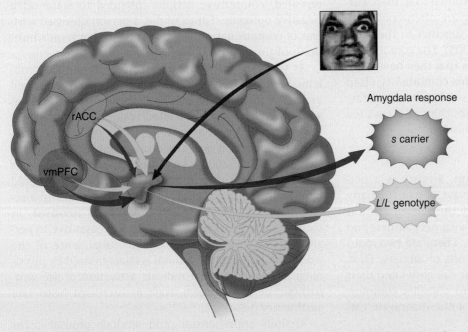

● **BOX FIGURE 14.2   Possible differences in interregion connectivity associated with serotonin transporter genotype.** The amygdala's response to a fearful face is stronger among those who are carriers of the S allele (S/S or S/L genotype) compared to those with the L/L genotype. One possible reason for this genotype difference is that the L/L genotype may be characterized by greater top-down control over the amygdala by the rostral anterior cingulate cortex (rACC). This difference in top-down control is depicted by the larger arrow from the rACC to the amygdala for the L/L group (yellow arrow) compared to the S carriers (blue arrow). In contrast, the amygdala may be more activated by the ventromedial prefrontal cortex (vmPFC) in S carriers compared to those with the L/L genotype. *Source:* Fig 1 in Hamann, S (2005). Nature Neuroscience, 8, 701–703.

other words, VNS might act to ameliorate the states of low arousal that are typical in depression. In addition, the nucleus of the solitary tract also connects to limbic structures, projecting directly to the amygdala and indirectly to the hippocampus. Therefore, stimulation of the vagus nerve has the potential to alter brain activity in these regions, which, as we have learned, appear to function atypically in depression.

As with rTMS and DBS, studies of the effectiveness of VNS have preceded a full understanding of its mechanism of action, and researchers continue to debate whether there is enough promising evidence to justify the risks. Nevertheless, research on these experimental treatments is being actively pursued in order to expand treatment options when traditional antidepressant drugs and cognitive therapies are not successful. Ultimately, researchers and patients must weigh the risks of these procedures against the risks of leaving depression untreated, as untreated depression can involve severe disability and risk of suicide.

Anxiety Disorders

Anxiety disorders are also very prevalent in the population; almost 20% of the population will be affected by an anxiety disorder within a given 12-month period (Kessler, Chiu et al., 2005). Like depression, anxiety disorders are more common among women than men. Furthermore, depression and anxiety are often comorbid, meaning that they tend to occur together in the same individuals (Kessler, Chiu et al., 2005). The comorbidity of anxiety and depression suggests that they have common origins. At the same time, this comorbidity often complicates research, because it is difficult to separate cognitive and neural characteristics that are associated uniquely with anxiety versus depression.

■ Symptoms and Features

Like schizophrenia and depression, anxiety is a heterogeneous syndrome. Anxiety plays a role in many different disorders, though all of the related clinical conditions share a preoccupation with nervousness and fear that interferes with daily life. There are two main ways of organizing all the variations of anxiety. First, we can consider separate diagnostic categories and their typical symptoms. Second, we can consider common dimensions that underlie many of the diagnostic categories, such as worry or panic.

The main diagnostic categories of anxiety disorders include phobias, panic disorder, posttraumatic stress disorder, generalized anxiety disorder, and obsessive-compulsive disorder. Although all these conditions involve the experience of fear and anxiety, they differ in the object, cause, and manifestation of the fear. **Phobias** are fears centered on specific objects or situations, such as spiders, snakes, heights, closed spaces,

or social settings. To qualify as a phobia, a fear must be irrational and interfere with normal functioning. People with phobias often go to great lengths to avoid situations in which they may encounter the feared object, and they may panic when confronted with that object. In contrast, when a person has repeated panic attacks—which include sensations of extreme bodily hyperarousal, dizziness, shortness of breath, elevated heart rate, and sense of losing control—he or she is diagnosed with a **panic disorder**. Panic disorder may be associated with fear of specific situations, such as being in a public space, but it need not be.

Whereas the origins of phobias and panic disorder may be uncertain, **posttraumatic stress disorder (PTSD)** has a clear origin: a deeply traumatic experience such as combat, rape, or survival of torture, natural disaster, or other life-threatening experience. Symptoms of PTSD include extremely vivid and intrusive recollections of the traumatic situation (such as nightmares), avoidance of situations related to that experience, chronically elevated bodily arousal, and feelings of survivor guilt and suicidal thoughts.

Generalized anxiety disorder involves a free-floating and chronic experience of anxiety. In this disorder, the anxiety is not tied to any specific triggering event or object, which makes it more difficult to address and treat. Finally, in **obsessive-compulsive disorder**, the afflicted person has obsessive thoughts about harm and, to cope with that anxiety, engages in repeated, compulsive actions intended to ward off a negative outcome. For example, a person obsessed with fear of contamination may wash his or her hands hundreds of times a day (*DSM-IV-TR*, 2000).

As you can see, there are a variety of clinical problems related to anxiety, and each has unique as well as shared features. To emphasize some commonalities across different anxiety-related conditions, researchers have identified two main dimensions of anxiety: anxious apprehension and anxious arousal (e.g., Nitschke, Heller, & Miller, 2000). **Anxious apprehension** refers to the nervous anticipation of something bad that could happen in the future; the one word that sums up anxious apprehension is "worry." **Anxious arousal**, in contrast, refers to a state of bodily and cognitive hyperarousal that corresponds with our usual sense of the word "panic." Anxious arousal is characterized by physiological symptoms that indicate activation of the sympathetic nervous system, such as increased heart rate and sweaty palms.

Anxious apprehension and anxious arousal occur in different mixes in the various anxiety disorders. For example, in generalized anxiety disorder, worry dominates. During panic attacks, anxious arousal dominates; however, a person with panic disorder often develops worries about a potential panic attack. Likewise, someone with a phobia about public speaking may worry in advance about an upcoming class presentation, and he or she may experience anxious arousal (panic) at the time of the presentation. As we will see later, anxious apprehension and arousal appear to have different neural correlates.

Cognitively, the main feature of anxiety disorders is an exaggerated bias to pay attention to threatening information in the world (Mineka, Rafaeli, & Yovel, 2003). This attentional bias has been demonstrated through various cognitive tasks. In the **emotional Stroop task**, the person must identify the ink color of words. Anxious individuals are slower to name the ink color of emotionally threatening words, such as "kill," than nonemotional words such as "sum," implying that attention has been automatically captured by the word's emotional meaning (● Figure 14.12A). Another task used to demonstrate attentional bias toward threatening information is the **dot probe task**. In this task, the person simply has to indicate the presence of a dot that is flashed on the screen. The dot is preceded by a pair of words, one of which is emotionally threatening. Researchers compare the speed of response to the dot depending on whether it appears at the same or opposite location in relation to the threatening word (● Figure 14.12B). Participants who shift attention toward the emotional word will be faster to respond to the dot when it appears at that location. In these tasks and in others that are similar, anxious individuals tend to show an increased attentional focus on threatening information, especially if the information is associated with the specific object of their anxiety (e.g., the word "web" for people who have a phobia of spiders).

■ Amygdala and Hippocampus

It should not be surprising that the amygdala is implicated in anxiety disorders. As we learned in Chapter 13, the amygdala is crucial for the acquisition of learned fears, and it is well situated to provoke the body's fight-or-flight response to stimuli. This structure is also important in directing attention to stimuli that are especially emotionally salient or urgent, and for this reason it plays a role in threat-related attentional biases in anxiety.

Numerous studies have found that activity in the amygdala is increased when anxious individuals are confronted with their fear-inducing objects or situations. For example, the amygdala's activity is increased in people who have a social phobia (compared to control groups) when viewing faces (Birbaumer et al., 1998; Schneider et al., 1999) or asked to make a public speech (Tillfors et al., 2001). Among social phobics who were treated with either anxiety-relieving drugs or cognitive therapy, improvement in symptoms was paralleled by decreases in amygdala activity during a public speaking task (Furmark et al., 2002). Other research has also found increased amygdala activity in combat-related PTSD patients viewing combat scenes (Rauch et al., 1996; Shin et al., 1997), listening to combat-related sounds (Pissiota, Frans, Fernandez, von Knorring, Fischer, & Fredrikson, 2002), or viewing pictures of fearful faces (Rauch et al., 2000). Although not all studies confronting an anxious person with the feared stimulus have found amygdala activation (see Kent & Rauch, 2009, for a review), the discrepant results may be due to

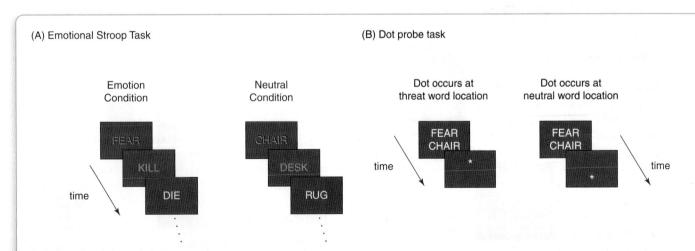

(A) Emotional Stroop Task

Emotion Condition

Neutral Condition

time

FEAR
KILL
DIE

CHAIR
DESK
RUG

(B) Dot probe task

Dot occurs at threat word location

Dot occurs at neutral word location

FEAR
CHAIR
*

FEAR
CHAIR
*

time

time

● **FIGURE 14.12   Cognitive tasks used to measure attentional biases in anxiety.** (A) Emotional Stroop task: The participant must identify the ink color while ignoring the word meaning. Anxious people are slower when the word is emotionally threatening (e.g., "fear") than when it is neutral (e.g., "chair"). (B) Dot probe task: The participant must press a button as quickly as possible when a dot appears somewhere on the screen. The dot is preceded by two words, one threatening and one neutral. These words are irrelevant to the main task. However, anxious people will tend to respond more quickly to the dot when it appears at the same location where a threatening word had just been shown than when it appears at the location where the neutral word was shown, indicating that attention has been shifted to that threatening word.

technical issues, such as imaging methods that were not optimized to detect amygdala activity.

Research also shows that anxiety influences the amygdala's sensitivity to threatening information that is presented outside the main focus of attention. In one study (Bishop, Duncan, & Lawrence, 2004), participants viewed a display that included pairs of faces and pairs of houses (Figure 14.13A). In one condition in the study, the participants made a decision about the houses while ignoring the faces; in the other condition, they made a decision about the faces while ignoring the houses. The expressions on the faces were sometimes fearful and sometimes neutral. Among participants with low self-reported levels of anxiety, the amygdala was responsive to the fearful faces only when the faces were the main focus of attention. However, for participants who reported high levels of anxiety, the amygdala was responsive to the fearful faces even when they were outside the main focus of attention, that is, when the participant was supposed to be paying attention to the houses and ignoring the faces (Figure 14.13B). These findings likely reflect the preferential processing of threatening information in anxious people, even when that information is not relevant to the task at hand (see also Bishop, Jenkins, & Lawrence, 2007).

The amygdala is also crucial in **extinction**, the process by which acquired fears are later lost. Typically, extinction is studied in animal models by first training an animal to associate a particular stimulus with an aversive outcome, and then presenting the stimulus repeatedly without the aversive outcome and measuring how long it takes the animal to learn that the stimulus is now "safe." Extinction learning in animals depends upon the activity of NMDA receptors within the amygdala; when those receptors are blocked, extinction is eliminated (Davis, Myers, Ressler, & Rothbaum, 2005). Further, when NMDA receptors within the amygdala are stimulated, extinction is facilitated (Ledgerwood, Richardson, & Cranney, 2003; Walker, Ressler, Lu, & Davis, 2002). Treatment for anxiety disorders such as phobias and PTSD has long taken advantage of the process of extinction by gradually and repeatedly exposing the person to the feared situation or cues in a safe setting, so that over time the fear is lost or inhibited. Recent studies have found that treating phobic patients with an NMDA agonist can speed up this process of extinction learning (Ressler et al., 2004).

Although the amygdala is clearly involved in the emotional learning that plays a role in anxiety disorders, the hippocampus is also implicated, particularly in PTSD. Several studies have found smaller hippocampal volumes in combat veterans who have PTSD compared to control groups (see Karl, Schaefer, Malta, Dörfel, Rohleder, & Werner, 2006, for a meta-analysis). The hippocampus is crucial in supporting aspects of memory encoding and consolidation (see Chapter 10), and some symptoms of PTSD, such as flashbacks, involve problems in controlling memory retrieval.

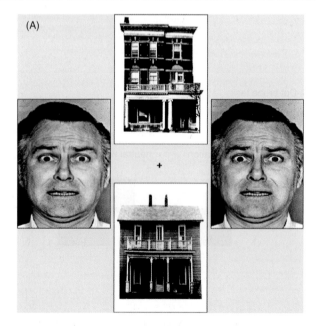

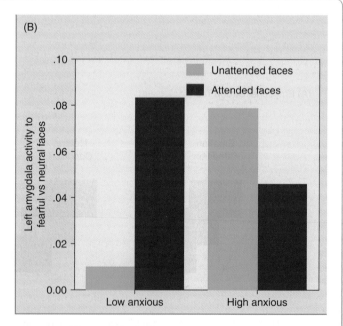

 FIGURE 14.13   Anxiety affects amygdala response to unattended threats. (A) Participants in this study viewed an array that included faces and houses. In some sets of trials, they were supposed to pay attention to the faces; in other sets, they were to pay attention to houses. (B) In low-anxious people, the amygdala showed greater response to fearful faces compared to neutral faces only when the participant was supposed to pay attention to the faces. In high-anxious people, the amygdala was responsive to the fearful faces even when the participant was supposed to ignore them. *Source:* Fig 1 and 3b from Bishop et al. (2004). State anxiety modulation of the amygdala response to unattended threat-related stimuli. Journal of Neuroscience, 24, 10364–10368

Therefore, it is logical to consider whether deficient hippocampal functioning may contribute to symptoms of PTSD. One question that immediately arises is whether people with a smaller hippocampus prior to the trauma are less able to cope and therefore more likely to develop PTSD, or, alternatively, whether the trauma itself has a direct influence on the hippocampus that leads to the development of PTSD. The latter possibility is plausible because animal studies have shown that stress, through its effects on hormone levels, can have a damaging effect on the hippocampus (McEwen, 2009).

To address whether hippocampal differences precede or follow the traumatic experience in PTSD, one group of researchers used a clever design involving identical twins (Gilbertson et al., 2002). The participants in the sample were all identical twins in which one twin of each pair was exposed to combat and the other was not. Some of those who were in combat later developed PTSD, and some did not. Replicating other findings, veterans with PTSD showed a smaller hippocampus than those without. More interestingly, the identical twins of veterans with PTSD had smaller hippocampi than the twins of veterans without PTSD. Furthermore, identical twins tended to have similarly sized hippocampi. These findings suggest that the small hippocampus seen in patients with PTSD may precede the trauma experience, rather than being a consequence of the trauma experience (see also Gurvits et al., 2006; Pitman et al., 2006). In this sense, a small hippocampus may be a vulnerability factor that makes some people more likely to develop the disorder when faced with an intense trauma.

■ Frontal Lobe

As we reviewed in Chapter 13, one mechanism of regulating emotional experience involves exerting top-down control of frontal regions over subcortical emotion structures such as the amygdala. Therefore, the functioning of the frontal lobes, and particularly their relationship to subcortical structures, has been examined in anxious people, in whom fear responses do not seem to be well regulated. As we discuss next, the functioning of both medial and dorsolateral frontal regions is relevant to understanding anxiety.

In the previous section, we discussed the role of the amygdala in fear extinction. However, the amygdala is not solely responsible for this process; regions of the medial prefrontal cortex contribute to extinction as well. Animal studies show that lesions in the medial prefrontal cortex can lead to an impairment in extinction, particularly in the ability to retain learned extinctions—the knowledge that a cue now signals a "safe" situation (Milad, Rauch, Pitman, & Quirk, 2006; Sotres-Bayon, Bush, & LeDoux, 2004). ● Figure 14.14 illustrates sample results from extinction learning in an animal study. Imaging studies in humans confirm that activity in the ventromedial prefrontal cortex occurs

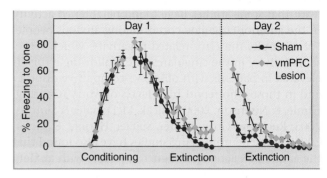

● **FIGURE 14.14   Effects of medial prefrontal lesions on extinction learning.** During the conditioning phase, the rat learns to associate a tone with a shock; freezing behavior to the tone (shown on the y axis) increases equally for sham-lesioned animals and those who received a lesion to the medial ventromedial prefrontal cortex (vmPFC) prior to conditioning. During the extinction phase, the tone is presented alone without the shock. As the number of trials without shock increases, freezing behavior to the tone decreases, slightly more for sham-lesioned than vmPFC-lesioned animals. More dramatically, however, rats with vmPFC lesions do not retain extinction learning from the first to the second day of testing to the same extent as sham-lesioned rats, and extinction must be relearned. *Source:* Fig. 2 in Milad, M. R. et al. (2006). Fear extinction in rats: Implications for human brain imaging and anxiety disorders. Biological Psychology, 73, 61–71. Reprinted by permission of Elsevier.

when an individual retains the knowledge learned during extinction training (Phelps, Delgado, Nearing, & LeDoux, 2004). Reduced activation of the ventromedial prefrontal cortex in anxious people, such as patients with PTSD (Milad et al., 2006), may lead to difficulty in learning that feared situations are actually safe.

Prefrontal-amygdala interactions may also contribute to the threat-related attentional bias that is characteristic of anxious people (Bishop, 2007). One study provided evidence that frontal lobe regions may not exert as much top-down control in anxious individuals when distracting threatening information is present (Bishop, Duncan, Brett, & Lawrence, 2004). In this study, as threatening distractors became more frequent, activity in dorsolateral frontal regions tended to increase, presumably as part of a system of cognitive control. However, this effect was reduced in people who reported high levels of anxiety. Highly anxious participants also had reduced activity in the rostral anterior cingulate cortex in this study. Together, the results suggest possible dysregulation of frontal lobe control systems in anxious people. Although the implications for treatment are not yet clear, one possibility is that cognitive training in controlling the focus of attention could benefit anxious people.

The anterior cingulate cortex has also been implicated in a number of different anxiety disorders. As we've learned previously, portions of the anterior cingulate are especially involved in detecting conflict. Its activity can serve as an important signal to other brain systems, indicating a matter of some urgency that the brain needs to attend to. It may not surprise you, then, to learn that some studies have found heightened activity in the anterior cingulate cortex among anxious people. For example, the error-related negativity, which represents activity in the cingulate cortex following errors, is elevated in patients with obsessive-compulsive disorder and in those who report high levels of worry (Gehring, Himle, & Nisenson, 2000; Hajcak, McDonald, & Simons, 2003; Ruchsow, Grön, Reuter, Spitzer, Hermle, & Kiefer, 2005). Some neuroimaging studies have also found that the cingulate's activity is higher in people with anxiety disorders compared to control participants, both during resting conditions and when provoked by threatening stimuli (Kent & Rauch, 2009). An overactive anterior cingulate region may reflect an overactive alarm system that keeps attention focused on potential threats.

One of the most controversial therapies for intractable anxiety disorders is a surgical intervention in the cingulate region. A procedure called **cingulotomy** involves the intentional creation of bilateral lesions in the anterior cingulate (see Mashour, Walker, & Martuza, 2005, for a review of cingulotomy and related procedures). Needless to say, this procedure has generated much debate, because brain surgery is highly invasive and brain lesions are not reversible. Therefore, the procedure should never be used unless the person's anxiety is so severe that daily functioning is impossible, and only when all other treatments have failed. Although some studies suggest potential benefits of cingulotomy in reducing anxiety (Cohen, Paul, Zawacki, Moser, Sweet, & Wilkinson, 2001; Dougherty et al., 2002), it is nearly impossible to conduct double-blind placebo-controlled tests of this surgical intervention. Cingulotomy reminds us of the limits of cognitive neuroscience approaches to mental disorders: Although current neuroimaging tools allow us to pinpoint malfunctioning brain regions, direct intervention in the brain itself is not always an advisable or feasible treatment option.

■ Hemispheric Asymmetries

The distinction between the two main dimensions of anxiety, anxious apprehension and anxious arousal, has been best articulated in the study of hemispheric asymmetries (Heller, Koven, & Miller, 2003). Generally, evidence indicates that anxious apprehension is associated with activity in the left frontal region, whereas anxious arousal is more closely associated with posterior right-hemisphere activity.

Anxious apprehension, or worry, is typically a verbal process. (This makes it difficult to study in animal models!) Uncontrollable thoughts run through the worrier's head, and these thoughts are more likely to take the form of words than images (Behar, Zuellig, & Borkovec, 2005). Therefore, it makes sense that the left frontal region, which generates speech, would be implicated. Several EEG studies have indeed found patterns of activity favoring the left frontal region among people prone to worry (Carter, Johnson, & Borkovec, 1986;

Heller, Nitschke, Etienne, & Miller, 1997; Hofmann, Moscovitch, Litz, Kim, Davis, & Pizzagalli, 2005).

At first blush, these findings might seem inconsistent with the approach-withdrawal model of frontal lobe asymmetry (see Chapter 13). Isn't activation of the left frontal lobe supposed to be associated with positive, approach-related emotions? It is difficult to conceive of worry as a positive or reward-related experience. A recent study helped to solve this dilemma by using the spatial resolution of fMRI (Engels et al., 2007). In this study, different subregions of the frontal lobe were associated with positive emotionality versus worry. In particular, Broca's region in the left inferior frontal gyrus was more activated in worriers, consistent with the experience of worry as internal verbalization. At the same time, a separate left dorsolateral frontal region became more active when positive than negative words were seen, consistent with the approach-withdrawal model (● Figure 14.15A).

Whereas worry is associated with left-hemisphere verbal systems, anxious arousal is more closely associated with right-hemisphere systems that govern attentional vigilance and autonomic arousal (Heller, Koven, & Miller, 2003). For example, during conditions intended to provoke anxious arousal, EEG activity increases in posterior regions of the right hemisphere (Heller et al., 1997). Increased EEG activity in the right posterior region is also associated with hyperarousal symptoms in patients with PTSD (Metzger et al., 2004). An fMRI study correlated anxious arousal with increased activity in the right inferior temporal gyrus during the processing of negative information in a Stroop task (● Figure 14.15B; Engels et al., 2007). Together, these findings indicate that experiences of heightened anxious arousal or panic activate the posterior right hemisphere.

As we have seen, different neural systems appear to underlie distinct aspects of anxiety, with anxious apprehension being linked to activity in left frontal regions and anxious arousal being linked to activity in right posterior regions. When designing new therapeutic interventions for anxious individuals, it may be fruitful to consider the nature of the person's anxiety, because distinct brain circuits are likely to be involved in anxious states characterized by worry compared to panic.

■ Action Systems in Obsessive-Compulsive Disorder

The brain regions that we have discussed so far—amygdala, prefrontal cortex, and hemispheric asymmetries—have been implicated in more than one anxiety disorder (such as phobias or posttraumatic stress disorder). In other words, these brain systems contribute to several different manifestations of anxiety, not just one diagnostic category. However, there is one additional brain system that appears to be uniquely implicated in *obsessive-compulsive disorder (OCD)*. The major behavioral feature that differentiates OCD from the other anxiety disorders is the compulsive and ritualistic

(A)

(B)

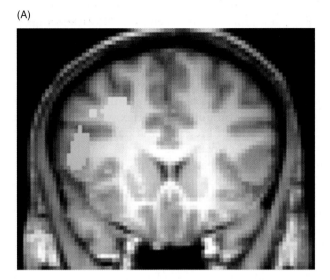
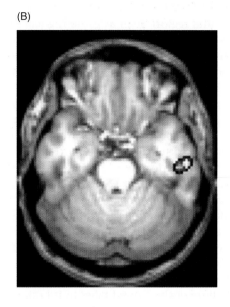

● FIGURE 14.15 Regions associated with individual differences in anxious apprehension and anxious arousal. (A) A region of left inferior frontal gyrus (shown in blue) was more activated in response to negative words in people who scored high on a measure of anxious apprehension, or worry, whereas regions of DLPFC (shown in yellow) were activated in response to positive words. (B) Among people who scored high on a measure of anxious arousal, or panic, a region of the right inferior temporal gyrus became especially activated by negative words. *Source:* From Fig 4 and 2 from Engels, AS et al. (2007). Specificity of regional brain activity in anxiety types during emotion processing. Psychophysiology, 44, 352–363. By permission of John Wiley & Sons, Inc.

actions that the person performs. Therefore, researchers have examined whether alterations in the circuits that initiate and inhibit actions may be disrupted in some way in OCD.

Of particular interest are the basal ganglia, an interconnected circuit of subcortical regions that control the initiation and cessation of movement (see Chapter 5). Numerous studies have found anatomical differences between people with OCD and control participants in the caudate nucleus, a part of the basal ganglia (● Figure 14.16) (Friedlander & Desrocher, 2006). Symptom provocation studies—in which stimuli are presented to provoke reactions in individuals with OCD—have found increased activity in the caudate and related basal ganglia regions (Chamberlain, Blackwell, Fineberg, Robbins, & Sahakian, 2005). Finally, successful treatment for OCD, whether through drugs or psychotherapy, appears to reduce functional activity within the basal ganglia (Nakatani et al., 2003; Saxena et al., 1999).

However, it is not only the basal ganglia that have been implicated in OCD; other related regions, such as the orbitofrontal cortex, also appear to show abnormalities. For example, patients with OCD are deficient in performing tasks of reversal learning, in which one must respond to an item that previously was not rewarded. These types of tasks are thought to depend upon the orbitofrontal region (Chamberlain et al., 2005).

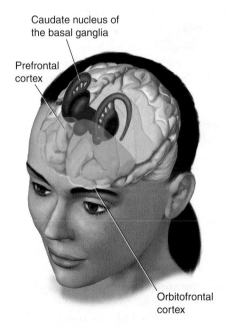

Caudate nucleus of the basal ganglia

Prefrontal cortex

Orbitofrontal cortex

● FIGURE 14.16 Basal ganglia are abnormal in obsessive-compulsive disorder. Patients with OCD display anatomical abnormalities in the caudate nucleus, and functional imaging studies show increased activity in this area in response to OCD-related images. Deficits in orbitofrontal cortex, shown in yellow, functioning have also been identified in people with OCD. © 2010 Cengage Learning

Likewise, people with OCD tend to perform poorly on decision-making tasks that are known to depend on the orbitofrontal region, such as gambling tasks (Cavedini, Gorini, & Bellodi, 2006). Therefore, OCD may be best characterized by disruptions in control loops that link orbitofrontal cortex with the basal ganglia (Graybiel & Rauch, 2000).

How could disruption in an orbitofrontal–basal ganglia circuit contribute to the compulsive behaviors seen in OCD? As you remember from Chapter 13, the orbitofrontal cortex plays an important role in representing the reward value of stimuli and actions. Therefore, a dysfunction in the orbitofrontal region in OCD could result in a skewed pairing of actions and rewards, such that certain actions (e.g., handwashing) become rigidly associated with reward (that is, the reduction of anxiety). This action-reward coupling may become reinforced and difficult to overcome. As a result of the skewed reward value of the compulsive action, as well as the failure of the frontal lobes to inhibit stereotyped actions generated by the basal ganglia, the compulsive actions are repeated again and again. These aspects of OCD share some features in common with addiction, to which we turn next.

Substance Abuse and Addiction

In addition to schizophrenia, depression, and anxiety disorders, substance abuse is one of the most common mental afflictions. In any 12-month period, about 4% of Americans are grappling with addiction, and the number increases to about 15% when lifetime prevalence is estimated (Kessler, Berglund et al., 2005; Kessler, Chiu et al., 2005). Substance abuse and addiction are more common among men than women, but the gender gap appears to be closing in recent years (Kessler, Berglund, et al., 2005). Substance abuse is also correlated with socioeconomic variables: those with lower levels of education are more likely to face substance abuse problems (Kessler, Berglund, et al., 2005). Finally, substance abuse can occur together with other psychological problems, such as depression and PTSD.

Needless to say, it is difficult to draw clear lines between "use" and "abuse" of substances such as alcohol, tobacco, and illicit drugs like cocaine and heroin. Drinking a glass of wine with dinner every night does not constitute alcohol abuse, but drinking to excess in ways that threaten the safety of oneself or others is generally considered to be a problem. The term *addiction* is usually applied in situations in which the person experiences withdrawal symptoms without the drug, and when the need to obtain the drug outweighs other priorities in life. However, the difficulty in defining exactly who qualifies as "addicted" poses a challenge for research on the neural correlates of addiction.

The major defining feature of substance abuse is that the person is unable to control the drug-seeking behavior even when the consequences are (or may be) severe. Severe consequences could include loss of a job and professional esteem, loss of relationships, financial losses, and even imprisonment. Yet, the addict has difficulty regulating behavior to avoid these losses; the desire for the drug outweighs these consequences.

The two main brain systems that have been related to drug abuse are the dopaminergic reward pathways and the orbitofrontal cortex, which together represent the values of rewards and punishments and act to govern behavior accordingly. In our discussion, we will consider research findings without regard to the substance abused (e.g., alcohol or cocaine) because many of the findings seem to hold true regardless of the specific substance.

■ Reward Pathways

All drugs of abuse appear to activate, either directly or indirectly, the reward pathways that stretch from the midbrain to the nucleus accumbens in the basal forebrain (see Chapter 13). Through activation of the reward pathways, the drugs exert their reinforcing effects, motivating the person to come back for more. Evidence implicates the nucleus accumbens in particular. For example, lesioning the nucleus accumbens or blocking dopamine's action within the nucleus accumbens can eliminate the rewarding effects of drugs in nonhuman animals (see Wise & Gardner, 2004, for review).

The development of drug dependence is likely to involve long-term changes in neurons within the reward system in response to the ongoing presence of the drugs. These changes are often thought of as "drug-opposite" adaptations because they counter the effects of the drugs themselves. For example, the reward pathways that are stimulated by addictive drugs may be especially underactive during the withdrawal state among chronic users (Wise & Gardner, 2004). Several different adaptations following chronic use have been investigated at the cellular and molecular levels, including changes in receptor concentrations, intracellular signaling pathways, and morphology of cells (Nestler, 2009). At this point it is unclear which of the many cellular changes accompanying drug use is most responsible for addiction observed at the behavioral level.

Given the role of the nucleus accumbens in responding to stimuli that are rewarding or reinforcing, you might expect that people would show elevated activity in this region when viewing pictures related to their drug of choice, particularly since such cues typically elicit a strong sense of craving. Some evidence supports this expectation; for example, one study found that smokers showed greater activity in the nucleus accumbens when viewing smoking-related pictures, compared to neutral pictures (● Figure 14.17A) (David et al., 2005; see also McClernon, Hiott, Huettel, & Rose, 2005). Another found that people who are heavy drinkers activate this region when given a small sip of alcohol (Filbey et al., 2008; ● Figure 14.17B). Other research has shown that

(A)

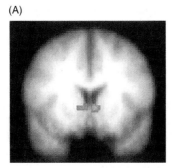

(B)

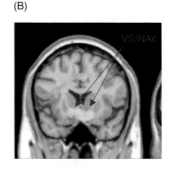

● **FIGURE 14.17   Increased activity in nucleus accumbens in addiction.** (A) When smokers viewed smoking-related pictures, compared to neutral pictures, activity was increased in the nucleus accumbens, shown here in a coronal view. (B) This same region was activated when heavy drinkers took a sip of alcohol. *Source:* From Fig 2 in David, SP et al. (2005). Ventral Striatum/Nucleus Accumbens Activation to Smoking-Related Pictorial Cues in Smokers and Nonsmokers: A Functional Magnetic Resonance Imaging Study. Biological Psychiatry, 58, 488–494. With permission from Elsevier. And Adapted by permission from Macmillan Publishers, LTD: Filbey, FM et al. (2008). Exposure to the Taste of Alcohol Elicits Activation of the Mesocorticolimbic Neurocircuitry, Neuropsychopharmacology, 33, 1391–1401.

exposure to cues associated with amphetamine led to increased dopamine release—measured by a decreased availability of "open" dopamine receptors—in the nucleus accumbens in human participants (Boileau et al., 2007).

Although the regions involved in the reward pathway are certainly implicated in substance abuse, a number of other studies have examined neural responsiveness to drug cues among chronic users and failed to find activity differences in the nucleus accumbens. However, these studies did observe group differences in a variety of other brain regions (e.g., Brody et al., 2002; Due, Huettel, Hall, & Rubin, 2002; Garavan et al., 2000; Wexler et al., 2001). These results imply that the nucleus accumbens is not necessarily the only brain region involved in addiction. In the next section, we consider the role of another brain region that is important in substance abuse, the orbitofrontal cortex.

■ Orbitofrontal Cortex

The orbitofrontal cortex (OFC) is known to be important in decision making; as we learned in Chapter 13, damage to this region often results in impaired decision making in real life situations. Because drug addicts appear to have made poor choices in their lives, the OFC is a logical place to expect dysfunctions among those with substance abuse problems (for reviews, see Dom, Sabbe, Hulstijn, & van den Brink, 2005; Schoenbaum, Roesch, & Stalnaker, 2006; Volkow & Fowler, 2000).

Studies of the behavior of addicted people confirm that they do not weigh costs and rewards normally when making decisions. For example, while all people tend to discount large future rewards in favor of immediate but

smaller payoffs, heroin addicts were even more likely than controls to undervalue long-term gains (Kirby, Petry, & Bickel, 1999). Interestingly, pathological gamblers showed the same effect, demonstrating a cognitive profile similar to that seen in those addicted to drugs (Petry, 2001). Another study found that, like patients with damage to the ventral frontal region, some substance abusers failed to show elevated skin conductance responses when considering risky options in a gambling task, and they also made more disadvantageous choices than did controls (● Figure 14.18) (Bechara & Damasio, 2002). Such performance deficits may stem from a difficulty in learning from past losses or mistakes (Garavan & Stout, 2005).

Neuroimaging evidence also indicates that the OFC region is dysfunctional in addicts. Anatomical studies show that chronic substance users have reduced gray matter in the OFC region (e.g., Brody et al., 2004; Franklin et al., 2002), as do those who had been drug abusers but are now abstinent (Tanabe et al., 2009). At the same time, exposure to drugs or drug-related cues results in increased activity in the OFC among users, and the amount of OFC activation is positively correlated with drug craving (e.g., Brody et al., 2002; Dalgleish et al., 2001; London, Ernst, Grant, Bonson, & Weinstein, 2000). OFC hyperactivity in response to drug cues is most reliably found in participants who are still actively taking the drug (Wilson, Sayette, & Fiez, 2004). Together with the decision-making deficits, these imaging findings make a compelling case that normal OFC function is disrupted in addicts.

But do these findings tell us that using addictive substances causes changes in OFC function, or do they tell

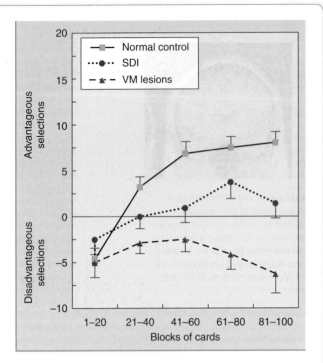

● **FIGURE 14.18 Performance on a gambling task in substance abusers, patients with ventromedial frontal damage, and control participants.** In this task, participants had to learn over time which of four decks of cards was most advantageous to select. Normal control participants show a pattern of increased selection from advantageous decks (those that return greater monetary reward). Participants with damage to the ventromedial prefrontal cortex (VM lesions) continue to choose from disadvantageous decks. Substance-dependent individuals (SDI) perform more poorly than controls but not as poorly as VM-lesioned patients. *Source:* Fig. 1 in Bechara, A., & Damasio, H. (2002). Decision-making and addiction (Part 1): Impaired activation of somatic states in substance dependent individuals when pondering decisions with negative future consequences. Neuropsychologic, 40, 1675–1689. Reprinted by permission of Elsevier.

us that people with OFC dysfunction are predisposed to become addicts? Studies of the brains of addicted people are inherently correlational; we cannot ask randomly selected people to take addictive drugs for a while and see how it may affect their brains. Therefore, the cause-and-effect relationship between substance use and OFC function is uncertain based on human studies alone. Experimental studies with nonhuman animals can offer more clues.

Some studies have found that ingestion of addictive substances can change the functioning of the OFC. For example, rats that received chronic doses of the drug amphetamine showed decreased density of dendritic spines in the OFC, in addition to increased density in the nucleus accumbens (● Figure 14.19) (Crombag, Gorny, Li, Kolb, & Robinson, 2005). Chronic cocaine administration also led rats to perform more poorly on behavioral tasks of OFC function, such as reversal learning (Schoenbaum, Saddoris, Ramus, Shaham, & Setlow,

2004). You can imagine a vicious cycle: ingesting addictive drugs disrupts the proper functioning of the OFC, and disruption of the OFC in turn leads to poor regard for the consequences of one's actions, influencing future decisions to continue drug use.

Other "vicious cycle" factors may also make it difficult to break out of a pattern of drug addiction. Some studies imply that in addiction, the substance of abuse "hijacks" the brain's frontal and limbic reward systems by lessening the reward value of other (nondrug) stimuli. In one study illustrating this phenomenon (Garavan et al., 2000), cocaine addicts and nonaddicts viewed films showing scenes of people smoking crack cocaine, sexually explicit scenes, or nature scenes. Not surprisingly, the nonaddicts showed greatest activity in prefrontal and limbic regions in response to the sexually explicit video. These same regions were activated for cocaine addicts when viewing people smoking crack cocaine, suggesting that substances of abuse activate the same brain regions that are relevant for biological rewards. Most notably, for cocaine addicts these brain regions responded *more* to the cocaine video than to the sexually explicit video. This hijacking of brain circuitry could make it doubly difficult to kick the habit, due to the diminished reward value of other, less-destructive activities that might otherwise provide a reward that is an alternative to the substance of abuse.

■ Other Brain Regions Implicated in Addiction

Although the vast majority of studies on addiction have focused either on the reward pathways or on the orbitofrontal cortex, other regions have been implicated as well. For example, neuroimaging studies comparing activation in response to drug cues between drug users and control participants have reported group differences in various regions such as the amygdala, insula, anterior cingulate cortex, and dorsolateral frontal cortex, even though these activations are not always consistent across studies (for reviews, see Bechara, 2005; Kalivas & Volkow, 2005).

Among these regions, the insula has recently received special attention for its possible role in addiction. As you remember from Chapter 13, the *insula* is a cortical region tucked inside the fissure between the frontal and temporal lobes, and it is thought to encode bodily states that contribute to emotional experience. Interestingly, a recent report found that smokers who suffered brain damage affecting the insula lost their addiction to cigarettes (Naqvi, Rudrauf, Damasio, & Bechara, 2007). Although no one is suggesting that removal of the insula ought to be considered as a treatment for addiction, these findings call attention to the possible role that bodily cues encoded by the insula may play in maintaining an addiction. One patient in this study reported that after the brain damage, his "body forgot the urge to smoke" (Naqvi et al., 2007, p. 534). Because addiction is closely associated with bodily sensations—the feel of

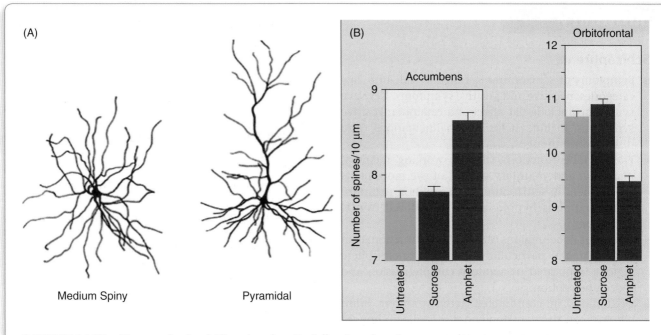

● **FIGURE 14.19   Changes in dendritic spine density following chronic exposure to amphetamines.** (A) Researchers quantified the dendritic spines of medium spiny neurons from the nucleus accumbens and pyramidal neurons from the orbitofrontal cortex. Rats who were given amphetamine for 14–20 days (depicted in red bars) showed an increase in spine density in the nucleus accumbens and a decrease in spine density in the orbitofrontal cortex, compared to sucrose-treated (blue bars) or untreated controls (green bars). *Source:* Figs. 1, 3, and 4 from Crombag, H. S., et al. (2005). Opposite effects of amphetamine self-administration experience on dendritic spines in the medial and orbital prefrontal cortex, CEREBRAL CORTEX, 15, 341–348. Reprinted by permission of Oxford University Press.

a cigarette between the lips, or the sensation of smoke in the throat—perhaps the loss of those sensations made it easier to quit.

Conclusions and Caveats

This chapter should convey that a great deal of research effort is being expended in trying to understand the neurocognitive correlates of mental disorders. This research is motivated both by the desire to develop treatments that will improve the lives of people suffering from these disorders, and by the desire to understand the basic science of the brain's workings. At the same time, you have probably become aware of some of the serious limitations on our knowledge in this area.

One major limitation is that each category of disorder is characterized by heterogeneity in symptoms, making it difficult to study "pure" profiles of disorder. Comorbidity between different disorders also adds to the problem of identifying unique features of specific disorders. For example, people with PTSD are also at increased risk for substance abuse, so studies of PTSD need to take possible substance abuse into account. Further, it is

often unclear whether a particular neural marker, such as activity in a certain brain region, is associated with a diagnostic category (e.g., major depressive disorder) or whether it is associated with a particular symptom (e.g., apathy) that might cut across different diagnostic categories. Some studies focus on people who score high on self-report measures of symptoms, even if those people do not meet the criteria for a clinical disorder.

You may also have noticed that many of the same brain regions are implicated in different disorders. For example, the prefrontal cortex, the amygdala, the cingulate cortex, and the reward systems are each implicated in more than one disorder covered in this chapter. In other words, there is no one-to-one correspondence between a dysfunctional brain region and an observable mental disorder. Ultimately, researchers want to know more about how a particular regional dysfunction contributes to a specific disorder. For example, we need to know not only that prefrontal function is disrupted in both schizophrenia and depression, but also how information is processed by that brain region, in interaction with other regions, in a way that manifests itself as schizophrenia in one case but depression in another case. The problems are extremely complex, but the motivation to solve them is strong and is likely to remain so.

Summary

Schizophrenia

- Symptoms of schizophrenia generally fall into two categories: negative and positive symptoms. Negative symptoms include flat affect and catatonia. Positive symptoms include delusions, hallucinations, and disorganized thought.

- Frontal lobe functions such as working memory, planning, and voluntary control of eye movements are deficient in schizophrenia. A common neuroimaging finding is hypofrontality, or reduced frontal activation.

- Temporal lobe regions are also dysfunctional in schizophrenia, particularly in the left-hemisphere regions implicated in auditory comprehension and speech perception.

- Disruptions in coordinated activity among brain regions may also contribute to disorganized thought and hallucinations in schizophrenia.

Depression

- Depression is defined by a loss of ability to feel pleasure, combined with feelings of helplessness, hopelessness, and disruptions in sleep and appetite.

- People who are depressed perform poorly on frontal lobe tasks, particularly tasks that require allocation of effort or learning from feedback. Dorsolateral prefrontal cortex and regions of the anterior cingulate cortex regions have been implicated as functioning atypically in depression.

- Evidence indicates decreased activity in the left frontal region, compared to the right frontal region, in people who are depressed or at risk for depression.

- Depression is also characterized by low levels of activity in posterior regions of the right hemisphere, which may contribute to visuospatial deficits.

- Depression is further characterized by changes in limbic-system structures such as the amygdala, reward pathways, and hippocampus.

- Experimental and controversial treatments for depression, such as rTMS, DBS, and VNS, attempt to intervene on a neurological level when mainstream treatments, such as pharmacotherapy and behavioral therapy, do not work.

Anxiety Disorders

- There are many different subtypes of anxiety disorders, including phobias, panic disorder, posttraumatic stress disorder, obsessive-compulsive disorder, and generalized anxiety disorder. All involve fear reactions that are out of proportion to the circumstances.

- The amygdala plays a key role in anxiety disorders, which is not surprising given its role in fear learning and extinction. Anxiety disorders may also be characterized by poor frontal lobe regulation of subcortical structures such as the amygdala. Such dysregulation can contribute to an inability to extinguish acquired fears and an increased attentional bias toward threatening cues.

- Two dimensions of anxiety, anxious apprehension and anxious arousal, have been linked to different neural correlates. Anxious apprehension, or worry, is associated with activity in the left frontal region near speech areas. Anxious arousal is associated with elevations in right-hemisphere systems of arousal and attentional vigilance.

- The basal ganglia motor structures, and the caudate nucleus in particular, are involved in the compulsive and ritualistic actions observed in obsessive-compulsive disorder.

- Individual differences in anxiety and depression are linked to variations in the serotonin transporter gene, which influences neurotransmission in the serotonin system. Individuals who have an "S" gene variant respond more strongly to negative information than do those with two copies of the "L" gene variant.

Substance Abuse and Addiction

- The main feature of substance abuse is the inability to stop drug-seeking behavior even when the consequences are very bad.

- Studies in nonhuman animals indicate that the reward pathway, from the midbrain to the nucleus accumbens, plays an important role in the reinforcing effects of addictive drugs and the neural adaptations that occur with chronic substance use.

- Accumulating evidence indicates that orbitofrontal cortex function, particularly the ability to weigh positive and negative outcomes, is disrupted in substance abusers. Other regions, such as the insula, amygdala, and cingulate cortex, have also been implicated in addiction, but their specific role is not yet certain.

Key Terms

anhedonia   410

anxious apprehension   416

anxious arousal   416

bipolar disorder   407

cingulotomy   420

deep brain stimulation (DBS)   413

dot probe task   417

dysthymia   407

emotional Stroop task   417

extinction   418

functional connectivity   402

gene-environment interaction   415

generalized anxiety disorder   416

hypofrontality   399

negative symptoms   397

neurodevelopmental
    hypothesis   403

obsessive-compulsive disorder   416

panic disorder   416

phobias   416

positive symptoms   397

posttraumatic stress disorder
    (PTSD)   416

repetitive transcranial magnetic
    stimulation (rTMS)   411

sensory gating   401

serotonin transporter gene   414

vagus nerve stimulation (VNS)   413

ventricular enlargement   398

Book Companion Site at www.cengage.com/psychology/Banich

This website provides instructors and students with a wealth of free information and resources, including tutorial quizzes, flashcards, and the glossary.

Brain Development and Plasticity

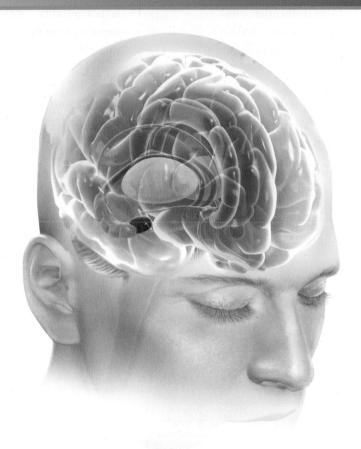

TO ALL WHO KNEW HIM, Dan appeared to be a relatively intelligent 12-year-old with a friendly and cooperative manner. Yet, he was struggling in his schoolwork, especially in spelling and reading. These troubles were nothing new. Despite considerable remedial training, these subjects had always been difficult for him. When a school counselor suggested neuropsychological assessment, his parents agreed willingly, hoping that it might shed some light on his problems.

Neuropsychological testing revealed no evidence of gross brain damage. His sensory, perceptual, and motor abilities all appeared normal and his overall IQ was in the average range. A more detailed analysis of his abilities revealed that his visuospatial skills were quite good. His score on the Perceptual Reasoning Index of the Wechsler Intelligence Scale for Children, Fourth Edition (WISC-IV), which emphasizes visuomotor and visuospatial abilities, was above average, and he performed well on a number of other tests assessing nonverbal problem solving. In contrast, his performance on the Verbal Comprehension Index of the WISC-IV was below average. A number of additional verbal tests revealed that he had little appreciation for the phonemic structure of words. He read words by guessing what they were on the basis of their salient visual features or configuration, rather than by trying to sound them out. For example, he read *form* as "farm," *theory* as "those," *grieve* as "great," and *tranquility* as "train track." He exhibited similar problems in the spelling of orally presented words, spelling *square* as "s-c-a-r," *cross* as "c-o-r-s," and *triangle* as "t-r-e-r-e."

Given that his difficulties were long-standing and that remediation so far had not been effective, the neuropsychologist diagnosed Dan as having a specific verbal learning disability that is commonly known as dyslexia. She suggested that further intervention for reading be geared to capitalize on Dan's good visuospatial abilities, such as teaching him to carefully distinguish words on the basis of their visual features and using flash cards to drill him on the form of words. An incremental approach could be taken; he could first acquire knowledge about simple words and then apply it toward reading more complicated material. For example, once Dan could learn to recognize *fly,* he could then use that knowledge to help read other words, such as *butterfly.*

The neuropsychologist also explained to Dan's parents that even with such remediation, he would probably never become a highly fluent reader, which meant that some aspects of formal schooling would remain challenging. However, she also emphasized that such difficulties did not preclude future occupational success for Dan. In fact, numerous famous individuals are known to be dyslexic, including the actor Tom Cruise, the artist Pablo Picasso, and William Hewitt, the co-founder of the Hewlett-Packard computer company. The neuropsychologist suggested to Dan's parents that they encourage him to pursue areas of study and interests that would capitalize on his above-average visuospatial abilities.

THE CASE STUDY in the opening vignette of this chapter illustrates some of the important ways in which neuropsychological disorders observed developmentally can differ from those observed later in life. In adults, the inability to read is often associated with damage to particular regions of the left hemisphere (see Chapter 9). However, in Dan's case, no evidence of localized brain damage was apparent. Whereas adults with alexia have acquired the ability to read and then lost it, Dan never acquired the ability to read with a reasonable degree of proficiency. Thus, cognitive deficits can have different origins and different neural correlates, depending on whether they were acquired in adulthood or during the process of development.

The case of Dan and children with other developmental disorders helps us to realize that the brain is dynamically changing: that is, the brain exhibits **plasticity**. A child's brain is not the same as an adult's brain, and yet in both children and adults the brain is exquisitely sensitive to environmental input. In this chapter, we examine how the brain develops and the ways in which it remains plastic or malleable across the life span. First we review the major processes of developmental change in the brain in childhood and adolescence. We also consider developmental disorders, such as dyslexia and autism, from a cognitive neuroscience perspective. We then discuss how the adult brain can adapt to changing experience. Finally we consider how the brain responds to damage or insult, and conclude with an examination of the changes in cognitive and neural processes associated with aging.

Development of the Brain

In this section, we review what is known about brain development from the beginning of life to adulthood. As you can imagine, an infant's brain does not look exactly like an adult's brain! You might think that the brain simply grows bigger as the child grows bigger, but the story is actually quite a bit more complex. As we will see, while some aspects of neural development can be thought of simply as "growth" or proliferation, other aspects involve a more complex sculpting of nerve cells, their pattern of connections, and their organization.

We will begin by studying the development of the brain during childhood, and then focus on the changes that occur during adolescence, the transition from childhood to adulthood. At all stages of development, the challenge for researchers is not only to document how the brain changes, but also to understand how physical changes in the brain relate to the developing cognitive and emotional skills of the child or adolescent.

■ Changes in the Brain during Childhood

● Figure 15.1 gives an overview of the time course of major events during neural development. You can immediately notice several things from this figure. First, many processes take place during development, including cell proliferation and migration, development of synapses, and myelination. Second, each of these processes has its own time course; some processes take place primarily before birth, whereas others continue throughout adolescence. Finally, development cannot be thought of simply as a linear progression of growth. As you can see from the figure, processes such as the generation of synapses show an inverted-U function, rising and then falling, indicating initial increases and proliferation followed by subsequent reduction, pruning, or sculpting.

To understand brain development, let us start at the beginning. Early in fetal development, after the simple primordial fertilized egg differentiates into specific types of tissue (e.g., muscle, skeletal, cardiovascular, nerve), the spinal cord and brain are nothing more than a hollow tube. The formation of this tube is referred to as **neurulation** (● Figure 15.2). With time, the tube folds, twists, turns, and expands to become the fetal brain, while the hole inside the tube becomes the ventricular system.

Around the seventh week of gestation, the nerve cells and glia near the inside of the tube divide, proliferate, and then begin to migrate outward. **Neurogenesis**, or the generation of new nerve cells, occurs in the area right around the ventricle (● Figure 15.3). In this process, the tube acts much like a port around which the initial neural settlers will reside. As more neurons are generated, the central areas around the ventricle become settled, and then the new neurons, like new immigrants to a city, must traverse farther out to find a place to live. As the brain grows, new neurons travel farther and farther out to the metaphorical suburbs of the brain. Glial cells provide the scaffolding or "roads" along which nerve cells can migrate to their ultimate destinations (● Figure 15.4) (see Lemke, 2001, for a review of the role of glial cells in development). Thus, the six layers of cortex are built from the inside out; the first set of cells migrates to the deepest layer of the cortex (the sixth), the second to the fifth, and so forth. By six months of gestation, most neurons have been produced. Because the development of the cortex is protracted during

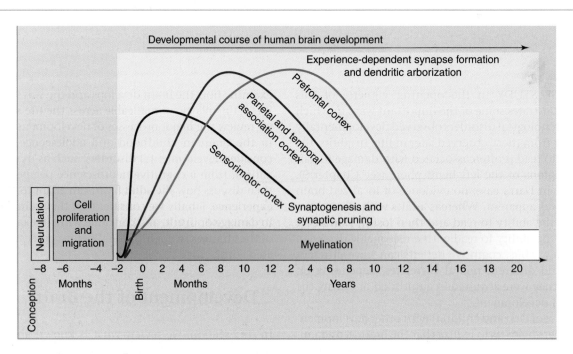

● **FIGURE 15.1   Overview of the time frame of human brain development.** Shown here is the time course of different processes involved in brain development, starting with those that occur at conception through those that occur up until the age of young adulthood. *Source:* Fig. 1 from Casey, B. J. et al (2005). Imaging the developing brain: what have we learned about cognitive development? Trends in Cognitive Sciences, 9, 104–110. Reprinted by permission of Elsevier.

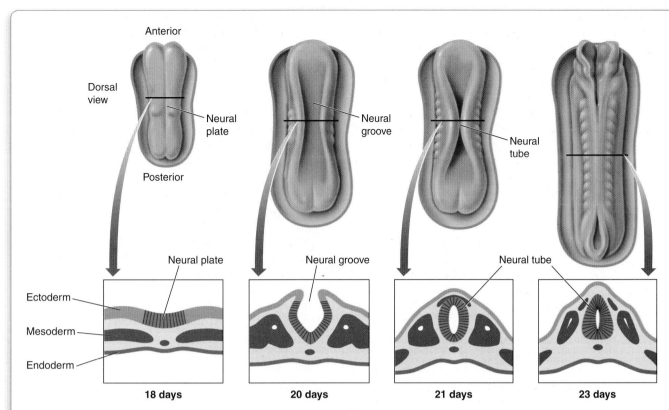

FIGURE 15.2   The closing of the neural tube. The nervous system has its origins in the neural tube, which is formed early in embryonic development. As the ectoderm folds, the neural plate forms into a groove, which then closes to create a tube. The tube will later become the ventricles and spinal canal, while the surrounding tissue will become the brain and spinal cord. © 2010 Cengage Learning

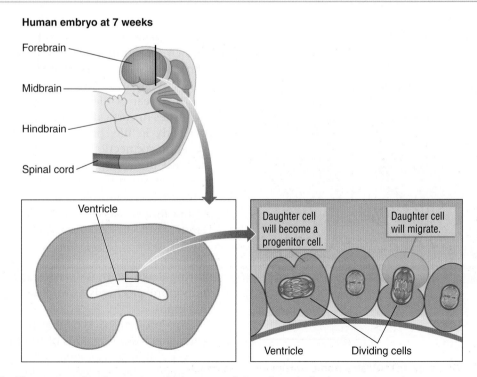

FIGURE 15.3   Neurogenesis. The creation of new nerve cells in embryonic development occurs in the ventricular zone. Progenitor cells that line the ventricles can divide, producing new daughter cells. The daughter cells can either stay in the ventricular zone and act as new progenitor cells, or they can migrate away from this zone and into other areas of the brain. © 2010 Cengage Learning

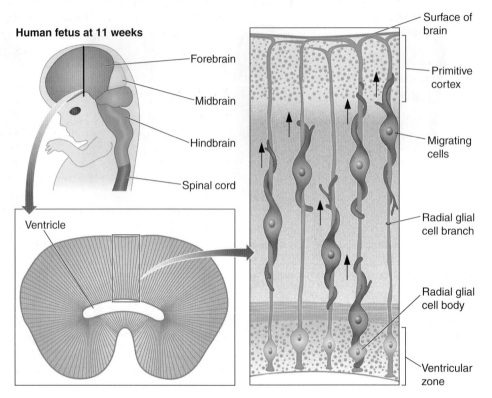

● FIGURE 15.4   Migration of nerve cells. Cells that migrate away from the ventricular zone often travel along radial glia, which form a kind of scaffolding along which the cells can migrate. © 2010 Cengage Learning

gestation, there is ample opportunity for disruption of the typical pattern. We will discuss syndromes involving disrupted development later in this chapter, including dyslexia and fetal alcohol syndrome.

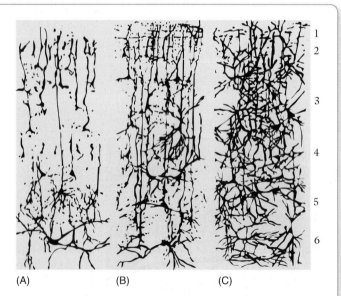

● FIGURE 15.5   Increases in dendrites during early development. Shown here are representative sections of the brain of (A) a 3-month-old child, (B) a 15-month-old child, and (C) a 24-month-old child. The numerals to the right of C indicate the six layers of cortex. © 2011 Cengage Learning

Synapse Formation and Pruning

One of the largest changes after birth is a dramatic increase in the number of connections (synapses) that neurons make with other neurons. This process is known as **synaptogenesis** (see Bourgeois, 2001). Synaptogenesis occurs so rapidly that the total number of synapses increases more than tenfold within the first year of life. As illustrated in ● Figure 15.5, dendrites in cortical regions increase greatly in number early in life, providing greater surface area for synaptic connections. One mystery that researchers are still unraveling is how so many neurons make the right synaptic connections to form functional circuits. A crucial role is played by a family of molecules known as *cadherins,* which help guide developing axons to synapse with certain targets and to adhere to those targets (Ranscht, 2000). The dramatic increase in synapses, combined with the subsequent paring-down of those synapses, is one of the most important mechanisms of plasticity in the developing brain.

The process of synaptogenesis does not occur equally across all regions of the human brain at the same point in development. Rather, there are regional differences (Huttenlocher, 2002; see Figure 15.1). Synaptogenesis occurs most rapidly in the primary sensory and motor areas first, followed by association areas and prefrontal cortex. This makes sense from a functional point of view; a baby needs to get basic sensory and motor skills up and running before more complex abilities can come online.

Another important feature of synapse formation is the inverted-U function that we have already mentioned (see Figure 15.1). After synapse proliferation, pruning occurs through the **elimination of synapses**, in which the number of connections between neurons is reduced. The pruning of neuronal connections occurs at a staggering rate. For example, researchers estimate that as many as 60 axons per *second* in the corpus callosum are lost during the first few weeks of a monkey's life (LaMantia & Rakic, 1990), and in humans the loss may be even greater—as many as 200 axons per second (Rakic, 1991). Such pruning happens in part because cells that do not receive so-called "survival factor" signals from their neighboring cells undergo apoptosis, or programmed cell death (Raff, 1998). In other cases, the cells themselves do not die, but their synapses are disassembled and their axons retract or degenerate (Low & Cheng, 2006).

Like synaptogenesis itself, the time course of synaptic elimination varies among cortical regions. For example, histological studies indicate that pruning is complete in the human visual cortex by 10 years of age, but continues in the frontal cortex until adolescence (Huttenlocher, 1979). More recent structural MRI studies have confirmed that changes in cortical thickness occur at different points during development depending on the brain region (Gogtay et al., 2004; Toga, Thompson, & Sowell, 2006). What is consistent across regions, however, is that the number of synapses in the adult is about 40% less than that at the peak value observed during childhood (Huttenlocher & de Courten, 1987).

Synaptic overproduction is a mechanism that allows the brain initially to have maximal capacity to respond to the environment. Then, during development, the neurons or connections that do not receive much stimulation wither away. This provides the brain with the capacity to fine-tune and specialize itself for its specific environment (Bourgeois, 2001; Huttenlocher, 2002). Interestingly, a recent longitudinal MRI study found that children with higher intelligence, measured by a standard IQ test, tend to show a greater rate of cortical thickening early in development, as well as a greater rate of cortical thinning later in development, particularly in frontal lobe regions (Shaw, Greenstein, et al., 2006). Assuming that cortical thickness is due in part to the number of synapses, these data suggest that superior intelligence may be correlated with faster rates of change in both the synaptic proliferation and pruning processes.

The importance of synaptic elaboration and pruning is also illustrated by developmental disorders in which these events go awry. For example, the brains of people who have disorders associated with mental retardation show reductions in the complexity of the dendritic trees, the length of dendrites, or both. Furthermore, the spines on their dendrites tend to have atypical form, such as being longer and thinner than usual (Kaufmann &

Moser, 2000). Other disorders, such as fragile X (which we discuss later in this chapter), are associated with an elevated density of spines along dendrites, suggesting a failure of synapse elimination (Grossman, Aldridge, Weiler, & Greenough, 2006).

Myelination

As you know, nerve cells are not the only cells in the brain; glial cells also play an important role in brain structure and function. We have already learned that certain types of glial cells form scaffolding during development that helps nerve cells find their way to distant destinations in the brain. Another very important role of glial cells is to provide the myelin sheath that coats axons in the brain. A baby's brain is relatively unmyelinated, which means that it lacks the oligodendrocytes that insulate neurons. Therefore, brain regions cannot interact quickly in the infant.

Myelination is a long, drawn-out process, with a developmental course that varies widely by region of the nervous system (Sampaio & Truwit, 2001). Myelination first begins to appear between the fourth gestational month and the first year after birth (● Figure 15.6). Not surprisingly, the brain regions that are most myelinated early in life, such as the spinal cord and the medulla, are those that support basic functions. During the first year after birth, basic sensory and motor systems become myelinated. Later in childhood, myelination occurs for connections between integrative systems, such as those connecting cortical and subcortical areas and those linking different cortical regions. For example, myelination of the corpus callosum continues through the teens into the early twenties (e.g., Giedd et al., 1996; Thompson, Giedd, Woods, MacDonald, Evans, & Toga, 2000). The net result of all this myelination is that the relative amount of white matter increases during childhood and the teenage years while the amount of gray matter decreases (Giedd et al., 1999; Paus, 2005).

The functional consequence of myelination is that communication between brain regions increases. It is as if the baby's brain were connected by a series of old country roads meandering from town to town. This system doesn't make for fast travel. Myelin transforms this infantile system into a faster one—the old country roads become regional highways, and even more myelin transforms them into national superhighways, over which large volumes of traffic can travel quickly. For example, the nerve-conduction velocity between the hemispheres reaches the adult value of approximately 5 ms during the late teen years, which is four to five times as quick as that observed in four-year-old children (Salamy, 1978). Faster transmission of neural signals can support quicker perception, cognition, and action.

Electrical and Biochemical Changes

Other generalized developmental changes also occur, such as those relating to the brain's electrical and biochemical activity. Two main trends emerge with regard

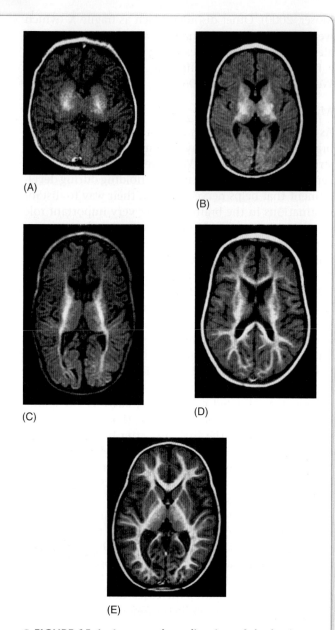

(A)

(B)

(C)

(D)

(E)

● **FIGURE 15.6   Increased myelination of the brain during infancy.** In these figures, myelin appears in white. (A) 1-month-old infant; (B) at 2 months; (C) 3–6 months; (D) 7–9 months; (E) older than 9 months. *Source:* M. S. van der Knaap and J. Valk, MR imaging of the various stages of normal myelination during the first year of life. Neuroradiology 31 (1990), pp. 459–470.

to electrophysiological activity: the dominant frequency of activity increases and the pattern of electrical activity becomes more cyclic. During the first two years of life, electrophysiological activity tends to be of low frequency (delta rhythm, < 3.5 Hz). Such low-frequency activity is not typically observed in awake adults. Between the ages of one year and five years, the dominant frequency band is theta (4–7 Hz), which in awake adults is associated with relaxation with the eyes closed. After the age of five years, the alpha rhythm (8–13 Hz) becomes discernible; this frequency band is associated with relaxation but alertness in adults. By

age 10 to 13 years, the alpha rhythm becomes similar to that of adults, and beta activity (> 14 Hz) becomes discernible. No obvious pattern of EEG cyclicity is evident in the infant, but as the child grows older, a clear sleep-wake cycle develops (Harmony, 1988).

Biochemical changes also occur in the brain during development. Aspects of brain metabolism, such as the rate of glucose consumption, change during childhood. As shown in ● Figure 15.7, during the first year after birth the metabolic rate of the entire cerebral cortex, as indexed by positron emission tomography (PET), is less than that for adults. After this point, the metabolic rate climbs steadily until it is double the adult value between the ages of three and eight years. After this peak, it begins to decrease, but remains above adult levels during the early teen years. The changes in brain metabolism do not occur equally across the brain, but, like myelination and synaptogenesis, vary across brain regions with age. For example, during the first year of life, the highest metabolic rate occurs in subcortical structures. High metabolic rates for the cortex are observed only after that time (Chugani, Phelps, & Mazziotta, 1987). The pattern of glucose consumption during childhood suggests that the brain needs fuel to support structural changes occurring during this time. The oligodendroglia may need extra energy to generate myelin, and neurons may need energy to undergo both elaboration and pruning.

Behavioral Changes

Needless to say, during the course of development the child's behavior also changes. That is, all these changes in brain physiology—changes in metabolic rate, myelination, and synaptic density—are mirrored by changes in the behavioral repertoire of the child. Children in all cultures tend to acquire both cognitive and motoric skills in an orderly fashion: Babbling precedes speaking, and crawling precedes walking. Furthermore, specific abilities are acquired within specific age ranges. Because these changes occur in an orderly fashion and at a particular age, they are known as **developmental milestones** (Spreen et al., 1984). The major behavioral changes during development are listed in Table 15.1. The table also lists the average size of the brain at each developmental stage, to give you a sense of the brain's overall growth. Of course, as you know from the preceding sections, it is not simply the growing size of the brain that supports different cognitive abilities. Rather, the complex pattern of interconnections among brain areas, sculpted by maturation and experience, is what drives behavioral and cognitive development.

Although development undoubtedly entails changes in brain functioning as well as changes in behavior, finding a direct causal link between a change in a specific aspect of neural functioning and the emergence of a certain cognitive function has proven surprisingly difficult. Currently, there are relatively few cases in which we can point to a biological marker that predicts development of a specific cognitive process. Furthermore, even when we do find such a marker, the connection between the physiological process and the cognitive function is unclear.

To illustrate this difficulty, consider some research conducted by Molfese and colleagues (reviewed in Molfese, Molfese, & Molfese, 2007). They found that an infant's electrical response to speech sounds (an auditory evoked response, or AER) recorded a week or so after birth can predict the child's language competence three years later (Molfese & Molfese, 1994). Follow-up studies indicated that the infant's AER can still predict language abilities at age five (Molfese & Molfese, 1997) and language and reading abilities at age eight (Molfese, Molfese, & Espy, 1999). It is fascinating to think about how a process that is evident in infancy can predict later cognitive competency.

Although the AER appears to act as a biological marker for future language competence, we do not know exactly what aspect of nervous system function is indexed by the AER. Moreover, we do not know how variations in that function lead to varying competence in language. One possibility is that a larger AER may reflect a heightened capacity to discriminate among different speech sounds (Molfese et al., 2007). Thus, children who can make fine discriminations sooner may have a head start in learning words early in life, which in turn helps them to have more developed language capacities at later ages. This explanation is logical, but it is hard to directly test the causal

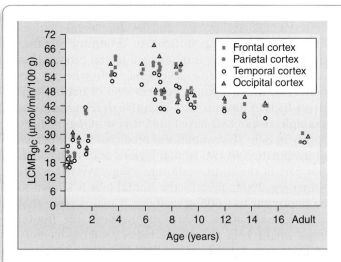

● **FIGURE 15.7 Changes in metabolic rate of the brain's four major lobes during development.** During the first few years of life, metabolic rates are less than those of an adult (far left-hand side of the graph). However, in preschool years the rate of brain metabolism begins to accelerate, reaching a peak value around the age of eight years, after which the metabolic rate slowly declines through the teenage years to adult values. LCMR$_{glc}$ = local cerebral metabolic rate for glucose. © 2011 Cengage Learning

role of the process that generates the AER; we cannot experimentally manipulate the underlying process reflected in the AER at infancy and see what happens to language development years later in childhood.

TABLE 15.1	Development Changes during Early Childhood		
Age	Visual and Motor Function	Social and Intellectual Function	Average Brain Weight (g)
Birth	Exhibits sucking, rooting, swallowing, and Moro reflexes; engages in infantile grasping; blinks to light	—	350
6 weeks	Extends and turns neck when prone; regards mother's face; follows objects with eyes	Smiles when played with	410
3 months	Exhibits infantile grasping and sucking modified by volition; keeps head above horizontal for long periods; turns to objects presented in visual field; may respond to sound	Watches own hands	515
6 months	Grasps objects with both hands; will place weight on forearms or hands when prone; rolls supine to prone; supports almost all weight on legs for brief periods; sits briefly	Laughs aloud and shows pleasure; emits primitive articulated sounds, "gagoo"; smiles at self in mirror	660
9 months	Sits well and pulls self to sitting position; uses thumb-forefinger grasp; crawls	Waves bye-bye; plays pat-a-cake; uses "dada," "baba"; imitates sounds	750
12 months	Is able to release objects; cruises and walks with one hand held; exhibits plantar reflex (50% of children)	Says two to four words with meaning; understands several proper nouns; may kiss on request	925
24 months	Walks up and down stairs (using two feet per step); bends over and picks up objects without falling; turns knob; can partially dress self; exhibits plantar reflex (100% of children)	Uses two- to three-word sentences; uses "I," "me," and "you" correctly; plays simple games; points to four to five body parts; obeys simple commands	1,065
36 months	Goes up stairs (using one foot per step); pedals tricycle; dresses and undresses fully except for shoelaces, belt, and buttons; visual acuity 20/20	Asks numerous questions; knows nursery rhymes; copies circle; plays with others	1,140

Even when we can find more specific correlations between biological markers and developmental changes in mental ability, it is difficult to determine whether the biological marker is indexing a neural process that is critical for cognitive development or whether the marker is just indexing a general level of brain maturity, which in turn predicts cognitive development. For example, researchers have found that working-memory ability in 8- to 18-year-olds was predicted by the degree of myelination in two frontal regions and in the anterior part of the corpus callosum (Nagy, Westerberg, & Klingberg, 2004). Because the frontal lobe is known to be important in working memory, it makes sense that greater myelination within and between the frontal lobes might help to support better working-memory abilities during development. However, we don't know whether increased myelination in the frontal lobes directly causes improved working memory. It is also possible that better working memory leads to more myelination, much the way working out more can lead to bigger muscles. Or, both increased myelination and improved working memory may just be characteristics of a more developed brain, even if one does not cause the other. Although a deeper understanding of the causal mechanisms of developmental change is elusive, researchers generally assume that a particular neurobiological substrate must be in place before specific motoric, cognitive, and emotional abilities can manifest themselves.

■ Changes in the Brain during Adolescence

Although much research on brain development has focused on the early childhood years, recent studies have also focused on understanding the transition from childhood to adulthood. This transitional period is generally known as *adolescence*. We've already seen in earlier sections that some aspects of brain development continue through adolescence. For example, changes in myelination and synaptic pruning occur well into the teen years (e.g., Paus, 2005).

Research on the adolescent brain has tended to focus on neural changes that can be related to the prominent cognitive and emotional characteristics of teenagers. For example, although adolescents are cognitively sophisticated, they tend to make riskier choices than adults (as you can probably confirm based on episodes from your own life!). In addition, social competency is especially important in adolescence, as navigating the complexities of peer groups becomes crucial. Finally, adolescence is a time of emotional turmoil. Therefore, maturation of brain areas that govern complex decision making, social cognition, and emotion regulation may have special implications for the development of the adolescent mind.

Can neuroscience explain why teenagers tend to drive too fast, fail to wear seatbelts, and engage in risky substance use? One viewpoint identifies the prefrontal cortex as the source of these risk-taking behaviors

(e.g., Yurgelun-Todd, 2007). According to this view, adolescents engage in risk-taking behavior because the prefrontal cortex, which exerts top-down control over lower brain regions, is still developing at this time of life. However, as other researchers point out (Casey, Getz, & Galvan, 2008), prefrontal maturation cannot be the whole story. The prefrontal cortex is more mature in adolescents than in younger children, and yet it is the adolescents, not the younger children, who typically display riskier behavior. To understand this pattern, we must consider the prefrontal cortex in relationship to the lower-level areas that it typically regulates (Casey, Getz, & Galvan, 2008; Steinberg, 2008). For example, in adolescents there may be increased activity in limbic reward regions such as the nucleus accumbens. As limbic structures mature in adolescence, they create more powerful incentives to seek exciting rewards. At the same time, the prefrontal cortex has not quite caught up, so it is unable to control these limbic regions in the same way as we typically see in adults.

Consistent with this model, a recent functional imaging study found that activity in the nucleus accumbens was increased in adolescents while they anticipated receiving a monetary reward, compared to the activity level in both children and adults (Galavan et al., 2006). At the same time, activity in the orbital region of the prefrontal cortex was lower in both children and adolescents compared to adults. Putting these two pieces together, the adolescents displayed a unique pattern, not seen in either children or adults, of elevated limbic responses in combination with relatively lower prefrontal responses to a reward incentive. The exaggerated limbic response to rewards could explain why adolescents tend to show adult-like skills in logical reasoning, but yet make risky choices in everyday life when strong emotional incentives are present (Steinberg, 2005).

Researchers are also especially interested in the adolescent brain because many forms of psychological distress either emerge for the first time or become worse during the adolescent years. For example, during adolescence, the risk for depression increases to adult levels for the first time, and the gender difference in depression emerges (e.g., Davey, Yücel, & Allen, 2008; Hyde, Mezulis, & Abramson, 2008). Substance abuse and schizophrenia may also have their first onset during the adolescent years. Of course, there are numerous social as well as biological reasons why psychological disorders may increase in this time period, as people's bodies and their social standing can both change dramatically, eliciting strong emotional reactions. We know from previous chapters that top-down control by the prefrontal regions over limbic regions is important in regulating emotions. During adolescence, the connection between these regions is still tenuous and social-emotional challenges are great. Therefore, it should not be surprising that difficulties in regulation of emotion may manifest during these years. In the long run, understanding the unique features of the adolescent brain may help explain why certain social-emotional problems emerge during this time period.

While controlling emotional impulses is an important key to surviving adolescence, understanding the complex social world is also crucial. Adolescents tend to be obsessed with social status and belonging to social groups; this in turn requires a level of cognitive sophistication in order to understand what other people think and feel. For example, adolescents are quicker than younger children in answering questions about another person's perspective (e.g., "A girl is not allowed to go to her best friend's party. How does she feel?"; Choudhury, Blakemore, & Charman, 2006). As discussed in Chapter 13, certain brain regions—such as the medial prefrontal region, temporoparietal junction, and superior temporal sulcus—are believed to be important in understanding the thoughts and feelings of others. These regions are activated in both adolescents and adults during tasks that require making inferences about another person's mental state (compared to tasks that require inferences about physical causality); however, the pattern of activation is slightly different, with adolescents showing stronger activity in the medial prefrontal region and adults showing stronger activity in the superior temporal sulcus (Blakemore, den Ouden, Choudhury, & Frith, 2007). These findings imply that adults and adolescents may be using different strategies to draw conclusions about other people's mental states. However, there is still much to be learned about how those differing strategies map onto developing brain circuits.

■ Influence of the Environment on the Developing Brain

The child's brain does not develop in a vacuum. Rather, it develops in a dynamic world full of sights, sounds, smells, tastes, and tactile sensations. As the child grows, he or she is not only receiving sensory experiences from the world, but is also actively exploring the world. How does the child's experience within the world influence the developing brain? What kinds of experiences are necessary for normal brain development, and what kinds of experiences can modulate the basic pattern of brain development? Does it matter when certain experiences occur in a child's life?

Researchers have distinguished between two broad categories of experience that can influence the developing nervous system (Bruer & Greenough, 2001; Greenough, Black, & Wallace, 1987). First, some kinds of experiences are common to nearly all members of the species. Any newborn human is virtually guaranteed to be exposed to patterned light, to social interactions, and to some kind of language; only in extreme cases are people deprived of these experiences. Therefore, evolution could count on these experiences to be present during development, and information from these sources, though essential for normal development, did not have to be specified in the genetic blueprint. Instead, the nervous system evolved to "expect" these kinds of experiences from the environment. The neural systems that respond to such experiences are known as **experience-expectant systems**; they develop normally when the expected input is received, but are seriously affected when the expected experience is absent. For example, in extremely rare cases in which an individual is exposed to no language, the development of the language system is grossly abnormal (Curtiss, 1977). Likewise, complete social deprivation produces abnormal social behavior (Harlow, Dodsworth, & Harlow, 1965). Within the visual system, the normal development of binocular depth perception depends on having normal exposure to light in both eyes during development (Horton & Hocking, 1997; Wiesel & Hubel, 1963).

Another category of environmental experiences is those that are known to vary quite a bit among people. For example, some children are exposed to musical training early in life, while other children are placed into pee-wee hockey clubs. These children are likely to develop different levels of musical and motor control skills. The nervous system does not require these specific experiences to develop normally; for example, a person without formal musical training still has a normal nervous system, unlike a child who is deprived of language input throughout childhood. **Experience-dependent systems**, in contrast to experience-expectant systems, are those that vary across individuals and are based on their personal, unique experiences.

One example of an experience-dependent effect is the influence of environmental enrichment on the brain. Numerous studies of rodents have found that an enriched or stimulating environment can affect the structure of neurons, causing the dendrites of the neurons to become bushier and the number of synapses per neuron to increase (e.g., Rosenzweig, Bennett, & Diamond, 1972; Turner & Greenough, 1985). An enriched environment for a laboratory rat typically consists of a spatially complex living area combined with social stimulation (● Figure 15.8A). In contrast, the control (impoverished) environment consists of a small standard-issue clear plastic cage where the animal lives alone (● Figure 15.8B). Enriched environments can influence synaptic connectivity not only during early development but also in adulthood, and changes persist to some degree even when the animals are later removed from the enriched setting (e.g., Briones, Klintsova, & Greenough, 2004).

Neural changes following environmental enrichment may provide for more and varied connections, increasing the brain's computational power so that it can effectively deal with a more cognitively demanding and complicated environment. Animals raised in complex environments are superior to control animals in aspects of perceptual sensitivity (e.g., Bourgeon, Xerri, & Coq, 2004) and in solving various maze-learning tasks (e.g., Leggio et al., 2005; Williams et al., 2001). Interestingly, female rats reared in enriched environments tend to transfer their superior maze performance to their

(A)

(B)

● **FIGURE 15.8   Enriched versus impoverished environments for rats.** (A) In the complex environment condition, the animals are allowed to spend hours each day in an environment characterized by a large area in which the spatial arrangement of items and toys is changed daily (for variety) and in which the rats have the opportunity to interact with other rats. (B) In contrast, in the control condition the rat remains alone in a small plastic cage all day. © 2011 Cengage Learning

exercise, intended to work on inhibitory control, children had to help a cartoon farmer bring sheep into a fenced area by clicking on sheep as quickly as possible, but withholding responses when the animal turned out to be a wolf instead of a sheep. Other training exercises developed skills of resolving discrepancies between conflicting information and remembering perceptual information. After five days of training, trained children (compared to untrained children) demonstrated ERP responses during a conflict resolution task that looked more like those of an adult. Similarly, the trained children had modest improvements in behavioral measures of resolving conflict. These results give some clues about how very specific learning experiences may affect development of executive functions (see also Diamond, Barnett, Thomas, & Munro, 2005).

Such training studies focus on experimental manipulation of certain aspects of a child's experience, but of course these manipulations represent only a tiny fraction of the varying experiences of different children in the real world. Taking a different approach to understanding the role of environmental factors on brain development, other researchers have compared children from economically impoverished versus well-off circumstances. These studies have the advantage of addressing real-life discrepancies in children's experience, but they also have the disadvantage that such experiences cannot be experimentally controlled or manipulated. In general, studies have found that children raised in less-than-ideal conditions, as indexed by lower socioeconomic status, show poorer cognitive performance than children raised in households with higher socioeconomic status. Interestingly, the performance decrement is more pronounced for tasks that rely on medial temporal areas, such as those linked to language and memory encoding, and those that rely on frontal cortex, such as those linked to working memory and executive control (e.g., Farah et al., 2006). Moreover, these groups differ in the degree to which they use language-related regions of the left hemisphere while performing phonological tasks (Noble, Wolmetz, Ochs, Farah, & McCandliss, 2006). Future research is necessary to determine which specific causal factors produce these neural and cognitive differences.

Although many studies focus on the role of the environment in early child development, others have

pups (Friske & Gammie, 2005)! Although it is not clear exactly how the benefits of environmental enrichment are transferred from mothers to pups, one possibility is that mothers raised in enriched environments bestow a more beneficial kind of maternal care upon their pups, which then enhances or aids the pups' ability to learn.

These studies have been conducted in other species, in which we can experimentally manipulate rearing conditions. Obviously, scientists cannot manipulate the entire environment in which a human child or adolescent is raised. However, some studies have begun to examine the influence of specific training experiences on children's cognitive and neural development. In one study (Rueda, Rothbart, McCandliss, Saccamanno, & Posner, 2005), researchers trained 4- and 6-year-old children in certain aspects of attention. In one training

focused on environmental influences in adolescence. In one study, researchers took anatomical brain scans of young adults at two time points, during the fall term of their first year of college and then about six months later. All the students had moved at least 100 miles from home, so the university environment was a significant change geographically, socially, and academically. After six months, the researchers observed increased MR signal, most likely reflecting changes in myelination, that was notable in both cortical and subcortical regions including the cingulate, basal ganglia, and insula (Bennett & Baird, 2006). Similar changes over a six-month period were not observed in an older sample of graduate students whose average age was around 25. Because this study lacked a control group of 19-year-olds who did not go away to college, we cannot rule out the possibility that these changes in the first year of college simply represent the typical developmental trajectory of a 19-year-old. Nonetheless, it suggests the possibility of large environmental influences on brain development, even during the late teen years.

For both experience-expectant and experience-dependent neural systems, the impact of an environmental experience may depend on the timing of its input. Although certain environmental effects can influence the organism across a lifetime, in other cases the organism is particularly sensitive to certain external stimuli during a specific developmental period, known as a **sensitive period**. Such time periods allow the brain to incorporate information from the environment and then to "lock in" that information.

Some examples of sensitive periods in development come from the visual system. For example, some children are born with cataracts, which make the lens of the eye opaque and therefore prevent light from entering the eye. Research has shown that it is crucial to have such cataracts removed immediately in order for vision to develop normally. Even a few months of early visual deprivation due to cataracts can disrupt the ability to develop normal face-perception skills (Le Grand, Mondloch, Maurer, & Brent, 2001, 2004). Having cataracts that develop after about age seven to nine is not as detrimental to visual acuity as having cataracts before that age, indicating that normal visual input for the first seven years of life is important in developing adult levels of acuity (Maurer & Lewis, 2001). Such evidence is consistent with research on other species, in which visual deprivation in early life has significant consequences for visual function. For example, suturing one eye shut during early development in cats or monkeys affects the responses of cells in the primary visual cortex (Horton & Hocking, 1997; Wiesel & Hubel, 1963). Research using animal models has identified particular molecular signals that influence the "opening and closing" of the sensitive period for visual development, including neurotrophins that promote plasticity in the developing visual cortex

and glycoproteins that inhibit axonal growth and therefore reduce plasticity in the adult visual cortex (Berardi, Pizzorusso, Ratto, & Maffei, 2003).

Sensitive periods exist not only for the development of visual functions, but for other cognitive and emotional functions as well. For example, the typical N_{170} ERP response to faces (see Chapter 7) is blunted in children who spent their early years in an orphanage, compared to noninstitutionalized children of the same age (Parker & Nelson, 2005; Parker, Nelson, & Bucharest Early Intervention Project Core Group, 2007). This result suggests that certain kinds of social input are important in developing normal face-perception processes in early life, although it is not yet known whether a similar social deprivation later in life would have parallel effects. Currently, researchers are investigating the extent to which interventions—such as moving to a foster care setting rather than an orphanage—can overcome these early cognitive deficits (e.g., Nelson, Zeanah, Fox, Marshall, Smyke, & Guthrie, 2007).

The development of language functions also seems to involve a period of maximal sensitivity to input, demonstrating that higher cognitive functions also depend upon input at particular time periods. For example, evidence from second-language acquisition supports the notion of a sensitive period for language development. If acquisition of a second language occurs before the ages of five to seven years, the person's competence will be equivalent to that of a native speaker (● Figure 15.9). For each year that passes after the age of seven without exposure to the language, there is an incremental decline in the ability to understand the grammatical constructions of that

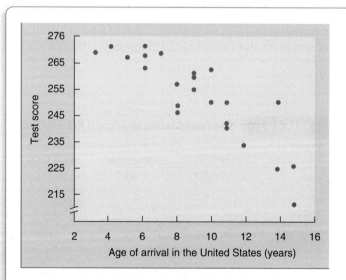

● **FIGURE 15.9   Sensitive period for acquiring grammatical competence in a second language.** The relationship between age of arrival in the United States and grammatical competence for individuals who arrive while between ages 3 and 15 years. With each year that passes after the age of five years, the ability to acquire grammatical competence decreases.
© 2011 Cengage Learning

language (Johnson & Newport, 1989; see also Gleitman & Newport, 2002; Newport, Bavelier, & Neville, 2001). This pattern of results suggests that the ability to acquire a high degree of grammatical competence in a second language is limited by biological factors (for alternative interpretations, see Flege, Yeni-Komshian, & Liu, 1999; MacDonald, 2006). However, it is not currently known what specific biological mechanisms control the end of the sensitive period for language acquisition.

In sum, the development of the brain and behavior involves marvelously complex processes that unfold over a period of more than 20 years. Developmental processes in the brain include cell proliferation and migration, synaptogenesis, synaptic pruning, and myelination, all of which take place over different time frames and at somewhat different rates in various brain regions. Some processes, such as cell migration, appear to progress relatively independently of environmental input, whereas others, such as synaptogenesis and synaptic pruning, appear to be exquisitely sensitive to the specific environments that the child encounters. Unfolding maturational processes combine with both universal and unique experiences at certain periods of development to produce a cognitively developed adult.

Developmental Disorders

Conditions such as mental retardation, dyslexia, autism, and attention-deficit disorder are known as *developmental disorders* because they typically make their first appearances during childhood, and because they represent a departure from the normal developmental path. Much is still unknown about the original causes of these conditions and how they unfold during development. Here we consider current understanding of several major classes of developmental disorders.

■ Mental Retardation

When children fail to acquire intellectual abilities across most cognitive domains at a normal rate and manner, and when they have difficulties in adaptive functioning such as self-care, the disorder is termed **mental retardation**. Mental retardation is not associated with a particular focal lesion, but rather tends to result from factors that have a pervasive effect on many developing brain systems.

Mental retardation is generally divided into four categories based on severity. This classification system and the characteristics of individuals in each category are presented in Table 15.2. Mental retardation can be caused by numerous factors, including genetic disorders, infections, toxins, and oxygen deprivation. As we learned earlier in this chapter, the developing brain is plastic and can be affected by the environment to a greater degree than can the adult brain. Although one of the virtues of this plasticity is that the brain can fine-tune itself to the environment, the downside of plasticity is that the brain is also more vulnerable to negative influences.

Genetic Disorders

Numerous genetic disorders can cause mental retardation (see Voeller, 2006, for a review). Here we review just two of these conditions—Down syndrome and fragile X syndrome—as examples of genetic conditions that have a pervasive influence on mental development.

Down syndrome is associated with severe retardation, with IQs typically in the lowest 2% of the general population. This syndrome, which occurs in about 1 in 1,000 births, is caused by trisomy 21, a condition in which the 21st pair of chromosomes contains three chromosomes (*trisomy*) rather than the usual

TABLE 15.2	The Four Classes of Mental Retardation Based on Severity		
Degree of Retardation	**IQ Level**	**Percentage***	**Typical Presentation**
Mild	50–55 to 70	85	Develop normally during preschool but do not acquire academic abilities above the sixth-grade level. As adults, can usually be self-supporting, and may live independently with community and social support.
Moderate	35–40 to 50–55	10	Can acquire communication skills during early childhood. As adults, need some supervision for living and work (such as group homes) but can take care of themselves in those contexts.
Severe	20–25 to 35–40	3–4	Can learn some elementary self-care and language skills. As adults, need supervision and assistance for living and work, but can perform simple tasks in closely supervised settings.
Profound	<20–25	1–2	Have impairments during childhood in sensorimotor functioning. Usually have an identifiable neurologic disorder that accounts for the retardation. Need highly structured environment with constant supervision by an individual caregiver.

*Percentage of all mentally retarded children who fall into that category.

two (● Figure 15.10). Down syndrome is characterized by a specific morphology of the body and face (● Figure 15.11A), which can aid early diagnosis. Individuals with Down syndrome have pronounced deficits in language and verbal memory, with somewhat better functioning in visuospatial and social tasks. Down syndrome appears to be characterized by abnormal dendritic development after birth, such that adults with Down syndrome have reduced dendritic branching and spine density compared to age-matched controls (Benavides-Piccione et al., 2004). As they enter the fourth or fifth decade of life, many individuals with Down syndrome begin to exhibit symptoms similar to those of Alzheimer's disease (see Chapter 16), and postmortem examination of the brain reveals the tangles and plaques typical of Alzheimer's disease (e.g., Karlinsky, 1986; Oliver & Holland, 1986).

Another inherited form of mental retardation is **fragile X syndrome**, which affects 1 in 1,500 boys and 1 in 2,500 girls (for review, see Koukoui & Chaudhuri, 2007). In this syndrome, an individual inherits an X chromosome with a "fragile" section. At this section of the chromosome, a normally repeating sequence of genetic material occurs an unusually large number of times, much like a genetic stutter (Ross, McInnis, Margolis, & Li, 1993). As a result,

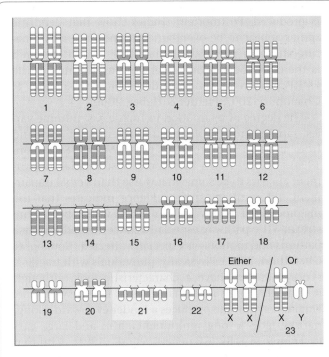

● **FIGURE 15.10   The inheritance of three copies of the 21st chromosome results in Down syndrome.** Notice that all other chromosomes are inherited in pairs, one from the mother and one from the father. © 2010 Cengage Learning

(A)

(B)

● **FIGURE 15.11   Physical features associated with genetic causes of mental retardation.**
(A) Individuals who have Down syndrome typically have certain physical features that make this type of retardation relatively easy to detect in infancy. These features include an upper eyelid that, at the corner of the eye, folds over the bottom eyelid, and a face with a relatively flat profile. (B) The physical features associated with fragile X syndrome are much less pronounced. As shown here in this adolescent male who has the syndrome, they include a long face, a prominent forehead, and large ears. However, as can be seen, these features are not so out of the ordinary as to make the diagnosis obvious.

less than the normal amount of a protein called FMRP is produced. Postmortem studies show that dendritic spines appear to be overabundant and have an immature shape in people with fragile X; current research is therefore focused on understanding the role of the FMRP protein in dendritic development (Koukoui & Chaudhuri, 2007; Pfeiffer & Huber, 2009).

The degree of retardation in fragile X syndrome varies, ranging from profound to borderline in boys and from mild to borderline in girls (Warren & Nelson, 1994). Unlike Down syndrome, visuospatial impairment appears to be somewhat worse than verbal impairment. Interestingly, some evidence indicates that the magnocellular pathway within the visual processing stream—the pathway especially concerned with coarse patterns and motion—is especially affected (Koukoui & Chaudhuri, 2007). Physically, individuals with fragile X syndrome often have a characteristic look, although it is much more subtle than that of Down syndrome. Fragile X syndrome produces a tendency toward a long, narrow face; a long, prominent chin; and large ears (● Figure 15.11B) (Cianchetti et al., 1991). Children with fragile X syndrome are often not diagnosed until later in childhood, when they begin to fall behind their peers in development.

Infections and Toxins

The developing fetus is exposed to many different substances that pass through the placenta, the membranous organ through which blood and nutrients are transferred from the mother to the fetus. Most of what is transferred through the placenta is beneficial and essential for the developing fetus, but some substances can be harmful. These include infectious organisms as well as toxic substances ingested by the mother.

Infections that can potentially damage the fetus—thought to occur in as many as 2% of all newborns—include toxoplasmosis, rubella, cytomegalovirus, and herpes simplex. One of the best known of these is rubella, also known as German measles. If rubella is acquired by the mother during the first month of gestation, the infant has a 50% chance of being mentally retarded (Brosco, Mattingly, & Sanders, 2006). Fortunately, this form of mental retardation has drastically decreased in areas of the world that have programs to vaccinate children against rubella.

Some substances ingested by the mother are toxic to the developing fetus and can cause mental retardation. For example, the long-term effects of alcohol abuse by the mother during pregnancy result in **fetal alcohol syndrome (FAS)**, a leading cause of mental retardation that occurs in 1 in 1,000 births even though it is entirely preventable. FAS causes hyperactivity, poor attention span, social and emotional difficulties, difficulties in learning and memory, and executive dysfunction. Generally speaking, children with FAS show greater cognitive impairments when they are tested on more complex and demanding tasks (Kodituwakku, 2007). Individuals with FAS also exhibit slowed physical growth and abnormalities of the face and cranium, as shown in ● Figure 15.12 (Manning & Hoyme, 2007). The syndrome is associated with changes in brain structure in the regions of the basal ganglia, corpus callosum, cerebellum, and hippocampus. It is not yet well understood what quantity of alcohol ingestion during pregnancy is sufficient to cause symptoms of FAS, so expectant mothers are typically advised to avoid alcohol altogether.

Although the effects of alcohol on the developing nervous system have been most widely studied, researchers have also examined the influence of other substances. For example, prenatal exposure to cocaine is thought to affect the developing neurotransmitter systems, in turn influencing structures that contribute to attention (Stanwood & Levitt, 2001). Ascertaining the specific effects of a mother's drug use on the subsequent mental status of the developing fetus is often difficult, because other factors that co-occur with drug use, such as poor nutrition and poor prenatal care, can also contribute to mental retardation.

Copyright © David Young-Wolff/Photo Edit

● **FIGURE 15.12   Physical facial features associated with fetal alcohol syndrome.** Some of these facial features include small eyes, a short upturned nose, and a smooth skin surface (without any indentation) between the nose and upper lip. © 2009 Cengage Learning

Anoxia

The brain is the most metabolically demanding of all organs. Because oxygen is critical for the conversion of glucose into energy, deprivation of oxygen for as little as three minutes is sufficient to cause brain death. Oxygen is especially critical for the developing nervous system, the metabolic needs of which can exceed those of the adult nervous system. **Anoxia** refers to complete deprivation of oxygen for some period of time, whereas **hypoxia** refers to reduced oxygen availability.

Oxygen deprivation can occur during development in a variety of ways. A child may experience reduced oxygen before birth because the placenta is underdeveloped or damaged, or because the mother herself is not getting adequate oxygen. During birth, damage to the placenta or entanglement of the umbilical cord may reduce the oxygen supply to the infant. Some populations of infants, such as those born very prematurely, are at risk for anoxia after birth because their lungs are not sufficiently developed for independent breathing. Children who have an anoxic episode early in life are at increased risk of later mental retardation (Lipper, Voorhies, Ross, Vannucci, & Auld, 1986) and cerebral palsy. **Cerebral palsy** is an umbrella term for many motor disorders resulting from nonprogressive damage to neural structures important for motor control (e.g., Krigger, 2006; Reddihough & Collins, 2003).

However, mental retardation is not an inevitable consequence of anoxia early in life, nor do all children with cerebral palsy have mental retardation. Some children, such as those with congenital heart problems, may exhibit substantial improvement if interventions are enacted to increase the oxygen supply to the brain (e.g., O'Dougherty, Wright, Loewenson, & Torres, 1985). Whereas those with moderate anoxia show deficits on tests of memory, perceptual-motor skills, and frontal lobe function, those with only mild hypoxia do not (Maneru, Junque, Botet, Tallada, & Guardia, 2001).

■ Dyslexia

Mental retardation describes a condition in which functioning is impaired across a broad range of domains. Other developmental disorders involve difficulty with acquiring cognitive skills in only one particular domain. When only one domain is affected, the condition is referred to as a **learning disability. Dyslexia**, sometimes referred to as a *specific reading disability,* is a specific inability to learn to read at an age-appropriate level, despite adequate opportunity, training, and intelligence. Other specific learning disabilities exist as well. For example, children with a *nonverbal learning disability* have a specific deficit in processing nonverbal material. Much less is known about this disorder, so we do not discuss it in detail here (see Forrest, 2004, for a review).

Children with difficulty reading are considered to have dyslexia when they have adequate intelligence to support the cognitive demands imposed by reading, can perform age- and grade-appropriate cognitive functions, and have been exposed to written language and instruction in reading. For example, an eight-year-old child with a specific reading disability would be unable to read but could solve age-appropriate math problems such as simple multiplication. As the child gets older, however, acquisition of knowledge in other subjects besides written language may be compromised, because knowledge is often conveyed via written materials. Simply put, in traditional schooling reading is an essential skill underlying the acquisition of knowledge in many other areas.

Dyslexia is one of the more common developmental disorders, affecting approximately 5–15% of school-age children in the United States (Shaywitz & Shaywitz, 2003), with a higher prevalence among boys than girls (Rutter et al., 2004). The number of individuals affected by dyslexia surpasses the combined total of those affected by cerebral palsy, epilepsy, and severe mental retardation.

Although many people incorrectly assume that the cardinal sign of dyslexia is writing letters backward, dyslexia is generally characterized by a deficit in phonological understanding (Ramus, 2004). Phonological processing involves linking a particular letter to a particular sound and being able to parse words into their constituent phonemes, a process sometimes referred to as *decoding*. For example, to decode the word *chart*, a person must be able to break the word down into separate sound units (*ch, ar, t*) and to know how those sound units are represented visually. People with dyslexia, in contrast, often learn to read using the whole-word route rather than by breaking words down into phonemes (refer to Chapter 9 for a discussion of different routes in reading). This reliance on visual form, rather than using the strategy of sounding out words, causes readers with dyslexia to make unusual errors, such as misreading *house* as "hose."

Although researchers generally agree that **phonological awareness** is disrupted in dyslexia, they are still trying to pin down exactly why it is disrupted. It may be that the deficit is in phonological awareness itself. An alternative possibility is that the requisite perceptual mechanisms needed to acquire phonological awareness are deficient. According to this idea (e.g., Tallal et al., 1996), difficulty with the fine temporal analysis of auditory information would prevent dyslexics from processing the critical acoustic parameters, such as voicing, that distinguish between phonemes (see Chapter 9). Indeed, evidence suggests that individuals with reading impairment do have difficulty with certain aspects of auditory processing, particularly in distinguishing the order of sounds presented in close succession (Wright, Bowen, & Zecker, 2000). Because reading requires the linkage of sound to visual symbol, still other researchers are

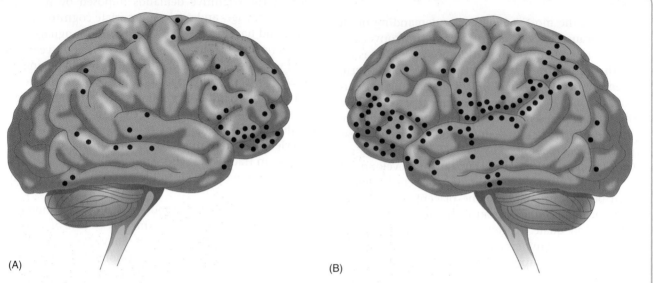

(A)   (B)

● **FIGURE 15.13   Location of developmental anomalies in the brains of males diagnosed with dyslexia.** Shown here as purple circles are sites that on postmortem examination were found to exhibit abnormalities in brain structure in (A) the right hemisphere and (B) the left hemisphere. Many more abnormalities can be seen in the left hemisphere than in the right. These abnormalities tend to occur in the perisylvian area (in the vicinity of the Sylvian fissure) and in frontal regions. © 2011 Cengage Learning

investigating the role that visual processing may play in reading problems (see Sperling, Lu, Manis, & Seidenberg, 2005; Stein, Talcott, & Walsh, 2000). It may be that reading difficulties can arise from more than one source,

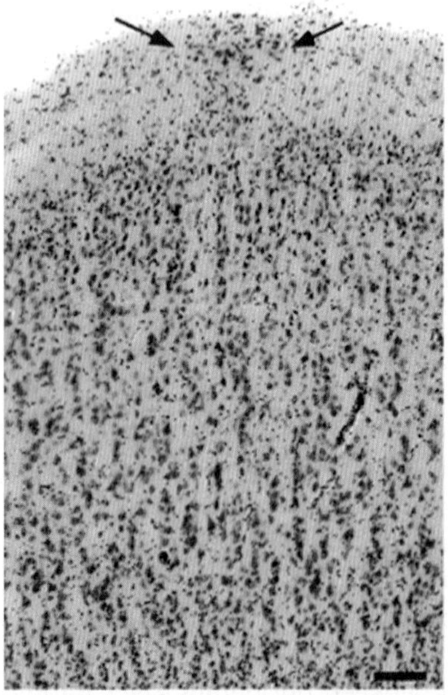

● **FIGURE 15.14   An ectopia, or abnormality of cell migration, in layer I of the cortex in a dyslexic individual.** The region of abnormal cell migration is shown between the two arrows. *Source:* Adapted by permission from Macmillan Publishers, Ltd. Fig. 2 from Galaburda, A. M., et al. (2006). From genes to behavior in developmental dyslexia. Nature Neuroscience, 9, 1213–1217. Adapted by permission from Macmillan Publishers, Ltd.

meaning that these explanations for dyslexia may not be mutually exclusive.

Since the late 1920s, researchers have been considering whether the reading difficulties observed in individuals with dyslexia might result from some type of neural miswiring (e.g., Orton, 1937). Postmortem anatomical examination of the brains of people with dyslexia reveals anatomical anomalies in the perisylvian area of the left hemisphere, a region that includes language-related areas around the Sylvian fissure, as well as in other areas of the left frontal lobe (Galaburda, Sherman, Rosen, Aboitiz, & Geschwind, 1985; Humphreys, Kaufmann, & Galaburda, 1990) (● Figure 15.13). In these areas, researchers observed *ectopias,* areas where cells appear to have migrated to the wrong layers of the cortex. An example of an ectopia is illustrated in ● Figure 15.14. Recent research has identified several genes that may be linked to dyslexia, and in most cases the genes appear to influence neuronal migration and axon growth (Galaburda, LoTurco, Ramus, Fitch, & Rosen, 2006). Therefore, one possibility is that due to genetic factors, cell migration in particular areas of the cortex is disrupted, leading to dyslexia. It is not known, however, why this abnormal migration would be restricted to the perisylvian region or how it might contribute to the cognitive function of phonological awareness that seems to be at the heart of dyslexia. Functional imaging studies also implicate the left perisylvian regions in dyslexia. Numerous studies, summarized in ● Figure 15.15, have found that during language-processing tasks, people with dyslexia tend to show less activity than controls in left perisylvian areas, particularly at the juncture of the parietal, temporal, and occipital lobes (Temple, 2002).

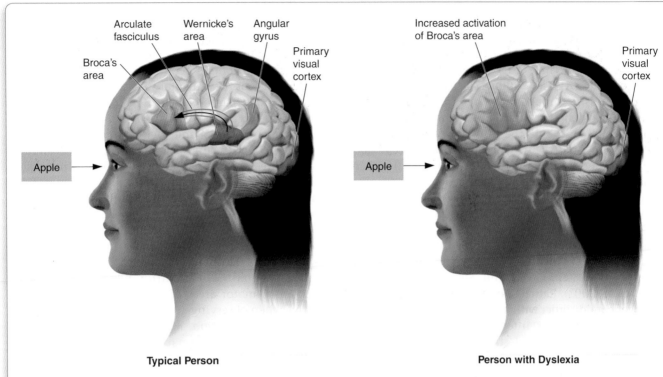

● FIGURE 15.15   **Areas in which dyslexic individuals show different brain activity than normal readers.** During a reading task, people with dyslexia tend to show less activity in Wernicke's area and the angular gyrus, and more activity in Broca's area, compared to typical readers. © 2010 Cengage Learning

These studies have focused on particular brain regions, but other studies implicate regional connectivity in dyslexia. One version of this position argues that dyslexia is caused by dysfunctional interaction between the cerebral hemispheres. By this account, learning to read necessitates that information about the visual form of letters (a purportedly right-hemisphere function) be linked via the corpus callosum with their phonetic representations (a purportedly left-hemisphere function). Indeed, some studies have reported correlations between reading ability and the size or shape of the corpus callosum (e.g., Fine, Semrud-Clikeman, Keith, Stapleton, & Hynd, 2007; Hynd et al., 1995; Robichon & Habib, 1998; von Plessen et al., 2002), while others report disrupted transfer of information between the hemispheres of dyslexics, both with regard to how well information is shared between hemispheres (e.g., Gladstone, Best, & Davidson, 1989; Henderson, Barca, & Ellis, 2007) and how quickly it is shared (e.g., Markee, Brown, Moore, & Theberge, 1996).

Another version of this position argues that dyslexia involves a disconnection between regions of the left hemisphere itself, rather than a disconnection between the hemispheres. Consistent with this viewpoint, dyslexics fail to coactivate temporoparietal and frontal regions during a rhyming task, and they exhibit less myelination of connections between left frontal and temporoparietal regions than do neurologically intact

individuals (Klingberg et al., 2000; for a longer review, see Banich & Scalf, 2003).

Before leaving the topic of dyslexia, we note that reading disability is an area where brain and culture meet. Children with difficulty in phonological awareness are especially challenged by languages such as English, in which there is no clear one-to-one correspondence or mapping between letters and sounds. (For example, in English, "f" and "ph" are linked to the same sound.) These difficulties are somewhat reduced in a language such as Italian, which has regular and consistent mappings between sounds and symbols (Ziegler & Goswami, 2005). Interestingly, though, a recent study found that dyslexic readers of Italian, French, or English exhibit a similar pattern of neural activation—decreased activity in the left posterior temporal region—regardless of their language (Paulesu et al., 2001). This finding indicates that although people with dyslexia may be less likely to display reading difficulties in one language, such as Italian, than another, such as French or English, the neural substrate that supports reading is altered in similar ways.

■ Autism and Pervasive Developmental Disorders

The four basic characteristics of **pervasive developmental disorders** (including **autism**) are: qualitative impairment in social interaction; delays and abnormalities in language as well as other aspects of communication; restricted, repetitive, and stereotyped patterns of behaviors, interests, or activities; and an onset of the problems in at least one of these three areas before the age of three years (American Psychiatric Association, [*DSM-IV-TR*]. 2000). You may have first heard about autism through news reports suggesting that autism is on the rise and that vaccines given in childhood may contribute the disorder. The scientific evidence suggests that increased public knowledge about the disorder, along with more liberal diagnostic criteria, have increased the rate at which people with the disorder are now correctly identified, but that the incidence rate is likely holding steady (Gernsbacher, Dawson, & Goldsmith, 2005). Moreover, vaccines do not appear to contribute to the disorder (Hviid, Stellfeld, Wohlfahrt, & Melbye, 2003; Institute of Medicine, 2004; Madsen et al., 2003; Stehr-Green, Tull, Stellfeld, Mortenson, & Simpson, 2003). Rather, autism is assumed to be a heterogeneous disorder with many potential causes, including genetic disorders, infectious diseases, birth injuries, metabolic diseases, and structural disorders of brain development (e.g., DiCicco-Bloom et al., 2006).

Although both autism and mental retardation are associated with IQs that are significantly below average, autistic children have profound social deficits that are not observed in children with mental retardation. Children with mental retardation seek interaction with adults and others, smile, and appreciate being held when hurt. Autistic children, in contrast, prefer to engage in routinized, robotic behavior such as hand flapping. They may scream if approached, as if being intruded upon too closely, and often avoid making eye contact with other people. They appear indifferent to the presence of others, acting as if other people are pieces of furniture or "looking through" them as if they didn't exist. Moreover, they tend to perform best on cognitive tasks that do not require human interaction. For example, on recognition tests, they often can identify inanimate objects, such as a screwdriver, more readily than objects representing something human, such as a face. The cognitive interests of people with autism are usually narrow and unemotional, such as an obsession with baseball statistics or an absorption with mechanical movement, like the spinning of an electric fan (*DSM-IV-TR*, 2000).

Throughout the history of thought on autism, a disorder that Kanner first described in 1943, people have debated whether its essence is primarily cognitive (e.g., Rutter, 1983) or primarily emotional (e.g., Fein, Pennington, Markowitz, Braverman, & Waterhouse, 1986). Now it appears that the cognitive and emotional deficits observed in autism are intertwined. For example, individuals with autism do not develop *joint attention,* in which attention is coordinated between the individual, another person, and an object or event (McArthur & Adamson, 1996). If you point to something in the distance, you expect your companion to look in the direction you are pointing; but autistic individuals do not do so. Although this can be viewed as an attentional problem, a lack of joint attentional focus is disruptive for social and emotional interaction as well. Autistic people also appear to lack "theory of mind," that is, the ability to understand that other people may have different mental states and that these mental states can be deduced from social signals (Baron-Cohen, 1995). For example, a look of surprise on someone's face can be a clue to the particular mental model under which that person has been operating. Once again, such an ability involves an interface between cognitive and social-emotional processing.

Because autism is characterized by social deficits, many researchers have focused on brain systems that participate in social cognition. Some researchers have proposed that the mirror neuron system (refer back to Chapter 5) may not operate normally in people with autism (Iacoboni & Dapretto, 2006; Oberman & Ramachandran, 2007). Mirror neurons, first identified in premotor areas of the monkey brain, become active when observing another individual carrying out a goal-directed action. Mirror neurons may provide a rudimentary mechanism for forming a common understanding of actions across individuals (Gallese, Keysers, & Rizzolatti, 2004). In a task that required participants to imitate facial expressions of emotion, autistic participants do not activate the premotor regions as extensively as do control participants (● Figure 15.16), adding credence to the idea that this neural system may be deficient in individuals with autism (Dapretto et al., 2006). However, because autistic children are able to correctly imitate goal-directed hand motions (Hamilton, Brindley, & Frith, 2007), it is not yet clear to what extent difficulties in mirroring constitute a core deficit in autism.

Another possibility is that the deficit in autism is more specific to perception and recognition of facial identity and emotional expression. Autistic people look at faces differently, fixating less on the eyes, than do neurologically intact people (e.g., Klin, Jones, Schultz, Volkmar, & Cohen, 2002; Spezio, Adolphs, Hurley, & Piven, 2007), consistent with clinical reports that autistic people tend not to make eye contact with others. Imaging studies have shown that people with autism do not engage the normal face-processing neural machinery when presented with pictures of faces. For example, when viewing face images, activity in both the amygdala and the fusiform face area is lower in autistic people compared to neurologically intact people (e.g., Ashwin, Baron-Cohen, Wheelwright, O'Riordan, & Bullmore, 2007; Pierce, Müller, Ambrose, Allen, & Courchesne, 2001). Moreover, they ignore information about faces that is especially useful for social interaction. In one study addressing this hypothesis, participants viewed faces that differed in the direction of gaze (Pelphrey, Morris, & McCarthy, 2005). Nonautistic participants showed a pattern of brain activity in the superior temporal sulcus that was sensitive to the gaze direction of the face, whereas autistic participants did not (● Figure 15.17). Although most of these studies focused on faces, other

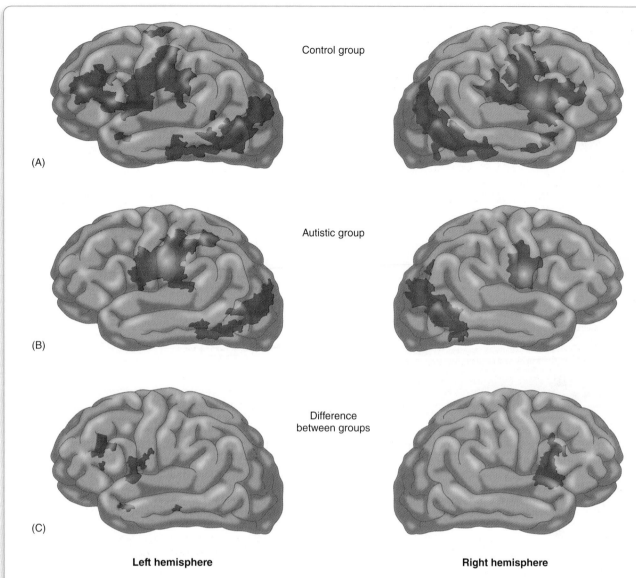

Control group

Autistic group

Difference
between groups

(A)

(B)

(C)

Left hemisphere   **Right hemisphere**

● **FIGURE 15.16   Brain activation during an imitation task in control participants (A) and autistic participants (B).** Panel (C) illustrates the areas that differed significantly between the two groups. The task required participants to imitate facial expressions of emotion. *Source:* Fig 1a–c from Dapretto, M. et al. (2006). Understanding emotions in others: Mirror neuron dysfunction in children with autism spectrum disorders. Nature Neuroscience, 9, 28–30.

studies indicate that the difficulty in engaging the neural systems for processing social cues extends to the auditory domain as well. For example, autistic individuals exhibit a lower response in the temporal lobe to human voices compared to neurologically intact people (Gervais et al., 2004).

At a more abstract level, when attempting to understand the viewpoint or motivations of others, autistic people do not tend to activate the brain regions that neurologically intact individuals do (see Zilbovicius, Meresse, Chabane, Brunelle, Samson, & Boddaert, 2006, for a review). In one intriguing study, participants viewed the movement of shapes that followed either a random pattern or a pattern suggesting that the shapes were intentionally interacting with one another (Castelli, Frith, Happé, & Frith, 2002). Most people

attribute mental states and intentions to the shapes in the latter condition, and these "mentalizing" attributions are associated with an increase in activity in the medial prefrontal cortex and superior temporal sulcus; however, autistic participants showed less activity in these regions compared to controls (see also Herrington et al., 2007). These results reinforce the idea that brain areas involved in social cognition, such as the superior temporal sulcus, are not activated normally in individuals with autism.

These theories represent some of the most prominent cognitive neuroscience approaches to understanding autism, but other approaches have also been taken. For example, some researchers have examined frontolimbic connectivity (Bachevalier & Loveland, 2006; Courchesne & Pierce, 2005); others have examined the

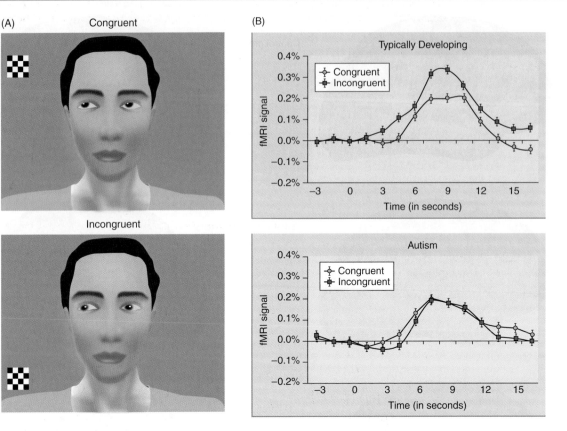

● **FIGURE 15.17   A task sensitive to gaze direction activates superior temporal sulcus in control participants but not autistic participants.** (A) Participants viewed a face whose eyes were looking either toward a target stimulus (congruent gaze) or toward an empty location (incongruent gaze). (B) Activity in the right superior temporal sulcus was sensitive to gaze direction in the typically developing (control) participants (top) but not the autistic participants (bottom). *Source:* Fig. 1 and Fig. 4a–b from Pelphrey et al. (2005). Neural basis of eye gaze processing deficits in autism. Brain: A Journal of Neurology, 128, 1038–1048.

role of the cerebellum, hypothesizing that mental timing may be disrupted in autism (Pierce & Courchesne, 2001). Still others have focused on the overall size of the brain (Redcay & Courchesne, 2005), on visual or auditory processing (Behrmann, Thomas, & Humphreys, 2006; Siegal & Blades, 2003), on the role of testosterone in prenatal development (Baron-Cohen, 2002; Baron-Cohen, Knickmeyer, & Belmonte, 2005), or on gene configurations that may contribute to autism (Persico & Bourgeron, 2006). If there is one general conclusion that we can draw from all of these different approaches, it is that autism is unlikely to be explained by any single unifying biological factor (Happé, Ronald, & Plomin, 2006).

■ **Attention-Deficit Hyperactivity Disorder**

Attention-deficit hyperactivity disorder (ADHD) is a developmental disorder in which the affected child is either inattentive, hyperactive/impulsive, or both compared to the average child of the same age (*DSM-IV-TR*, 2000). These children *can be* capable of paying attention and sitting still, as they may spend hours playing

a video game, but overall their ability to pay attention is much less than is typical for children their age, and they are often guided by environmental dependencies similar to those discussed in Chapter 12. Many people have expressed concern about the potential overdiagnosis of ADHD, particularly because some of its symptoms seem like common childhood behavior, such as fidgeting and difficulty in controlling impulses. To try to protect against labeling normal behavior as disordered, the *DSM-IV* diagnostic criteria require that the child have a clinically significant impairment that interferes with adaptive functioning in more than one setting (e.g., both school and home).

Not surprisingly, ADHD often impedes a child's progress in learning, especially in a structured environment, because the child's impulsivity and distractibility do not allow him or her to sit still long enough to absorb material or to listen to instructions. Because of these tendencies, such children may find themselves cherished by neither teachers nor parents. If their behavior leads to difficulty with peers and authority figures, their risk for engaging in antisocial behavior rises. Moreover, although ADHD is a distinct disorder, it regularly co-occurs with other learning disabilities such as dyslexia.

Although the name "attention-deficit disorder" implies that researchers have a clear idea of the cognitive difficulty—a deficit in attention—in fact there is disagreement in the literature about the core deficit in ADHD. One idea is that arousal mechanisms are disrupted in people with ADHD, leading to difficulty in sustaining attention over long periods of time (Sergeant, 2005). To assess sustained attention, researchers often use tasks such as the continuous performance task. In this task, the participant must respond to a certain stimulus anytime it appears; for example, pressing a key anytime an "X" appears in a continuous stream of letters. Typically, the task goes on for a long time, and the time delay between letters can be long. Thus, quick and accurate responses require the ability to sustain attention and arousal even when things get boring. Somewhat surprisingly, findings about the performance of children with ADHD on such tasks have been mixed; some studies have found deficits, but others have not (see Karatekin, 2001, for a review). Interestingly, on tasks in which participants must filter out irrelevant information, participants with ADHD performed better in the presence of white noise than under control conditions (Söderlund, Sikström, & Smart, 2007). One possible explanation is that under control conditions, ADHD participants experience very low states of arousal, whereas conditions of white noise provide enough external stimulation to maintain arousal and thus aid in performance (Sikström & Söderlund, 2007).

The deficit that has been most reliably observed in ADHD is in the ability to inhibit inappropriate responses (Barkley, 1997). Intuitively, behavioral inhibition seems naturally linked to ADHD, because such children often appear to act impulsively. To measure inhibitory control in the lab, researchers often use a task such as the stop-signal task (Logan, Cowan, & Davis, 1984). In this task, participants are trained to make a particular response to a particular stimulus; for example, press the right key when a circle appears, and the left key when a square appears. However, during some trials, just after the target item appears, participants are given a signal, such as a "beep" that indicates not to respond on that trial. Numerous studies have found that children with ADHD have particular difficulty overriding or aborting the prepared responses on the "stop" trials (Karatekin, 2001). This difficulty with overriding or controlling responses may be part of a more general disruption in executive functions observed in individuals with ADHD (Willcutt, Doyle, Nigg, Faraone, & Pennington, 2005).

Structural imaging studies support several conclusions about the brain in ADHD compared to control participants (for reviews, see Krain & Castellanos, 2006; Seidman, Valera, & Makris, 2005; Valera, Faraone, Murray, & Seidman, 2007). First, there is evidence of an overall reduction in brain volume in ADHD. Second, specific structures are especially implicated, including frontal cortex, regions of the striatum such as the caudate and globus pallidus, the splenium of the corpus callosum, and the cerebellum. Most of the existing studies have been conducted on children, but structural imaging also shows reductions in brain volume in some of these areas in adults with ADHD, particularly in regions implicated in attentional control (Makris et al., 2007). Furthermore, cortical volume has been linked to behavioral outcomes in ADHD. For example, one longitudinal study measured brain volumes in children with ADHD at two time points about six years apart (Shaw, Lerch, et al., 2006). A worse behavioral outcome at the second time point was associated with a relatively thinner cortex in the left medial prefrontal cortex, at both the initial and subsequent evaluations. However, for ADHD participants with good behavioral outcomes, there was a change in cortical thickness in the right parietal region, such that it more closely resembled that of control subjects at the second time point.

Functional imaging studies have examined the responsiveness of these and other brain regions while children perform tasks that involve attention and inhibitory control (see Bush, Valera, & Seidman, 2005, for a review). For example, in one study examining performance on the stop-signal task (Pliszka et al., 2006), healthy children showed significantly greater cingulate and left ventrolateral frontal cortex activation during unsuccessful inhibitions ("stop" trials in which the child was supposed to inhibit responding, but could not do so) compared to successful inhibitions. However, in children with ADHD, the activity in these regions was similar regardless of whether or not they were able to successfully inhibit their response (● Figure 15.18). Nevertheless, both groups showed greater right dorsolateral activity during "stop" trials compared to "go" trials. Therefore, at least based on this study, it seems that both ADHD and control children are activating frontal lobe inhibitory control systems, but in ADHD these systems may not be able to coordinate with the other regions needed to exert control over behavior. (For other functional imaging studies of ADHD children and adults, see Smith, Taylor, Brammer, Toone, & Rubia, 2006; Tamm, Menon, & Reiss, 2006.)

The brain's dopaminergic system is strongly implicated in ADHD. The drugs that are used to treat ADHD are known to influence the dopamine system, and these drugs have a beneficial effect on cognitive performance in children with ADHD (see Pietrzak, Mollica, Maruff, & Snyder, 2006, for review). Medications used to treat ADHD include those derived from amphetamine (trade names: Dexedrine, Adderall), methylphenidate (trade name: Ritalin), and pemoline (trade name: Cylert). Methylphenidate, for example, affects the dopaminergic neurotransmitter system by slowing the rate of dopamine reuptake on postsynaptic sites. In addition, candidate genes that are under study for their relationship to ADHD are generally genes that influence dopaminergic neurotransmission, such as the dopamine

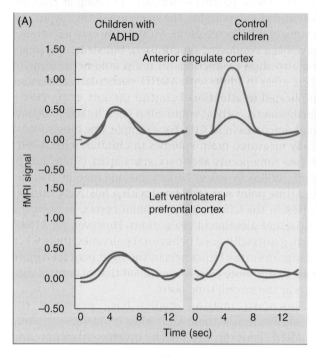

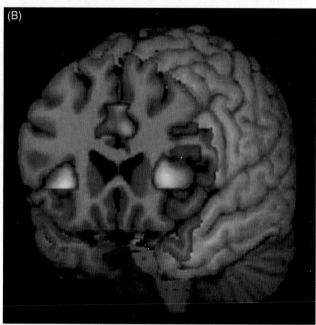

● **FIGURE 15.18**   **Frontal lobe activation during response inhibition in children with ADHD and controls.**   Control children show increased anterior cingulate cortex and left ventrolateral prefrontal activity in response to failures of inhibition, but children with ADHD do not. The red Line (put type in red) represents successful inhibitions and the blue line (put type in blue) represents unsuccessful inhibitions. *Source:* Fig. 2 from Pliszka, S. R., et al. (2006). Neuroimaging of inhibitory control areas in children with attention deficit hyperactivity disorder who were treatment naïve or in long-term treatment. American Journal of Psychiatry, 163, 1052–1060.

receptor genes (e.g., DRD₁, DRD₄); the COMT gene, which influences dopamine metabolism; and the dopa decarboxylase gene, which is crucial for dopamine synthesis (Waldman & Gizer, 2006). Because the frontal and striatal regions are heavily innervated by dopamine pathways, a dopamine-based hypothesis of ADHD is consistent with findings of anatomical and functional differences in the frontal-striatal regions in ADHD.

In addition to the typical treatment for ADHD, which involves the administration of medication, researchers have also explored behavioral interventions. Typically, such programs involve working with parents and teachers to better manage the child's behavior. Although some benefits may be obtained from behavioral treatments, studies that have directly compared medication and behavioral treatments find medication to be more effective on average (e.g., MTA Cooperative Group, 1999).

Before we leave the topic of developmental disorders, it is important to consider what happens when these children become adults. For some of the disorders we have discussed, the outcome is relatively straightforward. For instance, individuals who exhibit mental retardation or pervasive developmental disorders as children also exhibit intellectual impairment as adults. But what about some of the more specific learning disabilities, such as dyslexia and ADHD? Do children outgrow these disorders, or are they impaired for life?

One theory, the **maturational lag hypothesis**, postulated that individuals with specific learning disabilities are slower to mature than their peers, and that with time they will outgrow the problem much the way that children are thought to shed baby fat. This idea was fueled in part by observations that learning disabilities appear to become less severe with age in certain subpopulations of children. For example, some children with ADHD appear to become less impulsive around the age of 12 years, which is when children typically show an increase in attentional abilities. However, difficulties appear to manifest in a different form and manner as an individual matures. For example, at age 12 a child with ADHD may be able to sit in his chair in a classroom, something he could not do at age 7, but he may still have an inability to "sit with" a homework problem. Moreover, given our increasing knowledge regarding the neural bases for these disorders, the idea that these learning disabilities miraculously disappear at adulthood seems improbable. At the same time, it is important to remember that many people with dyslexia, ADHD, and other learning disabilities go on to have successful personal and professional lives, probably by emphasizing other cognitive strengths.

In the next section we examine the degree to which the brain can change and adapt, either in response to trauma and deprivation, or as a result of specific experiences or input. This adaptability, in fact, may account for some of the diminution in the severity of learning disabilities or changes in the nature of the symptoms that can occur as a child ages.

Brain Plasticity

As we discussed at the beginning of the chapter, the human brain is plastic and sensitive to environmental input. This applies not only during childhood but during adulthood as well. Logically, this must be true at some level; after all, if the brain were completely fixed at the time of adult maturation, you would never be able to learn a new skill or change your way of thinking! At a minimum, we know that adults can learn, and therefore their brains can respond to environmental input—that is, they can change. We also know that, contrary to long-standing dogma, new neurons are generated even in adulthood, though certainly not at anywhere near the rate of neurogenesis in the perinatal period. We have already discussed the basic mechanisms of learning and memory in Chapter 10, so here we focus on additional issues related to plasticity, emphasizing those that continue to occur in adulthood.

Numerous studies have shown that increased experience in adulthood can lead to changes in the representation of information in the brain. For example, training monkeys to distinguish between particular line orientations led to fine-tuning of the receptive fields for the cells coding those orientations in primary visual cortex (Schoups, Vogels, Qian, & Orban, 2001). In humans, learning to juggle in adulthood led to a growth in the size of visual area MT, which participates in coding for visual motion (Draganski, Gaser, Busch, Schuierer, Bogdahn, & May, 2004). The increase in MT size was

not maintained when participants stopped juggling for a few months, however, illustrating the "use it or lose it" phenomenon. Similarly, learning to read Braille is associated with expansion of the area in somatosensory cortex that represents the fingers used to read the Braille pattern (Hamilton & Pascual-Leone, 1998), and practicing specific motor sequences changes activation within primary motor cortex (Karni, Meyer, Jezzard, Adams, Turner, & Ungerleider, 1995).

All these examples suggest that training strengthens cortical representations—but what happens when input of a certain kind is lost? Do representations wither away? Research with other species suggests that the answer is yes. One type of experiment involved amputating fingers of monkeys and observing how the representation of those fingers in somatosensory cortex changed (Kaas, 2000; see also Buonomano & Merzenich, 1998; Jones, 2000). As you may remember from Chapter 1, the somatosensory cortex includes a map of the body, in which each section of the map consists of cells responsive to sensation from a distinct part of the body. When sensation from a particular body region is consistently missing, as in the case of an amputation, the map in somatosensory cortex is reorganized, such that the territory previously corresponding to that lost part is now responsive to a neighboring part of the body (i.e., a nearby finger) (● Figure 15.19). This research tells us that the "maps" that exist in our sensory cortices are not set in stone, but rather that they are maintained only through continual sensory input. When input changes systematically, the map changes. This change in cortical maps or the function of a brain region is referred to as **reorganization**.

These research findings have been applied to try to understand phantom sensations in people who have lost limbs. Even though they know that the limb is gone,

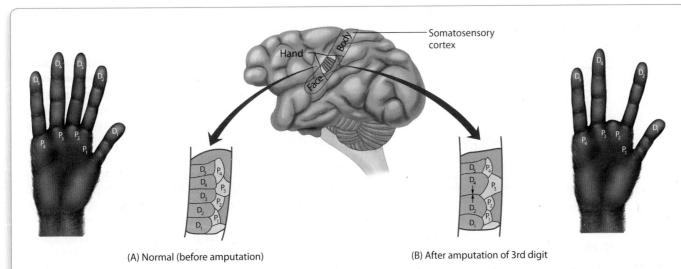

(A) Normal (before amputation)   (B) After amputation of 3rd digit

● **FIGURE 15.19   Somatosensory cortex reorganizes after amputation.** The region of somatosensory cortex that represents the hand surface changes after a monkey's finger is amputated. The region that used to represent the amputated finger begins to represent information from neighboring fingers and the palm surface. © 2009 Cengage Learning

some amputees continue to perceive sensations from the missing limb, and these sensations can be distracting and even painful. Some researchers have suggested that phantom limb sensations are elicited when cells that used to code for the lost limb are now being stimulated by new input from a different body location (Ramachandran & Hirstein, 1998) (● Figure 15.20). Because of this transition in the cells' coding—they used to code for one body part, but now code for another body part—phantom sensations may arise.

How dramatic can reorganization be? The examples we have just discussed pertain to reorganization on a relatively small scale, within a map in one sensory cortical region. But what if the person loses an entire sensory modality altogether? When a person becomes blind or deaf, what happens to the cortical regions that would normally respond to sight or sound? Several studies have found that congenital blindness leads to reorganization of the "visual" cortex for other functions. For example, in congenitally blind people, the "visual" cortex is activated by Braille reading and other tactile stimulation (Burton, Sinclair, & McLaren, 2004; Sadato et al., 1996; Sadato, Pascual-Leone, Grafman, Deiber, Ibañez, & Hallett, 1998), as well as by some auditory and verbal tasks (e.g., Amedi, Raz, Pianka, Malach, & Zohary, 2003; Röder, Stock, Bien, Neville, & Rösler, 2002). Further, transiently disrupting "visual" cortex function with

TMS leads to a decreased ability to read Braille in the blind but not in normally sighted people (Cohen et al., 1997). This evidence indicates that the "visual" cortex can reorganize to respond to nonvisual information in congenitally blind people, a phenomenon known as **cross-modal plasticity**. Several studies have found similar, though not as dramatic, cross-modal reorganization effects for people who became blind later in life, implying that reorganization of visual cortex can occur in adulthood, not just in response to congenital loss of vision (Burton, Snyder, Conturo, Akbudak, Ollinger, & Raichle, 2002; Burton, Snyder, Diamond, & Raichle, 2002). (See also the "In Focus" feature in this chapter, which discusses enhanced abilities in those who have lost a sensory modality.)

Another way of asking the plasticity question is to examine whether the cortex can reorganize when a sensory modality is restored. Imagine a person who was born blind or deaf due to defects in the eye or ear, but then later received a treatment that restored sensory input. For example, a person who was born with cataracts had those cataracts removed later in life; or a person who was born profoundly deaf, because of problems with the inner ear, but was later given cochlear implants that stimulate the auditory nerve.

There is currently much debate about the extent to which normal sensation can be restored in adulthood in such patients. Experimental studies with animals suggest that when sensory input is restored, the cortex associated with the sensory modality responds to such input. For example, in congenitally deaf cats, implantation of cochlear implants can elicit responses to auditory stimulation in the auditory cortex (Klinke, Kral, Heid, Tillien, & Hartmann, 1999; see Moore & Shannon, 2009, for review). Similarly, treatment of a defect in a dog's retina with gene therapy leads to a response to visual information in the dog's visual cortex, even when the treatment occurrs as late as ages one to four years (Aguirre et al., 2007), which would be about the equivalent of 15 to 40 years of age in humans. These studies imply that the relevant cortical regions still maintain some ability to respond to restored sensory input. But how well do these systems function? In clinical practice, cochlear implants to restore hearing are generally recommended only for adults who became deaf after learning language; for adults who have been deaf since early life, cochlear implants are not typically successful in restoring hearing, presumably because it is difficult to establish knowledge of speech patterns with the impoverished input from an implant (Copeland & Pillsbury, 2004; Moore & Shannon, 2009). In the visual domain, case studies of previously blind people whose visual input was restored in adulthood report that visual perception is abnormal (Fine et al., 2003; Sacks, 1995).

Thus, the possibility of recovery of perceptual function can be seen as a glass half-full or a glass half-empty: the adult cortex retains some ability to respond to sensory input even following severe deprivation of

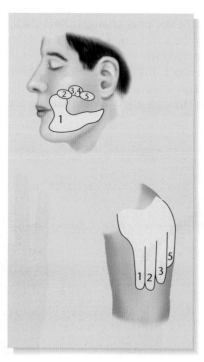

● **FIGURE 15.20   Phantom sensations in an amputee.** For an amputee who has lost the lower part of one arm, stimulation of certain regions of the face may give rise to phantom sensations in the (missing) fingers (numbered 1 through 5). Stimulation of the shoulder area may also give rise to phantom sensations in the fingers. © 2009 Cengage Learning

that sensory modality, but there are limits to that plasticity. Because the organization of the cortex has been affected by prior experiences without a specific sensory modality, it is no longer optimally organized to process information in that modality. This example shows how experience interacts with the biological organization of the brain to influence brain functioning.

Recovery of Function Following Brain Damage

In the previous section, we considered the plasticity in response to changing sensory input and experiences. Another kind of question is also important: How does the brain respond to damage? When the brain sustains a specific insult, such as a gunshot wound or stroke (● Figure 15.21), what is its capacity for reorganization and recovery? These issues are important not only for enriching our basic understanding of the brain's dynamic nature, but also for providing information that is clinically relevant to the many people who suffer brain damage. First, we describe, in a general manner, the brain's responses to injury on a neurophysiological level. We then discuss the possible mechanisms for recovery. Finally, we compare the differences in recovery of function between adults and children.

■ Neurophysiological Responses to Insult

Damage to the brain sets a number of physiological processes in motion, some of which occur directly at the site of the lesion and others of which occur at more distant points. ● Figure 15.22 provides an overview of these physiological processes and the time frame over which they occur. At the site of the lesion, cells begin to die, a process called **necrosis**. This process affects not only neurons, but also the glia that insulate neurons. In some cases, cell loss may extend past the actual site of damage to more distal neurons, a process called **transneuronal degeneration**. Such degeneration occurs because neurons require an optimal level of stimulation as well as certain chemical factors from other nerve cells. If a substantial proportion of a neuron's inputs are damaged, that cell may die. Transneuronal degeneration can occur across more than one synapse, having a domino-like effect. For example, if the optic nerve is cut, cells of the lateral geniculate body degenerate completely. Then, as the lateral geniculate begins to degenerate, cells in the visual cortex may degenerate as well. Often transneuronal degeneration is accompanied by accumulations of calcium, a process known as **calcification**, which is easily detected by brain imaging techniques.

Dead cells are engulfed and broken down (a process known as *phagocytosis*) by astrocytes and microglia. Because neurons have a far more limited capacity to regenerate than other cells in the body, fluid now fills the spaces where cells once resided. New capillaries may form in the region as well. The process of phagocytosis and capillary formation may continue for several months until only glial cells remain, a process known as **gliosis**. Astrocytes mark off the region, forming a scar.

In addition to changes in the neurons themselves, other processes occur with damage. One of these, **edema**, is the swelling of tissue after trauma, which occurs in the brain just as it does in any other part of the body (see Figure 15.21A). Swelling of the brain involves special dangers. When other body parts swell, they just take up more space under your clothing. But the brain and cerebrospinal fluid share a confined space within the skull; when the brain is bruised, the situation is like having a badly bruised toe that must be shoved into

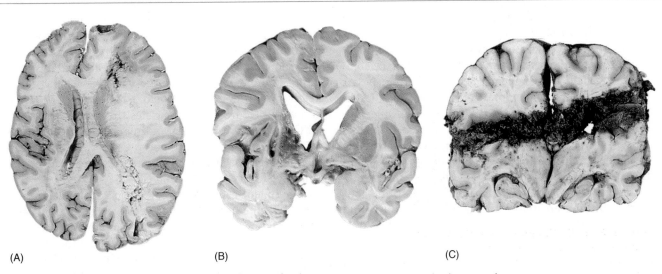

(A)   (B)   (C)

●**FIGURE 15.21   Types of damage to the human brain.** (A) Brain following a stroke that caused severe swelling on the right side of the brain. (B) Brain following a stroke that left cavities of lost cells on the left side. (C) Brain of a person who suffered a gunshot wound. Courtesy of Dr. Dana Copeland.

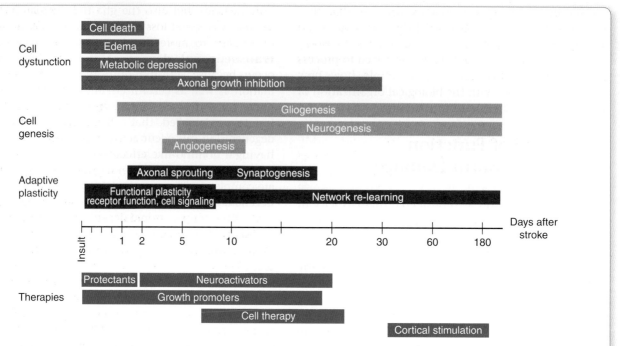

● **FIGURE 15.22   Overview of neurophysiological responses to brain injury.** In the first days after a stroke, dysfunctional responses at the cellular level include cell death, edema (swelling), depression in metabolism, and inhibition of axonal growth. Beginning within a few days are processes of cell genesis, including generation of glial cells and nerve cells, and development of new blood vessels (angiogenesis). Longer-term adaptive effects also include sprouting of axons, formation of new synapses, changes in receptor function, and reestablishment of connections among networks of neurons. Different therapies may be undertaken at various stages to protect against dysfunctional cellular responses to injury and to promote adaptive cellular and systems-level responses. *Source:* Figure 1 from Wieloch, T., & Nikolich, K. (2006). Mechanisms of neural plasticity following brain injury. Current Opinion in Neurobiology, 16, 258–264. Reprinted by permission of Elsevier.

your shoe. The edema associated with brain trauma leads to an increase in intracranial pressure, because more fluid now occupies the same amount of space. This increased pressure can interfere with neuronal function not only at the site of damage, but elsewhere as well. When the edema exerts pressure on brainstem regions controlling vital functions, it can cause a person to become comatose or even die. Therefore, medications and other treatments are given after cerebral trauma to help reduce edema. Because edema may last for some time, the behavioral consequences of a lesion may not become apparent until after the swelling subsides. In addition to these changes, some of the basic aspects of the brain's functioning, such as its metabolic rate, neurotransmitter release, and oxygen consumption, may also be disrupted by a lesion (Verma, 2000). Although there may be an initial increase in metabolism right after an injury, this is followed by a period of decreased metabolism (Bergsneider et al., 2001; Wieloch & Nikolich, 2006).

Given these multiple changes in brain function in response to injury, and the long time span during which they manifest themselves, you can appreciate why a clinician often cannot immediately assess the degree of damage sustained from an injury. If swelling is extensive, the person may show severe impairments at first but significant improvement as the edema decreases. In contrast, responses immediately after oxygen deprivation may lead one to overestimate later levels of functioning, because the detrimental effects of the oxygen deprivation continue to accrue over the time since injury. Thus, the person's behavior immediately after injury only crudely predicts the prognosis for functioning a month or even a year into the future.

Following the acute phase of cell death and dysfunction, a number of changes at the cellular level may aid in recovery of function (see Wieloch & Nikolich, 2006, for a review). Figure 15.22 illustrates the timeline of some of these processes. Understanding cellular mechanisms of recovery is important because new medical treatments might be able to stimulate those mechanisms to enhance recovery.

One major cellular process is the generation of new cells, both neurons and glia. Neurogenesis and gliogenesis are known to be enhanced following an injury to the brain. New blood vessels also grow, a process called *angiogenesis,* and this reestablishes blood supply to the damaged region. In addition, new axons begin to sprout, connecting regions that had not previously been connected, and new synapses form. One possible means by which **regeneration** and sprouting may occur is through a substance known as nerve growth factor

(NGF), which is transported to nerve cells from glia. NGF was discovered in the 1940s by Rita Levi-Montalcini and colleagues, a discovery for which she received the Nobel Prize. (For an interesting account of her experiments conducted in a closet while hiding from the Nazis during World War II, read Levi-Montalcini's autobiography, *In Praise of Imperfection.* As of the writing of this text, Levi-Montalcini is the oldest living Nobel laureate, at the age of 100.) NGF appears to be an important substance in sustaining neurons, especially after injury. Recent evidence indicates that treatments promoting such growth factors can aid in functional recovery following stroke in animal models, suggesting a possible route for clinical intervention (Wieloch & Nikolich, 2006).

■ Mechanisms for Recovery of Function

Damage to a discrete region of brain tissue affects more than the cells in that immediate area; an insult can also affect the surrounding tissue and even more distant tissue in the brain. For several reasons, much of what we know about this pattern of damage and recovery of function has come from studies of the motor system. The layout of motor cortex is well understood, changes in motor behavior are relatively easy to observe and measure, and motor cortex damage and recovery can be modeled in nonhuman animals, with whom we share the same basic pattern of motor system organization. In addition, recovery of movement is often a primary target of rehabilitation in people who have suffered strokes.

● Figure 15.23 schematically illustrates the regional changes that occur when a discrete area of motor cortex

is damaged on one side of the brain (Nudo, 2006). Generally, we can distinguish between three different regions of interest: the region right around the damaged area; other regions within that same hemisphere that are related to motor control, such as somatosensory cortex and premotor areas; and analogous regions in the intact opposite hemisphere (i.e., contralesional hemisphere).

In cases of relatively small lesions to motor cortex, recovery of function may be supported by the region adjacent to the damaged tissue. In this region, which is located in a ring around the lesion, changes in gene expression occur. These changes in gene expression result in an increase in proteins that facilitate growth and a decrease in proteins that inhibit growth (Nudo, 2006). The ability of the adjacent region to take over some function of the damaged tissue may be analogous to the ability of somatosensory and motor maps to reorganize in response to changing input, as we discussed in the preceding section. However, at least one fMRI study with humans found that postinjury activity in the adjacent region was lower than in controls, raising questions about how large a role it plays in recovery (Cramer, Shah, Juranek, Crafton, & Le, 2006).

Damage to a discrete region of primary motor cortex also alters activity in more distant regions of that hemisphere, such as the somatosensory cortex and higher-level motor areas (Nudo, 2006). For example, motor representations in premotor cortex expand (Frost, Barbay, Friel, Plautz, & Nudo, 2003), and pathways between premotor cortex and somatosensory cortex are strengthened as each of them loses connections with

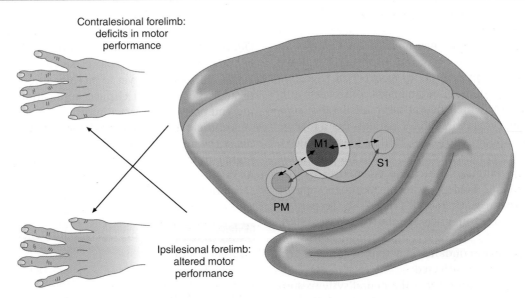

● **FIGURE 15.23   Regional effects of damage to a discrete area of primary motor cortex (M1).** The damaged region is shown in red, and the surrounding tissue is shown in pink. Following injury, changes in growth-stimulating and growth-inhibiting proteins occur in the surrounding tissue. Areas S1 (primary somatosensory cortex) and PM (premotor cortex) are also influenced by the lesion. For example, areas of premotor cortex may expand and illustrated by the light green regions. Solid lines represent strengthened pathways, and dashed lines represent lost pathways. *Source:* Figure 1 from Nudo, R. J. (2006). Mechanisms for recovery of motor function following cortical damage. Current Opinion in Neurobiology, 16, 638–644. Reprinted by permission of Elsevier.

the damaged primary motor cortex (see Figure 15.23) (Dancause et al., 2005). In this sense, the brain is developing a "work-around" strategy to keep somatosensory and motor areas in communication even though the hub that used to connect them has been damaged.

When the damaged area within primary motor cortex is relatively large, there may not be enough intact tissue in that hemisphere to support recovery of function. In such a case, function may be partly taken over by the parallel region of the opposite hemisphere (Cramer & Crafton, 2006). Numerous studies have shown changes in the contralesional hemisphere following unilateral primary motor cortex damage. For example, beginning about two weeks after unilateral damage, increased dendritic arborization is evident in the contralesional hemisphere (Jones & Schallert, 1994).

Changes in contralesional areas may occur for two different reasons. First, the person may begin to rely more upon the unaffected limb, which is controlled by the contralesional motor area. For example, after left-hemisphere damage that impairs movement of the right arm, a person might begin using the unaffected left arm more, stimulating neural changes in the right hemisphere. Alternatively, the contralesional area may begin to take over control of the impaired limb. For example, after left-hemisphere damage that impairs right-arm movement, the right hemisphere might begin to take control of the right arm. Supporting this idea, when patients were asked to tap fingers on the impaired hand (e.g., right hand if the lesion was in the left hemisphere), they activated a greater extent of cortex in the undamaged hemisphere than did neurologically intact individuals (Cramer et al., 1997). Thus, some functional recovery is likely to be supported by reorganization in the undamaged hemisphere.

Our discussion so far has focused on changes in brain organization that occur in sensorimotor regions. Do the same principles apply to recovery of cognitive functions? In the domain of language, controversy currently exists over which neural mechanisms best support language recovery in aphasic patients (for a review, see Muñoz-Cespedes, Rios-Lago, Paul, & Maestu, 2005). Is recovery due to reorganization within the left hemisphere, or are language functions taken over by the right hemisphere? Evidence can be found to support both viewpoints (e.g., Crinion & Price, 2005; Fernandez et al., 2004; Warburton, Price, Swinburn, & Wise, 1999), and it is difficult to untangle complicating factors such as the specific region of damage, extent of damage, and the aspect of language affected.

One recent study found that the neural systems supporting recovery in aphasia change over time following the injury (Saur et al., 2006). This study followed a set of aphasic patients longitudinally, assessing their functional recovery and measuring brain activity while the patients completed a task of sentence comprehension. When measured approximately two weeks after incurring brain damage, the patients tended to show increased activity in the right-hemisphere region homologous to Broca's area; further, greater activity in that region was associated with better task performance. However, when measured about a year after the injury, patients showed increased activity in intact left-hemisphere rather than right-hemisphere regions. These findings imply that strategies used shortly after the injury engage the right hemisphere, but that long-term recovery may depend upon reorganization within the damaged left hemisphere.

■ Factors Influencing Recovery of Function

Although these studies provide evidence of possible brain reorganization after trauma, there are many unanswered questions regarding the degree to which recovery from a traumatic lesion damage is possible. In this section we discuss some of the issues regarding recovery that apply to both adults and children and in the next section look more closely at issues more specific to recovery in children.

At present, we do not know all of the parameters that limit the extent of reorganization and recovery, nor do we know exactly how to manipulate conditions to make such reorganization possible. What is clear, however, is that there are multiple factors that influence recovery, and that more recovery is possible in adults than has been traditionally thought. The multiple factors that influence recovery are listed in Table 15.3.

Interestingly, research with animal models suggests that the surrounding environment may influence recovery. Earlier, we discussed evidence that environmental enrichment can influence synaptogenesis in the developing brain. Recent evidence also indicates that animals housed in enriched environments after a brain injury tend to have better outcomes, as shown by both physiological and behavioral measures, compared to animals housed in impoverished environments (e.g., Dhanushkodi, Bindu, Raju, & Kutty, 2007; Gobbo & O'Mara, 2004; Will, Galani, Kelche, & Rosenzweig, 2004). This issue has yet to be fully studied in humans, though the potential clinical applications are intriguing and potentially very important.

Another relevant factor is the premorbid cognitive status of the individual. It is thought that individuals with higher intelligence and education may recover better. As said by a noted scientist more than 70 years ago, "It is not only the kind of head injury that matters but the

TABLE 15.3	Factors Likely to Influence Recovery

Severity of insult
Number of insults
Spacing of insults
Age at time of insult
Premorbid cognitive status
Extent to which one function can be taken over by another
Overall brain integrity
Individual differences in brain structure
Motivation
Emotional factors
Extent and quality of rehabilitation

kind of head" (Symonds, 1937). However, the reason for this better recovery is unclear. On the one hand, more intelligent people may have a greater reserve of capacity, so that suffering a brain insult does not diminish their overall capacity as much as it does in a less intelligent person. On the other hand, it may be that more intelligent people are better at learning or devising strategies to overcome their disabilities.

Therapies aimed at brain-injured individuals are divided into two major camps: those aimed at restoration and those aimed at compensation. The goal of **restorative rehabilitation** is to gain increased function by repetitive exercise. The idea is that you will redevelop a mental muscle if you use it over and over again. Such therapy has been found effective in reducing hemiparesis of the arm after stroke, for example (Taub & Uswatte, 2000). However, it is less clear whether repetitive training works as well with cognitive functions such as language and memory. Relatively few studies have used controlled experimental designs to compare repetitive training to spontaneous recovery or other therapy methods, though some evidence indicates a benefit from training of specific attentional skills after brain injury (Park & Ingles, 2001). The goal of **compensatory rehabilitation**, in contrast to restorative rehabilitation, is to provide alternative strategies to achieve a particular goal. For example, a patient who becomes amnesic as a result of temporal lobe damage might carry a notebook or a personal digital assistant with a picture of her car and a note on where she parked it. This strategy generally would not be used by a neurologically intact person, but is invoked to minimize the loss of a specific skill by relying on functions that are still intact.

■ Recovery of Function in Children

If you had to choose between brain damage early in life and brain damage later in life, which would you choose? One factor you might want to consider is the extent to which the plasticity of the developing brain aids in recovery of function. Indeed, probably the most dramatic difference between adults and children after brain insult is the seemingly miraculous recovery that children appear to make. For decades, scientists have thought that the earlier in life damage is sustained, the better the recovery. This maxim became known as the **Kennard principle**, named after the individual who first proposed such an effect, Margaret Kennard (Kennard, 1936, 1942). As we learn in this section, the Kennard principle holds true in some cases but not in others.

Strong support for the Kennard principle comes from the study of language in brain-damaged children and adults. Lesions that would leave adults with little or no capacity for language do not have such dire consequences for children. For example, children with left-hemisphere brain damage do not typically exhibit aphasia. In one study (Bates et al.,

2001), researchers systematically assessed a number of linguistic functions in both children and adults with unilateral brain damage. The children in the study had congenital brain damage, whereas the adults had acquired brain damage during adulthood. The general pattern of results was that, across various measures, children with brain damage appeared to perform as well as their peers, regardless of the hemisphere of damage; in contrast, adults with left-hemisphere damage were especially impaired relative to age-matched controls.

However, the picture is not completely rosy for children with brain damage. While evidence from the domain of language appears to support the Kennard principle, studies in other domains illustrate the limits of plasticity. For example, children with damage to the right hemisphere of the brain develop difficulties in spatial cognition that seem analogous to those of right-hemisphere-damaged adults (Stiles, Reilly, Paul, & Moses, 2005). As illustrated in ● Figure 15.24, drawings

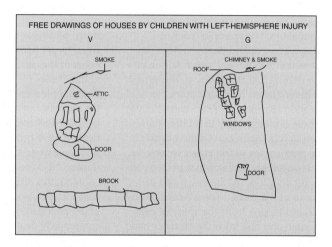

FREE DRAWINGS OF HOUSES BY CHILDREN WITH LEFT-HEMISPHERE INJURY

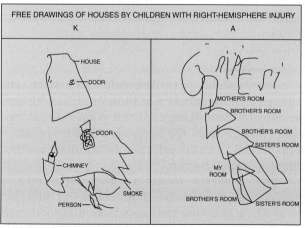

FREE DRAWINGS OF HOUSES BY CHILDREN WITH RIGHT-HEMISPHERE INJURY

● **FIGURE 15.24 Drawings made by children with left- and right-hemisphere brain damage early in life.** The deficits in the right-hemisphere-damaged children's drawings are similar to the deficits seen in adults with right-hemisphere damage. *Source:* Figure from Stiles-Davis, J. et al (1988). Drawing ability in four young children with congenital unilateral brain lesions. Neuropsychologia, 26, p. 365. Reprinted by permission from Elsevier.

IN FOCUS: Can Deprivation in One Sensory Modality Promote Extraordinary Abilities in Another?

In this chapter we have discussed how the brain's plasticity allows it to reorganize in response to insult or atypical environments (e.g., sensory deprivation), in some cases allowing the person to attain or reacquire a normal complement of abilities. But can reorganization actually enhance the brain's processing capacity beyond normal levels? You may have heard "common wisdom" that blind people can hear better, or deaf people can see better, compared to everyone else. Here we discuss the empirical evidence pertaining to this question.

First the bad news: It has been known for quite some time that deprivation of a particular sensory input from birth does not enhance basic sensitivity in the remaining sensory modalities. For example, auditory deprivation due to deafness does not alter the threshold at which light can be detected or the ability to distinguish different levels of visual contrast or motion (Bavelier, Dye, & Hauser, 2006). These findings imply that little, if any, reorganization occurs in the primary sensory cortex of the intact senses. Yet, the possibility remains that perception and cognition may be enhanced in more subtle ways. Here we consider two examples, one from the study of deaf people and one from the study of blind people.

Several pieces of evidence indicate that people who are deaf may be differentially responsive to visual information in the periphery, as opposed to central vision. Intuitively, this makes sense: normally, auditory cues in the periphery help us to reorient our gaze to fixate on a peripheral stimulus. For example, if you hear something near your left shoulder, you would probably shift your gaze toward the left, bringing the object into central vision. Because deaf people receive no auditory cues from the periphery, vision itself must be more sensitive to events in peripheral regions of space.

Evidence for enhanced attention to the visual periphery in deaf people comes from behavioral, ERP, and neuroimaging studies. In one behavioral study, participants had to respond to a visual target while a distractor appeared either in the center or the periphery of the display (Box Figure 15.1). Deaf people were more influenced by the distractor when it appeared in the periphery, whereas people with normal hearing were more influenced by the distractor when it appeared in the center (Proksch & Bavelier, 2002).

In another study, Neville and colleagues compared processing of peripheral information between congenitally deaf people who learned American Sign Language (ASL), hearing people who did not know ASL, and hearing people who knew ASL (usually because a parent or sibling was deaf). This last group is an especially important control; ASL is a visual language that involves movement across space, so the researchers wanted to be able to tell whether it was deafness itself or experience with ASL that influenced visual perception. These three groups of individuals were tested with both behavioral and event-related potential (ERP) methods. Signers who were deaf were more than 100 ms faster to respond to peripheral visual stimuli than either hearing signers or hearing nonsigners. Moreover, deaf individuals exhibited an attention-related N_{150} over occipital regions that was much larger than that observed in either group of hearing individuals. These findings suggest an enhancement of visuospatial attention to peripheral regions in the deaf (Neville, 1990; Neville & Lawson, 1987a–c).

Studies using fMRI have helped to provide information on what parts of the brain seem to be related to these abilities in the deaf. The superior performance of deaf individuals in directing attention to peripheral locations, as compared to hearing signers and nonsigners, is associated with increased activation in MT/MST (motion perception areas) and posterior parietal cortex, which is

by right-hemisphere-damaged children show the same patterns of disorganization as those of adults with similar areas of brain damage. At this point it is not clear why evidence from the language domain appears to support the Kennard principle better than evidence from the spatial domain.

Other evidence points to the importance of considering the whole time course of development when assessing the impact of childhood brain damage. In other words, researchers must consider not only the age at which a child sustains a lesion, but also the age at which the child is being assessed and the amount of time that has passed since the injury. Children may appear to be relatively resilient early in development, with deficits emerging only later as the child is expected to demonstrate more and more complex skills. For example, one recent study

found that children with congenital brain damage showed declines in IQ after the age of seven, as they failed to keep up with their peers in cognitive development (Levine, Kraus, Alexander, Suriyakham, & Huttenlocher, 2005; see also Banich, Levine, Kim, & Huttenlocher, 1990).

One possible explanation of the phenomenon of later-emerging deficits is the **crowding hypothesis** (e.g., Teuber & Rudel, 1962). According to this idea, the intact areas of the child's brain are now expected to carry out the functions that they would normally implement, as well as the functions that the damaged area would normally have implemented. In other words, too many functions are crowded into the intact brain tissue. If we only needed three-quarters of a brain to function optimally, evolution probably would have given us a three-quarters-sized brain! Thus, it should

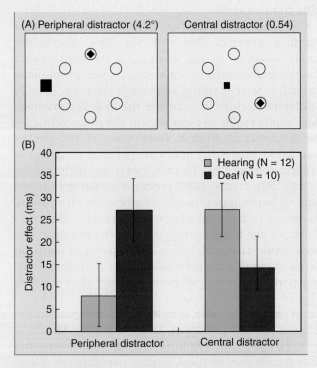

(A) Peripheral distractor (4.2°)   Central distractor (0.54)

(B)

● **BOX FIGURE 15.1   Attention to peripheral versus central visual information in deaf versus hearing individuals.** When making a decision about the symbol in the circle, deaf people are more influenced by a distracting shape in the periphery, whereas hearing people are more influenced by a distracting shape in the center. *Source:* Figure from Bavelier, D. et al (2006). Do deaf individuals see better? Trends in Cognitive Sciences, 10, 512–518. Reprinted by permission of Elsevier.

involved in spatial attention (Bavelier, Brozinsky, Tomann, Mitchell, Neville, & Liu, 2001). Area MT/MST is more responsive when people with normal hearing attended to central versus peripheral visual motion, but this pattern is reversed in deaf people.

These studies focused on visual perception in the deaf, but other studies have focused on cognition in blind people. One interesting line of research has examined the verbal memory abilities of blind people. Many cultural traditions feature blind storytellers, who pass on narrative histories reliably by word-of-mouth. It is logical that blind people might need to rely on verbal memory more than sighted people, because they cannot refer back to written texts. Indeed, several studies have reported superior verbal memory in the blind (e.g., Röder, Rösler, & Neville, 2001).

Somewhat surprisingly, neuroimaging studies have found that verbal tasks activate primary visual cortex (area V1) in congenitally blind people but not in sighted controls (Amedi, Raz, Pianka, Malach, & Zohary, 2003; Röder, Stock, Bein, Neville, & Rösler, 2002). Further, disruption of visual cortex activity with TMS leads to semantic errors in a verbal task in blind but not sighted people (Amedi, Floel, Knecht, Zohary, & Cohen, 2004). These studies imply that "visual" cortex has been reorganized to support verbal functions. Linking these findings together, in one study the degree of activity in V1 predicted verbal memory performance among blind (but not sighted) people (Amedi et al., 2003).

It may seem amazing that an area that is normally so clearly dedicated to representing visual features can be reorganized to represent a very different kind of information. It is easier to think of how visual cortex could be reorganized to support Braille reading (see earlier discussion in this chapter), because Braille letters have a kind of spatial organization that could map onto the spatial layout of area V1. Because researchers do not have a good understanding of how verbal information is organized even in the normal brain, it is still unclear how such information could be represented in V1 in the brain of someone who is blind. Nevertheless, existing studies provide at least preliminary evidence that reorganization of V1 to serve verbal functions may contribute to enhanced verbal-memory skills in people who are blind.

not be surprising that childhood brain damage does have a cost, even given the remarkable plasticity of the developmental period.

Finally, we cannot think of "childhood" as simply one category of time compared to "adulthood." Damage to the brain at different points in childhood may have different consequences. For example, research on rats has shown that damage to the brain produces the worst functional outcomes when the damage occurs just after neurogenesis is complete, whereas damage occurring slightly later, during the period of synaptogenesis, is associated with better outcomes (Kolb & Gibb, 2001). This evidence reminds us that the brain is in a different state at different points during early development, and we must also remember that the adult brain differs at different ages as well. This brings us to the topic of the aging brain.

Changes in the Brain with Aging

Changes in brain functioning occur not only during childhood and as a result of brain damage, but also as a result of the aging process. These changes become more noticeable as a person approaches the later adult years. In this last section, we consider some of the cognitive and neural changes that accompany old age. Here, we focus on change associated with healthy aging; the topic of dementia, such as accompanies Parkinson's and Alzheimer's disease, is addressed in Chapter 16.

■ Cognitive Changes with Aging

Broadly speaking, there are several different ways to view the changes in mental function that accompany age. We can focus on the nature of decline with aging, considering whether decline is general (that is, everything gets worse with age) or specific to certain abilities (that is, some functions get worse at a faster rate than others). In addition, instead of focusing solely on mental decline with age, we can also consider how the cognitive strategy employed by an older person differs from that of the young adult mind, and whether there are some ways in which older people actually may perform better than younger people.

Most studies of aging have taken a decline-related approach. One viewpoint argues that there is a general decline across all abilities with age. This decline is believed to represent a general reduction in mental resources or a general slowing in the speed of processing (e.g., Craik & Byrd, 1982; Salthouse, 1996). Evidence for this theory comes from comparing the performance of young adults and older adults (usually early retirement age or older) across a variety of tasks. Generally, older people perform worse than younger people on a wide range of tasks (● Figure 15.25).

Another decline-related view is that the deficits that emerge with age are not general, but rather more specific. According to this view, some aspects of processing are compromised in older persons but other aspects are not. For example, cognitive declines in aging appear to be most pronounced for explicit memory recall tasks (e.g., memorizing and recalling lists of words) and for tasks of executive functioning. In contrast, autobiographical memory, vocabulary, and implicit memory processes seem relatively intact (see Hedden & Gabrieli, 2004, for a review). As we will see, data from cognitive neuroscience studies support the idea that specific brain regions are especially affected by age and that the

functions associated with those regions are differentially compromised.

One issue that researchers must consider is whether cognitive strategies shift with age. This issue is not simply answered by just examining the performance of older individuals. In some cases, older people may perform as well as young adults, but they may employ a different strategy to complete the task. For example, older adults might rely more upon stored knowledge—the accumulated wisdom from years of life—rather than upon processing speed to perform a particular problem-solving task. In such cases, we might not be able to detect age-related processing changes on the basis of performance measures alone. In other cases, the way a task is framed can influence the degree to which an age-related effect is seen. For example, one study found that instructing participants to focus on the meaning of a memory task (rather than simply letting participants use whatever strategy they wanted) reduced the age discrepancy in performance and produced patterns of brain activity that were more similar between age groups (Logan, Sanders, Snyder, Morris, & Buckner, 2002). Such findings indicate that young and older people may at times tend to use different cognitive strategies for the same task.

Finally, we need to consider the possibility that aging may actually be associated with improved performance on some tasks. This is a counterintuitive idea, because many people assume that aging is one long, slow, degenerative, inevitable glide into the grave. However, recent studies suggest at least one domain in which aged people outperform young people: emotion regulation (Mather & Carstensen, 2005). Whereas older people are generally impaired on working memory tasks compared to younger people, they show no impairment when the task involves emotional information (Mikels, Larkin, Reuter-Lorenz, & Carstensen, 2005). Older people appear to be better able to cope with emotionally distressing situations; their negative moods tend not to persist as long as those of younger people and their positive moods persist longer (Carstensen, Pasupathi, Mayr, & Nesselroade, 2000). Older people also tend to show positive attentional biases, shifting attention toward positive information and away from negative information in standard lab tasks (Mather & Carstensen, 2003; Mather et al., 2004). Although we may question whether it is always good to see the world through rose-colored glasses, it certainly can make the later years of life more enjoyable!

■ Neural Changes with Aging

In recent years, there has been an explosion of studies focused on changes in the brain with aging (for recent reviews, see Grady, 2008; Minati, Grisoli, & Bruzzone, 2007). Brain imaging studies indicate that some age-related changes in brain structure and activity are region-specific. For example, volume declines measured by structural imaging are more

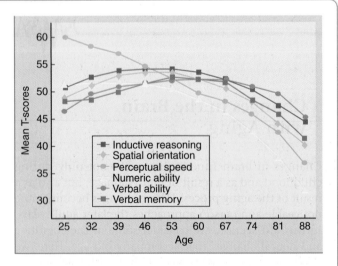

● **FIGURE 15.25   Age-related declines across a wide range of cognitive tasks.** These results are from a longitudinal study of people whose cognitive performance was measured at numerous time points. *Source:* From Hedden, T., & Gabrieli, J. D. E. (2004). Insights into the ageing mind: A view from cognitive neuroscience. Nature Reviews Neuroscience, 5, 87–97.

prominent in the frontal lobes and less pronounced in primary sensory areas (● Figure 15.26) (Raz, Torres, Spencer, Baertschie, Millman, & Sarpel, 1993; Raz et al., 2005). Reduced activity is also seen in medial temporal regions, associated with memory processing, and visual regions across a wide variety of tasks (Grady, 2008).

These physiological changes in brain function appear to have behavioral consequences. Over the years, studies have confirmed that cognitive functions supported by frontal regions and temporal regions are particularly compromised with age (Hedden & Gabrieli, 2004). For example, older adults exhibit deficits on a battery of tests sensitive to frontal lobe damage, such as the self-ordered pointing task, the Wisconsin Card Sorting Test, verbal and design fluency, and the Stroop task (Daigneault, Braun, & Whitaker, 1992). They also show clear declines in memory tasks that rely on frontal regions. These include working-memory tasks; "meta-memory" tasks, such as knowing the temporal order in which information was received (Parkin, Walter, & Hunkin, 1995); prospective-memory tasks, which require remembering to carry out a function at a future time; and **source memory**, which is the ability to remember the specific circumstances or context in which particular information was learned (e.g., knowing that you learned that the earth orbits the sun in your third-grade class taught by Ms. Frost) (McIntyre & Craik, 1987). As we learned in Chapter 10, the temporal lobes, and particularly the hippocampus, are critically important for creating new long-term declarative memories, memories that allow information to be used flexibly and in a variety of contexts. By the sixth and seventh decades of life, healthy older adults begin to perform more poorly than younger individuals on direct tests of declarative memory (see Grady & Craik, 2000, for a review).

Yet, interestingly, there are many cases in which older adults show increased brain activation compared to younger adults. These increases are often prominent in exactly the regions that are affected by aging, such as prefrontal cortex. How are we to understand this seemingly counterintuitive finding? One possibility is that these regions are neurally inefficient—they must work doubly hard because they are working poorly, leading to increased activation (e.g., Cabeza, Anderson, Mangels, Nyberg, & Houle, 2000). However, an intriguing alternative explanation is that these regions become more active in a compensatory manner to overcome declines in functioning in other brain regions (Park & Reuter-Lorenz, 2009). Supporting this idea, older individuals who perform better on working-memory tasks seem to show the greatest degree of engagement of prefrontal regions (Rypma, Eldreth, & Rebbechi, 2007).

Aging affects not only the integrity of specific brain regions, but also the global pattern of activation across the brain. One prominent theory is that of **dedifferentiation**, which suggests that localization of function becomes less defined with age (Li & Lindenberger, 1999). For example, older adults show less specificity in activity in the fusiform face area, parahippocampal place area, and lateral occipital area in response to stimuli that typically activate these regions (faces, houses, and letters/words, respectively) (Park, Polk, Park, Minear, Savage, & Smith, 2004). These findings, however, do not mean that the elderly brain becomes one large, undifferentiated mush. In fact, one elegant series of studies suggests that this more diffuse pattern of activation may reflect increased activation to compensate for increasing demand. Unlike younger adults, who activate left prefrontal regions during verbal working-memory tasks and right prefrontal regions during spatial working-memory tasks, elderly adults tend to exhibit bilateral activation for both verbal and spatial working memory (Reuter-Lorenz, Marshuetz, Jones, Smith, Hartley, & Koeppe, 2001). This pattern

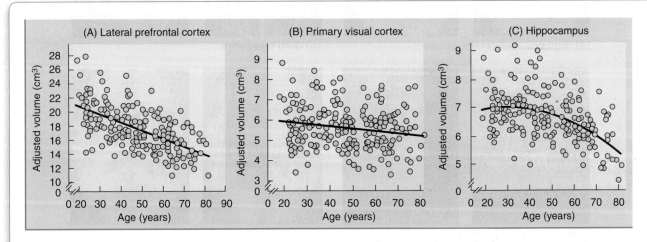

● **FIGURE 15.26   Changes in brain volume with age for three different brain regions.** Notice that the loss of brain volume with age varies by area with relatively little drop off for primary visual areas, a linear drop off for lateral prefrontal cortex, and a steep drop off for the hippocampus after middle age. *Source:* From Hedden, T., & Gabrieli, J. D. E. (2004). Insights into the ageing mind: A view from cognitive neuroscience. *Nature Reviews Neuroscience, 5,* 87–97.

of bilateral activation is seen across a variety of tasks (Cabeza, 2002; Cabeza, Daselar, Dolcos, Prince, Budde, & Nyberg, 2004) (● Figure 15.27). One possibility is that the bilateral pattern of performance indicates that the elderly adults need to engage both hemispheres because of reduced abilities in each hemisphere. As we discussed in Chapter 4, it is advantageous to have the hemispheres pool their resources under demanding conditions (Banich, 2003). Indeed, the hemispheres of elderly adults show an advantage for coupling the hemispheres at lower levels of task demand than do younger adults (Reuter-Lorenz, Stanczak, & Miller, 1999). In another study, older adults who performed better on a memory encoding task had more bilateral frontal activation than those who performed worse (Rosen et al., 2002). These results imply that bilateral patterns of activation in the elderly reflect a **compensatory mechanism** of recruiting additional brain regions to support performance (Reuter-Lorenz, 2002).

In other cases, the relative activation of brain regions within a network will change with age. For example, in the Stroop task, in which an individual must identify the ink color of a word even when it conflicts with the word meaning, younger individuals show large activation of dorsolateral prefrontal regions, with lesser activation of the anterior cingulate cortex. Dorsolateral prefrontal regions are involved in top-down attentional control,

enabling one to direct attention to the task-relevant ink color while tuning out the task-irrelevant word. In contrast, the anterior cingulate is involved in resolving any remaining conflict before a response is emitted (refer back to Chapter 12 for a longer discussion). Compared to young adults, the elderly tend to show more interference from conflicting information and less activation in dorsolateral prefrontal regions, suggesting that they are having difficulty ignoring the word and paying attention to ink color. However, older adults also show increased activation in cingulate cortex; this suggests that this region is working doubly hard to select the correct response, perhaps attempting to compensate for the reduced activity in dorsolateral prefrontal cortex (Milham et al., 2002).

Another possible reason why the pattern of activation might change in the elderly is that there is a greater disconnection between brain regions as a result of a loss of myelin. Studies of white-matter loss in aging have shown generalized declines that are most pronounced in the frontal lobes and the anterior corpus callosum (Head et al., 2004). This greater disconnection could explain in part why executive control by frontal regions is compromised by aging. Older people would be less able to exert top-down attentional control over other parts of the brain; for example, they might be unable to rev up activation of brain regions involved in

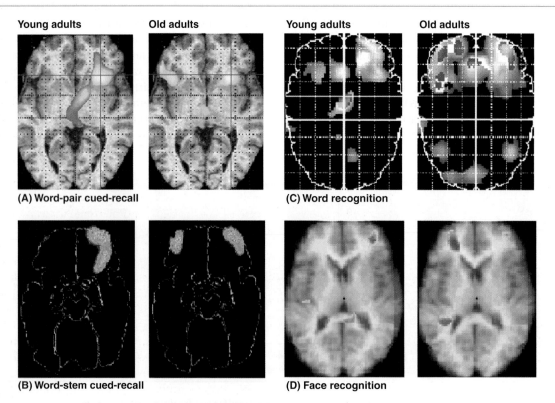

(A) Word-pair cued-recall

(B) Word-stem cued-recall

(C) Word recognition

(D) Face recognition

● **FIGURE 15.27 Changes in brain activation associated with aging.** Notice that across a variety of tasks, brain activation is more bilateral in older adults than in younger adults. *Source:* Copyright 2002 by the American Psychological Association. Reproduced by permission. Cabeza, R., 2002. Hemispheric asymmetry reduction in older adults: The HAROLD model. Psychology and Aging, 17, No.1 p.87. The use of APA information does not imply endorsement by APA.

processing task-relevant information (such as identifying the ink color in the Stroop task) while dampening down activation of brain regions involved in processing task-irrelevant information (such as the irrelevant word information in the Stroop task). In fact, measures of white-matter integrity are found to be better predictors of cognitive performance in the elderly than the degree of gray-matter loss. In particular, one study found that white-matter integrity in the frontal lobe predicted executive function, whereas that in the temporal and parietal lobe predicted episodic memory, the ability to remember certain events or episodes (Ziegler, Piguet, Salat, Prince, Connally, & Corkin, 2008).

■ Slowing the Effects of Aging

Just as Ponce de Leon went searching for the fountain of youth, scientists have embarked on a voyage to determine what can help keep the elderly mentally young. Two factors have emerged as helping to slow the effects of aging: aerobic exercise and remaining intellectually active. Our knowledge of the importance of these factors was initially gleaned from animal research and then shown to be equally important for people. Each factor helps to sustain the brain by a distinct mechanism. Aerobic exercise produces a greater proliferation of blood vessels to the brain, resulting in enhanced oxygen supply. In addition, as we discussed earlier, a mentally stimulating environment produces an elaboration of dendritic trees, allowing more numerous and varied synaptic connections. We discuss each in turn.

Increasing evidence now supports the conclusion that aerobic exercise has beneficial effects on cognitive tasks during aging (see Kramer & Erickson, 2007, for a review). Research with animals indicates that exercising leads to greater proliferation of the blood supply to the brain (e.g., Black, Isaacs, Anderson, Alcantara, & Greenough, 1990). Oxygen insufficiency, whether caused by pulmonary disease, cigarette smoking, or living on a high mountaintop where the air is thin, can lead to deterioration in neuropsychological functioning (Hjalmarsen, Waterloo, Dahl, Rolf, & Viitanen, 1999; Kramer, Coyne, & Strayer, 1993). It is not surprising, therefore, that people who engage in aerobic exercise have better neurocognitive functioning than their non-exercising peers (Clarkson-Smith & Hartley, 1989; van Boxtel, Paas, Houx, Adam, Teeken, & Jolles, 1997). One issue with such findings, however, is that these people might be particularly blessed physical specimens, which is why they retain their mental faculties and can continue to exercise into old age. In other words, the correlation between physical health and cognitive functioning does not necessarily tell us about the causal role of exercise upon mental functioning.

To examine whether exercise can aid the average individual, one group of researchers (including the first author of this textbook) selected people aged 60–75 who did not exercise, being "couch potatoes" who preferred to watch television or read (Kramer et al., 1999).

These individuals were enrolled in a six-month program of either light aerobic exercise (e.g., 30 minutes of brisk walking three times a week) or a toning and stretching program that involved no aerobic exercise (e.g., 30 minutes of stretching exercises three times a week). At the end of the six-month period, the aerobic-exercise group showed fewer age-related deficits on attentional and memory functions that rely on prefrontal regions of the brain, compared to the stretching-and-toning group. This study demonstrated that the beneficial effect of exercise on cognition was specific to aerobic exercise, and that even relatively low levels of such exercise can have significant effects.

There is also evidence that a stimulating environment may stave off some of the more negative effects of aging (see Kramer, Bherer, Colcombe, Dong, & Greenough, 2004; Milgram, Siwak-Tapp, Araujo, & Head, 2006, for recent reviews). For example, a long-term study of more than 5,000 adults found that being involved in intellectually stimulating and challenging activities, both at work and at home, reduces the risk of cognitive decline in old age. These activities include having a job involving high complexity and low routine, participating in continuing education, having a habit of extensive reading, being active in social groups, and engaging in travel (Schaie, 1994). Such an effect is also found when biological factors are kept constant. A study of twins discordant for dementia (one has dementia, one does not) found that the twin with a lower level of education and who tended not be mentally active was more likely to get Alzheimer's disease (Gatz, Svedberg, Pedersen, Mortimer, Berg, & Johansson, 2001).

Neurogenesis, the formation of new neurons, may help to stave off the effects of cognitive decline typically observed in old age (see Gould, Tanapat, Hastings, & Shors, 1999). Until relatively recently, it was taken as gospel that at birth people had all the neurons they would ever have, and that it was all downhill from there. Scientists presumed that unlike skin, which replaces itself every three days or so, no additional neurons are created after birth, and those that exist at birth must be retained over a lifetime. If neurons came and went, then so might memory and learning from earlier in your life! Instead, recent research suggests that the adult brains of both animals (Kuhn, Dickinson-Anson, & Gage, 1996) and humans (Eriksson et al., 1998) have a limited ability to form new neurons (for a recent review, see Zhao, Deng, & Gage, 2008). This effect has been demonstrated most clearly in the hippocampus. These new cells first appear as undifferentiated *stem cells* (which are primordial cells from which all tissue derives) and then evolve into neurons. A certain proportion of these neurons never become functional, probably because they do not make adequate connections with other neurons (similar to the pruning process in development).

Aerobic exercise and enriched environments are both known to affect neurogenesis, albeit in different ways: Aerobic exercise affects the production of stem cells, whereas an enriched environment affects their survival. Rats given aerobic exercise produce more of these stem cells than rats that are not given exercise. Because the exercising rats have more stem cells to begin with, they end up with more new neurons (e.g., Van Praag, Kempermann, & Gage, 1999). In contrast, although mice in an enriched environment do not produce any more new stem cells than do mice in a less stimulating environment, not as many of their stem cells die while transforming into functional neurons, presumably because

these neurons have made useful functional connections (e.g., Kempermann, Kuhn, & Gage, 1997). As a result, aged animals housed in an enriched environment had nearly five times the number of new neurons as animals housed in an impoverished environment (Kempermann, Gast, & Gage, 2002). The presence of neurogenesis even among aging animals, and the possibility for increasing it through environmental manipulations, points to greater possibilities for effective intervention than were previously presumed to exist.

Summary

Development of the Brain

- Nerve cells proliferate during gestation, whereas glia proliferate after birth.
- Physiological changes during childhood include an increase in the brain's metabolic rate, a greater coherence in electrical activity, an overproduction and then pruning of synaptic connections, and increased myelination.
- Developmental changes in brain structure and function are accompanied by changes in the cognitive skills of the child that occur in an orderly fashion, such as crawling before walking.
- Recently research has shown that adolescence is also a time period in which there is continued brain development, especially with regards to the prefrontal cortex and its connections with limbic areas.
- The environment can have profound effects on the developing brain, especially during sensitive periods, during which information from the environment has a lifelong effect on the brain's organization and capacity.

Developmental Disorders

- Mental retardation is characterized by a lack of intellectual ability across a wide range of cognitive skills. It is caused by various factors, including infections, genetic disorders, toxins, anoxia, and malnutrition.
- Dyslexia is an inability to read despite adequate intelligence in other domains and schooling in the reading process. It is associated with atypical anatomy and function of language regions of the left hemisphere, and possibly poor integration of information between brain regions.
- Autism and pervasive developmental disorders are characterized by a profound lack of desire to interact emotionally or socially with other people, and profound delays and disturbances in cognitive functioning, especially in functions that relate to communication and language. These disorders are thought to involve a large number of brain regions that may include the temporal and frontal lobes, portions of the limbic system, and the cerebellum.

- Children with attention-deficit hyperactivity disorder have difficulty concentrating, are physically restless, cannot focus their attention on a task, and tend to be impulsive. Dysregulation of the dopaminergic system is implicated in this disorder, as well as prefrontal regions of the brain, the basal ganglia, and possibly the anterior cingulate.
- Children with learning disabilities rarely outgrow them, although the disorder may manifest itself differently in adulthood. For example, whereas a hyperactive child might have trouble sitting in a chair in class, a hyperactive adult might not be able to "sit with" a problem.

Brain Plasticity

- The adult brain can reorganize in response to changes in sensory input and experience, although there are limits to the capacity for reorganization.
- A vast physiological response occurs to brain injury, including the degeneration and death of nerve cells, the cleaning-up of debris by glia, swelling (known as edema), and eventually the formation of a scar. Lesions may disrupt other aspects of brain functioning, such as metabolic rate, neurotransmitter release, and oxygen consumption.
- At the cellular level, compensatory mechanisms for neural injury include an increased sensitivity to neurotransmitters and the formation of new connections by rerouting and sprouting.
- Injury to a specific region of the brain can affect activity in neighboring regions, as well as parallel regions in the opposite hemisphere. These regional activity changes may aid in compensating for the loss of the damaged tissue.
- Factors influencing recovery of function include the premorbid status of the individual, repetitive training, and the use of compensatory or alternative strategies.
- Although the Kennard principle posited that recovery of function in children is superior to that in adults, recent studies suggest that the deficits observed after brain damage in children may emerge or recede depending on the time since the lesion and the developmental stage at which a function is examined.

Changes in the Brain with Aging

- Some theories posit a general slowing or overall reduction in capacity with age, but evidence from cognitive neuroscience suggests that the changes with age are more specific.
- Brain regions most susceptible to the effects of aging include the frontal and temporal regions.

- With aging, the brain appears to exhibit less localization of function, which may occur because older individuals attempt to recruit more brain areas to aid in performing a task.
- Engaging in aerobic exercise and being in a stimulating environment appear to stave off the effects of aging, possibly because both processes aid in the formation of new neurons in the adult brain.

Key Terms

anoxia 443

attention-deficit hyperactivity disorder (ADHD) 448

autism 445

calcification 453

cerebral palsy 443

compensatory mechanism 462

compensatory rehabilitation 457

cross-modal plasticity 452

crowding hypothesis 458

dedifferentiation 461

developmental milestones 434

Down syndrome 440

dyslexia 443

edema 453

elimination of synapses 433

experience-dependent systems 437

experience-expectant systems 437

fetal alcohol syndrome (FAS) 442

fragile X syndrome 441

gliosis 453

hypoxia 442

Kennard principle 457

learning disability 443

maturational lag hypothesis 450

mental retardation 440

necrosis 453

neurogenesis 430

neurulation 430

pervasive developmental disorders 445

phonological awareness 443

plasticity 429

regeneration 454

reorganization 451

restorative rehabilitation 457

sensitive period 439

source memory 461

synaptogenesis 432

transneuronal degeneration 453

Book Companion Site at www.cengage.com/psychology/Banich

This website provides instructors and students with a wealth of free information and resources, including tutorial quizzes, flashcards, and the glossary.

Generalized Cognitive Disorders

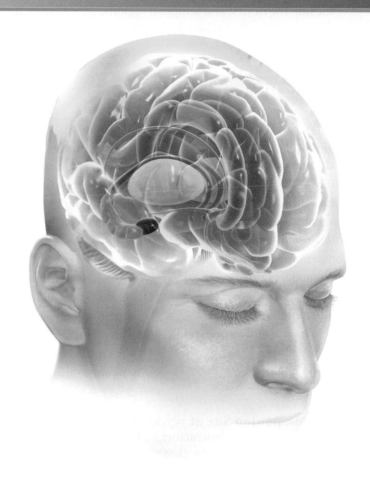

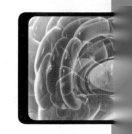

A STRONG AND DETERMINED WOMAN, L.F. immigrated to the United States from Italy in the early 1900s when she was in her twenties. She came alone, without family or friends—a journey that few women dared to make at that time, especially under such circumstances. After arriving in the United States, she bucked tradition, setting out on her own and not marrying immediately, even though she was already considered an "old maid." Eventually she met a fellow Italian immigrant who suited her taste, and they married.

Their life together started out well. Her husband was a successful small businessman, and along came four children, the last two of whom were born when L.F. was in her forties. However, when the financial markets collapsed at the beginning of the Great Depression, the debt her husband had incurred building multifamily dwellings caused him to lose everything. Determined that all her children would nonetheless get a college education (which they all eventually did), L.F. worked 10- to 14-hour days for years as a seamstress, doing intricate embroidery and beadwork for numerous garment makers in New York City. Despite the family's dire poverty, she instilled in her children a strong work ethic, a love of learning, and a sense of pride.

When she was in her early eighties, L.F. and her husband were forced to leave the apartment building and neighborhood in which they had lived for the past 40 years. The property had been sold to a new owner and was to be converted into a bank. So they went to live with their second-eldest daughter's family. L.F.'s memory had been deteriorating for some time, and moving into a new home was exceedingly difficult for her. Beset by forgetfulness and disorientation, this once vibrant, resourceful, and proud woman, who had traveled the streets of New York City with ease, now had difficulty navigating from one room to the next. She was disoriented in both space and time, often confusing whether it was morning or night. L.F. would wander aimlessly around the house, especially at night, searching for an item whose location she couldn't remember. On rare occasions she would even have a brief bout of paranoia. Once, for example, while her daughter was adjusting her seat belt for a trip to the grocery store, L.F. muttered in Italian that her ungrateful daughter was taking her to be killed.

The strain on L.F.'s daughter's family was great. The house was small, and L.F.'s wanderings, especially at night, disrupted everyone in the house. During these jaunts, she would move various items all over the house, open and close cabinets, turn lights on and off, and sometimes leave her dentures in bizarre locations. Because she found the world so confusing, it was important to keep the house as orderly as possible. This degree of order was sometimes difficult for her grandchildren to maintain. They were still in grade school and junior high, so just keeping their own rooms clean was a challenge! And L.F.'s grandchildren found it difficult to have their friends come over to play because L.F.'s paranoia might cause her to follow their friends around the house to ensure that they weren't stealing anything.

About nine months later, L.F. and her husband moved to the other half of the duplex in which their eldest daughter and family lived. These new living arrangements were much more suitable for the couple. L.F. could wander without disturbing others and the house could be organized specifically to accommodate her mental deterioration. Because her daughter's family was next door, L.F.'s husband, who was also in his eighties, received generous help whenever he had difficulty handling her or the daily chores. However, even with these new arrangements, L.F.'s ability to care for herself continued to decline. Eventually she needed almost constant care, although she was never institutionalized because of the love and patience of her husband of more than 50 years. He outlived his wife, and, unlike her, remained intellectually sharp and physically active until a few weeks before his death at the age of 90 years.

THE CASE HISTORY in the opening vignette describes the maternal grandmother of one of the authors (M.T.B.). Although the disease was never formally diagnosed, she surely had Alzheimer's or some similar dementia. In many ways, her case was typical, characterized by loss of memory, difficulties in spatial processing, disorientation, and changes in personality, especially paranoia. The course was unremittingly downward, although she died from heat stroke before becoming totally bedridden.

In this chapter, we discuss disorders, such as Alzheimer's disease, that are distinct from the neuropsychological syndromes covered elsewhere in this book. In our discussions so far, we have emphasized the breakdown of specific cognitive functions, such as visual recognition, and precisely described the circumscribed nature of the deficits. For example, in the case of visual object agnosia, we noted the specificity of the disruption, an inability to visually identify objects because of perceptual difficulties that prevent the association between visual form and meaning. However, in many clinical syndromes, including Alzheimer's disease, the breakdown of function is not restricted to one cognitive domain; rather, multiple cognitive abilities are affected simultaneously. We refer to these syndromes as **generalized (nonspecific) disorders**.

You should not be surprised to learn that the causes of generalized disorders are quite different from the causes of specific disorders we discussed in earlier chapters. Specific disorders usually result from focal damage to the brain, such as that caused by bullet wounds or strokes, which confine damage to the path of the projectile or the brain regions deprived of oxygen, respectively. In contrast, the causes of generalized disorders include closed head injury (which results from falls, vehicular accidents, assaults, and sports injuries), dementing disorders (which result from pathological changes in the brain), demyelinating diseases (which result from damage to the myelin sheath surrounding neurons), and exposure to toxins, all of which are likely to have more distributed, rather than focal, effects on brain tissue.

Even though all these causes of brain damage are likely to influence more than one cognitive system at the same time, their effects are not identical, so we can observe subtle but important differences in their neuropsychological manifestations. We now turn to a more detailed discussion of these various etiologies and the nature of the generalized cognitive disorders that they produce.

Closed Head Injury

Often the brain sustains damage because the head forcefully comes into contact with another object (e.g., a car windshield, the ground, or a blunt instrument such as a baseball bat), but no object penetrates the brain. This damage, known as **closed head injury**, is the leading cause of *traumatic brain injury (TBI)*, which is a more general term referring to any sudden trauma that causes damage to the brain, either because the head suddenly and violently hits (or is hit by) an object (as in closed head injury), or because an object pierces the skull and enters the brain (as in the case of a bullet wound). Traumatic brain injury is a significant source of neuropsychological dysfunction, with approximately 1.5 million new cases a year in the United States alone (Rutland-Brown, Langlois, Thomas, & Xi, 2006). It may surprise you to learn that this rate is higher than the combined rate of three other well-known neuropsychological disorders: Alzheimer's disease, multiple sclerosis, and Parkinson's disease.

Closed head injury is most common in adolescents and young adults 15–24 years of age, caused mainly by motor vehicle, bicycle, or vehicle-pedestrian accidents. In older people (65 years or older), closed head injury is predominantly attributed to falls. Other causes include assault and sport-related injuries (see the "In Focus" feature). Alcohol is involved in more than half of the incidents of closed head injury, either with regard to the person causing the injury, the person injured, or both (NIH Consensus Development Panel, 1999). The brain injury is typically diffuse, as is seen most commonly after motor vehicle accidents, but it may also have focal elements, as is usually the case with falls (Alberico, Ward, Choi, Marmarou, & Young, 1987). We now briefly discuss the mechanisms by which both diffuse and focal damage can occur in closed head injury and then discuss the neuropsychological consequences of such damage.

■ Etiology

The main mechanism of damage in closed head injury is a rapid acceleration of the head followed by a deceleration; thus, it is sometimes referred to as **acceleration-deceleration injury**. The energy imparted to the brain causes it to move within the skull. This movement can lead to diffuse damage as a result of the twisting and shearing of neurons, as well as focal damage due to the impact of the brain with the hard inner surface of the skull. The neurons most vulnerable to twisting are those that compose white-matter tracts, which have long axons and connect distant brain regions (e.g., Adams, Graham, Murray, & Scott, 1982) (● Figure 16.1).

At the time of injury, such diffuse damage is not readily revealed by anatomical brain imaging studies because it does not produce a focal lesion. Instead, the major telltale

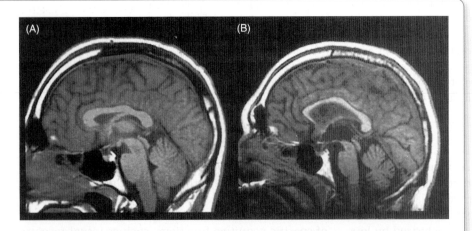

● **FIGURE 16.1** **Effects of closed head injury on long myelinated nerve-fiber tracts in the brain.** Compared with an age- and gender-matched neurologically intact person (A), a person who sustained a closed head injury (B) exhibits a neuronal loss in white matter that is especially prominent in the corpus callosum, as shown in these midsagittal MRI images. *Source:* From "Nonspecific White Matter Degeneration Following Traumatic Brain Injury," by S. D. Gale, S. C. Johnson, E. D. Bigler, and D. D. Blatter, 1995, Journal of the International Neuropsychological Society, 1, p. 26. Copyright © 1995 Cambridge University Press, Reprinted with the permission of the Cambridge University Press.

sign of closed head injury that can be detected at the time of injury is edema (swelling). As time passes, a diffuse loss of neural tissue may lead to detectable enlargement of the ventricles and a loss of volume in large myelinated tracts such as the corpus callosum. Some of these anatomical changes, such as ventricular enlargement (e.g., Levin, Meyers, Grossman, & Sarwar, 1981) and the degree of damage to specific white-matter tracts (e.g., Gale, Johnson, Bigler, & Blatter, 1995), have been found to correlate with the degree of intellectual impairment. More recent neuroanatomical imaging techniques, such as diffusion tensor imaging (see Chapter 3) are also used to detect white-matter damage after closed head injury, and they too predict subsequent problems with memory and learning (Salmond et al., 2006). Diffusion tensor imaging appears to be more sensitive than conventional anatomical imaging in detecting white-matter abnormalities that are associated with lasting cognitive deficits after mild traumatic brain injury (Niogi et al., 2008).

The brain regions most likely to sustain injury are the orbitofrontal and temporal regions, because the bones at these points in the skull are rough and protruding (e.g., Adams, Graham, Murray, & Scott, 1982). Focal damage at the site of impact is known as a **coup injury**, whereas focal damage opposite the site of impact is known as a **contrecoup injury** (Figure 16.2). For example, if the head strikes a windshield, a coup injury in the frontal areas might be sustained, as well as a contrecoup injury at occipital sites.

Efforts to understand the mechanisms of closed head injury, as well as their cognitive and emotional consequences, have increased recently as veterans return to the United States with head injuries. It is estimated that 10–20% of all veterans of the conflicts in Iraq and Afghanistan have sustained traumatic brain injury. Although motor vehicle crashes and blunt trauma (hitting or being hit by an object) are the most common causes of nonbattle injuries, the event typically causing injury in battle is a blast from an improvised explosive device (Galarneau, Woodruff, Dye, Mohrle, & Wade, 2008). Not only do the shock waves from the explosion cause shearing of the brain tissue, but there may also be damage if the blast hurls the person into an object or if the blast propels an object that then penetrates the brain. As in other types of brain injury, diffuse axonal damage is common (Elder & Cristian, 2009).

■ Neuropsychological Consequences

One of the most prominent clinical signs of closed head injury is a significant alteration in consciousness. As you may remember from Chapter 1, basic aspects of wakefulness and consciousness are controlled by the brainstem. Consequently, the degree to which the injury interferes with these aspects of brainstem function can serve as a proxy for the overall impact on the brain. For this reason, scales such as the **Glasgow Coma Scale (GCS)** (Teasdale & Jennett, 1974), which assess the level

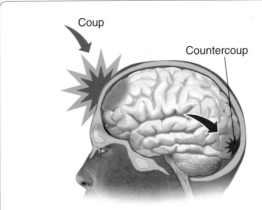

● **FIGURE 16.2   Coup and contrecoup.** In closed head injuries, the brain may be damaged at the site of the impact (coup site) as well as at the site on the opposite side of the head (contrecoup or countercoup site). © 2010 Cengage Learning

of consciousness, are widely used in emergency rooms around the world to provide a gross method for classifying the severity of damage in someone who has just sustained a head injury. This scale, which is shown in Table 16.1, evaluates three realms of functioning: visual responsiveness, motor capabilities, and verbal responsiveness.

Medical personnel find the GCS score useful because it has prognostic value for survival rates and the future level of functioning. For example, a study of thousands of cases found that the survival rate for patients who scored less than 6 on the GCS was about 60%, compared to those with a score above 6, for whom the survival rate was approximately 90% (Udekwu, Kromhout-Schiro, Vaslef, Baker, & Oller, 2004; see also Davis et al., 2006). The same study found that the GCS score at the time of injury predicted subsequent scores on a measure called the Functional Independence Measure, which assesses how well the patient is able to engage in activities like feeding and walking. However, the GCS is not a perfect predictor of outcomes, as varied circumstances can make one patient's outcome better than another's outcome even if their GCS scores are the same.

The profile of neuropsychological deficits observed after closed head injury can vary widely due to dissimilarities in the nature of the damage (e.g., Thomas & Trexler, 1982). Nonetheless, certain difficulties are commonly observed, most notably in memory and attention. In the realm of memory, such patients tend to have posttraumatic amnesia (the inability to acquire new information for events after the injury; see Chapter 10) (e.g., Ahmed, Bierley, Sheikh, & Date, 2000). The initial presentation of these memory problems tends to predict the severity of injury and the subsequent level of functioning. For example, posttraumatic amnesia extending longer than three weeks is associated with a poor level of subsequent cognitive functioning. Some memory problems may arise from damage to the cholinergic system

TABLE 16.1		Glasgow Coma Scale Used to Predict Severity of Brain Trauma
Response	**Points**	**Index of Wakefulness**
Eye Opening		
None	1	Not attributable to ocular swelling
To pain	2	Pain stimulus is applied to chest or limbs
To speech	3	Nonspecific response to speech or shout, but does not imply that patient obeys command to open eyes
Spontaneous	4	Eyes are open, but this does not imply intact awareness
Motor Response		
No response	1	Flaccid
Extension	2	"Decerebrate." Adduction, internal rotation of shoulder, and pronation of the forearm
Abnormal flexion	3	"Decorticate." Abnormal flexion, adduction of the shoulder
Withdrawal	4	Normal flexor response; withdraws from pain stimulus with abduction of the shoulder
Localizes pain	5	Pain stimulus applied to supraocular region or fingertip causes limb to move so as to attempt to remove it
Obeys command	6	Follows simple commands
Verbal Response		
No response	1	(self-explanatory)
Incomprehensible	2	Moaning and groaning, but no recognizable words
Inappropriate	3	Intelligible speech (e.g., shouting or swearing), but no sustained or coherent conversation
Confused	4	Patient responds to questions in a conversational manner, but the responses indicate varying degrees of disorientation and confusion
Oriented	5	Normal orientation to time, place, and person

An individual's consciousness is assessed in three separate arenas: visual responsiveness, motor capabilities, and verbal responsiveness. The scores obtained in each of these three arenas are totaled to provide the overall score. Scores less than or equal to 8 indicate severe head injury, scores of 9 to 12 indicate moderate head injury, and scores of 13 or greater indicate mild head injury.

(see Chapter 2), which tends to be more compromised by closed head injury than other neurotransmitter systems (Schmidt & Grady, 1995). We will revisit the role of the cholinergic system in memory later in this chapter when we discuss Alzheimer's disease.

Another commonly affected ability is attentional functioning. Although people with closed head injury maintain vigilance and alertness, they have particular difficulty in selective attention, divided attention, response inhibition and cognitive flexibility (Zoccolotti et al., 2000). Their behavioral control is often poor, and they may appear impulsive, impatient, and distractible. Deficits in executive function are also observed (e.g., van Donkelaar et al., 2005). For example, the ability to plan toward a goal, or the motivation to do so, is compromised. Motivational problems are related to emotional changes after injury, such as depression or a lack of understanding of deficits. In addition, deficits in cognitive functions performed by the brain region at the site of coup or contrecoup injury are often observed (Orsini, Van Gorp, & Boone, 1988).

Head injuries can vary in their severity, and not surprisingly the severity of the injury affects cognitive consequences. **Mild head injury**, also known as *concussion*, occurs when a person has a change in consciousness for 2 to 30 minutes and does not have other gross signs of neurological damage. A loss of consciousness is often considered to be the hallmark of a concussion, but loss of consciousness is not necessary for the diagnosis of concussion. Behaviors that are often associated with concussion are listed in Table 16.2.

Even mild damage can have consequences for mental functioning (see Frencham, Fox, & Maybery, 2005, for a review). Concussions, like more serious head injuries, result in a cascade of changes within the brain, including changes in neurotransmitter release, glucose metabolism, blood flow, and axonal structure and function (Giza & Haovda, 2001). Symptoms tend to fall into three major areas. First, difficulties in cognition are noted, especially in attention, concentration, and memory. Second, the person experiences somatic symptoms, such as dizziness, blurred vision, sensitivity to noise and bright lights, sleep disturbances, fatigue, headaches, lightheadedness, alterations in taste and smell, and changes in

TABLE 16.2	Frequently Observed Behaviors Associated with Mild Head Injury
Vacant stare	Befuddled facial expression
Delayed responses	Slower to answer questions or follow instructions
Inability to focus	Easily distracted; unable to follow through with normal activities
Disorientation	Unaware of time, date, place; walking in wrong direction
Atypical speech	Slurred speech; incoherent, disjointed, or incomprehensible statements
Gross incoordination	Stumbling; inability to walk a straight line
Hyperemotionality	Acting distraught; crying for no reason
Memory deficits	Asking the same question; inability to remember what happened five minutes ago
Loss of consciousness	Nonresponsiveness to stimulus

appetite. Third, the individual undergoes emotional changes, including depression, anxiety, loss of patience, and increased temper (Riggio & Wong, 2009). Despite apparent recovery as demonstrated on neuropsychological tests, some of these symptoms, such as irritability, anxiety, depression, insomnia, and fatigue, may persist (e.g., Binder, 1986). Nevertheless, the prognosis for cognitive recovery is better following mild head injury compared to more severe injury (Schretlen & Shapiro, 2003).

Closed head injury is a risk factor for longer-term neurological problems. First, having had a closed head injury puts a person at higher risk for sustaining another head injury (see Salcido & Costich, 1992), increasing the risk four to six times more than someone who has never had a head injury (e.g., Zemper, 1994). The subsequent head injury may occur, in part, because some people have personality and social characteristics (e.g., risk taking, alcohol abuse) that predispose them to accidents (e.g., Tsuang, Boor, & Fleming, 1985). However, decrements in attention and poor judgment resulting from the initial head injury may also predispose someone to another head injury (e.g., failing to notice a traffic light might lead to another motor vehicle accident). The risk of additional head injury is problematic, as both neuropsychological and neurophysiological effects are cumulative, even when the injuries are separated by months or years (Gronwall & Wrightson, 1975; Jordan & Zimmerman, 1990).

Closed head injury is also associated with posttraumatic epilepsy, which does not always manifest itself immediately but may begin more than a year after the head injury. (Later in this chapter, we discuss epilepsy in more detail.) A closed head injury that occurs in early adulthood is associated with a significant increase in the risk of depression over the person's lifetime (Holsinger et al., 2002). Furthermore, even a mild closed head injury may put an individual at higher risk for dementing disorders such as Alzheimer's disease (e.g., Lye & Shores, 2000; Nemetz et al., 1999).

Dementing Diseases

The term for a debilitating syndrome involving a loss of cognitive functions, sometimes accompanied by personality changes, that interferes significantly with work or social activities, is **dementia**. Although a person can become demented after an acute neurological incident (i.e., very severe head injury), dementias typically progress in stages, generally termed *mild, moderate,* and *severe,* and eventually lead to death. In mild dementia, the person retains judgment, can live alone, and can maintain adequate personal hygiene, although work and social activities are significantly impaired. As the disease progresses to the moderate stage, independent living becomes hazardous (e.g., the person forgets to turn off the stove) and some degree of supervision becomes necessary. In severe dementia, the person's abilities are so impaired that he or she requires constant supervision (e.g., the person is mute or cannot maintain minimal personal hygiene).

Dementia is a growing problem for industrialized societies, because the average life span continues to lengthen and the risk of dementia increases with age. Based on current rates of Alzheimer's disease and a population of older people that is expected to swell as the baby-boom generation ages, researchers project that by the year 2050, nearly a million new cases of Alzheimer's will be diagnosed each year in the United States (Alzheimer's Association, 2009). The burden of dementia can be staggering, both in terms of the emotional impact on families and the financial impact of long-term medical care on the health care system and economy.

Although all dementias lead to the same depressing end, different varieties are distinct in both the specific constellation of cognitive functions affected and the course of decline. Typically, dementias are divided into three major varieties, loosely based on the region of the brain most affected: (1) *cortical dementias*; (2) *subcortical dementias*; and (3) *mixed-variety dementias,* which encompass both cortical and subcortical damage.

The cortical dementias—Alzheimer's disease, Pick's disease, and Creutzfeldt-Jakob disease—manifest as the co-occurrence of many deficits with which we are already familiar, such as aphasia, apraxia, agnosia, acalculia, spatial deficits, and memory problems. They generally have an insidious onset in which the first symptoms are difficulty remembering events, disorientation in familiar surroundings, problems in finding the correct words to use or difficulty in naming objects, and changes in personality and mood. The cognitive decline thereafter is steady and slow (except for Creutzfeldt-Jakob disease, which progresses rapidly).

In contrast, subcortical dementias, which occur with Huntington's disease and Parkinson's disease, do not result in specific and striking cognitive deficits, such as aphasia and apraxia. Instead, they are much more likely to manifest first as changes in personality, slowness in the speed of cognitive processing, lapses in attention, and difficulties in accomplishing goal-directed tasks or tasks that require formation of a strategy (Bonelli & Cummings, 2008). Moreover, people with subcortical dementias have relatively few difficulties with recognition tasks, showing impairment mainly on recall. Table 16.3 on page 474 lists the major features that distinguish cortical and subcortical dementias.

Mixed-variety dementias are disorders in which both cortical and subcortical involvement seems to occur, such as vascular dementia (previously referred to as *multi-infarct dementia*) and the dementia associated with AIDS. These dementias manifest as patterns of cognitive performance that are midway between those observed in cortical and subcortical dementias. We now turn our attention to a more detailed discussion of each syndrome.

IN FOCUS: Closed Head Injury and Sports

In October 2009, the U.S. Congress opened hearings on the issue of brain injuries in professional football players (Schwarz, 2009a). Although the outcome of those hearings is unresolved at the time of this writing, the hearings underscore the increasing—and publicly voiced—concerns about the long-term consequences of repeated head traumas suffered by football players. The hearings were prompted, in part, by a study, commissioned by the National Football League, that found an elevated rate of early-onset dementias such as Alzheimer's among retired football players compared to the general population (Schwarz, 2009b). Though these hearings focus specifically on American football, concerns about head injuries are relevant to other contact sports as well, such as boxing, rugby, lacrosse, hockey, and soccer (called football in most of the world). In this feature, we explore what is known about how repeated concussions during a sports career can influence cognitive functioning.

Probably the clearest case of sports-related head trauma occurs in boxing, in the syndrome known as *dementia pugilistica,* or *chronic traumatic encephalopathy* (McCrory, Zazryn, & Cameron, 2007). This syndrome was described as early as 1928 by a doctor who called it the "punch-drunk" syndrome (Martland, 1928). The features typically begin to manifest at the end of a boxing career or soon thereafter, and are initially evident as tremors, slurred speech, and abnormal gait and reflexes (due to damage to the cerebellum and other motor areas). Insidiously, these difficulties become worse, and disorders in thinking and emotion emerge, indicating the extensive nature of damage to more wide-ranging regions of the brain. Regardless of whether a boxer is a professional or an amateur, heavyweight or lightweight, the probability of developing these symptoms is related to the number of bouts in which the person fought (Mortimer & Pirozzolo, 1985). In fact, so clear is the association between head trauma sustained in the ring and subsequent neurological deficits that the American Academy of Neurology has called for a ban on boxing (see Lundberg, 1983, 1984, 1986; Rowland, 2006).

Head injuries in other contact sports tend to be associated with collisions between players, explaining why U.S. football accounts for more than half the reported injuries (Powell & Barber-Foss, 1999) (● Box Figure 16.1). To appreciate the frequency of head trauma, consider the following: In one study of college football players, researchers found that 1 in 10 players received a head injury within any given season and that more than 40% of the athletes sustained at least one head injury during their high school and college careers (Barth et al., 1989). Concussion rates are also high among ice hockey and rugby players, including both youth and professional players (see Toth, 2008, for comparisons across sports). These injuries occur despite the use of protective headgear.

Research on the consequences of sports-related head injuries is methodologically challenging. Obviously, researchers cannot randomly assign people to participate in sports that could lead to a concussion merely to observe the effects on their cognitive functioning. Instead, people themselves choose to participate in such sports, so researchers must rule out the possibility that preexisting factors, rather than the head injuries sustained during the sport, account for differences in cognitive functioning between athletes who play contact sports and the general population. For that reason, good studies require a carefully selected control group that is matched to the contact sports group in as many relevant variables as possible, such as fitness level, education, and lifestyle factors such as substance use. Other studies employ a pre/post design, in which they examine cognitive functioning in members of a team at the beginning of a season, and then again at the end of the season after some players have endured concussions (e.g., Collins et al., 1999; McCrea et al., 2003). A third approach is to simply look for correlations between the number of past head injuries reported and present cognitive performance. Of course, such correlations can be difficult to interpret; for example, poor attention or slowed reflexes might lead to a head injury rather than the other way around. In addition to these study design issues, researchers must also consider whether the sample consists of amateur or professional players, as such samples differ in their skill level and the speed and impact of play.

Despite these methodological challenges, accumulating evidence does indicate that head injuries sustained during sports can take a toll on mental functioning. Acute effects of sports-related concussion on cognitive functioning within 24 hours after the injury have been well documented, across a wide range of cognitive domains, including memory, attention, and executive function (Belanger & Vanderploeg, 2005). Longer-term consequences are more subtle, but have also been documented. Indeed, even when the player feels that symptoms have subsided, the effect of mild head injury can still be detected in the laboratory. For example, one study examined Australian professional

■ Cortical Dementias

For each of the major cortical dementias—Alzheimer's, Pick's, and Creutzfeldt-Jakob—we first discuss its neuropsychological profile, then its neurophysiological bases and putative causes.

Alzheimer's Disease

Most people associate Alzheimer's disease with memory loss. Indeed, this association is reasonable, considering that the ability to remember a list of words after a delay is the best measure for distinguishing between a mildly demented individual and a healthy older adult, or for distinguishing between someone who is presymptomatic but later develops Alzheimer's versus someone who does not (e.g., Chen, Ratcliff, Belle, Cauley, DeKosky, & Ganguli, 2000; Welsh, Butters, Hughes, Mohs, & Heyman, 1991). However, the consequences of the disease reach far beyond memory impairment. **Alzheimer's disease** (or, as it is often called, **dementia of the Alzheimer's type [DAT]**) is defined by a decline not only in memory but also in many other aspects of cognitive function, including at least one

MIKE RANSDELL/MCT/Landov

● **BOX FIGURE 16.1** Collisions between players in contact sports, such as the one here that was forceful enough to remove protective headgear, account for many of the head injuries sustained while playing sports.

football players who had suffered a mild head injury, defined as any 2- to 20-minute change in consciousness with no accompanying gross signs of neurological damage, and a posttraumatic amnesia that lasted less than 24 hours (Cremona-Meteyard & Geffen, 1994). The players were tested two weeks after the injury and again one year later. Two weeks after injury, they exhibited a slowing of overall reaction time and an inability to direct attention to a cued location. A year later, when the players claimed that all the behavioral signs of the concussion had disappeared, reaction times had indeed returned to normal, but the deficit in directing visual attention remained. These findings suggest that even mild head injuries may have long-term consequences.

The long-term effects of mild head injury are not limited to the orienting or directing of visual attention, but can affect more central aspects of processing as well. One study found that people who incur mild head injury as a result of contact sports, including rugby, soccer, and wrestling, may exhibit a decrease in the amplitude of the P_{300} ERP component, which reflects central aspects of attentional

control. The amount of the decrease was related to the degree of postconcussive symptoms (Dupuis, Johnston, Lavoie, Lepore, & Lassonde, 2000). Another study found that one out of every four serious amateur soccer players (playing on average 4 hours a week for more than 15 years) was moderately impaired on tests of memory, and four out of ten were impaired on executive function as measured by the Wisconsin Card Sorting Test (WCST) (Matser, Kessels, Lezak, & Jordan, 1999). Although concussions are less frequent in soccer than in American football or hockey, soccer involves "heading," the intentional use of the head to play the ball. Repeated impacts from heading may have a detrimental impact on the brain that is more subtle than that from a full-blown concussion, yet still detectable by neuropsychological testing (e.g., Rutherford, Stephens, & Potter, 2003; Rutherford, Stephens, Potter, & Fernie, 2005).

Although the effect of head trauma on cognitive performance has been demonstrated, it is still controversial whether sports-related head injury leads to a greater likelihood of severe dementias such as Alzheimer's disease. Traumatic brain injury from nonsports head trauma is known to increase the risk for dementia (Lye & Shores, 2000), so it stands to reason that sports-related injury may have the same effects. However, the NFL-commissioned study, which has not yet been published in the peer-reviewed scientific literature, is the only study to date that establishes an increased risk of dementia in professional athletes other

than boxers. Certainly, not all athletes who have suffered multiple concussions will go on to develop dementia, a fact that raises the question of why some do and some don't. Interestingly, the increased risk of dementia following sports-related head trauma may be specific to people with a particular variant of the ApoE gene, which influences a protein that aids in cell membrane repair (Jordan, Relkin, Ravdin, Jacobs, Bennett, & Gandy, 1997; Kutner, Erlanger, Tsai, Jordan, & Relkin, 2000). (We discuss this gene later in this chapter, in the section on Alzheimer's disease.)

What are the implications of such findings for coaches, athletes, and fans? One obvious implication is that coaches and trainers must be aware of the potential consequences of a head injury when deciding whether to put a player back into the game. A player who has suffered a concussion may be at greater risk for sustaining another head injury with more devastating consequences, in what is known as "second impact syndrome" (Erlanger, Kutner, Barth, & Barnes, 1999). These issues are especially important for young athletes, whose brains are still developing. Therefore, guidelines have been developed to assist coaches and trainers in determining when an injured player is ready to go back into the game (Guskiewicz et al., 2004). More broadly, professional teams must be aware of long-term medical issues that players may face in retirement, and must be prepared to offer just compensation and coverage of the related medical expenses. Players themselves should be made fully aware of the potential consequences of their choices to play bruising professional sports. Finally, fans may be sobered to realize that what is entertainment to them can lead to neurological impairment in players long after they have left their days of fame and glory on the field.

of the following: language, visuospatial skills, abstract thinking, motor performance, and judgment. In addition, emotional dysfunction and personality changes, which at first are subtle but later become profound, are typically observed as well. As we will learn later, the brain damage sustained is diffuse, which accounts for the broad nature of the cognitive deficits observed.

Because Alzheimer's disease has been estimated to account for more than half of all cases of dementia in older people (Alzheimer's Association, 2009), researchers are intensely examining it in an attempt to

understand both its neuropsychological consequences and its causes. Generally, Alzheimer's disease is considered to comprise two subsyndromes. One, known as *early-onset Alzheimer's,* is characterized by onset of the disease before the age of 65 years, and progresses rapidly. The other, known as *late-onset Alzheimer's,* is characterized by an onset after the age of 65 years, and is usually associated with a slower decline (American Psychiatric Association, 2000). As we discuss later, different genetic factors are thought to be linked to each of these syndromes.

TABLE 16.3	Major Characteristics Distinguishing Cortical and Subcortical Dementias	
Characteristic	**Subcortical**	**Cortical**
Mental Status		
Language	No aphasia	Aphasia
Memory	Forgetful (difficulty retrieving learned material)	Amnesia (difficulty learning new material)
Cognition	Impaired (poor problem solving produced by slowness, forgetfulness, and impaired strategy and planning)	Severely disturbed (agnosia, aphasia, acalculia, and amnesia)
	Slow processing time	Response time relatively normal
Personality	Apathetic	Unconcerned or euphoric
Mood	Affective disorder common (depression or mania)	Normal
Motor System		
Speech	Dysarthric (poor articulation of sounds)	Normal*
Posture	Abnormal	Normal, upright*
Gait	Abnormal	Normal*
Motor speed	Slow	Normal*
Movement disorder	Common (chorea, tremor, rigidity, ataxia)	Absent
Anatomy		
Cortex	Largely spared	Involved
Basal ganglia, thalamus, mesencephalon	Involved	Largely spared
Metabolism		
Neurotransmitters preferentially involved	Huntington's disease: γ-aminobutyric acid	Alzheimer's disease: acetylcholine
	Parkinson's disease: dopamine	

*Motor system involvement occurs late in the course of Alzheimer's disease and Pick's disease.

At present, no specific physiological test can definitively reveal the presence of Alzheimer's disease in living people. The defining characteristics of the disease, specific neuroanatomical changes to the brain (discussed later), can be determined only by postmortem examination of brain tissue, so a probable diagnosis is made on the basis of behavior. When other causes of dementia have been ruled out (e.g., dementia due to substance abuse) and the person's behavioral pattern is consistent with the disease, a diagnosis of Alzheimer's disease is made. These behavioral criteria do quite well, in the best cases agreeing with the diagnosis at autopsy as much as 90% of the time (e.g., Blacker, Albert, Bassett, Go, Harrell, & Folstein, 1994). Some research has focused on the potential for biomarkers (e.g., substances in the cerebrospinal fluid or blood plasma) to serve as additional indicators of disease presence (Estrada & Soto, 2009; Minati, Edginton, Bruzzone, & Giaccone, 2009). However, it has been difficult to find biomarkers that are unique to Alzheimer's, and it is not clear whether the presence of such a biomarker would change the treatment approach when cognitive symptoms are already known to be present. Thus, the vast majority of diagnoses are made on the basis of cognition and behavior.

From its typically gradual onset, the course of the disease is progressively downward. Because of the variability of impairment seen at different stages of the disease, scales are widely used to quantify the degree to which the abilities of patients with Alzheimer's disease are compromised. One such scale, the Global Deterioration Scale (e.g., Reisberg, Ferris, deLeon, & Crook, 1988; Reisberg et al., 1989), uses an interview to examine memory, orientation to the world, and self-care skills to provide a seven-stage rating (from 1, no decline, to 7, very severe decline). An overview of the characteristics of each stage and its typical duration is provided in Table 16.4.

Neuropsychological Profile Memory impairment is one of the most prominent aspects of the disease, as we've already mentioned. People with Alzheimer's disease show a severe and global anterograde amnesia (see Minati et al., 2009, for a review). Thus, like patients with amnesia, they cannot acquire new information. Not surprisingly, they have significant discrepancies between their IQ scores (which tend to rely more on previously acquired information) and their scores on tests such as the Wechsler Memory Scale (which measure the acquisition of new memories) (e.g., Weingartner, Kaye, Smallberg, Ebert, Gillin, & Sitaram, 1981). Often family members will not realize how debilitated a loved one is because the patient instinctively remains in familiar environments and engages in behaviors that are routine, so that new information need not be acquired. The severity of the deficit becomes evident only when the person is confronted with unfamiliar circumstances, such as those encountered on a vacation away from home or with the institution of new procedures at work.

TABLE 16.4	A Typical Rating Scale for Alzheimer's Dementia (AD)		
Stage	Diagnosis	Characteristics	Estimated Duration*
1	Normal adult	No decrement noted	
2	Normal older adult	Subjective deficit in word finding and other aspects of memory	
3	Compatible with incipient AD	Deficits noted on demanding job-related tasks and may be apparent to family members	7 years
4	Mild AD	Assistance required for complex tasks (e.g., handling finances, planning a dinner party, traveling to a new location)	2 years
		Person's knowledge of current and recent events diminishes	
5	Moderate AD	Assistance required for many daily tasks	18 months
		May not know the day, location, or time	
		Is likely to still remember family member	
6	Moderately severe AD	a. Assistance required for dressing	5 months
		b. Assistance required for proper bathing	5 months
		c. Assistance required with mechanics of toileting (e.g., flushing, wiping)	5 months
		d. Urinary continence lost	4 months
		e. Fecal continence lost	10 months
7	Severe AD	a. Speech ability limited to about one-half dozen intelligible words	12 months
		b. Intelligible vocabulary limited to a single word	18 months
		c. Ambulatory ability lost	12 months
		d. Ability to sit up lost	12 months
		e. Ability to smile lost	18 months
		f. Ability to hold up head lost	Unknown

*In subjects who survive and progress to the next stage.

Although patients with Alzheimer's disease exhibit amnesia, the pattern of memory impairment in Alzheimer's disease differs in important ways from patients with medial temporal lobe amnesia (see Chapter 10). First, unlike typical amnesic patients, procedural knowledge is not spared in those with Alzheimer's disease. As discussed in Chapter 10, procedural memory is independent of the hippocampal system and depends on activating the same cortical processors that were used in the acquisition of a skill. Procedural knowledge is affected in Alzheimer's disease to the degree that a particular cortical processor is affected by the disease. For example, whereas amnesics typically are biased to complete a stem (e.g., *mot__*) with a word that they recently read in a list of words (e.g., *motel*), Alzheimer's patients do not show evidence of implicit learning in this way (e.g., Shimamura, Salmon, Squire, & Butters, 1987). Such a task requires knowledge about language and word meaning, and thus presumably relies on the frontal and parietotemporal regions that are often compromised in Alzheimer's disease. In contrast, Alzheimer's patients exhibit intact perceptual priming for visual form, which presumably relies on occipital regions that are relatively spared in the disease process (Keane, Gabrieli, Fennema, Growdon, & Corkin, 1991). Patients with Alzheimer's disease also exhibit extensive retrograde amnesia, unlike typical amnesic patients (e.g., Beatty, Salmon, Butters, Heindel, & Granholm, 1988). Finally, unlike typical amnesics, patients in the later stages of Alzheimer's disease may have problems with working memory, such as performance on digit-span tasks (e.g., Wilson, Bacon, Fox, & Kaszniak, 1983).

In later stages of the disease, language problems, such as aphasia, usually become prominent, affecting semantic aspects of language more than syntax or phonology. At this time, the patient's speech becomes sparse and empty of meaning. For example, when asked to name an orange pictured in a photograph, a moderately demented patient replied, "Same thing, this is no, no, they may be this here and it didn't get here, but it got there, there, there" (Bayles, 1982, p. 276). Despite the lack of content, the syntactic structure of these individuals' language remains intact (e.g., Hier, Hagenlocker, & Shindler, 1985), and they show few phonemic disturbances or articulatory problems (e.g., Appell, Kertesz, & Fisman, 1982). They also exhibit difficulty in other functions, such as visuospatial processing and the conceptual aspects of motor behavior often observed in apraxic individuals. The exact functions compromised, especially in the early phases of the disorder, vary from person to person and tend to be predicted by regional decreases in brain metabolism (e.g., Haxby et al., 1990). For example, low metabolism in right parietal regions is associated with disturbances in spatial functions, whereas low metabolism in left parietal regions is associated with apraxia symptoms and language problems (Hart & Semple, 1990).

Alzheimer's disease also causes changes in emotional functioning and personality. Relative to their premorbid personalities, patients are rated by caregivers as more neurotic, vulnerable, and anxious; less extroverted; more passive; less agreeable; less open to new ideas; and more depressed, though not profoundly so. Patients with Alzheimer's disease tend not to exhibit odd or socially inappropriate behaviors, which are more common in people with subcortical dementias. For the most part, personality changes are not correlated with the duration of the illness and may begin to manifest relatively early in the disease. In some cases, the patients may exhibit psychiatric symptoms. For example, at later stages of the disease, delusions, especially of persecution, infidelity, and theft, may occur. However, these delusions tend not to be elaborate and they pass quickly. The more atypical an individual's personality before she or he is diagnosed with the disease, the more likely the person is to exhibit psychiatric symptoms such as depression and paranoid delusions (Chatterjee, Strauss, Smyth, & Whitehouse, 1992).

Neurophysiological Bases   One of the main challenges in Alzheimer's research is to characterize the pathological features of the brain and to determine which of these features reflects the essential cause of the disorder. Great progress has been made in describing the pathology, but understanding of the causal chain that leads to the presence of these pathological features has been more elusive (for a review of all aspects of Alzheimer's pathology, see Duyckaerts, Delatour, & Potier, 2009; Maccioni & Perry, 2009).

The defining characteristic of Alzheimer's disease is a brain riddled with large numbers of neurofibrillary tangles and amyloid plaques. **Neurofibrillary tangles** are twisted pairs of helical filaments found within the neuron (● Figure 16.3). They are similar to but distinct from microtubules, which are normal cell structures that allow neurotransmitters and other proteins made within the cell body to be transported to other regions of the cell. Because of their structure, neurofibrillary tangles are thought to disrupt a neuron's structural matrix. Although these tangles can be found in the brain of the average healthy older individual, they are found in greatly increased numbers in the cortex of a person with Alzheimer's disease (e.g., Tomlinson, 1980, 1982), and their number predicts the severity of the dementia (e.g., Bierer et al., 1995; Nagy et al., 1995). However, large numbers of neurofibrillary tangles are not unique to Alzheimer's disease, but are also observed in other neurological conditions such as Down syndrome, dementia from boxing, and Parkinson's disease resulting from encephalitis. These tangles are not equally distributed throughout the brain: they show an affinity for medial temporal, inferior parietal, and frontal regions, while sparing primary motor and sensory areas (e.g., Kemper, 1984).

Amyloid plaques are deposits consisting of aluminum silicate and amyloid peptides, meaning that they are basically a buildup or a conglomeration of proteins (Figure 16.3). These plaques often include

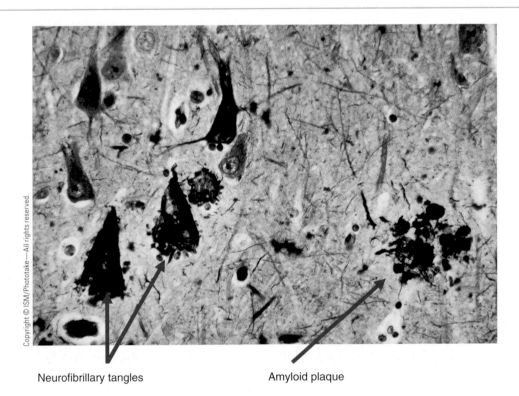

Neurofibrillary tangles   Amyloid plaque

● **FIGURE 16.3**   **Neurofibrillary tangles and plaques that are typically observed in Alzheimer's disease.** Shown here is a section of cortex from a patient with Alzheimer's disease. The neurofibrillary tangles are the dark cone-shaped objects, and the plaques are the brown clumps.

tau protein and apolipoprotein E (ApoE), which, as we will soon learn, are implicated in the genetic aspects of Alzheimer's disease. The plaques, typically surrounded by neurons containing neurofibrillary tangles, are believed to cause vascular damage and neuronal cell loss. The accumulation of tau protein appears to be especially important in contributing to cell death, so intense research has focused on attempting to understand the molecular mechanisms of tau accumulation (Spires-Jones, Stoothoff, de Calignon, Jones, & Hyman, 2009).

As with neurofibrillary tangles, amyloid plaques can be observed in the brain of the average older person without dementia. What distinguishes patients with Alzheimer's disease from the neurologically intact older population is the number of plaques, which tend to concentrate in the cortex and the hippocampus. Plaques are also observed in other brain diseases, such as amyotrophic lateral sclerosis (ALS), a demyelinating disease. There is usually evidence of inflammation in the vicinity of the plaque (McNaull, Todd, McGuinness, & Passmore, 2010) and a deficiency of nerve growth factor (Tonnaer & Dekker, 1994). The importance of these findings will be discussed later in connection with potential therapeutic interventions to slow the course of the disease.

The net result of all these tangles and amyloid deposits is the loss of synapses and then the loss of cells (Arendt, 2009). At later stages of the disease, the cell loss is very visible on anatomical brain images, as the cortex is atrophied and the ventricles enlarged (● Figure 16.4). As might be expected from the description of the location of tangles and plaques, cell loss in the cortex is widely distributed across frontal, anterior temporal, and parietal regions (e.g., Du et al., 2007; Lerch, Pruessner, Zijdenbos, Hampel, Teipel, & Evans,

2005). The subcortical and midbrain structures most affected include the hippocampus, amygdala, and olfactory system.

Not surprisingly, the degree of tissue loss is closely tied to behavioral changes. For example, the amount of cortical thinning measured with structural MRI can predict symptom severity even in early stages of the disease (Dickerson et al., 2009). Loss of gray matter can distinguish people with Alzheimer's disease from those with a **mild cognitive impairment** that is often seen as a precursor to Alzheimer's (Desikan et al., 2009). Mild cognitive impairment is characterized by a cognitive decline that is greater than typical for a person's age, but not of sufficient severity to warrant a diagnosis of dementia (see Nelson & O'Connor, 2008). Gray-matter loss tracks the progression of symptoms over time as patients with mild cognitive impairment develop diagnosable Alzheimer's disease (Whitwell et al., 2007). Furthermore, enlargement of the cerebral ventricles, which is a marker of tissue-volume loss, is greater in people with mild cognitive impairment who go on to develop Alzheimer's within the next six months, compared to those whose cognitive function remains stable (Nestor et al., 2008; see also Querbes et al., 2009). Therefore, although gray-matter loss is not the original cause of the disease, it is closely associated with the characteristic cognitive decline of the disease. Indeed, some research has found that cognitive decline is better predicted by volume loss than by the amount of amyloid plaque deposits (Jack et al., 2009).

Among the brain's neurotransmitter systems, the cholinergic system is most affected in Alzheimer's, and the disruption to this system correlates with the severity of dementia (Wilcock, Esiri, Bowen, & Smith, 1982). The main route for cholinergic input to the cortex and hippocampus is lost, as up to 90% of cells are destroyed

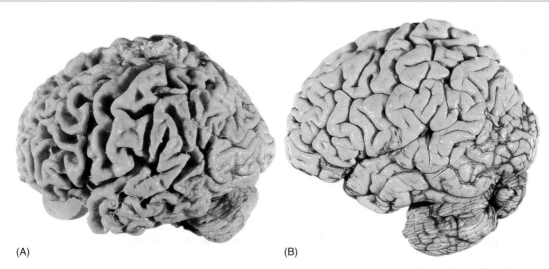

(A)   (B)

● **FIGURE 16.4   Cortical loss due to Alzheimer's disease.** The gyri of the cortex are clearly shrunken in a patient with Alzheimer's disease (A) compared to a normal person (B). *Source:* Dr. Robert D. Terry, Department of Neurosciences, School of Medicine, University of California at San Diego.

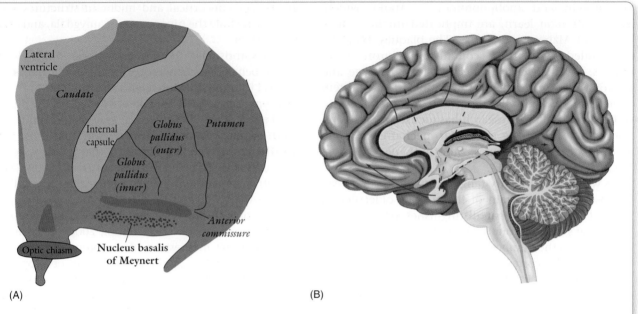

● **FIGURE 16.5   The nucleus basalis of Meynert and cholinergic projections, which are affected by Alzheimer's disease.** (A) A coronal section at the level of the optic chiasm illustrating the position of the nucleus basalis of Meynert relative to the striatum and anterior commissure. (B) A midsagittal view of the brain showing cholinergic projections (in blue) to the cortex from the nucleus basalis of Meynert. © 2011 Cengage Learning

in the *nucleus basalis of Meynert* (e.g., Whitehouse, Price, Clark, Coyle, & DeLong, 1981; Whitehouse, Price, Stubble, Clark, Coyle, & DeLong, 1982). ● Figure 16.5A shows the location of the nucleus basalis of Meynert in relation to midbrain structures, and ● Figure 16.5B depicts cholinergic projections from this region to cortical areas. Although cholinergic transmission is most affected, the noradrenergic and serotonergic systems are also compromised. To a lesser extent, reductions can also be observed in levels of glutamate and dopamine (Parnetti, Senin, & Mecocci, 1997).

Genetic Bases and Risk Factors   Much research has examined genetic factors that are related to Alzheimer's disease (see Bertram & Tanzi, 2008, for review). One set of genetic factors involves mutations that *lead* to Alzheimer's disease. They are associated with Alzheimer's dementia of early onset and all involve increased production of the amyloid beta protein. Another set of genes is associated with the *risk* of late-onset Alzheimer's disease, either increasing or decreasing the likelihood of disease. These genetic contributions to Alzheimer's disease are outlined in Table 16.5.

A number of genes have been found to cause the early-onset varieties of Alzheimer's disease. One is a mutation of the gene on chromosome 21 coding for amyloid precursor protein (Goate et al., 1991). Aberrant catabolism of amyloid precursor protein is linked to the formation of amyloid deposits. Interestingly, by the age of 30, people with Down syndrome, which involves an extra copy of chromosome 21, have pathology of the brain similar to that seen in people with Alzheimer's disease and start to exhibit dementia with increasing age (Wisniewski, Wisniewski, & Wen, 1985). Two genes that code for presenilin are also linked to early-onset Alzheimer's. The gene on chromosome 1 that codes

TABLE 16.5	Genetic Associations for Alzheimer's Dementia (AD)	
Gene	**Chromosome**	**Effect**
Mutations Causing AD		
Presenilin 2	1	Disease typically occurs between age 30 and 40 years, but can be wide-ranging
Presenilin 1	14	Disease occurs between age 50 and 65 years
Trisomy 21 (Down syndrome)	21	Disease occurs between age 30 and 40 years
Amyloid precursor protein	21	Disease occurs between age 40 and 50 years
Factors Modulating AD		
Apolipoprotein—ApoE-4 allele	19	Increased risk of late-onset AD
Apolipoprotein—ApoE-2 allele	19	Decreased risk of late-onset AD

for presenilin 2 has been found in a small group of German families that migrated to the Volga region of Russia (Levy-Lahad et al., 1995), and the gene on chromosome 14 that codes for presenilin 1 has been linked to the majority of cases of early-onset Alzheimer's disease (Sherrington et al., 1995). These early-onset varieties of Alzheimer's disease account for less than 5% of all patients with Alzheimer's dementia, so additional research is needed to understand genetic contributions in the more typical late-onset type.

The gene that has been most closely associated with the risk of getting late-onset Alzheimer's disease is the ApoE gene, which codes for apolipoprotein E, a protein that is thought to play a role in clearing amyloid plaques (see Bu, 2009, for a review). Commonly the gene has three alleles (i.e., possible forms): e-2, e-3, and e-4. The ApoE-4 allele is associated with an increased risk of Alzheimer's. For example, this allele is present in approximately 15% of the general population but in 40% of patients with Alzheimer's, and people with one copy of the allele are three to four times more likely to develop Alzheimer's than participants without any ApoE-4 alleles (Bu, 2009). Interestingly, the presence of the ApoE-2 allele, which is relatively rare, seems to be associated with a decreased risk of developing the disease.

The presence of the higher-risk ApoE-4 allele appears to affect the degenerative course of the disease. For example, among Alzheimer's patients, those who possess the ApoE-4 allele show faster rates of hippocampal atrophy compared to those with no alleles of this type (Schuff et al., 2009). In addition, Alzheimer's patients with the ApoE-4 allele have greater levels of amyloid plaque accumulation than do patients with other genotypes (Drzezga et al., 2009). Some studies have suggested that ApoE genotype may even influence cognitive abilities in older people who do not have Alzheimer's disease (e.g., Caselli, Dueck, Osborne, & Sabbagh, 2009; Luciano et al., 2009).

Factors other than genes have also been linked to the risk of getting Alzheimer's. Factors that increase risk include smoking (Merchant, Tang, Albert, Manly, Stern, & Mayeux, 1999), cardiovascular disease (Stewart, 1998), diabetes mellitus (Leibson et al., 1997), and head injury (Lye & Shores, 2000). On the other side of the coin, a number of factors are associated with decreased risk of Alzheimer's disease. These include the use of non-steroidal anti-inflammatory drugs (McGeer, Schulzer, & McGeer, 1996), having higher education and being involved in mentally challenging work and activities (Stern, Gurland, Tatemichi, Tang, Wilder, & Mayeux, 1994), receiving estrogen replacement therapy (Ohkura et al., 1994), and engaging in high levels of physical activity (Scarmeas, Luchsinger, et al., 2009).

Cognitive abilities prior to the elderly years also seem to predict risk for dementia. For example, in one study of elderly nuns, the complexity of a nun's writing exhibited 50 years earlier, when she first entered the convent, predicted her likelihood of getting Alzheimer's

in old age (Snowdon, Kemper, Mortimer, Greiner, Wekstein, & Markesbery, 1996). One possibility is that the processes leading to Alzheimer's may start at an early age and accumulate over a lifetime. Alternatively, these results might also provide evidence for *cognitive reserve*, which is the idea that people with greater mental capacity can sustain more insult before exhibiting symptoms. For example, some people may just be endowed with a greater-than-average elaboration of dendritic branching and synaptic density. Their brains can sustain more degradation before the damage to the matrix of their synaptic connections makes them incapable of handling complex cognitive thought.

Recent work also suggests that dietary factors may influence risk for the disease. Specifically, epidemiological studies have reported that people who adhere to a Mediterranean diet (lots of fruits, vegetables, fish, and olive oil, with low saturated fat intake) have a reduced risk of developing dementia (Féart et al., 2009; Scarmeas, Stern, Mayeux, Manly, Schupf, & Luchsinger, 2009) and a lower mortality rate if Alzheimer's is diagnosed (Scarmeas, Luchsinger, Mayeux, & Stern, 2007). Although the causal mechanism is still unknown, it is possible that the high levels of antioxidants in a Mediterranean diet may counteract processes of oxidative stress that damage cells in the brain (for reviews, see Pratico, 2008; Sultana, Perluigi, & Butterfield, 2009; Uttara, Singh, Zamboni, & Mahajan, 2009). These intriguing correlational studies suggest possible routes for treatment and prevention.

Treatment and Prevention   At present, no treatment can cure Alzheimer's disease. At best, treatments may postpone the cognitive decline for some period of time. Given the staggering cost of the condition and the numbers of people affected, enormous effort is currently being invested in attempting to discover new approaches that could potentially yield a more effective treatment. Research has also focused on possible avenues for prevention. Because mild cognitive impairment is viewed as a potential precursor to Alzheimer's disease, it is being investigated intensely. The hope is that a better understanding of mild cognitive impairment will yield insights into the early pathophysiology that might lead to Alzheimer's disease, and could help to identify people who might benefit from early intervention (Petersen & Negash, 2008).

The vast majority of therapeutic interventions for Alzheimer's disease attempt to influence the cholinergic system, because acetylcholine levels are linked to the severity of memory loss and dementia. Initial drug trials attempted to increase acetylcholine levels by providing more precursors to acetylcholine, such as lecithin and choline. This approach did not meet with much success, because the enzyme needed to create acetylcholine from these precursors (choline acetyltransferase) is also reduced in the disease. More successful are drugs that inhibit the action of acetylcholinesterase, the enzyme that breaks down acetylcholine in the synaptic cleft. The drugs that are most commonly used to treat Alzheimer's disease—tacrine, donepezil, rivastigmine, and galantamine—are all acetylcholinesterase inhibitors (see Fuentes, 2009, for a review). In addition to these drugs, another drug used to treat Alzheimer's disease is memantine, a drug that blocks NMDA receptors. This drug reduces the neurotoxicity that is induced by excess levels of excitatory amino acids in Alzheimer's disease.

These drugs can slow the course of Alzheimer's disease, but they cannot stop its progression. They cannot do so because they do not directly address the core pathology of Alzheimer's, the formation of plaques and tangles. However, slowing the progression of the disease can have a real-life impact. In one study, long-term treatment with tacrine significantly extended the time before nursing home care was required for the affected individual (Knopman et al., 1996). Although this benefit may seem at first glance to be rather trivial, a delay in nursing home placement can be very important. For the affected person and his or her family, it provides time to make the necessary financial, living, social, and emotional adjustments to prepare for the patient's decline. For society as a whole, it can mean a savings of about $1 billion a year, both in direct costs, such as nursing home, acute, and in-home care; and indirect costs, including unpaid home care provided by family and friends (Brookmeyer, Gray, & Kawas, 1998).

Researchers continue to search for new drugs in the hopes of further slowing or even stopping the degeneration that is characteristic of Alzheimer's disease. Some candidate drugs attempt to influence the core pathology of amyloid plaque deposition and tau protein formation (e.g., Brunden, Trojanowski, & Lee, 2009). Others address different steps in the pathological cascade of events. For example, some anti-inflammatory drugs are being investigated, because plaque formation is associated with inflammatory processes. Antioxidant drugs are also under study because they protect against oxidative stress that damages cells. In addition, neurotrophic drugs, such as nerve growth factor, may be useful because they can stimulate the growth of new neurons and therefore protect against cell loss.

Because lifestyle factors are associated with the likelihood of disease, nonpharmacological prevention methods may also be warranted. As discussed earlier, diet, exercise, smoking, and degree of mental activity are all predictors of the risk of developing the disease. If each of these makes some contribution to the development of the disease, then perhaps interventions in these areas could lead to a reduced prevalence of the disease. It may be that you can start making choices in your twenties that will reduce your chances of getting Alzheimer's in your eighties!

Frontotemporal Dementia

Another type of cortical dementia, which accounts for about 15–20% of all dementias (Jackson & Lowe, 1996), is **frontotemporal dementia**. Although

frontotemporal dementia is a cortical dementia like Alzheimer's disease, it differs from Alzheimer's in a number of key aspects of behavior, cognition, and neuropathology. In addition, its average age of onset, approximately 56–58 years of age, is much younger than is typical in Alzheimer's disease (Mendez, 2006).

Unlike the initial symptom in Alzheimer's disease, which tends to be memory impairment, the first symptoms of frontotemporal dementia usually occur in the realm of social-emotional functioning (see Mendez, 2006, for a review). Persons with this variety of dementia generally have difficulty modulating their behavior, especially in a socially appropriate manner. They lack inhibition and are impulsive, doing things such as swearing at inappropriate times, having outbursts of frustration, and impulsively grabbing what they want, such as snatching food off someone's plate or shoplifting. Their lack of concern for social norms usually extends to a lack of concern for their personal appearance, so they often are unkempt. In some cases, they may also exhibit inappropriate sexual behaviors. Furthermore, they have no insight into or awareness of the inappropriateness of their behavior.

Another characteristic that is sometimes observed is a preoccupation with repetitive or routinized behavior. They may read the same book over and over again or always take a walk to the same place. In addition, they tend to be hyperoral, overeating and obsessively focusing on food. Mood changes can occur as well, tending toward depression and anxiety. In addition to these behavioral changes, there are cognitive changes that manifest mainly in the domain of language. People with frontotemporal dementia tend to have difficulty in verbal expression and in naming of persons and things. With time, their speech has less and less content, and eventually they can become practically mute. Difficulties in reading and writing also develop. Later in the disease, they may have Parkinson-like motor difficulties, with tremor and rigidity.

Other aspects of mental functioning, however, remain surprisingly intact. For example, spatial cognition and higher-order motor programming seem to be relatively preserved in those with frontotemporal dementia. In one case report, a former computer engineer took to wandering miles from his home to collect cans, and never had any trouble returning home. However, his wife had to start managing his behavior when he started peering into people's windows in search of his prized cans. Memory problems are less prominent at first, as these individuals tend to be oriented to time and place and are able to keep track of recent events, at least in the initial stages of the disease (Kaye, 1998; McKhann, Albert, Grossman, Miller, Dickson, & Trojanowski, 2001).

The neural characteristics of frontotemporal dementia also differ from those of Alzheimer's disease. For example, cell loss appears to follow a different pattern than in Alzheimer's disease. Whereas patients with Alzheimer's disease have cortical thinning across all major cortical regions (frontal, temporal, parietal, and occipital), patients with frontotemporal dementia have characteristic thinning primarily in frontal and temporal regions, with less thinning in the parietal lobe than Alzheimer's patients (Du et al., 2007). The relative preservation of parietal cortex likely accounts for relatively preserved spatial cognition. In addition, patients with frontotemporal dementia have greater loss of white matter in the frontal lobes than do patients with Alzheimer's disease (Zhang et al., 2009). An example of the severe atrophy of the frontal regions in frontotemporal dementia is shown in ● Figure 16.6.

Cellular characteristics also distinguish frontotemporal dementias from Alzheimer's disease. For example, Pick's disease, a subtype of frontotemporal dementia, is characterized by two main features: pale neurons swollen as if they had "ballooned," and clumps of fibers in the cytoplasm that are stained by silver and are known as *Pick's bodies*. These fibers are distinguishable from the neurofibrillary tangles of Alzheimer's disease because they are straight rather than paired and helical (see Scully, 1986, for a particularly vivid case report of Pick's disease).

The largest risk factor for frontotemporal dementia is familial; that is, the presence of the same dementia in a closely related family member. This pattern suggests a strong genetic component, though researchers are still working to identify the exact genetic mechanisms that give rise to the disease. Genes that are linked to frontotemporal dementia tend to involve chromosome 17, which includes the gene coding for the tau protein (Mendez, 2006; Spillantini, Bird, & Ghetti, 1998). Interestingly, although the ApoE genotype is associated with risk for frontotemporal dementia, the association does not seem as strong as for Alzheimer's. Furthermore, the effect of the high-risk ApoE-4 variant on the brain appears to be different for Alzheimer's than for frontotemporal dementia. For example, one study found that ApoE-4 carriers with Alzheimer's disease had greater atrophy in parietal and hippocampal regions than noncarriers with Alzheimer's, but ApoE-4 carriers with frontotemporal dementia had greater atrophy in frontal regions than noncarriers (Agosta et al., 2009). This finding implies that the ApoE-4 genotype modulates the course of the disease process differently in these two types of dementia.

Creutzfeldt-Jakob Disease

Another cortical dementia, **Creutzfeldt-Jakob disease (CJD)**, is starkly different from both Alzheimer's and frontotemporal dementia in a few key respects. First, it is very rare (1 in every 1 million persons). Second, mental deterioration in CJD is quite rapid, rather than following the slow time course of other degenerative disorders. Third, and perhaps most importantly, CJD has a known cause: a group of transmissible protein agents known as *prions* (*pro*teinaceous *in*fectious particles) (e.g., Gibbs et al., 1968).

Prions cause disease when a prion protein, which is a normal brain protein, undergoes a change of shape

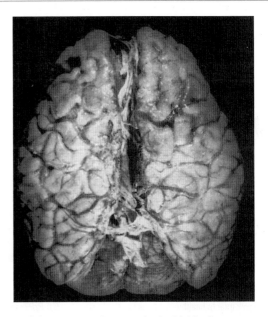

● **FIGURE 16.6 Brain atrophy in Pick's disease.** Shown here is the brain of a patient with Pick's disease, as viewed from above. Note the amount of degeneration in the frontal regions relative to that in other areas of the cortex. *Source:* From "Case Records of the Massachusetts General Hospital: Case 16-1986," by R. E. Scally, 1986, New England Journal of Medicine, 314, p. 1108. Copyright © 1986, Massachusetts Medical Society. Reprinted by permission of The New England Journal of Medicine.

that makes it insoluble (● Figure 16.7) (for a review of prion diseases, see Aguzzi & Heikenwalder, 2006; Johnson, 2005). Once insoluble, it can no longer be broken down, so it accumulates, leading to cell death. The prion responsible for CJD is highly transmissible. It can be transmitted from one person to the next during medical procedures, such as corneal implants, injections of human growth factor, and the implantation of intracranial electroencephalography (EEG) electrodes. It can even be contracted from contact with brain tissue during dissection if gloves are not worn. The prion that causes the disease is known to be hardy (unlike the HIV virus) because it is resistant to boiling, formalin, alcohol, and ultraviolet radiation. Fortunately, the prion can be inactivated by autoclaving or by bleach. In most cases, doctors are unable to determine how a particular patient acquired the disease-causing prion. Because it occurs sporadically (rather than clustering in certain families, geographic areas, or occupations), the typical form of CJD is often known as "sporadic CJD."

Sporadic CJD has behavioral characteristics that easily distinguish it from Alzheimer's and frontotemporal dementias. CJD dementia is accompanied by involuntary movements and a characteristic EEG pattern consisting of periodic sharp, synchronous spikes at a rate of 0.5 to 2 Hz (Wieser, Schindler, & Zumsteg, 2006). The initial complaints tend to be fatigue, anxiety, problems with concentration, difficulties with appetite or sleep, and occasionally an elated mood. Because of these

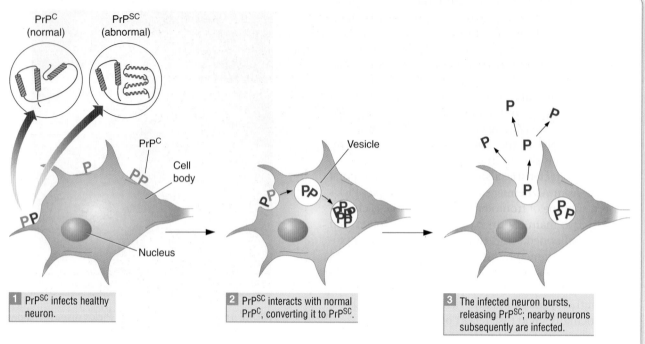

PrP^C (normal)

PrP^{SC} (abnormal)

PrP^C

Cell body

Vesicle

Nucleus

1 PrP^{SC} infects healthy neuron.

2 PrP^{SC} interacts with normal PrP^C, converting it to PrP^{SC}.

3 The infected neuron bursts, releasing PrP^{SC}; nearby neurons subsequently are infected.

● **FIGURE 16.7** **How abnormal prion proteins infect a cell.** Normal prion proteins (PrP^C, shown in green) can change to an abnormal form (PrP^{SC}, shown in red), which then turns other normal prions into the abnormal form, infecting the cell. © 2010 Cengage Learning

symptoms, patients are sometimes given a psychiatric diagnosis. Several weeks later, these symptoms are typically followed by motor symptoms, such as contractions of muscle groups, which may then be followed by a lack of coordination, involuntary movements, difficulty in gait, and altered vision. A swift and progressive neurological collapse follows, invariably including dementia (e.g., Brown, Cathala, Sadowski, & Gajdusek, 1979; Will & Matthews, 1984). The incubation period for CJD can be quite long, with symptoms beginning to manifest years or even decades after the person is infected (Fleminger & Curtis, 1997). However, once symptoms appear, the course of the disease is so rapid that the patient usually lives less than one year thereafter. The decline may be seen week by week, or in some cases even day by day.

Neuropathologically, the changes seen in the cortex in CJD are widespread neuronal loss and a proliferation of glial cells. In addition, the brain appears "spongy," which is why this disease is sometimes referred as to as *spongiform encephalopathy* (● Figure 16.8). Although the sponginess of the brain in CJD is most evident upon autopsy, MRI findings may also assist in confirming the presence of the disease while the patient is still living (e.g., Lodi et al., 2009; Zerr et al., 2009).

A new variant of this disorder (called variant CJD) was identified in the United Kingdom and France in the 1990s. This variant afflicted people younger than 40 years of age, including some adolescents (● Figure 16.9). In these cases, the initial presentation tended to involve behavioral changes, and the decline was more protracted (up to 22 months), with dementia occurring only later on. The characteristic EEG abnormalities of sporadic CJD are not observed in variant CJD. Although there are sparse spongy cells in both variant and sporadic CJD, with damage mainly in the basal ganglia and thalamus, variant CJD is also characterized by amyloid plaques, which are typically absent in sporadic CJD (for a review, see Johnson, 2005).

It is thought that people acquired variant CJD by eating cattle infected with the prion disease bovine spongiform encephalopathy, also known as *mad cow disease*. Observed first in British cattle starting in 1986, the disorder appears to have been transmitted across species from cattle to humans through butchering practices that allowed brain and spinal tissue to taint the meat prepared for consumption. Because of such concerns, other European countries banned imports of British meat during the spring of 1996 (Epstein & Brown, 1997). This bovine disorder has now been found in countries outside Europe, including Japan. Although the incidence of variant CJD appears to have decreased since the 1990s, the long incubation period of the disease makes it difficult to know for certain whether the window of danger for variant CJD has closed.

■ Subcortical Dementias

Patients with subcortical dementias display a pattern of cognitive disabilities that is distinct from those observed in patients with cortical dementias. Thought tends to be

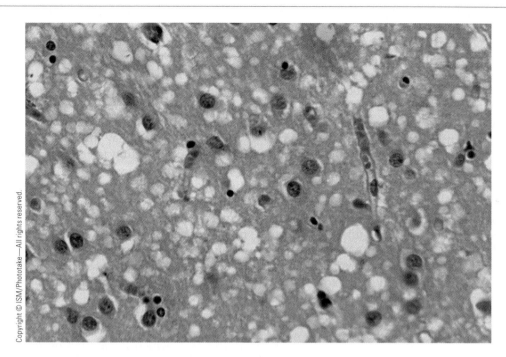

● **FIGURE 16.8   Brain tissue showing spongiform encephalopathy.** This image was taken from a cow with bovine spongiform encephalopathy. The pathology is similar in humans with Creutzfeldt-Jakob disease.

slowed, and symptoms related to frontal lobe dysfunction are prominent. These latter difficulties probably result because the main subcortical regions affected in these dementias have intimate connections with frontal regions. Here we discuss two subcortical diseases: Parkinson's and Huntington's.

Parkinson's Disease

As we learned in Chapter 5, patients with Parkinson's disease have a specific cell loss in the substantia nigra, the major source of dopaminergic neurons in the brain, and to a lesser degree in the locus ceruleus. Along with the

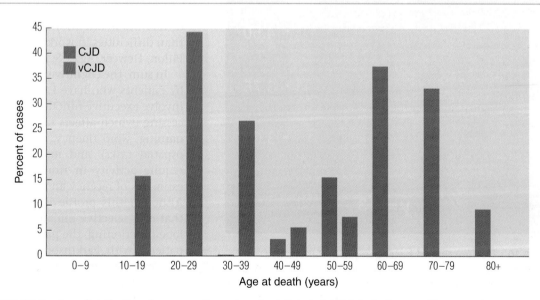

● **FIGURE 16.9   Age distribution for sporadic and variant Creutzfeldt-Jakob disease.** The variant form of the disease (vCJD), thought to be acquired by eating infected meat, has affected much younger people than the classic sporadic form (CJD). © 2010 Cengage Learning

motor symptoms that accompany the disease, dementia manifests in approximately 30% of these patients (Tison, Dartigues, Auriacombe, Letenneur, Boller, & Alperovitch, 1995). The cardinal neuropsychological symptoms of Parkinson's disease are dysfunction of executive processes, slowing in motor and thought processes, and impairment in memory retrieval (but not retention) (for a review, see Jacobs, Levy, & Marder, 2006).

Patients with Parkinson's disease exhibit cognitive dysfunction in the realm of executive function (e.g., Dalrymple, Kalders, Jones, & Watson, 1994). For example, these patients have difficulty with the Wisconsin Card Sorting Task, not so much because they act in a perseverative manner but because they are not able to think abstractly, being deficient at identifying the categories into which the cards should be sorted. They exhibit deficits in switching between categories, in overriding stereotypic responses, in responding to novel situations, and in developing plans of action (e.g., Henik, Singh, Beckley, & Rafal, 1993) (● Figure 16.10).

The second area of cognitive compromise exhibited by individuals with Parkinson's disease is the slowing of motor and thought processes known as **bradyphrenia** (Mahurin, 2008). Although patients with Parkinson's disease can arrive at a correct answer, they do so slowly, seeming to need to overcome some sort of mental inertia. Such slowing is more likely to occur on tasks requiring planning (e.g., Tower of London) than on simpler tasks. This slowness may influence a variety of mental functions, contributing to poor performance in other domains, such as language and visuospatial functioning. For example, mental slowing can reduce the ability to name items and can disrupt articulatory capacities. Some of the slowing of mental and motoric functions may also be exacerbated by the depression that often accompanies the disease.

A third area of difficulty is in certain aspects of memory, specifically in retrieving information in unstructured situations and in spatial working memory (Postle, Jonides, Smith, Corkin, & Growdon, 1997). The ability to plan a strategic search through memory, which is required by recall, is impaired. However, long-term memory for both verbal and visuospatial material appears to be intact when recognition procedures are used (e.g., "Have you seen this item before?"). The pattern of memory functions observed in Parkinson's disease suggests that memory functions dependent on the temporal lobes are spared, whereas memory dependent on the integrity of the frontal lobes is more severely compromised (e.g., memory for recency). Finally, working memory is generally spared in Parkinson's disease, although performance deteriorates if a distracting stimulus intervenes, probably because of difficulties in attentional processes rather than difficulties in working memory (e.g., Pillon, Deweer, Agid, & Dubois, 1993).

In sum, the cognitive deficits exhibited by patients who have Parkinson's disease involve executive functions, speed of processing (which affects tasks such as word naming, word fluency, and certain visuospatial tasks), and memory tasks that require activity in frontal regions (e.g., estimates of recency and temporal order). Although this profile is consistent with that of a selective impairment in frontal lobe functioning, the pattern observed in patients with Parkinson's disease differs in subtle ways from that in patients with frontal lobe damage. For example, patients with Parkinson's disease are less likely to perseverate (Owen, Roberts, Hodges, Summers, Polkey, & Robbins, 1993), to lack insight into their behavior, or to be

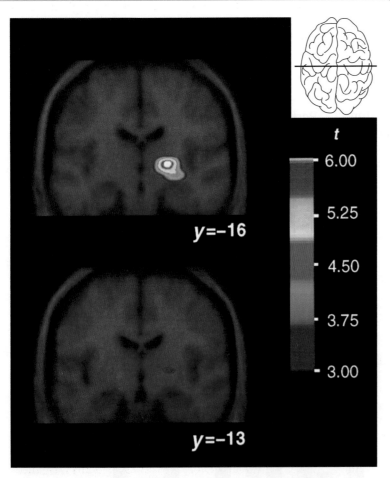

● **FIGURE 16.10   Dysfunction of basal ganglia in Parkinson's disease.** Regions shown here are those that are significantly more activated in neurologically intact people than in people with Parkinson's disease when performing a complex planning task. Red indicates the highest degree of activation. *Source:* Adapted from Owen et al, 1998. Abnormal basal ganglia outflow in Parkinson's disease identified with PET: Implications for higher cortical functions, Brain, 121, p. 955. By permission of Oxford University Press.

disinhibited than are patients with frontal lobe damage (Dubois, Boller, Pillon, & Agid, 1991).

Patients with Parkinson's disease also show changes in emotional functioning (Borek, Amick, & Friedman, 2006). Approximately 40–50% of Parkinson's patients exhibit depression. This depression appears to be linked more to the neurobiological substrate of the disease than to the disabilities imposed by the illness. Levels of depression in patients with Parkinson's disease are higher than those observed in patients with other debilitating motor impairments, such as paraplegia and hemiplegia. Also, the depression may precede motor symptoms and be uncorrelated with their severity. Compromise of the dopaminergic system, which is associated with reward, may explain some of the apathy and lack of pleasure associated with depression in these patients.

In addition to mood changes, other aspects of emotional function are compromised. One prominent symptom of the disease is the **Parkinsonian mask**, which is an expressionless face. This masklike facial appearance may, in part, reflect a dampening of movements, because the patients can identify which facial expression should go with an emotional situation and can produce a particular facial expression when asked (although they rarely do so spontaneously). In part, though, it seems to reflect a dampening of emotional responsiveness. The facial expressions and tone of voice of people with Parkinson's disease lack emotional intensity, even in response to pictures with strong affective value.

Parkinson's appears to be caused by a combination of genetic and environmental factors. First-degree relatives of people with Parkinson's are between 2 and 10 times more likely to get the disease than people with no affected relatives; and siblings are likely to get the disorder at a similar age. From the environmental side, increased risk has been associated with a rural or farming environment, drinking well water, exposure to pesticides or herbicides, head trauma, and exposure to industrial pollutants (Maher et al., 2002). For example, long-term exposure to metals such as manganese, copper, iron, and lead, which are occupational hazards for pipefitters, electrical workers, engineers, chemists, machinists, firefighters, steamfitters, and toolmakers, has been linked to neuropsychological disorders such as Parkinson's disease. These metals may lead to the generation of free radicals, which are neurotoxic (Gorell et al., 1997).

The standard treatment for Parkinson's has been to try to offset the dopamine deficiency by giving patients L-dopa, a precursor to dopamine that can cross the blood-brain barrier. This drug can improve at least some of the cognitive deficits associated with Parkinson's by influencing dopamine levels in the prefrontal cortex (e.g., Cools, Stefanova, Barker, Robbins, & Owen, 2002). Unfortunately, it is associated with dyskinesias in about 35% of patients and with hallucinations in other patients, and there is a loss of drug efficacy over time. Consequently, other dopamine agonists are now preferred for early stages of the disorder when they are effective, with L-dopa reserved for later stages when the dopamine agonists become ineffective (Jenner, 2002).

When a patient becomes resistant to L-dopa and the symptoms are extremely problematic, more invasive treatment options may be considered, such as ablation of the thalamus or the internal portion of the globus pallidus, or deep brain stimulation of these structures via an implanted electrode (e.g., Deuschl et al., 2006). Although these procedures are thought to improve motor functioning, controversy presently exists as to whether they have any positive cognitive consequences (Fields & Troster, 2000; Hugdahl & Wester, 2000). Moreover, in some cases, specific negative effects on mental processes have been documented (e.g., Scott et al., 2002).

A final therapeutic avenue is the prospect of using fetal stem cells to replace neurons that are lost in the substantia nigra. Such therapeutic interventions are still in the exploratory stages. Some research has found that stem cells implanted into the substantia nigra or striatum can improve motor functions in rodent and nonhuman primate models of Parkinson's (e.g., Qing feng, Ji, Ling li, & Chong gang, 2009; Redmond et al., 2007). Clinical trials testing the effectiveness of stem cell therapy in humans have not yet been performed. However, some studies have grafted neural tissue from the fetal midbrain into the midbrain of Parkinson's patients, with mixed results (see Lindvall & Kokaia, 2009, for a review). These studies have focused primarily on motor symptoms to measure the potential beneficial effects of implants, so it is not yet known how such treatments would affect the cognitive deterioration in this disease.

Huntington's Disease

As discussed in Chapter 5, Huntington's disease is an inherited, progressive neurological disease that generally first manifests around age 35–42 and inevitably leads to death about 14–17 years later. The incidence of this disease is about 5 cases per 100,000 people. The disease destroys GABAergic (and cholinergic) neurons in the striatum (caudate nucleus and putamen) and to some degree in the globus pallidus, leading to a movement disorder characterized by jerky, rapid, and uncontrollable movements (i.e., *choreiform* movements). ● Figure 16.11 illustrates the loss of tissue in the basal ganglia in Huntington's disease.

The decline in cognitive functioning in individuals with Huntington's disease approximately parallels the decline in motor functioning, with practically all patients eventually becoming demented (Jacobs et al., 2006; Lieberman et al., 1979). These patients have difficulty with executive aspects of attention (e.g., Josiassen, Curry, & Mancall, 1982), with processing of spatial information (e.g., Brouwers, Cox, Martin, Chase, & Fedio, 1984), and with retrieval of information from memory (e.g., Butters, Wolfe, Martone, Granholm, & Cermak, 1985). The foregoing symptoms are often accompanied by disorganized speech and changes in personality

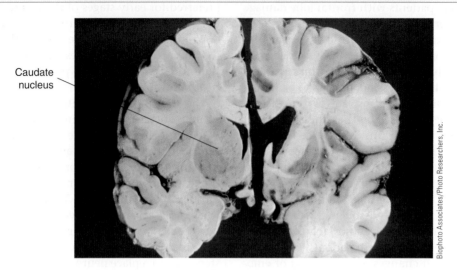

Caudate nucleus

Biophoto Associates/Photo Researchers, Inc.

● **FIGURE 16.11   Neurological degeneration in Huntington's disease.** The caudate nucleus is much smaller in an individual with Huntington's disease (right) compared to a neurologically intact individual (left). Also notice that the ventricle is enlarged in the Huntington's patient due to the loss of tissue in this region.

and emotional functioning. As with other subcortical dementias, profound aphasia and apraxia are rare, a factor that allows clinicians to easily differentiate between Alzheimer's disease (or other cortical dementias) and Huntington's disease (or other subcortical dementias). We now examine the constellation of cognitive and emotional deficits in Huntington's disease in more detail (for a good review, see Brandt, 1991).

One broad domain of cognitive dysfunction observed in Huntington's disease is in the realm of executive control and other abilities mediated by the frontal lobe. Patients with this disease have specific difficulties in initiating behavior, selecting a response, selecting a stimulus on the basis of particular attributes, and switching mental sets. In addition, they have reduced verbal fluency, perseverative tendencies, and a loss of cognitive flexibility. Such deficits are manifest on tasks such as the Wisconsin Card Sorting Test and the Stroop test. The existence of such deficits is not surprising if you consider that the head of the caudate nucleus, which is damaged by Huntington's disease, receives much input from the dorsolateral and orbital frontal cortex. The disintegration of connections between the frontal lobe and the basal ganglia manifests early in the course of the disease. One of the most common early complaints of people with Huntington's disease is that they have difficulty planning their activities and scheduling their lives.

A second broad domain affected in this disorder is spatial processing. One might speculate that because spatial tests often emphasize motor speed, these difficulties are a consequence of the motor difficulties associated with Huntington's disease rather than a specific deficit in spatial processing. Arguing against such a conclusion, however, is the fact that deficits are observed even on tasks in which motor demands are not prominent, especially on tasks of spatial learning. Such findings are consistent with research performed on monkeys in which damage to the caudate nucleus has been found to cause difficulty with spatial learning tasks, such as spatial alternation (e.g., respond to the left stimulus on Trial 1, to the right stimulus on Trial 2, to the left stimulus on Trial 3, etc.).

Patients with Huntington's disease also often exhibit problems in certain aspects of memory. In fact, these are often one of the earliest signs of cognitive impairment. The memory disorder is characterized by two main features, each of which distinguishes it from the memory problems observed in patients with Alzheimer's disease. The first main feature of memory dysfunction in patients with Huntington's disease is that they are much better at recognition than at recall. In contrast, patients with Alzheimer's disease are equally impaired at both. These findings suggest that although patients with Huntington's disease can store new information, they have difficulty making the kind of self-guided search through memory that is required to recall (rather than recognize) information. However, they are able to retrieve information when given cues, such as those provided in multiple-choice recognition memory tasks; this indicates that the information has indeed been successfully stored in memory.

The second main feature of memory dysfunction in patients with Huntington's disease is the lack of a temporal gradient to the memory impairment. Unlike patients in the early stages of Alzheimer's disease, who have better memory for historical events that occurred earlier in life (e.g., when they were 20 or 30 years old) than for events that occurred more recently (e.g., when they were 40, 50, or 60 years old), patients with Huntington's disease show more equal memory impairment across all time periods (e.g., Beatty et al., 1988).

Besides being affected cognitively, more than 80% of all patients with Huntington's disease manifest changes in emotional functioning (Lieberman et al., 1979). About half of all people with this disease have major depressive episodes or exhibit a depressed mood. The depression often precedes motor symptoms and is similar to that observed in people with Parkinson's disease. Patients with Huntington's disease may also be irritable, apathetic, impulsive, aggressive, and emotionally labile. At times they even exhibit psychotic symptoms such as delusions (e.g., thinking they are being persecuted by the FBI or that they are Napoleon reincarnated). Hallucinations (e.g., hearing voices) are rarer. These patients often act in socially inappropriate ways that are reminiscent of the behavior of individuals with frontal lobe damage (Cummings & Benson, 1988). Finally, they often show a lack of awareness of their own deficits across cognitive and emotional domains (Hoth, Paulsen, Moser, Tranel, Clark, & Bechara, 2007).

Huntington's disease is classified as a subcortical dementia because it is caused by changes to the striatum, as discussed in Chapter 5. Researchers have therefore examined the relationship between behavioral deficits and anatomical and functional changes in the basal ganglia. Atrophy or metabolically decreased function of the caudate nucleus is a good predictor of performance, especially on psychomotor and executive attentional tasks (e.g., Bamford, Caine, Kido, Cox, & Shoulson, 1995). However, Huntington's disease is also associated with changes in the cortex itself, such as cortical thinning, and such cortical changes can also predict symptom severity (Montoya, Price, Menear, & Lepage, 2006; Rosas et al., 2008). This reminds us that, unlike the focal lesions that we discussed earlier in the book, degenerative diseases affect large portions of the brain, making it challenging to establish firm structure-function associations.

Because the gene for Huntington's disease is known, it is possible to identify people who will develop the disease but have not yet done so. People who carry the Huntington's gene, but who are asymptomatic with regard to motor signs, exhibit poorer performance than noncarriers on tasks of memory and executive functioning (Lawrence, Hodges, et al., 1998; Wahlin, Lundin, & Dear, 2007). Furthermore, these cognitive deficits are associated with reduced dopamine binding in the striatum (Lawrence, Weeks, et al., 1998). Functional imaging studies have also shown that the left dorsolateral prefrontal cortex is less activated in Huntington's carriers than noncarriers when performing a working-memory task (Wolf, Vasic, Schönfeldt-Lecuona, Landwehrmeyer, & Ecker, 2007). Thus, it appears that Huntington's disease has a progressive degenerative effect on the brain even before the onset of motor symptoms.

Because there is no cure for Huntington's disease, the aim of treatment is generally to address the motor and psychiatric symptoms. As with Parkinson's disease, there is interest in determining whether implantation of neural tissue or stem cells could slow or reverse the progression of the disease. In one study, researchers implanted embryonic tissue in the striatum of five patients with Huntington's disease, and found that three of the five showed cognitive improvements for the first two years after implantation; by four to six years after the surgery, these patients continued to show stabilized performance on untimed cognitive tasks, although performance decreased on timed tasks (Bachoud-Lévi et al., 2006). Whether such therapies will ultimately be beneficial for treating Huntington's disease remains to be further investigated.

■ Mixed-Variety Dementias

Mixed-variety dementias are characterized by a substantial degree of both cortical and subcortical damage, which makes the clinical profile of these disorders an amalgam of the cortical and subcortical dementias. At present, our ability to clearly characterize the constellation of the two main types of mixed-variety dementias—vascular dementia and AIDS dementia—is not as good as for the other types of dementia we discussed. One reason for this murkiness is that the mixed-variety dementias affect the nervous system in a heterogeneous manner. In vascular dementia, the regions of the circulatory system that fail may vary from person to person. In the case of AIDS dementia, the profile of some aspects of neuropsychological functioning may vary between different groups of individuals (e.g., gay or bisexual men vs. intravenous drug users; e.g., Martin, Pitrak, Pursell, Mullane, & Novak, 1995).

Vascular (Multi-Infarct) Dementia

Vascular dementia, formerly known as *multi-infarct dementia*, is the second most common form of dementia. It results not from a single stroke, which tends to compromise a specific mental capacity (e.g., speech output), but from the cumulative effects of many small strokes that tend to create both cortical and subcortical lesions. In some cases, the vascular damage is mainly cortical, and in such cases there is a higher frequency of lesions in the frontal lobes than in other lobes of the cortex (e.g., Erkinjuntti, Haltia, Palo, & Paetau, 1988). In other cases, especially with hypertension, lesions occur in the small blood vessels supplying subcortical areas, primarily those that supply the basal ganglia, internal capsule, thalamus, and pons. When the damage is restricted to the subcortical white matter, the dementia is sometimes referred to as *Binswanger's disease* (e.g., Libon, Scanlon, Swenson, & Coslet, 1990).

The presentation of patients with vascular dementia is often similar to that of patients with Alzheimer's disease (Mathias & Burke, 2009). Ways to distinguish between the two include the patient's medical history, brain imaging, and neuropsychological testing. Evidence for a vascular contribution to dementia comes from a long-standing medical history of arterial hypertension, focal neurological signs (such as weakness of an extremity) that suggest a stroke, and MRI scans revealing specific and multiple infarcts of the cortex in either the white or gray matter. Typically, vascular dementia occurs with a relatively abrupt onset (due to a stroke), is accompanied by a stepwise rather than gradual course (because the effects are compounded by each additional stroke), and is not restricted to onset in the later years. This pattern contrasts with that observed in Alzheimer's disease, which has an insidious onset, slow progression, and an unremittingly downward course, and tends to occur later in life. Finally, because vascular dementia is associated with stroke, the pattern of impairment can fluctuate, being worse initially and then improving. Moreover, treatment of hypertension may help prevent further progression of the disease, whereas hypertension is not a factor that characterizes or influences Alzheimer's disease (*DSM-IV-TR*, 2000).

In terms of their neuropsychological profile, patients with vascular dementia usually demonstrate the same type of pattern observed in patients with Alzheimer's disease. For this reason, it is difficult to distinguish the two disorders definitively based on cognitive functioning alone (see Mathias & Burke, 2009, for a review). Patients with vascular dementia are somewhat more likely to exhibit deficits on tasks relying on frontal lobe function and to display a pattern suggestive of subcortical involvement (e.g., Kertesz & Clydesdale, 1994). For example, patients with vascular dementia and Alzheimer's disease usually perform similarly on tests assessing visuospatial ability, language, and memory, but patients with vascular dementia usually perform more poorly on tests measuring executive function, verbal fluency, and attention, all of which are believed to rely on the frontal lobes. Consistent with the idea of greater subcortical involvement in vascular dementia than in Alzheimer's disease, patients with vascular dementia tend to exhibit slowing of performance on motor tasks and, to a lesser degree, on cognitive tasks in general (Almkvist, Backman, Basun, & Wahlund, 1993).

AIDS Dementia

AIDS is a viral disease that is passed through the exchange of blood or bodily fluids (mainly during sexual relations between male-female, male-male, and possibly female-female partners) and that devastates the immune system, eventually leading to death. Because no cure exists for the disease, prevention is paramount, requiring the one-time use or bleaching of hypodermic needles; the wearing of latex gloves to protect against contamination by infected blood; the practice of "safe sex," in which a barrier is used to prevent the exchange of bodily fluids; adherence to monogamy with a noninfected partner; or abstinence from any sexual activity that involves the exchange of bodily fluids.

AIDS ravages the systems of the body evenhandedly, not sparing the brain. Studies suggest that brain pathology exists in 75–90% of all people who have died of AIDS. Some of the effects are direct. As soon as a few weeks after infection, the human immunodeficiency virus (HIV) that causes AIDS can be found in cerebrospinal fluid; therefore, we know that it crosses the blood-brain barrier, although the exact mechanism by which it does so is not yet clear. Once in the brain, the virus appears to destroy both neurons and oligodendrocytes, leading to a loss of both gray and white matter. Although the virus does not directly enter neurons, it infects non-neural cells in the brain (such as glial cells, immune cells, and cells that line the blood vessels), and those cells in turn release substances that can damage synapses and lead to neuronal death (Ellis, Calero, & Stockin, 2009) (● Figure 16.12). Brain imaging studies suggest that AIDS is associated with both cortical and subcortical damage, particularly in the striatum, thalamus, and frontal cortex (Navia, Cho, Petito, & Price, 1986; Woods, Moore, Weber, & Grant, 2009). This pattern of regional brain atrophy significantly influences the nature of the neuropsychological disorders that accompany AIDS.

AIDS dementia, which affects 6–30% of all adult AIDS patients, almost always occurs in the late stages of the disease when immunosuppression exists and other AIDS-defining illnesses, such as Kaposi's sarcoma, manifest (e.g., Day et al., 1992). As with any dementia, AIDS dementia causes serious declines in cognitive functioning (see Woods et al., 2009, for a review). The most notable consequences are slowing of mental and motor functions, disruptions in concentration and attention, and memory disturbances. In contrast, naming and vocabulary are more likely to be spared. Often, AIDS dementia is also accompanied by changes in affect. Emotionally, individuals tend toward a flattened affect manifesting as apathy, reduced spontaneity, social withdrawal, increased irritability, and emotional lability. Depression is often noted as well. As in patients with Parkinson's and Huntington's disease, the changes in mood for people with AIDS dementia, especially apathy and irritability, appear to be linked to frontal-subcortical dysfunction rather than just being a response to having a terminal illness. These mood changes tend to be associated with deficits in dual-task performance and attentional control in the face of salient distracting information (Castellon, Hinkin, & Myers, 2000). In addition, as the disease progresses, difficulty in executive function, such as poor performance on the Wisconsin Card Sorting Task, becomes more apparent (e.g., Bornstein, Nasrallah, Para, Whitacre, Rosenberger, & Fass, 1993; Heaton et al., 1995; Woods et al., 2009). The progression of the dementia is variable, and at present no good predictors of its course are known (e.g., Maj, 1990; Navia, Jordan, & Price, 1986).

The effects of AIDS on neuropsychological function may not be limited to cases in which it causes

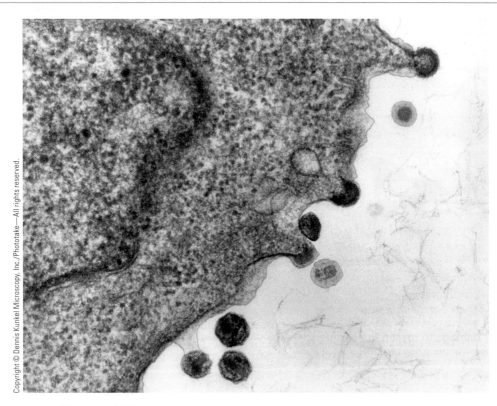

● **FIGURE 16.12**   Packets containing HIV are released from an infected cell.

dementia. Indeed, subtler forms of cognitive dysfunction can be evident in earlier stages of HIV infection as well (Ellis et al., 2009). These milder dysfunctions are important to understand, as drug treatment that slows disease progression has allowed patients to live longer in earlier stages of the disease. The rates of impairment for patients who are seropositive (i.e., test positive for the virus) but asymptomatic are about three times higher than those for individuals who are seronegative (i.e., 35% vs. 12%) (White, Heaton, Monsch, & the HNRC Group, 1995). Tests on which asymptomatic seropositive patients are likely to perform poorly include those requiring speeded psychomotor or mental functioning and those that require new learning (e.g., Bornstein et al., 1993; Heaton et al., 1995). These data have implications for everyday functioning, as individuals who have some neuropsychological impairment are more likely to have difficulty in performing their jobs (Heaton et al., 1996) and to be involved in motor vehicle accidents, as indicated by results of driving-simulation tasks (Marcotte et al., 1997). The rates of neuropsychological compromise are even higher in children, with 75–90% exhibiting neuropsychological deficits (Levenson & Mellins, 1992).

At one time, little or nothing could be done for people diagnosed with AIDS, but now a variety of drug therapies are available. Most notably, antiretroviral treatment (ART) is typically used to treat HIV-infected people in the industrialized world. This raises the question of whether ARTs can slow cognitive declines as well as addressing other aspects of HIV infection. Indeed, recent data suggest that ARTs have dramatically reduced the incidence of AIDS dementia, though milder cognitive deficits may still remain (Cysique & Brew, 2009). This good news is tempered by the fact that many people in the developing world, which is ravaged by AIDS, do not have access to such treatment. Acknowledging that most cases of AIDS occur in developing countries, researchers have begun to examine how AIDS dementia emerges across international settings that differ widely in environmental, cultural, economic, and genetic factors (e.g., Robertson, Liner, & Heaton, 2009).

Demyelinating Diseases

One of the most common neurological diseases of non-traumatic origin, **multiple sclerosis (MS)**, affects the cognitive functioning of young and middle-aged adults. It is so named because it is characterized by multiple discrete areas of scarring (*sclerosis*), ranging in size from 1 mm to several centimeters, in which neurons have absent or damaged myelin (● Figure 16.13). The destruction of myelin in MS is traditionally thought to result from an immunological disruption in which the body incorrectly identifies part of its own system as a foreign

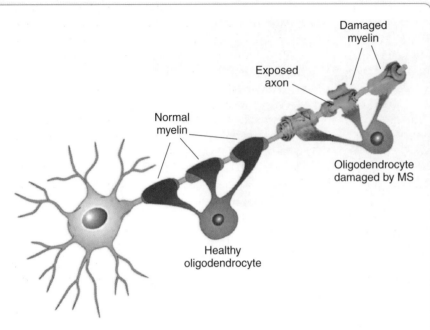

● **FIGURE 16.13   Damage to myelin in multiple sclerosis.** When the myelin is damaged, transmission of the action potential along the axon is impaired. © 2010 Cengage Learning

agent or invader and attacks it (i.e., an autoimmune disorder). However, other researchers argue that the death of oligodendrocytes, which form myelin, may precede the autoimmune response rather than resulting from it (for discussion, see Matute & Pérez-Cerdá, 2005; Trapp & Nave, 2008). In either scenario, demyelination leads to axonal degeneration and interferes with neural transmission. The sites affected tend to be diffuse and multifocal, occurring in both the central and peripheral nervous system. However, certain sites, such as those in the periventricular regions (*peri*, "near"; *ventricular*, "having to do with the ventricles"), tend to be more affected. Although MS is generally considered to be a disease of the brain's white-matter tracts, gray matter may also be lost in the disease (e.g., Inglese, Ge, Filippi, Falini, Grossman, & Gonen, 2004; Rovaris et al., 2006).

MS occurs in approximately 85 of every 100,000 individuals, affecting women about twice as often as men (Alonso & Hernán, 2008; Noonan, Kathman, & White, 2002). Its etiology is unknown, although evidence suggests both an environmental and a genetic contribution. In general, MS is linked to geographical locale; it is less prevalent near the equator and more prevalent toward the geographic poles. People who change their geographical location after the age of 15 years retain the risk rate associated with their birthplace, a fact that has led some researchers to suggest that the causative agent may be a slow virus that is more common in temperate and colder locales (Kurtzke, 1980).

A genetic risk for the disease is suggested by findings that one in five patients with MS have a family member with the disease. In addition, a higher concordance rate (20–30%) occurs in monozygotic twins (who share identical genetic material) than in dizygotic twins (2–5%) (who have only half their genetic endowment in common). MS is associated with genes that influence the body's immunologic response, most notably the human leukocyte antigen gene on the short arm of chromosome 6 (Oksenberg, Baranzini, Sawcer, & Hauser, 2008). The genetic risk factor appears to be independent of the environmental factor because, for example, the incidence rate among ethnic Japanese is low regardless of whether they live in Japan, Hawaii, or the Pacific Coast of the United States (Martin & McFarland, 1993).

Because of the diffuse nature of the lesions in MS and the variability of their location, MS has multiple manifestations. The exact symptoms depend on the sites in the nervous system where myelin is damaged. Initial symptoms often involve weakness in the extremities or difficulty in some aspect of sensory processing. Sensory and motor tracts are especially susceptible to MS, because they are often myelinated to allow speedy transfer of information along the long distances from the peripheral receptor to the brain or from the brain to the muscle. For the person affected, the first manifestations of the disease can be petrifying. Common initial symptoms include a blurring or loss of vision, persistent tingling or numbness of a body part, weakness of a body part, or difficulty in coordination. Unlike many of the other syndromes we have discussed in this chapter, the course of MS is highly variable. A person can have an acute flare-up that results in a hemianopsia, only to have the hemianopsia dissipate and remit—but a subsequent attack could then leave the person with a permanent visual loss. Because MS usually affects people in the prime of their lives and its progression is highly unpredictable, the disease is extremely stressful for those who have it, as well as for their families. An MS patient never knows whether he or she will have the next attack 20 years later or if a series of exacerbations will lead to permanent blindness or paralysis in the near future.

Some people with MS exhibit little if any cognitive disability, whereas others clearly show cognitive compromise. Researchers have estimated that cognitive deficits occur in 40–60% of all MS patients (e.g., Rao, Leo, Bernardin, & Unverzagt, 1991). The degree of cognitive impairment predicts how effectively the patient is able to carry out everyday tasks of life (Kalmar, Gaudino, Moore, Halper, & DeLuca, 2008). When cognitive difficulties do occur, they tend to be variable and do not affect as large a range of function as observed in patients with dementia. If a typical pattern of cognitive disability exists in MS, it involves difficulty in memory and conceptual reasoning along with a general sparing of knowledge systems (see Chiaravalloti & DeLuca, 2008, for a review). On memory tasks, people with MS have difficulty recalling information but display good recognition memory, which suggests an impairment of memory search patterns. Consistent with such an interpretation, they also tend to have difficulty in verbal fluency, which also requires an atypical search through memory. Patients with MS also have difficulty on the types of tasks that require conceptual abstraction, and they may exhibit deficits on visuospatial tasks. However, many of these tasks rely on either speeded performance or manual dexterity, making it difficult to determine whether the deficits are due to peripheral sensory or motor problems or whether they reflect central cognitive problems. The pattern of neuropsychological difficulties suggests a disruption of processing involving both subcortical structures (such as the thalamus and the basal ganglia) and the cortex, mainly the frontal lobes (Rao, 1986), as well as the connections between these regions.

The cognitive changes in MS are usually accompanied by changes in mood and personality. The most common disorder in MS is depression, occurring in 30–60% of all affected individuals (Aikens, Fischer, Namey, & Rudick, 1997; Siegert & Abernethy, 2005). These mood changes are difficult to interpret because they could be normal reactions to having a debilitating, chronic disease, or they could reflect the fatigue that is often associated with the disorder. They also may, in part, reflect some of the organic changes that accompany the disease.

Over time, cognitive skills of patients with MS may either continue to deteriorate or may be maintained. Once again, we see that the course of the disease varies widely from one person to the next. In one longitudinal study of approximately 100 patients with progressive MS, cognitive function declined over a period of two years for approximately one-third of the sample and remained stable or even improved in the other two-thirds (Camp et al., 2005). Interestingly, changes in MRI measurements did not predict changes in cognitive function, but better cognitive performance at the beginning of the study predicted a greater likelihood of maintaining cognitive function over the two years. Thus, initial cognitive performance was a better predictor of the course of the disease than the MRI variables (which included brain volume and the amount of white-matter lesions).

No cure exists yet for MS. Currently, a drug known as interferon beta-1b is considered the standard treatment. *Interferons* are proteins produced by the body that have antiviral characteristics and modulate the immune response. Unlike other therapies, which just stayed the course of the disease, interferon appears to actually reduce exacerbations of the disease (Jacobs, Munschauer, & Pullicino, 1993). Over a period of a year or more, interferon beta-1b was found to have a beneficial effect on cognitive performance for patients with a relapsing-remitting, rather than continually progressive, form of MS. In particular, the drug aided visual memory, learning, problem solving, and complex attentional control, skills that tend to decline over a similar time period in patients who do not receive such medication (Barak & Achiron, 2000; Fischer et al., 2000). Some researchers have proposed giving interferon to people who have symptoms that are suggestive but not definitive of MS, because it may prevent the onset of the full disorder (Comi, 2009).

Ultimately, researchers are aiming for treatments that will do more than just limit the degree of future myelin loss; they would like to be able to repair the damage to cells so as to help patients recover lost functions. Potential strategies include promoting axonal regeneration and promoting myelin repair (Colman, Lubetzki, & Reingold, 2003). Stem cells may prove to be especially beneficial in repairing myelin (Keirstead, 2005). However, most of these research directions are still in the exploratory stages, and it is not known how any such therapies would affect sensory, motor, or cognitive symptoms of the disorder.

Epilepsy

Throughout much of history, epilepsy has had a negative connotation; epileptic seizures have been referred to as "fits," and people with epilepsy have been stigmatized. We now know that such characterizations are unfair and that epilepsy is a neurological problem that has nothing to do with the person's character. *Epilepsy* is a disease in which seizure activity is recurrent but intermittent. **Epileptic seizures** are episodes in which synchronous activity of nerve cells increases so that a gigantic hyperpolarization of neurons spreads over a large area in an atypical and abnormal manner.

Seizures come in many varieties, which are divided into two major classes. One major class is *generalized seizures,* so called because they involve the entire body. The second class is *partial (or focal) seizures,* in which the activity starts in a particular region of the brain and then spreads. In both cases, the abnormal electrical activity spreads throughout the brain (● Figure 16.14). The major types of seizures, along with their motoric effects and usual changes in consciousness, are outlined in Table 16.6. Generalized seizures can be further subdivided into *grand mal seizures,* in which a loss of consciousness is followed by large jerky movements of the body, and *petit mal seizures,* which involve smaller and less generalized movements. Because they involve abnormal electrical activity, these types of seizures are identifiable by characteristic abnormalities in the EEG (● Figure 16.15).

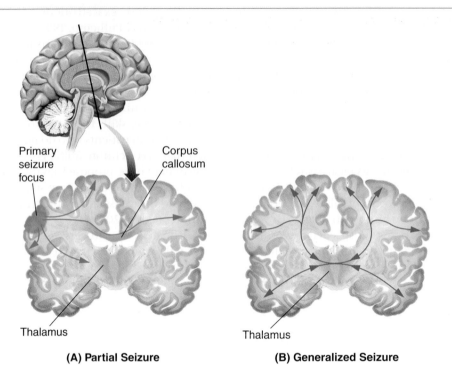

(A) Partial Seizure   **(B) Generalized Seizure**

● **FIGURE 16.14   Seizures spread throughout the brain.** The abnormal electrical activity generated from a partial (focal) seizure (A) or a generalized seizure (B) can spread rapidly through the brain over fiber pathways. © 2010 Cengage Learning

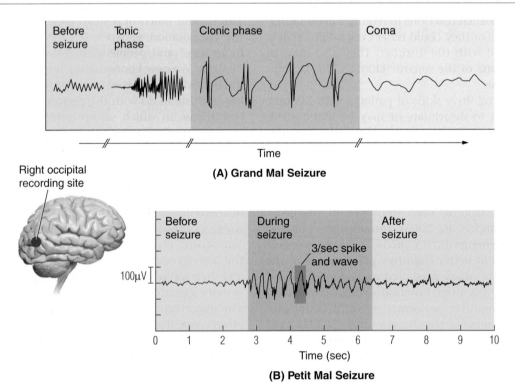

● **FIGURE 16.15   Seizure disorders are detectable by characteristic patterns in the EEG.**
(A) Grand mal seizures are characterized by unique patterns of spiking in both the tonic phase, accompanied by loss of consciousness, and the clonic phase, accompanied by jerky movements. (B) Petit mal seizures, which involve smaller movements, are also characterized by a unique EEG signature. © 2010 Cengage Learning

TABLE 16.6	Classification of Epileptic Seizures and Their Manifestations	
Type of Seizure	Motor Manifestations	Changes in Consciousness
Generalized Seizures		
Grand mal (tonic-clonic)	1. *Tonic phase:* The person shouts or makes a loud noise and falls. Then the person exhibits upward or sideways turning of the eyes and tonic tension of the muscles in which the whole body stiffens and breathing stops. 2. *Clonic phase:* Rhythmic jerking of body parts begins and continues for minutes.	1. *Tonic phase:* The person loses conscious control of movement and loses consciousness. 2. *Clonic phase:* Disorientation or comatose behavior is exhibited following clonic motor activity.
Clonic	Same as clonic phase of grand mal seizures.	Same as clonic phase of grand mal seizures.
Tonic	Same as tonic phase of grand mal seizures.	Same as tonic phase of grand mal seizures.
Petit mal	A slight movement of the eyes or turning of the head can be observed.	A brief change in consciousness occurs, which is often not noticed or overlooked by untrained individuals. The person seems to "space out" briefly (i.e., is unresponsive for about 10 seconds).
Focal Seizures		
Jacksonian (originate in a specific region of the motor strip, but sometimes in other regions such as the somatosensory strip)	The seizure starts as a clonic movement of one specific body part. The seizure spreads in an orderly progression down the motor strip to neighboring regions, involving more and more body parts; this progression is known as a *Jacksonian march.*	Little impairment of consciousness occurs.
Complex partial seizures (originate in the temporal or frontal lobe)	*During seizures:* The person engages in automatisms—repetitive motions including buttoning and unbuttoning the same button, lip smacking, swallowing, and chewing. This phase may then be followed by one in which the person seems catatonic, or frozen.	*Preceding seizures:* The person experiences an aura, which is a feeling, sensation, smell, or taste that signals the onset of the seizure. In some cases, these auras can be elaborate and may involve mood changes, feelings of déjà vu, hallucinations, repetitive thoughts, or a warping of the sense of time and place. *During seizures:* A limited clouding of consciousness occurs.

Sometimes the cause of a seizure disorder is known, and then the seizure disorder is termed *symptomatic*. Typical causes include head trauma, metabolic disorders, infection, toxins, and tumors. For example, approximately 20% of all patients who sustain a penetrating brain injury develop epilepsy. Seizure disorders with no known cause are called *idiopathic*. Individual seizure episodes can be triggered by a variety of stimuli, with the likely trigger varying from person to person. It often takes an affected individual some time to determine exactly what the exacerbating stimulus is. Once the trigger is identified, the individual will try to avoid the situation or stimulus that leads to a seizure. Stressful situations, especially those induced by sleep deprivation, can lead to seizure activity. In fact, so potent is sleep deprivation in bringing on seizure activity that neurologists will evaluate the likelihood of a diagnosis of epilepsy by recording an individual's EEG after he or she has gone without a night's sleep. Seizures may also be triggered by certain sensory stimuli, such as flashing lights; particular sounds; reading or laughing; certain classes of drugs, including alcohol; specific foods; and hormonal changes. For example, hormonal changes at puberty often cause a seizure (Kolb & Whishaw, 1990; Spreen, Tupper, Risser, Tuokko, & Edgell, 1984).

Epilepsy impairs cognitive and psychosocial functioning in about half of all cases (Binnie, 1994). Clearly, consciousness is disrupted during the seizure and this disruption impairs cognition, but *interictal* (i.e., between-seizure) consequences occur as well. Some neuropsychological deficits reflect dysfunction of the area from where the seizure originates, such as the memory problems and word-finding difficulties associated with temporal lobe seizures. Other difficulties are more generalized. These include poor sustained attention, compromised executive function, and lengthening of reaction time (for reviews, see Dodrill, 1992; Thompson & Trimble, 1996).

Epilepsy is sometimes associated with psychiatric disorders that occur postictally or chronically (Perrine & Kiobasa, 1999). Patients may show psychotic features similar to those observed in schizophrenia except that they retain interpersonal skills and appropriate emotional affect. Other commonly observed psychiatric symptoms are anxiety and depression. People with temporal lobe epilepsy may also exhibit an odd constellation of personality traits interictally. The characteristics of this syndrome are an interpersonal "stickiness," in which the person doesn't know when to disengage from interaction with someone else; empty, verbose, and pedantic speech; a preoccupation with religious concepts, though not usually of an organized nature; and excessive writing, such as excessive note-taking or writing in diaries. The existence of such a syndrome, however, is controversial (see Blumer, 1999; and Devinsky & Najjar, 1999, for differing viewpoints).

The two main forms of therapy for epilepsy are drug therapy and surgery. The first step in any treatment involves the administration of anticonvulsant medication, which reduces the likelihood of epileptic discharges. Three major classes of drugs are used. One class, which includes barbiturates (such as phenobarbital), mimics the neurotransmitter GABA or potentiates its transmission. GABA, as we learned in Chapter 2, is the main inhibitory neurotransmitter in the brain. Another class of anticonvulsants, which is known as *hydantoins* and includes phenytoin (Dilanin) and carbamazepine (Tegretol), acts to block the influx of sodium into the neuron, which reduces the ability of neurons to fire at high rates. More recent anti-epileptic drugs (such as lamotrigine) work by attenuating glutamate release, which, as you may remember from Chapter 2, is the main excitatory neurotransmitter in the brain (Julien, 2005; Ketter, Post, & Theodore, 1999). As with all other drugs, they can have side effects, such as excessive sedation, and when given in too large a dose can impair cognition (Nichols, Meador, & Loring, 1993). Therefore, drug administration must be *titrated*—that is, adjusted bit by bit—so that the physician can find the dosage that has the greatest efficacy against seizures with the fewest side effects on cognition (Bannister, 1992).

If the focal origin for the seizure is clear, the physician and the patient may opt for surgery to remove the source of the seizure activity, especially if it seems to be recruiting previously healthy areas. As discussed in the preceding section, focal seizures are most often localized to temporal and frontal areas. Especially when the focus is in the temporal areas, resection of epileptiform tissue may be associated with memory loss.

Researchers continue to search for new treatments, because medication is not effective for all patients, and because surgery is highly invasive and appropriate only for those with focal seizures. Currently, some research is exploring whether cell or gene therapies may be effective (Löscher, Gernert, & Heinemann, 2008). For example, transplantation of fetal tissue or genetically engineered cells into the hippocampus may be beneficial in reducing temporal lobe epilepsies. However, these avenues are still limited to investigations with animal models and have produced mixed success.

Brain and Cognitive Function in Vegetative States

When a patient suffers a very severe brain injury that results in a sustained loss of conscious awareness, family members face questions fraught with fear and anxiety: How can we tell what the patient is thinking and feeling? Is he or she able to think or feel anything at all? In this final section, we consider the level of mental function that may be possible when a severe brain injury leaves a patient in a persistent vegetative state. The topic is highly controversial, not only because of scientific and philosophical challenges in defining and measuring conscious awareness, but also because of the ethical implications for compassionate treatment at the end of life. (For thoughtful reviews, see Jennett, 2005; Laureys, 2005; Owen & Coleman, 2008; Zeman, 1997.)

Physicians must distinguish between several different disorders of consciousness that may follow a severe brain injury (Laureys, Owen, & Schiff, 2004). Generally, a *coma* is a condition in which the patient does not show any evidence of awareness or communication, does not open his eyes, and does not exhibit any kind of sleep-wake cycle. Comas typically last for a limited period of time (from a few days to a few months), and they typically resolve in one of two basic ways: the patient may die, or the patient may emerge from the coma and recover some level of functioning. For example, a patient may move from a coma into a vegetative state. In contrast to a coma, a **vegetative state** is a condition in which the patient shows no evidence of awareness or communication, but exhibits a sleep-wake cycle and has eyes open during the wakeful periods. Such patients may exhibit some simple behaviors, such as smiling, but these behaviors seem random, rather than elicited in response to external stimulation. In addition, the condition is marked by the absence of even the most basic form of communication. For example, if asked to blink twice to answer "yes" to a question, the patient will continue to stare blankly. Generally speaking, the vegetative state involves a patient who is deemed awake but unaware. If this state lasts more than one month, it is called a *persistent vegetative state (PVS)*. The chances of emerging from a PVS and regaining some level of conscious awareness are extremely low, but very rare cases of recovery have been reported (Kotchoubey, 2009; Zeman, 1997). A vegetative state must be distinguished from a **minimally conscious state**, in which there are intermittent signs of awareness and purposeful action, and from **locked-in syndrome**, in which cortical function and awareness are normal but a brainstem injury prevents almost all motor output. Locked-in patients are able to communicate using simple eye movements.

As you can probably appreciate, it can be very difficult for a clinician to assess a patient's level of awareness based on behavior alone. Distinguishing between the vegetative state and the minimally conscious state is particularly difficult, because the clinician must judge whether any emitted behaviors are simple reflexes being spontaneously performed, or whether they represent consciously aware and intentional actions. The diagnosis of a PVS is based on absence of evidence of awareness, and making decisions based on absence of evidence is always tricky from a logical standpoint because it assumes that the clinician hasn't missed anything in her observations. Furthermore, the distinction between PVS and minimally conscious states, while subtle and prone to misdiagnosis, can have serious ethical and legal implications.

In recent years, researchers have argued that functional brain imaging evidence may help doctors and families to better understand the patient's level of mental function (Owen & Coleman, 2008). Structural imaging findings have long been used to provide some clues; for example, if a patient's cerebral cortex is totally destroyed, it is safe to assume that little higher-level cognition is possible. Likewise, EEG can distinguish overall states of consciousness (e.g., coma vs. alertness, evidence of sleep-wake cycles). However, functional brain imaging has a unique ability to probe specific higher-level cognition functions in patients with disordered awareness.

One of the most dramatic fMRI studies suggested that a vegetative patient may have retained much more higher-level cognition than could have been inferred on the basis of her behavior alone (Owen, Coleman, Boly, Davis, Laureys, & Pickard, 2006). The patient, who was classified as being in a vegetative state, was instructed to perform mental imagery tasks that typically activate certain brain regions. For example, imagining a particular

motor sequence such as playing tennis activates the supplementary motor area, and imagining walking around one's house activates the parahippocampal gyrus and parietal cortex, which are important in spatial navigation. In a startling finding, the vegetative patient showed the same patterns of brain activity as did normal controls when asked to engage in such mental imagery tasks (● Figure 16.16). These findings imply that the patient understood the instructions and was able to imagine complex activities like playing tennis or walking around her house. Other studies have found that some (though not all) patients classified as being in vegetative states showed activation of language areas in response to linguistic stimuli (Coleman et al., 2007; Di et al., 2007; see also Schiff et al., 2005), or activation of the right fusiform gyrus in response to familiar faces (Menon et al., 1998).

These findings challenge the current system for classifying patients as "unaware" based on behavioral observations, and they have raised a host of additional questions. First, does fMRI activation in response to a task necessarily reflect "awareness"? Second, how representative are the few patients who have been studied? Do most vegetative patients show such evidence of higher-level cognition, or are those who have been studied unique in some way? Could fMRI evidence be used

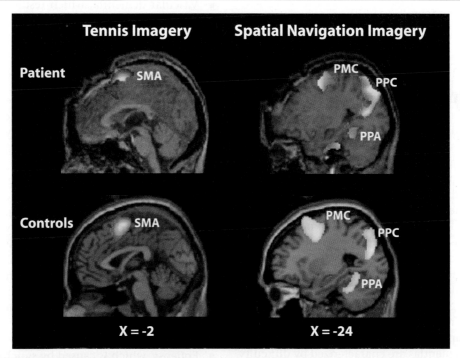

● **FIGURE 16.16   Brain activity indicates possibility of high-level cognition in vegetative states.** Participants were asked to imagine playing tennis or navigating through the rooms of their home. The brain activity generated by a patient in a vegetative state (top row) is highly similar to the pattern generated by neurologically normal people (bottom row). Thus, even though the patient is unable to show overt signs of awareness or intentional action in her behavior, she is able to generate some kinds of mental imagery on command. SMA = supplementary motor area; PMC = premotor cortex; PPC = posterior parietal cortex; PPA = parahippocampal place area. *Source:* Owen, A. M., Coleman, M. R., Boly, M., Davis, M. H., Laureys, S., & Pickard, J. D. (2006). Detecting awareness in the vegetative state. Science, 313, 1402. Reprinted with permission from AAAS.

to predict which patients have a better likelihood of emerging from a vegetative state (see Di et al., 2007)?

Perhaps most difficult are the ethical issues. If a patient is behaviorally unresponsive to stimulation, seeming to stare blankly for months at a time and failing to respond in any way to others, but her brain shows evidence that she can imagine activities of daily life like playing tennis, what efforts should be made to sustain her life? Vegetative patients typically are able to breathe on their own, so they do not need to be on respirators, but they do need to be given food and water if they are to survive. Thus, families are faced with wrenching decisions about end-of-life care, with limited ability to fully understand the mental states of their loved one. Indeed, this complex issue illustrates both the promise and the limitations of cognitive neuroscience methods in addressing challenging clinical issues of the relationships between brain activity and mental function.

Summary

Closed Head Injury

- Closed head injury, which occurs when the head hits or is hit by a blunt object, as happens in vehicular accidents, falls, and sport-related injuries, is generally associated with changes in consciousness.
- Acute consequences of head injury include difficulties in concentration, attentional problems, and posttraumatic amnesia; longer-term effects include difficulties with abstract thought, anxiety, depression, and anger.

Dementing Diseases

- Cortical dementias compromise a wide range of mental functions, including memory, language, spatial abilities, and object recognition.
- The main feature of Alzheimer's disease is prominent memory impairment, with compromise of other cognitive functions as well.
- Alzheimer's disease is associated with specific neuroanatomical changes: the presence of neurofibrillary tangles and amyloid plaques in brain tissue.
- There is evidence of both a genetic and an environmental contribution to Alzheimer's disease.
- Drug therapies designed to delay the effects of Alzheimer's disease concentrate on boosting the amount of acetylcholine in the nervous system.
- Frontotemporal dementia is characterized by difficulty with language and changes in personality.
- Creutzfeldt-Jakob disease, which leads to a fast decline in cognitive function, is caused by a prion that is easily transmissible, although symptoms typically do not appear until decades after exposure.
- Subcortical dementias are characterized by difficulty with tasks related to motor functioning, attention, and executive control, along with poor memory recall but intact recognition, and symptoms of depression.
- In Parkinson's disease, there is a general slowing of both motor functioning and thinking, dysfunction of executive processes, difficulty in memory retrieval, apathy, and depression.

- Therapies for Parkinson's disease are aimed at ameliorating the loss of dopamine.
- Huntington's disease is characterized by a constellation of cognitive disturbances in executive functioning, spatial processing, and retrieval of information from memory, along with emotional symptoms including depression, irritability, impulsivity, and aggression.
- Mixed-variety dementias have symptoms that are a blend of those seen in cortical and subcortical dementias.
- Vascular dementia, which results from the cumulative effect of many small strokes, has a variable profile of neuropsychological dysfunction depending on the brain regions affected.
- Individuals with AIDS dementia have difficulties with attention, problem solving, and memory, and may exhibit psychiatric symptoms. Mild neuropsychological dysfunction may occur in individuals who are infected with HIV but asymptomatic.

Demyelinating Diseases

- The most common demyelinating disease is multiple sclerosis (MS), which seems to be caused by a genetic vulnerability combined with exposure to an environmental pathogen, which is as yet undefined.
- Because the regions of brain tissue affected differ among individuals, some variability in the cognitive dysfunction is observed, although sensory and motor deficits, along with difficulties in memory, conceptual reasoning, and attention, are common.

Epilepsy

- Epilepsy, which is caused by synchronous and atypical firing of nerve cells, usually results from exposure to toxins, head injury, or metabolic disturbances.
- Cognitive deficits are usually seen in tasks dependent on the region from which the seizures originate. Sometimes changes in personality occur as well.
- Typically, epilepsy is treated by drugs that dampen down the activity of the nervous system; in more

severe cases, surgery is employed when the focus of the seizure can be clearly defined.

Vegetative States

- Severe brain injuries may result in persistent vegetative states, in which the patient is awake but seemingly unaware. Such conditions present difficult challenges for doctors and families.
- Brain imaging may yield important clues to the level of cognitive processing possible by persons in vegetative states.

Key Terms

acceleration-deceleration injury 468

Alzheimer's disease 472

amyloid plaques 476

bradyphrenia 484

closed head injury 468

contrecoup injury 469

coup injury 469

Creutzfeldt-Jakob disease (CJD) 481

dementia 471

dementia of the Alzheimer's type (DAT) 472

epileptic seizures 491

frontotemporal dementia 480

generalized (nonspecific) disorders 468

Glasgow Coma Scale (GCS) 469

locked-in syndrome 494

mild cognitive impairment 477

mild head injury 470

minimally conscious state 494

multiple sclerosis (MS) 489

neurofibrillary tangles 476

Parkinsonian mask 485

vascular dementia 487

vegetative state 494

Book Companion Site at www.cengage.com/psychology/Banich
This website provides instructors and students with a wealth of free information and resources, including tutorial quizzes, flashcards, and the glossary.

Glossary

acceleration-deceleration injury   Diffuse damage created by a rapid acceleration of the head followed by a deceleration, in which the energy imparted to the brain causes it to move within the skull; main mechanism of damage in closed head injury.

acetylcholine   Neurotransmitter; plays an important role in overall arousal and excitability.

acetylcholinesterase   Enzyme that divides the neurotransmitter acetylcholine into its two constituent parts, choline and acetate, thereby deactivating it.

action potential   Sequence of events occurring when a neuron fires: reversal of electrical charge to a peak of +40 mV (*depolarization*), retreat toward the baseline resting potential (*repolarization*), brief negative voltage (*hyperpolarization*), and return to resting potential.

action tremor   Staggered, jerky, and zigzag motion that occurs during the performance of an act, especially as the person zeroes in on a target.

activating-orienting model   Model of how perceptual asymmetries occur: Engaging in a particular type of process causes greater activation in the hemisphere best suited to the task, increasing its activity. This causes an attentional bias to the side of space contralateral to the more active hemisphere; thus, perceptual information on that side of space is more salient, allowing it to be processed better.

affective prosody   Emotional context or tone of an utterance.

agnosia   Modality-specific deficit in recognizing objects that occurs in the absence of major deficits in basic sensory processing.

agonists   Chemicals that mimic or facilitate the effect of a neurotransmitter on a target neuron.

agrammatic aphasia   Compromised ability to produce and comprehend the grammatical aspects of language; also called *anterior aphasia.*

agraphia   Loss of the ability to write, as a consequence of brain damage.

akinesia   Inability to initiate spontaneous movement.

alertness and arousal   The most basic levels of attention; conditions of responsiveness to the outside world.

alexia (acquired dyslexia)   Loss of the ability to read, as a consequence of brain damage.

alien limb syndrome   Rare disorder of motor function in which patients feel as if one of their limbs, usually a hand, does not belong them, either because it seems to move on its own, does not obey them, makes involuntary and complex movements, or seems to have its own personality.

allocentric reference frame   Category of reference frames that specify an object's location in relation to other objects, independent of one's own location.

alpha suppression   Decrease in the amount of electrical brain activity in the alpha band: Typically observed when individuals are involved in cognitive processing.

Alzheimer's disease   Type of dementia characterized by a decline in memory and many other aspects of cognitive function, including at least one of the following: language, visuospatial skills, abstract thinking, motor performance, and judgment. Emotional dysfunction and personality changes are also typically observed.

amino acids   Smallest and most basic building blocks of proteins; act as the main excitatory and inhibitory neurotransmitters in the brain.

amnesia   Loss of memory that is global with regard to modality and material; inability to form most new long-term memories.

amyloid plaques   Deposits consisting of aluminum silicate and amyloid peptides (a buildup or conglomeration of proteins), often including tau protein and apolipoprotein E; implicated in Alzheimer's disease and believed to cause vascular damage and neuronal cell loss.

anhedonia   Inability to find any pleasure in life; a characteristic of depression.

anoxia   Complete deprivation of oxygen for some period of time.

antagonists   Chemicals that oppose, block, or diminish the effect of a neurotransmitter on a target neuron.

anterior   Front; in front of.

anterior cingulate cortex   Brain region located above the corpus callosum and below the cingulate sulcus, extending as far back as the central fissure; resides mainly in Brodmann areas 24 and 32, but also has portions in BA 25 and 33. It has been implicated in aspects of attentional selection, motivation and emotion, and pain.

anterograde amnesia   Deficit in learning new information after the onset of an injury causing amnesia.

anterograde disorientation   Inability to construct new representations of environments, although patients are still able to navigate successfully around previously learned environments.

anxious apprehension   Nervous anticipation of something bad that could happen in the future; worry.

anxious arousal   State of bodily and cognitive hyperarousal characterized by physiological symptoms indicating activation of the sympathetic nervous system; panic.

apperceptive agnosia   Fundamental difficulty in forming a percept (a mental impression of something perceived by the senses); although sensory information is processed in a rudimentary way, the data cannot be bound together to allow the person to perceive a meaningful whole.

approach-withdrawal model   Theory based on basic and rudimentary actions that organisms take in responding adaptively to the environment. Proposes that the left frontal region houses a system involved in approach behaviors and associated with (mostly positive) emotions that accompany approach behaviors; the right frontal region is posited to house a system involved in withdrawal behaviors and associated with (mostly negative) emotions that accompany withdrawal behaviors.

apraxia   Inability to link skilled motor movement to ideas or representations; inability to perform skilled, sequential, purposeful movement that cannot be accounted for by disruptions in more basic motor processes such as muscle weakness, abnormal posture or tone, or movement disorders; most common after damage to the left hemisphere.

aprosodia   Impairment or deficits in comprehension of prosody, resulting from brain damage.

aprosodic   All at one pitch or lacking a varied intonation pattern; description of the type of speech deficit observed after damage to anterior regions of the right hemisphere.

area MT   Brain region crucial to the ability to perceive and represent motion; also known as area V5.

association area   Area of the brain where information from multiple modalities is processed.

associative agnosia   Disorder in which basic visual information can be integrated to form a meaningful perceptual whole, yet that particular perceptual whole cannot be linked to stored knowledge about the objective.

athetosis   Type of hyperkinesia characterized by involuntary writhing contractions and twisting of the body into abnormal postures.

attention   Selective process by which specific information is chosen for further processing; necessary because the brain can only process a limited amount of information at any one time.

attention-deficit hyperactivity disorder (ADHD)   Developmental disorder in which the affected child is either inattentive, hyperactive/impulsive, or both compared to the average child of the same age.

attentional dyslexia Syndrome in which the person can recognize a single letter or word in isolation but cannot recognize the same letter or word if it is presented along with items of the same kind.

attentional set Attentional process that designates which information is relevant to the current task at hand.

auditory agnosia Inability to recognize the meaning of sounds, even though other cognitive functions are normal.

auditory-verbal working memory Phonological store; a short-term buffer for verbal information in the auditory modality (e.g., speech sounds).

autism Pervasive developmental disorder associated with IQs that are significantly below average and profound cognitive, emotional, and social deficits.

autoreceptors Receptors located on the presynaptic neuron that bind the same neurotransmitter as released by that neuron; regulate the responsiveness of cells by working as a negative feedback mechanism.

axon Major structure of the neuron, along which information is carried from the cell body to the synaptic cleft.

axon hillock Part of the neuron near the cell body where post-synaptic potentials are summated and the action potential is first produced.

barbiturates Class of CNS depressants, derived from barbituric acid, that reduce the activity of the CNS by binding to GABA receptors.

basal ganglia Complex collection of subcortical nuclei located near the thalamus, consisting of the caudate nucleus, putamen, and nucleus accumbens (known collectively as the *striatum*); the globus pallidus (or *pallidum*); the substantia nigra; and the subthalamic nucleus. Important in motor control.

belt Region of auditory cortex that surrounds (and receives most of its input from) the core; also receives some direct input from the medial geniculate.

benzodiazepines Tranquilizing drugs that act by binding to GABA receptors.

bilateral Both sides; two-sided.

binocular disparity Discrepancy between the images seen by the two eyes; arises because the image that falls on each retina is slightly different, since the eyes are positioned in different locations. Acts as a cue for depth perception.

binocular rivalry Oscillation of conscious perception of a visual scene or object that occurs when different stimuli are presented simultaneously to the left eye and the right eye.

bipolar disorder Disorder in which depression is interspersed between periods of mania, or mania alone; formerly called *manic-depressive illness*.

blind spot Area in the retina where there are no photoreceptors; the point at which all the ganglion cell fibers are gathered together in a bundle to exit the eye as the optic nerve.

blindsight Retention of some visual capabilities after damage to cortical visual areas without the conscious experience of seeing; is thought to be supported by the functioning of intact subcortical brain regions.

blood-brain barrier Mechanism by which substances are prevented from reaching the brain; consists of tightly packed glial cells between blood vessels and neurons, which create a physical obstruction that keeps materials in the bloodstream from directly reaching the nervous system.

bottom-up attentional selection Mechanisms by which some intrinsic aspect of the stimulus itself, such as its brightness or emotional significance, causes it to be attended or to receive priority in processing.

bradykinesia Slowness of movement; one of the motor symptoms often observed in individuals with Parkinson's disease.

bradyphrenia Slowing of thought processes; part of the cognitive compromise exhibited by individuals with Parkinson's disease.

Broca's aphasia Syndrome in which a lesion to a specific region of the left hemisphere causes a loss of fluent speech even though the person's speech comprehension is relatively spared.

Brodmann map Map (named after its creator) that divides the brain into distinct areas based on similarities in the laminar organization and nature of cells.

calcification Accumulation of calcium; often accompanies transneuronal degeneration.

callosal apraxia Disconnection syndrome that selectively disrupts the ability to perform movements or manipulate objects with the left hand in response to verbal commands; associated with damage to the corpus callosum.

callosal relay model Model explaining the origin of perceptual asymmetries: concept that information received by the hemisphere less adept at a given task is transferred to the opposite hemisphere via the corpus callosum; this callosal transfer degrades the information and leads to poorer performance than if the information were received directly by the hemisphere more suited to the task.

caloric stimulation Neglect-reducing technique in which water at least 7°C colder than body temperature is introduced into the ear canal, thereby inducing motion in the semicircular canals of the vestibular system and drawing attention to the neglected field or side of the body.

catecholamines Monoamine neurotransmitters (dopamine and noradrenaline) derived from the amino acid tyrosine.

categorical spatial relations Schema that specifies the position of one location relative to another in dichotomous categorical terms, such as above versus below; may be specialized to the left hemisphere.

category-specific deficit Inability to recognize or identify a certain category of objects even though the ability to recognize other categories of items in that same modality is retained.

caudal Toward the back (in an animal, toward the tail).

caudate nucleus Part of the basal ganglia.

cell body Part of the cell containing the nucleus and other cellular apparatus responsible for manufacturing the proteins and enzymes that sustain cell functioning.

center-surround receptive field Receptive-field structure of retinal ganglion cells and LGN cells; light stimulation in the center (or surround) excites cell firing, whereas light stimulation in the surround (or center) inhibits cell firing; helps to enhance contrast.

central executive Theoretical construct in working memory; performs the mental work of (1) controlling slave subsystems that mediate the storage process and (2) forming strategies for using the information the subsystems contain.

central fissure Split or chasm that separates each hemisphere of the brain in an anterior-posterior dimension; sometimes called the *Rolandic fissure*.

central nervous system (CNS) Body system encompassing the brain and the spinal cord.

cerebellar ataxia Difficulty in the coordination of movement that is observed after cerebellar damage.

cerebellum Region at the back of the brain, located posterior to the medulla, that plays a major role in motor control through the regulation of muscle tone and guidance of motor activity; especially important in the coordination of muscle movement timing, the planning of movements, and the learning of motor skills.

cerebral dominance Concept that one hemisphere dominates or leads mental function.

cerebral hemisphere One of two physically separated halves of the cortex.

cerebral palsy Umbrella term for many motor disorders resulting from nonprogressive damage to neural structures important for motor control.

cerebrospinal fluid (CSF) Fluid found between neurons and their bony encasements; similar in composition to blood plasma.

chorea Type of hyperkinesia that produces uncontrollable, jerky movements such as twitching and abrupt jerking of the body.

cingulotomy Surgical creation of bilateral lesions in the anterior cingulate.

closed head injury Brain damage sustained when the head forcefully contacts another object, such as occurs in falls and motor vehicle accidents, but no object penetrates the brain.

coarticulation Differences in how the vocal muscles produce sounds (most notably vowels) depending on what precedes or follows them; phenomenon suggestive of motor planning.

cochlea Spiral-shaped inner-ear structure containing the hair cells that translate sound energy into neural impulses; has a set of membranes that move in relation to one another when sound waves enter the ear.

cochlear nucleus   Area in the medulla where the auditory nerve synapses.

cognitive control   Process of guiding or controlling one's thoughts, actions or emotions. *See also* executive functions.

cognitive neuroscience   Field of study comprised of investigations of all mental functions that are linked to neural processes.

cogwheel rigidity   Symptom of Parkinson's disease that causes limbs to move in specific, rigid steps, rather than moving smoothly; occurs because of increased muscle tone in the extensor and flexor muscles.

coincidence detectors   Cells in brainstem areas that take into account the different arrival times of a sound at the left and right ears; maximally stimulated when the signals from the right and left ears arrive at the cell simultaneously; codes for spatial location of the sound.

coma   State in which a person is unresponsive to and unaware of the outside world.

compensation (neural)   Recruitment of additional brain regions to support performance that was previously performed by a damaged region.

compensatory rehabilitation   Therapy for brain-damaged patients that aims to provide alternative strategies to achieve a particular goal, such as training individuals with memory deficits to write information down for future reference.

complex cells   Type of striate cortex cells; respond best to certain line orientations and motion in a particular direction.

components   Characteristic portions of an electrical waveform recorded from the brain that have been linked to certain psychological processes.

computational models   Computer models, often called neural networks, that simulate human mental functions; the basic component of most computational models is a "unit," which exhibits behavior like an individual neuron.

computerized axial tomography (CAT, CT)   Process that uses X-rays to determine density of brain structures; in a CAT scan, dense tissue appears white and material with the least density appears black.

conduction aphasia   Disconnection syndrome characterized by inability to repeat what was just heard, although language comprehension and speech production are intact; caused by damage that severs the connection between Broca's and Wernicke's areas.

connectionist networks   Computational model composed of interconnected layers of units that exhibit neuron-like behavior.

consolidation   *See* memory consolidation.

constructional apraxia   Disorder which disrupts the ability to correctly manipulate items with regard to their spatial relationships; generally observed after right-hemisphere lesion and often associated with spatial-processing difficulties and hemineglect.

constructional praxis   Ability to motorically produce or manipulate items so that they have a particular spatial relationship.

contention scheduling   One component of a two-component system that influences the choice of behavior; a cognitive system that enables relatively automatic processing, which has been developed over time through learning.

contextual fear conditioning   Conditioning in which a fear response is evoked by a previously neutral context or environment due to its repeated association with an aversive stimulus.

contextual modulation   Process by which cell responsiveness is modified by surrounding context; although information outside a cell's receptive field cannot by itself cause the cell to fire, such information can change the cell's response when presented together with the cell's favored stimulus.

contralateral   On the opposite side.

contrecoup (countercoup) injury   Focal damage opposite the site of impact.

core   Area of auditory cortex that receives input from the medial geniculate nucleus; subdivided into areas A1 (primary auditory cortex) and regions anterior to A1, referred to as the rostral and rostrotemporal fields.

corollary discharge   Signal to sensory areas about upcoming motor movements, sent by motor-planning regions of the brain; helps the brain to distinguish between changes in incoming sensory information that result from motor movements initiated by the animal (e.g., such as eye movements) as opposed to movement of objects and entities in the outside world.

coronal view   Planar view of the brain in which the brain is sliced ear-to-ear to separate the front from the back.

corpus callosum   Massive tract of more than 250 million nerve fibers that connects the cerebral hemispheres.

cortical blindness   Blindness caused by damage to primary visual cortex rather than by a problem in the eye or optic nerve.

cortical magnification factor   Describes the millimeters of cortical surface that are devoted to one degree of angle in the visual world.

coup injury   Focal damage at the site of impact.

cranial nerves   Twelve major nerves originating in the brain; some are responsible for receipt of sensory information and motor control of the head, others are responsible for the neural control of internal organs.

Creutzfeldt-Jakob disease (CJD)   Rare cortical dementia with rapid mental deterioration (also known as *spongiform encephalopathy*); caused by transmissible protein agents known as *prions* that result in widespread neuronal loss and a proliferation of glial cells.

crossed aphasia   Loss of speech ability (aphasia) resulting from a right-hemisphere lesion in a right-handed individual.

cross-modal plasticity   Brain reorganization in which cortex normally devoted to one sensory modality becomes able to respond to information supplied in another modality; may occur when a person loses input from an entire sensory modality.

crowding hypothesis   Theory regarding the phenomenon of later-emerging deficits following brain damage early in life; posits that the intact brain tissue takes on too many functions (by picking up the load of the damaged areas) to allow normal or optimal development of all functions.

cued recall   Memory test in which the person is given prompts to help him or her remember information that was previously encoded. An example of cued recall would be a test paradigm in which an individual is read a list of words to remember and then, 30 minutes later, is told, "Report all the words from the study list that were examples of buildings or that began with the letter 'b.'"

customized neuropsychological assessment   Evaluation in which the examiner initially uses information from a small set of tests to generate hypotheses about the abilities that were compromised by the brain damage. Each hypothesis is then evaluated with a specific neuropsychological test, and, depending on the patient's performance, the hypothesis is either pursued further with another test or abandoned.

declarative memory system   Memory system, supported by the hippocampus, that allows particular information to be used flexibly in contexts not linked to the situation in which the information was acquired.

decomposition of movement   Strategy of moving one joint at a time in a serial manner to accomplish movement; used when multijoint coordination breaks down, as is often observed after damage to the cerebellum.

dedifferentiation   Theory that the neural localization of function becomes less defined with age.

deep brain stimulation (DBS)   Treatment in which electrodes are implanted deep within the brain to administer electrical current that modulates activity in the targeted brain region; has been used for Parkinson's disease and severe depression.

deep cerebellar nuclei   Nuclei within the cerebellum, each of which serves to form a distinct loop with other cortical and subcortical regions that modulate motor control; the fastigial nucleus, interpositus nucleus, and dentate nucleus.

deep dyslexia (alexia)   Syndrome in which affected individuals show many of the deficits exhibited in phonological alexia (such as inability to read nonwords), and also show additional difficulties such as semantic paralexias, problems with reading abstract words, and trouble with reading small function words that serve as grammatical markers; thought to be the represent right-hemisphere reading.

delay lines   Part of a brainstem system that assists in computing spatial location based on inter-aural time differences; signals representing incoming sounds travel along the delay lines, with activity in the cells along the delay line representing different offsets of time between when a sound arrived at the left and right ears.

delayed nonmatch-to-sample task   Test in which an animal is exposed to one of a large set of objects and, following a delay, is presented again with the object just viewed, together with another from the set of available objects; to receive a reward, the animal must select the object that was not previously presented. Reveals dissociation between long-term-memory deficit and fully functional working memory.

dementia   Debilitating syndrome involving a progressive loss of cognitive functions that interferes significantly with work or social activities; sometimes accompanied by personality changes.

dementia of the Alzheimer's type (DAT)   *See* Alzheimer's disease.

dendritic tree   Part of the neuron that receives input from other cells.

dentate nucleus   Deep cerebellar nucleus to which the lateral zone projects.

developmental (congenital) prosopagnosia   Condition of being "face-blind" from birth, without any known brain damage.

developmental milestones   Changes during childhood that occur in an orderly fashion and at a particular age; include behavioral changes, acquisition of cognitive and motoric skills, and acquisition of other specific abilities.

dichaptic presentation   Method applied to investigate hemispheric differences in the somatosensory (touch) modality; the test subject (typically blindfolded) is asked to feel two items simultaneously, one in each hand, and then to identify these items in some manner.

dichotic presentation   Method for examining hemispheric differences in the auditory modality; different information is presented simultaneously to each ear so that each hemisphere receives two competing pieces of information, one from the ipsilateral ear and one from the contralateral ear. Under these conditions, a hemisphere mainly processes information from the contralateral ear.

diencephalon   Brain structure that contains the thalamus and hypothalamus.

diffusion tensor imaging (DTI)   Anatomical MRI method that can provide information not only about the structural integrity of white matter, but also about the anatomical connectivity between different brain regions via white matter tracts.

digit span task   Test in which a person must report back a sequence of digits read one at a time by the experimenter; reveals the person's working-memory span.

dipole   Small region of electrical current with a relatively positive end and a relatively negative end; the signal that is recorded in event-related potentials (EEG).

direct access theory   Concept asserting that the hemisphere receiving sensory information processes it; when information is received by the hemisphere less suited to a task, performance is poorer than if the information is received by the hemisphere better suited to the task.

direct (lexical) route to reading   Method of reading in which print is directly associated with meaning, without the use of a phonological intermediary.

disconnection syndrome   Behavioral deficit that occurs when information carried by fibers of passage cannot be transmitted from one brain region to another.

distal   Far.

disturbances of posture   Symptoms of Parkinson's disease that affect muscle groups throughout the body, causing difficulty in body position and locomotion, especially in movements that require postural adjustments or transitions.

divided attention   Distribution of attention when it must be split across two or more tasks.

divided visual field technique   Technique to investigate hemispheric differences in processing. Information is separately in each visual field for a brief amount of time while an individual maintains fixation. Under such conditions, information in the right visual field projects exclusively to the primary visual cortex of the left hemisphere and information presented in the left visual field projects exclusively to the primary visual cortex of the right hemisphere. Faster reaction time or higher accuracy in one visual field is taken to index superiority of the contralateral hemisphere for that task.

dopamine   Monoamine neurotransmitter (a catecholamine). Dopaminergic pathways have been implicated in motor control, reward processing and executive function.

dorsal   Above or superior (in a four-legged animal, toward the animal's back).

dot probe task   Test in which the participant has to indicate the presence of a dot flashed on a screen; the dot is preceded by a pair of words, one of which is emotionally threatening. Faster response to the dot when it appears in the location of the threatening word, compared to the neutral word, demonstrates attentional bias to threatening information.

double dissociation   Pattern of performance across brain-damaged individuals in which damage to a given brain region leads to a deficit for a particular cognitive function while sparing another, whereas damage to a different brain region leads to the opposite outcome: a deficit for the latter function but not the former. Such a pattern suggests that these two cognitive functions can be independent of one another.

double filtering by frequency theory   Theory regarding hemispheric differences in information processing. Posits that after task-relevant information has been identified, filtering causes information of relatively higher spatial frequency to be preferentially processed by the left hemisphere and information of relatively lower spatial frequency to be processed by the right hemisphere.

double simultaneous stimulation   Condition in which identical stimuli are presented at the same time in both visual fields.

Down syndrome   Genetic disorder associated with severe retardation and characterized by a specific morphology of the body and face; caused by trisomy 21, a condition in which the 21st pair of chromosomes contains three chromosomes rather than the usual two.

dressing apraxia   Disorder in which the affected person has difficulty manipulating and orienting both clothes and his or her limbs so that clothes can be put on correctly; generally observed after right-hemisphere lesion and often associated with spatial-processing difficulties and hemineglect.

dysarthria   Difficulty in speech output that is observed after cerebellar damage; characterized by slurred speech with sometime explosive variations in voice intensity.

dyslexia   Also called *specific reading disability;* a specific inability to learn to read at an age-appropriate level, despite adequate opportunity, training, and intelligence.

dysprosodic   With disordered intonation; type of speech deficit exhibited after damage to the left hemisphere.

dysthymia   Mild state of chronic depression lasting at least two years.

early-selection viewpoint   Theory regarding the time frame of attentional selection with regards to incoming stimuli; suggests that attentional selection occurs at an early stage of processing, before items are identified.

echolalia   Compulsive repetition of a sound or word.

edema   Swelling of tissue after trauma.

egocentric disorientation   Inability to represent the location of objects in relationship to the self; associated with damage to the posterior parietal region, either bilaterally or unilaterally in the right hemisphere.

egocentric reference frame   Category of reference frames that specify an object's location in relation to some aspect of the self.

electrical potential   Summed or superimposed signal of the postsynaptic electrical fields of similarly aligned neuronal dendrites, recorded at the scalp as a waveform; has a particular voltage and frequency.

electroencephalography (EEG)   Recordings of the brain's electrical activity; used clinically to detect aberrant activity, and used experimentally to detect psychological states associated with particular patterns of electrical activity.

elimination of synapses   Pruning of neuronal connections during which the number of connections between neurons is reduced; a process that occurs during normal development but which occurs at different ages for different brain regions.

emotion regulation   General term for the process by which a person attempts to manage the emotions that one experiences, so that they are socially appropriate and do not spiral out of control.

emotional Stroop task   Cognitive test in which the participant must identify the ink color of either emotionally threatening words or non-emotional words; slower color identification of threatening words than non-emotional words demonstrates attentional bias to threatening information.

endogenous components Components of event-related potentials (ERPs) that appear to be driven by internal cognitive states, independent of stimulus characteristics; typically occur later in the waveform.

environmental dependency syndrome Disorder in which behavior is triggered by stimuli in the environment; involves automatic invocation of contention scheduling schemes because the supervisory attentional system has been lost; most often observed after frontal lobe lesions.

enzymatic deactivation Process in which an enzyme cleaves transmitter molecules so they become incapable of binding to the receptor.

enzyme Any molecule that controls a chemical reaction, either by binding together two substances or by cleaving a substance into parts.

epileptic seizures Episodes in which synchronous activity of nerve cells increases so that a gigantic hyperpolarization of neurons spreads over a large area in an atypical and abnormal manner; during a seizure, neurons in the brain fire in an abnormal manner typified by great bursts or volleys, often called *spikes*. May be generalized or partial.

episodic memory Autobiographical memories that are specific to one's experience of a particular episode; includes context about the time, space, and emotion associated with that event.

error positivity (Pe) ERP signal that is thought to indicate awareness of an error; typically follows the error-related negativity (ERN) by about 200–300 ms.

error-related negativity (ERN) ERP signal that occurs approximately 100 ms after an individual makes a response that is likely to be evaluated as being incorrect or suboptimal.

estimate of premorbid functioning A reasonable guess as to how well a person was performing before an injury.

event-related potentials (ERPs) Recordings of brain activity that is time-locked to the occurrence of an event; derived from scalp-recorded EEG.

excitatory postsynaptic potential (EPSP) Makes a cell's electrical charge slightly more positive by reducing the difference in electrical charge between the inside and the outside of the cell; this reduction brings the differential closer to the threshold value of −55 mV at which the cell will fire.

excitotoxicity Excessive activity of receptors that can kill neurons by overstimulation (excite neurons to death).

executive functions Abilities to plan actions to reach a goal, to use information flexibly, to think abstractly, and to make inferences (among other capabilities). *See also* cognitive control.

exogenous components Components linked to the physical characteristics of a stimulus; usually occur early in the waveform.

experience-dependent systems Neural systems that vary across people and are based on the individuals' personal, unique experiences, such as those that support musical training.

experience-expectant systems Neural systems that respond to experiences universally present in normal development, relying upon external information essential for development but not specified in the genetic blueprint, such as language input.

explicit memory system Memory system that permits the conscious recollection of prior experiences and facts; lost in amnesia.

extended digit span Test in which the same digit string is presented on each trial but with an additional digit added to extend the span; requires use of long-term storage in addition to working memory.

extinction In fear conditioning paradigms, process by which acquired fears are later lost through the de-coupling of the neutral stimulus from the stimulus that elicits fear.

extrastriate body area Neural module in the ventral visual-processing stream (located in Brodmann area 18 in the occipitotemporal cortex); responds preferentially to human bodies and body parts.

fastigial nucleus Deep cerebellar nucleus to which the vermis projects.

fear conditioning Method in which a formerly neutral stimulus comes to invoke fear because it is paired with an aversive event.

fetal alcohol syndrome (FAS) Preventable mental-retardation disorder caused by the mother's alcohol abuse during pregnancy; results in hyperactivity, poor attention span, social and emotional difficulties, difficulties in learning and memory, executive dysfunction, slowed physical growth, and abnormalities of the face and cranium.

fiber tract Group of axons from different neurons that project to the same brain structure.

figure-ground separation Visual process by which an object is distinguished from its background or surroundings.

fissure Deep valley between brain convolutions or gyri.

flocculus Brain structure that constitutes part of the vestibulocerebellum.

forward model A model that predicts the sensory consequences of motor plans; the cerebellum is thought to be involved in creating such a model.

fovea Region in the center of the retina where cones are packed more densely; it provides for the highest degree of visual acuity.

fragile X syndrome Inherited form of mental retardation in which a person's X chromosome has a section where a normally repeating sequence of genetic material occurs an unusually large number of times; reduces production of a protein called FMRP (fragile X mental retardation protein).

frames of reference Sets of spatial coordinates that are linked to a particular reference point; for example, a frame of reference might be linked to the location of the head, the focus of gaze, or the position of the body.

free recall Memory test in which a person is asked to recall previously encoded information without any cues or prompts.

frontal eye field (FEF) Portion of dorsal premotor region that controls the voluntary execution of eye movements.

frontal lobe Brain area in front of the central fissure.

frontotemporal dementia Type of cortical dementia characterized by degeneration of frontal and temporal regions; characterized by social-emotional dysfunction, with difficulty in modulating behavior; impulsivity and lack of inhibition; lack of concern for social norms and personal appearance; inappropriate sexual behaviors; and a preoccupation with repetitive or routinized behavior. Mood disorders and language/speech difficulties are also common, though other mental functions (e.g., spatial processing) remain intact.

functional connectivity Communication or synchronization of activity between brain regions that allows the regions to work together in service of a task.

functional magnetic resonance imaging (fMRI) MRI technique that measures changes in brain physiology (or function) as a result of engaging in a particular cognitive task or emotional process; method most commonly used by cognitive neuroscientists to discern which areas of the brain are physiologically active in response to a cognitive or emotional process.

fusiform body area Brain region located in the fusiform gyrus (within the ventral visual-processing stream) that responds preferentially to human bodies and body parts.

fusiform face area (FFA) Brain region located in the fusiform gyrus (within the ventral visual-processing stream) that exhibits a greater response to faces than to other objects.

G protein Guanyl nucleotide-binding protein; works with neurotransmitter to control ion channels in the neuron and hence to control neuronal responding.

GABA Gamma-aminobutyric acid; an amino acid that acts as an inhibitory neurotransmitter in the central nervous system.

ganglion cells The retina's output layer of cells, whose axons form the optic nerve running between the retina and the brain.

gene-environment interactions Situations in which a combination of specific environmental and genetic factors are necessary to bring about a certain result or behavior.

generalized anxiety disorder Free-floating, chronic experience of anxiety that is not tied to any specific triggering event or object.

generalized (nonspecific) disorders Clinical syndromes, including Alzheimer's disease, in which the breakdown of function is not restricted to one cognitive or emotional domain, but rather simultaneously affects multiple cognitive (and emotional) processes.

geniculostriate pathway Neural pathway from the lateral geniculate nucleus of the thalamus (LGN) to visual cortex; enables the conscious experience of seeing.

Glasgow Coma Scale (GCS) Tool for assessing level of consciousness, which evaluates three realms of functioning: visual responsiveness, motor capabilities, and verbal responsiveness;

widely used in emergency rooms to classify the severity of damage in someone who has just sustained a head injury.

glia Cells of the nervous system that serve as support cells; although they do not convey information like neurons, they can nonetheless influence neuronal transmission; in addition, they are involved in processes that occur in response to brain damage.

gliosis Process of phagocytosis (that removes cellular debris) and capillary formation that occurs after insult to the nervous system, which continues until only glial cells remain.

global aphasia Inability to comprehend or produce language; associated with extensive left-hemisphere damage that typically includes both Wernicke's and Broca's areas and the area between them.

globus pallidus Portion of the basal ganglia; most of the output from the basal ganglia occurs via the globus pallidus.

glutamate Amino acid that acts as the main excitatory neurotransmitter in the central nervous system.

Go/No-Go task Test in which participants respond by pushing a button when certain visual stimuli appear (Go trials) and withholding response to other stimuli (No-Go); measures response inhibition.

gradient field Magnetic field that varies in intensity over the area being imaged in an MRI; provides a way to identify the location from which signals are emanating.

grandmother cell theory Theory that there is a particular cell in the ventral processing stream whose job is to fire when you see a particular object or person (such as your grandmother).

grapheme-to-phoneme correspondence rules Rules whereby print is associated with sound.

group studies Research method in which patients with brain damage who have similar characteristics (e.g., lesions in similar areas) are studied as a group.

gyrus Convolution, or bump, of the brain formed by a giant sheath of neurons wrapped around other brain structures (plural: *gyri*).

habit learning Category of skill learning; gradual and incremental learning of specific items, actions or processes that may not necessarily generalize to new exemplars of those items, actions or processes.

hair cells Cells in the inner ear that have tiny hairs called *cilia* sticking out of them; movement of the cilia in response to sound vibrations ultimately causes the cell to emit action potentials. The axons of the hair cells synapse on spiral ganglion cells, which make up the auditory nerve.

hemi-extinction Condition occurring as a result of brain damage that causes information on one side of space to be extinguished from consciousness (neglected) when two pieces of information are presented simultaneously, one on each side of space.

hemi-inattention Term synonymous with hemineglect; syndrome in which patients ignore, or do not pay attention to, information on one side of space (usually the left), and act as if that side of the world does not exist, despite having intact sensory and motor functioning.

hemineglect Term synonymous with hemi-inattention; syndrome in which patients ignore, or do not pay attention to, information on one side of space (usually the left), and act as if that side of the world does not exist, despite having intact sensory and motor functioning.

hemiplegia Paralysis of the side of the body contralateral to the site of brain damage.

hemispherectomy Procedure in which a malformed hemisphere is removed, typically at birth in order to prevent debilitating seizures.

hemispheric specialization Differences in processing between the left and right hemispheres of the brain.

Heschl's gyrus Superior portion of the posterior temporal lobe where the human primary auditory cortex is located.

higher-order thinking Set of abilities involving complicated aspects of thought, such as being able to think in an abstract and conceptual rather than concrete manner, the ability to deduce rules or regularity, and the ability to be flexible and respond to novelty.

hippocampal system A series of related structures located at the midline of the temporal lobe that include the hippocampus; Damage to this region may result in amnesia or other memory-related disorders.

homonymous hemianopsia Condition in which the entire occipital cortex of one hemisphere is damaged, so that no visual information can be detected in the contralateral visual field.

horizontal view Planar view of the brain in which the brain is sliced so that the top of the brain is separated from the bottom; also called *axial* or *transverse*.

human neuropsychology Field of study that emphasizes examination of the changes in behavior as a result of brain trauma to understand mental processes in humans.

Huntington's disease Inherited neurologic disease caused by degeneration of the striatum; produces abnormal movements, cognitive deficits (eventually dementia), and psychiatric symptoms.

hyper-complex cells Type of striate cortex cells that fire most strongly in response to lines of certain lengths.

hyperkinesias Involuntary, undesired movements.

hypofrontality Hypoactivation (reduced activation) of frontal regions, often observed in people with schizophrenia.

hypothalamus Brain area controlling behaviors that help the body maintain equilibrium including the control of eating, drinking, fleeing and fighting.

hypoxia Reduced oxygen availability.

ideational apraxia Also called *conceptual apraxia;* impairment of the ability to form an "idea" of a movement, so that a person cannot determine which actions are necessary and in what order they should occur.

ideomotor apraxia Disconnection between the idea of a movement and execution of the movement.

implicit memory system Memory system that allows prior experience to affect behavior without conscious retrieval or awareness of the memory.

indolamine Monoamine neurotransmitter (serotonin) derived from the amino acid tryptophan.

inference Ability to "fill in the blanks" and make assumptions about material that is not explicitly stated (implied material).

inferior Bottom; underneath; below.

inferior colliculus One of two dorsal midbrain structures; acts as a relay point for auditory information and contributes to reflexive movements of the head and eyes in response to sound.

inhibitory postsynaptic potential (IPSP) Electrical potential on the postsynaptic side of the synapse that makes the inside of a cell slightly more negative than the outside, thus moving the cell farther away from the threshold at which it will fire.

input phonological buffer Buffer that holds on line auditory-verbal information received by the listener online while an utterance is being parsed.

intention tremor *See* action tremor.

interaural intensity difference Difference in the intensity of sound reaching each ear; one of the cues that the brain uses to deduce the spatial location of a sound source.

interaural time difference Difference in the time at which sound reaches each ear; from this information; one of the cues that the brain uses to deduces the spatial location of a sound source.

interference resolution Ability to resolve conflict between competing information or distracting information that might interfere with performing a task.

intermediate zone Region of the cerebellar hemisphere that projects to the interpositus nucleus.

interoception Ability to perceive the internal state of the body.

interpositus nucleus Deep cerebellar nucleus to which the intermediate zone projects.

intralaminar nucleus (of the thalamus) Portion of the thalamus specifically implicated in the functions of alertness and wakefulness; acts by modulating the level of arousal of the cortex.

inverse model Model of motor actions that describes what motor commands are required to reach each point along a trajectory of a desired sensory outcome.

inversion effect Phenomenon in which recognition (particularly of faces) is poorer when an object is turned upside down; thought to reflect the disruption to which recognition of the object relies on configural relationships.

ionotropic receptors Receptors that work directly to either open or close an ion channel.

ipsilateral On the same side.

irregular words Words that do not follow grapheme-to-phoneme correspondence rules and so are impossible to sound out correctly, such as "colonel."

ischemia Form of brain damage in which neurons die due to a lack of oxygen, most typically after blockage of a blood vessel in the brain.

Kennard principle Theory that the earlier in life brain damage is sustained, the better the recovery.

landmark agnosia Object recognition deficit in which patients lose the ability to recognize certain landmarks that are usually used for navigation.

lateral Toward the outside (of the brain).

lateral corticospinal tract One of two major sets of pathways that link the brain to muscle. This tract, whose cell bodies are located mainly in primary motor cortex, crosses entirely from one side of the brain to the opposite side of the body in the medulla; thus, damage to this tract results in profound deficits in motor movement on the opposite side of the body, including the ability to reach, grasp, and manipulate objects.

lateral geniculate nucleus (LGN) Complex layered structure in the thalamus that receives visual information from the retina and sends information on to the striate cortex.

lateral zone Region of the cerebellar hemisphere that projects to the dentate nucleus.

lateralization of function *See* hemispheric specialization.

late-selection viewpoint Theory suggesting that attentional selection occurs only after sensory processing is complete and items have been identified and categorized.

L-dopa Metabolic precursor of dopamine; when taken orally, can reach the brain and stimulate pre- and postsynaptic dopaminergic receptors.

learning disability Difficulty during childhood in acquiring cognitive skills in only one particular domain.

left visual field Area/information to the left of the fixation point of gaze.

lesion method Method of determining which regions of the brain are important for a given mental function: If damage to a particular brain region results in an inability to perform a specific mental function, scientists usually assume that the function must have depended on that brain region.

letter-by-letter reading Syndrome in which individual letters can be identified, but cannot be integrated to form a word; patients may say each letter aloud and then use the sound information to deduce the word. Also called *spelling dyslexia* or *pure alexia.*

lexical agraphia Syndrome in which the person can produce reasonable spelling, both manually and orally, for regular words or nonwords, but cannot spell irregular words.

limb apraxia Disruption of the ability to use the limbs to manipulate items, to perform a complex series of movements, and/or to use motor movements in a symbolic or gestural way; usually produced by damage to left parietal or parietotemporal regions.

limbic system Series of subcortical structures—including the amygdala, hypothalamus, cingulate cortex, anterior thalamus, mammillary body, and hippocampus—that sit below the neocortex; contributes to emotional and other functions.

localization of function Concept that a processing subsystem uniquely dedicated to a single function is located in a specific region of brain tissue.

locked-in syndrome Condition in which cortical function and awareness are normal but a brainstem injury prevents almost all motor output; locked-in patients are able to communicate using simple eye movements.

longitudinal fissure Fissure in the brain that separates the right cerebral hemisphere from the left.

long-term potentiation (LTP) Neuronal mechanism that allows processing of the conjunctions or co-occurrences of inputs, in which brief, patterned activation of particular pathways produces a stable increase in synaptic efficacy lasting for hours to weeks.

M and P ganglion cells Retinal cells (also called *parasol cells* and *midget cells,* respectively) that form functional pathways with similarly named cells in the thalamus.

magnetic resonance imaging (MRI) Technique that relies on the use of magnetic fields to distort the behavior of protons; information about how long the protons take to recover from this distortion is used to create an image of the brain.

magnetoencephalography (MEG) Method related to EEG that relies on the recording of magnetic potentials at the scalp (rather than electrical potentials) to index brain activity.

mammillary bodies Parts of the hypothalamus; damage to these structures may result in amnesia.

mass action Theory holding that all pieces of brain contribute to all functions; opposite of theory of localization of function.

material-specific memory disorders Selective impairments of memory and/or recall; left-hemisphere damage impairs memory for verbal material, right-hemisphere damage impairs memory for nonverbal materials.

maturational lag hypothesis Theory that children with specific learning disabilities are merely slower to mature than their peers, and that with time they will outgrow the problem.

medial In the middle or center (of the brain).

medial dorsal nucleus (of the thalamus) Portion of the thalamus specifically implicated in the functions of alertness and wakefulness; acts by modulating the level of arousal of the cortex.

medial geniculate nucleus Structure in the thalamus that acts as a stopover point on the pathway relaying auditory information to the cortex.

medial pathway One of two major sets of pathways that link the brain to muscles; involved in control of movements of the trunk and proximal limb muscles. This tract projects both contralaterally and ipsilaterally, and is mainly involved in the control of posture, as well as bilateral movements such as standing, bending, turning, and walking.

medulla Section of the brain directly superior to the spinal cord; contains the cell bodies of most cranial nerves and controls many vital functions and reflexes.

memory consolidation Process by which memories are strengthened over time to allow for long-term retention. Theoretically, the hippocampus aids in slowly binding together pieces of a memory trace in separate neocortical processors; once they are bound in this way, they can be retrieved without involvement of the hippocampal system.

mental retardation Developmental disorder in which children fail to acquire intellectual abilities across most cognitive domains at a normal rate and manner, and have difficulties in adaptive functioning; generally divided into four categories based on severity.

mesocortical system Dopaminergic subsystem with cell bodies located in the ventral tegmental area and projecting to much of the cortex; influences a variety of mental functions, notably working memory.

mesolimbic system Dopaminergic subsystem with cell bodies in the ventral tegmental area, projecting to several parts of the limbic system; linked to reward-related behavior.

metabotropic receptors Receptors that work indirectly to either open or close an ion channel by attaching to and activating an enzyme situated in the postsynaptic membrane.

metacognition The ability to reflect upon a cognitive process.

method of converging operations Research method of examining whether all the answers obtained from a set of interrelated experiments using different approaches or techniques lead to the same conclusion; if so, then scientists can have greater confidence in the validity of their conclusion.

metric (coordinate) spatial relations Spatial relations described in terms of the distance between two locations; proposed to rely more on processing of the right hemisphere than the left.

midbrain Brain region superior to the pons; contains the nuclei of some of the cranial nerves. Also contains the inferior and superior colliculi, which are important in orientation to stimuli in the auditory and visual modalities, respectively.

midline diencephalic region Portions of the diencephalon, including the mammillary bodies, which when damaged may result in amnesia.

midsagittal Planar view of the brain in which the brain is cut down the middle, separating the left side from the right side.

mild cognitive impairment Cognitive decline with aging that is greater than is typical for a person's age, but not of sufficient severity to warrant a diagnosis of dementia; may be a precursor to Alzheimer's disease.

mild head injury Also known as *concussion;* occurs when a person has a change in consciousness for 2 to 30 minutes and does not have other gross signs of neurological damage.

minimally conscious state Condition in which a brain-damaged patient shows intermittent signs of awareness and purposeful action.

mirror-reading task Test in which word triplets are presented in mirror-image orientation, and the viewer reads them aloud as quickly and accurately as possible; can be used to determine whether a skill generalizes to new exemplars.

mirror tracing task Test in which the person must trace the outline of a figure by looking in a mirror; is considered a test of skill-learning and implicit/procedural memory.

mixed auditory agnosia Disorder that affects the ability to attach meaning to both verbal and nonverbal sounds; however, the person can determine whether two sounds are identical or different and whether one sound is louder than the other.

modality specific Pertaining to or manifesting in only one of the senses.

monoamines Neurotransmitters derived from amino acids that have undergone a chemical transformation via an enzymatic process; produced by neurons with cell bodies located subcortically and in the brainstem.

Morris water maze Test of learning and memory of spatial relations in animals. A rat is placed in a circular tank filled with an opaque liquid that obscures a slightly submerged platform, which is positioned at a constant location relative to various visual cues outside the maze. Normal animals learn the position of the platform, and across trials there is a decrease in the time it takes them to swim to the platform; the ability to perform this task is disrupted in animals with hippocampal damage.

motor program Plan of action; an abstract representation of an intended movement.

motor unit Motor neuron and the muscle fibers it innervates.

multiple-case-study approach Research technique in which research findings are validated on a series of patients, each of whom is also treated as a single-case study. In this approach, data for each person within each group are provided, so that researchers can determine the variability across people as well as the degree to which the overall group average typifies the behavior of individuals within the group.

multiple-resource theory Suggests that a limited set of distinct attentional resource pools may exist, each of which can be applied only to certain types of processes.

multiple sclerosis (MS) Neurological disease of nontraumatic origin in which demyelination leads to axonal degeneration and neuronal damage that interferes with neural transmission. Symptoms may include weakness in the extremities, difficulty in some aspect of sensory processing, and changes in cognition, mood, and personality; however, the course and effects of the disease vary.

myelin Fatty sheath that insulates the axon.

narrative Aspect of language in which different events or ideas are linked together to form a coherent story or theme.

necrosis Cell death.

negative symptoms Absence of normal behavior that is characteristic of individuals with schizophrenia (e.g., catatonia, flat affect).

neglect dyslexia Syndrome in which the person consistently misreads the beginning or end of a word; neglect is exhibited for a particular portion of a word, regardless of the word's length or orientation.

neologisms Made-up words that follow the rules for combining sounds in the language, yet are not real words; often exhibited by individuals with aphasia.

neural networks Computer modeling techniques that simulate the action of the brain and its processes.

neurodevelopmental hypothesis Theory regarding the etiology of schizophrenia. Argues that neural functions are subtly altered early in life, leaving the person with a vulnerable neural organization that may lead to emergence of the disorder after puberty or at the onset of young adulthood.

neurofibrillary tangles Twisted pairs of helical filaments found within the neuron; thought to disrupt a neuron's structural matrix; a characteristic of aged individuals, especially those with Alzheimer's disease.

neurogenesis Generation of new nerve cells (neurons).

neuromuscular junction Synapse between a neuron and muscle fibers; is larger and has a more specialized structure than a typical synapse.

neurons Nervous system cells that carry information from one place to another by means of a combination of electrical and chemical signals.

neuropsychological assessment Evaluation performed to determine the degree to which damage to the central nervous system may have compromised a person's cognitive, behavioral, and emotional functioning.

neuropsychological test battery Multiple tests used to detect any type of brain dysfunction of either neurological or psychiatric origin; most common is the Halstead-Reitan battery.

neurotransmitter Molecules that are released from the presynaptic neuron and received by the postsynaptic neuron; enable transmission of information from one neuron to another.

neurulation Formation of a tube, early in fetal development, that later becomes the spinal cord and brain.

nigrostriatal bundle Structure by which the striatum receives input from the substantia nigra.

nigrostriatal system Dopaminergic subsystem with cell bodies located in the substantia nigra and projecting to the neostriatum (the basal ganglia); regulates the selection, initiation, and cessation of motor behaviors.

nodes of Ranvier Gaps between myelinated sections of an axon; they enable the strength of the action potential to be maintained over the entire length of the axon.

nodulus Brain structure that constitutes part of the vestibulocerebellum.

nonmatch-to-sample paradigm Test procedure in which the participant must choose which of two test items does not match the previously shown sample item; often used with a short delay between the sample item and the test items to assess working memory.

nonverbal auditory agnosia Disorder characterized by inability to attach meaning to nonverbal sounds, although ability to attach meaning to words remains intact.

noradrenaline/norepinephrine Monoamine neurotransmitter (a catecholamine); it is involved in overall arousal and vigilance.

nuclei Distinct groups of neurons whose cell bodies are all situated in the same region.

nucleus accumbens Part of the basal ganglia; a cluster of cells in the basal forebrain (also called the *ventral striatum*). One of the brain areas where electrical stimulation is most rewarding.

object-based neglect Condition in which the individual neglects half of the stimulus regardless of the position of the stimulus in space.

object-based attention Attention directed on the basis of particular objects (rather than on the basis of locations in space).

object-centered neglect Condition in which the patient ignores one half of an object with regards to its canonical orientation regardless of how that object is displayed or oriented.

obsessive-compulsive disorder Syndrome in which the afflicted person has obsessive thoughts, usually about harm, and copes with that anxiety by engaging in repeated, compulsive actions intended to ward off a negative outcome.

occipital lobe Brain region behind the parieto-occipital sulcus; involved in processing visual information.

olfactory bulb Thin strand of neural tissue located directly below the frontal lobe; one of two bulbs (one in each hemisphere) that receive and project sensory information about smells.

oligodendrocytes Glial cells that produce the insulating myelin sheath for a neuron.

optic ataxia Failure in visually guided reaching; caused by superior parietal lobe damage.

optic chiasm Crossover point where some information from the left eye is transmitted to the right side of the brain, and vice versa; place where information from the inside half of each retina crosses the midline of the body and projects to the contralateral lateral geniculate.

optic flow Pattern of movement of images on the retina as one moves actively through an environment.

optical imaging Imaging technique in which a laser source of near-infrared light is positioned on the scalp, with detectors composed of optic fiber bundles located a few centimeters away from the light source. The detectors sense how the path of light is altered, either through absorption or scattering, as it traverses brain tissue. Can provide cognitive neuroscientists with simultaneous information about the source and time course of neural activity.

optimal feedback control Viewpoint (derived from computational models) that conceptualizes the motor regions of the brain working together as a circuit to reach a goal, which can met by a number of different movement options.

oral (buccofacial) apraxia Difficulty in performing voluntary movements with the muscles of the tongue, lips, cheek, and larynx, although automatic movements are usually preserved; usually produced by a frontotemporal lesion.

orbitofrontal cortex (OFC) Brain region that resides directly over the eye orbits and areas that extend into the medial wall of the frontal lobes (*ventromedial prefrontal cortex*); implicated in integrating emotion and decision making.

output phonological buffer Working memory buffer that holds a phonological code online as a speaker is preparing his or her own utterance.

paired-associate learning Memory-task format in which the participant must learn to associate pairs of items with one another; emphasizes declarative memory and engages hippocampal regions.

panic disorder Repeated attacks with sensations of extreme bodily hyperarousal, dizziness, shortness of breath, elevated heart rate, and sense of losing control; may be associated with fear of specific situations.

parabelt Region of auditory cortex that surrounds the belt; receives input from the belt and the medial geniculate.

paraphasias Errors in producing specific words; usually produced by individuals with aphasia.

parietal lobe Brain region directly behind the central fissure and above the Sylvian fissure.

Parkinson's disease Disease resulting from damage to the cells of the substantia nigra, which stop producing the neurotransmitter dopamine; may be caused by genetic predisposition, toxins, trauma, inflammation, or viral infection; disrupts motor control and affects cognitive processing.

Parkinsonian mask Expressionless face that is a prominent symptom of Parkinson's disease; may reflect a dampening of both movements and emotional responsiveness.

pattern completion Process by which the interaction of the hippocampal system with neocortical storage sites may allow one piece of information to be used to reconstitute a whole memory (allows for the reactivation of long-term memories).

perceptual asymmetries Differences in the perception of information depending on which hemisphere receives that information; taken to reflect underlying hemispheric asymmetries in information processing.

peripheral nervous system All neural tissue beyond the central nervous system, such as neurons that receive sensory information from the body or send information to muscles, and neurons that relay information to or from the spinal cord or the brain.

perseverate To perform a behavior repeatedly.

perseveration Behavior of repeating the same action (or thought) over and over again.

pervasive developmental disorders Syndromes characterized by qualitative impairment in social interaction; delays and abnormalities in language as well as other aspects of communication; restricted, repetitive, and stereotyped patterns of behaviors, interests, or activities; and an onset of the problems in at least one of these three areas before the age of three years.

phobias Irrational fears, centered on specific objects or situations, that interfere with normal functioning.

phonemic paraphasia Error in which the substituted word sounds similar to that of the intended word.

phonological agraphia Syndrome in which the person can manually or orally spell regular and irregular words in dictation but performs poorly with nonwords.

phonological awareness Ability to link a particular letter to a particular sound and to parse words into their constituent phonemes.

phonological dyslexia (alexia) Syndrome in which the affected person does not have an association between the visual form of words and meaning; due to a disrupted phonological route but an intact direct route, the person can read previously learned words (whether regular or irregular), but cannot read nonwords or unfamiliar words.

phonological (nonlexical) route to reading Method of reading that links information in a visual linguistic format to meaning by identifying each letter and blending the sounds to produce a word; word recognition occurs because the sound pattern is associated with the concept that the word represents.

phonology Study of the sounds that compose a language and the rules that govern their combination.

photoreceptors Sensory receptors in the eye, called rods and cones, which contain pigments that absorb light.

place fields Particular places in the environment to which hippocampal neurons fire preferentially.

place of articulation Location in the vocal tract where airflow is obstructed during normal speech/sound production.

planum temporale Temporal plane; the region at the end of the Sylvian fissure in the temporal lobe; involved in processing sounds, especially those that are language-related.

plasticity Malleability; quality of dynamic changes in the nervous system in response to environmental and developmental factors or in response to damage.

pons Multifunctional brain area directly superior to the medulla and anterior to the cerebellum. Contains the superior olive (which relays auditory information from the ear to the brain); acts as the main connective bridge from the rest of the brain to the cerebellum; is the point of synapse of some cranial nerves; and acts to control certain types of eye movements and vestibular functions.

population coding Theory that the pattern of activity across a large population of cells codes for information, such as particular movements or individual objects.

positive symptoms In schizophrenia, excesses or distortions in normal behavior (e.g., delusions, hallucinations).

positron emission tomography (PET) Imaging method that uses a radioactive agent to trace and determine the brain's metabolic activity.

posterior Back; behind.

post-error slowing A more cautious and slowed response on the next trial after an error; generally thought to indicate awareness of having made an error.

posttraumatic stress disorder (PTSD) Disorder caused by a deeply traumatic or life-threatening experience. Symptoms include vivid, intrusive recollections of the traumatic situation; avoidance of situations related to the traumatic experience; chronically elevated bodily arousal; feelings of survivor guilt; and suicidal thoughts.

praxis System responsible for production of skilled motor movement; probably requires a wide variety of brain regions, including the parietal, prefrontal, motor, and subcortical regions, each contributing in a different manner to the planning, retrieval, and/or implementation of motor action plans.

premotor area Region located on the lateral surface of the brain just in front of primary motor cortex; sends commands about the type of movement to be performed (e.g., a pinching movement of the index finger and thumb) to the primary motor area, which sends specific commands that direct the movement.

primal sketch Proposed rudimentary representation of objects in the visual-system that distinguishes dark from light regions and allows for simple grouping of regions by Gestalt principles.

primary motor cortex Cortical region that is the final exit point for neurons responsible for fine motor control of the body's muscles.

primary sensory cortex Cortical region that initially receives information about a particular sensory modality from receptors in the periphery.

procedural memory system Supports memory of "how" things should be done, allowing for the acquisition and expression of skill; learning in this system is probabilistic, integrating information across events rather than storing each event separately; thought to rely on the specific brain regions required for the skill, as well as portions of the basal ganglia.

propositional prosody Intonation pattern of speech that communicates lexical or semantic information, such as whether an utterance is a question or a declaration.

proprioception Perception of the position of body parts and their movements.

prosody The intonation pattern, or sound envelope, of an utterance; tone of voice in which a phrase is spoken.

prosopagnosia   Selective inability to recognize the identity of faces or to differentiate among them, although the ability to correctly identify other objects in the visual modality is retained.

proximal   Near.

psychic blindness   Disconnection between the ability to process the sensory properties of objects and the understanding of the affective properties of those same objects.

psychological inertia   Reduced ability to initiate or start an action or a behavior and/or the reduced ability to stop a behavior once it has been initiated; often observed in individuals with a dysexecutive syndrome and frontal lobe damage.

pulse sequence   Oscillating magnetic field that creates a perturbation in the static magnetic field.

pulvinar (of the thalamus)   Thalamic structure that plays a role in attention and the filtering-out of distracting information.

pure-word deafness   *See* verbal auditory agnosia.

putamen   Portion of the basal ganglia that receives much of its input.

pyramidal cell   Specific type of neuron; involved in controlling muscle movement.

quadranopsia   Disorder in which one quadrant of the visual world is lost; caused by damage to a dorsal or ventral portion of the occipital cortex in one hemisphere.

receiver coil   Radio-frequency apparatus that records the time it takes for protons perturbed in an MRI machine to revert to their original state.

receptive field   That specific region of visual space to which a particular cell responds or is sensitive; a part of visual space in which light will affect the cell's firing rate.

receptors   Specially configured proteins, embedded within the postsynaptic membrane, that create binding sites for neurotransmitter.

recognition memory   Test paradigm in which a person views a list of items to remember, and then later is shown both old and new items and is asked which of them were previously seen.

regeneration   Process of creation of new cells, both neurons and glia; also involves sprouting of new axons, connection of regions that were not previously connected, and formation of new synapses.

reinforcement contingency   Degree to which a reward or punishment is associated with a particular stimulus or action.

relational learning   Learning and memory for the relations among items, especially items associated only arbitrarily; thought to rely mainly on the hippocampal memory system.

relay center   Region of the brain whose neurons receive information from one area of the brain and then go on to synapse elsewhere in the brain; often a site where information is combined or recoded.

reorganization   Changes in the brain that occur when one cortical region "takes over" the functions of another damaged or dysfunctional region.

repetition priming   Enhancement or biasing of performance as a result of previous exposure to an item; major category of preserved learning and memory in amnesia.

repetitive transcranial magnetic stimulation (rTMS)   Procedure in which repetitive magnetic pulses are applied to the brain from a generator held outside the scalp; under certain conditions it may disrupt processing, in other cases it may enhance processing; also an experimental treatment for depression.

resource   Theoretical construct in attention that describes the effort that can be applied to processing information or performing a task.

response inhibition   Ability to override or interrupt ongoing processing, or to abort inappropriate responses.

resting potential   Difference in electrical charge between the inside and outside of the neuron; typically about −70 millivolts.

restorative rehabilitation   Therapy for brain-injured patients aimed at gaining increased function by repetitive exercise.

reticular activating system (RAS)   Set of brainstem neurons that projects diffusely to many other regions of the brain; relies on the excitatory neurotransmitter glutamate. Important for overall arousal and attention, and for regulation of sleep-wake cycles.

reticular nucleus (of the thalamus)   Portion of the thalamus specifically implicated in the functions of alertness and wakefulness; acts by modulating the level of arousal of the cortex.

retina   Structure at the back of the eye that registers light and processes visual information before sending it on to the brain.

retinotopic map   Characteristic of some areas of the visual system (e.g., in LGN or striate cortex), in which visual information is mapped onto brain tissue following the same spatial layout as visual information reaching the retina itself, such that neighboring regions of brain tissue process information from neighboring regions on the retina, and hence the world.

retrograde amnesia   Memory impairment for information that was acquired prior to the event that caused the amnesia; a deficit for memories stretching back in time to some point prior to onset of amnesia.

reuptake   Rapid removal of neurotransmitter back into the terminal bouton by special transporter molecules embedded in the presynaptic membrane.

reversal learning   Ability to change behavior when contingencies change; ability to reverse a previously learned association.

Ribot's Law   Law regarding the amount of time over which retrograde amnesias extend: generally, it states that there is greater compromise of more recent memories than of more remote memories.

right visual field   Area/information to the right of the fixation of gaze.

rostral   Toward the front (in an animal, toward the head).

rotary pursuit   Task in which a person has to track a circularly moving target; reveals ability to learn a perceptual-motor skill, which is not compromised in individuals with hippocampal damage.

saccade   Eye movement in which the eyes, rather than moving smoothly across space, jump from one position to the next with no processing of the intervening visual information.

sagittal   Planar view of the brain in which the brain is cut so that the left side is separated from the right side.

scotomas   Blind spots; particular regions of the visual field in which light-dark contrast cannot be detected. Caused by damage to small portions of the visual cortex.

selective attention   An aspect of attention that allows certain information to be selected for additional processing, often conceptualized as a filtering process that allows homing in on critical information from the vast amount of information available; this process can be performed on incoming sensory information, on information being kept "in mind," or on the set of possible responses.

self-ordered pointing task   Test of sequencing ability. The person is shown an array of items laid out on a page, followed by a series of pages with those same items positioned in a different arrangement. The participant must point to a unique item on each successive page, which requires keeping track of which items were previously selected.

semantic dementia   Disorder in which the affected person progressively loses the ability to retain semantic information.

semantic memory   Knowledge that allows the formation and retention of facts, concepts, categories, and word meaning and retention of information about ourselves and the people we know—all of which are expressed across many different contexts.

semantic paralexias   Reading errors in which a word is misread as a word with a related meaning.

semantic paraphasia   Error in which the substituted word has a meaning similar to that of the intended word.

semantics   Meaning of language.

sensitive period   Specific time during development when the organism is particularly responsive (sensitive) to certain external stimuli.

sensory gating   Phenomenon in which the neural response to the second of two successive auditory tones or clicks is less than the response to the first stimulus; a mechanism whereby repetitive or similar stimuli receive a reduced amount of attention.

sequencing   One of the basic processes involved in reaching a goal; ability to determine what steps to take to attain the goal, and the order in which those steps must be taken.

serotonin   Monoamine neurotransmitter (an indolamine).

serotonin transporter gene   Gene that codes for the serotonin reuptake protein, which takes the neurotransmitter serotonin from the synapse back up into the presynaptic cell.

simple cells   Type of striate cortex cells; responsive to bars of light oriented in particular ways.

simulation   Mimicking or acting like another person in order to comprehend that person's mental state.

single-case studies   Research method in which a single patient with brain damage is studied intensively with a variety of neuropsychological tests to determine the relationship between a particular region of brain tissue and the cognitive or emotional processes that the region supports.

skill learning   Acquisition—usually gradually and incrementally through repetition—of motor, perceptual, or cognitive operations or procedures that aid performance.

somatosensory agnosia   Condition in which a person is unable to recognize an item by touch but can recognize the object in other modalities.

source memory   Ability to recall or remember the specific circumstances or context in which particular information was learned.

space-based attention   Attention that is directed on the basis of locations in space.

sparse coding   Theory that a small but specific group of cells responds to the presence of a given object.

spatial frequency hypothesis   Proposes that the hemispheres differ in their ability to process a particular attribute of visual information known as spatial frequency, which describes how quickly visual information transitions from dark to light.

spinal cord   Portion of the nervous system through which many sensory neurons relay information to the brain, and through which motor commands from the brain are sent to the muscles.

split-brain procedure   Surgical procedure in which the corpus callosum—the primary route by which the left and right cerebral hemispheres interact—is severed, thereby splitting the brain in half; also sometimes referred to as *commissurotomy*.

static field   Constant magnetic field; MRI machines are classified by the strength of this field.

stimulus-centered neglect   Condition in which a person ignores (neglects) one side of a stimulus regardless of what information is contained on that side of the stimulus.

striate cortex   Primary visual cortex; first region of the cortex that receives visual information; contains a map that is retinotopically organized.

subsequent memory effect   Effect in which subsequently remembered items are associated with greater brain activity at encoding than items that are not subsequently remembered.

substantia nigra   Part of the basal ganglia; provides dopaminergic input to other portions of the basal ganglia.

subthalamic nucleus   Part of the basal ganglia; a portion of the indirect pathway of the basal ganglia.

sulcus   Valley between brain convolutions (plural: *sulci*).

superior   Top; above.

superior colliculus   Dorsal midbrain structures that allows orientation of eyes toward large moving objects in the periphery, so that the object falls in the center of vision. Also permits one to move the focus of visual attention from one position or object to another.

superior olivary nucleus   Structure in the medulla to which the cochlear nucleus relays auditory information.

supervisory attentional system   One component of a two-component system that influences the choice of behavior; cognitive system required to effortfully direct attention and guide action through decision processes. Active only in certain situations: when no preexisting processing schemes are available, as occurs in novel situations; when the task is technically difficult; when problem solving is required; and when certain typical response tendencies must be overridden.

supplementary motor area (SMA)   Specific brain region that is involved in the creation of a motor program, which is an abstract plan that specified the type and nature of actions as well as their sequence; this information is transmitted to other brain regions that; transmits this information to other brain regions that are involved in the execution of the motor program.

supplementary motor complex (SMC)   One of the main regions of the brain that plays a role in planning, preparing, and initiating movements. Located mainly on the medial surface of the brain, and is composed of the more posteriorly located supplementary motor area, the more anteriorly located pre-SMA, and the supplementary eye field.

surface dyslexia (alexia)   Syndrome in which the affected person cannot link the visual form of a word directly to meaning; involves disruption in the direct route but not the phonological route.

switch cost   Time (or other resources) needed to change from the current task set to an alternative task set; considered an executive process that is independent of the tasks being performed.

Sylvian (lateral) fissure   Separates each hemisphere of the brain in the dorsal-ventral dimension; sometimes called the *fissure of Sylvius*.

synapse   Region of contact between neurons containing the pre-synaptic terminal bouton, the synaptic cleft between the neurons, and the postsynaptic region.

synaptic vesicles   Small balloonlike structures in and on the neuron that are filled with neurotransmitter; these vesicles merge with the cell wall to release the neurotransmitter into the synaptic cleft.

synaptogenesis   Creation of connections (synapses) that neurons make with other neurons; increases dramatically after birth, but then goes through a pruning process later during childhood and adolescence.

syntax   Rules of grammar.

tactile agnosia   *See* somatosensory agnosia.

tactile asymbolia   Disorder in which a person can form a percept from tactile information, but cannot link that percept to its symbolic meaning.

tectopulvinar path   Neural pathway from the retina to the superior colliculus to the pulvinar of the thalamus; allows quick orientation to important visual information; especially sensitive to motion and appearance of novel objects in the visual periphery.

telegraphic speech   Nonfluent speech in which sentences are structured like a telegram or text message; uses primarily content words, such as nouns and verbs, and omits function words (such as conjunctions and prepositions) and word endings.

temporal gradient   Characteristics of amnesia in which there is greater compromise of more recent memories than more remote memories.

temporal lobe   Brain area below the Sylvian fissure; plays an important role in memory, emotion, and auditory perception.

temporally limited retrograde amnesia   Memory loss that extends back only a certain amount of time from the point of injury; often limited to minutes, hours or days before injury, but possibly extending to years or decades earlier.

thalamus   Part of the diencephalon; a large relay center for almost all sensory information coming into the cortex and almost all motor information leaving it.

theory of mind   Theory that assumes that we have a cognitive representation of other people's mental states, including their feelings and their knowledge.

three-dimensional (3-D) representation   Proposed abstract, viewpoint-invariant mental construct of an object.

tics   Repetitive involuntary movements of a compulsive nature that wax and wane in severity; characteristic of Tourette's syndrome.

tonotopic   Organized with regard to the frequency of a tone or sound.

tonotopic map   Area in the brain (e.g., in auditory cortex) that organizes information according to sound frequency.

top-down attentional selection   Process by which the individual determines how to direct attention based on task goals, instructions, or higher-level decisions.

Tourette's syndrome   Relatively rare disorder that manifests as a variety of vocal and motor tics; appears in childhood.

Tower of London task   Test of planning and sequencing; the task requires the person to move a set of balls, one at a time, from an initial position on prongs to a target configuration in as few moves as possible while keeping in mind the constraints imposed by the height of each prong.

tractography   Method that builds on diffusion tensor information to ascertain information about probable white-matter tracts in the brain.

transcortical motor aphasia   Syndrome in which ability to produce fluent speech is lost, except that the ability to repeat sounds is retained; associated with lesions in the premotor area of the frontal lobe.

transcortical sensory aphasia   Syndrome that prevents an individual from interpreting the meaning of words, although the ability to repeat words is retained; associated with lesions at the border of the temporal and occipital lobes.

transcranial magnetic stimulation (TMS)   Methodology by which brain activity can be modulated or changed in individuals through a pulsed magnetic field, created by a coil or series of coils placed on the scalp; induces an electrical field that alters the pattern of brain activity in the underlying tissue.

transneuronal degeneration   Cell loss and death that extends past the actual site of damage to more distal neurons.

tremors   Repetitive rhythmic motions that result from oscillatory movement of agonist and antagonist muscles; a characteristic observed in Parkinson's disease as well as cerebellar damage.

tuning curve   Description of a cell's relative sensitivity to different sensory stimuli (e.g., an auditory system cell's sensitivity to sounds of different frequencies).

unilateral   One side; one-sided.

vagus nerve stimulation   Experimental treatment for depression in which a device containing stimulating electrodes is implanted in the upper chest, near the collarbone, where it can stimulate the vagus nerve before it enters the brain.

vascular dementia   Formerly known as *multi-infarct dementia;* results from the cumulative effects of many small strokes that tend to create both cortical and subcortical lesions. Patients usually demonstrate similar dysfunctions as observed in Alzheimer's disease.

vegetative state   Condition in which the patient shows no evidence of awareness or communication, but exhibits a sleep-wake cycle, has eyes open during the wakeful periods, and may perform some simple behaviors at random; characterized by the absence of even the most basic form of communication.

ventral   Below or inferior (in a four-legged animal, toward the animal's stomach).

ventral visual-processing stream   Areas of the occipital, occipitotemporal, and temporal regions that are devoted to processing visual stimuli; portion of the brain that is especially well-suited for object recognition.

ventricular enlargement   Enlargement of the lateral ventricles, resulting from widespread atrophy of brain tissue.

verbal auditory agnosia   Disorder in which auditory words cannot be understood, although the ability to attach meaning to nonverbal sounds is intact as are other aspects of language processing.

vermis   Region of the cerebellar hemisphere that projects to the fastigial nucleus.

viewer-centered representation   Representation of visual information from the vantage point of the viewer; multiple such stored representations of objects, each from a distinct viewpoint, are proposed to be interpolated to allow the recognition of objects from any particular viewpoint.

vigilance   Sustained attention; the ability to maintain alertness continuously over time.

visual agnosia   Inability to recognize objects in the visual modality that cannot be explained by other causes, such as blindness, memory problems and so forth.

visual-verbal working memory   That portion of working memory that allows visual-verbal information to be held online.

visuospatial scratch pad   Portion of working memory that allows nonverbal visual information to be held on-line while performing perceptual analyses of a stimulus array.

voicing   Timing between the release of air for a stop consonant and the vibration of the vocal cords; this aspect of speech production distinguishes between phonemes such as b and d.

Wada technique   Procedure in which a sedative is introduced into the carotid artery supplying blood to one hemisphere, after which the experimenter observes whether disruptions in speech output occurs; used to determine which hemisphere is responsible for speech output in patients about to undergo tissue removal to control epileptic seizures.

Wernicke's aphasia   Syndrome typically due to damage of the temporo-parietal regions of the left hemisphere, in which there is disrupted speech comprehension along with fluent (but nonsensical) speech output; speech output occurs without hesitation, sounds are well formed, and all parts of speech are present, but output is a jumble of words, often referred to as a *word salad.*

Wisconsin Card Sorting Test (WCST)   Classic neuropsychological test used to examine task switching. The participant is to sort a stack of cards into four piles based either on the color, number, or shape of the items on the card. No explicit criteria for sorting are given, but as the participant places each card onto one of the four piles, the experimenter indicates whether the response is correct or incorrect. From the experimenter's feedback, the participant must deduce the dimension by which the card should be sorted. At some point in the trial, the experimenter changes the sorting criterion, and the participant must deduce the new order.

word-stem completion task   Test used to examine implicit memory; participants are given a list of words to study, and after a delay, individuals are to report "the first word that comes to mind" that completes each stem; performance is contrasted with explicit recall in which participants are asked to recall the word from the study list that started with that stem.

References

Abi-Dargham, A., Mawlawi, O., Lombardo, I., Gil, R., Martinez, D., Huang, Y., Hwang, D.-R., Keilp, J., Kochan, L., Van Heertum, R., Gorman, J. M., & Laruelle, M. (2002). Prefrontal dopamine D1 receptors and working memory in schizophrenia. *Journal of Neuroscience, 22,* 3708–3719.

Aboitiz, F., Carrasco, X., Schröter, C., Zaidel, D., Zaidel, E., & Lavados, M. (2003). The alien hand syndrome: Classification of forms reported and discussion of a new condition. *Neurological Sciences, 24,* 252–257.

Abutalebi, J., Brambati, S. M., Annoni, J. M., Moro, A., Cappa, S. F., & Perani, D. (2007). The neural cost of the auditory perception of language switches: An event-related fMRI study in bilinguals. *Journal of Neuroscience, 27,* 13762–13769.

Ackermann, H., Mathiak, K., & Riecker, A. (2007). The contribution of the cerebellum to speech production and speech perception: Clinical and functional imaging data. *Cerebellum, 6,* 202–213.

Adair, J. C., & Barrett, A. M. (2008). Spatial neglect: Clinical and neuroscience review: A wealth of information on the poverty of spatial attention. *Annals of the New York Academy of Sciences, 1142,* 21–43.

Adams, J. H., Graham, D. I., Murray, L. S., & Scott, G. (1982). Diffuse axonal injury due to nonmissile head injury in humans: An analysis of 45 cases. *Annals of Neurology, 12,* 557–563.

Adams, J. R., Troiano, A. R., & Caine, D. B. (2004). Functional imaging in Tourette's syndrome. *Journal of Neural Transmission, 111,* 1495–1506.

Adolphs, R., Cahill, L., Schul, R., & Babinsky, R. (1997). Impaired declarative memory for emotional material following bilateral amygdala damage in humans. *Learning & Memory, 4,* 291–300.

Adolphs, R., Gosselin, F., Buchanan, T. W., Tranel, D., Schyns, P., & Damasio, A. R. (2005). A mechanism for impaired fear recognition after amygdala damage. *Nature, 433,* 68–72.

Adolphs, R., Tranel, D., & Damasio, A. R. (1998). The human amygdala in social judgment. *Nature, 393,* 470–474.

Adolphs, R., Tranel, D., & Damasio, H. (2001). Emotion recognition from faces and prosody following temporal lobectomy. *Neuropsychology, 15,* 396–404.

Adolphs, R., Tranel, D., Hamann, S., Young, A. W., Calder, A. J., Phelps, E. A., et al. (1999). Recognition of facial emotion in nine individuals with bilateral amygdala damage. *Neuropsychologia, 37,* 1111–1117.

Afraz, S.-R., Kiani, R., & Esteky, H. (2006). Microstimulation of inferotemporal cortex influences face categorization. *Nature, 442,* 692–695.

Aggleton, J. P., & Young, A. W. (2000). The enigma of the amygdala: On its contribution to human emotion. In R. D. Lane & L. Nadel (Eds.), *Cognitive neuroscience of emotion* (pp. 106–128). New York: Oxford University Press.

Agosta, F., Vossel, K. A., Miller, B. L., Migliaccio, R., Bonasera, S. J., Filippi, M., et al. (2009). Apolipoprotein E ε4 is associated with disease-specific effects on brain atrophy in Alzheimer's disease and frontotemporal dementia. *Proceedings of the National Academy of Sciences, 106,* 2018–2022.

Aguirre, G. K. (2003). Topographical disorientation: A disorder of way-finding ability. In M. D'Esposito (Ed.), *Neurological foundations of cognitive neuroscience* (pp. 89–108). Cambridge, MA: MIT Press.

Aguirre, G. K., Detre, J. A., Alsop, D. C., & D'Esposito, M. (1996). The parahippocampus subserves topographical learning in man. *Cerebral Cortex, 6,* 823–829.

Aguirre, G. K., Komáromy, A. M., Cideciyan, A. V., Brainard, D. H., Aleman, T. S., Roman, A. J., et al. (2007). Canine and human visual cortex intact and responsive despite early retinal blindness from RPE65 mutation. *PLoS Medicine, 4,* 1117–1128.

Aguirre, G. K., Zarahn, E., & D'Esposito, M. (1998). An area within human ventral cortex sensitive to "building" stimuli: Evidence and implications. *Neuron, 21,* 373–383.

Aguzzi, A., & Heikenwalder, M. (2006). Pathogenesis of prion diseases: Current status and future outlook. *Nature Reviews Microbiology, 4,* 765–775.

Aharon, I., Etcoff, N., Ariely, D., Chabris, C. F., O'Connor, E., & Breiter, H. C. (2001). Beautiful faces have variable reward value: fMRI and behavioral evidence. *Neuron, 32,* 537–551.

Ahmed, S., Bierley, R., Sheikh, J. I., & Date, E. S. (2000). Posttraumatic amnesia after closed head injury: A review of the literature and some suggestions for further research. *Brain Injury, 14,* 765–780.

Ahveninen, J., Jääskeläinen, I. P., Raij, T., Bonmassar, G., Devore, S., Hämäläinen, M., et al. (2006). Task modulated "what" and "where" pathways in human auditory cortex. *Proceedings of the National Academy of Sciences, USA, 103,* 14608–14613.

Aikens, J. E., Fischer, J. S., Namey, M., & Rudick, R. A. (1997). A replicated prospective investigation of life stress, coping, and depressive symptoms in multiple sclerosis. *Journal of Behavioral Medicine, 20,* 433–445.

Akshoomoff, N. A., & Courchesne, E. (1992). A new role for the cerebellum in cognitive operations. *Behavioral Neuroscience, 106*(5), 731–738.

Alberico, A. M., Ward, J. M., Choi, S. C., Marmarou, A., & Young, H. F. (1987). Outcome after severe head injury: Relationship to mass lesions, diffuse injury, and ICP course in pediatric and adult patients. *Journal of Neurosurgery, 67,* 648–656.

Albert, M. L. (1973). A simple test of visual neglect. *Neurology, 23,* 658–664.

Albert, M. S., Butters, N., & Levin, J. (1979). Temporal gradients in the retrograde amnesia of patients with Korsakoff's disease. *Archives of Neurology, 36,* 211.

Albery, W. B. (2007). Multisensory cueing for enhancing orientation information during flight. *Aviation, Space, & Environmental Medicine, 78,* B186–B190.

Albin, R. L., & Mink, J. W. (2006). Recent advances in Tourette syndrome research. *Trends in Neurosciences, 29,* 175–182.

Albin, R. L., Young, A. B., & Penney, J. B. (1989). The functional anatomy of basal ganglia disorders. *Trends in Neurosciences, 12,* 366–375.

Alexander, G. E., & Crutcher, M. D. (1990). Functional architecture of basal ganglia circuits: Neural substrates of parallel processing. *Trends in Neurosciences, 13,* 266–271.

Alexander, G. E., DeLong, M. R., & Strick, P. L. (1986). Parallel organization of functionally segregated circuits linking basal ganglia and cortex. *Annual Review of Neuroscience, 9,* 357–381.

Alkire, M. T., Gruver, R., Miller, J., McReynolds, J. R., Hahn, E. L., & Cahill, L. (2008). Neuroimaging analysis of an anesthetic gas that blocks human emotional memory. *Proceedings of the National Academy of Sciences, 105,* 1722–1727.

Allen, J. S., Emmorey, K., Bruss, J., & Damasio, H. (2008). Morphology of the insula in relation to hearing status and sign language experience. *Journal of Neuroscience, 28,* 11900–11905.

Allen, L. S., Richey, M. F., Chai, Y. M., & Gorski, R. A. (1991). Sex differences in the corpus callosum of the living human being. *Journal of Neuroscience, 11,* 933–942.

Allison, T., McCarthy, G., Nobre, A., Puce, A., & Belger, A. (1994). Human extrastriate visual cortex and the perception of faces, words, numbers, and colors. *Cerebral Cortex, 5,* 544–554.

Allison, T., Puce, A., & McCarthy, G. (2000). Social perception from visual cues: Role of the STS region. *Trends in Cognitive Sciences, 4*(7), 267–278.

Allman, J. M., Hakeen, A., Erwin, J. M., Nimchinsky, E., & Hof, P. (2001). The anterior cingulate cortex: The evolution of an interface between emotion and cognition. In A. R. Damasio, A. Harrington, J. Kagan, B. S. McEwen, H. Moss, & R. Shaikh (Eds.), *Unity of knowledge: The convergence of natural and human science. Annals of the New York Academy of Sciences, Vol. 935* (pp. 107–117). New York: The New York Academy of Sciences.

Almkvist, O., Backman, L., Basun, H., & Wahlund, L. O. (1993). Patterns of neuropsychological performance in Alzheimer's disease and vascular dementia. *Cortex, 29,* 661–673.

Alonso, A., & Hernán, M.A. (2008). Temporal trends in the incidence of multiple sclerosis: A systematic review. *Neurology, 71,* 129–135.

Alossa, N., & Castelli, L. (2009). Amusia and musical functioning. *European Neurology, 61,* 269–277.

Alzheimer's Association. (2009). 2009 Alzheimer's disease facts and figures. *Alzheimer's & Dementia, 5,* 234–270.

Amedi, A., Floel, A., Knecht, S., Zohary, E., & Cohen, L. G. (2004). Transcranial magnetic stimulation of the occipital pole interferes with verbal processing in blind subjects. *Nature Neuroscience, 7,* 1266–1270.

Amedi, A., Jacobson, G., Hendler, T., Malach, R., & Zohary, E. (2002). Convergence of visual and tactile shape processing in the human lateral occipital complex. *Cerebral Cortex, 12,* 1202–1212.

Amedi, A., Malach, R., Hendler, T., Peled, S., & Zohary, E. (2001). Visuo-haptic object-related activation in the ventral visual pathway. *Nature Neuroscience, 4,* 324–330.

Amedi, A., Raz, N., Pianka, P., Malach, R., & Zohary, E. (2003). Early "visual" cortex activation correlates with superior verbal memory performance in the blind. *Nature Neuroscience, 6,* 758–766.

American Psychiatric Association. (2000). *Diagnostic and statistical manual of mental disorders,* Fourth Edition, Text Revision (*DSM-IV-TR*). Washington, D.C.: American Psychiatric Association.

Amiez, C., & Petrides, M. (2007). Selective involvement of the mid-dorsolateral prefrontal cortex in the coding of the serial order of visual stimuli in working memory. *Proceedings of the National Academy of Sciences, USA, 104,* 13786–13791.

Amodio, D. M., Devine, P. G., & Harmon-Jones, E. (2007). A dynamic model of guilt: Implications for motication and self-regulation in the context of prejudice. *Psychological Science, 18,* 524–530.

Amodio, D. M., Harmon-Jones, E., Devine, P. G., Curtin, J. J., Hartley, S. L., & Covert, A. E. (2004). Neural signals for the detection of unintentional race bias. *Psychological Science, 15,* 88–93.

Amodio, D. M., Kubota, J. T., Harmon-Jones, E., & Devine, P. G. (2006). Alternative mechanisms for regulating racial responses according to internal vs. external cues. *Social Cognitive & Affective Neuroscience, 1,* 26–36.

Amunts, K., Schleicher, A., Burgel, U., Mohlberg, H., Uylings, H. B. M., & Zilles, K. (1999). Broca's region revisited: Cytoarchitecture and intersubject variability. *Journal of Comparative Neurology, 412,* 319–341.

Anand, A., Li, Y., Wang, Y., Wu, J., Gao, S., Bukhari, L., et al. (2005). Antidepressant effect on connectivity of the mood-regulating circuit: An fMRI study. *Neuropsychopharmacology, 30,* 1334–1344.

Anders, S., Eippert, F., Weiskopf, N., & Veit, R. (2008). The human amygdala is sensitive to the valence of pictures and sounds irrespective of arousal: An fMRI study. *Social Cognitive & Affective Neuroscience, 3,* 233–243.

Andersen, R. A., & Mountcastle, V. B. (1983). The influence of the angle of gaze upon the excitability of the light-sensitive neurons of the posterior parietal cortex. *Journal of Neuroscience, 3,* 532–548.

Anderson, A. K., & Phelps, E. A. (2001). Lesions of the human amygdala impair enhanced perception of emotionally salient events. *Nature, 411,* 305–309.

Anderson, A. K., Christoff, K., Stappen, I., Panitz, D., Ghahremani, D. G., Glover, G., et al. (2003). Dissociated neural representations of intensity and valence in human olfaction. *Nature Neuroscience, 6,* 196–202.

Anderson, B., Mishory, A., Nahas, Z., Borckardt, J. J., Yamanaka, K., Rastogi, K., & George, M. S. (2006). Tolerability and safety of high daily doses of repetitive transcranial magnetic stimulation in healthy young men. *Journal of ECT, 22,* 49–53.

Anderson, M. C., & Green, C. (2001). Suppressing unwanted memories by executive control. *Nature, 410,* 366–369.

Anderson, M. C., Ochsner, K. N., Kuhl, B., Cooper, J., Robertson, E., Gabrieli, S.W., et al. (2004). Neural systems underlying the suppression of unwanted memories. *Science, 303,* 232–235.

Anderson, S. W., Bechara, A., Damasio, H., Tranel, D., & Damasio, A. R. (1999). Impairment of social and moral behavior related to early damage in human prefrontal cortex. *Nature Neuroscience, 2,* 1032–1037.

Anderson, S. W., Damasio, H., Jones, R. D., & Tranel, D. (1991). Wisconsin Card Sorting Test performance as a measure of frontal lobe damage. *Journal of Clinical & Experimental Neuropsychology, 13,* 909–922.

Andresen, D. R., Vinberg, J., & Grill-Spector, K. (2009). The representation of object viewpoint in human visual cortex. *NeuroImage, 45,* 522–536.

Andrew, R. D., & MacVicar, B. A. (1994). Imaging cell volume changes and neuronal excitation in the hippocampal slice. *Neuroscience, 62,* 371–383.

Andrews, G. (2001). Should depression be managed as a chronic disease? *British Medical Journal, 322,* 419–421.

Andrews, G., & Titov, N. (2007). Depression is very disabling. *Lancet, 370,* 808–809.

Anilo-Vento, L., Luck, S. J., & Hillyard, S. A. (1998). Spatiotemporal dynamics of attention to color: Evidence from human electrophysiology. *Human Brain Mapping, 6,* 216–238.

Annett, M. (1985). *Left, right, hand and brain: The right shift theory.* London: Lawrence Erlbaum Associates.

Annett, M. (1995). The right shift theory of a genetic balanced polymorphism for cerebral dominance and cognitive processing. *Current Psychology of Cognition, 14,* 427–480.

Anton, P. S., Granger, R., & Lynch, G. (1993). Simulated dendritic spines influence reciprocal synaptic strengths and lateral inhibition in the olfactory bulb. *Brain Research, 628,* 157–165.

Appell, J., Kertesz, A., & Fisman, M. (1982). A study of language functioning in Alzheimer patients. *Brain & Language, 17,* 73–91.

Arborelius, L., Owens, M. J., Plotsky, P. M., & Nemeroff, C. B. (1999). The role of corticotropin-releasing factor in depression and anxiety disorders. *Journal of Endocrinology, 160,* 1–12.

Arendt, T. (2009). Synaptic degeneration in Alzheimer's disease. *Acta Neuropathologica, 118,* 167–179.

Aretz, A. J. (1991). The design of electronic map displays. *Human Factors, 33,* 85–101.

Aretz, A. J., & Wickens, C. D. (1992). The mental rotation of map displays. *Human Performance, 5,* 303–328.

Armony, J. L., & LeDoux, J. E. (2000). How danger is encoded: Toward a systems, cellular, and computational understanding of cognitive-emotional interactions in fear. In M. S. Gazzaniga (Ed.), *The new cognitive neurosciences* (pp. 1067–1079). Cambridge, MA: MIT Press.

Arnsten, A. F. T. (1998). Catecholamine modulation of prefrontal cortical cognitive function. *Trends in Cognitive Sciences, 2,* 436–447.

Aron, A. R., Fletcher, P. C., Bullmore, E. T., Sahakian, B. J., & Robbins, T. W. (2003). Stop-signal inhibition disrupted by damage to right inferior frontal gyrus in humans. *Nature Neuroscience, 6,* 115–116.

Aron, A. R., Monsell, S., Sahakian, B. J., & Robbins, T. W. (2004). A componential analysis of task-switching deficits associated with lesions of left and right frontal cortex. *Brain, 127,* 1561–1573.

Aron, A. R., Robbins, T. W., & Poldrack, R. A. (2004). Inhibition and the right inferior frontal cortex. *Trends in Cognitive Sciences, 8,* 170–177.

Arruda, J. E., Walker, K. A., Weiler, M. D., & Valentino, D. A. (1999). Validation of a right hemisphere vigilance system as measured by principal component and factor analyzed quantitative electroencephalogram. *International Journal of Psychophysiology, 32,* 119–128.

Ashbridge, E., Walsh, V., & Cowey, A. (1997). Temporal aspects of visual search studies by transcranial magnetic stimulation. *Neuropsychologia, 35,* 1121–1131.

Ashwin, C., Baron-Cohen, S., Wheelwright, S., O'Riordan, M., & Bullmore, E. T. (2007). Differential activation of the amygdala and the "social brain" during fearful face-processing in Asperger syndrome. *Neuropsychologia, 45,* 2–14.

Astafiev, S. V., Shulman, G. L., Stanley, C. M., Snyder, A. Z., Van Essen, D. C., & Corbetta, M. (2003). Functional organization of human intraparietal and frontal cortex for attending, looking, and pointing. *Journal of Neuroscience, 23,* 4689–4699.

Astafiev, S. V., Stanley, C. M., Shulman, G. L., & Corbetta, M. (2004). Extrastriate body area in human occipital cortex responds to the performance of motor actions. *Nature Neuroscience, 7,* 542–548.

Atallah, H., Frank, M. J., & O'Reilly, R. (2004). Hippocampus, cortex, and basal ganglia: Insights from computational models of complementary learning systems. *Neurobiology of Learning & Memory, 82*(3), 253–267.

Avery, D. H., Holtzheimer, P. E., Fawaz, W., Russo, J., Neumaier, J., Dunner, D. L., et al. (2006). A controlled study of repetitive transcranial magnetic stimulation in medication-resistant major depression. *Biological Psychiatry, 59,* 187–194.

Avillac, M., Deneve, S., Olivier, E., Pouget, A., & Duhamel, J.-R. (2005). Reference frames for representing visual and tactile locations in parietal cortex. *Nature Neuroscience, 8,* 941–949.

Axmacher, N., Draguhn, A., Elger, C. E., & Fell, J. (2009). Memory processes during sleep: Beyond the standard consolidation theory. *Cellular & Molecular Life Sciences, 66,* 2285–2297.

Bachevalier, J., & Loveland, K. A. (2006). The orbitofrontal-amygdala circuit and self-regulation of social-emotional behavior in autism. *Neuroscience & Biobehavioral Reviews, 30,* 97–117.

Bachoud-Lévi, A.-C., Gaura, V., Brugiéres, P., Lefaucheur, J.-P., Boissé, M.-F., Maison, P., et al. (2006). Effect of fetal neural transplants in patients with Huntington's disease 6 years after surgery: A long-term follow-up study. *Lancet Neurology, 5,* 303–309.

Baddeley, A. (1992). Working memory. *Science, 255*(5044), 556–559.

Baddeley, A. (1996). The fractionation of working memory. *Proceedings of the National Academy of Science, USA, 93*(24), 13468–13472.

Baddeley, A. D. (1986). *Working memory.* Oxford, UK: Oxford University Press.

Baddeley, A. D., & Hitch, G. (1974). Working memory. In G. A. Bower (Ed.), *The psychology of learning and motivation* (pp. 47–90). New York: Academic Press.

Badre, D. (2008). Cognitive control, hierarchy, and the rostro-caudal organization of the frontal lobes. *Trends in Cognitive Sciences, 12,* 193–200.

Badre, D., & Wagner, A. (2007). Left ventrolateral prefrontal cortex and the cognitive control of memory. *Neuropsychologia, 45,* 2883–2901.

Badre, D., Poldrack, R. A., Pare-Blagoev, E. J., Insler, R. Z., & Wagner, A. D. (2005). Dissociable controlled retrieval and generalized selection mechanisms in ventrolateral prefrontal cortex. *Neuron, 47*(6), 907–918.

Bains, J. S., & Oliet, S. H. (2007). Glia: They make your memories stick! *Trends in Neurosciences, 30*(8), 417–424.

Baker, C. I., Behrmann, M., & Olson, C. R. (2002). Impact of learning on representation of parts and wholes in monkey inferotemporal cortex. *Nature Neuroscience, 5,* 1210–1216.

Baker, D. P., Chabris, C. F., & Kosslyn, S. M. (1999). Encoding categorical and coordinate spatial relations without input-output correlations: New simulation models. *Cognitive Science, 23,* 33–51.

Baker, E., Blumstein, S. E., & Goodglass, H. (1981). Interaction between phonological and semantic factors in auditory comprehension. *Neuropsychologia, 19,* 1–16.

Ball, K. K., Roenker, D. L., Wadley, V. G., Edwards, J. D., Roth, D. L., McGwin, G., et al. (2006). Can high-risk older drivers be identified through performance-based measures in a Department of Motor Vehicles setting? *Journal of the American Geriatrics Society, 54,* 77–86.

Balslev, D., & Miall, R. C. (2008). Eye position representation in human anterior parietal cortex. *Journal of Neuroscience, 28,* 8968–8972.

Bamford, K. A., Caine, E. D., Kido, D. K., Cox, C., & Shoulson, I. (1995). A prospective evaluation of cognitive decline in early Huntington's disease: Functional and radiographic correlates. *Neurology, 45,* 1867–1873.

Bandettini, P. (2007). Functional MRI today. *International Journal of Psychophysiology, 63,* 138–145.

Banich, M. T. (1998). The missing link: The role of interhemispheric interaction in attentional processing. *Brain & Cognition, 36*(2), 128–157.

Banich, M. T. (2003). Interaction between the hemispheres and its implications for the processing capacity of the brain. In R. Davidson & K. Hugdahl (Eds.), *Brain asymmetry* (2d ed.) (pp. 261–302). Cambridge, MA: MIT Press.

Banich, M. T. (2009). Executive function: The search for an integrated account. *Current Directions in Psychological Science, 18,* 89–94.

Banich, M. T., & Belger, A. (1990). Interhemispheric interaction: How do the hemispheres divide and conquer a task? *Cortex, 26,* 77–94.

Banich, M. T., & Brown, W. S. (2000). A life-span perspective on interaction between the cerebral hemispheres. *Developmental Neuropsychology, 18*(1), 1–10.

Banich, M. T., & Federmeier, K. (1999). Categorical and metric spatial processing distinguished by task demands and practice. *Journal of Cognitive Neuroscience, 2,* 153–166.

Banich, M. T., & Scalf, P. E. (2003). The neurocognitive bases of developmental reading disorders. In M. T. Banich & M. Mack (Eds.), *Mind, brain, and language: Multidisciplinary perspectives* (pp. 283–306). Mahwah, NJ: Lawrence Erlbaum Associates.

Banich, M. T., & Shenker, J. I. (1994). Dissociations in memory for item identity and item frequency: Evidence from hemispheric interactions. *Neuropsychologia, 32,* 1179–1194.

Banich, M. T., Levine, S. C., Kim, H., & Huttenlocher, P. (1990). The effects of developmental factors on IQ in hemiplegic children. *Neuropsychologia, 28,* 35–47.

Banich, M. T., Passarotti, A. M., & Janes, D. (2000). Interhemispheric interaction during childhood: I. Neurologically intact children. *Developmental Neuropsychology, 18*(1), 33–51.

Banich, M. T., Stokes, A., & Elledge, V. C. (1989). Neuropsychological evaluation of aviators: A review. *Aviation Space & Environmental Medicine, 60,* 361–366.

Banich, M. T., Milham, M. P., Atchley, R. A., Cohen, N. J., Webb, A., Wszalek, T., et al. (2000). Prefrontal regions play a predominant role in imposing and attentional "set": evidence from fMRI. *Cognitive Brain Research, 10,* 1–9.

Banks, G., Short, P., Martinez, A. J., Latchaw, R., Ratcliff, G., & Boller, F. (1989). The alien hand syndrome: Clinical and postmortem findings. *Archives of Neurology, 46,* 456–459.

Bannister, R. (1992). *Brain and Bannister's clinical neurology* (7th ed.). Oxford, UK: Oxford University Press.

Barak, Y., & Achiron, A. (2000). Effect of interferon-beta-1b on cognitive functions in multiple sclerosis. *Annals of Neurology, 48,* 885–892.

Barch, D. M. (2005). The cognitive neuroscience of schizophrenia. *Annual Review of Clinical Psychology, 1,* 321–353.

Barch, D. M., Braver, T. S., Akbudak, E., Conturo, T., Ollinger, J., & Snyder, A. (2001). Anterior cingulate cortex and response conflict: Effects of response modality and processing domain. *Cerebral Cortex, 11,* 837–848.

Barch, D. M., Csernansky, J. G., Conturo, T., & Snyder, A. Z. (2002). Working and long-term memory deficits in schizophrenia: Is there a common prefrontal mechanism? *Journal of Abnormal Psychology, 111,* 478–494.

Barkley, R. A. (1997). Behavioral inhibition, sustained attention, and executive functions: Constructing a unifying theory of ADHD. *Psychological Bulletin, 121,* 65–94.

Barlow, H. B. (1985). The twelfth Bartlett Memorial Lecture: The role of single neurons in the psychology of perception. *Quarterly Journal of Experimental Psychology, 37A,* 121–145.

Baron-Cohen, S. (1995). *Mindblindness: An essay on autism and theory of mind.* Cambridge, MA: The MIT Press.

Baron-Cohen, S. (2002). The extreme male brain theory of autism. *Trends in Cognitive Sciences, 6,* 248–254.

Baron-Cohen, S., Knickmeyer, R., & Belmonte, M. (2005). Sex differences in the brain: Implications for explaining autism. *Science, 310,* 819–823.

Barr, C. L. (2001). Genetics of childhood disorders: XXII. ADHD, Part 6: The dopamine D4 receptor gene. *Journal of the American Academy of Child and Adolescent Psychiatry, 40,* 118–120.

Bartels, A. L., & Leenders, K. L. (2009). Parkinson's disease: the syndrome, the pathogenesis and pathophysiology. *Cortex, 45,* 915–921.

Bartels, A., & Zeki, S. (2000). The architecture of the colour centre in the human visual brain: New results and a review. *European Journal of Neuroscience, 12,* 172–193.

Bartels, A., & Zeki, S. (2000). The neural basis of romantic love. *Neuroreport, 11,* 3829–3834.

Barth, J. T., Alves, W. M., Ryan, T. V., Macchiocchi, S. N., Rimel, R. W., Jane, J. A., & Nelson, W. E. (1989). Mild head injury in sports: Neuropsychological sequelae and recovery of function. In H. S. Levin, H. M. Eisenberg, & A. L. Benton (Eds.), *Mild head injury.* New York: Oxford University Press.

Bartolo, A., Benuzzi, F., Nocetti, L., Baraldi, P., & Nichelli, P. (2006). Humor comprehension and appreciation: An FMRI study. *Journal of Cognitive Neuroscience, 18,* 1789–1798.

Bartus, R. T. (2000). On neurodegenerative diseases, models, and treatment strategies: Lessons learned and lessons forgotten a generation following the cholinergic hypothesis. *Experimental Neurology, 163,* 495–529.

Bastian, A. J. (2006). Learning to predict the future: The cerebellum adapts feedforward movement control. *Current Opinion in Neurobiology, 16,* 645–649.

Bastian, A. J., Martin, T. A., Keating, J. G., & Thach, W. T. (1996). Cerebellar ataxia: Abnormal control of interaction torques across multiple joints. *Journal of Neurophysiology, 76,* 492–509.

Bates, E., Reilly, J., Wulfeck, B., Dronkers, N., Opie, M., Fenson, J., et al. (2001). Differential effects of unilateral lesions on language production in children and adults. *Brain & Language, 79,* 223–265.

Batista, A. P., Buneo, C. A., Snyder, L. H., & Andersen, R. A. (1999). Reach plans in eye-centered coordinates. *Science, 285,* 257–260.

Bauer, R. M., & McDonald, C. R. (2006). Auditory agnosia and amusia. In M. J. Farah & T. E. Feinberg (Eds.), *Patient-based approaches to cognitive neuroscience* (2d ed., pp. 133–146). Cambridge, MA: MIT Press.

Baumann, O., Chan, E., & Mattingley, J. B. (2010). Dissociable neural circuits for encoding and retrieval of object locations during active navigation in humans. *NeuroImage, 49,* 2816–2825.

Bavelier, D., Brozinsky, C., Tomann, A., Mitchell, T., Neville, H., & Liu, G. (2001). Impact of early deafness and early exposure to sign language on the cerebral organization for motion processing. *Journal of Neuroscience, 21,* 8931–8942.

Bavelier, D., Dye, M. W. G., & Hauser, P. C. (2006). Do deaf individuals see better? *Trends in Cognitive Sciences, 10,* 512–518.

Baxendale, S. (2009). The Wada test. *Current Opinion in Neurology, 22,* 185–189.

Baxter, M. G. (2009). Prefrontal cortex and rule abstraction: Where and whether? Theoretical comment on Moore et al. (2009). *Behavioral Neuroscience, 123,* 459–462.

Baxter, M. G., & Murray, E. A. (2002). The amygdala and reward. *Nature Reviews Neuroscience, 3,* 563–573.

Bayles, K. A. (1982). Language function in senile dementia. *Brain & Language, 16,* 265–280.

Bayley, P. J., Hopkins, R. O., & Squire, L. R. (2006). The fate of old memories after medial temporal lobe damage. *Journal of Neuroscience, 26*(51), 13311–13317.

Bayley, P. J., O'Reilly, R. C., Curran, T., & Squire, L. R. (2008). New semantic learning in patients with large medial temporal lobe lesions. *Hippocampus, 18,* 575–583.

Baylis, G. C., Baylis, L. L., & Gore, C. L. (2004). Visual neglect can be object-based or scene-based depending on task representation. *Cortex, 40,* 237–246.

Beatty, W. W., Salmon, D. P., Butters, N., Heindel, W. C., & Granholm, E. L. (1988). Retrograde amnesia in patients with Alzheimer's disease or Huntington's disease. *Neurobiology of Aging, 9,* 181–186.

Beaubrun, G., & Gray, G. E. (2000). A review of herbal medicines for psychiatric disorders. *Psychiatric Services, 51,* 1130–1134.

Beauchamp, M. S., Haxby, J. V., Jennings, J. E., & DeYoe, E. A. (1999). An fMRI version of the Farnsworth-Munsell 100-Hue Test reveals multiple color-selective areas in human ventral occipitotemporal cortex. *Cerebral Cortex, 9,* 257–263.

Beauregard, M., Levesque, J., & Bourgouin, P. (2001). Neural correlates of conscious self-regulation of emotion. *Journal of Neuroscience, 21,* RC165(1–6).

Beauvois, M.-F., & Derouesne, J. (1981). Lexical or orthographic dysgraphia. *Brain, 104,* 21–50.

Bechara, A. (2004). The role of emotion in decision-making: Evidence from neurological patients with orbitofrontal damage. *Brain and Cognition, 55*(1), 30–40.

Bechara, A. (2005). Decision making, impulse control and loss of willpower to resist drugs: A neurocognitive perspective. *Nature Neuroscience, 8,* 1458–1463.

Bechara, A., & Damasio, H. (2002). Decision-making and addiction (Part I): Impaired activation of somatic states in substance dependent individuals when pondering decisions with negative future consequences. *Neuropsychologia, 40,* 1675–1689.

Bechara, A., Damasio, A. R., Damasio, H., & Anderson, S. W. (1994). Insensitivity to future consequences following damage to human prefrontal cortex. *Cognition, 50,* 7–15.

Bechara, A., Damasio, H., & Damasio, A. R. (2000). Emotion, decision making and the orbitofrontal cortex. *Cerebral Cortex, 10,* 295–307.

Bechara, A., Tranel, D., Damasio, H., Adolphs, R., Rockland, C., & Damasio, R. A. R. (1995). Double dissociation of conditioning and declarative knowledge relative to the amygdala and hippocampus in humans. *Science, 269*(5227), 1115–1118.

Beckmann, M., Johansen-Berg, H., & Rushworth, M. F. S. (2009). Connectivity-based parcellation of human cingulate cortex and its relation to functional specialization. *Journal of Neuroscience, 29,* 1175–1190.

Beeman, M. (1993). Semantic processing in the right hemisphere may contribute to drawing inferences during comprehension. *Brain & Language, 44,* 80–120.

Beeman, M. J., & Chiarello, C. (1998a). Complementary right- and left-hemisphere language comprehension. *Current Directions in Psychological Science, 7*(1), 2–8.

Beeman, M. J., & Chiarello, C. (Eds.) (1998b). *Right hemisphere language comprehension: Perspectives from cognitive neuroscience.* Mahwah, NJ: Lawrence Erlbaum & Associates.

Beevers, C. G., Gibb, B. E., McGeary, J. E., & Miller, I. W. (2007). Serotonin transporter genetic variation and biased attention for emotional word stimuli among psychiatric inpatients. *Journal of Abnormal Psychology, 116,* 208–212.

Behar, E., Zuellig, A. R., & Borkovec, T. D. (2005). Thought and imaginal activity during worry and trauma recall. *Behavior Therapy, 36,* 157–168.

Behrens, S. (1988). The role of the right hemisphere in the production of linguistic stress. *Brain & Language, 33,* 104–127.

Behrmann, M. (2000). The mind's eye mapped onto the brain's matter. *Current Directions in Psychological Science, 9,* 50–54.

Behrmann, M., & Avidan, G. (2005). Congenital prosopagnosia: Face-blind from birth. *Trends in Cognitive Sciences, 9,* 180–187.

Behrmann, M., & Ewell, C. (2003). Expertise in tactile pattern recognition. *Psychological Science, 14,* 480–486.

Behrmann, M., & Moscovitch, M. (1994). Object-centered neglect in patients with unilateral neglect. *Journal of Cognitive Neuroscience, 6,* 1–16.

Behrmann, M., Moscovitch, M., & Winocur, G. (1994). Intact visual imagery and impaired visual perception in a patient with visual agnosia. *Journal of Experimental Psychology: Human Perception and Performance, 20,* 1068–1087.

Behrmann, M., Peterson, M. A., Moscovitch, M., & Suzuki, S. (2006). Independent representation of parts and the relations between them: Evidence from integrative agnosia. *Journal of Experimental Psychology: Human Perception and Performance, 32,* 1169–1184.

Behrmann, M., Thomas, C., & Humphreys, K. (2006). Seeing it differently: Visual processing in autism. *Trends in Cognitive Sciences, 10,* 258–264.

Belanger, H. G., & Vanderploeg, R. D. (2005). The neuropsychological impact of sports-related concussion: A meta-analysis. *Journal of the International Neuropsychological Society, 11,* 345–357.

Belger, A., & Banich, M. T. (1992). Interhemispheric interaction affected by computational complexity. *Neuropsychologia, 30,* 923–931.

Belger, A., & Banich, M. T. (1998). Costs and benefits of integrating information between the cerebral hemispheres: A computational perspective. *Neuropsychology, 12*(3), 380–988.

Belin, P., Zatorre, R. J., Lafaille, P., Ahad, P., & Pike, B. (2000). Voice-selective areas in human auditory cortex. *Nature, 403,* 309–312.

Ben-Shachar, M., Dougherty, R. F., & Wandell, B. A. (2007). White matter pathways in reading. *Current Opinion in Neurobiology, 17,* 258–270.

Benabid, A. L., Chabardes, S., Mitrofanis, J., & Pollak, P. (2009). Deep brain stimulation of the subthalamic nucleus for the treatment of Parkinson's disease. *Lancet Neurology, 8,* 67–81.

Benavides-Piccione, R., Ballesteros-Yáñez, I., de Lagrán, M. M., Elston, G., Estivill, X., Fillat, C., et al. (2004). On dendrites in Down syndrome and DS murine models: A spiny way to learn. *Progress in Neurobiology, 74,* 111–126.

Bengtsson, S. L., Haynes, J. D., Sakai, K., Buckley, M. J., & Passingham, R. E. (2009). The representation of abstract task rules in the human prefrontal cortex. *Cerebral Cortex, 19,* 1929–1936.

Benishin, C. G., Lee, R., Wang, L. C. H., & Liu, H. J. (1991). Effects of ginsenoside Rb$_1$ on central cholinergic metabolism. *Pharmacology, 42,* 223–229.

Benjamin, J., Li, L., Patterson, C., Greenberg, B. D., Murphy, D. L., & Hamer, D. H. (1996). Population and familial association between the D4 dopamine receptor gene and measures of Novelty Seeking. *Nature Genetics, 12,* 81–84.

Benke, T., Köylü, B., Visani, P., Karner, E., Brenneis, C., Bartha, L., et al. (2006). Language lateralization in temporal lobe epilepsy: A comparison between fMRI and the Wada test. *Epilepsia, 47,* 1308–1319.

Bennett, C. M., & Baird, A. A. (2006). Anatomical changes in the emerging adult brain: A voxel-based morphometry study. *Human Brain Imaging, 27,* 766–777.

Benowitz, L. I., Bear, D. M., Rosenthal, R., Mesulam, M.-M., Zaidel, E., & Sperry, R. W. (1983). Hemispheric specialization in nonverbal communication. *Cortex, 19,* 5–12.

Benson, D. F., & Geschwind, N. (1972). Aphasia and related disturbances. In A. B. Baker (Ed.), *Clinical neurology.* New York: Harper & Row.

Bentin, S., Allison, T., Puce, A., Perez, E., & McCarthy, G. (1996). Electrophysiological studies of face perception in humans. *Journal of Cognitive Neuroscience, 8,* 551–565.

Bentin, S., Taylor, M. J., Rousselet, G. A., Itier, R. J., Caldara, R., Schyns, P. G., Jacques, C., & Rossion, B. (2007). Controlling for interstimulus perceptual variance does not abolish N170 face sensitivity. *Nature Neuroscience, 10,* 801–802.

Benton, A. L. (1967). Constructional apraxia and the minor hemisphere. *Confinia Neurologica, 29,* 1–16.

Benton, A. L. (1969). Disorders of spatial orientation. In P. J. Vinken & G. W. Bruyn (Eds.), *Handbook of clinical neurology.* Amsterdam: North Holland.

Benton, A. L. (1985). Body schema disturbances: Finger agnosia and right-left disorientation. In K. M. Heilman & E. Valenstein (Eds.), *Clinical neuropsychology* (2d ed., pp. 115–129). New York: Oxford University Press.

Benton, A. L., Hannay, H. J., & Varney, N. R. (1975). Visual perception of line direction in patients with unilateral brain disease. *Neurology, 25,* 907–910.

Berardi, N., Pizzorusso, T., Ratto, G. M., & Maffei, L. (2003). Molecular basis of plasticity in the visual cortex. *Trends in Neurosciences, 26,* 369–378.

Bergman, H., & Deuschl, G. (2002). Pathophysiology of Parkinson's disease: from clinical neurology to basic neuroscience and back. *Movement Disorders, 17,* s28–s40.

Bergsneider, M., Hovda, D. A., McArthur, D. L., Etchepare, M., Huang, S.-C., Sehati, N., et al. (2001). Metabolic recovery following human traumatic brain injury based on FDG-PET: Time course and relationship to neurological disability. *Journal of Head Trauma Rehabilitation, 16,* 135–148.

Berman, K. F., & Meyer-Lindenberg, A. (2004). Functional brain imaging studies in schizophrenia. In D. S. Charney & E. J. Nestler (Eds.), *Neurobiology of mental illness* (2d ed.; pp. 311–323). Oxford, UK: Oxford University Press.

Berman, R. M., Sporn, J., Charney, D. S., & Mathew, S. (2009). Principles of the pharmacotherapy of depression. In D. S. Charney & E. J. Nestler (Eds.), *Neurobiology of mental illness* (3d ed.; pp. 491–514). Oxford, UK: Oxford University Press.

Bernheimer, H., Birkmayer, W., Hornykiewicz, O., Jellinger, K., & Seitelberg, F. (1973). Brain dopamine and the syndromes of Parkinson and Huntington: Clinical, morphological and neurochemical correlations. *Journal of Neuroscience, 20,* 415–455.

Berns, G. S., McClure, S. M., Pagnoni, G., & Montague, P. R. (2001). Predictability modulates human brain response to reward. *Journal of Neuroscience, 21,* 2793–2798.

Berntson, G. G., Bechara, A., Damasio, H., Tranel, D., & Cacioppo, J. T. (2007). Amygdala contribution to selective dimensions of emotion. *Social Cognitive & Affective Neuroscience, 2,* 123–129.

Berridge, C. W. (2008). Noradrenergic modulation of arousal. *Brain Research Reviews, 58,* 1–17.

Berridge, C. W., & Waterhouse, B. D. (2003). The locus-coeruleus-noradrenergic system: Modulation of behavioral state and state-dependent cognitive processes. *Brain Research Reviews, 42,* 33–84.

Berridge, K. C. (2003). Pleasures of the brain. *Brain & Cognition, 5,* 106–128.

Berridge, K. C., & Robinson, T. E. (1998). What is the role of dopamine in reward: Hedonic impact, reward learning, or incentive salience? *Brain Research Reviews, 28,* 309–369.

Berridge, K. C., & Robinson, T. E. (2003). Parsing reward. *Trends in Neurosciences, 26,* 507–513.

Berryhill, M. E., Phuong, L., Picasso, L., Cabeza, R., & Olson, I. R. (2007). Parietal lobe and episodic memory: Bilateral damage causes impaired free recall of autobiographical memory. *Journal of Neuroscience, 27,* 14415–14423.

Berti, A., & Rizzolatti, G. (1992). Visual processing without awareness: Evidence from unilateral neglect. *Journal of Cognitive Neuroscience, 4,* 345–351.

Berton, O., & Nestler, E. J. (2006). New drug approaches to antidepressant drug discovery: Beyond monoamines. *Nature Reviews Neuroscience, 7,* 137–151.

Bertoncini, J., Morais, J., Bijeljac-Babic, R., McAdams, S., Peretz, I., & Mehler, J. (1989). Dichotic perception and laterality in neonates. *Brain and Language, 37,* 591–605.

Bertram, L., & Tanzi, R. E. (2008). Thirty years of Alzheimer's disease genetics: The implications of systematic meta-analyses. *Nature Reviews Neuroscience, 9,* 768–778.

Best, C. T., Hoffman, H., & Glanville, B. B. (1982). Development of infant ear asymmetries for speech and music. *Perception and Psychophysics, 31*(1), 75–85.

Bialystok, E., Craik, F. I. M., Klein, R., & Viswanathan, M. (2004). Bilingualism, aging, and cognitive control: Evidence from the Simon task. *Psychology & Aging, 19,* 290–303.

Biederman, J., & Spencer, T. (1999). Attention-deficit/hyperactivity disorder (ADHD) as a noradrenergic disorder. *Biological Psychiatry, 46,* 1234–1242.

Biederman, J., Arnsten, A. F. T., Faraone, S. V., Doyle, A. E., Spencer, T. J., Wilens, T. E., Weiss, M. D., Safren, S. A., & Culpepper, L. (2006). New developments in the treatment of ADHD. *Journal of Clinical Psychiatry, 67,* 148–159.

Bierer, L. M., Hof, P. R., Purohit, D. P., Carlin, L., Schmeidler, J., Davis, K. L., & Perl, D. P. (1995). Neocortical neurofibrillary tangles correlate with dementia severity in Alzheimer's disease. *Archives of Neurology, 52,* 81–88.

Binder, J. R., Frost, J. A., Hammeke, T. A., Cox, R. W., Rao, S. M., & Pricto, T. (1997). Human brain language areas identified by functional magnetic resonance imaging. *Journal of Neuroscience, 17,* 353–362.

Binder, J. R., Frost, J. A., Hammeke, T. A., Rao, S. M., & Cox, R. W. (1996). Function of the left planum temporale in auditory and linguistic processing. *Brain, 119,* 1239–1247.

Binder, L. M. (1986). Persisting symptoms after mild head injury: A review of the post-concussive syndrome. *Journal of Clinical & Experimental Neuropsychology, 8,* 323–346.

Binkofski, F., Buccino, G., Stephan, K. M., Rizzolatti, G., Seitz, R. J., & Freund, H. J. (1999). A parieto-premotor network for object manipulation: Evidence from neuroimaging. *Experimental Brain Research, 128,* 210–213.

Binnie, C. D. (1994). Cognitive impairment: Is it inevitable? *Seizure, 3*(Suppl. A), 17–22.

Biran, I., & Chatterjee, A. (2004). Alien hand syndrome. *Archives of Neurology, 61,* 292–294.

Birbaumer, N., Grodd, W., Diedrich, O., Klose, U., Erb, M., Lotze, M., et al. (1998). fMRI reveals amygdala activation to human faces in social phobics. *NeuroReport, 9,* 1223–1226.

Birnbaum, S. G., Gobeske, K. T., Auerbach, J., Taylor, J. R., & Arnsten, A. F. T. (1999). A role for norepinephrine in stress-induced cognitive deficits: Alpha-1-adrenoceptor mediation in prefrontal cortex. *Biological Psychiatry, 46,* 1266–1274.

Bisazza, A., Cantalupo, C., Capocchiano, M., & Vallortigara, G. (2000). Population lateralization and social behavior: A study with sixteen species of fish. *Laterality, 5,* 269–284.

Bishop, K. M., & Wahlsten, D. (1997). Sex differences in the human corpus callosum: Myth or reality? *Neuroscience and Biobehavioral Reviews, 21,* 581–601.

Bishop, S. J. (2007). Neurocognitive mechanisms of anxiety: An integrative account. *Trends in Cognitive Sciences, 11,* 307–316.

Bishop, S. J., Duncan, J., & Lawrence, A. D. (2004). State anxiety modulation of the amygdala response to unattended threat-related stimuli. *Journal of Neuroscience, 24,* 10364–10368.

Bishop, S. J., Duncan, J., Brett, M., & Lawrence, A. D. (2004). Prefrontal cortical function and anxiety: Controlling attention to threat-related stimuli. *Nature Neuroscience, 7,* 184–188.

Bishop, S. J., Jenkins, R., & Lawrence, A. D. (2007). Neural processing of fearful faces: Effects of anxiety are gated by perceptual capacity limitations. *Cerebral Cortex, 17,* 1595–1603.

Bisiach, E., & Luzzatti, C. (1978). Unilateral neglect of representational space. *Cortex, 14,* 129–133.

Bisiach, E., & Rusconi, M. L. (1990). Breakdown of perceptual awareness in unilateral neglect. *Cortex, 24,* 643–649.

Bisiach, E., Geminiani, G., Berti, A., & Rusconi, M.L. (1990). Perceptual and premotor factors of unilateral neglect. *Neurology, 40,* 1278–1281.

Bisiach, E., Neppi-Modona, M., & Ricci, R. (2002). Space anisometry in unilateral neglect. In H. O. Karnath, A. D. Milner, & G. Villar (Eds.), *The cognitive and neural bases of spatial neglect* (pp. 145–152). Oxford, UK: Oxford University Press.

Bisiach, E., Rusconi, M. L., & Vallar, G. (1991). Remission of somatoparaphrenic delusion through vestibular stimulation. *Neuropsychologia, 29,* 1029–1031.

Black, F. W., & Strub, R. L. (1976). Constructional apraxia in patients with discrete missile wounds of the brain. *Cortex, 12,* 212–220.

Black, J. E., Isaacs, K. R., Anderson, B. J., Alcantara, A. A., & Greenough, W. T. (1990). Learning causes synaptogenesis, whereas motor activity causes angiogenesis, in cerebellar cortex of adult rats. *Proceedings of the National Academy of Science, USA, 87*(14), 5568–5572.

Blacker, D., Albert, M. S., Bassett, S. S., Go, R. C. P., Harrell, L. E., & Folstein, M. F. (1994). Reliability and validity of NINCDS-ADRDA criteria for Alzheimer's disease: The National Institute of Mental Health Genetics Initiative. *Archives of Neurology, 51,* 1198–1024.

Blair, R. J. R., Morris, J. S., Frith, C. D., Perrett, D. I., & Dolan, R. J. (1999). Dissociable neural responses to facial expressions of sadness and anger. *Brain, 122,* 883–893.

Blakemore, S. J., Wolpert, D. M., & Frith, C. D. (1998). Central cancellation of self-produced tickle sensation. *Nature Neuroscience, 1,* 635–640.

Blakemore, S. J., den Ouden, H., Choudhury, S., & Frith, C. (2007). Adolescent development of the neural circuitry for thinking about intentions. *Social, Cognitive & Affective Neuroscience, 2,* 130–139.

Blangero, A., Menz, M., McNamara, A., & Binkofski, F. (2009). Parietal modules for reaching. *Neuropsychologia, 47,* 1500–1507.

Bloch, C., Kaiser, A., Kuenzli, E., Zappatore, D., Haller, S., Franceschini, R., et al. (2009). The age of second language acquisition determines the variability in activation elicited by narration in three languages in Broca's and Wernicke's area. *Neuropsychologia, 47,* 625–633.

Bloom, F. E. (1993). Advancing a neurodevelopmental origin for schizophrenia. *Archives of General Psychiatry, 50,* 224–227.

Blumenfeld, R. S., & Ranganath, C. (2007). Prefrontal cortex and long-term memory encoding: An integrative review of findings from neuropsychology and neuroimaging. *The Neuroscientist, 13,* 280–291.

Blumer, D. (1999). Evidence supporting the temporal lobe epilepsy personality syndrome. *Neurology, 53*(Suppl. 2), S9–S12.

Blumstein, S. (1991). Phonological aspects of aphasia. In M. Sarno (Ed.), *Acquired aphasia* (pp. 129–155). New York: Academic Press.

Bobes, M. A., Lopera, F., Diaz Comas, L., Galan, L., Carbonell, F., Bringas, M. L., & Valdes-Sosa, M. (2004). Brain potentials reflect residual face processing in a case of prosopagnosia. *Cognitive Neuropsychology, 21,* 691–718.

Boileau, I., Dagher, A., Leyton, M., Welfeld, K., Booij, L., Diksic, M., & Benkelfat, C. (2007). Conditioned dopamine release in humans: A positron emission tomography [11][C] raclopride study with amphetamine. *Journal of Neuroscience, 27,* 3998–4003.

Bolger, D. J., Perfetti, C. A., & Schneider, W. (2005). Cross-cultural effect on the brain revisited: Universal structures plus writing system variation. *Human Brain Mapping, 25,* 92–104.

Boll, T. J. (1981). The Halstead-Reitan Neuropsychological Battery. In S. B. Filskov & T. J. Boll (Eds.), *Handbook of clinical neuropsychology.* New York: Wiley Interscience.

Bonelli, R. M., & Cummings, J. L. (2008). Frontal-subcortical dementias. *Neurologist, 14,* 100–107.

Bookheimer, S. (2002). Functional MRI of language: New approaches to understanding the cortical organization of semantic processing. *Annual Review of Neuroscience, 25,* 151–188.

Boorman, E. D., Behrens, T. E., Woolrich, M. W., & Rushworth, M. F. (2009). How green is the grass on the other side? Frontopolar cortex and the evidence in favor of alternative courses of action. *Neuron, 62,* 733–743.

Booth, M. C. A., & Rolls, E. T. (1998). View-invariant representations of familiar objects by neurons in the inferior temporal cortex. *Cerebral Cortex, 8,* 510–523.

Borek, L. L., Amick, M. M., & Friedman, J. H. (2006). Non-motor aspects of Parkinson's disease. *CNS Spectrums, 11,* 541–554.

Borgwardt, S. J., Riecher-Rössler, A., Dazzan, P., Chitnis, X., Aston, J., Drewe, M., et al. (2007). Regional gray matter volume abnormalities in the at risk mental state. *Biological Psychiatry, 61,* 1148–1156.

Born, R. T., & Bradley, D. C. (2005). Structure and function of visual area MT. *Annual Review of Neuroscience, 28,* 157–189.

Bornstein, B. (1963). Prosopagnosia. In L. Hapern (Ed.), *Problems of dynamic neurology* (pp. 283–318). Jerusalem: Hadassah Medical School.

Bornstein, B., Sroka, M., & Munitz, H. (1969). Prosopagnosia with animal face agnosia. *Cortex, 5,* 164–169.

Bornstein, R. A., Nasrallah, H. A., Para, M. F., Whitacre, C. C., Rosenberger, P., & Fass, R. J. (1993). Neuropsychological performance in symptomatic and asymptomatic HIV infection. *AIDS, 7,* 519–524.

Borod, J. C., Carper, M., Naeser, M., & Goodglass, H. (1985). Left-handed and right-handed aphasics with left hemisphere lesions compared on nonverbal performance measures. *Cortex, 21,* 81–90.

Borod, J. C., Cicero, B. A., Obler, L. K., Welkowitz, J., Erhan, H. M., Santschi, C., et al. (1998). Right hemisphere emotional perception: Evidence across multiple channels. *Neuropsychology, 12,* 446–458.

Bosco, G., Carrozzo, M., & Lacquaniti, F. (2008). Contributions of the human temporoparietal junction and MT/V51 to the timing of interception revealed by transcranial magnetic stimulation. *Journal of Neuroscience, 28,* 12071–12804.

Bottini, G., Corcoran, R., Sterzi, R., Paulesu, E., Schenone, P., Scarpa, P., Frackowiak, R. S., & Frith, C. D. (1994). The role of the right hemisphere in the interpretation of figurative aspects of language. A positron emission tomography activation study. *Brain, 117,* 1241–1253.

Botvinick, M. M., Braver, T. S., Barch, D. M., Carter, C. S., & Cohen, J. D. (2001). Conflict monitoring and cognitive control. *Psychological Review, 108,* 624–652.

Botvinick, M., Cohen, J. D., & Carter, C. S. (2004). Conflict monitoring and anterior cingulate cortex: An update. *Trends in Cognitive Sciences, 8,* 539–546.

Bourgeois, J.-P. (2001). Synaptogenesis in the neocortex of the newborn: The ultimate frontier for individuation? In C. A. Nelson & M. Luciana (Eds.), *Handbook of developmental cognitive neuroscience* (pp. 23–34). Cambridge, MA: MIT Press.

Bourgeon, S., Xerri, C., & Coq, J. O. (2004). Abilities in tactile discrimination of textures in adult rats exposed to enriched or impoverished environments. *Behavioural Brain Research, 153,* 217–231.

Boutros, N., Belger, A, Campbell, D., D'Souza, C., & Krystal, J. (1999). Comparison of four components of sensory gating in schizophrenia and normal subjects: A preliminary report. *Psychiatry Research, 88*(2), 119–130.

Bouvier, S. E., & Engel, S. A. (2006). Behavioral deficits and cortical damage loci in cerebral achromatopsia. *Cerebral Cortex, 16,* 183–191.

Bowers, D., Bauer, R. M., Coslett, H. B., & Heilman, K. M. (1985). Processing of faces by patients with unilateral hemispheric lesions. I. Dissociations between judgements of facial affect and facial identity. *Brain and Cognition, 4,* 258–272.

Bowyer, S. M., Hsieh, L., Moran, J. E., Young, R. A., Manoharan, A., Liao, C. C., et al. (2009). Conversation effects on neural mechanisms underlying reaction time to visual events while viewing a driving scene using MEG. *Brain Research, 1251,* 151–161.

Brüne, M., & Brüne-Cohrs, U. (2006). Theory of mind: Evolution, ontogeny, brain mechanisms, and psychopathology. *Neuroscience & Biobehavioral Reviews, 30,* 437–455.

Braak, H., & Del Tredici, K. (2008). Assessing fetal nerve cell grafts in Parkinson's disease. *Nature Medicine, 14,* 483–485.

Bradshaw, J. L., Phillips, J. G., Dennis, C., Mattingley, J. B., Andrewes, D., Chiu, E., Pierson, J. M., & Bradshaw, J. A. (1992). Initiation and execution of movement sequences in those suffering from and at-risk of developing Huntington's disease. *Journal of Clinical and Experimental Neuropsychology, 14,* 179–192.

Braff, D. L. (2004). Psychophysiological and information processing approaches to schizophrenia. In D. S. Charney & E. J. Nestler (Eds.), *Neurobiology of mental illness* (2d ed.; pp. 324–338). Oxford, UK: Oxford University Press.

Braff, D. L., & Light, G. A. (2004). Preattentional and attentional cognitive deficits as targets for treating schizophrenia. *Psychopharmacology, 174,* 75–85.

Brainin, M., Seiser, A., & Matz, K. (2008). The mirror world of motor inhibition: The alien hand. *Journal of Neurology, Neurosurgery & Psychiatry, 79,* 246–252.

Brambilla, P., Cerini, R., Gasparini, A., Versace, A., Andreone, N., Vittorini, E., et al. (2005). Investigation of corpus callosum in schizophrenia with diffusion imaging. *Schizophrenia Research, 79,* 201–210.

Brandt, J. (1991). Cognitive impairments in Huntington's disease: Insights into the neuropsychology of the striatum. In F. Boller & J. Grafman (Eds.), *Handbook of neuropsychology* (Vol. 5, pp. 241–264). New York: Elsevier.

Braun, A. R., Guillemin, A., Hosey, L., & Varga, M. (2001). The neural organization of discourse: An H2 15O-PET study of narrative production in English and American sign language. *Brain, 124,* 2028–2024.

Braver, T. S., & Bongiolatti, S. R. (2002). The role of frontopolar cortex in subgoal processing during working memory. *NeuroImage, 15,* 523–536.

Breiter, H. C., Etcoff, N. L., Whalen, P. J., Kennedy, W. A., Rauch, S. L., Buckner, R. L., et al. (1996). Response and habituation of the human amygdala during visual processing of facial expression. *Neuron, 17,* 875–887.

Brewer, J. B., Zhao, Z., Desmond, J. E., Glover, G. H., & Gabrieli, J. D. (1998). Making memories: Brain activity that predicts how well visual experience will be remembered. *Science, 281*(5380), 1151–1152.

Briggs, F., & Usrey, W. M. (2009). Parallel processing in the corticogeniculate pathway of the macaque monkey. *Neuron, 62,* 135–146.

Brighina, F., Bisiach, E., Oliveri, M., Piazza, A., La Bua, V., Daniele, O., & Fierro, B. (2003). 1 Hz repetitive transcranial magnetic stimulation of the unaffected hemisphere ameliorates contralesional visuospatial neglect in humans. *Neuroscience Letters, 336,* 131–133.

Bright, P., Buckman, J., Fradera, A., Yoshimasu, H., Colchester, A. C., & Kopelman, M. D. (2006). Retrograde amnesia in patients with hippocampal, medial temporal, temporal lobe, or frontal pathology. *Learning & Memory, 13*(5), 545–557.

Brinkman, C. (1984). Supplementary motor area of the monkey's cerebral cortex: Short- and long-term deficits after unilateral ablation and the effects of subsequent callosal section. *Journal of Neuroscience, 4,* 918–929.

Briones, T. L., Klintsova, A. Y., & Greenough, W. T. (2004). Stability of synaptic plasticity in the adult rat visual cortex induced by complex environment exposure. *Brain Research, 1018,* 130–135.

Britten, K. H. (2008). Mechanisms of self-motion perception. *Annual Review of Neuroscience, 31,* 389–410.

Broadbent, D. E. (1958). *Perception and communication.* London: Pergamon Press.

Brodal, P. (1998). *The central nervous system: Structure and function* (2d ed). New York: Oxford University Press.

Brody, A. L., Mandelkern, M. A., Jarvik, M. E., Lee, G. S., Smith, E. C., Huang, J. C., et al. (2004). Differences between smokers and nonsmokers in regional gray matter volumes and densities. *Biological Psychiatry, 55,* 77–84.

Brody, A. L., Mandelkern, M. A., London, E. D., Childress, A. R., Lee, G. S., Bota, R. G., et al. (2002). Brain metabolic changes during cigarette craving. *Archives of General Psychiatry, 59,* 1162–1172.

Brookmeyer, R., Gray, S., & Kawas, C. (1998). Projections of Alzheimer's disease in the United States and the public health impact of delaying disease onset. *American Journal of Public Health, 88,* 1337–1342.

Brooks, D. N., & Baddeley, A. (1976). What can amnesic patients learn? *Neuropsychologia, 14,* 111–122.

Brosco, J. P., Mattingly, M., & Sanders, L. M. (2006). Impact of specific medical interventions on reducing the prevalence of mental retardation. *Archives of Pediatric & Adolescent Medicine, 160,* 302–309.

Brouwers, P., Cox, C., Martin, A., Chase, T. N., & Fedio, P. (1984). Differential perceptual-spatial impairment in Huntington's and Alzheimer's dementias. *Archives of Neurology, 41,* 1073–1076.

Brown, A. S. (2002). Consolidation theory and retrograde amnesia in humans. *Psychonomic Bulletin & Review, 9,* 403–425.

Brown, P., & Marsden, C. D. (1998). What do the basal ganglia do? *Lancet, 351,* 1801–1804.

Brown, P., Cathala, F., Sadowski, D., & Gajdusek, D. (1979). Creutzfeldt-Jakob disease in France: II. Clinical characteristics of 124 consecutively verified cases during the decade 1968–1977. *Annals of Neurology, 6,* 430–437.

Brownell, H. (1988). Appreciation of metaphoric and connotative word meaning by brain-damaged patients. In C. Chiarello (Ed.), *Right hemisphere contributions to lexical semantics* (pp. 19–31). New York: Springer-Verlag.

Brownell, H. H., Michel, D., Powelson, J. A., & Gardner, H. (1983). Surprise but not coherence: Sensitivity to verbal humor in right hemisphere patients. *Brain & Language, 18,* 20–27.

Brozoski, T. J., Brown, R. M., Rosvold, H. E., & Goldman, P. S. (1979). Cognitive deficit caused by regional depletion of dopamine in prefrontal cortex of rhesus monkey. *Science, 205,* 929–932.

Bruder, G. E., Fong, R., Tenke, C. E., Leite, P., Towey, J. P., Stewart, J. E., et al. (1997). Regional brain asymmetries in major depression with or without an anxiety disorder: A quantitative electroencephalographic study. *Biological Psychiatry, 41,* 939–948.

Bruder, G. E., Tenke, C. E., Warner, V., & Weissman, M. M. (2007). Grandchildren at high and low risk for depression differ in EEG measures of regional brain asymmetry. *Biological Psychiatry, 62,* 1317–1323.

Bruder, G. E., Tenke, C. E., Warner, V., Nomura, Y., Grillon, C., Hille, J., et al. (2005). Electroencephalographic measures of regional hemispheric activity in offspring at risk for depressive disorders. *Biological Psychiatry, 57,* 328–335.

Bruer, J. T., & Greenough, W. T. (2001). The subtle science of how experience affects the brain. In D. B. Bailey, J. T. Bruer, F. J. Symons, & J. W. Lichtman (Eds.), *Critical thinking about critical periods* (pp. 209–232). Baltimore, MD: Paul H. Brookes Publishing.

Bruggeman, R., van der Linden, C., Buitelaar, J. K., Gericke, G. S., Hawkridge, S. M., & Temlett, J. A. (2001). Risperidone versus pimozide in Tourette's disorder: A comparative double-blind parallel-group study. *Journal of Clinical Psychiatry, 62,* 50–56.

Brunden, K. R., Trojanowski, J. Q., & Lee, V. M.-Y. (2009). Advances in tau-focused drug discovery for Alzheimer's disease and related tauopathies. *Nature Reviews Drug Discovery, 8,* 783–793.

Bruyer, R., Laterre, C., Seron, X., Feyereisen, P., Strypstein, E., Pierrard, E., & Rectem, D. (1983). A case of prosopagnosia with some preserved covert remembrance of familiar faces. *Brain and Cognition, 2,* 257–284.

Bryden, M. P. (1965). Tachistoscopic recognition, handedness, and cerebral dominance. *Neuropsychologia, 3,* 1–8.

Bu, G. (2009). Apolipoprotein E and its receptors in Alzheimer's disease: Pathways, pathogenesis and therapy. *Nature Reviews Neuroscience, 10,* 333–344.

Buccino, G., Lui, F., Canessa, N., Patteri, I., Lagravinese, G., Benuzzi, F., Porro, C. A., & Rizzolatti, G. (2004). Neural circuits involved in the recognition of actions performed by nonconspecifics: An FMRI study. *Journal of Cognitive Neuroscience, 16,* 114–126.

Buchanan, T. W., Lutz, K., Mirzazade, S., Specht, K., Shah, N. J., Zilles, K., & Jancke, L. (2000). Recognition of emotional prosody and verbal components of spoken language: An fMRI study. *Cognitive Brain Research, 9,* 227–238.

Büchel, C., Bornhovd, K., Qunate, M., Glauche, V., Bromm, B., & Weiler, C. (2002). Dissociable neural responses related to pain intensity, stimulus intensity, and stimulus awareness within the anterior cingulate cortex: A parametric single-trial laser functional magnetic resonance imaging study. *Journal of Neuroscience, 22,* 970–976.

Buckner, R. L. (1996). Beyond HERA: Contributions of specific prefrontal brain areas to long-term memory retrieval. *Psychonomic Bulletin & Review, 3*(2), 149–158.

Buckner, R. L., Andrews-Hanna, J. R., & Schacter, D. L. (2008). The brain's default network: Anatomy, function, and relevance to disease. *Annals of the New York Academy of Sciences, 1124,* 1–38.

Buckner, R. L., Koutstaal, W., Schacter, D. L., Wagner, A. D., & Rosen, B. R. (1998). Functional-anatomic study of episodic retrieval using fMRI. I. Retrieval effort versus retrieval success. *NeuroImage, 7*(3), 151–162.

Buckner, R. L., Wheeler, M. E., & Sheridan, M. A. (2001). Encoding processes during retrieval tasks. *Journal of Cognitive Neuroscience, 13*(3), 406–415.

Buhot, M.-C., Martin, S., & Segu, L. (2000). Role of serotonin in memory impairment. *Annals of Medicine, 32,* 210–221.

Bukach, C. M., Gauthier, I., & Tarr, M. J. (2006). Beyond faces and modularity: The power of an expertise framework. *Trends in Cognitive Sciences, 10,* 159–166.

Bumiller, E. (1982, March 31). Jim Brady's long ordeal. *Washington Post.*

Buneo, C. A., & Andersen, R. A. (2006). The posterior parietal cortex: Sensorimotor interface for the planning and online control of visually guided movements. *Neuropsychologia, 44,* 2594–2604.

Buneo, C. A., Jarvis, M. R., Batista, A. P., & Andersen, R. A. (2002). Direct visuomotor transformations for reaching. *Nature, 416*(6881), 632–636.

Bunge, S. A. (2004). How we use rules to select actions: A review of evidence from cognitive neuroscience. *Cognitive, Affective, & Behavioral Neuroscience, 4*(4), 564–579.

Bunge, S. A., Hazeltine, E., Scanlon, M. D., Rosen, A. C., & Gabrieli, J. D. (2002). Dissociable contributions of prefrontal and parietal cortices to response selection. *NeuroImage, 17,* 1562–1571.

Buonomano, D. V., & Merzenich, M. M. (1998). Cortical plasticity: From synapses to maps. *Annual Review of Neuroscience, 21,* 149–186.

Burgess, C., & Simpson, G. B. (1988). Cerebral hemispheric mechanisms in the retrieval of ambiguous word meanings. *Brain & Language, 33,* 86–103.

Burgund, E. D., & Marsolek, C. J. (1997). Letter-case-specific priming in the right cerebral hemisphere with a form-specific perceptual identification task. *Brain & Cognitive Sciences, 35,* 239–258.

Burianova, H., McIntosh, A. R., & Grady, C. L. (2010). A common functional brain network for autobiographical, episodic, and semantic memory retrieval. *NeuroImage, 49*(1), 865–874.

Burke, K. A., Letsos, A., & Butler, R. A. (1994). Asymmetric performances in biaural localization of sound in space. *Neuropsychologia, 32,* 1409–1417.

Burton, H., Sinclair, R. J., & McLaren, D. G. (2004). Cortical activity to vibrotactile stimulation: An fMRI study in blind and sighted individuals. *Human Brain Mapping, 23,* 210–228.

Burton, H., Snyder, A. Z., Conturo, T. W., Akbudak, E., Ollinger, J. M., & Raichle, M. E. (2002). Adaptive changes in early and late blind: A fMRI study of Braille reading. *Journal of Neurophysiology, 87,* 589–607.

Burton, H., Snyder, A. Z., Diamond, J. B., & Raichle, M. E. (2002). Adaptive changes in early and late blind: A fMRI study of verb generation to heard nouns. *Journal of Neurophysiology, 88,* 3359–3371.

Buschsbaum, M. S., Friedman, J., Buschsbaum, B. R., Chu, K.-W., Hazlett, E. A., Newmark, R., et al. (2006). Diffusion tensor imaging in schizophrenia. *Biological Psychiatry, 60,* 1181–1187.

Busey, T. A., & Vanderkolk, J. R. (2005). Behavioral and electrophysiological evidence for configural processing in fingerprint experts. *Vision Research, 45,* 431–448.

Bush, G., Luu, P., & Posner, M. I. (2000). Cognitive and emotional influences in anterior cingulate cortex. *Trends in Cognitive Sciences, 4,* 215–222.

Bush, G., Valera, E. M., & Seidman, L. J. (2005). Functional neuroimaging of attention-deficit/hyperactivity disorder: A review and suggested future directions. *Biological Psychiatry, 57,* 1273–1284.

Buss, K. A., Schumacher, J. R. M., Dolski, I., Kalin, N. H., Goldsmith, H. H., & Davidson, R. J. (2003). Right frontal brain activity, cortisol, and withdrawal behavior in 6-month-old infants. *Behavioral Neuroscience, 117,* 11–20.

Butler, R. A. (1994). Asymmetric performances in monaural localization of sound in space. *Neuropsychologia, 32,* 221–229.

Butters, N., Wolfe, J., Martone, M., Granholm, E., & Cermak, L. S. (1985). Memory disorders associated with Huntington's disease: Verbal recall, verbal recognition, and procedural memory. *Neuropsychologia, 23,* 729–743.

Cabeza, R. (2002). Hemispheric asymmetry reduction in older adults: The HAROLD model. *Psychology & Aging, 17,* 85–100.

Cabeza, R., Anderson, N. D., Mangels, J. A., Nyberg, L., & Houle, S. (2000). Age-related differences in neural activity during item and temporal order memory retrieval: A positron emission tomography study. *Journal of Cognitive Neuroscience, 12*(1), 197–206.

Cabeza, R., Ciaramelli, E., Olson, I. R., & Moscovitch, M. (2008). The parietal cortex and episodic memory: An attentional account. *Nature Reviews Neuroscience, 9*(8), 613–625.

Cabeza, R., Daselar, S. M., Dolcos, F., Prince, S. E., Budde, M., & Nyberg, L. (2004). Task-independent and task-specific age effects on brain activity during working memory, visual attention and episodic retrieval. *Cerebral Cortex, 14,* 364–375.

Cabeza, R., Locantore, J. K., & Anderson, N. D. (2003). Lateralization of prefrontal activity during episodic memory retrieval: Evidence for the production-monitoring hypothesis. *Journal of Cognitive Neuroscience, 15*(2), 249–259.

Cacioppo, J. T., Visser, P. S., & Pickett, C. L. (Eds.). (2006). *Social neuroscience: People thinking about people.* Cambridge, MA: MIT Press.

Cahill, L. (2006). Why sex matters for neuroscience. *Nature Reviews Neuroscience, 7,* 477–484.

Cahill, L., Babinsky, R., Markowitsch, H. J., & McGaugh, J. L. (1995). The amygdala and emotional memory. *Nature, 377*(6547), 295–296.

Cahill, L., Haier, R. J., Fallon, J., Alkire, M. T., Tang, C., Keator, D., et al. (1996). Amygdala activity at encoding correlated with long-term, free recall of emotional information. *Proceedings of the National Academy of Science, USA, 93*(15), 8016–8021.

Cahill, L., Pham, C. A., & Setlow, B. (2000). Impaired memory consolidation in rats produced with beta-adrenergic blockade. *Neurobiology of Learning & Memory, 74,* 259–266.

Cahill, L., Weinberger, N. M., Roozendaal, B., & McGaugh, J. L. (1999). Is the amygdala a locus of "conditioned fear"? Some questions and caveats. *Neuron, 23*(2), 227–228.

Calder, A. J., Keane, J., Manes, F., Antoun, N., & Young, A. W. (2000). Impaired recognition and experience of disgust following brain injury. *Nature Neuroscience, 3,* 1077–1078.

Calder, A. J., Young, A. W., Rowland, D., Perrett, D. I., Hodges, J. R., & Etcoff, N. L. (1996). Facial emotion recognition after bilateral amygdala damage: Differentially severe impairment of fear. *Cognitive Neuropsychology, 13,* 699–745.

Callicott, J. H., Egan, M. F., Mattay, V. S., Bertolino, A., Bone, A. D., Verchinksi, B., & Weinberger, D. R. (2003). Abnormal fMRI response of the dorsolateral prefrontal cortex in cognitively intact siblings of patients with schizophrenia. *American Journal of Psychiatry, 160,* 709–719.

Camille, N., Coricelli, G., Sallet, J., Pradat-Diehl, P., Duhamel, J.-R., & Sirigu, A. (2004). The involvement of the orbitofrontal cortex in the experience of regret. *Science, 304,* 1167–1170.

Camp, S. J., Stevenson, V. L., Thompson, A. J., Ingle, G. T., Miller, D. H., Borras, C., et al. (2005). A longitudinal study of cognition in primary progressive multiple sclerosis. *Brain, 128,* 2891–2898.

Campanella, S., & Guerit, J. M. (2009). How clinical neurophysiology may contribute to the understanding of a psychiatric disease such as schizophrenia. *Neurophysiologie Clinique, 39,* 31–39.

Campbell, R., MacSweeney, M., & Waters, D. (2007). Sign language and the brain: A review. *Journal of Deaf Studies & Deaf Education, 13,* 3–20.

Cancelliere, A., & Kertesz, A. (1990). Lesion localization in acquired deficits of emotional expression and comprehension. *Brain & Cognition, 13,* 133–147.

Canli, T., & Lesch, K.-P. (2007). Long story short: The serotonin transporter in emotion regulation and social cognition. *Nature Neuroscience, 10,* 1103–1109.

Canli, T., Omura, K., Haas, B. W., Fallgatter, A., Constable, R. T., & Lesch, K. P. (2005). Beyond affect: A role for genetic variation of the serotonin transporter during a cognitive attention task. *Proceedings of the National Academy of Sciences, 102,* 12224–12229.

Cantalupo, C., & Hopkins, W. D. (2001). Asymmetric Broca's area in great apes. *Nature, 414,* 505.

Capek, C. M., Grossi, G., Newman, A. J., McBurney, S. L., Corina, D., Roeder, B., & Neville, H. J. (2009). Brain systems mediating semantic and syntactic processing in deaf native signers: Biological invariance and modality specificity. *Proceedings of the National Academy of Sciences USA, 106,* 8784–8789.

Capitani, E., Laiacona, M., Mahon, B., & Caramazza, A. (2003). What are the facts of semantic category-specific deficits? A critical review of the clinical evidence. *Cognitive Neuropsychology, 20,* 213–261.

Cappa, S., Sterzi, R., Vallar, G., & Bisiach, E. (1987). Remission of hemineglect and anosognosia during vestibular stimulation. *Neuropsychologia, 25,* 775–782.

Caramazza, A., & Badecker, W. (1989). Patient classification in neuropsychological research. *Brain and Cognition, 10,* 256–295.

Caramazza, A., & Hillis, A. (1990). Spatial representation of words in the brain implied by studies of a unilateral neglect patient. *Nature, 346,* 267–269.

Caramazza, A., & Mahon, B. Z. (2003). The organization of conceptual knowledge: The evidence from category-specific semantic deficits. *Trends in Cognitive Sciences, 7,* 354–361.

Caramazza, A., & Shelton, J. R. (1998). Domain-specific knowledge systems in the brain: The animate-inanimate distinction. *Journal of Cognitive Neuroscience, 10,* 1–34.

Caramazza, A., Miceli, G., Silveri, M. C., & Laudanna, A. (1985). Reading mechanisms and the organization of the lexicon: Evidence from acquired dyslexia. *Cognitive Neuropsychology, 2,* 81–114.

Carey, B. (2008, December 4). H. M., an Unforgettable Amnesic, Dies at 82. *NY Times.*

Carey, S., & Diamond, R. (1977). From piecemeal to configurational representation of faces. *Science, 195,* 312–314.

Carlin, D., Bonerba, J., Phipps, M., Alexander, G., Shapiro, M., & Grafman, J., 2000. Planning impairments in frontal lobe dementia and frontal lobe lesions. *Neuropsychologia, 38,* 655–665.

Carp, J., Halenar, M., Quandt, L. C., Sklar, A., & Compton, R. J. (2009). Perceived similarity and neural mirroring: Evidence from vicarious error processing. *Social Neuroscience, 4,* 85–96.

Carpenter, P., Just, M., Keller, T., Eddy, W., & Thulborn, K. (1999). Graded functional activation in the visuospatial system in the amount of task demand. *Journal of Cognitive Neuroscience, 11,* 9–24.

Carstensen, L. L., Pasupathi, M., Mayr, U., & Nesselroade, J. R. (2000). Emotional experience in everyday life across the adult life span. *Journal of Personality & Social Psychology, 79,* 644–655.

Carter, C. S. (2005). Applying new approaches from cognitive neuroscience to enhance drug development for the treatment of impaired cognition in schizophrenia. *Schizophrenia Bulletin, 31,* 810–815.

Carter, C. S., & Barch, D. M. (2007). Cognitive neuroscience-based approaches to measuring and improving treatment effects on cognition in schizophrenia: The CNTRICS Initiative. *Schizophrenia Bulletin, 33,* 1131–1137.

Carter, C. S., Braver, T. S., Barch, D. M., Botvinick, M. M., Noll, D., & Cohen, J. D. (1998). Anterior cingulate cortex, error detection, and the online monitoring of performance. *Science, 280,* 747–749.

Carter, W. R., Johnson, M. C., & Borkovec, T. D. (1986). Worry: An electrocortical analysis. *Advances in Behavioral Research & Therapy, 8,* 193–204.

Caselli, R. J., Dueck, A. C., Osborne, D., Sabbagh, M. N., et al. (2009). Longitudinal modeling of age-related memory decline and the APOE-4 effect. *New England Journal of Medicine, 361,* 255–263.

Casey, B. J., Getz, S., & Galvan, A. (2008). The adolescent brain. *Developmental Review, 28,* 62–77.

Caspi, A., Sugden, K., Moffit, T. E., Taylor, A., Craig, I. W., Harrington, H., et al. (2003). Influence of life stress on depression: Moderation by a polymorphism in the 5-HTT gene. *Science, 301,* 386–389.

Castelli, F., Frith, C., Happé, F., & Frith, U. (2002). Autism, Asperger syndrome and brain mechanisms for the attribution of mental states to animated shapes. *Brain, 125,* 1839–1849.

Castellon, S. A., Hinkin, C. H., & Myers, H. F. (2000). Neuropsychiatric disturbance is associated with executive dysfunction in HIV-1 infection. *Journal of the International Neuropsychological Society, 6,* 336–347.

Castles, A., Bates, T. C., & Coltheart, M. (2006). John Marshall and the developmental dyslexias. *Aphasiology, 20,* 871–892.

Cavalli, M., DeRenzi, E., Faglioni, P., & Vitale, A. (1981). Impairment of right brain-damaged patients on a linguistic cognitive task. *Cortex, 17,* 545–556.

Cavedini, P., Gorini, A., & Bellodi, L. (2006). Understanding obsessive-compulsive disorder: Focus on decision-making. *Neuropsychology Review, 16,* 3–15.

Cermak, L. S., Lewis, R., Butters, N., & Goodglass, H. (1973). Role of verbal mediation in performance of motor tasks by Korsakoff patients. *Perceptual & Motor Skills, 37,* 259–262.

Chabris, C. F., & Kosslyn, S. M. (1998). How do the cerebral hemispheres contribute to encoding spatial relations? *Current Directions in Psychological Science, 7*(1), 8–14.

Chafee, M. V., Averbeck, B. B., & Crowe, D. A. (2007). Representing spatial relationships in posterior parietal cortex: Single neurons code object-referenced position. *Cerebral Cortex, 17,* 2914–2932.

Chamberlain, S. R., Blackwell, A. D., Fineberg, N. A., Robbins, T. W., & Sahakian, B. J. (2005). The neuropsychology of obsessive-compulsive disorder: The importance of failures in cognitive and behavioural inhibition as candidate endophenotypic markers. *Neuroscience & Biobehavioral Reviews, 29,* 399–419.

Chamberlain, S. R., Müller, U., Blackwell, A. D., Robbins, T. W., & Sahakian, B. J. (2006). Noradrenergic modulation of working memory and emotional memory in humans. *Psychopharmacology, 188,* 397–407.

Chambers, C. D., Bellgrove, M. A., Gould, I. C., English, T., Garavan, H., McNaught, E., Kamke, M., & Mattingley, J. B. (2007). Dissociable mechanisms of cognitive control in prefrontal and premotor cortex. *Journal of Neurophysiology, 98,* 3638–3647.

Chang, S. W. C., Dickinson, A. R., & Snyder, L. H. (2008). Limb-specific representation for reaching in the posterior parietal cortex. *Journal of Neuroscience, 28,* 6128–6140.

Chapman, H. A., Kim, D. A., Susskind, J. M., & Anderson, A. K. (2009). In bad taste: Evidence for the oral origins of moral disgust. *Science, 323,* 1222–1226.

Charlton, S. G. (2009). Driving while conversing: Cell phones that distract and passengers who react. *Accident; Analysis & Prevention, 41,* 160–173.

Chatterjee, A., Strauss, M. E., Smyth, K. A., & Whitehouse, P. J. (1992). Personality changes in Alzheimer's disease. *Archives of Neurology, 49,* 486–491.

Chee, M. W., Hon, N., Lee, H. L., Soon, C. S. (2001). Relative language proficiency modulates BOLD signal change when bilinguals perform semantic judgments: Blood oxygen level dependent. *NeuroImage, 13*(6), 1155–1163.

Chen, C.-H., Ridler, K., Suckling, J., Williams, S., Fu, C. H. Y., Merlo-Pich, E., & Bullmore, E. (2007). Brain imaging correlates of depressive symptom severity and predictors of symptom improvement after antidepressant treatment. *Biological Psychiatry, 62,* 407–414.

Chen, L. L., & Wise, S. P. (1996). Evolution of directional preferences in the supplementary eye field during acquisition of conditional oculomotor associations. *Journal of Neuroscience, 16,* 3067–3081.

Chen, P., Ratcliff, G., Belle, S. H., Cauley, J. A., DeKosky, S. T., & Ganguli, M. (2000). Cognitive tests that best discriminate between presymptomatic AD and those who remain nondemented. *Neurology, 55,* 1847–1853.

Chen, W., Zhu, X. H., Thulborn, K. R., & Ugurbil, K. (1999). Retinotopic mapping of lateral geniculate nucleus in humans using functional magnetic resonance imaging. *Proceedings of the National Academy of Sciences, 96,* 2430–2434.

Chen, X., Riley, B., & Kendler, K. S. (2009). Molecular genetics of schizophrenia. In D. S. Charney & E. J. Nestler (Eds.), *Neurobiology of mental illness* (3d ed.; pp. 252–262). Oxford, UK: Oxford University Press.

Chiaravalloti, N. D., & DeLuca, J. (2008). Cognitive impairment in multiple sclerosis. *Lancet Neurology, 7,* 1139–1151.

Chiarello, C. (1991). Interpretation of word meanings by the cerebral hemispheres: One is not enough. In P. J. Schwanenflugel (Ed.), *The psychology of word meanings* (pp. 251–278). Hillsdale, NJ: Erlbaum.

Chikazoe, J., Jimura, K., Asari, T., Yamashita, K., Morimotor, H., Hirose, S., Miyashita, Y., & Konishi, S. (2009). Functional dissociation in right inferior frontal cortex during performance of a go/no-go task. *Cerebral Cortex, 19,* 146–152.

Chou, T. L., Booth, J. R., Burman, D. D., Bitan, T., Bigio, J. D., Lu, D., & Cone, N. E. (2006). Developmental changes in the neural correlates of semantic processing. *NeuroImage, 29,* 1141–1149.

Choudhury, S., Blakemore, S.-J., & Charman, T. (2006). Social cognitive development during adolescence. *Social, Cognitive & Affective Neuroscience, 1,* 165–174.

Chouinard, P. A., & Paus, T. (2006). The primary motor and premotor areas of the human cerebral cortex. *Neuroscientist, 12,* 143–152.

Chugani, H. T., Phelps, M. E., & Mazziotta, J. C. (1987). Positron emission tomography study of human brain functional development. *Annals of Neurology, 22*(4), 487–497.

Chun, M. M., & Phelps, E. A. (1999). Memory deficits for implicit contextual information in amnesic subjects with hippocampal damage. *Nature Neuroscience, 2,* 844–847.

Çiçek, M., Gitelman, D., Hurley, R. S., Nobre, A., & Mesulam, M. (2007). Anatomical physiology of spatial extinction. *Cerebral Cortex, 17,* 2892–2898.

Cianchetti, C., Sannio-Fancello, G., Fratta, A. L., Manconi, F., Orano, A., Pischedda, M. P., et al. (1991). Neuropsychological, psychiatric, and physical manifestations in 140 members from 18 fragile X families. *American Journal of Medical Genetics, 40,* 234–243.

Ciccarelli, O., Catani, M., Johansen-Berg, H., Clark, C., & Thompson, A. (2008). Diffusion-based tractography in neurological disorders: Concepts, applications and future developments. *Lancet Neurology, 7,* 715–727.

Cicerone, K., Lazar, R., & Shapiro, W. (1983). Effects of frontal lobe lesions on hypothesis sampling during concept formation. *Neuropsychologia, 21,* 513–524.

Cicone, M., Wapner, W., & Gardner, H. (1980). Sensitivity to emotional expressions and situations in organic patients. *Cortex, 16,* 145–158.

Cincotti, F., Mattia, D., Aloise, F., Bufalari, S., Schalk, G., Oriolo, G., Cherubini, A., Marciani, M. G., & Babiloni, F. (2008). Non-invasive brain-computer interface system: Towards its application as assistive technology. *Brain Research Bulletin, 75,* 796–803.

Cipolotti, L., & Bird, C. M. (2006). Amnesia and the hippocampus. *Current Opinion in Neurology, 19*(6), 593–598.

Clarkson-Smith, L., & Hartley, A. A. (1989). Relationships between physical exercise and cognitive abilities in older adults. *Psychology & Aging, 4,* 183–189.

Clementz, B. A., Geyer, M. A., & Braff, D. L. (1997). P50 suppression among schizophrenia and normal comparison subjects: A methodological analysis. *Biological Psychiatry, 41,* 1035–1044.

Clower, W. T., & Alexander, G. E. (1998). Movement sequence-related activity reflecting numerical order of components in supplementary and presupplementary motor areas. *Journal of Neurophysiology, 80,* 1562–1566.

Coan, J. A., & Allen, J. J. B. (2004). Frontal EEG asymmetry as a moderator and mediator of emotion. *Biological Psychology, 67,* 7–49.

Cohen, E. D., Mariol, M. C., Wallace, R. M. H., Weyers, J., Kamberov, Y. G., Pradel, J., & Wilder, E. L. (2002). DWnt4 regulates cell movement and focal adhesion kinase during *Drosophila* ovarian morphogenesis. *Developmental Cell 2*(4), 437–448.

Cohen, J. C., Braver, T. S., & O'Reilly, R. C. (1996). A computational approach to prefrontal cortex, cognitive control, and schizophrenia: Recent developments and current challenges. *Philosophical Transactions of the Royal Society of London, B, 351,* 1515–1527.

Cohen, L. G., Celnik, P., Pascual-Leone, A., Corwell, B., Faiz, L., Dambrosia, J., et al. (1997). Functional relevance of cross-modal plasticity in blind humans. *Nature, 389,* 180–183.

Cohen, L., Dehaene, S., Naccache, L., Lehéricy, S., Dehaene-Lambertz, G., Hénaff, M.-A., & Michel, F. (2000). The visual word form area: Spatial and temporal characterization of an initial stage of reading in normal subjects and posterior split-brain patients. *Brain, 123,* 291–307.

Cohen, M. S., Kosslyn, S. M., Breiter, H. D., DiGirolamo, G. J., Thompson, W. L., Anderson, A. K., et al. (1996). Changes in cortical activity during mental rotation: A mapping study using functional MRI. *Brain, 199,* 89–100.

Cohen, M. X., Ridderinkhof, K. R., Haupt, S., Elger, C. E., & Fell, J. (2008). Medial frontal cortex and response conflict: Evidence from human intracranial EEG and medial frontal cortex lesion. *Brain Research, 1238*, 127–142.

Cohen, N. J. (1984). Preserved learning capacity in amnesia: Evidence for multiple memory systems. In L. R. Squire & N. Butters (Eds.), *Neuropsychology of memory* (pp. 83–103). New York: Guilford Press.

Cohen, N. J., & Squire, L. R. (1980). Preserved learning and retention of pattern-analyzing skill in amnesia: Dissociation of knowing how and knowing that. *Science, 210*, 207–210.

Cohen, N. J., Ryan, J., Hunt, C., Romine, L., Wszalek, T., & Nash, C. (1999). Hippocampal system and declarative (relational) memory: Summarizing the data from functional neuroimaging studies. *Hippocampus, 9*(1), 83–98.

Cohen, R. A., Kaplan, R. F., Zuffante, P., Moser, D. J., Jenkins, M. A., Salloway, S., & Wilkinson, H. (1999). Alteration of intention and self-initiated action associated with bilateral anterior cingulotomy. *Journal of Neuropsychiatry & Clinical Neurosciences, 11*, 444–453.

Cohen, R. A., Paul, R., Zawacki, T. M., Moser, D. J., Sweet, L., & Wilkinson, H. (2001). Emotional and personality changes following cingulotomy. *Emotion, 1*, 38–50.

Cohen, Y. E., & Knudsen, E. I. (1999). Maps versus clusters: Different representations of auditory space in the midbrain and forebrain. *Trends in Neurosciences, 22*, 128–135.

Colby, C. L., Duhamel, J.-R., & Goldberg, M. E. (1996). Visual, presaccadic and cognitive activation of single neurons in monkey lateral intraparietal area. *Journal of Neurophysiology, 76*, 2841–2852.

Cole, M., Schutta, H. S., & Warrington, E. K. (1962). Visual disorientation in homonymous half fields. *Neurology, 12*, 257–263.

Coleman, M. R., Rodd, J. M., Davis, M. H., Johnsrude, I. S., Menon, D. K., Pickard, J. D., & Owen, A. M. (2007). Do vegetative patients retain aspects of language comprehension? Evidence from fMRI. *Brain, 130*, 2494–2507.

Collins, M. W., Grindle, S. H., Lovell, M. R., Dede, D. E., Moser, D. J., Phalin, B. R., et al. (1999). Relationship between concussion and neuropsychological performance in college football players. *JAMA, 282*, 964–970.

Colman, D., Lubetzki, C., & Reingold, S. (2003). Multiple paths towards repair in multiple sclerosis. *Trends in Neurosciences, 26*, 59–61.

Coltheart, M. (1982). The psycholinguistic analysis of acquired dyslexias: Some illustrations. *Philosophical Transactions of the Royal Society of London, B298*, 151–164.

Coltheart, M. (2000). Deep dyslexia is right-hemisphere reading. *Brain & Language, 71*, 299–309.

Coltheart, M., Rastle, K., Perry, C., Langdon, R., & Ziegler, J. (2001). DRC: A dual route cascaded model of visual word recognition and reading aloud. *Psychological Review, 108*, 204–256.

Comi, G. (2009). Shifting the paradigm toward earlier treatment of multiple sclerosis with interferon beta. *Clinical Therapeutics, 31*, 1142–1157.

Compton, R. J. (1999). Manipulating attentional asymmetry affects self-reported arousal. *Neuropsychology, 13*, 128–134.

Compton, R. J. (2003). The interface between emotion and attention: A review of evidence from psychology and neuroscience. *Behavioral & Cognitive Neuroscience Reviews, 2*, 115–129.

Compton, R. J., Banich, M. T., Mohanty, A., Milham, M. P., Herrington, J., Miller, G. A., et al. (2003). Paying attention to emotion: An fMRI investigation of cognitive and emotional Stroop tasks. *Cognitive, Affective, & Behavioral Neuroscience, 3*, 81–96.

Compton, R. J., Lin, M., Vargas, G., Carp, J., Fineman, S., & Quandt, L. C. (2008). Error detection and post-error behavior in depressed undergraduates. *Emotion, 8*, 58–67.

Conturo, T. E., Lori, N. F., Cull, T. S., Akbudak, E., Synder, A. Z., Shimony, J. S., McKinstry, R. C., Burton, H., & Raichle, M. E. (1999). Tracking neuronal fiber pathways in the living human brain. *Proceedings of the National Academy of Sciences, 96*, 10422–10427.

Conway, B. R., & Tsao, D. Y. (2006). Color architecture in alert macaque cortex revealed by fMRI. *Cerebral Cortex, 16*, 1604–1613.

Conway, B. R., Moeller, S., & Tsao, D. Y. (2007). Specialized color modules in macaque extrastriate cortex. *Neuron, 56*, 560–573.

Cools, R., Clark, L., & Robbins, T. W. (2004). Differential responses in human striatum and prefrontal cortex to changes in object and rule relevance. *Journal of Neuroscience, 24*, 1129–1135.

Cools, R., Stefanova, E., Barker, R. A., Robbins, T. W., & Owen, A. M. (2002). Dopaminergic modulation of high-level cognition in Parkinson's disease: The role of the prefrontal cortex revealed by PET. *Brain, 125*, 584–594.

Coombs, B. D., Best, A., Brown, M. S., Miller, D. E., Corboy, J., Baier, M., & Simon, J. H. (2004). Multiple sclerosis pathology in the normal and abnormal appearing white matter of the corpus callosum by diffusion tensor imaging. *Multiple Sclerosis, 10*, 392–397.

Cooper, B. G., & Mizumori, S. J. Y. (2001). Temporary inactivation of the retrosplenial cortex causes a transient reorganization of spatial coding in the hippocampus. *Journal of Neuroscience, 21*, 3986–4001.

Cooper, J. M., & Strayer, D. L. (2008). Effects of simulator practice and real-world experience on cell-phone-related driver distraction. *Human Factors, 50*, 893–902.

Copeland, B. J., & Pillsbury III, H. C. (2004). Cochlear implantation for the treatment of deafness. *Annual Review of Medicine, 55*, 157–167.

Corballis, M. C. (1991). Memory, growth, evolution, and laterality. In W. E. Hockley, & S. Lewandowsky (Eds.), *Relating theory and data: Essays on human memory in honor of Bennet B. Murdock* (pp. 23–38). Hillsdale, NJ: Lawrence Erlbaum & Associates.

Corballis, M. C. (1997). The genetics and evolution of handedness. *Psychological Review, 104*, 714–727.

Corbetta, M., & Shulmann, G. L. (2002). Control of goal-directed and stimulus-driven attention in the brain. *Nature Reviews Neuroscience, 3*, 201–215.

Corbetta, M., Miezin, F. M., Dobmeyer, S., Shulman, G. L., & Petersen, S. E. (1991). Selective and divided attention during visual discriminations of shape, color, and speed: Functional anatomy by positron emission tomography. *Journal of Neuroscience, 11*, 2383–2402.

Corbetta, M., Miezin, F. M., Shulman, G. L., & Petersen, S. E. (1993). A PET study of visuospatial attention. *Journal of Neuroscience, 13*, 1202–1226.

Coricelli, G., Critchley, H. D., Joffily, M., O'Doherty, J. P., Sirigu, A., & Dolan, R. J. (2005). Regret and its avoidance: A neuroimaging study of choice behavior. *Nature Neuroscience, 8*, 1255–1262.

Corina, D. P., McBurney, S. L., Dodrill, C., Hinshaw, K., Brinkley, J., & Ojemann, G. (1999). Functional roles of Broca's area and SMG: Evidence from cortical stimulation mapping in a deaf signer. *NeuroImage, 10*, 570–581.

Corkin, S. (1968). Acquisition of motor skill after bilateral medial temporal-lobe excision. *Neuropsychologia, 6*, 255–265.

Corkin, S. (1984). Lasting consequences of bilateral medial temporal lobectomy: Clinical course and experimental findings in H. M. *Seminars in Neurology, 4*, 249–259.

Corkin, S. (2002). What's new with the amnesic patient H. M.? *Nature Reviews Neuroscience, 3*(2), 153–160.

Coslett, H. B. (2000). Acquired dyslexia. *Seminars in Neurology, 20*, 419–426.

Coslett, H. B., Bowers, D., & Heilman, K. M. (1987). Reduction in cerebral activation after right hemisphere stroke. *Neurology, 37*, 957–962.

Costafreda, S. G., Fu, C. H., Lee, L., Everitt, B., Brammer, M. J., & David A. S. (2006). A systematic review and quantitative appraisal of fMRI studies of verbal fluency: Role of the left inferior frontal gyrus. *Human Brain Mapping, 27*, 799–810.

Coull, J. T. (2004). fMRI studies of temporal attention: Allocating attention within, or towards time. *Cognitive Brain Research, 21*, 216–226.

Coull, J. T., & Nobre, A. C. (1998). Where and when to pay attention: The neural systems for directing attention to spatial locations and to time intervals as revealed by both PET and fMRI. *Journal of Neuroscience, 18*, 7426–7435.

Coull, J. T., Middleton, H. C., Robbins, T. W., & Sahakian, B. J. (1995). Clonidine and diazepam have differential effects on tests of attention and learning. *Psychopharmacology, 120,* 322–332.

Coull, J. T., Nobre, A. C., & Frith, C. D. (2001). The noradrenergic alpha-2 agonist clonidine modulates behavioural and neuroanatomical correlates of human attentional orienting and alerting. *Cerebral Cortex, 11,* 73–84.

Coull, J. T., Sahakian, B. J., Middleton, H. C., Young, A. H., Park, S. B., McShane, R. H., Cowen, P. J., & Robbins, T. W. (1995). Differential effects of clonidine, haloperidol, diazepam, and tryptophan depletion on focused attention and attentional search. *Psychopharmacology, 121,* 222–230.

Courchesne, E., & Pierce, K. (2005). Why the frontal cortex in autism might be talking only to itself: Local over-connectivity but long-distance disconnection. *Current Opinion in Neurobiology, 15,* 225–230.

Couturier, J. L. (2005). Efficacy of rapid-rate repetitive transcranial magnetic stimulation in the treatment of depression: A systematic review and meta-analysis. *Journal of Psychiatry & Neuroscience, 30,* 83–90.

Cowey, A., & Heywood, C. A. (1997). Cerebral achromatopsia: Colour blindness despite wavelength processing. *Trends in Cognitive Sciences, 1,* 133–139.

Cox, D. D., & DiCarlo, J. J. (2008). Does learned shape selectivity in inferior temporal cortex automatically generalize across retinal position? *Journal of Neuroscience, 28,* 10045–10055.

Craig, A. D. (2002). How do you feel? Interoception: The sense of the physiological condition of the body. *Nature Reviews Neuroscience, 3,* 655–666.

Craig, A. D. (2009). How do you feel—now? The anterior insula and human awareness. *Nature Reviews Neuroscience, 10,* 59–70.

Craik, F. I. M., & Byrd, M. (1982). Aging and cognitive deficits: The role of attentional resources. In F. I. M. Craik & S. Trehub (Eds.), *Aging and cognitive processes* (pp. 191–211). New York: Plenum Press.

Cramer, S. C., & Crafton, K. R. (2006). Somatotopy and movement representation sites following cortical stroke. *Experimental Brain Research, 168,* 25–32.

Cramer, S. C., Nelles, G., Benson, R. R., Kaplan, J. D., Parker, R. A., Kwong, K. K., et al. (1997). A functional MRI study of subjects recovered from hemiparetic stroke. *Stroke, 28,* 2518–2527.

Cramer, S. C., Shah, R., Juranek, J., Crafton, K. R., & Le, V. (2006). Activity in the peri-infarct rim in relation to recovery from stroke. *Stroke, 37,* 111–115.

Crawford, J. R. (1992). Current and premorbid intelligence measures in neuropsychological assessment. In J. R. Crawford, D. M. Parker, & W. W. McKinlay (Eds.), *A handbook of neuropsychological assessment.* Hillsdale, NJ: Erlbaum.

Cremona-Meteyard, S. L., & Geffen, G. M. (1994). Persistent visuospatial attention deficits following mild head injury in Australian Rules football players. *Neuropsychologia, 32,* 649–662.

Crinion, J., & Price, C. J. (2005). Right anterior superior temporal activation predicts auditory sentence comprehension following aphasic stroke. *Brain, 128,* 2858–2871.

Critchley, H. D., Rothstein, P., Öhman, A., & Dolan, R. J. (2004). Neural systems supporting interoceptive awareness. *Nature Neuroscience, 7,* 189–195.

Critchley, H. D., Tang, J., Glaser, D., Butterworth, B., & Dolan, R. J. (2005). Anterior cingulate activity during error and autonomic response. *NeuroImage, 27,* 885–895.

Crombag, H. S., Gorny, G., Li, Y., Kolb, B., & Robinson, T. E. (2005). Opposite effects of amphetamine self-administration experience on dendritic spines in the medial and orbital prefrontal cortex. *Cerebral Cortex, 15,* 341–348.

Crottaz-Herbette, S., & Menon, V. (2006). Where and when the anterior cingulate cortex modulates attentional response: Combined fMRI and ERP evidence. *Journal of Cognitive Neuroscience, 18,* 766–780.

Crowe, D. A., Averbeck, B. B., & Chafee, M. V. (2008). Neural ensemble coding reveals a correlate of viewer- to object-centered spatial transformation in monkey parietal cortex. *Journal of Neuroscience, 28,* 5218–5228.

Cummings, J. L., & Benson, D. F. (1988). Psychological dysfunction accompanying subcortical dementias. *Annual Review of Medicine, 39,* 53–61.

Curran, T. (2000). Brain potentials of recollection and familiarity. *Memory & Cognition, 28,* 923–938.

Curtiss, S. (1977). *Genie: A psycholinguistic study of a modern-day "wild child."* New York: Academic Press.

Cysique, L. A., & Brew, B. J. (2009). Neuropsychological functioning and antiretroviral treatment in HIV/AIDS: A review. *Neuropsychology Review, 19,* 169–185.

Cytowic, R. E. (1981, September 27). The long ordeal of James Brady. *New York Times.*

D'Esposito, M., Cooney, J. W., Gazzaley, A., Gibbs, S. E., & Postle, B. R. (2006). Is the prefrontal cortex necessary for delay task performance? Evidence from lesion and FMRI data. *Journal of the International Neuropsychological Society, 12*(2), 248–260.

Dacey, D. M., Peterson, B. B., Robinson, F. R., & Gamlin, P. D. (2003). Fireworks in the primate retina: In vitro photodynamics reveals diverse LGN-projecting ganglion cell types. *Neuron, 37,* 15–27.

Daigneault, S., Braun, C. M. J., & Whitaker, H. A. (1992). Early effects of normal aging on perseverative and non-perseverative prefrontal measures. *Developmental Neuropsychology, 8,* 99–114.

Dalgleish, M. R. C., Weinstein, A., Malizia, A. L., Wilson, S., Melichar, J. K., Britten, S., et al. (2001). Changes in regional cerebral blood flow elicited by craving memories in abstinent opiate-dependent subjects. *American Journal of Psychiatry, 158,* 1680–1686.

Dalrymple, A. J. C., Kalders, A. S., Jones, R. D., & Watson, R. W. (1994). A central executive deficit in patients with Parkinson's disease. *Journal of Neurology, Neurosurgery & Psychiatry, 57,* 360–367.

Daly, J. J., & Wolpaw, J. R. (2008). Brain-computer interfaces in neurological rehabilitation. *Lancet Neurology, 7,* 1032–1043.

Damasio, A. R. (1994). *Descartes' error: Emotion, reason, and the human brain.* New York: Avon Books.

Damasio, A. R., Damasio, H., & Chui, H. C. (1980). Neglect following damage to frontal lobe or basal ganglia. *Neuropsychologia, 18,* 123–132.

Damasio, A. R., Damasio, H., & Van Hoesen, G. W. (1982). Prosopagnosia: Anatomical basis and behavioral mechanisms. *Neurology, 32,* 331–341.

Damasio, H. C. (1991). Neuroanatomical correlates of the aphasias. In M. T. Sarno (Ed.), *Acquired aphasia* (2d ed., pp. 45–70). New York: Academic Press.

Damasio, H., & Damasio, A. R. (1989). *Lesion analysis in neuropsychology.* New York: Oxford University Press.

Dambeck, N., Sparing, R., Meister, I. G., Wienemann, M., Weidemann, J., Topper, R., & Boroojerdi, B. (2006). Interhemispheric imbalance during visuospatial attention investigated by unilateral and bilateral TMS over human parietal cortices. *Brain Research, 1072,* 194–199.

Dancause, N., Barbay, S., Frost, S. B., Plautz, E. J., Chen, D., Zoubina, E. V., et al. (2005). Extensive cortical rewiring after brain injury. *Journal of Neuroscience, 25,* 10167–10179.

Danly, M., & Shapiro, B. (1982). Speech prosody in Broca's aphasia. *Brain & Language, 16,* 171–190.

Dapretto, M., Davies, M. S., Pfeifer, J. H., Scott, A. A., Sigman, M., Bookheimer, S. Y., & Iacoboni, M. (2006). Understanding emotions in others: Mirror neuron dysfunction in children with autism spectrum disorders. *Nature Neuroscience, 9,* 28–30.

Darwin, C. (1873). *The expression of the emotions in man and animals.* Reprinted 1965, Chicago: University of Chicago Press.

Davey, C. G., Yücel, M., & Allen, N. B. (2008). The emergence of depression in adolescence: Development of the prefrontal cortex and the representation of reward. *Neuroscience & Biobehavioral Reviews, 32,* 1–19.

David, D. J., Samuels, B. A., Rainer, Q., Wang, J.-W., Marsteller, D., Mendez, I., et al. (2009). Neurogenesis-dependent and -independent effects of fluoxetine in an animal model of anxiety/depression. *Neuron, 62,* 479–493.

David, S. P., Munafo, M. R., Johansen-Berg, H., Smith, S. M., Rogers, R. D., Matthews, P. M., & Walton, R. T. (2005). Ventral striatum/nucleus accumbens activation to smoking-related pictorial cues in smokers and nonsmokers: A functional magnetic resonance imaging study. *Biological Psychiatry, 58,* 488–494.

David, S. V., Hayden, B. Y., & Gallant, J. L. (2006). Spectral receptive field properties explain shape selectivity in area V4. *Journal of Neurophysiology, 96,* 3492–3505.

Davidson, R. J. (1995). Cerebral asymmetry, emotion, and affective style. In R. J. Davidson & K. Hugdahl (Eds.), *Brain asymmetry* (pp. 361–387). Cambridge, MA: MIT Press.

Davidson, R. J. (2004). What does the prefrontal cortex "do" in affect: Perspectives on frontal EEG asymmetry research. *Biological Psychology, 67,* 219–233.

Davidson, R. J., & Fox, N. A. (1989). Frontal brain asymmetry predicts infants' response to maternal separation. *Journal of Abnormal Psychology, 98,* 127–131.

Davidson, R. J., Ekman, P., Saron, C. D., Senulis, J. A., & Friesen, W. V. (1990). Approach-withdrawal and cerebral asymmetry: Emotional expression and brain physiology I. *Journal of Personality & Social Psychology, 58,* 330–341.

Davidson, R. J., Pizzagalli, D., Nitschke, J. B., & Putnam, K. (2002). Depression: Perspectives from affective neuroscience. *Annual Review of Psychology, 53,* 545–574.

Davies, P. L., Segalowitz, S. J., Dywan, J., & Pailing, P. E. (2001). Error-negativity and positivity as they relate to other ERP indices of attentional control and stimulus processing. *Biological Psychology, 56*(3), 191–206.

Davis, D. P., Serrano, J. A., Vilke, G. M., Sise, M. J., Kennedy, F., Eastman, B., et al. (2006). The predictive value of field versus arrival Glasgow Coma Scale score and TRISS calculations in moderate-to-severe traumatic brain injury. *Journal of Trauma Injury, Infection, & Critical Care, 60,* 985–990.

Davis, K. D., Taylor, K. S., Hutchinson, W. D., Dostrovsky, J. O., McAndrews, M. P., Richter, E. O., & Lozano, A. M. (2005). Human anterior cingulate cortex neurons encode cognitive and emotional demands. *Journal of Neuroscience, 25,* 8402–8406.

Davis, M. (1992). The role of the amygdala in fear and anxiety. *Annual Review of Neuroscience, 15,* 353–375.

Davis, M. (1994). The role of the amygdala in emotional learning. *International Review of Neurobiology, 36,* 225–266.

Davis, M., Myers, K. M., Ressler, K. J., & Rothbaum, B. O. (2005). Facilitation of extinction of conditioned fear by D-cycloserine. *Current Directions in Psychological Science, 14,* 214–219.

Dawson, G., Ashman, S. B., Hessl, D., Spieker, S., Frey, K., Panagiotides, H., & Embry, L. (2001). Autonomic and brain electrical activity in securely- and insecurely-attached infants of depressed mothers. *Infant Behavior & Development, 24,* 135–149.

Day, J. J., Grant, I., Atkinson, J. H., Brysk, L. T., McCutchan, J. A., Hesselink, J. R., et al. (1992). Incidence of dementia in a two-year follow-up of AIDS and ARC patients on an initial Phase II AZT placebo-controlled study: San Diego Cohort. *Journal of Neuropsychiatry, 4,* 15–20.

De Haan, E. H., Young, A., & Newcombe, F. (1987). Faces interfere with name classification in a prosopagnosic patient. *Cortex, 23,* 309–316.

De Santis, L., Clarke, S., & Murray, M. M. (2007). Automatic and intrinsic auditory "what" and "where" processing in humans revealed by electrical neuroimaging. *Cerebral Cortex, 17,* 9–17.

De Stefano, N., Bartolozzi, M. L., Guidi, L., Stromillo, M. L., & Federico, A. (2005). Magnetic resonance spectroscopy as a measure of brain damage in multiple sclerosis. *Journal of the Neurological Sciences, 233,* 203–208.

De Witt, K. (1990, December 18). James Brady relives the day he became a symbol. *New York Times.*

DeAngelis, G. C., Cumming, B. G., & Newsome, W. T. (1998). Cortical area MT and the perception of stereoscopic depth. *Nature, 394,* 677–680.

Debener, S., Ullsperger, M., Siegel, M., Fiehler, K., von Cramon, D. Y., & Engel, A. K. (2005). Trial-by-trial coupling of concurrent electroencephalogram and functional magnetic resonance imaging identifies the dynamics of performance monitoring. *Journal of Neuroscience, 25,* 11730–11737.

Decety, J., Perani, D., Jeannerod, M., Bettinardi, V., Tadary, B., Woods, R., Mazziotla, J. C., & Fazio, F. (1994). Mapping motor representations with positron emission tomography. *Nature, 371,* 600–602.

deCharms, R. C., Maeda, F., Glover, G. H., Ludlow, D., Pauly, J. M., Soneji, D., et al. (2005). Control over brain activation and pain learned by using real-time functional MRI. *Proceedings of the National Academy of Sciences, USA, 102,* 18626–18631.

Dee, H. L., Benton, A. L., & Van Allen, M. W. (1970). Apraxia in relation to hemisphere locus of lesion and aphasia. *Transactions of the American Neurological Association, 95,* 147–148.

Dehaene, S., Posner, M. I., & Tucker, D. M. (1994). Localization of a neural system for error detection and compensation. *Psychological Science, 5,* 303–305.

Dehaene-Lambertz, G., Dehaene, S., & Hertz-Pannier, L. (2002). Functional neuroimaging of speech perception in infants. *Science, 298,* 2013–2015.

Deierborg, T., Soulet, D., Roybon, L., Hall, V., & Brundin, P. (2008). Emerging restorative treatments for Parkinson's disease. *Progress in Neurobiology, 85,* 407–432.

DeKosky, S. T., Heilman, G. E., Bowers, D., & Valenstein, I. (1980). Recognition and discrimination of emotional faces and pictures. *Brain & Language, 9,* 206–214.

DeKosky, S. T., Williamson, J. D., Fitzpatrick, A. L., Kronmal, R. A., Ives, D. G., Saxton, J. A., et al. (2008). Ginkgo biloba for prevention of dementia. *JAMA, 300,* 2253–2730.

deLacoste-Utamsing, C., & Holloway, R. L. (1982). Sexual dimorphism in the human corpus callosum. *Science, 216,* 1431–1432.

Deldin, P. J., Keller, J., Gergen, J. A., & Miller, G. A. (2000). Right-posterior face processing anomaly in depression. *Journal of Abnormal Psychology, 109,* 116–121.

Delis, D. C., Robertson, L. C., & Efron, R. (1986). Hemispheric specialization of memory for visual hierarchical stimuli. *Neuropsychologia, 24,* 205–214.

Delis, D. C., Squire, L. R., Bihrle, A., & Massman, P. (1992). Componential analysis of problem-solving ability: Performance of patients with frontal lobe damage and amnesic patients on a new sorting test. *Neuropsychologia, 30,* 683–697.

Delis, D. C., Wapner, W., Gardner, H., & Moses, J. A. (1983). The contribution of the right hemisphere to the organization of paragraphs. *Cortex, 19,* 43–50.

Della Malva, C. L., Stuss, D. T., D'Alton, J., & Willmer, J. (1993). Capture errors and sequencing after frontal brain lesions. *Neuropsychologia, 31,* 363–372.

Della-Maggiore, V., Malfait, N., Ostry, D. J., & Paus, T. (2004). Stimulation of the posterior parietal cortex interferes with arm trajectory adjustments during the learning of new dynamics. *Journal of Neuroscience, 24,* 9971–9976.

Demakis, G. J. (2003). A meta-analytic review of the sensitivity of the Wisconsin Card Sorting Test to frontal and lateralized frontal brain damage. *Neuropsychology, 17,* 255–264.

Demb, J. B. (2007). Cellular mechanisms for direction selectivity in the retina. *Neuron, 55,* 179–186.

Denes, G., Semenza, C., Stoppa, E., & Lis, A. (1982). Unilateral spatial neglect and recovery from hemiplegia: A follow-up study. *Brain, 105,* 543–552.

Dennis, M., & Kohn, B. (1975). Comprehension of syntax in infantile hemiplegics after cerebral hemidecortication: Left-hemisphere superiority. *Brain and Language, 2,* 472–482.

Dennis, M., & Whitaker, W. (1976). Language acquisition following hemidecortication: Linguistic superiority of left over right hemisphere. *Brain and Language, 3,* 404–433.

Depue, B. E., Curran, T., & Banich, M. T. (2007). Prefrontal regions orchestrate suppression of emotional memories via a two-phase process. *Science, 317,* 215–219.

DeRenzi, E. (1980). The Token Test and the Reporter's Test: A measure of verbal input and a measure of verbal output. In M. T. Sarno & O. Hook (Eds.), *Aphasia: Assessment and treatment* (pp. 158–169). New York: Masson.

DeRenzi, E. (1986). Current issues in prosopagnosia. In H. D. Ellis, M. A. Jeeves, F. Newcombe, & A. Young (Eds.), *Aspects of face processing.* Dordrecht, The Netherlands: Martinus Nijhoff.

DeRenzi, E. (2000). Prosopagnosia. In M. J. Farah & T. E. Feinberg (Eds.), *Patient-based approaches to cognitive neuroscience* (pp. 85–95). Cambridge, MA: MIT Press.

DeRenzi, E., & Lucchelli, F. (1988). Ideational apraxia. *Brain, 111,* 1173–1188.

DeRenzi, E., Motti, F., & Nichelli, P. (1980). Imitating gestures: A quantitative approach. *Archives of Neurology, 37,* 6–10.

DeRenzi, E., Perani, D., Carlesimo, G. A., Silveri, M. C., & Fazio, F. (1994). Prosopagnosia can be associated with damage confined to the right hemisphere: An MRI and PET study and review of the literature. *Neuropsychologia, 32,* 893–902.

DeRenzi, E., Pieczuro, A., & Vignolo, L. A. (1968). Ideational apraxia: A quantitative study. *Neuropsychologia, 6,* 41–52.

Derrfuss, J., Brass, M., Neumann, J., & von Cramon, D. Y. (2005). Involvement of the inferior frontal junction in cognitive control: Meta-analyses of switching and Stroop studies. *Human Brain Mapping, 25,* 22–34.

Desikan, R. S., Cabral, H. J., Hess, C. P., Dillon, W. P., Glastonbury, C. M., Weiner, M. W., et al. (2009). Automated MRI measures identify individual with mild cognitive impairment and Alzheimer's disease. *Brain, 132,* 2048–2057.

Desimone, R., & Duncan, J. (1995). Neural mechanisms of selective visual attention. *Annual Review of Neuroscience, 18,* 193–222.

Desimone, R., & Gross, C. G. (1979). Visual areas in the temporal cortex of the macaque. *Brain Research, 178,* 363–380.

Desimone, R., & Schein, S. J. (1987). Visual properties of neurons in area V4 of the macaque: Sensitivity to stimulus form. *Journal of Neurophysiology, 57,* 835–868.

Desimone, R., Albright, T. D., Gross, C. G., & Bruce, C. (1984). Stimulus selective properties of inferior temporal neurons in the macaque. *Journal of Neuroscience, 4,* 2051–2062.

Desimone, R., Wessinger, M., Thomas, L., & Schneider, W. (1990). Attentional control of visual perception: Cortical and subcortical mechanisms. *Cold Spring Harbor Symposia on Quantitative Biology, 55,* 963–971.

Desmedt, J. E., & Robertson, D. (1977). Differential enhancement of early and late components of the cerebral somatosensory evoked potentials during forced-paced cognitive tasks in man. *Journal of Physiology (London), 271,* 761–782.

Desmurget, M., & Grafton, S. (2000). Forward modeling allows feedback control for fast reaching movements. *Trends in Cognitive Sciences, 4,* 423–443.

Desmurget, M., Epstein, C. M., Turner, R. S., Prablanc, C., Alexander, G. E., & Grafton, S. T. (1999). Role of the posterior parietal cortex in updating reaching movements to a visual target. *Nature Neuroscience, 2(6),* 563–567.

Deuschl, G., Raethjen, J., Baron, R., Lindemann, M., Wilms, H., & Krack, P. (2000). The pathophysiology of Parkinsonian tremor: A review. *Journal of Neurology, 247(Suppl 5),* V33–V48.

Deuschl, G., Scade-Brittinger, C., Krack, P., Volkmann, J., et al. (2006). A randomized trial of deep-brain stimulation for Parkinson's disease. *New England Journal of Medicine, 355,* 896–908.

Deuschl, G., Toro, C., Zeffiro, T., Massaquoi, S., & Hallett, M. (1996). Adaptation motor learning of arm movements in patients with cerebellar disease. *Journal of Neurology, Neurosurgery & Psychiatry, 60,* 515–519.

Deutsch, G., Bourbon, W., Papanicolaou, A., & Eisenberg, H. (1988). Visuospatial tasks compared during activation of regional cerebral blood flow. *Neuropsychologia, 26,* 445–452.

Deutsch, J. A., & Deutsch, D. (1963). Attention: Some theoretical considerations. *Psychological Review, 70,* 80–90.

Deveney, C. M., & Deldin, P. J. (2004). Memory of faces: A slow wave ERP study of major depression. *Emotion, 4,* 295–304.

Devinsky, O., & Najjar, S. (1999). Evidence against the existence of temporal lobe epilepsy personality syndrome. *Neurology, 53(Suppl. 2),* S13–S25.

Devlin, J. T., & Watkins, K. E. (2007). Stimulating language: Insights from TMS. *Brain, 130,* 610–622.

Dhamala, M., Assisi, C. G., Jirsa, V. K., Steinberg, F. L., & Kelso, J. A. S. (2007). Multisensory integration for timing engages different brain networks. *Neuroimage, 34,* 764–773.

Dhanushkodi, A., Bindu, B., Raju, T. R., & Kutty, B. M. (2007). Exposure to enriched environment improves spatial learning performances and enhances cell density but not choline acetyltransferase activity in the hippocampus of ventral subicular-lesioned rats. *Behavioral Neuroscience, 121,* 491–500.

Di, H. B., Yu, S. M., Weng, X. C., Laureys, S., Yu, D., Li, J. Q., et al. (2007). Cerebral response to patient's own name in the vegetative and minimally conscious states. *Neurology, 68,* 895–899.

Di Russo, F., Aprille, T., Spitoni, G., & Spinelli, D. (2008). Impaired visual processing of contralesional stimuli in neglect patients: A visual-evoked potential study. *Brain, 131,* 842–854.

Diamond, A. (1990). Developmental time course in human infants and infant monkeys, and the neural bases of inhibitory control in reading. *Annals of the New York Academy of Sciences, 608,* 637–676.

Diamond, A., Barnett, W. S., Thomas, J., & Munro, S. (2005). Preschool program improves cognitive control. *Science, 318,* 1387–1388.

Diamond, R., & Carey, S. (1986). Why faces are and are not special: An effect of expertise. *Journal of Experimental Psychology: General, 115,* 107–117.

DiCarlo, J. J., & Cox, D. D. (2007). Untangling invariant object recognition. *Trends in Cognitive Sciences, 11,* 333–341.

DiCarlo, J. J., & Maunsell, J. H. R. (2003). Anterior inferotemporal neurons of monkeys engaged in object recognition can be highly sensitive to object retinal position. *Journal of Neurophysiology, 89,* 3264–3287.

DiCicco-Bloom, E., Lord, C., Zwaigenbaum, L., Courchesne, E., Dager, S. R., Schmitz, C., et al. (2006). The developmental neurobiology of autism spectrum disorder. *Journal of Neuroscience, 26,* 6897–6906.

Dickerson, B. C., Bakkour, A., Salat, D. H., Feczko, E., Pacheco, J., Greve, D. N., et al. (2009). The cortical signature of Alzheimer's disease: Regionally specific cortical thinning relates to symptom severity in very mild to mild AD dementia and is detectable in asymptomatic amyloid-positive individuals. *Cerebral Cortex, 19,* 497–510.

Dickter, C. L., & Bartholow, B. D. (2007). Racial ingroup and outgroup attention biases revealed by event-related brain potentials. *Social Cognitive & Affective Neuroscience, 2,* 189–198.

Diego, M. A., Field, T., Hernandez-Reif, M., Cullen, C., Schanberg, S., & Kuhn, C. (2004). Prepartum, postpartum, and chronic depression effects on newborns. *Psychiatry, 67,* 63–80.

Dien, J. (2009). The neurocognitive basis of reading single words as seen through early latency ERPs: A model of converging pathways. *Biological Psychology, 80,* 10–22.

Dimond, S. J., & Beaumont, J. G. (1973). Difference in the vigilance performance of the right and left hemisphere. *Cortex, 9,* 259–265.

Ditunno, P., & Mann, V. (1990). Right hemisphere specialization for mental rotation in normals and brain damaged subjects. *Cortex, 26,* 177–188.

Dockery, C. A., Hueckel-Weng, R., Birbaumer, N., & Plewnia, C. (2009). Enhancement of planning ability by transcranial direct current stimulation. *Journal of Neuroscience, 29,* 7271–7277.

Dodrill, C. B. (1992). Neuropsychological aspects of epilepsy. *Psychiatric Clinics of North America, 15,* 383–394.

Dolan, R. J., & Morris, J. S. (2000). The functional anatomy of innate and acquired fear: Perspectives from neuroscience. In R. D. Lane & L. Nadel (Eds.), *Cognitive neuroscience of emotion* (pp. 156–191). New York: Oxford University Press.

Dolcos, F., LaBar, K. S., & Cabeza, R. (2004). Interaction between the amygdala and the medial temporal lobe memory system predicts better memory for emotional events. *Neuron, 42,* 855–863.

Dom, G., Sabbe, B., Hulstijn, W., & van den Brink, W. (2005). Substance use disorders and the orbitofrontal cortex: Systematic review of behavioural decision-making and neuroimaging studies. *British Journal of Psychiatry, 187,* 209–220.

Donaldson, D. I., Petersen, S. E., & Buckner, R. L. (2001). Dissociating memory retrieval processes using fMRI: Evidence that priming does not support recognition memory. *Neuron, 31(6),* 1047–1059.

Donchin, E. (1981). Surprise! . . . Surprise? *Psychophysiology, 18,* 493–513.

Donchin, E., & Coles, M. (1988). Is the P_{300} component a manifestation of context updating? *Behavioral and Brain Sciences, 11,* 406–417.

Doody, R. S., & Jankovic, J. (1992). The alien hand and related signs. *Journal of Neurology, Neurosurgery & Psychiatry, 55,* 806–810.

Douaud, G., Gaura, V., Ribeiro, M. J., Lethimonnier, F., Maroy, R., Verny, C., et al. (2006). Distribution of grey matter atrophy in Huntington's disease patients: A combined ROI-based and voxel-based morphometric study. *Neuroimage, 32*, 1562–1567.

Dougherty, D. D., Baer, L., Cosgrove, G. R., Cassem, E. H., Price, B. H., Nierenberg, A. A., et al. (2002). Prospective long-term follow-up of 44 patients who received cingulotomy for treatment-refractory obsessive-compulsive disorder. *American Journal of Psychiatry, 159*, 269–275.

Downing, P. E., Jiang, Y., Shuman, M., & Kanwisher, N. (2001). A cortical area selective for visual processing of the human body. *Science, 293*, 2470–2473.

Downing, P., Liu, J., & Kanwisher, N. (2001). Testing cognitive models of visual attention with fMRI and MEG. *Neuropsychologia, 39*, 1329–1342.

Doyon, J. (2008). Motor sequence learning and movement disorders. *Current Opinion in Neurology, 21*, 478–483.

Drachman, D. A., & Arbit, J. (1966). Memory and hippocampal complex. II. Is memory a multiple process? *Archives of Neurology, 15*, 52–61.

Drachman, D. A., & Leavitt, J. (1974). Human memory and the cholinergic system. *Archives of Neurology, 30*, 113–121.

Draganski, B., Gaser, C., Busch, V., Schuierer, G., Bogdahn, U., & May, A. (2004). Changes in gray matter induced by training. *Nature, 427*, 311–312.

Dreher, J. C., Koechlin, E., Tierney, M., & Grafman, J. (2008). Damage to the fronto-polar cortex is associated with impaired multitasking. *PLoS ONE, 3*, e3227.

Drevets, W. C., & Raichle, M. E. (1998). Reciprocal suppression of regional cerebral blood flow during emotional versus higher cognitive processes: Implications for interaction between emotion and cognition. *Cognition & Emotion, 12*, 353–385.

Driver, J., & Vuilleumier, P. (2001). Perceptual awareness and its loss in unilateral neglect and extinction. *Cognition, 79*, 39–88.

Driver, J., Baylis, G., Goodrich, S. J., & Rafal, R. D. (1994). Axis-based neglect of visual shapes. *Neuropsychologia, 32*, 1353–1365.

Dronkers, N. F. (2000). The pursuit of brain-language relationships. *Brain & Language, 71*, 59–61.

Dronkers, N. F., Plaisant, O., Iba-Zizen, M. T., & Cabanis, E. A. (2007). Paul Broca's historic cases: High-resolution MR imaging of the brain of Leborgne and Lelong. *Brain, 130*, 1432–1441.

Dror, I. E., Kosslyn, S. M., & Waag, W. L. (1993). Visual-spatial abilities of pilots. *Journal of Applied Psychology, 78*, 763–773.

Drzezga, A., Grimmer, T., Henriksen, G., Muhlau, M., Perneczky, R., Miederer, I., et al. (2009). Effect of APOE genotype on amyloid plaque load and gray matter volume in Alzheimer disease. *Neurology, 72*, 1487–1494.

Du, A.-T., Schuff, N., Kramer, J. H., Rosen, H. J., Gorno-Tempini, M. L., Rankin, K., et al. (2007). Different regional patterns of cortical thinning in Alzheimer's disease and frontotemporal dementia. *Brain, 130*, 1159–1166.

Dubois, B., Boller, F., Pillon, B., & Agid, Y. (1991). Cognitive deficits in Parkinson's disease. In F. Boller & J. Grafman (Eds.), *Handbook of neuropsychology* (Vol. 5, pp. 195–240). New York: Elsevier.

Duchaine, B. C., & Nakayama, K. (2006). Developmental prosopagnosia: A window to content-specific face processing. *Current Opinion in Neurobiology, 16*, 166–173.

Due, D. L., Huettel, S. A., Hall, W. G., & Rubin, D. C. (2002). Activation in mesolimbic and visuospatial neural circuits elicited by smoking cues: Evidence from functional magnetic resonance imaging. *American Journal of Psychiatry, 159*, 954–960.

Duggan, P. S., Siegel, A. W., Blass, D. M., Bok, H., Coyle, J. T., Faden, R., et al. (2009). Unintended changes in cognition, mood, and behavior arising from cell-based interventions for neurological conditions: Ethical challenges. *American Journal of Bioethics, 9*, 31–36.

Duman, R. S. (2004). Depression: A case of neuronal life and death? *Biological Psychiatry, 56*, 140–145.

Duman, R. S. (2009). Neurochemical theories of depression: Preclinical studies. In D. S. Charney & E. J. Nestler (Eds.), *Neurobiology of mental illness* (3d ed; pp. 413–434). Oxford, UK: Oxford University Press.

Duncan, J. (1986). Disorganization of behavior after frontal lobe damage. *Cognitive Neuropsychology, 3*, 271–290.

Duncan, J., & Owen, A. M. (2000). Cognitive regions of the human frontal lobe recruited by diverse cognitive demands. *Trends in Neurosciences, 23*, 475–483.

Duncan, J., Seitz, R. J., Kolodny, J., Bor, D., Herzog, H., Ahmed, A., et al. (2000). A neural basis for general intelligence. *Science, 289*, 457–460.

Dunlop, B. W., Garlow, S. J., & Nemeroff, C. B. (2009). The neurochemistry of depressive disorders: Clinical studies. In D. S. Charney & E. J. Nestler (Eds.), *Neurobiology of mental illness* (3d ed.; pp. 435–460). Oxford, UK: Oxford University Press.

Dunn, J. C. (2004). Remember-know: A matter of confidence. *Psychological Review, 111*, 524–542.

Dupont, S., Van de Moortele, P. F., Samson, S., Hasboun, D., Poline, J. B., Adam, C., et al. (2000). Episodic memory in left temporal lobe epilepsy: A functional MRI study. *Brain, 123*, 1722–1732.

Dupuis, F., Johnston, K. M., Lavoie, M., Lepore, F., & Lassonde, M. (2000). Concussions in athletes produce brain dysfunction as revealed by event-related potentials. *NeuroReport, 11*, 4087–4092.

Duyckaerts, C., Delatour, B., & Potier, M.-C. (2009). Classification and basic pathology of Alzheimer disease. *Acta Neuropathologica, 118*, 5–36.

Ebmeier, K. P., Donaghey, C., & Steele, J. D. (2006). Recent developments and current controversies in depression. *Lancet, 367*, 153–167.

Edwards, R., Xiao, D., Keysers, C., Földiák, P., & Perrett, D. (2003). Color sensitivity of cells responsive to complex stimuli in the temporal cortex. *Journal of Neurophysiology, 90*, 1245–1256.

Egan, M. F., Goldberg, T. E., Kolachana, B. S., Callicott, J. H., Mazzanti, C. M., Straub, R. E., et al. (2001). Effect of COMT Val[108/158] Met genotype on frontal lobe function and risk for schizophrenia. *Proceedings of the National Academy of Sciences, 98*, 6917–6922.

Eichenbaum, H. (1997). How does the brain organize memories? *Science, 277*(5324), 330–332.

Eichenbaum, H. (2000). A cortical-hippocampal system for declarative memory. *Nature Reviews Neuroscience, 1*(1), 41–50.

Eichenbaum, H., & Cohen, N. J. (2001). *From conditioning to conscious recollection: Memory systems of the brain.* New York: Oxford University Press.

Eichenbaum, H., Dudchenko, P., Wood, E., Shapiro, M., & Tanila, H. (1999). The hippocampus, memory, and place cells: Is it spatial memory or a memory space? *Neuron, 23*, 209–226.

Eichenbaum, H., Stewart, C., & Morris, R. G. M. (1990). Hippocampal representation in spatial learning. *Journal of Neuroscience, 10*, 331–339.

Eichenbaum, H., Yonelinas, A. P., & Ranganath, C. (2007). The medial temporal lobe and recognition memory. *Annual Review of Neuroscience, 30*, 123–152.

Eisenberger, N. I., Jarcho, J. M., Lieberman, M. D., & Naliboff, B. D. (2006). An experimental study of shared sensitivity to physical pain and social rejection. *Pain, 126*, 132–138.

Eisenberger, N. I., Lieberman, M. D., & Williams, K. D. (2003). Does rejection hurt? An fMRI study of social exclusion. *Science, 302*, 290–292.

Ekman, P., Sorenson, E. R., & Friesen, W. V. (1969). Pan-cultural elements in facial displays of emotion. *Science, 164*, 86–88.

Ekstrom, A. D., Kahana, M. J., Caplan, J. B., Fields, T. A., Isham, E. A., Newman, E. L., & Fried, I. (2003). Cellular networks underlying human spatial navigation. *Nature, 425*, 184–187.

Elder, G. A., & Cristian, A. (2009). Blast-related mild traumatic brain injury: Mechanisms of injury and impact on clinical care. *Mount Sinai Journal of Medicine, 76*, 111–118.

Elfenbein, H. A., & Ambady, N. (2002). On the universality and cultural specificity of emotion recognition: A meta-analysis. *Psychological Bulletin, 128*, 203–235.

Elhwuegi, A. S. (2004). Central monoamines and their role in major depression. *Progress in Neuro-Psychopharmacology & Biological Psychiatry, 28*, 435–451.

Ellenbogen, J. M., Hulbert, J. C., Stickgold, R., Dinges, D. F., & Thompson-Schill, S. L. (2006). Interfering with theories of sleep and memory: Sleep, declarative memory, and associative interference. *Current Biology, 16*, 1290–1294.

Ellenbogen, J. M., Payne, J. D., & Stickgold, R. (2006). The role of sleep in declarative memory consolidation: Passive, permissive, active or none? *Current Opinion in Neurobiology, 16*, 716–722.

Elliott, R. (1998). The neuropsychological profile in unipolar depression. *Trends in Cognitive Sciences, 2*, 447–454.

Elliott, R., Rubinsztein, J. S., Sahakian, B. J., & Dolan, R. J. (2002). The neural basis of mood-congruent processing biases in depression. *Archives of General Psychiatry, 59*, 597–604.

Ellis, A. W., Flude, B. M., & Young, A. W. (1987). "Neglect dyslexia" and the early visual processing of letters in words. *Cognitive Neuropsychology, 4*, 439–464.

Ellis, R. J., Calero, P., & Stockin, M. D. (2009). HIV infection and the central nervous system: A primer. *Neuropsychology Review, 19*, 144–151.

Ellison, A., Rushworth, M., & Walsh, V. (2003). The parietal cortex in visual search: A visuomotor hypothesis. *Supplements to Clinical Neurophysiology, 56*, 321–330.

Ellsworth, P. C. (1994). William James and emotion: Is a century of fame worth a century of misunderstanding? *Psychological Review, 101*, 222–229.

Emery, N. J., Capitanio, J. P., Mason, W. A., Machado, C. J., Mendoza, S. P., & Amaral, D. G. (2001). The effects of bilateral lesions of the amygdala on dyadic social interactions in rhesus monkeys (*Macaca mulatta*). *Behavioral Neuroscience, 115*, 515–544.

Emmorey, K., Grabowski, T., McCullough, S., Damasio, H., Ponto, L. L., Hichwa, R. D., & Bellugi, U. (2003). Neural systems underlying lexical retrieval for sign language. *NeuroImage, 41*, 85–95.

Emmorey, K., Mehta, S., & Grabowski, T. J. (2007). The neural correlates of sign versus word production. *NeuroImage, 36*, 202–208.

Engels, A. S., Heller, W., Mohanty, A., Herrington, J. D., Banich, M. T., Webb, A. G., & Miller, G. A. (2007). Specificity of regional brain activity in anxiety types during emotion processing. *Psychophysiology, 44*, 352–363.

Entus, A. K. (1977). Hemispheric asymmetry in processing of dichotically presented speech and nonspeech stimuli by infants. In S. J. Segalowitz & F. A. Gruber (Eds.), *Language development and neurological theory* (pp. 64–73). New York: Academic Press.

Epstein, J., Pan, H., Kocsis, J. H., Yang, Y., Butler, T., Chusid, J., et al. (2006). Lack of ventral striatal response to positive stimuli in depressed versus normal subjects. *American Journal of Psychiatry, 163*, 1784–1790.

Epstein, L., & Brown, P. (1997). Bovine spongiform encephalopathy and a new variant of Creutzfeldt-Jakob disease. *Neurology, 48*, 569–571.

Epstein, R. A., & Kanwisher, N. (1998). A cortical representation of the local visual environment. *Nature, 392*, 598–601.

Epstein, R. A., Higgins, J. S., Jablonski, K., & Feiler, A. M. (2007). Visual scene processing in familiar and unfamiliar environments. *Journal of Neurophysiology, 97*, 3670–3683.

Epstein, R. A., Parker, W. E., & Feiler, A. M. (2007). Where am I now? Distinct roles for parahippocampal and retrosplenial cortices in place recognition. *Journal of Neuroscience, 27*, 6141–6149.

Epstein, R., DeYoe, E. A., Press, D. Z., Rosen, A. C., & Kanwisher, N. (2001). Neuropsychological evidence for a topographical learning mechanism in parahippocampal cortex. *Cognitive Neuropsychology, 18*, 481–508.

Epstein, R., Harris, A., Stanley, D., & Kanwisher, N. (1999). The parahippocampal place area: Recognition, navigation or encoding? *Neuron, 23*, 115–125.

Eriksson, P. S., Perfilieva, E., Björk-Eriksson, T., Alborn, A. M., Nordborg, C., Peterson, D. A., & Gage, F. H. (1998). Neurogenesis in adult human hippocampus. *Nature Medicine, 4*, 1313–1317.

Erkinjuntti, T., Haltia, M., Palo, J., & Paetau, A. (1988). Accuracy of the clinical diagnosis of vascular dementia: A prospective clinical and post-mortem neuropathological study. *Journal of Neurology, Neurosurgery & Psychiatry, 51*, 1037–1044.

Erlanger, D. M., Kutner, K. C., Barth, J. T., & Barnes, R. (1999). Neuropsychology of sports-related head injury: Dementia pugilistica to post concussion syndrome. *Clinical Neuropsychologist, 13*, 193–209.

Estrada, L. D., & Soto, C. (2009). Strategies for Alzheimer's disease diagnosis. In R. B. Maccioni & G. Perry (Eds.), *Current hypotheses and research milestones in Alzheimer's disease* (pp. 217–226). New York: Springer.

Féart, C., Samieri, C., Rondeau, V., Amieva, H., Portet, F., Dartigues, J.-F., et al. (2009). Adherence to a Mediterranean diet, cognitive decline, and risk of dementia. *JAMA, 302*, 638–648.

Földiák, P., Xiao, D., Keysers, C., Edwards, R., & Perrett, D. I. (2004). Rapid serial visual presentation for the determination of neural selectivity in area STSa. *Progress in Brain Research, 144*, 107–116.

Fabiani, M., & Donchin, E. (1995). Encoding processes and memory organization: A model of the von Restorff effect. *Journal of Experimental Psychology: Learning, Memory, & Cognition, 21*(1), 224–240.

Fabiani, M., Gratton, G., & Federmeier, K. (2007). Event-related brain potentials: Methods, theory and applications. In J. T. Cacioppo, L. G. Tassinary, & G. G. Berntson (Eds.), *Handbook of Psychophysiology* (3d ed., pp. 85–119). Cambridge: Cambridge University Press.

Fadiga, L., Craighero, L., & D'Ausilio, A. (2009). Broca's area in language, action, and music. *Annals of the New York Academy of Sciences, 1169*, 448–458.

Fairhall, S. L., & Macaluso, E. (2009). Spatial attention can modulate audiovisual integration at multiple cortical and subcortical sites. *European Journal of Neuroscience, 29*, 1247–1257.

Falchier, A., Clavagnier, S., Barone, P., & Kennedy, H. (2002). Anatomical evidence of multimodal integration in primate striate cortex. *Journal of Neuroscience, 22*, 5749–5759.

Falkenstein, M., Hohnsbein, J., Hoormann, J., & Blanke, L. (1991). Effects of cross-modal divided attention on late ERP components: II. Error processing in choice reaction tasks. *Clinical Neurophysiology, 78*(6), 447–455.

Fan, J., Gu, X., Guise, K. G., Liu, X., Fossella, J., Wang, H., & Posner, M. I. (2009). Testing the behavioral interaction and integration of attentional networks. *Brain & Cognition, 70*, 209–220.

Farah, M. J. (1988). Is visual imagery really visual? Overlooked evidence from neuropsychology. *Psychological Review, 95*, 307–317.

Farah, M. J. (2000). *The cognitive neuroscience of vision*. Malden, MA: Blackwell Publishers.

Farah, M. J. (2004). *Visual agnosia* (2d ed.). Cambridge, MA: MIT Press.

Farah, M. J., & Feinberg, T. E. (2000). Visual object agnosia. In M. J. Farah & T. E. Feinberg (Eds.), *Patient-based approaches to cognitive neuroscience* (pp. 79–84). Cambridge, MA: MIT Press.

Farah, M. J., & McClelland, J. L. (1991). A computational model of semantic memory impairment: Modality-specificity and emergent category-specificity. *Journal of Experimental Psychology: General, 120*, 339–357.

Farah, M. J., Levine, D. N., & Calvanio, R. (1988). A case study of a mental imagery deficit. *Brain and Cognition, 8*, 147–164.

Farah, M. J., O'Reilly, R. C., & Vecera, S. P. (1993). Dissociated overt and covert recognition as an emergent property of a lesioned neural network. *Psychological Review, 100*, 571–588.

Farah, M. J., Rabinowitz, C., Quinn, G. E., & Liu, G. T. (2000). Early commitment of neural substrates for face recognition. *Cognitive Neuropsychology, 17*, 117–123.

Farah, M. J., Shera, D. M., Savage, J. H., Betancourt, L., Giannetta, J. M., Brodsky, N. L., et al. (2006). Childhood poverty: Specific associations with neurocognitive development. *Brain Research, 1110*, 166–174.

Farah, M. J., Soso, M. J., & Dasheiff, R. M. (1992). Visual angle of the mind's eye before and after unilateral occipital lobectomy. *Journal of Experimental Psychology: Human Perception and Performance, 18*, 241–246.

Fauth, C., Meyer, B. U., Prosiegel, M., Zihl, J., & Conrad, B. E. (1992). Seizure induction and magnetic stimulation after stroke. *Lancet, 339*, 362.

Federmeier, K. D. (2007). Thinking ahead: The role and roots of prediction in language comprehension. *Psychophysiology, 44,* 491–505.

Feigin, A., Ghilardi, M. F., Huang, C., Ma, Y., Carbon, M., Guttman, M., Paulsen, J. S., Ghez, C. P., & Eidelberg, D. (2006). Preclinical Huntington's disease: Compensatory brain responses during learning. *Annals of Neurology, 59,* 53–59.

Fein, D., Pennington, B., Markowitz, P., Braverman, M., & Waterhouse, L. (1986). Towards a neuropsychological model of infantile autism: Are the social deficits primary? *Journal of the American Academy of Child Psychiatry, 25*(2), 198–212.

Feinberg, T. E., Schindler, R. J., Ochoa, E., Kwan, P. C., & Farah, M. J. (1994). Associative visual agnosia and alexia without prosopagnosia. *Cortex, 30,* 395–411.

Feldman-Barrett, L., & Russell, J. A. (1999). The structure of current affect: Controversies and emerging consensus. *Current Directions in Psychological Science, 8,* 10–14.

Felleman, D. J., & Van Essen, D. C. (1991). Distributed hierarchical processing in the primate cerebral cortex. *Cerebral Cortex, 1,* 1–47.

Fellows, L. K., & Farah, M. J. (2005). Is anterior cingulate cortex necessary for cognitive control? *Brain, 128,* 788–796.

Fendrich, R., Wessinger, C. M., & Gazzaniga, M. S. (1992). Residual vision in a scotoma: Implications for blindsight. *Science, 258,* 1489–1491.

Fernandez, B., Cardebat, D., Demonet, J.-F., Joseph, P. A., Mazaux, J. M., Barat, M., & Allard, M. (2004). Functional MRI follow-up study of language processes in healthy subjects and during recovery in a case of aphasia. *Stroke, 35,* 2171–2176.

Fernandez, G., Effern, A., Grunwald, T., Pezer, N., Lehnertz, K., Dumpelmann, M., et al. (1999). Real-time tracking of memory formation in the human rhinal cortex and hippocampus. *Science, 285*(5433), 1582–1585.

Fernandez-Carriba, S., Loeches, A., Morcillo, A., & Hopkins, W. D. (2002). Asymmetry in facial expression of emotions by chimpanzees. *Neuropsychologia, 40,* 1523–1533.

Ferraro, F. R., Balota, D. A., & Connor, L. T. (1993). Implicit memory and the formation of new associations in nondemented Parkinson's disease individuals and individuals with senile dementia of the Alzheimer type: A serial reaction time (SRT) investigation. *Brain & Cognition, 21*(2), 163–180.

Ferstl, E. C., Neumann, J., Bogler, C., & von Cramon, D. Y. (2008). The extended language network: A meta-analysis of neuroimaging studies on text comprehension. *Human Brain Mapping, 29,* 581–593.

Field, G. D., & Chichilnisky, E. J. (2007). Information processing in the primate retina: Circuitry and coding. *Annual Review of Neuroscience, 30,* 1–30.

Fields, J. A., & Troster, A. I. (2000). Cognitive outcomes after deep brain stimulation for Parkinson's Disease: A review of initial studies and recommendations for future research. *Brain & Cognition, 42,* 268–293.

Fierro, B., Brighina, F., Piazza, A., Oliveri, M., & Bisiach, E. (2001). Timing of right parietal and frontal cortex activity in visuospatial perception: A TMS study in normal individuals. *NeuroReport, 12,* 2605–2607.

Fierro, B., Brighina, F., & Bisiach, E. (2006). Improving neglect by TMS. *Behavioural Neurology, 17,* 169–176.

Fiez, J. A., & Petersen, S. E. (1998). Neuroimaging studies of word reading. *Proceedings of the National Academy of Sciences, USA, 95,* 914–921.

Fiez, J. A., Tallal, P., Raichle, M. E., Miezin, F. M., Katz, W. F., & Petersen, S. E. (1995). PET studies of auditory and phonological processing: Effects of stimulus characteristics and task demands. *Journal of Cognitive Neuroscience, 7,* 357–375.

Fiez, J. A., Tranel, D., Seager-Frerichs, D., & Damasio, H. (2006). Specific reading and phonological processing deficits are associated with damage to the left frontal operculum. *Cerebral Cortex, 42,* 624–643.

Filbey, F. M., Claus, E., Audette, A. R., Niculescu, M., Banich, M. T., Tanabe, J., et al. (2008). Exposure to the taste of alcohol elicits activation of the mesocorticolimbic neurocircuitry. *Neuropsychopharmacology, 33,* 1391–1401.

Filimon, F., Nelson, J. D., Huang, R. S., & Sereno, M. I. (2009). Multiple parietal reach regions in humans: Cortical representations for visual and proprioceptive feedback during on-line reaching. *Journal of Neuroscience, 29,* 2961–2971.

Fine, I., Wade, I. R., Brewer, A. A., May, M. G., Goodman, D. F., Boynton, G. M., et al. (2003). Long-term deprivation affects visual perception and cortex. *Nature Neuroscience, 6,* 915–916.

Fine, J. G., Semrud-Clikeman, M., Keith, T. Z., Stapleton, L. M., & Hynd, G. W. (2007). Reading and the corpus callosum: An MRI family study of volume and area. *Neuropsychology, 21,* 235–241.

Fink, G. R., Dolan, R. J., Halligan, P. W., Marshall, J. C., & Frith, C. D. (1997). Space-based and object-based visual attention: Shared and specific neural domains. *Brain, 120,* 2013–2028.

Fink, G. R., Marshall, J. C., Weiss, P. H., Shah, N. J., Toni, I., Halligan, P. W., & Zilles, K. (2000). "Where" depends on "what": A differential functional anatomy for position discrimination in one- versus two-dimensions. *Neuropsychologia, 38,* 1741–1748.

Fink, M., Wadsak, W., Savli, M., Stein, P., Moser, U., Hahn, A., et al. (2007). Lateralization of the serotonin-1A receptor distribution in language areas revealed by PET. *Neuroimage, 45,* 598–605.

Fiorillo, C. D., Tobler, P. N., & Schultz, W. (2003). Discrete coding of reward probability and uncertainty by dopamine neurons. *Science, 299,* 1898–1902.

Fischer, J. S., Priore, R. L., Jacobs, L. D., Cookfair, D. L., Rudick, R. A., Herndon, R. M., et al. (2000). Neuropsychological effects of interferon beta-1a in relapsing multiple sclerosis. Multiple Sclerosis Collaborative Research Group. *Annals of Neurology, 48,* 885–892.

Fischer, S., Hallschmid, M., Elsner, A. L., & Born, J. (2002) Sleep forms memory for finger skills. *Proceedings of the National Academy of Sciences, USA, 99,* 11987–11991.

Fisher, M., Holland, C., Merzenich, M. M., & Vinogradov, S. (2009). Using neuroplasticity-based auditory training to improve verbal memory in schizophrenia. *American Journal of Psychiatry, 166,* 805–811.

Fisher, M., Holland, C., Subramaniam, K., & Vinogradov, S. (2009). Neuroplasticity-based cognitive training in schizophrenia: An interim report on the effects 6 months later. *Schizophrenia Bulletin,* Epub ahead of print, doi:10.1093/schbul/sbn170.

Fitzgerald, K. D., Welsh, R. C., Gehring, W. J., Abelson, J. L., Himle, J. A., Liberzon, I., & Taylor, S. F. (2005). Error-related hyperactivity of the anterior cingulate cortex in obsessive-compulsive disorder. *Biological Psychiatry, 57*(3), 287–294.

Fitzgerald, P. B., & Daskalakis, Z. J. (2008). The use of repetitive transcranial magnetic stimulation and vagal nerve stimulation in the treatment of depression. *Current Opinion in Psychiatry, 21,* 25–29.

Fitzgerald, P. B., Brown, T. L., Marston, N. A. U., Daskalakis, J., de Castella, A., & Kulkarni, J. (2003). Transcranial magnetic stimulation in the treatment of depression. *Archives of General Psychiatry, 60,* 1002–1008.

Fitzgerald, P. B., Huntsman, S., Gunewardene, R., Kulkarmi, J., & Daskalskis, Z. J. (2006). A randomized trial of low-frequency right-prefrontal-cortex transcranial magnetic stimulation as augmentation in treatment-resistant major depression. *International Journal of Neuropsychopharmacology, 9,* 655–666.

Flament, D., Ellermann, J. M., Kim, S. G., Ugurbil, K., & Ebner, T. J. (1996). Functional magnetic resonance imaging of cerebellar activation during the learning of a visuo-motor dissociation task. *Human Brain Mapping, 4*(3), 210–226.

Flavell, J. H. (2004). Theory-of-mind development: Retrospect and prospect. *Merrill-Palmer Quarterly, 50,* 274–290.

Flege, J. E., Yeni-Komshian, G. H., & Liu, S. (1999). Age constraints on second language acquisition. *Journal of Memory & Language, 41,* 78–104.

Fleminger, S., & Curtis, D. (1997). Prion diseases. *British Journal of Psychiatry, 170,* 103–105.

Fodor, J. (1985). The modularity of mind. *Behavioral and Brain Sciences, 8,* 1–42.

Foldi, N. S. (1987). Appreciation of pragmatic interpretation of indirect commands: Comparison of right and left brain-damaged patients. *Brain & Language, 31,* 88–108.

Forbes, E. E., Christopher May, J., Siegle, G. J., Ladouceur, C. D., Ryan, N. D., Carter, C. S., et al. (2006). Reward-related decision-making in pediatric major depressive disorder: An fMRI study. *Journal of Child Psychology & Psychiatry & Allied Disciplines, 47,* 1031–1040.

Forbes, E. E., Hariri, A. R., Martin, S. L., Silk, J. S., Moyles, D. L., Fisher, P. M., et al. (2009). Altered striatal activation predicting real-world positive affect in adolescent major depression. *American Journal of Psychiatry, 166,* 64–73.

Forbes, E. E., Shaw, D. S., & Dahl, R. E. (2007). Alterations in reward-related decision making in boys with recent and future depression. *Biological Psychiatry, 61,* 633–639.

Ford, J. M. (1999). Schizophrenia: The broken P300 and beyond. *Psychophysiology, 36,* 667–682.

Ford, J. M., Mathalon, D. H., Whitfield, S., Faustman, W. O., & Roth, W. T. (2002). Reduced communication between frontal and temporal lobes during talking in schizophrenia. *Biological Psychiatry, 51,* 485–492.

Ford, J. M., Sullivan, E. V., Marsh, L., White, P. M., Lim, K. O., & Pfefferbaum, A. (1994). The relationship between P300 amplitude and regional gray matter volumes depends upon the attentional system engaged. *Electroencephalography & Clinical Neurophysiology, 90,* 214–228.

Forrest, B. J. (2004). The utility of math difficulties, internalized psychopathology, and visual-spatial deficits to identify children with the nonverbal learning disability syndrome: Evidence for a visual-spatial disability. *Child Neuropsychology, 10,* 129–146.

Forstmann, B. U., Brass, M., Koch, I., & von Cramon, D. Y. (2006). Voluntary selection of task sets revealed by functional magnetic resonance imaging. *Journal of Cognitive Neuroscience, 18,* 388–398.

Foti, D., & Hajcak, G. (2008). Deconstructing reappraisal: Descriptions preceding arousing pictures modulate the subsequent neural response. *Journal of Cognitive Neuroscience, 20,* 977–988.

Foundas, A. L., Leonard, D. M., Gilmore, R., Fennell, E., & Heilman, K. M. (1994). Planum temporale asymmetry and language dominance. *Neuropsychologia, 10,* 1225–1231.

Fowler, J. S., Wang, G. J., Volkow, N. D., Logan, J., Franceschi, D., Franceschi, M., MacGregor, R., Shea, C., Garza, V., Liu, N., & Ding, Y. S. (2000). Evidence that ginkgo biloba extract does not inhibit MAO A and B in living human brain. *Life Science, 66,* 141–146.

Fox, C. M., Raming, L. O., Ciucci, M. R., Sapir, S., McFarland, D., & Farley, B. G. (2006). The science and practice of LSVT/LOUD: Neural plasticity-principled approach to treating individuals with Parkinson disease and other neurological disorders. *Seminars in Speech and Language, 27,* 283–299.

Fox, M., Snyder, A. Z., Vincent, J. L., Corbetta, M., Van Essen, D. C., & Raichle, M. E. (2005). The human brain is intrinsically organized into dynamic, anticorrelated functional networks. *Proceedings of the National Academy of Sciences, USA, 102,* 9673–9678.

Fox, N. A., & Davidson, R. J. (1986). Taste-elicited changes in facial signs of emotion and the asymmetry of brain electrical activity in human newborns. *Neuropsychologia, 24,* 417–422.

Fox, P. T., Raichle, M. E., Mintun, M. A., & Dence, C. (1988). Nonoxidative glucose consumption during focal physiologic neural activity. *Science, 241,* 462–464.

Frank, M. J., Loughry, B., & O'Reilly, R. C. (2001). Interactions between frontal cortex and basal ganglia in working memory: A computational model. *Cognitive, Affective and Behavioral Neuroscience, 1,* 136–160.

Frank, M. J., O'Reilly, R., & Curran, T. (2006). When memory fails, intuition reigns: Midazolam enhances implicit inference in humans. *Psychological Science, 17,* 700–707.

Franklin, T. R., Acton, P. S., Maldjian, J. A., Gray, J. D., Croft, J. R., Dackis, C. A., et al. (2002). Decreased gray matter concentration in the insular, orbitofrontal, cingulate, and temporal cortices of cocaine patients. *Biological Psychiatry, 51,* 134–142.

Fraser, L. M., O'Carroll, R. E., & Ebmeier, K. P. (2008). The effect of electroconvulsive therapy on autobiographical memory: A systematic review. *Journal of ECT, 24*(1), 10–7.

Frassinetti, F., Rossi, M., & Làdavas, E. (2001). Passive limb movements improve visual neglect. *Neuropsychologia, 39,* 725–733.

Freedman, R., Waldo, M. C., Bickford-Wimer, P., & Nagamoto, H. (1991). Elementary neuronal dysfunctions in schizophrenia. *Schizophrenia Research, 4*(2), 233–243.

Freese, J. L., & Amaral, D. G. (2009). Neuroanatomy of the primate amygdala. In P. J. Whalen & E. A. Phelps (Eds.), *The human amygdala* (pp. 3–42). New York: Guilford.

Freiberg, L., Olsen, T. S., Roland, P. E., Paulson, O. B., & Lassen, N. A. (1985). Focal increase of blood flow in the cerebral cortex of man during vestibular stimulation. *Brain, 108,* 609–623.

Frencham, K. A. R., Fox, A. M., & Maybery, M. T. (2005). Neuropsychological studies of mild traumatic brain injury: A meta-analytic review of research since 1995. *Journal of Clinical & Experimental Neuropsychology, 27,* 334–351.

Frey, S. H., Vinton, D., Norlund, R., & Grafton, S. T. (2005). Cortical topography of human anterior intraparietal cortex active during visually guided grasping. *Cognitive Brain Research, 23,* 397–405.

Friederici, A. D. (2009). Pathways to language: Fiber tracts in the human brain. *Trends in Cognitive Sciences,13*(4), 175–181.

Friederici, A. D., Hahne, A., & Mecklinger, A. (1996). Temporal structure of syntactic parsing: Early and late event-related brain potential effects. *Journal of Experimental Psychology: Learning, Memory, & Cognition, 22,* 1219–1248.

Friedlander, L., & Desrocher, M. (2006). Neuroimaging studies of obsessive-compulsive disorder in adults and children. *Clinical Psychology Review, 26,* 32–49.

Friedman, D., Cycowicz, Y. M,, & Gaeta, H. (2001). The novelty P3: An event-related brain potential (ERP) sign of the brain's evaluation of novelty. *Neuroscience & Biobehavioral Reviews, 25,* 355–373.

Friedman, D., Goldman, R., Stern, Y., & Brown, T. R. (2009). The brain's orienting response: An event-related functional magnetic resonance imaging investigation. *Human Brain Mapping, 30,* 1144–1154.

Friedman, N. P., Miyake, A., Corley, R. P., Young, S. E., Defries, J. C., & Hewitt, J. K. (2006). Not all executive functions are related to intelligence. *Psychological Science, 17,* 172–179.

Friedman-Hill, S. R., Robertson, L. C., & Treisman, A. M. (1995). Parietal contributions to visual feature binding: Evidence from a patient with bilateral lesions. *Science, 269,* 853–855.

Friske, J. E., & Gammie, S. C. (2005). Environmental enrichment alters plus maze, but not maternal defense performance in mice. *Physiology & Behavior, 85,* 187–194.

Frith, C. D., Friston, K. J., Liddle, P. F., & Frackowiak, R. S. J. (1991). A PET study of word finding. *Neuropsychologia, 29,* 1137–1148.

Frith, U., & Frith, C. D. (2003). Development and neurophysiology of mentalizing. *Philosophical Transactions of the Royal Society of London, Series B, Biological Sciences, 358,* 459–473.

Frost, J. A., Binder, J. R., Springer, J. A., Hammeke, T. A., Bellgowan, P. S., Rao, S. M., & Cox, R. W. (1999). Language processing is strongly left lateralized in both sexes. Evidence from functional MRI. *Brain, 122,* 199–208.

Frost, S. B., Barbay, S., Friel, K. M., Plautz, E. J., & Nudo, R. J. (2003). Reorganization of remote cortical regions after ischemic brain injury: A potential substrate for stroke recovery. *Journal of Neurophysiology, 89,* 3205–3214.

Fuentes, P. (2009). Current anti-dementia drugs: Hypothesis and clinical benefits. In R. B. Maccioni & G. Perry (Eds.), *Current hypotheses and research milestones in Alzheimer's disease* (pp. 237–241). New York: Springer.

Fujita, I., Tanaka, K., Ito, M., & Cheng, K. (1992). Columns for visual features of objects in monkey inferotemporal cortex. *Nature, 360,* 343–346.

Funahashi, S. (2006). Prefrontal cortex and working memory processes. *Neuroscience, 139,* 251–261.

Funahashi, S., Bruce, C. J., & Goldman-Rakic, P. S. (1991). Neuronal activity related to saccadic eye movements in the monkey's dorsolateral prefrontal cortex. *Journal of Neurophysiology, 65*(6), 1464–1483.

Funahashi, S., Bruce, C. J., & Goldman-Rakic, P. S. (1993). Dorsolateral prefrontal lesions and oculomotor delayed-response performance: Evidence for mnemonic "scotomas." *Journal of Neuroscience, 13*(4), 1479–1497.

Furey, M. L., Pietrini, P., & Haxby, J. V. (2000). Cholinergic enhancement and increased selectivity of perceptual processing during working memory. *Science, 290,* 2315–2319.

Furmark, T., Tillford, M., Marteinsdottir, I., Fischer, H., Pissiota, A., Langstrom, B., & Fredrikson, M. (2002). Common changes in cerebral blood flow in patients with social phobia treated with citalopram or cognitive-behavioral therapy. *Archives of General Psychiatry, 59,* 425–433.

Fusar-Poli, P., Perez, J., Broome, M., Borgwardt, S., Placentino, A., Caverzasi, E., et al. (2007). Neurofunctional correlates of vulnerability to psychosis: A systematic review and meta-analysis. *Neuroscience & Biobehavioral Reviews, 31,* 465–484.

Fuster, J. M. (1985). The prefrontal cortex, mediator of cross-temporal contingencies. *Human Neurobiology, 4,* 169–179.

Fyhn, M., Molden, S., Witter, M. P., Moser, E. I., & Moser, M.-B. (2004). Spatial representation in the entorhinal cortex. *Science, 305,* 1258–1264.

Gabrieli, J. D. (1995). A systematic view of human memory processes. *Journal of the International Neuropsychological Society, 1*(1), 115–118.

Gabrieli, J. D. (1998). Cognitive science of human memory. *Annual Review of Psychology, 49,* 87–115.

Gabrieli, J. D. E., Fleischman, D. A., Keane, M. M., Reminger, S. L., & Morrell, F. (1995). Double dissociation between memory systems underlying explicit and implicit memory in the human brain. *Psychological Science, 6*(2), 76–82.

Gabrieli, J. D., Cohen, N. J., & Corkin, S. (1988). The impaired learning of semantic knowledge following bilateral medial temporal-lobe resection. *Brain & Cognition, 7*(2), 157–177.

Gaffan, D. (1974). Recognition impaired and association intact in the memory of monkeys after transection of the fornix. *Journal of Comparative & Physiological Psychology, 86,* 1100–1109.

Gaffan, D. (1977). Monkey's recognition memory for complex pictures and the effects of fornix transection. *Quarterly Journal of Experimental Psychology, 29,* 505–514.

Gaillard, W. D., Balsamo, L., Xu, B., McKinney, C., Papero, P. H., Weinstein, S., et al. (2004). fMRI language task panel improves determination of language dominance. *Neurology, 63,* 1403–1408.

Gais, S., Lucas, B., & Born, J. (2006) Sleep after learning aids memory recall. *Learning & Memory, 13,* 259–262.

Galaburda, A. M., LoTurco, J., Ramus, F., Fitch, R. H., & Rosen, G. D. (2006). From genes to behavior in developmental dyslexia. *Nature Neuroscience, 9,* 1213–1217.

Galaburda, A. M., Sherman, G. F., Rosen, G. D., Aboitiz, F., & Geschwind, N. (1985). Developmental dyslexia: Four consecutive patients with cortical anomalies. *Annuals of Neurology, 18,* 222–233.

Galarneau, M. R., Woodruff, S. I., Dye, J. L., Mohrle, C. R., & Wade, A. L. (2008). Traumatic brain injury during Operation Iraqi Freedom: Findings from the United States Navy-Marine Corps Combat Trauma Registry. *Journal of Neurosurgery, 108,* 950–957.

Galavan, A., Hare, T. A., Parra, C. E., Penn, J., Voss, H., Glover, G., & Casey, B. J. (2006). Earlier development of the accumbens relative to orbitofrontal cortex might underlie risk-taking behavior in adolescents. *Journal of Neuroscience, 26,* 6885–6892.

Gale, S. D., Johnson, S. C., Bigler, E. D., & Blatter, D. D. (1995). Nonspecific white matter degeneration following traumatic brain injury. *Journal of the International Neuropsychological Society, 1,* 17–28.

Gallese, V., Keysers, C., & Rizzolatti, G. (2004). A unifying view of the basis of social cognition. *Trends in Cognitive Sciences, 8,* 396–403.

Garavan, H., & Stout, J. C. (2005). Neurocognitive insights into substance abuse. *Trends in Cognitive Sciences, 9,* 195–201.

Garavan, H., Pankiewicz, J., Bloom, A., Cho, J.-K., Sperry, L., Ross, T. J., et al. (2000). Cue-induced cocaine craving: Neuroanatomical specificity for drug users and drug stimuli. *American Journal of Psychiatry, 157,* 1789–1798.

Garavan, H., Ross, T. J., & Stein, E. A. (1999). Right hemispheric dominance of inhibitory control: An event-related functional MRI study. *Proceedings of the National Academy of Sciences, USA, 96,* 8301–8306.

Garpenstrand, H., Annas, P., Ekblom, J., Oreland, L., & Fredrikson, M. (2001). Human fear conditioning is related to dopaminergic and serotonergic biological markers. *Behavioral Neuroscience, 115,* 358–364.

Gasquet, I., Haro, J. M., Novick, D., Edgell, E. T., Kennedy, L., & Lepine, J. P. (2005). Pharmacological treatment and other predictors of treatment outcomes in previously untreated patients with schizophrenia: Results from the European Schizophrenia Outpatient Health Outcomes (SOHO) study. *International Clinical Psychopharmacology, 20,* 199–205.

Gatley, J., Volkow, N. D., Wang, G. J., Fowler, J. S., Logan, J., Ding, Y. S., & Gerasimov, M. (2005). PET imaging in clinical drug abuse research. *Current Pharmaceutical Design, 11,* 3203–3219.

Gatz, M., Svedberg, P., Pedersen, N. L., Mortimer, J. A., Berg, S., & Johansson, B. (2001). Education and the risk of Alzheimer's disease: Findings from the study of dementia in Swedish twins. *Journal of Gerontology Series B—Psychological Sciences & Social Sciences, 56B,* 292–300.

Gauthier, I., Behrmann, M., & Tarr, M. J. (2004). Are Greebles like faces? Using the neuropsychological exception to test the rule. *Neuropsychologia, 42,* 1961–1970.

Gauthier, I., Skudlarski, P., Gore, J. C., & Anderson, A. W. (2000). Expertise for cars and birds recruits brain areas involved in face recognition. *Nature Neuroscience, 3,* 191–197.

Gauthier, I., Tarr, M. J., Anderson, A. W., Skudlarski, P., & Gore, J. C. (1999). Activation of the middle fusiform "face area" increases with expertise in recognizing novel objects. *Nature Neuroscience, 2,* 568–573.

Gazzaniga, M. S. (1970). *The bisected brain.* New York: Appleton-Century-Crofts.

Gazzaniga, M. S. (1983a). Reply to Levy and Zaidel. *American Psychologist, 38,* 547–549.

Gazzaniga, M. S. (1983b). Right hemisphere language following brain bisection: A 20-year perspective. *American Psychologist, 38,* 525–537.

Gazzaniga, M. S. (2000). Cerebral specialization and interhemispheric communication: Does the corpus callosum enable the human condition? *Brain, 123,* 1293–1326.

Gazzaniga, M. S. (2005). Forty-five years of split-brain research and still going strong. *Nature Reviews Neuroscience, 6,* 653–659.

Gazzaniga, M. S., Bogen, J. E., & Sperry, R. W. (1962). Some functional effects of sectioning the cerebral commissures in man. *Proceedings of the National Academy of Science, USA, 48,* 1765–1769.

Gazzaniga, M. S., Fendrich, R., & Wessinger, C. M. (1994). Blindsight reconsidered. *Current Directions in Psychological Science, 3,* 93–96.

Geffen, G., Bradshaw, J. L., & Wallace, G. (1971). Interhemispheric effects on reaction time to verbal and nonverbal visual stimuli. *Journal of Experimental Psychology, 87,* 415–422.

Gegenfurtner, K. R., & Kiper, D. C. (2004). The processing of color in extrastriate cortex. In L. M. Chalupa & J. S. Werner (Eds.), *The visual neurosciences* (pp. 1017–1028). Cambridge, MA: MIT Press.

Gehring, W. J., & Knight, R. T. (2000). Prefrontal-cingulate interactions in action monitoring. *Nature Neuroscience, 3,* 516–520.

Gehring, W. J., & Willoughby, A. R. (2002). The medial frontal cortex and the rapid processing of monetary gains and losses. *Science, 295,* 2279–2282.

Gehring, W. J., Himle, J., & Nisenson, L. G. (2000). Action-monitoring dysfunction in obsessive-compulsive disorder. *Psychological Science, 11,* 1–6.

Gehring, W. P., Goss, B., Coles, M. G. H., Meyer, D. E., & Donehin, E. (1993). A neural system for error detection and compensation. *Psychological Science, 4*(6), 385–390.

George, M. S., Ketter, T. A., Parekh, P. I., Rosinsky, N., Ring, H. A., Pazzaglia, P. J., Marangell, L. B., Callahan, A. M., & Post, R. M. (1997). Blunted left cingulate activation in mood disorder subjects during a response interference task (the Stroop). *Journal of Neuropsychiatry, 9,* 55–63.

George, M. S., Parekh, P. I., Rosinsky, N., Ketter, T. A., Kimbrell, T. A., Heilman, K. M., et al. (1996). Understanding emotional prosody activates right hemisphere regions. *Archives of Neurology, 53,* 665–670.

George, M. S., Rush, A. J., Marangell, L. B., Sackeim, H. A., Brannan, S. K., Davis, S. M., et al. (2005). A one-year comparison of vagus nerve stimulation with treatment as usual for treatment-resistant depression. *Biological Psychiatry, 58,* 364–373.

Georgopolous, A. P., Lurito, J. T., Petrides, M., Schwartz, A. B., & Massey, J. T. (1989). Mental rotation of the neuronal population vector. *Science, 243,* 234–236.

Georgopoulos, A. P. (2000). Neural aspects of cognitive motor control. *Current Opinion in Neurobiology, 10,* 238–241.

Georgopoulos, A. P., Schwartz, A. B., & Kettner, R. E. (1986). Neuronal population coding of movement direction. *Science, 233,* 1416–1419.

Gerardin, E., Sirigu, A., Lehéricy, S., Poline, J. B., Gaymard, B., Marsault, C., Agid, Y., & Le Bihan, D. (2000). Partially overlapping neural networks for real and imagined hand movements. *Cerebral Cortex, 10,* 1093–1104.

Gernsbacher, M. A., Dawson, M., & Goldsmith, H. H. (2005). Three reasons not to believe in an autism epidemic. *Current Directions in Psychological Science, 14,* 55–58.

Gershberg, F. B., & Shimamura, A. P. (1995). Impaired use of organizational strategies in free recall following frontal lobe damage. *Neuropsychologia, 33*(10), 1305–1333.

Gerstner, W., Kempter, R., van Hemmen, J. L., & Wagner, H. (1996). A neuronal learning rule for submillisecond temporal coding. *Nature, 383*(6595), 76–78.

Gervais, H., Belin, P., Boddaert, N., Leboyer, M., Coez, A., Sfaello, I., et al. (2004). Abnormal cortical voice processing in autism. *Nature Neuroscience, 7,* 801–802.

Gerwig, M., Kolb, F. P., & Timmann, D. (2007). The involvement of the human cerebellum in eyeblink conditioning. *Cerebellum, 6,* 38–57.

Geschwind, N., & Levitsky, W. (1968). Human brain: Left-right asymmetrics in temporal speech region. *Science, 161,* 186–187.

Ghahremani, D. G., Monterosso, J., Jentsch, J. D., Bilder, R. M., & Poldrack, R. A. (2009). Neural components underlying behavioral flexibility in human reversal learning. *Cerebral Cortex,* Epub ahead of print.

Ghazanfar, A. A., Chandrasekaran, C., & Logothetis, N. K. (2008). Interactions between the superior temporal sulcus and auditory cortex mediate dynamic face/voice integration in rhesus monkeys. *Journal of Neuroscience, 28,* 4457–4469.

Ghazanfar, A. A., Maier, J. X., Hoffman, K. L., & Logothetis, N. K. (2005). Multisensory integration of dynamic faces and voices in rhesus monkey auditory cortex. *Journal of Neuroscience, 25,* 5004–5012.

Gibbs, C. J., Gajdusek, D. C., Asher, D. M., Alpers, M. P., Beck, E., Daniel, P. M., & Matthews, W. B. (1968). Creutzfeldt-Jakob disease (spongiform encephalopathy): Transmission to the chimpanzee. *Science, 161,* 388–389.

Gibson, C., & Bryden, M. P. (1983). Dichaptic recognition of shapes and letters in children. *Canadian Journal of Psychology, 37,* 132–143.

Giedd, J. N., Blumenthal, J., Jeffries, N. O., Castellanos, F. X., Lui, H., Zijdenbos, A., et al. (1999). Brain development during childhood and adolescence: A longitudinal MRI study. *Nature Neuroscience, 2*(10), 861–863.

Giedd, J. N., Rumsey, J. M., Castellanos, F. X., Rajapakse, J. C., Kaysen, D., Vaituzis, A. C., et al. (1996). A quantitative MRI study of the corpus callosum in children and adolescents. *Development Brain Research, 91,* 274–280.

Giedd, J. N., Rumsey, J. M., Castellanos, F. X., Rajapakse, J. C., Kaysen, D., Vaituzis, A. C., Vauss, Y. C., Hamburger, S. D., & Rapoport, J. L. (1996). A quantitative MRI study of the corpus callosum in children and adolescents. *Development Brain Research, 91,* 274–280.

Gilbert, C. D., & Sigman, M. (2007). Brain states: Top-down influences in sensory processing. *Neuron, 54,* 677–696.

Gilbertson, M. W., Shenton, M. E., Ciszewski, A., Kasai, K., Lasko, N. B., Orr, S. P., & Pitman, R. K. (2002). Smaller hippocampal volume predicts pathologic vulnerability to psychological trauma. *Nature Neuroscience, 5,* 1242–1247.

Giussani, C., Roux, F. E., Lubrano, V., Gaini, S. M., & Bello, L. (2007). Review of language organisation in bilingual patients: What can we learn from direct brain mapping? *Acta Neurochirurgica, 149,* 1109–1116.

Giza, C. C., & Haovda, D. A. (2001). The neurometabolic cascade of concussion. *Journal of Athletic Training, 36,* 228–235.

Gladstone, M., Best, C. T., & Davidson, R. J. (1989). Anomalous bimanual coordination among dyslexic boys. *Developmental Psychology, 25,* 236–246.

Gleitman, L., & Newport, E. (2002). The invention of language by children: Environmental and biological influences. In D. J. Levitin (Ed.), *Foundations of cognitive psychology: Core readings* (pp. 685–704). Cambridge, MA: MIT Press.

Glick, S. D., Ross, A. D., & Hough, L. B. (1982). Lateral asymmetry of neurotransmitters in human brain. *Brain Research, 234,* 53–63.

Glover, S., Miall, R. C., & Rushworth, M. F. S. (2005). Parietal rTMS disrupts the initiation but not the execution of on-line adjustments to a perturbation of object size. *Journal of Cognitive Neuroscience, 17,* 124–136.

Goate, A., Chartierharlin, M. C., Mullan, M., Brown, J., Crawford, F., Fidani, L., et al. (1991). Segregation of a missense mutation in the amyloid precursor protein gene with familial Alzheimer's disease. *Nature, 349,* 704–706.

Gobbo, O. L., & O'Mara, S. M. (2004). Impact of enriched-environment housing on brain-derived neurotrophic factor and on cognitive performance after a transient global ischemia. *Behavioural Brain Research, 152,* 231–241.

Goel, V., & Dolan, R. J. (2001). The functional anatomy of humor: Segregating cognitive and affective components. *Nature Neuroscience, 4,* 237–238.

Gogtay, N., Giedd, J. N., Lusk, L., Hayashi, K. M., Greenstein, D., Vaituzis, A. C., et al. (2004). Dynamic mapping of human cortical development during childhood through early adulthood. *Proceedings of the National Academy of Sciences, 101,* 8174–8179.

Gold, J. M. (2004). Cognitive deficits as treatment targets in schizophrenia. *Schizophrenia Research, 72,* 21–28.

Goldapple, K., Segal, Z., Garson, C., Lau, M., Bieling, P., Kennedy, S., & Mayberg, H. (2004). Modulation of cortical-limbic pathways in major depression: Treatment-specific effects of cognitive behavior therapy. *Archives of General Psychiatry, 61,* 34–41.

Goldberg, T. E., Saint-Cyr, J. A., & Weinberger, D. R. (1990). Assessment of procedural learning and problem-solving in schizophrenic patients by Tower of Hanoi type tasks. *Journal of Neuropsychiatry & Clinical Neurosciences, 2,* 165–173.

Golden, C. J. (1981). A standardized version of Luria's neuropsychological tests. In S. Filskov & T. J. Boll (Eds.), *Handbook of clinical neuropsychology.* New York: Wiley Interscience.

Goldenberg, G. (2009). Apraxia and the parietal lobes. *Neuropsychologia, 47,* 1449–1459.

Goldman-Rakic, P. S. (1988). Topography of cognition: Parallel distributed networks in primate association cortex. *Annual Review of Neuroscience, 11,* 137–156.

Goldman-Rakic, P. S. (1995). Anatomical and functional circuits in prefrontal cortex of nonhuman primates. Relevance to epilepsy. *Advances in Neurology, 66,* 51–63.

Goldman-Rakic, P. S. (1996). The prefrontal landscape: Implications of functional architecture for understanding human mentation and the central executive. *Philosophical Transactions of the Royal Society of London, B Biological Sciences, 351*(1346), 1445–1453.

Golestani, N., & Zatorre, R. J. (2004) Learning new sounds of speech: Reallocation of neural substrates. *NeuroImage, 21,* 494–506.

Golestani, N., Molko, N., Dehaene, S., LeBihan, D., & Pallier, C. (2007). Brain structure predicts the learning of foreign speech sounds. *Cerebral Cortex, 17*(3), 575–582.

Goodale, M. A., & Milner, A. D. (1992). Separate visual pathways for perception and action. *Trends in Neurosciences, 15,* 20–25.

Goodale, M. A., & Westwood, D. A. (2004). An evolving view of duplex vision: Separate but interacting cortical pathways for perception and action. *Current Opinion in Neurobiology, 14,* 203–211.

Goodglass, H. (1976). Agrammatism. In H. Whitaker & H. A. Whitaker (Eds.), *Studies in neurolinguistics* (pp. 237–260). New York: Academic Press.

Gordon, H. W. (1980). Degree of ear asymmetries for perception of dichotic chords and for illusory chord localization in musicians of different levels of competence. *Journal of Experimental Psychology: Human Perception and Performance, 6,* 516–527.

Gorell, J. M., Johnson, C. C., Rybicki, B. A., Peterson, E. L., Kortsha, G. X., Brown, G. G., & Richardson, R. J. (1997). Occupational exposure to metals as risk factors for Parkinson's disease. *Neurology, 48,* 650–658.

Gosselin, N., Peretz, I., Johnsen, E., & Adolphs, R. (2007). Amygdala damage impairs emotion recognition from music. *Neuropsychologia, 45,* 236–244.

Gotlib, I. H., & Hamilton, J. P. (2008). Neuroimaging and depression: Current status and unresolved issues. *Current Directions in Psychological Science, 17,* 159–163.

Gottesman, I. I. (1991). *Schizophrenia genesis: The origins of madness.* New York: W.H. Freeman.

Gottlieb, J., Balan, P., Oristaglio, J., & Suzuki, M. (2009). Parietal control of attentional guidance: The significance of sensory, motivational and motor factors. *Neurobiology of Learning & Memory, 91,* 121–128.

Gould, E., Tanapat, P., Hastings, N. B., & Shors, T. J. (1999). Neurogenesis in adulthood: A possible role in learning. *Trends in Cognitive Sciences, 3,* 186–192.

Gowen, E., & Miall, R. C. (2007). The cerebellum and motor dysfunction in neuropsychiatric disorders. *Cerebellum, 6,* 268–279.

Grady, C. L. (2008). Cognitive neuroscience of aging. *Annals of the New York Academy of Sciences, 1124,* 127–144.

Grady, C. L., & Craik, F. I. M. (2000). Changes in memory processing with age. *Current Opinion in Neurobiology, 10,* 224–231.

Grady, C. L., Haxby, J. V., Horwitz, B., Schapiro, M. B., Rapoport, S. I., Ungerleider, L. G., et al. (1992). Dissociation of object and spatial vision in human extrastriate cortex: Age-related changes in activation of regional cerebral blood flow measured with (O_{15}) water and positron emission tomography. *Journal of Cognitive Neuroscience, 4*(1), 23–34.

Graf, P., Squire, L. R., & Mandler, G. (1984). The information that amnesic patients do not forget. *Journal of Experimental Psychology: Learning, Memory, & Cognition, 10*(1), 164–178.

Grafman, J., Jones, B., & Salazar, A. (1990). Wisconsin Card Sorting Test performance based on location and size of neuroanatomical lesion in Vietnam veterans with penetrating head injury. *Perceptual & Motor Skills, 71,* 1120–1122.

Grafton, S. T., Hazeltine, E., & Ivry, R. (1995). Functional mapping of sequence learning in normal humans. *Journal of Cognitive Neuroscience, 7*(4), 497–510.

Grafton, S. T., Mazziotta, J. C., Presty, S., Friston, K. J., Frackowiak, R. S., & Phelps, M. E. (1992). Functional anatomy of human procedural learning determined with regional cerebral blood flow and PET. *Journal of Neuroscience, 12*(7), 2542–2548.

Grafton, S. T., Schmitt, P., Van Horn, J., & Diedrichsen, J. (2008). Neural substrates of visuomotor learning based on improved feedback control and prediction. *Neuroimage, 39,* 1383–1389.

Grafton, S. T., Woods, R. P., & Tyszka, M. (1994). Functional imaging of procedural motor learning: Relating cerebral blood flow with individual subject performance. *Human Brain Mapping, 1*(3), 221–234.

Gratton, G., & Fabiani, M. (2001). The event-related optical signal: A new tool for studying brain function. *International Journal of Psychophysiology, 42,* 109–121.

Gratton, G., Wee, E, Rykhlevskaia, E. I., Leaver, E. E., & Fabiani, M. (2009). Does white matter matter? Spatio-temporal dynamics of task switching in aging. *Journal of Cognitive Neuroscience, 21,* 1380–1395.

Gray, D. P. (1998). Forty-seven minutes a year for the patient. *British Journal of General Practice, 48*(437), 1816–1817.

Graybiel, A. (1998). The basal ganglia and chunking of action repertoires. *Neurobiology of Learning and Memory, 70,* 119–136.

Graybiel, A. M., & Rauch, S. L. (2000). Toward a neurobiology of obsessive-compulsive disorder. *Neuron, 28,* 343–347.

Graybiel, A. M., Aosaki, T., Flaherty, A. W., & Kimura, M. (1994). The basal ganglia and adaptive motor control. *Science, 265,* 1826–1831.

Graziano, M. (2006). The organization of behavioral repertoire in motor cortex. *Annual Review of Neuroscience, 29,* 105–134.

Green, A. E., Fugelsang, J. A., Kraemer, D. J., Shamosh, N. A., & Dunbar, K. N. (2006). Frontopolar cortex mediates abstract integration in analogy. *Brain Research, 1096,* 125–137.

Green, M. F., Kern, R. S., & Heaton, R. K. (2004). Longitudinal studies of cognition and functional outcome in schizophrenia: Implications for MATRICS. *Schizophrenia Research, 72,* 41–51.

Greenberg, B. D., Li, Q., Lucas, F. R., Hu, S., Sirota, L. A., Benjamin, J., et al. (2000). Association between the serotonin transporter promoter polymorphism and personality traits in a primarily female population sample. *American Journal of Medical Genetics, 96,* 202–216.

Greenblatt, S. H. (1973). Alexia without agraphia or hemianopia. Anatomical analysis of an autopsied case. *Brain, 96,* 307–316.

Greene, J. D., Nystrom, L. E., Engell, A. D., Darley, J. M., & Cohen, J. D. (2004). The neural bases of cognitive conflict and control in moral judgment. *Neuron, 44,* 389–400.

Greene, J. D., Sommerville, R. B., Nystrom, L. E., Darley, J. M., & Cohen, J. D. (2001). An fMRI investigation of emotional engagement in moral judgment. *Science, 293,* 2105–2108.

Greenough, W., Black, J., & Wallace, C. (1987). Experience and brain development. *Child Development, 58,* 539–559.

Griffiths, T. D., & Warren, J. D. (2002). The planum temporale as a computational hub. *Trends in Neurosciences, 25,* 348–353.

Griffiths, T. D., Warren, J. D., Scott, S. K., Nelken, I., & King, A. J. (2004). Cortical processing of complex sound: A way forward? *Trends in Neurosciences, 27,* 181–185.

Grill-Spector, K., Knouf, N., & Kanwisher, N. (2004). The fusiform face area subserves face perception, not generic within-category identification. *Nature Neuroscience, 7,* 555–562.

Grill-Spector, K., Kushnir, T., Edelman, S., Avidan, G., Itzchak, Y., & Malach, R. (1999). Differential processing of objects under various viewing conditions in the human lateral occipital complex. *Neuron, 24,* 187–203.

Grill-Spector, K., Sayres, R., & Ress, D. (2006). High-resolution imaging reveals highly selective nonface clusters in the fusiform face area. *Nature Neuroscience, 9,* 1177–1185.

Grimm, S., Beck, J., Schuepbach, D., Hell, D., Boesiger, P., Bermpohl, F., et al. (2008). Imbalance between left and right dorsolateral prefrontal cortex in major depression is linked to negative emotional judgment: An fMRI study in severe major depressive disorder. *Biological Psychiatry, 63,* 369–376.

Grimshaw, G. M., Kwasny, K. M., Covell, E., & Johnson, R. A. (2003). The dynamic nature of language lateralization: Effects of lexical and prosodic factors. *Neuropsychologia, 41,* 1008–1019.

Grodzinsky, Y., & Friederici, A. D. (2006). Neuroimaging of syntax and syntactic processing. *Current Opinion in Neurobiology, 16,* 240–246.

Gronwall, D., & Wrightson, P. (1975). Cumulative effect of concussion. *Lancet, 2*(7943), 995–997.

Gross, C. G. (2005). Processing the facial image: A brief history. *American Psychologist, 60,* 755–763.

Gross, C. G. (2008). Single neuron studies of inferior temporal cortex. *Neuropsychologia, 46,* 841–852.

Gross, C. G., & Mishkin, M. (1977). The neural basis of stimulus equivalence across retinal translation. In S. Harnad, R. Doty, J. Jaynes, L. Goldstein, & G. Krauthamer (Eds.), *Lateralization in the nervous system* (pp. 109–122). New York: Academic Press.

Gross, C. G., Bender, D. B., & Rocha-Miranda, C. E. (1969). Visual receptive fields of neurons in inferotemporal cortex of the monkey. *Science, 166,* 1303–1306.

Gross, C. G., Rocha-Miranda, C. E., & Bender, D. B. (1972). Visual properties of neurons in inferotemporal cortex of the macaque. *Journal of Neurophysiology, 35,* 96–111.

Gross, R. G., & Grossman, M. (2008). Update on apraxia. *Current Neurology and Neuroscience Reports, 8,* 490–496.

Grossman, A. W., Aldridge, G. M., Weiler, I. J., & Greenough, W. T. (2006). Local protein synthesis and spine morphogenesis: Fragile X syndrome and beyond. *Journal of Neuroscience, 26,* 7151–7155.

Grote, C. L., Wierenga, C., & Smith M. C. (1999). Wada difference a day makes: Interpretive cautions regarding same-day injections. *Neurology, 52*, 1577–1582.

Groves, D. A., & Brown, V. J. (2005). Vagal nerve stimulation: A review of its applications and potential mechanisms that mediate its clinical effects. *Neuroscience & Biobehavioral Reviews, 29*, 493–500.

Grueter, M., Grueter, T., Bell, V., Horst, J., Laskowski, W., Sperling, K., Halligan, P. W., Ellis, H. D., & Kennerknecht, I. (2007). Hereditary prosopagnosia: The first case series. *Cortex, 43*, 734–749.

Gu, Y., DeAngelis, G. C., & Angelaki, D. E. (2007). A functional link between area MSTd and heading perception based on vestibular signals. *Nature Neuroscience, 10*, 1038–1047.

Guillery-Girard, B., Desgranges, B., Urban, C., Piolino, P., de la Sayette, V., & Eustache, F. (2004). The dynamic time course of memory recovery in transient global amnesia. *Journal of Neurology, Neurosurgery, & Psychiatry, 75*(11), 532–540.

Guitton, D., Buchtel, H. A., & Douglas, R. M. (1985). Frontal lobe lesions in man cause difficulties in suppressing reflexive glances and in generating goal-directed saccades. *Experimental Brain Research, 58*, 455–472.

Gujar, S. K., Maheshwari, S., Björkman-Burtscher, I., & Sundgren, P. C. (2005). Magnetic resonance spectroscopy. *Journal of Neuro-Ophthalmology, 25*, 217–226.

Gur, R. C., Mozley, L. H., Mozley, P. D., Resnick, S. M., Karp, J. S., Alvai, B., Arnold, S. E., & Gur, R. E. (1995). Sex differences in regional cerebral glucose metabolism during a resting state. *Science, 267*, 528–531.

Gurvits, T. V., Metzger, L. J., Lasko, N. B., Cannistraro, P. A., Tarhan, A. S., Gilbertson, M. W., et al. (2006). Subtle neurologic compromise as a vulnerability factor for combat-related posttraumatic stress disorder. *Archives of General Psychiatry, 63*, 571–576.

Guskiewicz, K. M., Bruce, S. L., Cantu, R. C., Ferrara, M. S., Kelly, J. P., McCrea, M., et al. (2004). National Athletic Trainers' Association position statement: Management of sports-related concussion. *Journal of Athletic Training, 39*, 280–297.

Hécaen, H. (1962). Clinical symptomology in right and left hemisphere lesions. In V. B. Mountcastle (Ed.), *Interhemispheric relations and cerebral dominance* (pp. 215–243). Baltimore, MD: Johns Hopkins University Press.

Hécaen, H., & Kremin, H. (1976). Neurolinguistic research on reading disorder from left hemisphere lesions: Aphasic and "pure" alexias. In H. A. Whitaker & H. Whitaker (Eds.), *Studies in neurolinguistics II* (pp. 269–329). New York: Academic Press.

Haarmeier, T., Thier, P., Repnow, M., & Petersen, D. (1997). False perception of motion in a patient who cannot compensate for eye movements. *Nature, 389*, 849–852.

Habib, M., Gayraud, D., Oliva, A., Regis, J., Salamon, G., & Khalil, R. (1991). Effects of handedness and sex on the morphology of the corpus callosum: A study with brain magnetic resonance imaging. *Brain and Cognition, 16*, 41–61.

Habib, R., & Lepage, M. (2000). Novelty assessment in the brain. In E. Tulving (Ed.), *Memory, consciousness, and the brain: The Tallinn Conference* (pp. 265–277). Philadelphia: Psychology Press/Taylor & Francis.

Hackett, T. A., & Kaas, J. H. (2004). Auditory cortex in primates: Functional subdivisions and processing streams. In M. S. Gazzaniga (Ed.), *The cognitive neurosciences III* (pp. 215–232). Cambridge, MA: MIT Press.

Hadjikhani, N., Liu, A. K., Dale, A.M., Cavanaugh, P., & Tootell, R. B. H. (1998). Retinotopy and color sensitivity in human visual cortical area V8. *Nature Neuroscience, 1*, 235–241.

Hadland, K. A., Rushworth, M. F. S., Gaffan, D., & Passingham, R. E. (2003). The effect of cingulate lesions on social behaviour and emotion. *Neuropsychologia, 41*, 919–931.

Hagoort, P., & Brown, C. (1994). Brain responses to lexical ambiguity resolution and parsing. In C. Clifton, Jr., L. Frazier, & K. Rayner (Eds.), *Perspectives on sentence processing* (pp. 45–80). Hillsdale, NJ: Lawrence Erlbaum.

Hagoort, P., & Brown, C. (2000a). ERP effects of listening to speech: Semantic ERP effects. *Neuropsychologia, 38*(11), 1518–1530.

Hagoort, P., & Brown, C. (2000b). ERP effects of listening to speech compared to reading: The P600/SPS to syntactic violations in spoken sentences and rapid serial visual presentation. *Neuropsychologia, 38*(11), 1531–1549.

Hahn, B., Wolkenberg, F. A., Ross, T. J., Myers, C. S., Heishman, S. J., Stein, D. J., et al. (2008). Divided versus selective attention: Evidence for common processing mechanisms. *Brain Research, 1215*, 137–146.

Haijima, A., & Ichitani, Y. (2008). Anterograde and retrograde amnesia of place discrimination in retrosplenial cortex and hippocampal lesioned rats. *Learning & Memory, 15*, 477–482.

Haist, F., Bowden Gore, J., & Mao, H. (2001). Consolidation of human memory over decades revealed by functional magnetic resonance imaging. *Nature Neuroscience, 4*(11), 1139–1145.

Hajcak, G., & Nieuwenhuis, S. (2006). Reappraisal modulates the electrocortical response to unpleasant pictures. *Cognitive, Affective, & Behavioral Neuroscience, 6*, 291–297.

Hajcak, G., McDonald, N., & Simons, R. F. (2003). Anxiety and error-related brain activity. *Biological Psychology, 64*, 77–90.

Halgren, E. (1984). Human hippocampal and amygdal recording and stimulation: Evidence for a neural model of recent memory. In L. R. Squire & N. Butters (Eds.), *The neuropsychology of memory* (pp. 165–182). New York: Guilford Press.

Hallett, M. (2007). Transcranial magnetic stimulation: A primer. *Neuron, 55*, 187–199.

Halligan, P. W., Fink, G. R., Marshall, J. C., & Vallar, G. (2003). Spatial cognition: Evidence from visual neglect. *Trends in Cognitive Sciences, 7*, 125–133.

Halpern, M. E., Güntürkün, O., Hopkins, W. D., & Rogers, L. J. (2005). Lateralization of the vertebrate brain: Taking the side of model systems. *Journal of Neuroscience, 25*, 10351–10357.

Halpern, M. E., Liang, J. O., & Gamse, J. T. (2003). Leaning to the left: Laterality in the zebrafish forebrain. *Trends in Neurosciences, 26*, 308–313.

Hamberger, M. J. (2007). Cortical language mapping in epilepsy: A critical review. *Neuropsychology Review, 17*, 477–489.

Hamilton, A. F. C., Brindley, R. M., & Frith, U. (2007). Imitation and action understanding in autistic spectrum disorders: How valid is the hypothesis of a deficit in the mirror neuron system? *Neuropsychologia, 45*, 1859–1868.

Hamilton, C. R., & Vermeire, B. A. (1988). Complementary hemispheric specialization in monkeys. *Science, 242*(4886), 1691–1694.

Hamilton, J. P., & Gotlib, I. H. (2008). Neural substrates of increased memory sensitivity for negative stimuli in major depression. *Biological Psychiatry, 63*, 1155–1162.

Hamilton, R. H., & Pascual-Leone, A. (1998). Cortical plasticity associated with Braille learning. *Trends in Cognitive Sciences, 2*, 168–174.

Hammen, C. (2005). Stress and depression. *Annual Review of Clinical Psychology, 1*, 293–319.

Hampshire, A., Chamberlain, S. R., Monti, M. M., Duncan, J., & Owen, A. M. (2010). The role of the right inferior frontal gyrus: Inhibition and attentional control. *NeuroImage, 50*, 1313–1319.

Hanna-Pladdy, B., Heilman, K. M., & Foundas, A. L. (2001). Cortical and subcortical contributions to ideomotor apraxia: Analysis of task demands and error types. *Brain, 124*, 2513–2527.

Hannay, H. J., Varney, N., & Benton, A. L. (1976). Visual localization in patients with unilateral cerebral brain disease. *Journal of Neurology, Neurosurgery & Psychiatry, 39*, 307–313.

Happé, F., Ronald, A., & Plomin, R. (2006). Time to give up on a single explanation for autism. *Nature Neuroscience, 9*, 1218–1220.

Hardesty, D. E., & Sackeim, H. A. (2007). Deep brain stimulation in movement and psychiatric disorders. *Biological Psychiatry, 61*, 831–835.

Hariri, A. R., & Holmes, A. (2006). Genetics of emotional regulation: The role of the serotonin transporter in neural function. *Trends in Cognitive Sciences, 10*, 182–191.

Hariri, A. R., Mattay, V. S., Tessitore, A., Kolachana, B., Fera, F., Goldman, D., et al. (2002). Serotonin transporter genetic variation and the response of the human amygdala. *Science, 297*, 400–403.

Harlow, H. F., Dodsworth, R. O., & Harlow, M. K. (1965). Total social isolation in monkeys. *Proceedings of the National Academy of Sciences, 54,* 90–97.

Harmon-Jones, E. (2004). Contributions from research on anger and cognitive dissonance to understanding the motivational functions of asymmetrical brain activity. *Biological Psychology, 67,* 51–76.

Harmon-Jones, E. (2007). Trait anger predicts relative left frontal cortical activation to anger-inducing stimuli. *International Journal of Psychophysiology, 66,* 154–160.

Harmon-Jones, E., & Sigelman, J. (2001). State anger and prefrontal brain activity: Evidence that insult-related relative left-prefrontal activation is associated with experienced anger and aggression. *Journal of Personality & Social Psychology, 80,* 797–803.

Harmony, T. (1988). Psychophysiological evaluation of children's neuropsychological disorders. In C. R. Reynolds (Ed.), *Handbook of Child Clinical Neuropsychology* (pp. 265–290). New York: Plenum.

Harrington, A. (1987). *Medicine, mind, and the double brain.* Princeton, NJ: Princeton University Press.

Harris, I. M., & Miniussi, C. (2003). Parietal lobe contribution to mental rotation demonstrated with rTMS. *Journal of Cognitive Neuroscience, 15,* 1–9.

Harris, L. J., & Gitterman, S. R. (1978). University professors' self-descriptions of left-right confusability: Sex and handedness differences. *Perceptual & Motor Skills, 47,* 819–823.

Hart, J., Berndt, R. S., & Caramazza, A. (1985). Category-specific naming deficit following cerebral infarction. *Nature, 316,* 439–440.

Hart, S., & Semple, J. M. (1990). *Neuropsychology and the dementias.* London: Erlbaum.

Harwood, K., & Wickens, C. D. (1991). Frames of reference for helicopter electronic maps: The relevance of spatial cognition and componential analysis. *International Journal of Aviation Psychology, 1,* 5–23.

Hauser, M. (1993). Right hemisphere dominance in the production of facial expression in monkeys. *Science, 261,* 475–477.

Hauser, T. (1991). *Muhammad Ali: His life and times.* New York: Simon & Schuster.

Haxby, J. V., Grady, C. L., Koss, E., Horwitz, B., Heston, L., Scapiro, M., et al. (1990). Longitudinal study of cerebral metabolic asymmetries and associated neuropsychological patterns in early dementia of the Alzheimer type. *Archives of Neurology, 47,* 753–760.

Haxby, J. V., Hoffman, E. A., & Gobbini, M. I. (2000). The distributed human neural system for face perception. *Trends in Cognitive Sciences, 4,* 223–232.

Haxby, J. V., Horwitz, B., Ungerleider, L. G., Maisog, J. M., Pietrini, P., & Grady, C. L. (1994). The functional organization of human extrastriate cortex: A PET-rCBF study of selective attention to faces and locations. *Journal of Neuroscience, 14*(11), 6336–6353.

Haynes, J. D., Sakai, K., Rees, G., Gilbert, S., Frith, C., & Passingham, R. E. (2007). Reading hidden intentions in the human brain. *Current Biology, 17,* 323–328.

Hayward, W. G., & Tarr, M. J. (1997). Testing conditions for viewpoint invariance in object recognition. *Journal of Experimental Psychology: Human Perception and Performance, 23,* 1511–1521.

Hazy, T. E., Frank, M. J., & O'Reilly, R. C. (2006). Banishing the homunculus: Making working memory work. *Neuroscience, 139,* 105–118.

Head, D., Buckner, R. L., Shimony, J. S., Williams, L. E., Akbudak, E., Conturo, T. E., et al. (2004). Differential vulnerability of anterior white matter in nondemented aging with minimal acceleration in dementia of the Alzheimer type: Evidence from diffusion tensor imaging. *Cerebral Cortex, 14,* 410–423.

Heath, M., Roy, E. A., Westwood, D, & Black, S. E. (2001). Patterns of apraxia associated with the production of intransitive limb gestures following left and right hemisphere stroke. *Brain & Cognition, 46,* 165–169.

Heaton, R. K., Grant, I., Butters, N., White, D. A., Kirson, D., Atkinson, J. H., et al. (1995). The HNRC 500—Neuropsychology of HIV infection at different disease stages. *Journal of the International Neuropsychological Society, 1,* 231–251.

Heaton, R. K., Marcotte, T. D., White, D. A., Ross, D., Meredith, K., Taylor, M. J., et al. (1996). Nature and vocational significance of neuropsychological impairment associated with HIV infection. *Clinical Neuropsychologist, 10,* 1–14.

Hebben, N., Corkin, S., Eichenbaum, H., & Shedlack, K. (1985). Diminished ability to interpret and report internal states after bilateral medial temporal resection: Case H. M. *Behavioral Neuroscience, 99*(6), 1031–1039.

Hecaen, H., & Rondot, P. (1985). Apraxia as a disorder of a system of signs. In E. A. Roy (Ed.), *Neuropsychological studies of apraxia and related disorders* (pp. 75–97). Amsterdam: Elsevier Science Publishers BV, North-Holland.

Hedden, T., & Gabrieli, J. D. E. (2004). Insights into the aging mind: A view from cognitive neuroscience. *Nature Reviews Neuroscience, 5,* 87–97.

Hegdé, J., & Van Essen, D. C. (2005). Role of primate visual area V4 in the processing of 3-D shape characteristics defined by disparity. *Journal of Neurophysiology, 94,* 2856–2866.

Heilman, K. M., & Rothi, L. J. G. (1985). Apraxia. In K. M. Heilman & E. Valenstein (Eds.), *Clinical neuropsychology* (2d ed., pp. 131–150). New York: Oxford University Press.

Heilman, K. M., & Valenstein, E. (1972). Frontal lobe neglect in man. *Neurology, 22,* 660–664.

Heilman, K. M., Rothi, L. J., & Valenstein, E. (1982). Two forms of ideomotor apraxia. *Neurology, 32,* 342–346.

Heilman, K. M., Watson, R. T., & Valenstein, E. (1985). Neglect and related disorders. In K. M. Heilman & E. Valenstein (eds.). *Clinical Neuropsychology* (2nd ed.). (pp 243–293). New York: Oxford University Press.

Heilman, K., Bowers, D., Speedie, L., & Coslett, H. B. (1984). Comprehension of affective and nonaffective prosody. *Neurology, 34,* 917–921.

Heimer, G., Rivlin-Etzion, M., Bar-Gad, I., Goldberg, J. A., Haber, S. N., & Bergman, H. (2006). Dopamine replacement therapy does not restore the full spectrum of normal pallidal activity in the 1-methyl-4-phenyl-1,2,3,6-tetra-hydropyridine primate model of Parkinsonism. *Journal of Neuroscience, 26,* 8101–8114.

Heinz, A., Braus, D. F., Smolka, M. N., Wraase, J., Puls, I., Hermann, D., et al. (2005). Amygdala-prefrontal coupling depends on a genetic variation of the serotonin transporter. *Nature Neuroscience, 8,* 20–21.

Heinz, A., Romero, B., Gallinat, J., Juckel, G., & Weinberger, D. R. (2003). Molecular brain imaging and the neurobiology and genetics of schizophrenia. *Pharmacopsychiatry, 36*(Suppl. 3), S152–S157.

Heinz, A., Smolka, M. N., Braus, D. F., Wrase, J., Beck, A., Flor, H., et al. (2007). Serotonin transporter genotype (5-HTTLPR): Effects of neutral and undefined conditions on amygdala activation. *Biological Psychiatry, 61,* 1011–1014.

Heinze, H. J., Luck, S. J., Mangun, G. R., & Hillyard, S. A. (1990). Visual event-related potentials index focused attention within bilateral stimulus arrays: 1. Evidence for early selection. *Electroencephalography & Clinical Neurophysiology, 75*(6), 511–527.

Heinze, H. J., Mangun, G. R., Burchert, W., Hinrichs, H., Scholz, M., Munte, T. F., et al. (1994). Combined spatial and temporal imaging of brain activity during visual selective attention in humans. *Nature, 372,* 543–546.

Heiser, M., Iacoboni, M., Maeda, F., Marcus, J., & Mazziotta, J. C. (2003). The essential role of Broca's area in imitation. *European Journal of Neuroscience, 17,* 1123–1128.

Heller, W. (1993). Neuropsychological mechanisms of individual differences in emotion, personality, and arousal. *Neuropsychology, 7,* 476–489.

Heller, W., & Nitschke, J. B. (1998). The puzzle of regional brain activity in depression and anxiety: The importance of subtypes and comorbidity. *Cognition & Emotion, 12,* 421–447.

Heller, W., Koven, N. S., & Miller, G. A. (2003). Regional brain activity in anxiety and depression, cognition/emotion interaction, and emotion regulation. In K. Hugdahl & R. J. Davidson (Eds.), *The asymmetrical brain* (pp. 533–564). Cambridge, MA: MIT Press.

Heller, W., Nitschke, J. B., & Lindsay, D. L. (1997). Neuropsychological correlates of arousal in self-reported emotion. *Cognition & Emotion, 11,* 383–402.

Heller, W., Nitschke, J. B., Etienne, M. A., & Miller, G. A. (1997). Patterns of regional brain activity differentiate types of anxiety. *Journal of Abnormal Psychology, 106,* 376–385.

Hellige, J. B., & Michimata, C. (1989). Categorization versus distance: Hemispheric differences for processing spatial information. *Memory & Cognition, 17,* 770–776.

Henderson, L., Barca, L., & Ellis, A. W. (2007). Interhemispheric cooperation and non-cooperation during word recognition: Evidence for callosal transfer dysfunction in dyslexic adults. *Brain & Language, 103,* 276–291.

Hendry, S. H., & Reid, R. C. (2000). The koniocellular pathway in primate vision. *Annual Review of Neuroscience, 23,* 127–153.

Henik, A., Singh, J., Beckley, R. J., & Rafal, R. D. (1993). Disinhibition of automatic word reading in Parkinson's disease. *Cortex, 29,* 589–599.

Henke, K., Buck, A., Weber, B., & Weiser, H. G. (1997). Human hippocampus establishes associations in memory. *Hippocampus, 7*(3), 249–256.

Henley, S. M. D., Wild, E. J., Hobbs, N. Z., Scahill, R. I., Ridgway, G. R., Macmanus, D. G., et al. (2009). Relationship between CAG repeat length and brain volume in premanifest and early Huntington's disease. *Journal of Neurology, 256,* 203–212.

Hennenlotter, A., & Schroeder, U. (2006). Partly dissociable neural substrates for recognizing basic emotions: A critical review. *Progress in Brain Research, 156,* 443–456.

Henriques, J. B., & Davidson, R. J. (1990). Regional brain electrical asymmetries discriminate between previously depressed and healthy control subjects. *Journal of Abnormal Psychology, 99,* 22–31.

Henriques, J. B., & Davidson, R. J. (1997). Brain electrical asymmetries during cognitive task performance in depressed and nondepressed subjects. *Biological Psychiatry, 42,* 1039–1050.

Henson, R. N., Rugg, M. D., Shallice, T., Josephs, O., & Dolan, R. J. (1999). Recollection and familiarity in recognition memory: An event-related functional magnetic resonance imaging. *Journal of Neuroscience, 19*(10), 3962–3972.

Herd, S. A., Banich, M. T., & O'Reilly, R. C. (2006). Neural mechanisms of cognitive control: An integrative model of Stroop task performance and fMRI data. *Journal of Cognitive Neuroscience, 18,* 22–32.

Herrington, J. D., Baron-Cohen, S., Wheelwright, S. J., Singh, K. D., Bullmore, E. T., Brammer, M., & Williams, S. C. R. (2007). The role of MT1/V5 during biological motion perception in Asperger syndrome: An fMRI study. *Research in Autism Spectrum Disorders, 1,* 14–27.

Herrington, J. D., Mohanty, A., Koven, N. S., Fisher, J. E., Stewart, J. L., Banich, M. T., et al. (2005). Emotion-modulated performance and activity in left dorsolateral prefrontal cortex. *Emotion, 5,* 200–207.

Herrmann, M. J., Römmler, J., Ehlis, A. C., Heidrich, A., & Fallgatter, A. J. (2004). Source localization (LORETA) of the error-related-negativity (ERN/Ne) and positivity (Pe). *Cognitive Brain Research, 20,* 294–299.

Hertel, P. T. (2000). The cognitive-initiative account of depression-related impairments in memory. In D. Medin (Ed.), *The psychology of learning and motivation* (vol. 39, pp. 47–71). New York: Academic Press.

Hertel, P.T., & Calcaterra, G. (2005). Intentional forgetting benefits from thought substitution. *Psychonomic Bulletin & Review, 12,* 484–489.

Hess, R. F., Baker, C. L., & Zihl, J. (1989). The motion-blind patient: Low-level spatial and temporal filters. *Journal of Neuroscience, 9,* 1628–1640.

Hesselmann, G., Kell, C. A., & Kleinschmidt, A. (2008). Ongoing activity fluctuations in hMT+ bias the perception of coherent visual motion. *Journal of Neuroscience, 28,* 14481–14485.

Hester, R., Foxe, J. J., Molholm, S., Shpaner, M., & Garavan, H. (2005). Neural mechanisms involved in error processing: A comparison of errors made with and without awareness. *NeuroImage, 27*(3), 602–608.

Heuer, H. W., & Britten, K. H. (2007). Linear responses to stochastic motion signals in area MST. *Journal of Neurophysiology, 98,* 1115–1124.

Hickok, G., Love-Geffen,T., Klima, E. (2002). Left temporal lobe supports sign language comprehension. *Brain and Language, 82,* 167–178.

Hickok, G., Wilson, M., Clark, K., Klima, E.S., Kritchevsky, M., & Bellugi, U. (1999). Discourse deficits following right hemisphere damage in deaf signers. *Brain and Language, 66,* 233–248.

Hier, D. B., Hagenlocker, K., & Shindler, A. G. (1985). Language disintegration in dementia: Effects of etiology and severity. *Brain & Language, 25,* 117–133.

Hillis, A. E. (2007). Aphasia: Progress in the last quarter of a century. *Neurology, 69,* 200–213.

Hillis, A. E., & Caramazza, A. (1991). Deficit to stimulus-centered, letter shape representations in a case of "unilateral neglect." *Neuropsychologia, 29*(12), 1223–1240.

Hillyard, S. A., Hink, R. F., Schwent, V. L., & Picton, T. W. (1973). Electrical signs of selective attention in the human brain. *Science, 182,* 177–180.

Himmelbach, M., & Karnath, H.-O. (2005). Dorsal and ventral visual stream interaction: Contributions from optic ataxia. *Journal of Cognitive Neuroscience, 17,* 632–640.

Hinton, G. E. (1992). How neural networks learn from experience. *Scientific American, 267*(3), 145–151.

Hiscock, M., Inch, R., Jacek, C., Hiscock-Kalil, C., & Kalil, K. M. (1994). Is there a sex difference in human laterality? I. An exhaustive survey of auditory laterality studies from six neuropsychology journals. *Journal of Clinical and Experimental Neuropsychology, 16,* 423–435.

Hiscock, M., Israelian, M., Inch, R., Jacek, C., Hiscock-Kalil, C. (1995). Is there a sex difference in human laterality? II. An exhaustive survey of visual laterality studies from six neuropsychology journals. *Journal of Clinical and Experimental Neuropsychology, 17,* 590–610.

Hjalmarsen, A., Waterloo, K., Dahl, A., Rolf, J., & Viitanen, M. (1999). Effect of long-term oxygen therapy on cognitive and neurological dysfunction in chronic obstructive pulmonary disease. *European Neurology, 42,* 27–35.

Hochberg, F., & LeMay, M. (1975). Arteriographic correlates of handedness. *Neurology, 25*(3), 218–222.

Hoefgen, B., Schulze, T. G., Ohlraun, S., von Widdern, O., Höfels, S., Gross, M., et al. (2005). The power of sample size and homogeneous sampling: Association between the 5-HTTLPR serotonin transporter polymorphism and major depressive disorder. *Biological Psychiatry, 57,* 247–251.

Hoekstra, P. J., Anderson, G. M., Limburg, P. C., Korf, J., Kallenberg, C. G., & Minderaa, R. B. (2009). Neurobiology and neuroimmunology of Tourette's syndrome: An update. *Cellular and Molecular Life Sciences, 61,* 886–898.

Hoffman, E. A., & Haxby, J. V. (2000). Distinct representations of eye gaze and identity in the distributed human neural system for face perception. *Nature Neuroscience, 3,* 80–84.

Hofmann, S. G., Moscovitch, D. A., Litz, B. T., Kim, H. J., Davis, L. L., & Pizzagalli, D. A. (2005). The worried mind: Autonomic and prefrontal activation during worrying. *Emotion, 5,* 464–475.

Holland, S. K., Vannest, J., Mecoli, M., Jacola, L. M., Tillema, J.-M., Karunanayaka, P. R., et al. (2007). Functional MRI of language lateralization during development in children. *International Journal of Audiology, 46,* 533–551.

Hollerman, J. R., & Schultz, W. (1998). Dopamine neurons report an error in the temporal prediction of reward during learning. *Nature Neuroscience, 1,* 304–309.

Holloway, R. L. (1983) Human paleontological evidence relevant to language behavior. *Human Neurobiology, 2,* 105–114.

Holmes, A. J., & Pizzagalli, D. A. (2008). Spatiotemporal dynamics of error processing dysfunctions in major depressive disorder. *Archives of General Psychiatry, 65,* 179–188.

Holmes, G. (1918). Disturbances of visual orientation. *British Journal of Ophthalmology, 2,* 449–468.

Holmes, G., & Horax, G. (1919). Disturbances of spatial orientation and visual attention, with loss of stereoscopic vision. *Archives of Neurology & Psychiatry, 1,* 385–407.

Holroyd, C. B., & Coles, M. G. (2002). The neural basis of human error processing: Reinforcement learning, dopamine, and the error-related negativity. *Psychological Review, 109,* 679–709.

Holroyd, C. B., & Coles, M. G. (2008). Dorsal anterior cingulate cortex integrates reinforcement history to guide voluntary behavior. *Cortex, 44*, 548–559.

Holroyd, C. B., & Coles, M. G. H. (2002). The neural basis of human error processing: Reinforcement learning, dopamine, and the error-related negativity. *Psychological Review, 109*, 679–709.

Holroyd, C. B., & Coles, M. G. H. (2008). Dorsal anterior cingulate cortex integrates reinforcement history to guide voluntary behavior. *Cortex, 44*, 548–559.

Holroyd, C. B., Nieuwenhuis, S., Yeung, N., & Cohen, J. D. (2003). Errors in reward prediction are reflected in the event-related brain potential. *NeuroReport, 14*(18), 2481–4.

Holsinger, T., Steffens, D. C., Phillips, C., Helms, M., Havlik, R. J., Brietner, J. C. S., et al. (2002). Head injury in early adulthood and the lifetime risk of depression. *Archives of General Psychiatry, 59*, 17–22.

Hopkins, W. D. (1997). Hemispheric specialization for local and global processing of hierarchical visual stimuli in chimpanzees (*Pan troglodytes*). *Neuropsychologia, 35*(3), 343–348.

Hopkins, W. D., Marino, L., Rilling, J. K., & MacGregor, L. A. (1998). Planum temporale asymmetries in great apes as revealed by magnetic resonance imaging (MRI). *Neuroreport: An International Journal for the Rapid Communication of Research* in *Neuroscience, 9*(12), 2913–2918.

Horton, J. C., & Hocking, D. R. (1997). Timing of the critical period for plasticity of ocular dominance columns in the macaque striate cortex. *Journal of Neuroscience, 17*, 3684–3709.

Horwitz, B., Amunts, K., Bhattacharyya, R., Patkin, D., Jeffries, K., Zilles, K., & Braun, A. R. (2003). Activation of Broca's area during the production of spoken and signed language: A combined cytoarchitectonic mapping and PET analysis. *Neuropsychologia, 41*, 1868–1876.

Hosford, D. A., Clark, S., Cao, Z., Wilson, W. A., Jr., Lin, F. H., Morriset, R. A., & Huin, A. (1992). The role of GABA$_B$ receptor activation in absence seizures of lethargic (lh/lh) mice. *Science, 257*, 398–401.

Hoth, K. F., Paulsen, J. S., Moser, D. J., Tranel, D., Clark, L. A., & Bechara, A. (2007). Patients with Huntington's disease have impaired awareness of cognitive, emotional, and functional abilities. *Journal of Clinical & Experimental Neuropsychology, 29*, 365–376.

Howes, D., & Boller, F. (1975). Simple reaction time: Evidence for focal impairment from lesions of the right hemisphere. *Brain, 98*, 317–332.

Hsieh, L., Young, R. A., Bowyer, S. M., Moran, J. E., Genik, R. J., Green, C. C., et al. (2009). Conversation effects on neural mechanisms underlying reaction time to visual events while viewing a driving scene: fMRI analysis and asynchrony model. *Brain Research, 1251*, 162–175.

Hsiung, G-Y. R., & Feldman, H. H. (2008). Pharmacological treatment in moderate-to-severe Alzheimer's disease. *Expert Opinion on Pharmacotherapy, 9*, 2575–2582.

Hubel, D. H. (1982). Exploration of the primary visual cortex, 1955–78. *Nature, 299*, 515–524.

Huber, S. J., Christy, J. A., & Paulson, G. W. (1991). Cognitive heterogeneity associated with clinical subtypes of Parkinson's disease. *Neuropsychiatry, Neuropsychology and Behavioral Neurology, 4*, 147–157.

Hubl, D., Koenig, T., Strik, W., Federspiel, A., Kreis, R., Boesch, C., et al. (2004). Pathways that make voices: White matter changes in auditory hallucinations. *Archives of General Psychiatry, 61*, 658–668.

Huddleston, W. E., & DeYoe, E. A. (2008). The representation of spatial attention in human parietal cortex dynamically modulated with performance. *Cerebral Cortex, 18*, 1272–1280.

Hugdahl, K., & Wester, K. (2000). Neurocognitive correlates of stereotactic thalamotomy and thalamic stimulation in Parkinsonian patients. *Brain & Cognition, 42*, 231–252.

Humphreys, G. W., & Forde, E. M. E. (2001). Hierarchies, similarity, and interactivity in object recognition: "Category-specific" neuropsychological deficits. *Behavioral and Brain Sciences, 24*, 453–509.

Humphreys, P., Kaufmann, W. E., & Galaburda, A. M. (1990). Developmental dyslexia in women: Neuropathological findings in three patients. *Annuals of Neurology, 28*, 727–738.

Hung, C. P., Kreiman, G., Poggio, T., & DiCarlo, J. J. (2005). Fast readout of object identity from macaque inferior temporal cortex. *Science, 310*, 863–866.

Hurlemann, R., Hawellek, B., Matusch, A., Kolsch, H., Wollersen, H., Madea, B., Vogeley, K., Maier, W., & Dolan, R. J. (2005). Noradrenergic modulation of emotion-induced forgetting and remembering. *Journal of Neuroscience, 25*, 6343–6349.

Husain, M., & Nachev, P. (2007). Space and the parietal cortex. *Trends in Cognitive Sciences, 11*, 30–36.

Husain, M., & Rorden, C. (2003). Non-spatially lateralized mechanisms in hemispatial neglect. *Nature Reviews Neuroscience, 4*, 26–36.

Hutsler, J., & Galuske, R. A. W. (2003). Hemispheric asymmetries in cerebral cortical networks. *Trends in Neurosciences, 26*, 429–435.

Huttenlocher, P. R. (1979). Synaptic density in human frontal cortex: Developmental changes and effects of aging. *Brain Research, 163*, 195–205.

Huttenlocher, P. R. (2002). *Neural plasticity: The effects of environment on the development of the cerebral cortex*. Cambridge, MA: Harvard University Press.

Huttenlocher, P. R., & de Courten, C. (1987). The development of synapses in striate cortex of man. *Human Neurobiology, 6*, 1–9.

Hviid, A., Stellfeld, M., Wohlfahrt, J., & Melbye, M. (2003). Association between thimerosal-containing vaccine and autism. *JAMA, 290*, 1763–1766.

Hyafil, A., Summerfield, C., & Koechlin, E. (2009). Two mechanisms for task switching in the prefrontal cortex. *Journal of Neuroscience, 29*, 5135–5142.

Hyde, J. S., Mezulis, A. H., & Abramson, L. Y. (2008). The ABCs of depression: Integrating affective, biological, and cognitive models to explain the emergence of the gender difference in depression. *Psychological Review, 115*, 291–313.

Hynd, G. W., Hall, J., Novey, E. S., Eliopulos, D., Black, K., Gonzalez, J. J., et al. (1995). Dyslexia and corpus callosum morphology. *Archives of Neurology, 52*, 32–38.

Iacoboni, M. (2006). Visuo-motor integration and control in the human posterior parietal cortex: Evidence from TMS and fMRI. *Neuropsychologia, 44*, 2691–2699.

Iacoboni, M., & Dapretto, M. (2006). The mirror neuron system and the consequences of its dysfunction. *Nature Reviews Neuroscience, 7*, 942–951.

Iacoboni, M., Woods, R. P., Brass, M., Bekkering, H., Mazziotta, J. C., & Rizzolatti, G. (1999). Cortical mechanisms of human imitation. *Science, 286*, 2526–2528.

Iaria, G., Chen, J.-K., Guariglia, C., Ptito, A., & Petrides, M. (2007). Retrosplenial and hippocampal brain regions in human navigation: Complementary functional contributions to the formation and use of cognitive maps. *European Journal of Neuroscience, 25*, 890–899.

Ilg, W., & Thier, P. (2008). The neural basis of smooth pursuit eye movements in the rhesus monkey brain. *Brain and Cognition, 68*, 229–240.

Imaizumi, S., Mori, K., Kiritani, S., Kawashima, R., Sugiura, M., Fukuda, H., et al. (1997). Vocal identification of speaker and emotion activates different brain regions. *NeuroReport, 8*, 2809–2812.

Inglese, M., Ge, Y., Filippi, M., Falini, A., Grossman, R. I., & Gonen, O. (2004). Indirect evidence for early widespread gray matter involvement in relapsing-remitting multiple sclerosis. *NeuroImage, 21*, 1825–1829.

Ino, T., Nakai, R., Azuma, T., Kimura, T., & Fukuyama, H. (2009). Recognition and reading aloud of kana and kanji word: An fMRI study. *Brain Research Bulletin, 78*, 232–239.

Institute of Medicine (2004). *Immunization safety review: Vaccines and autism*. Washington, DC: National Academies Press.

Ioannides, A. A. (2007). Magnetoencephalography as a research tool in neuroscience: State of the art. *Neuroscientist, 12*, 524–544.

Isomura, Y., Ito, Y., Akazawa, T., Nambu, A., & Takada, M. (2003). Neural coding of "attention for action" and "response selection" in primate anterior cingulate cortex. *Journal of Neuroscience, 23*, 8003–8012.

Ito, M. (2008). Control of mental activities by internal models in the cerebellum. *Nature Reviews Neuroscience, 9,* 304–313.

Ito, T. A., Thompson, E., & Cacioppo, J. T. (2004). Tracking the timecourse of social perception: The effects of racial cues on event-related brain potentials. *Personality & Social Psychology Bulletin, 30,* 1267–1280.

Ivry, R. (1997). Cerebellar timing systems. *International Review of Neurobiology, 41,* 555–573.

Ivry, R. B., & Lebby, P. C. (1993). Hemispheric differences in auditory perception are similar to those found in visual perception. *Psychological Science, 4,* 41–45.

Ivry, R. B., & Robertson, L. C. (1998). *The two sides of perception.* Cambridge, MA: MIT Press.

Ivry, R. B., & Spencer, R. M. (2004). The neural representation of time. *Current Opinions in Neurobiology, 14,* 225–232.

Ivry, R. B., Spencer, R. M., Zelaznik, H. N., & Diedrichsen, J. (2002). The cerebellum and event timing. *Annals of the New York Academy of Sciences, 978,* 302–317.

Jabbi, M., Bastiaansen, J., & Keysers, C. (2008). A common anterior insula representation of disgust observation, experience and imagination shows divergent functional connectivity patterns. *PLoS ONE, 3,* e2939.

Jack, C. R., Lowe, V. J., Weigand, S. D., Wiste, H. J., Senjem, M. L., Knopman, D. S., et al. (2009). Serial PIB and MRI in normal, mild cognitive impairment and Alzheimer's disease: Implications for sequence of pathological events in Alzheimer's disease. *Brain, 132,* 1355–1365.

Jackson, M., & Lowe, J. (1996). The new neuropathology of degenerative frontotemporal dementias. *Acta Neuropathologica, 91,* 127–134.

Jackson, P. L., Meltzoff, A. N., & Decety, J. (2005). How do we perceive the pain of others? A window into the neural processes involved in empathy. *NeuroImage, 24,* 771–779.

Jacobs, B. L. (2004). Depression: The brain finally gets into the act. *Current Directions in Psychological Science, 13,* 103–106.

Jacobs, D. M., Levy, G., & Marder, K. (2006). Dementia in Parkinson's disease, Huntington's disease, and related disorders. In M. J. Farah & T. E. Feinberg (Eds.), *Patient-based approaches to cognitive neuroscience* (2d ed.; pp. 381–395). Cambridge, MA: MIT Press.

Jacobs, L., Munschauer, F. E., & Pullicino, P. (1993). Current treatment strategies and perspectives of multiple sclerosis. In U. Halbreich (Ed.), *Multiple sclerosis: A neuropsychiatric disorder* (pp. 97–117). Washington, DC: American Psychiatric Press.

Jacoby, L. L. (1984). Incidental versus intentional retrieval: Remembering and awareness as separate issues. In L. R. Squire & N. Butters (Eds.), *Neuropsychology of memory* (pp. 145–156). New York: Guilford Press.

Jager, G., & Postma, A. (2003). On the hemispheric specialization for categorical and coordinate spatial relations: A review of the current evidence. *Neuropsychologia, 41,* 504–515.

Jakobson, L. S., Archibald, Y. M., Carey, D. P., & Goodale, M. A. (1991). A kinematic analysis of reaching and grasping movements in a patient recovering from optic ataxia. *Neuropsychologia, 29,* 803–809.

James, T. W., Culham, J., Humphrey, G. K., Milner, A. D., & Goodale, M. A. (2003). Ventral occipital lesions impair object recognition but not object-directed grasping: An fMRI study. *Brain, 126,* 2463–2475.

James, W. (1884). What is an emotion? *Mind, 9,* 188–205.

Janicak, P. G., O'Reardon, J. P., Sampson, S. M., Husain, M. M., Lisanby, S. H., Rado, J. T., Heart, K. L., & Demitrack, M. A. (2008). Transcranial magnetic stimulation in the treatment of major depressive disorder: A comprehensive summary of safety experience from acute exposure, extended exposure, and during reintroduction treatment. *Journal of Clinical Psychiatry, 69,* 222–232.

Janssen, P., Srivastava, S., Ombelet, S., & Orban, G. A. (2008). Coding of shape and position in macaque lateral intraparietal area. *Journal of Neuroscience, 28,* 6679–6690.

Janzen, G., & van Turennout, M. (2004). Selective neural representations of objects relevant for navigation. *Nature Neuroscience, 7,* 673–677.

Jech, R., Klempír, J., Vymazal, J., Zidovská, J., Klempírová, O., Růzicka, E., & Roth, J. (2007). Variation of selective gray and white matter atrophy in Huntington's disease. *Movement Disorders, 22,* 1783–1789.

Jellema, T., Baker, C. I., Wicker, B., & Perrett, D. I. (2000). Neural representation for the perception of the intentionality of actions. *Brain & Cognition, 44,* 280–302.

Jellinger, K. A. (1999). Post mortem studies in Parkinson's disease: Is it possible to detect brain areas for specific symptoms? *Journal of Neural Transmission Supplementum, 56,* 1–29.

Jenkins, I. H., Brooks, D. J., Nixon, P. D., Frackowiak, R. S., & Passingham, R. E. (1994). Motor sequence learning: A study with positron emission tomography. *Journal of Neuroscience, 14*(6), 3775–3790.

Jenner, P. (2002). Pharmacology of dopamine agonists in the treatment of Parkinson's disease. *Neurology, 58,* S1–S8.

Jennett, B. (2005). Thirty years of the vegetative state: Clinical, ethical and legal problems. *Progress in Brain Research, 150,* 537–543.

Jensen, O., Kaiser, J., & Lachaux, J.-P. (2007). Human gamma-frequency oscillations associated with attention and memory. *Trends in Neurosciences, 30,* 317–324.

Ji, D., & Wilson, M. A. (2007). Coordinated memory replay in the visual cortex and hippocampus during sleep. *Nature Neuroscience, 10,* 100–107.

Jobard, G., Crivello, F., & Tzourio-Mazoyer, N. (2003). Evaluation of the dual-route theory of reading: A metanalysis of 35 neuroimaging studies. *NeuroImage, 20,* 693–712.

Johannsen, L., Ackermann, H., & Karnath, H. O. (2003). Lasting amelioration of spatial neglect by treatment with neck muscle vibration even without concurrent training. *Journal of Rehabilitation Medicine, 35,* 249–253.

Johnson, J. A., & Zatorre, R. J. (2006). Neural substrates for dividing and focusing attention between simultaneous auditory and visual events. *NeuroImage, 31,* 1673–1681.

Johnson, J. A., Strafella, A. P., & Zatorre, R. J. (2007). The role of the dorsolateral prefrontal cortex in bimodal divided attention: Two transcranial magnetic stimulation studies. *Journal of Cognitive Neuroscience, 19,* 907–920.

Johnson, J. S., & Newport, E. L. (1989). Critical period effects in second language learning: The influence of maturational state on the acquisition of English as a second language. *Cognitive Psychology, 21*(1), 60–99.

Johnson, R. T. (2005). Prion diseases. *Lancet Neurology, 4,* 635–642.

Johnson-Frey, S. H., Newman-Norlund, R., & Grafton, S. T. (2005). A distributed left hemisphere network active during planning of everyday tool use skills. *Cerebral Cortex, 15,* 681–695.

Jones, B. E. (2003). Arousal systems. *Frontiers in Bioscience, 8,* s438–s451.

Jones, E. G. (2000). Cortical and subcortical contributions to activity-dependent plasticity in primate somatosensory cortex. *Annual Review of Neuroscience, 23,* 1–37.

Jones, T. A., & Schallert, T. (1994). Use-dependent growth of pyramidal neurons after cortical damage. *Journal of Neuroscience, 14,* 2140–2152.

Jones-Gotman, M., & Milner, B. (1977). Design fluency: The invention of nonsense drawings after focal cortical lesions. *Neuropsychologia, 15,* 653–674.

Jonides, J., Smith, E. E., Marshuetz, C., Koeppe, R. A., & Reuter-Lorenz, P. A. (1998). Inhibition in verbal working memory revealed by brain activation. *Proceedings of the National Academy of Sciences, USA, 95*(14), 8410–8413.

Jordan, B. D., & Zimmerman, R. D. (1990). Computed tomography and magnetic resonance imaging comparisons in boxers. *JAMA, 263,* 1670–1674.

Jordan, B. D., Relkin, N. R., Ravdin, L. D., Jacobs, A. R., Bennett, A., & Gandy, S. (1997). Apolipoprotein E ε4 associated with chronic traumatic brain injury in boxing. *JAMA, 278,* 136–140.

Josiassen, R. C., Curry, L. M., & Mancall, E. L. (1982). Patterns of intellectual deficit in Huntington's disease. *Journal of Clinical Neuropsychology, 4,* 173–183.

Julien, R. M. (2005). *A primer of drug action* (10th ed.). New York: Worth Publishers.

Jung-Beeman, M. (2005). Bilateral brain processes for comprehending natural language. *Trends in Cognitive Sciences, 9,* 512–518.

Jurgens, C. K., van de Wiel, L., van Es, A. C., Grimbergen, Y. M., Witjes-Ané, M. N. W., van der Grond, J., Middelkoop, H. A. M., & Roos, R. A. C. (2008). Basal ganglia volume and clinical correlates in "preclinical" Huntington's disease. *Journal of Neurology, 255,* 1785–1791.

Just, M. A., Keller, T. A., & Cynkar, J. (2008). A decrease in brain activation associated with driving while listening to someone speak. *Brain Research, 1205,* 70–80.

Kaas, J. (2000). The reorganization of sensory and motor maps after injury in adult mammals. In M. S. Gazzaniga (Ed.), *The new cognitive neurosciences* (pp. 223–236). Cambridge, MA: MIT Press.

Kaas, J. H., Hackett, T. A., & Tramo, M. J. (1999). Auditory processing in primate cerebral cortex. *Current Opinion in Neurobiology, 9,* 164–170.

Kahneman, D. (1973). *Attention and effort.* Englewood Cliffs, NJ: Prentice Hall.

Kalin, N. H., Larson, C., Shelton, S. E., & Davidson, R. J. (1998). Asymmetric frontal brain activity, cortisol, and behavior associated with fearful temperament in rhesus monkeys. *Behavioral Neuroscience, 112,* 286–292.

Kalin, N. H., Shelton, S. E., & Davidson, R. J. (2000). Cerebrospinal fluid corticotropin-releasing hormone levels are elevated in monkeys with patterns of brain activity associated with a fearful temperament. *Biological Psychiatry, 47,* 579–585.

Kalisch, R., Wiech, K., Critchley, H. D., Seymour, B., O'Doherty, J. P., Oakley, D. A., et al. (2005). Anxiety reduction through detachment: Subjective, physiological, and neural effects. *Journal of Cognitive Neuroscience, 17,* 874–883.

Kalivas, P. W., & Volkow, N. D. (2005). The neural basis of addiction: A pathology of motivation and choice. *American Journal of Psychiatry, 162,* 1403–1413.

Kalmar, J. H., Gaudino, E. A., Moore, N. B., Halper, J., & DeLuca, J. (2008). The relationship between cognitive deficits and everyday functional activities in multiple sclerosis. *Neuropsychology, 22,* 442–449.

Kamitani, Y., & Tong, F. (2005). Decoding the visual and subjective contents of the human brain. *Nature Neuroscience, 8,* 679–685.

Kampe, K. K. W., Frith, C. D., Dolan, R. J., & Frith, U. (2001). Reward value of attractiveness and gaze. *Nature, 413,* 589.

Kandel, E. R. (2009). An introduction to the work of David Hubel and Torsten Wiesel. *Journal of Physiology, 587,* 2733–2741.

Kanwisher, N. (2000). Domain specificity in face perception. *Nature Neuroscience, 3,* 759–763.

Kanwisher, N., & Yovel, G. (2006). The fusiform face area: A cortical region specialized for the perception of faces. *Philosophical Transactions of the Royal Society of London, 361,* 2109–2128.

Kanwisher, N., McDermott, J., & Chun, M. M. (1997). The fusiform face area: A module in human extrastriate cortex specialized for face perception. *Journal of Neuroscience, 17,* 4302–4311.

Kaplan, E. (2004). The M, P, and K pathways of the primate visual system. In L. M. Chalupa & J. S. Werner (Eds.), *The visual neurosciences* (pp. 481–493). Cambridge, MA: MIT Press.

Kaplan, J. A., Brownell, H. H., Jacobs, J. R., & Gardner, H. (1990). The effects of right hemisphere damage on the pragmatic interpretation of conversational remarks. *Brain & Language, 38,* 315–333.

Kapur, N. (1999). Syndromes of retrograde amnesia: A conceptual and empirical analysis. *Psychological Bulletin, 125,* 800–825.

Kapur, N., & Brooks, D. J. (1999). Temporally-specific retrograde amnesia in two cases of discrete bilateral hippocampal pathology. *Hippocampus, 9*(3), 247–254.

Karatekin, C. (2001). Developmental disorders of attention. In C. A. Nelson & M. Luciana (Eds.), *Handbook of developmental cognitive neuroscience* (pp. 561–576). Cambridge, MA: MIT Press.

Karl, A., Schaefer, M., Malta, L. S., Dörfel, D., Rohleder, N., & Werner, A. (2006). A meta-analysis of structural brain abnormalities in PTSD. *Neuroscience & Biobehavioral Reviews, 30,* 1004–1031.

Karlinsky, H. (1986). Alzheimer's disease and Down's syndrome: A review. *Journal of the American Geriatrics Society, 34,* 728–734.

Karnath, H. O., Fruhmann Berger, M., Küker, W., & Rorden, C. (2004). The anatomy of spatial neglect based on voxelwise statistical analysis: A study of 140 patients. *Cerebral Cortex, 14,* 1164–1172.

Karnath, H. O., Sievering, D., & Fetter, M. (1994). The interactive contribution of neck muscle proprioception and vestibular stimulation to subjective "straight ahead" orientation in man. *Experimental Brain Research, 101,* 140–146.

Karni, A., Meyer, G., Jezzard, P., Adams, M. M., Turner, R., & Ungerleider, L. G. (1995). Functional MRI evidence for adult motor cortex plasticity during motor skill learning. *Nature, 377,* 155–157.

Karni, A., Meyer, G., Jezzard, P., Adams, M. M., Turner, R., & Ungerleider, L. G. (1995). Functional MRI evidence for adult motor cortex plasticity during motor skill learning. *Nature, 377,* 155–158.

Karni, A., Meyer, G., Jezzard, P., Adams, M. M., Turner, R., & Ungerleider, L. G. (1998). The acquisition of skilled motor performance: Fast and slow experience-driven changes in primary motor cortex. *Proceedings of the National Academy of Sciences, USA, 95,* 861–868.

Kasai, K., Shenton, M. E., Salisbury, D. F., Hirayasu, Y., Onitsuka, T., Spencer, M. H., et al. (2003). Progressive decrease of left Heschl gyrus and planum temporale gray matter volume in first-episode schizophrenia. *Archives of General Psychiatry, 60,* 766–775.

Kasper, S., Gastpar, M., Müller, W. E., Volz, H. P., Dienl, A., Kieser, M., & Möller, H. J. (2008). Efficacy of St. John's wort extract WS 5570 in acute treatment of mild depression. *European Archives of Psychiatry and Clinical Neurosciences, 258,* 59–63.

Kassel, J. (1997). Smoking and attention: A review and reformulation of the stimulus-filter hypothesis. *Clinical Psychology Review, 17,* 451–478.

Kassubek, J., Hickok, G., & Erhard, P. (2004). Involvement of classical anterior and posterior language areas in sign language production, as investigated by 4T functional magnetic resonance imaging. *Neuroscience Letters, 364,* 168–172.

Kastner, S., & Pinsk, M. A. (2004). Visual attention as a multilevel selection process. *Cognitive, Affective & Behavioral Neuroscience, 4,* 483–500.

Kastner, S., De Weerd, P., Desimone, R., & Ungerleider, L. G. (1998). Mechanisms of directed attention in the human extrastriate cortex as revealed by functional MRI. *Science, 282,* 108–111.

Kastner, S., Pinsk, M. A., De Weerd, P., Desimone, R., & Ungerleider, L. G. (1999). Increased activity in human visual cortex during directed attention in the absence of visual stimulation. *Neuron, 22,* 751–761.

Kastner, S., Schneider, K. A., & Wunderlich, K. (2006). Beyond a relay nucleus: Neuroimaging views on the human LGN. *Progress in Brain Research, 155,* 125–143.

Katz, N., Ring, H., Naveh, Y., Kizony, R., Feintuch, U., & Weiss, P. L. (2005). Interactive virtual environment training for safe street crossing of right hemisphere stroke patients with unilateral spatial neglect. *Disability & Rehabilitation, 27,* 1235–1243.

Kaufman, J., Yang, B.-Z., Douglas-Palumberi, H., Houshyar, S., Lipschitz, D., Krystal, J. H., & Gelernter, J. (2004). Social supports and serotonin transporter gene moderate depression in maltreated children. *Proceedings of the National Academy of Sciences, 101,* 17316–17321.

Kaufmann, W. E., & Moser, H. W. (2000). Dendritic anomalies in disorders associated with mental retardation. *Cerebral Cortex, 10,* 981–991.

Kawahata, N., Nagata, K., & Shishido, F. (1988). Alexia with agraphia due to the left posterior inferior temporal lobe lesion: Neuropsychological analysis and its pathogenetic mechanisms. *Brain & Language, 33,* 296–310.

Kawamura, M., Hirayama, K., Hasegawa, K., Takahashi, N., & Yamaura, A. (1987). Alexia with agraphia of kanji (Japanese morphograms). *Journal of Neurology, Neurosurgery & Psychiatry, 50,* 1125–1129.

Kawasaki, Y., Sumiyoshi, T., Higuchi, Y., Ito, T., Takeuchi, M., & Kurachi, M. (2007). Voxel-based analysis of P300 electrophysiological topography associated with positive and negative symptoms of schizophrenia. *Schizophrenia Research, 94,* 164–171.

Kaye, J. (1998). Diagnostic challenges in dementia. *Neurology, 51* (Suppl. 1), S45–S52.

Keane, M. M., Clarke, H., & Corkin, S. (1992). Impaired perceptual priming and intact conceptual priming in a patient with bilateral posterior cerebral lesions. *Society for Neuroscience Abstracts, 18,* 386.

Keane, M. M., Gabrieli, J. D., Fennema, A. C., Growdon, J. H., & Corkin, S. (1991). Evidence for a dissociation between perceptual and conceptual priming in Alzheimer's disease. *Behavioral Neuroscience, 105,* 326–342.

Keedwell, P. A., Andrew, C., Williams, S. C. R., Brammer, M. J., & Phillips, M. L. (2005). The neural correlates of anhedonia in major depressive disorder. *Biological Psychiatry, 58,* 843–853.

Keele, S. (1968). Movement control in skilled motor performance. *Psychological Bulletin, 70,* 387–403.

Keirstead, H. S. (2005). Stem cells for the treatment of myelin loss. *Trends in Neurosciences, 28,* 677–683.

Keller, J., Nitschke, J. B., Bhargava, T., Deldin, P. J., Gergen, J. A., Miller, G. A., & Heller, W. (2000). Neuropsychological differentiation of depression and anxiety. *Journal of Abnormal Psychology, 109,* 3–10.

Kelley, T. A., Serences, J. T., Giesbrecht, B., & Yantis, S. (2008). Cortical mechanisms for shifting and holding visuospatial attention. *Cerebral Cortex, 18,* 114–125.

Kelley, W. M., Miezin, F. M., McDermott, K. B., Buckner, R. L., Raichle, M. E., Cohen, N. J., et al. (1998). Hemispheric specialization in human dorsal frontal cortex and medial temporal lobe for verbal and nonverbal memory encoding. *Neuron, 20*(5), 927–936.

Kemper, T. (1984). Neuroanatomical and neuropathological changes in normal aging and dementia. In M. A. Albert (Ed.), *Clinical neurology of aging.* New York: Oxford University Press.

Kempermann, G., & Kronenberg, G. (2003). Depressed new neurons? Adult hippocampal neurogenesis and a cellular plasticity hypothesis of major depression. *Biological Psychiatry, 54,* 499–503.

Kempermann, G., Gast, D., & Gage, F. H. (2002). Neuroplasticity in old age: Sustained fivefold induction of hippocampal neurogenesis by long-term environmental enrichment. *Annals of Neurology, 52,* 135–143.

Kempermann, G., Kuhn, H. G., & Gage, F. H. (1997). More hippocampal neurons in adult mice living in an enriched environment. *Nature, 386,* 493–495.

Kennard, M. A. (1936). Age and other factors in motor recovery from precentral lesions in monkeys. *Journal of Neurophysiology, 1,* 477–496.

Kennard, M. A. (1942). Cortical reorganization of motor function. *Archives of Neurological Psychiatry, 48,* 227–240.

Kennedy, S. H., Evans, K. R., Kruger, S., Mayberg, H. S., Meyer, J. H., McCann, S., et al. (2001). Changes in regional brain glucose metabolism measured with positron emission tomography after paroxetine treatment of major depression. *American Journal of Psychiatry, 158,* 899–905.

Kent, J. M., & Rauch, S. L. (2009). Neuroimaging studies of anxiety disorders. In D. S. Charney & E. J. Nestler (Eds.), *Neurobiology of mental illness* (3d ed.; pp. 703–730). Oxford, UK: Oxford University Press.

Kent, R. D., & Rosenbek, J. (1982). Prosodic disturbance and neurologic lesion. *Brain & Language, 15,* 259–291.

Kentgen, L. M., Tenke, C. E., Pine, D. S., Fong, R., Klein, R. G., & Bruder, G. E. (2000). Electroencephalographic asymmetries in adolescents with major depression: Influence of comorbidity with anxiety disorders. *Journal of Abnormal Psychology, 109,* 797–802.

Kerkhoff, G. (2003). Modulation and rehabilitation of spatial neglect by sensory stimulation. *Progress in Brain Research, 142,* 257–271.

Kerkhoff, G., Keller, I., Ritter, V., & Marquardt, C. (2006). Repetitive optokinetic stimulation induces lasting recovery from visual neglect. *Restorative Neurology & Neuroscience, 24,* 357–369.

Kerns, J. G., Cohen, J. D., MacDonald, A. W., Johnson, M. K., Stenger, V. A., Aizenstein, H., & Carter, C. S. (2005). Decreased conflict- and error-related activity in the anterior cingulate cortex in subjects with schizophrenia. *American Journal of Psychiatry, 162,* 1833–1839.

Kertesz, A., & Clydesdale, S. (1994). Neuropsychological deficits in vascular dementia vs. Alzheimer's disease: Frontal lobe deficits prominent in vascular dementia. *Archives of Neurology, 51,* 1226–1231.

Kesler-West, M. L., Andersen, A. H., Smith, C. D., Avison, M. J., Davis, C. E., Kryscio, R. J. & Blonder, L. X. (2001). Neural substrates of facial emotion processing using fMRI. *Cognitive Brain Research, 11,* 213–226.

Kessler, R. C., Berglund, P., Demler, O., Jin, R., Merikangas, K. R., & Walters, E. E. (2005). Lifetime prevalence and age-of-onset distributions of DSM-IV disorders in the National Comorbidity Survey Replication. *Archives of General Psychiatry, 62,* 593–602.

Kessler, R. C., Chiu, W. T., Demler, O., Merikangas, K. R., & Walters, E. E. (2005). Prevalence, severity, and comorbidity of 12-month DSM-IV disorders in the National Comorbidity Survey replication. *Archives of General Psychiatry, 62,* 617–627.

Ketter, T. A., Post, R. M., & Theodore, W. H. (1999). Positive and negative psychiatric effects of antiepileptic drugs in patients with seizure disorders. *Neurology, 53*(Suppl. 2), S53–S67.

Kharitonova, M., Chien, S., Colunga, E., & Munakata, Y. (2009). More than a matter of getting 'unstuck': flexible thinkers use more abstract representations than perseverators. *Developmental Science, 12,* 662–669.

Khedr, E. M., Hamed, E., Said, A., & Basahi, J. (2002). Handedness and language cerebral lateralization. *European Journal of Applied Physiology, 87,* 469–473.

Kiang, M., Kutas, M., Light, G. A., & Braff, D. L. (2008). An event-related brain potential study of direct and indirect semantic priming in schizophrenia. *American Journal of Psychiatry, 165,* 74–81.

Kiehl, K.A., Laurens, K.R., Duty, T.L., Forster, B.B., & Liddle, P.F. (2001). Neural sources involved in auditory target detection and novelty processing: an event-related fMRI study. *Psychophysiology, 38,* 133–142.

Kiehl, K.A., Liddle, P. F., & Hopfinger, J. B. (2000). Error processing and the rostral anterior cingulate: An event-related fMRI study. *Psychophysiology, 37,* 216–223.

Kihlstrom, J.F. (2002). No need for repression. *Trends in Cognitive Science, 6,* 502.

Kikkert, M. A., Ribbers, G. M., & Koudstaal, P. J. (2006). Alien hand syndrome in stroke: A report of 2 cases and review of the literature. *Archives of Physical Medicine and Rehabilitation, 87,* 728–732.

Kim, A., & Osterhout, L. (2005). The independence of combinatory semantic processing: Evidence from event-related potentials. *Journal of Memory & Language, 52,* 205–225.

Kim, K. H. S., Relkin, N. R., Lee, K.-M., & Hirsch, J. (1997). Distinct cortical areas associated with native and second languages. *Nature, 388,* 171–174.

Kim, S. H., & Hamann, S. (2007). Neural correlates of positive and negative emotion regulation. *Journal of Cognitive Neuroscience, 19,* 776–798.

Kim, Y.-H., Min, S.-J., Ko, M.-H., Park, J.-W., Jang, S. H., & Lee, P. K. W. (2005). Facilitating visuospatial attention for the contralateral hemifield by repetitive TMS on the posterior parietal cortex. *Neuroscience Letters, 382,* 280–285.

Kimura, D. (1967). Functional asymmetry of the brain in dichotic listening. *Cortex, 3,* 164–178.

Kimura, D. (1969). Spatial localization in left and right visual fields. *Canadian Journal of Psychology, 23,* 445–458.

Kimura, D. (1977). Acquisition of a motor skill after left hemisphere damage. *Brain, 100,* 337–350.

Kimura, D. (1993). *Neuromotor mechanisms in human communication.* New York: Clarendon Press/Oxford University Press.

Kinomura, S., Larsson, J., Gulyas, B., & Roland, P. E. (1996). Activation by attention of the human reticular formation and thalamic intralaminar nuclei. *Science, 271,* 512–515.

Kinsbourne, M. (1974). Lateral interaction in the brain. In M. Kinsbourne & W. L. Smith (Eds.), *Hemispheric disconnections and cerebral function* (pp. 239–259). Springfield, IL: Charles C Thomas.

Kinsbourne, M. (1975). The mechanisms of hemispheric control of the lateral gradient of attention. In P. M. A. Rabbitt & S. Dornic (Eds.), *Attention and performance.* New York: Academic Press.

Kinsbourne, M. (1987). Mechanisms of unilateral neglect. In M. Jeannerod (Ed.), *Neurophysiological and neuropsychological aspects of spatial neglect* (pp. 69–83). North-Holland: Elsevier.

Kinsbourne, M. (1993). Orientational bias model of unilateral neglect: Evidence from attentional gradients within hemispace. In I. H. Robertson & J.C. Marshall (Eds.), *Unilateral neglect: Clinical and experimental studies* (pp. 63–88). Hillsdale, NJ: Erlbaum.

Kinsbourne, M., & Wood, F. (1975). Short-term memory processes and the amnesic syndrome. In D. Deutsch & A. J. Deutsch (Eds.), *Short-term memory* (pp. 258–291). New York: Academic Press.

Kirby, K. N., Petry, N. M., & Bickel, W. K. (1999). Heroin addicts have higher discount rates for delayed rewards than non-drug-use controls. *Journal of Experimental Psychology: General, 128,* 78–87.

Kircher, T. T. J., Brammer, M., Andreu, N. T., Steven, C. R., Williams, S. C. R., & McGuire, P. K. (2001). Engagement of right temporal cortex during processing of linguistic context. *Neuropsychologia, 39*(8), 798–809.

Kirchhoff, B. A., Wagner, A. D., Maril, A., & Stern, C. E. (2000). Prefrontal-temporal circuitry for episodic encoding and subsequent memory. *Journal of Neuroscience, 20*(16), 6173–6180.

Kito, S., Fujita, K., & Koga, Y. (2008). Changes in regional cerebral blood flow after repetitive transcranial magnetic stimulation of the left dorsolateral prefrontal cortex in treatment-resistant depression. *Journal of Neuropsychiatry & Clinical Neurosciences, 20,* 74–80.

Kitterle, F. L., Hellige, J. B., & Christman, S. (1992). Visual hemispheric asymmetries depend on which spatial frequencies are task relevant. *Brain and Cognition, 20,* 308–314.

Klüver, H., & Bucy, P. C. (1937). "Psychic blindness" and other symptoms following bilateral temporal lobectomy in rhesus monkeys. *American Journal of Physiology, 119,* 352–353.

Kleim, J. A., Lussnig, E., Schwarz, E. R., Comery, T. A., & Greenough, W. T. (1996). Synaptogenesis and Fos expression in the motor cortex of the adult rat after motor skill learning. *Journal of Neuroscience, 16*(14), 4529–4535.

Klin, A., Jones, W., Schultz, R., Volkmar, F., & Cohen, D. (2002). Visual fixation patterns during viewing of naturalistic social situations as predictors of social competence in individuals with autism. *Archives of General Psychiatry, 59,* 809–816.

Klingberg, T., Hedehus, M., Emple, E., Satz, T., Gabrieli, J. D. E., Moseley, M. E., & Poldrack, R. A. (2000). Microstructure of temporo-parietal white matter as a basis for reading ability: Evidence from diffusion tensor magnetic resonance imaging. *Neuron, 25,* 493–500.

Klinke, R., Kral, A., Heid, S., Tillien, J., & Hartmann, R. (1999). Recruitment of the auditory cortex in congenitally deaf cats by long-term cochlear electrostimulation. *Science, 285,* 1729–1733.

Knight, R. T., Scabini, D., Woods, D. L., & Clayworth, C. C. (1989). Contribution of temporal-parietal junction to the human auditory P$_3$. *Brain Research, 502,* 109–116.

Knight, R.T. (1984). Decreased response to novel stimuli after prefrontal lesions in man. *Electroencephalography and Clinical Neurophysiology, 59,* 9–20.

Knoblich, G., Ohlsson, S., Haider, H., & Rhenius, D. (1999). Constraint relaxation and chunk decomposition in insight problem solving. *Journal of Experimental Psychology: Learning, Memory & Cognition, 25,* 1534–1555.

Knopman, D., Schneider, L., Davis, K., Talwalker, S., Smith, F., Hoover, T., et al. (1996). Long-term tacrine (Cognex) treatment: Effects on nursing home placement and mortality. *Neurology, 47,* 166–177.

Knowlton, B. J., Mangels, J. A., & Squire, L. R. (1996). A neostriatal habit learning system in humans. *Science, 273*(5280), 1399–1402.

Knowlton, B. J., Ramus, S. J., & Squire, L. R. (1992). Intact artificial grammar learning in amnesia: Dissociation of classification learning and explicit memory for specific instances. *Psychological Science, 3,* 172–179.

Knowlton, B. J., Squire, L. R., Paulsen, J. S., Swerdlow, N. R., Swenson, M., & Butters, N. (1996). Dissociations within nondeclarative memory in Huntington's disease. *Neuropsychology, 10,* 538–548.

Knutson, B., Adams, C. M., Fong, G. W., & Hommer, D. (2001). Anticipation of increasing monetary reward selectively recruits nucleus accumbens. *Journal of Neuroscience, 21,* RC159(1–5).

Knutson, B., Westdorp, A., Kaiser, E., & Hommer, D. (2000). fMRI visualization of brain activity during a monetary incentive delay task. *NeuroImage, 12,* 20–27.

Kodituwakku, P. W. (2007). Defining the behavioral phenotype in children with fetal alcohol spectrum disorders: A review. *Neuroscience & Biobehavioral Reviews, 31,* 192–201.

Koechlin, E., & Summerfield, C. (2007). An information theoretical approach to prefrontal executive function. *Trends in Cognitive Sciences, 11,* 229–235.

Koepp, M. J., Gunn, R. N., Lawrence, A. D., Cunningham, V. J., Dagher, A., Jones, T., Brooks, D. J., Bench, C. J., & Grasby, P. M. (1998). Evidence for striatal dopamine release during a video game. *Nature, 393,* 266–268.

Kohn, B., & Dennis, M. (1974). Selective impairments of visuospatial abilities in infantile hemiplegics after right cerebral hemidecortication. *Neuropsychologia, 12,* 505–512.

Kolb, B., & Gibb, R. (2001). Early brain injury, plasticity, and behavior. In C. A. Nelson & M. Luciana (Eds.), *Handbook of developmental cognitive neuroscience* (pp. 175–190). Cambridge, MA: MIT Press.

Kolb, B., & Milner, B. (1981). Performance of complex arm and facial movements after focal brain lesions. *Neuropsychologia, 19,* 291–308.

Kolb, B., & Whishaw, I. Q. (1990). *Fundamentals of human neuropsychology* (3d ed.). New York: Freeman.

Komatsu, H. (2006). The neural mechanisms of perceptual filling-in. *Nature Reviews Neuroscience, 7,* 220–231.

Komatsu, H., Kinoshita, M., & Murakami, I. (2000). Neural responses in the retinotopic representation of the blind spot in the macaque V1 to stimuli for perceptual filling-in. *Journal of Neuroscience, 20,* 9310–9319.

Konishi, M. (2003). Coding of auditory space. *Annual Review of Neuroscience, 26,* 31–55.

Konishi, S., Morimoto, H., Jimura, K., Asari, T., Chikazoe, J., Yamashita, K., Hirose, S., & Miyashita, Y. (2008). Differential superior prefrontal activity on initial versus subsequent shifts in naive subjects. *NeuroImage, 41,* 575–580.

Konishi, S., Wheeler, M. E., Donaldson, D. I., & Buckner, R. L. (2000). Neural correlates of episodic retrieval success. *NeuroImage, 12*(3), 276–286.

Kopelman, M. D., Stanhope, N., & Kingsley, D. (1999). Retrograde amnesia in patients with diencephalic, temporal lobe or frontal lesions. *Neuropsychologia, 37*(8), 939–958.

Kosslyn, S. M. (1973). Scanning visual images. Some structural implications. *Perception and Psychophysics, 14,* 90–94.

Kosslyn, S. M. (1987). Seeing and imagining in the cerebral hemispheres: A computational approach. *Psychological Review, 94,* 148–175.

Kosslyn, S. M. (1990). Mental imagery. In D. N. Osherson, S. M. Kosslyn, & J. M. Hollerbach (Eds.), *Visual cognition and action* (pp. 73–97). Cambridge, MA: MIT Press.

Kosslyn, S. M. (2006). You can play 20 questions with nature and win: Categorical versus coordinate spatial relations as a case study. *Neuropsychologia, 44,* 1519–1523.

Kosslyn, S. M., Alpert, N. M., Thompson, W. L., Maljkovic, V., Weise, S. B., Chabris, C. F., Hamilton, S. E., Rauch, S. L., & Buonanno, F. S. (1993). Visual mental imagery activates topographically organized visual cortex: PET investigations. *Journal of Cognitive Neuroscience, 5,* 263–287.

Kosslyn, S. M., Chabris, C. F., Marsolek, C. J., & Koenig, O. (1992). Categorical versus coordinate spatial relations: Computational analyses and computer simulations. *Journal of Experimental Psychology: Human Perception & Performance, 18,* 562–577.

Kosslyn, S. M., Koenig, O., Barrett, A., Cave, C., Tang, J., & Gabrieli, J. D. E. (1989). Evidence for two types of spatial representations: Hemispheric specialization for categorical and coordinate relations. *Journal of Experimental Psychology: Human Perception & Performance, 15,* 723–735.

Kosslyn, S. M., Pascual-Leone, A., Felician, O., Camposano, S., Keenan, J. P., Thompson, W. L., Ganis, G., Sukel, K. E., &

Alpert, N. M. (1999). The role of Area 17 in visual imagery: Convergent evidence from PET and rTMS. *Science, 284*(5411), 167–170.

Kosslyn, S. M., Thompson, W. L., & Alpert, N. M. (1997). Neural systems shared by visual imagery and visual perception: A positron emission tomography study. *NeuroImage, 6*(4), 320–334.

Kosslyn, S. M., Thompson, W. L., Gitelman, D. R., & Alpert, N. M. (1998). Neural systems that encode categorical versus coordinate spatial relations: PET investigations. *Psychobiology, 26*, 333–347.

Kosslyn, S. M., Thompson, W. L., Kim, I. J., & Alpert, N. M. (1995). Topographical representations of mental images in primary visual cortex. *Nature, 378*(6556), 496–498.

Kotchoubey, B. (2009). Vegetative state. In L. R. Squire (Ed.), *Encyclopedia of neuroscience* (pp. 61–66). Oxford, UK: Academic Press.

Kotecha, A., Spratt, A., & Viswanathan, A. (2008). Visual function and fitness to drive. *British Medical Bulletin, 87*, 164–174.

Kotz, S. A., Meyer, M., Alter, K., Besson, M., von Cramon, D. Y., & Friederici, A. D. (2003). On the lateralization of emotional prosody: An event-related functional MR investigation. *Brain & Language, 86*, 366–376.

Koukoui, S. D., & Chaudhuri, A. (2007). Neuroanatomical, molecular genetic, and behavioral correlates of fragile X syndrome. *Brain Research Reviews, 53*, 27–38.

Kounios, J., Frymiare, J. L., Bowden, E. M., Fleck, J. I., Subramaniam, K., Parrish, T. B., & Jung-Beeman, M. (2006). The prepared mind: Neural activity prior to problem presentation predicts subsequent solution by sudden insight. *Psychological Science, 17*, 882–890.

Kourtzi, Z., & Kanwisher, N. (2000). Cortical regions involved in perceiving object shape. *Journal of Neuroscience, 20*, 3310–3318.

Kovelman, I., Shalinsky, M. H., Berens, M. S., & Petitto, L. A. (2008). Shining new light on the brain's "bilingual signature": A functional near-infrared spectroscopy investigation of semantic processing. *NeuroImage, 39*, 1457–1771.

Krain, A. L., & Castellanos, F. X. (2006). Brain development and ADHD. *Clinical Psychology Review, 26*, 433–444.

Kramer, A. F., & Erickson, K. I. (2007). Capitalizing on cortical plasticity: Influence of physical activity on cognition and brain function. *Trends in Cognitive Sciences, 11*, 342–348.

Kramer, A. F., Bherer, L., Colcombe, S. J., Dong, W., & Greenough, W. T. (2004). Environmental influences on cognitive and brain plasticity during aging. *Journals of Gerontology, 59A*, 940–957.

Kramer, A. F., Coyne, J. T., & Strayer, D. L. (1993). Cognitive function at high altitude. *Human Factors, 35*, 329–344.

Kramer, A. F., Hahn, S., Cohen, N. J., Banich, M. T., McAuley, E., Harrison, C. R., et al. (1999). Aging, fitness and neurocognitive function. *Nature, 400*(6743), 418–419.

Kramer, A. F., Wickens, C. D., & Donchin, E. (1985). Processing of stimulus properties: Evidence for dual-task integrality. *Journal of Experimental Psychology: Human Perception & Performance, 11*(4), 393–408.

Kreiman, G., Hung, C. P., Kraskov, A., Quiroga, R. Q., Poggio, T., & DiCarlo, J. J. (2006). Object selectivity of local field potentials and spikes in the macaque inferior temporal cortex. *Neuron, 49*, 433–445.

Krekelberg, B., Boynton, G. M., & van Wezel, R. J. A. (2006). Adaptation: From single cells to BOLD signals. *Trends in Neurosciences, 29*, 250–256.

Krigger, K. W. (2006). Cerebral palsy: An overview. *American Family Physician, 73*, 91–100.

Kringelbach, M. L. (2005). The human orbitofrontal cortex: Linking reward to hedonic experience. *Nature Reviews Neuroscience, 6*, 691–702.

Kringelbach, M. L., O'Doherty, J., Rolls, E. T., & Andrews, C. (2003). Activation of the human orbitofrontal cortex to a liquid food stimulus is correlated with its subjective pleasantness. *Cerebral Cortex, 13*, 1064–1071.

Krompinger, J. W., Moser, J. S., & Simons, R. F. (2008). Modulations of the electrophysiological response to pleasant stimuli by cognitive reappraisal. *Emotion, 8*, 132–137.

Kronbichler, M., Klackl, J., Richlan, F, Schurz, M., Staffen, W., Ladurner, G., & Wimmer, H. (2009). On the functional neuroanatomy of visual word processing: effects of case and letter deviance. *Journal of Cognitive Neuroscience, 21*, 222–229.

Krystal, J. H., & Neumeister, A. (2009). Noradrenergic and serotonergic mechanisms in the neurobiology of posttraumatic stress disorder and resilience. *Brain Research, 1293*, 13–23.

Kuhn, A. A., Kupsch, A., Schneider, G. H., & Brown, P. (2006). Reduction in subthalamic 8–35 Hz oscillatory activity correlates with clinical improvement in Parkinson's disease. *European Journal of Neuroscience, 23*, 1956–1960.

Kuhn, H. G., Dickinson-Anson, H., & Gage, F. H. (1996). Neurogenesis in the dentate gyrus of the adult rat: Age-related decrease of neuronal progenitor proliferation. *Journal of Neuroscience, 16*, 2027–2033.

Kumar, A., Ghosal, S., & Bigl, V. (1997). Systematic administration of defined extracts from *Withania somnifera* (Indian Ginseng) and Shilajit differentially affects cholinergic but not glutamatergic and GABAergic markers in rat brain. *Neurochemistry International, 30*, 181–190.

Kuperberg, G. (2007). Neural mechanisms of language comprehension: Challenges to syntax. *Brain Research, 1146*, 23–49.

Kuperberg, G. R., Deckersbach, T., Holt, D. J., Goff, D., & West, W. C. (2007). Increased temporal and prefrontal activity in response to semantic associations in schizophrenia. *Archives of General Psychiatry, 64*, 138–151.

Kuroki, N., Shenton, M. E., Salisbury, D. F., Hirayasu, Y., Onitsuka, T., Ersner-Herschfield, H., et al. (2006). Middle and inferior temporal gyrus gray matter volume abnormalities in first-episode schizophrenia: An MRI study. *American Journal of Psychiatry, 163*, 2103–2110.

Kurtzer, I., Herter, T. M., & Scott, S. H. (2005). Random change in cortical load representation suggests distinct control of posture and movement. *Nature Neuroscience, 8*, 498–504.

Kurtzke, J. F. (1980). Epidemiologic contributions to multiple sclerosis: An overview. *Neurology, 30*, 61–79.

Kusunoki, M., Moutoussis, K., & Zeki, S. (2006). Effect of background colors on the tuning of color-selective cells in monkey area V4. *Journal of Neurophysiology, 95*, 3047–3059.

Kutas, M., & Hillyard, S. A. (1980). Reading senseless sentences: Brain potentials reflect semantic incongruity. *Science, 207*, 203–205.

Kutner, K. C., Erlanger, D. M., Tsai, J., Jordan, B., & Relkin, N. R. (2000). Lower cognitive performance of older football players possessing Apolipoprotein ε4. *Neurosurgery, 47*, 651–658.

Kwong, K. K., Belliveau, J. W., Chesler, D. A., Goldberg, I. E., Weisskoff, R. M., Poncelet, B. P., Kennedy, P. N., Hoppel, B. E., Cohen, M. S., Turner, R., Cheng, H.-M., Brady, T. J., & Rosen, B. R. (1992). Dynamic magnetic resonance imaging of human brain activity during primary sensory stimulation. *Proceedings of the National Academy of Sciences, USA, 89*, 5675–5679.

LaBar, K. S., & Cabeza, R. (2006). Cognitive neuroscience of emotional memory. *Nature Reviews Neuroscience, 7*, 54–64.

LaBerge, D., & Buchsbaum, M. S. (1990). Positron emission tomographic measurements of pulvinar activity during an attention task. *Journal of Neuroscience, 10*, 613–619.

Ladavas, E., Umilta, C., & Ricci-Bitti, P. E. (1980). Evidence for sex differences in right hemisphere dominance for emotions. *Neuropsychologia, 18*, 361–367.

Laeng, B. (1994). Lateralization of categorical and coordinate spatial functions: A study of unilateral stroke patients. *Journal of Cognitive Neuroscience, 6*, 189–203.

LaMantia, A. S., & Rakic, P. (1990). Axon overproduction and elimination in the corpus callosum of the developing rhesus monkey. *Journal of Neuroscience, 10*, 2156–2175.

Lamme, V. A. (2004). Beyond the classical receptive field: Contextual modulation of V1 responses. In L. M. Chalupa & J. S. Werner (Eds.), *The visual neurosciences* (pp. 720–732). Cambridge, MA: MIT Press.

Langenecker, S. A., Kennedy, S. E., Guidotti, L. M., Briceno, E. M., Own, L. S., Hooven, T., et al. (2007). Frontal and limbic activation during inhibitory control predicts treatment response in major depressive disorder. *Biological Psychiatry, 62*, 1272–1280.

Larson, C. L., Schaefer, H. S., Siegle, G. J., Jackson, C. A. B., Anderle, M. J., & Davidson, R. J. (2006). Fear is fast in phobic individuals: Amygdala activation in response to fear-relevant stimuli. *Biological Psychiatry, 60*, 410–417.

Lashley, K. S. (1929). *Brain mechanisms and intelligence*. Chicago: University of Chicago Press.

Lau, H., Rogers, R. D., Haggard, P., & Passingham, R. E. (2004). Attention to intention. *Science, 303*, 1208–1210.

Laureys, S. (2005). The neural correlate of (un)awareness: Lessons from the vegetative state. *Trends in Cognitive Sciences, 9*, 556–559.

Laureys, S., Owen, A. M., & Schiff, N. D. (2004). Brain function in coma, vegetative state, and related disorders. *Lancet Neurology, 3*, 537–546.

Lavi-Avnon, Y., Weller, A., Finberg, J. P. M., Gispan-Herman, I., Kinor, N., Stern, Y., et al. (2008). The reward system and maternal behavior in an animal model of depression: A microdialysis study. *Psychopharmacology, 196*, 281–291.

Lavie, N. (1995). Perceptual load as a necessary condition for selective attention. *Journal of Experimental Psychology: Human Perception & Performance, 21*, 451–468.

Lavie, N., & Tsal, Y. (1994). Perceptual load as a major determinant of the locus of selection in visual attention. *Perception & Psychophysics, 56*, 183–197.

Lawrence, A. D., Hodges, J. R., Rosser, A. E., Kershaw, A., French-Constant, C., Rubinstein, D. C., et al. (1998). Evidence for specific cognitive deficits in preclinical Huntington's disease. *Brain, 121*, 1329–1341.

Lawrence, A. D., Weeks, R. A., Brooks, D. J., Andrews, T. C., Watkins, L. H., Harding, A. E., et al. (1998). The relationship between striatal dopamine receptor binding and cognitive performance in Huntington's disease. *Brain, 121*, 1343–1355.

Lawrie, S. M., Buechel, C., Whalley, H. C., Frith, C. D., Firston, K. J., & Johnstone, E. C. (2002). Reduced frontotemporal functional connectivity in schizophrenia associated with auditory hallucinations. *Biological Psychiatry, 51*, 1008–1011.

Laws, K. R. (2005). Category-specific effects in object identification: What is "normal"? *Cortex, 41*, 833–841.

Lazeron, R. H. C., Rombouts, S. A. R. B., Machielsen, W. C. M., Scheltens, P., Witter, M. P., Uylings, H. B. M., & Barkhof, F. (2000). Visualizing brain activation during planning: The Tower of London test adapted for functional MR imaging. *American Journal of Neuroradiology, 21*, 1407–1414.

Le Grand, R., Mondloch, C. J., Maurer, D., & Brent, H. P. (2001). Early visual experience and face processing. *Nature, 410*, 890.

Le Grand, R., Mondloch, C. J., Maurer, D., & Brent, H. P. (2004). Impairment in holistic face processing following early visual deprivation. *Psychological Science, 15*, 762–768.

LeBars, P. L., Katz, M. M., Berman, N., Itil, T. M., Freedman, A. M., & Schatzberg, A. F. (1997). A placebo-controlled, double-blind, randomized trial of an extract of Ginkgo biloba for dementia. North American EGb study group. *JAMA, 278*, 1327–1332.

Leckman, J. F. (2002). Tourette's syndrome. *Lancet, 360*, 577–1586.

Ledgerwood, L., Richardson, R., & Cranney, J. (2003). Effects of D-cycloserine on extinction of conditioned freezing. *Behavioral Neuroscience, 117*, 341–349.

LeDoux, J. (1996). *The emotional brain: The mysterious underpinnings of emotional life*. New York: Touchstone.

LeDoux, J. E. (1992). Brain mechanisms of emotion and emotional learning. *Current Opinion in Neurobiology, 2*(2), 191–197.

LeDoux, J. E. (1994). Emotion, memory and the brain. *Scientific American, 270*(6), 50–57.

Lee, J.-H., Ryu, J., Jolesz, F., Cho, Z.-H., & Yoo, S.-S. (2009). Brain-machine interface via real-time fMRI: Preliminary study on thought-controlled robotic arm. *Neuroscience Letters, 450*, 1–6.

Lee, K.-H., Williams, L. M., Breakspear, M., & Gordon, E. (2003). Synchronous gamma activity: A review and contribution to an integrative neuroscience model of schizophrenia. *Brain Research Reviews, 41*, 57–78.

Lee, S.-H., Blake, R., & Heeger, D. J. (2007). Hierarchy of cortical responses underlying binocular rivalry. *Nature Neuroscience, 10*(8), 1048–1054.

Leehey, S. C., Carey, S., Diamond, R., & Cahn, A. (1978). Upright and inverted faces: The right hemisphere knows the difference. *Cortex, 14*, 411–419.

Lees, A. J., Hardy, J., & Revesz, T. (2009). Parkinson's disease. *Lancet, 373*, 2055–2066.

Leggio, M. G., Madolesi, L., Federico, F., Spirito, F., Ricci, B., Gelfo, F., & Petrosini, L. (2005). Environmental enrichment promotes improved spatial abilities and enhanced dendritic growth in the rat. *Behavioural Brain Research, 163*, 78–90.

Leh, S. E., Johansen-Berg, H., & Ptito, A. (2006). Unconscious vision: New insights into the neuronal correlate of blindsight using diffusion tractography. *Brain, 129*, 1822–1832.

Leh, S. E., Mullen, K. T., & Ptito, A. (2006). Absence of S-cone input in human blindsight following hemispherectomy. *European Journal of Neuroscience, 24*, 2954–2960.

Lehmkuhl, G., & Poeck, K. (1981). A disturbance in the conceptual organization of actions in patients with ideational apraxia. *Cortex, 17*, 153–158.

Leibson, C. L., Rocca, W. A., Hanson, V. A., Cha, R., Kokmen, E., O'Brien, P. C., & Palumbo, P. J. (1997). Risk of dementia among persons with diabetes mellitus: A population based cohort study. *American Journal of Epidemiology, 145*, 301–308.

Leiguarda, R. C., & Marsden, C. D. (2000). Limb apraxias: Higher-order disorders of sensorimotor integration. *Brain, 123*, 860–879.

Lemke, G. (2001). Glial control of neuronal development. *Annual Review of Neuroscience, 24*, 87–105.

Lenneberg, E. H. (1967). *Biological foundations of language*. New York: Wiley.

Lepage, M., Habib, R., & Tulving, E. (1998). Hippocampal PET activations of memory encoding and retrieval: The HIPER model. *Hippocampus, 8*(4), 313–322.

Lerch, J. P., Pruessner, J. C., Zijdenbos, A., Hampel, H., Teipel, S. J., & Evans, A. C. (2005). Focal decline of cortical thickness in Alzheimer's disease identified by computational neuroanatomy. *Cerebral Cortex, 15*, 995–1001.

Lesch, K.-P., Bengel, D., Heils, A., Sabol, S. Z., Greenberg, B. D., Petri, S., et al. (1996). Association of anxiety-related traits with a polymorphism in the serotonin transporter gene regulatory region. *Science, 274*, 1527–1531.

Leung, H. C., & Cai, W. (2007). Common and differential ventrolateral prefrontal activity during inhibition of hand and eye movements. *Journal of Neuroscience, 27*, 9893–9900.

Levenson, R. L., & Mellins, C. A. (1992). Pediatric HIV and disease: What psychologists need to know. *Professional Psychology: Research & Practice, 23*, 410–415.

Leveroni, C., Seidenberg, M., Mayer, A. R., Mead, L. A., Binder, J. R., & Rao, S. M. (2000). Neural systems underlying the recognition of familiar and newly learned faces. *Journal of Neuroscience, 20*, 876–886.

Levin, H. S., Meyers, C. A., Grossman, R. G., & Sarwar, M. (1981). Ventricular enlargement after closed head injury. *Archives of Neurology, 38*, 623–629.

Levin, R. L., Heller, W., Mohanty, A., Herrington, J. D., & Miller, G. A. (2007). Cognitive deficits in depression and functional specificity of regional brain activity. *Cognitive Therapy & Research, 31*, 211–233.

Levine, D. N., Kaufman, K. J., & Mohr, J. P. (1978). Inaccurate reaching associated with a superior parietal lobe tumor. *Neurology, 28*, 556–561.

Levine, S. C. (1984). Developmental changes in right-hemisphere involvement in face recognition. In C. Best (Ed.), *Hemispheric function and collaboration in the child* (pp. 157–191). New York: Academic Press.

Levine, S. C., & Banich, M. T. (1982). Lateral asymmetries in the naming of words and corresponding line drawings. *Brain and Language, 17*, 34–45.

Levine, S. C., Banich, M. T., & Koch-Weser, M. (1988). Face recognition: A general or specific right hemisphere capacity? *Brain and Cognition, 8*, 303–325.

Levine, S. C., Kraus, R., Alexander, E., Suriyakham, L. W., & Huttenlocher, P. (2005). IQ decline following early unilateral brain injury: A longitudinal study. *Brain & Cognition, 59*, 114–123.

Levy, J. (1983). Language, cognition, and the right hemisphere: A response to Gazzaniga. *American Psychologist, 38*, 538–541.

Levy, J., & Trevarthen, C. W. (1977). Perceptual, semantic and phonetic aspects of elementary language processes in split-brain patients. *Brain, 100*, 105–118.

Levy, J., Heller, W., Banich, M. T., & Burton, L. A. (1983). Asymmetry of perception in free viewing of chimeric faces. *Brain & Cognition, 2,* 404–419.

Levy, J., Trevarthen, C. W., & Sperry, R. W. (1972). Perception of bilateral chimeric figures following "hemispheric deconnexion." *Brain, 95,* 61–78.

Levy-Lahad, E., Wasco, W., Poorkaj, P., Romano, D. M., Oshima, J., Pettingell, W. H., et al. (1995). Candidate gene for the chromosome 1 familial Alzheimer's disease locus. *Science, 269,* 973–977.

Lewis, J. W., Brefczynski, R. E., Phinney, R. E., Janik, J. J., & DeYoe, E. A. (2005). Distinct cortical pathways for processing tool versus animal sounds. *Journal of Neuroscience, 25,* 5148–5158.

Lewis, J. W., Wightman, F. L., Brefczynski, R. E., Phinney, R. E., Binder, J. R., & DeYoe, E. A. (2004). Human brain regions involved in recognizing environmental sounds. *Cerebral Cortex, 14,* 1008–1021.

Ley, R. G., & Bryden, M. P. (1982). A dissociation of right and left hemispheric effects for recognizing emotional tone and verbal content. *Brain and Cognition, 1,* 3–9.

Lezak, M. D. (1983). *Neuropsychological assessment* (2d ed.). New York: Oxford University Press.

Lezak, M. D., Howieson, D. B., Loring, D. W., Hannay, H. J., & Fischer, J. S. (2004). *Neuropsychological assessment* (4th ed.). Oxford, UK: Oxford University Press.

Lhermitte, F. (1983). "Utilization behavior" and its relation to lesions of the frontal lobes. *Brain, 106,* 237–255.

Lhermitte, F. (1986). Human autonomy and the frontal lobes: Part II. Patient behavior in complex and social situations: The "Environmental Dependency Syndrome." *Annals of Neurology, 19*(4), 335–343.

Lhermitte, F., Pillon, B., & Serdaru, M. (1986). Human autonomy and the frontal lobes: Part I. Imitation and utilization behavior: A neuropsychological study of 75 patients. *Annals of Neurology, 19,* 326–334.

Li, C. S., Huang, C., Constable, R. T., & Sinha, R. (2006). Imaging response inhibition in a stop-signal task: Neural correlates independent of signal monitoring and post-response processing. *Journal of Neuroscience, 26,* 186–192.

Li, S.-C., & Lindenberger, U. (1999). Cross-level unification: A computational exploration of the link between deterioration of neurotransmitter systems and dedifferentiation of cognitive abilities in old age. In L.-G. Nilsson & H. J. Markowitsch (Eds.), *Cognitive neuroscience of memory* (pp. 103–146). Seattle, WA: Hogrefe & Huber.

Libon, D. J., Scanlon, M., Swenson, R., & Coslet, H. B. (1990). Binswanger's disease: Some neuropsychological considerations. *Journal of Geriatric Psychiatry & Neurology, 3,* 31–40.

Liddell, B. J., Brown, K. J., Kemp, A. H., Barton, M. J., Das, P., Peduto, A., et al. (2005). A direct brainstem-amygdala-cortical "alarm" system for subliminal signals of fear. *NeuroImage, 24,* 235–243.

Liddle, P. F., Kiehl, K. A., & Smith, A. M. (2001). Event-related fMRI study of response inhibition. *Human Brain Mapping, 12,* 100–109.

Lidow, M. S., Williams, C. V., & Goldman-Rakic, P. S. (1998). The cerebral cortex: A case for a common site of action for antipsychotics. *Trends in Pharmacological Sciences, 91,* 136–140.

Lieberman, A., Dziatolowski, M., Neophytides, A., Kupersmith, M., Aleksic, S., Serby, M., et al. (1979). Dementias of Huntington's and Parkinson's disease. In T. N. Chase, N. Wexler, & A. Barbeau (Eds.), *Advances in neurology* (pp. 273–289). New York: Raven Press.

Lieberman, M. D. (2007). Social cognitive neuroscience: A review of core processes. *Annual Review of Psychology, 58,* 259–289.

Linde, K., Berner, M., Egger, M., & Mulrow, C. (2005). St. John's wort for depression: Meta-analysis of randomized controlled trials. *British Journal of Psychiatry, 186,* 99–107.

Lindell, A. K. (2006). In your right mind: Right hemisphere contributions to language processing and production. *Neuropsychology Review, 16,* 131–148.

Lindvall, O., & Kokaia, Z. (2009). Prospects of stem cell therapy for replacing dopamine neurons in Parkinson's disease. *Trends in Pharmacological Sciences, 30,* 260–267.

Lipper, E. G., Voorhies, T. M., Ross, G., Vannucci, R. C., & Auld, P. A. M. (1986). Early predictors of one-year outcome for infants asphyxiated at birth. *Developmental Medicine & Child Neurology, 28,* 303–309.

Liu, J., & Newsome, W. T. (2005). Correlation between speed perception and neural activity in the middle temporal visual area. *Journal of Neuroscience, 25,* 711–722.

Liu, X., Banich, M. T., Jacobson, B. L., & Tanabe, J. L. (2006). Functional dissociation of attentional selection within PFC: Response and non-response related aspects of attentional selection as ascertained by fMRI. *Cerebral Cortex, 16,* 827–834.

Lledo, P.-M., Alonso, M., & Grubb, M. S. (2006). Adult neurogenesis and functional plasticity in neuronal circuits. *Nature Reviews Neuroscience, 7,* 179–193.

Lodi, R., Parchi, P., Tonon, C., Manners, D., Capellari, S., Strammiello, R., et al. (2009). Magnetic resonance diagnostic markers in clinical sporadic prion disease: A combined brain magnetic resonance imaging and spectroscopy study. *Brain, 132,* 2669–2679.

Loftus, E. (2003). Make-believe memories. *American Psychologist, 58,* 867–873.

Logan, G. D., Cowan, W. B., & Davis, K. A. (1984). On the ability to inhibit simple and choice reaction time responses: A model and a method. *Journal of Experimental Psychology: Human Perception & Performance, 10,* 276–291.

Logan, J. M., Sanders, A. L., Snyder, A. Z., Morris, J. C., & Buckner, R. L. (2002). Under-recruitment and nonselective recruitment: Dissociable neural mechanisms associated with aging. *Neuron, 33,* 827–840.

Logothetis, N. K., & Pauls, J. (1995). Psychophysical and physiological evidence for viewer-centered object representations in the primate. *Cerebral Cortex, 3,* 270–288.

London, E. D., Ernst, M., Grant, S., Bonson, K., & Weinstein, A. (2000). Orbitofrontal cortex and human drug abuse: Functional imaging. *Cerebral Cortex, 10,* 334–342.

Lorenzen, B., & Murray, L. L. (2008). Bilingual aphasia: A theoretical and clinical review. *American Journal of Speech-Language Pathology, 17,* 299–317.

Löscher, W., Gernert, M., & Heinemann, U. (2008). Cell and gene therapies in epilepsy: Promising avenues or blind alleys? *Trends in Neurosciences, 31,* 62–73.

Low, L. K., & Cheng, H.-J. (2006). Axon pruning: An essential step underlying the developmental plasticity of neuronal connections. *Philosophical Transactions of the Royal Society B, 361,* 1531–1544.

Lozano, A. M., Mayberg, H. S., Giacobbe, P., Hamani, C., Craddock, R. C., & Kennedy, S. H. (2008). Subcallosal cingulate gyrus deep brain stimulation for treatment-resistant depression. *Biological Psychiatry, 64,* 461–467.

Lu, B. Y., Martin, K. E., Edgar, J. C., Smith, A. K., Lewis, S. F., Escamilla, M. A., et al. (2007). Effect of catechol-O-methyltransferase val[158]met polymorphism on the P50 gating endophenotype in schizophrenia. *Biological Psychiatry, 62,* 822–825.

Lu, Z.-L., Williamson, S. J., & Kaufmann, L. (1992). Behavioral lifetime of human auditory sensory memory predicted by physiological measures. *Science, 258,* 1668–1670.

Lucas, T. H., McKhann, G. M., & Ojemann, G. A. (2004). Functional separation of languages in the bilingual brain: A comparison of electrical stimulation language mapping in 25 bilingual patients and 117 monolingual control patients. *Journal of Neurosurgery, 101,* 449–457.

Luciano, M., Gow, A. J., Harris, S. E., Hayward, C., Allerhand, M., Starr, J. M., & Visscher, P. M. (2009). Cognitive ability at age 11 and 70 years, information processing speed, and APOE variation: The Lothian birth cohort 1936 study. *Psychology & Aging, 24,* 129–138.

Luck, S. J., & Hillyard, S. A. (1994). Spatial filtering during visual search: Evidence from human electrophysiology. *Journal of Experimental Psychology: Human Perception & Performance, 20,* 1000–1014.

Lundberg, G. D. (1983). Boxing should be banned in civilized countries. *JAMA, 249,* 250.

Lundberg, G.D. (1984). Boxing should be banned in civilized countries—round 2. *JAMA, 251,* 2696–2698.

Lundberg, G.D. (1986). Boxing should be banned in civilized countries—round 3. *JAMA, 255,* 2483–2485.

Luria, A. R. (1966). *Higher cortical functions in man.* New York: Basic Books.

Luu, P., Collins, P., & Tucker, D. M. (2000). Mood, personality, and self-monitoring: Negative affect and emotionality in relation to frontal lobe mechanisms of error monitoring. *Journal of Experimental Psychology General, 129,* 43–60.

Lye, T. C., & Shores, E. A. (2000). Traumatic brain injury as a risk factor for Alzheimer's disease: A review. *Neuropsychology Review, 10,* 115–129.

Lynch, J. C. (1980). The functional organization of posterior parietal association cortex. *Behavioral and Brain Sciences, 3,* 485–534.

Lynch, J. C., Mountcastle, V. B., Talbot, W. H., & Yin, T. C. (1977). Parietal lobe mechanisms for directed visual attention. *Journal of Neurophysiology, 40,* 362–389.

Müller, N. G., & Knight, R. T. (2006). The functional neuroanatomy of working memory: Contributions of human brain lesion studies. *Neuroscience, 139*(1), 51–58.

Maccioni, R. B., & Perry, G. (Eds.). (2009). *Current hypotheses and research milestones in Alzheimer's disease.* New York: Springer.

MacDonald, A. W., Cohen, J. D., Stenger, V. W., & Carter, C. S. (2000). Dissociating the role of the dorsolateral prefrontal and anterior cingulate cortex in cognitive control. *Science, 288,* 1835–1838.

MacDonald, G., & Leary, M. R. (2005). Why does social exclusion hurt? The relationship between social and physical pain. *Psychological Bulletin, 131,* 202–223.

MacDonald, J. L. (2006). Beyond the critical period: Processing-based explanations for poor grammaticality judgment performance by late second language learners. *Journal of Memory & Language, 55,* 381–401.

Machado, C. J., Kazama, A. M., & Bachevalier, J. (2009). Impact of amygdala, orbital frontal, or hippocampal lesions on threat avoidance and emotional reactivity in nonhuman primates. *Emotion, 9,* 147–163.

MacLean, P. D. (1949). Psychosomatic disease and the "visceral brain": Recent developments' bearing on the Papez theory of emotion. *Psychosomatic Medicine, 11,* 338–353.

MacLean, P. D. (1952). Some psychiatric implications of physiological studies on frontotemporal portion of limbic system (visceral brain). *Electroencephalography & Clinical Neurophysiology, 4,* 407–418.

Madsen, K. M., Lauritsen, M. B., Pedersen, C. B., Thorsen, P., Plesner, A.-M., Andersen, P. H., & Mortensen, P. B. (2003). Thimerosal and the occurrence of autism: Negative ecological evidence from Danish population-based data. *Pediatrics, 112,* 604–606.

Maeder, P. P., Meuli, R. A., Adriani, M., Bellmann, A., Fornari, E., Thiran, J.-P., et al. (2001). Distinct pathways involved in sound recognition and localization: A human fMRI study. *NeuroImage, 14,* 802–816.

Maess, B., Koelsch, S., Gunter, T. C., & Friederici, A. D. (2001). Musical syntax is processed in Broca's area: An MEG study. *Nature Neuroscience, 4,* 540–545.

Maguire, E. A., Frackowiak, R. S., & Frith, C. D. (1997). Recalling routes around London: Activation of the right hippocampus in taxi drivers. *Journal of Neuroscience, 17*(18), 7103–7110.

Maguire, E. A., Frith, C. D., Burgess, N., Donnett, J. G., & O'Keefe, J. (1998). Knowing where things are: Parahippocampal involvement in encoding object locations in virtual large-scale space. *Journal of Cognitive Neuroscience, 10,* 61–76.

Maguire, E. A., Henson, R. N., Mummery, C. J., & Frith, C. D. (2001). Activity in prefrontal cortex, not hippocampus, varies parametrically with the increasing remoteness of memories. *NeuroReport, 12*(3), 441–444.

Maher, N. E., Golbe, L. I., Lazzarini, M. A. M., Mark, M. H., Currie, J. L. J., Wooten, G. F., et al. (2002). Epidemiologic study of 203 sibling pairs with Parkinson's disease: The *Gene*PD study. *Neurology, 58,* 79–84.

Mahurin, R. K. (2008). Frontal-subcortical determinants of processing speed in Parkinson's disease. In J. DeLuca & J. Kalmar (Eds.) *Information processing speed in clinical populations* (pp. 195–220). New York: Taylor & Francis.

Maillet, M., Robert, S. J., & Lezoualc'h, F. (2004). New insights into serotonin 5-HT4 receptors: A novel therapeutic target for Alzheimer's disease? *Current Alzheimer Research, 1,* 79–85.

Mainy, N., Jung, J., Baciu, M., Kahane, P., Schoendorff, B., Minotti, L., et al. (2008). Cortical dynamics of word recognition. *Human Brain Mapping, 29,* 1215–1230.

Maj, M. (1990). Psychiatric aspects of HIV-1 infection and AIDS. *Psychological Medicine, 20,* 547–563.

Makris, N., Biederman, J., Valera, E. M., Bush, G., Kaiser, J., Kennedy, D. N., et al. (2007). Cortical thinning of the attention and executive function networks in adults with attention-deficit/hyperactivity disorder. *Cerebral Cortex, 17,* 1364–1375.

Makuuchi, M., Kaminaga, T., & Sugishita, M. (2003). Both parietal lobes are involved in drawing: A functional MRI study and implications for constructional apraxia. *Cognitive Brain Research, 16,* 338–347.

Malaschichev, Y. B., & Wasserug, R. J. (2004). Left and right in the amphibian world: Which way to develop and where to turn? *BioEssays, 26,* 512–523.

Malhotra, P., Coulthard, E. J., & Husain, M. (2009). Role of right posterior parietal cortex in maintaining attention to spatial locations over time. *Brain, 132,* 645–660.

Malone, D. A., Dougherty, D. D., Rezai, A. R., Carpenter, L. L., Friehs, G. M., Eskandar, E. N., et al. (2009). Deep brain stimulation of the ventral capsule/ventral striatum for treatment-resistant depression. *Biological Psychiatry, 65,* 267–275.

Mancuso, G., Andres, P., Ansseau, M., & Tirelli, E. (1999). Effects of nicotine administered via a transdermal delivery system on vigilance: A repeated measure study. *Psychopharmacology, 142,* 18–23.

Maneru, C., Junque, C., Botet, F., Tallada, M., & Guardia, J. (2001). Neuropsychological long-term sequelae of perinatal asphyxia. *Brain Injury, 15,* 1029–1039.

Mangun, G. R., & Hillyard, S. A. (1988). Spatial gradients of visual attention: Behavioral and electrophysiological evidence. *Electroencephalography & Clinical Neurophysiology, 70,* 417–428.

Mangun, G. R., & Hillyard, S. A. (1990). Electrophysiological studies of visual selective attention in humans. In A. R. Scheibel & A. F. Wechsler (Eds.), *Neurobiology of higher cognitive function* (pp. 271–295). New York: Guilford Press.

Mangun, G. R., Buonocore, M. H., Girelli, M., & Jha, A. P. (1998). ERP and fMRI measures of visual spatial selection attention. *Human Brain Mapping, 6,* 383–389.

Manning, M. A., & Hoyme, H. E. (2007). Fetal alcohol spectrum disorders: A practical clinical approach to diagnosis. *Neuroscience & Biobehavioral Reviews, 31,* 230–238.

Marangell, L. B., Rush, A. J., George, M. S., Sackeim, H. A., Johnson, C. R., Husain, M. M., et al. (2002). Vagus nerve stimulation (VNS) for major depressive episodes: One year outcomes. *Biological Psychiatry, 51,* 280–287.

Marcotte, T. D., Heaton, K. R. K., Alhassoon, O., Taylor, J. M. J., Arffa, K., Grant, I., & HNRC Group (1997). Mild HIV-related cognitive impairment is associated with reduced performance on a driving simulator. *Journal of the International Neuropsychological Society, 3,* 14.

Mark, V. W., Kooistra, C. A., & Heilman, K. M. (1988). Hemispatial neglect affected by non-neglected stimuli. *Neurology, 38,* 1207–1211.

Markee, T., Brown, W. S., Moore, L. H., & Theberge, D. C. (1996). Callosal function in dyslexia: Evoked potential interhemispheric transfer time and bilateral field advantage. *Developmental Neuropsychology, 12,* 409–428.

Marois, R., Leung, H.-C., & Gore, J. C. (2000). A stimulus-driven approach to object identity and location processing in the human brain. *Neuron, 25,* 717–728.

Marr, D. (1982). *Vision.* San Francisco: Freeman.

Marsh, A. A., Elfenbein, H. A., & Ambady, N. (2003). Nonverbal "accents": Cultural differences in facial expressions of emotion. *Psychological Science, 14,* 373–376.

Marsh, R., Alexander, G. M., Packard, M. G., Zhu, H., Wingard, J. C., Quackenbush, G., & Peterson, B. S. (2004). Habit learning in Tourette syndrome: A translational neuroscience approach to a developmental psychopathology. *Archives of General Psychiatry, 61,* 1259–1268.

Marshall, J. C., & Halligan, P. W. (1988). Blindsight and insight in visuospatial neglect. *Nature, 336,* 766–767.

Marshall, L., & Born, J. (2007). The contribution of sleep to hippocampus-dependent memory consolidation. *Trends in Cognitive Sciences, 11,* 442–450.

Marshall, R. S. (2009). Rehabilitation approaches to hemineglect. *Neurologist, 15,* 185–192.

Martin, A., Wiggs, C. L., Ungerleider, L. G., & Haxby, J. V. (1996). Neural correlates of category-specific knowledge. *Nature, 379,* 649–652.

Martin, C. D., Dering, B., Thomas, E. M., & Thierry, G. (2009). Brain potentials reveal semantic priming in both the "active" and the "non-attended" language of early bilinguals. *NeuroImage, 47,* 326–333.

Martin, E. M., Pitrak, D. L., Pursell, K. J., Mullane, K. M., & Novak, R. M. (1995). Delayed recognition memory span in HIV-1 infection. *Journal of the International Neuropsychological Society, 1,* 575–580.

Martin, G. M., Harley, C. W., Smith, R. A. R., Hoyles, E. S., & Hynes, C. A. (1997). Spatial disorientation blocks reliable goal location on a plus maze but does not prevent goal location in the Morris maze. *Journal of Experimental Psychology: Animal Behavior Processes, 23*(2), 183–193.

Martin, L. F., Kern, W. R., & Freedman, R. (2004). Alpha-7 nicotinic receptor agonists: Potential new candidates for the treatment of schizophrenia. *Psychopharmacology, 174,* 54–64.

Martin, P. R., & Grünert, U. (2004). Ganglion cells in mammalian retinae. In L. M. Chalupa & J. S. Werner (Eds.), *The visual neurosciences* (pp. 410–421). Cambridge, MA: MIT Press.

Martin, R., & McFarland, H. F. (1993). Role of genetic factors for the autoimmune pathogenesis of multiple sclerosis. In U. Halbreich (Ed.), *Multiple sclerosis: A neuropsychiatric disorder* (pp. 73–96). Washington, DC: American Psychiatric Press.

Martland, H. (1928). Punch drunk. *JAMA, 91,* 1103–1107.

Martone, M., Butters, N., Payne, M., Becker, J. T., & Sax, D. (1984). Dissociations between skill learning and verbal recognition in amnesia and dementia. *Archives of Neurology, 41*(9), 965–970.

Mashour, G. A., Walker, E. E., & Martuza, R. L. (2005). Psychosurgery: Past, present, and future. *Brain Research Reviews, 48,* 409–419.

Masland, R. H. (2004). Direction selectivity in retinal ganglion cells. In L. M. Chalupa & J. S. Werner (Eds.), *The visual neurosciences* (pp. 451–462). Cambridge, MA: MIT Press.

Masterton, R. B. (1992). Role of the central auditory system in hearing: The new direction. *Trends in Neurosciences, 15*(8), 280–285.

Materna, S., Dicke, P. W., & Thier, P. (2008). The posterior superior temporal sulcus is involved in social communication not specific for the eyes. *Neuropsychologia, 46,* 2759–2765.

Mathalon, D. H., Fedor, M., Faustman, W. O., Gray, M., Askari, N., & Ford, J. M. (2002). Response-monitoring dysfunction in schizophrenia: An event-related brain potential study. *Journal of Abnormal Psychology, 111,* 22–41.

Mathalon, D. H., Whitfield, S. L., & Ford, J. M. (2003). Anatomy of an error: ERP and fMRI. *Biological Psychology, 64,* 119–141.

Mather, M., & Carstensen, L. L. (2003). Aging and attentional biases for emotional faces. *Psychological Science, 14,* 409–415.

Mather, M., & Carstensen, L. L. (2005). Aging and motivated cognition: The positivity effect in attention and memory. *Trends in Cognitive Sciences, 9,* 497–502.

Mather, M., Canli, T., English, T., Whitfield, S., Waid, P., Ochsner, K., et al. (2004). Amygdala responses to emotionally valenced stimuli in older and younger adults. *Psychological Science, 15,* 259–267.

Mathias, J. L., & Burke, J. (2009). Cognitive functioning in Alzheimer's and vascular dementia: A meta-analysis. *Neuropsychology, 23,* 411–423.

Matser, E. J. T., Kessels, A. G., Lezak, M. D., & Jordan, B. D. (1999). Neuropsychological impairment in amateur soccer players. *JAMA, 282,* 971–973.

Matsumoto, D., Yoo, S. H., Hirayama, S., & Petrova, G. (2005). Development and validation of a measure of display-rule knowledge: The display rule assessment inventory. *Emotion, 5,* 23–40.

Matsumoto, M., & Komatsu, H. (2005). Neural responses in the macaque V1 to bar stimuli with various lengths presented on the blind spot. *Journal of Neurophysiology, 93,* 2374–2387.

Matsumoto, N., Okada, M., Sugase-Miyamoto, Y., Yamane, S., & Kawano, K. (2005). Population dynamics of face-responsive neurons in the inferior temporal cortex. *Cerebral Cortex, 15,* 1103–1112.

Matthews, P. M., Honey, G. D., & Bullmore, E. T. (2006). Applications of fMRI in translational medicine and clinical practice. *Nature Reviews Neuroscience, 7,* 732–744.

Matthews, S. C., Paulus, M. P., Simmons, A. N., Nelesen, R. A., & Dimsdale, J. E. (2004). Functional subdivisions within anterior cingulate cortex and their relationship to autonomic nervous system function. *NeuroImage, 22,* 1151–1156.

Matute, C., & Pérez-Cerdá, F. (2005). Multiple sclerosis: Novel perspectives on newly forming lesions. *Trends in Neurosciences, 28,* 173–175.

Mauk, M. D., Medina, J. F., Nores, W. L., & Ohyama, T. (2000). Cerebellar function: Coordination, learning or timing? *Current Biology, 10,* R522–R525.

Maurer, A. H. (2008). Combined imaging modalities: PET/CT and SPECT/CT. *Health Physics 95,* 571–576.

Maurer, D., & Lewis, T. I. (2001). Visual acuity and spatial contrast sensitivity: Normal development and underlying mechanisms. In C. A. Nelson & M. Luciana (Eds.), *Handbook of developmental cognitive neuroscience* (pp. 237–253). Cambridge, MA: MIT Press.

Mayberg, H. S. (2003). Modulating dysfunctional limbic-cortical circuits in depression: Towards development of brain-based algorithms for diagnosis and optimised treatment. *British Medical Bulletin, 65,* 193–207.

Mayberg, H. S., Liotti, M., Brannan, S. K., McGinnis, S., Mahurin, R. K., Jerabek, P. A., et al. (1999). Reciprocal limbic-cortical function and negative mood: Converging PET findings in depression and normal sadness. *American Journal of Psychiatry, 156,* 675–682.

Mayberg, H. S., Lozano, A. M., Voon, V., McNeely, H. E., Seminowicz, D., Hamani Schwalb, J.M., & Kennedy, S. H. (2005). Deep brain stimulation for treatment-resistant depression. *Neuron, 45,* 651–660.

Mayes, A. R., Downes, J. J., McDonald, C., Poole, V., Rooke, S., Sagar, H. J., & Meudell, P. R. (1994). Two tests for assessing remote public knowledge: A tool for assessing retrograde amnesia. *Memory, 2*(2), 183–210.

Mayes, A., Montaldi, D., & Migo, E. (2007). Associative memory and the medial temporal lobes. *Trends in Cognitive Science, 11,* 126–135.

Mazer, J. A., & Gallant, J. L. (2000). Object recognition: Seeing us seeing shapes. *Current Biology, 10,* R668–R670.

Mazza, M., Capuano, A., Bria, P., & Mazza, S. (2006). Ginkgo biloba and donepezil: A comparison in the treatment of Alzheimer's dementia in a randomized placebo-controlled double-blind study. *European Journal of Neurology, 13,* 981–985.

McArthur, D., & Adamson, L. B. (1996). Joint attention in preverbal children: Autism and developmental language disorder. *Journal of Autism & Developmental Disorders, 26,* 481–496.

McCandliss, B. D., Cohen, L., & Dehaene, S. (2003). The visual word form area: Expertise for reading in the fusiform gyrus. *Trends in Cognitive Sciences, 7,* 293–299.

McCarley, R. W., Salisbury, D. F., Hirayasu, Y., Yurgelun-Todd, D. A., Tohen, M., Zarate, C., et al. (2002). Association between smaller left posterior superior temporal gyrus volume on magnetic resonance imaging and smaller left temporal P300 amplitude in first-episode schizophrenia. *Archives of General Psychiatry, 59,* 321–331.

McClernon, F. J., Hiott, F. B., Huettel, S. A., & Rose, J. E. (2005). Abstinence-induced changes in self-report craving correlated with event-related fMRI responses to smoking cues. *Neuropsychopharmacology, 30,* 1940–1947.

McCloskey, M. (2009). *Visual reflections: A perceptual deficit and its implications*. New York: Oxford.

McCloskey, M., Rapp, B., Yantis, S., Rubin, G., Bacon, W. F., Dagnelie, G., et al. (1995). A developmental deficit in localizing objects from vision. *Psychological Science, 6,* 112–117.

McCrea, M., Guskiewicz, K. M., Marshall, S. W., Barr, W., Randolph, C., Cantu, R. C., et al. (2003). Acute effects and recovery time following concussion in collegiate football players. *JAMA, 290,* 2556–2563.

McCrory, P., Zazryn, T., & Cameron, P. (2007). The evidence for chronic traumatic encephalopathy in boxing. *Sports Medicine, 37,* 467–476.

McDermott, K. B., Buckner, R. L., Peterson, S. E., Kelley, W. M., & Sanders, A. L. (1999). Set- and code-specific activation in the frontal cortex: An fMRI study of encoding and retrieval of faces and words. *Journal of Cognitive Neuroscience, 11*(6), 631–640.

McDonald, C., & Murphy, K. C. (2003). The new genetics of schizophrenia. *Psychiatric Clinics of North America, 26,* 41–63.

McEwen, B. S. (2009). Stress-induced structural and functional plasticity in the brain: Protection, damage, and brain-body communication. In D. S. Charney & E. J. Nestler (Eds.), *Neurobiology of mental illness* (3d ed.; pp. 627–654). Oxford, UK: Oxford University Press.

McFie, J., & Zangwill, O. L. (1960). Visual-constructive disabilities associated with lesions of the left cerebral hemisphere. *Brain, 83,* 242–260.

McGaughey, J., Kaiser, T., & Sarter, M. (1996). Behavioral vigilance following infusions of 192 IgG-saporin into the basal forebrain: Selectivity of the behavioral impairment and relation to cortical AChE-positive fiber density. *Behavioral Neuroscience, 110*(2), 247–265.

McGeer, P. L., Schulzer, M., & McGeer, E. G. (1996). Arthritis and anti-inflammatory agents as possible protective factors for Alzheimer's disease: A review of 17 epidemiological studies. *Neurology, 47,* 425–432.

McGlinchey-Berroth, R., Milberg, W. P., Verfaellie, M., Alexander, M., & Kilduff, P. T. (1993). Semantic processing in the neglected visual field: Evidence from a lexical decision task. *Cognitive Neuropsychology, 10,* 79–108.

McGlone, J. (1980). Sex differences in human brain asymmetry: A critical survey. *Behavioral and Brain Sciences, 3*(2), 215–263.

McGrew, W. C., & Marchant, L. F. (1999). Laterality of hand use pays off in foraging success for wild chimpanzees. *Primates, 40,* 509–513.

McGuire, P. K., Shah, G. M., & Murray, R. M. (1993). Increased blood flow in Broca's area during auditory hallucinations in schizophrenia. *Lancet, 342,* 703–706.

McGurk, S. R., Twamley, E. W., Sitzer, D. I., McHugo, G. J., & Mueser, K. T. (2007). A meta-analysis of cognitive remediation in schizophrenia. *American Journal of Psychiatry, 164,* 1791–1802.

McIntyre, J. S., & Craik, F. I. M. (1987). Age differences in memory for item and source information. *Canadian Journal of Psychology, 41,* 175–192.

McIntyre, J., Stratta, F., & Lacquaniti, F. (1997). Viewer-centered frame of reference for pointing to memorized targets in three-dimensional space. *Journal of Neurophysiology, 78*(3), 1601–1618.

McKeefry, D. J., & Zeki, S. (1997). The position and topography of the human colour centre as revealed by functional magnetic resonance imaging. *Brain, 120,* 2229–2242.

McKhann, M. G. M., Albert, M., Grossman, M., Miller, B., Dickson, D., & Trojanowski, J. Q. (2001). Clinical and pathological diagnosis of frontotemporal dementia: Report of the work group on frontotemporal dementia and Pick's disease. *Archives of Neurology, 58,* 1803–1809.

McKone, E., Kanwisher, N., & Duchaine, B. C. (2006). Can generic expertise explain special processing for faces? *Trends in Cognitive Sciences, 11,* 8–15.

McLaughlin, N. C., Paul, R. H., Grieve, S. M., Williams, L. M., Laidlaw, D., DiCarlo, M., Clark, C. R., Whelihan, W., Cohen, R. A., Whitford, T. J., & Gordon, E. (2007). Diffusion tensor imaging of the corpus callosum: A cross-sectional study across the lifespan. *International Journal of Developmental Neuroscience, 25,* 215–221.

McLeod, P., Shallice, T., & Plaut, D. C. (2000). Attractor dynamics in word recognition: Converging evidence from errors by normal subjects, dyslexic patients and a connectionist model. *Cognition, 74*(1), 91–113.

McManus, C. (2002). *Right hand, left hand: The origins of asymmetry in brains, bodies, atoms and cultures.* Cambridge, MA: Harvard University Press.

McManus, I. C. (1985). Handedness, language dominance and aphasia: A genetic model. *Psychological Medicine, 8*(Suppl.), 1–40.

McManus, I. C., & Humphrey, N. K. (1973). Turning the left cheek. *Nature, 243,* 271–272.

McNaull, B. B. A., Todd, S., McGuinness, B., & Passmore, A. P. (2010). Inflammation and anti-inflammatory strategies for Alzheimer's disease: A mini-review. *Gerontology, 56,* 3–14.

McNeil, J. E., & Warrington, E. K. (1993). Prosopagnosia: A face-specific disorder. *Quarterly Journal of Experimental Psychology, 46A,* 1–10.

Mechelli, A., Crinion, J. T., Long, S., Friston, K. J., Lambon Ralph, M. A., Patterson, K., McClelland, J. L., & Price, C. J. (2005). Dissociating reading processes on the basis of neuronal interactions. *Journal of Cognitive Neuroscience, 17,* 1753–1756.

Mechelli, A., Crinion, J. T., Noppeney, U., O'Doherty, J., Ashburner, J., Frackowiak, R. S., & Price, C. J. (2004). Neurolinguistics: Structural plasticity in the bilingual brain. *Nature, 431,* 757.

Medina, J., Kannan, V., Pawlak, M., Kleinman, J. T., Newhart, M., Davis, C., et al. (2009). Neural substrates of visuospatial processing in distinct reference frames: Evidence from unilateral spatial neglect. *Journal of Cognitive Neuroscience. 21,* 2073–2084.

Meeter, M., Eijsackers, E. V., & Mulder, J. L. (2006). Retrograde amnesia for autobiographical memories and public events in mild and moderate Alzheimer's disease. *Journal of Clinical & Experimental Neuropsychology, 28*(6), 914–927.

Meister, I. G., Wienemann, M., Buelte, D., Grünewald, C., Sparing, R., Dambeck, N., & Boroojerdi, B. (2006). Hemiextinction induced by transcranial magnetic stimulation over the right temporo-parietal junction. *Neuroscience, 142,* 119–123.

Mendez, M. F. (2006). Frontotemporal dementia. In M. J. Farah & T. E. Feinberg (Eds.), *Patient-based approaches to cognitive neuroscience* (2d ed.; pp. 371–379). Cambridge, MA: MIT Press.

Meng, M., Remus, D. A., & Tong, F. (2005). Filling-in of visual phantoms in the human brain. *Nature Neuroscience, 8,* 1248–1254.

Menon, D. K., Owen, A. M., Williams, E. J., Minhas, P. S., Allen, C. M. C., Boniface, S. J., Pickard, J. D., & Wolfson Brain Imaging Centre Team. (1998). Cortical processing in persistent vegetative state. *Lancet, 352,* 200.

Merchant, C., Tang, M.-X., Albert, S., Manly, J., Stern, Y., & Mayeux, R. (1999). The influence of smoking on the risk of Alzheimer's disease. *Neurology, 52,* 1408–1412.

Merzenich, M. M., Recanzone, G. H., Jenkins, W. M., & Grajski, K. A. (1990). Adaptive mechanisms in cortical networks underlying cortical contributions to learning and nondeclarative memory. In *Cold Spring Harbor Symposia on Quantitative Biology: Vol. 55: The brain.* New York: Cold Spring Harbor Laboratory.

Mesulam, M.-M. (1981). A cortical network for directed attention and unilateral neglect. *Annals of Neurology, 10,* 309–325.

Mesulam, M.-M. (Ed.). (1985). *Principles of behavioral neurology.* Philadelphia: F. A. Davis.

Metzger, L. J., Paige, S. R., Carson, M. A., Lasko, N. B., Paulus, L. A., Pitman, R. K., & Orr, S. P. (2004). PTSD arousal and depression symptoms associated with increased right-sided parietal EEG asymmetry. *Journal of Abnormal Psychology, 113,* 324–329.

Miall, R. C., & Jenkinson, E. W. (2005). Functional imaging of changes in cerebellar activity related to learning during a novel eye-hand tracking task. *Experimental Brain Research, 166,* 170–183.

Miall, R. C., Reckess, G. Z., & Imamizu, H. (2001). The cerebellum coordinates eye and hand tracking movements. *Nature Neuroscience, 4,* 638–644.

Miceli, G., Gainotti, G., Caltagirone, C., & Masullo, C. (1980). Some aspects of phonological impairment in aphasia. *Brain & Language, 11,* 159–169.

Middlebrooks, J. C. (2002). Auditory space processing: Here, there, or everywhere? *Nature Neuroscience, 5,* 824–826.

Middleton, F. A., & Strick, P. L. (2000). Basal ganglia and cerebellar loops: Motor and cognitive circuits. *Brain Research Reviews, 31,* 236–250.

Mikels, J. A., Larkin, G. R., Reuter-Lorenz, P. A., & Carstensen, L. L. (2005). Divergent trajectories in the aging mind: Changes in working memory for affective versus visual information with age. *Psychology & Aging, 20,* 542–553.

Milad, M. R., Rauch, S. L., Pitman, R. K., & Quirk, G. J. (2006). Fear extinction in rats: Implications for human brain imaging and anxiety disorders. *Biological Psychology, 73,* 61–71.

Milgram, N. W., Siwak-Tapp, C. T., Araujo, J. A., & Head, E. (2006). Neuroprotective effects of cognitive enrichment. *Ageing Research Reviews, 5,* 354–369.

Milham, M. P., Banich, M. T., Webb, A., Barad, V., Cohen, N. J., Wszalek, T., & Kramer, A. F. (2001). The relative involvement of anterior cingulate and prefrontal cortex in attentional control depends on nature of conflict. *Cognitive Brain Research, 12,* 467–473.

Milham, M. P., Erickson, K. I., Banich, M. T., Kramer, A. F., Webb, A., Wszalek, T., & Cohen, N. J. (2002). Attentional control in the aging brain: Insights from an fMRI study of the Stroop task. *Brain & Cognition, 49,* 277–296.

Milivojevic, B., Hamm, J. P., & Corballis, M. C. (2008). Functional neuroanatomy of mental rotation. *Journal of Cognitive Neuroscience, 21,* 945–959.

Miller, E. K., & Cohen, J. D. (2001). An integrative theory of prefrontal cortex function. *Annual Review of Neuroscience, 24,* 167–202.

Milner, A. D., & McIntosh, R. D. (2005). The neurological basis of visual neglect. *Current Opinion in Neurology, 18,* 748–753.

Milner, A. D., Dijkerman, H. C., McIntosh, R. D., Rossetti, Y., & Pisella, L. (2003). Delayed reaching and grasping in patients with optic ataxia. *Progress in Brain Research, 142,* 225–242.

Milner, B. (1962). Les troubles de la mémoire accompagnat des lésions hippocampiques bilatérales [Memory troubles accompanying bilateral hippocampal lesions]. In P. Passouant (Ed.), *Physiologic de l'hippocampe [Physiology of the hippocampus]* (pp. 257–272). Paris: Centre National de la Recherche Scientifique.

Milner, B. (1963). Effects of different brain lesions on card sorting: The role of the frontal lobes. *Archives of Neurology, 9,* 100–110.

Milner, B. (1964). Some effects of frontal lobectomy in man. In Warren, J.M. & Akert, K. (eds.) *The frontal granular cortex and behavior,* pp. 313–334. New York: McGraw Hill.

Milner, B. (1968). Visual recognition and recall after temporal lobe excisions in man. *Neuropsychologia, 6,* 191–209.

Milner, B. (1971). Interhemispheric differences in the localization of psychological processes in man. *British Medical Bulletin, 27,* 272–277.

Milner, B. (1978). Clues to the cerebral organization of memory. In P. Buser & A. Rougeul-Buser (Eds.), *Cerebral correlates of conscious experience.* Amsterdam: Elsevier.

Milner, B. (1982). Some cognitive effects of frontal-lobe lesions in man. *Philosophical Transactions of the Royal Society of London, B298,* 211–226.

Milner, B., & Petrides, M. (1984). Behavioural effects of frontal-lobe lesions in man. *Trends in Neurosciences, 7,* 403–407.

Milner, B., Corkin, S., & Teuber, H. L. (1968). Further analysis of the hippocampal amnesia syndrome. *Neuropsychologia, 6,* 215–234.

Milner, B., Corsi, P., & Leonard, G. (1991). Frontal-lobe contribution to recency judgements. *Neuropsychologia, 29,* 601–618.

Milner, B., Taylor, L., & Sperry, R. W. (1968). Lateralized suppression of dichotically presented digits after commissural section in man. *Science, 161,* 184–185.

Minati, L., Edginton, T., Bruzzone, M. G., & Giaccone, G. (2009). Current concepts in Alzheimer's disease: A multidisciplinary review. *American Journal of Alzheimer's Disease & Other Dementias, 24,* 95–121.

Minati, L., Grisoli, M., & Bruzzone, M. G. (2007). MR spectroscopy, functional MRI, and diffusion-tensor imaging in the aging brain: A conceptual review. *Journal of Geriatric Psychiatric & Neurology, 20,* 3–21.

Mineka, S., Rafaeli, E., & Yovel, I. (2003). Cognitive biases in emotional disorders: Information processing and social-cognitive perspectives. In R. J. Davidson, K. R. Scherer, & H. H. Goldsmith (Eds.), *Handbook of affective sciences* (pp. 976–1009). Oxford, UK: Oxford University Press.

Mink, J. W. (2001). Basal ganglia dysfunction in Tourette's syndrome: A new hypothesis. *Pediatric Neurology, 25,* 190–198.

Minzenberg, M., Ober, B. A., & Vinogradov, S. (2002). Semantic priming in schizophrenia: A review and synthesis. *Journal of the International Neuropsychological Society, 8,* 699–720.

Mishkin, M. (1978). Memory in monkeys severely impaired by combined but not separate removal of the amygdala and hippocampus. *Nature, 273,* 297–298.

Mishkin, M. (1982). A memory system in the monkey. *Philosophical Transactions of the Royal Society of London, B298,* 85–95.

Mishkin, M., & Delacour, J. (1975). An analysis of short-term visual memory in the monkey. *Journal of Experimental Psychology: Animal Behavior Processes, 104,* 326–334.

Mishkin, M., Ungerleider, G., & Macko, K. A. (1983). Object vision and spatial vision: Two cortical pathways. *Trends in Neurosciences, 6,* 414–417.

Mitchell, R. L. C., Elliott, R., & Woodruff, P. W. R. (2001). fMRI and cognitive dysfunction in schizophrenia. *Trends in Cognitive Sciences, 5,* 71–81.

Mitz, A. R., & Wise, S. P. (1987). The somatotopic organization of the supplementary motor area: Intracortical microstimulation mapping. *Journal of Neuroscience, 7,* 1010–1021.

Miwa, H., Iijima, M., Tanaka, S., & Mizuno, Y. (2001). Generalized convulsions after consuming a large amount of ginkgo nuts. *Epilepsia, 42,* 280–281.

Miyake, A., Friedman, N. P., Emerson, M. J., Witzki, A. H., Howerter, A., & Wager, T. D. (2000). The unity and diversity of executive functions and their contributions to complex "frontal lobe" tasks: A latent variable analysis. *Cognitive Psychology, 41,* 49–100.

Mobbs, D., Greicius, M. D., Abdel-Azim, E., Menon, V., & Reiss, A. L. (2003). Humor modulates the mesolimbic reward centers. *Neuron, 40,* 1041–1048.

Mobbs, D., Yu, R., Meyer, M., Passamonti, L., Seymour, B., Calder, A. J., et al. (2009). A key role for similarity in vicarious reward. *Science, 324,* 900.

Mogg, A., Purvis, R., Eranti, S., Contell, F., Taylor, J. P., Nicholson, T., et al. (2007). Repetitive transcranial magnetic stimulation for negative symptoms of schizophrenia: A randomized controlled pilot study. *Schizophrenia Research, 93,* 221–228.

Mohanty, A., Engels, A. S., Herrington, J. D., Heller, W., Ho, M.-H. R., Banich, M. T., et al. (2007). Differential engagement of anterior cingulate cortex subdivisions for cognitive and emotional function. *Psychophysiology, 44,* 343–351.

Mohr, J. P., Pessin, M. S., Finkelstein, S., Funkenstein, H. H., Duncan, G. W., & Davis, K. R. (1978). Broca aphasia: Pathologic and clinical. *Neurology, 28,* 311–324.

Molfese, D. L., & Molfese, V. J. (1994). Short-term and long-term developmental outcomes: The use of behavioral and electrophysiological measures as predictors. In G. Dawson & K. W. Fischer (Eds.), *Human behavior and the developing brain* (pp. 493–517). New York: Guilford Press.

Molfese, D. L., & Molfese, V. J. (1997). Discrimination of language skills at five years of age using event-related potentials recorded at birth. *Developmental Neuropsychology, 13,* 135–156.

Molfese, D. L., Freeman, R. B., & Palermo, D. S. (1975). The ontogeny of brain lateralization for speech and nonspeech stimuli. *Brain and Language, 2,* 356–368.

Molfese, D. L., Molfese, V. J., & Espy, K. A. (1999). The predictive use of event-related potentials in language development and the treatment of language disorders. *Developmental Neuropsychology, 13,* 373–377.

Molfese, D. L., Molfese, V. J., & Molfese, P. J. (2007). Relation between early measures of brain responses to language performance on language and language-related tasks. In D. Coch, G. Dawson, & K. W. Fischer (Eds.), *Human behavior, learning, and the developing brain: Atypical development* (pp. 191–211). New York: Guilford Press.

Molholm, S., Ritter, W., Javitt, D. C., & Foxe, J. J. (2004). Multisensory visual-auditory object recognition in humans: A high-density electrical mapping study. *Cerebral Cortex, 14,* 452–465.

Molko, N., Cohen, L., Mangin, J. F., Chochon, F., Lehéricy, S., Le Bihan, D., & Dehaene, S. (2002). Visualizing the neural bases of a disconnection syndrome with diffusion tensor imaging. *Journal of Cognitive Neuroscience, 14,* 629–636.

Moll, J., & de Oliveira-Souza, R. (2007). Moral judgments, emotions and the utilitarian brain. *Trends in Cognitive Science, 11*(8), 319–321.

Monk, C. S., Klein, R. G., Telzer, E. H., Schroth, E. A., Mannuzza, S., Moulton III, J. L., et al. (2008). Amygdala and nucleus accumbens activation to emotional facial expressions in children and adolescents at risk for major depression. *American Journal of Psychiatry, 165,* 90–98.

Monrad-Krohn, G. H. (1947). Dysprosody of altered "melody of language." *Brain, 70,* 405–415.

Monsell, S. (2003). Task switching. *Trends in Cognitive Sciences, 7,* 134–140.

Montoya, A., Price, B. H., Menear, M., & Lepage, M. (2006). Brain imaging and cognitive dysfunctions in Huntington's disease. *Journal of Psychiatry & Neuroscience, 31,* 21–29.

Montreys, C. R., & Borod, J. C. (1998). A preliminary evaluation of emotional experience and expression following unilateral brain damage. *International Journal of Neuroscience, 96,* 269–283.

Moore, D. R., & Shannon, R. V. (2009). Beyond cochlear implants: Awakening the deafened brain. *Nature Neuroscience, 12,* 686–691.

Moran, J., & Desimone, R. (1985). Selective attention gates visual processing in the extrastriate cortex. *Science, 229,* 782–784.

Moritz, C. T., Perlmutter, S. I., & Fetz, E. E. (2008). Direct control of paralysed muscles by cortical neurons. *Nature, 456,* 639–642.

Morland, A. B., Lê, S., Carroll, E., Hoffmann, M. B., & Pambakian, A. (2004). The role of spared calcarine cortex and lateral occipital cortex in the responses of human hemianopes to visual motion. *Journal of Cognitive Neuroscience, 16,* 204–218.

Morris, P. L., Robinson, R. G., Raphael, B., & Hopwood, M. J. (1996). Lesion location and poststroke depression. *Journal of Neuropsychiatry & Clinical Neurosciences, 8,* 399–403.

Morris, R. G. M. (1981). Spatial localization does not require the presence of local cues. *Learning & Motivation, 12,* 239–260.

Morris, R. G., Ahmed, S., Syed, G. M., & Toone, B. K. (1993). Neural correlates of planning ability: Frontal lobe activation during the Tower of London test. *Neuropsychologia, 31,* 1367–1378.

Morselli, P. L., & Lloyd, K. G. (1985). Mechanisms of action of antiepileptic drugs. In R. J. Porter & P. L. Morselli (Eds.), *The epilepsies* (pp. 40–81). Boston: Butterworth.

Mort, D. J., Malhotra, P., Mannan, S. K., Rorden, C., Pambakian, A., Kennard, C., & Husain, M. (2003). The anatomy of visual neglect. *Brain, 126,* 1986–1997.

Mortimer, J. A., & Pirozzolo, F. J. (1985). Remote effects of head trauma. *Developmental Neuropsychology, 1,* 215–229.

Morton, S. M., & Bastian, A. J. (2004). Cerebellar contributions to balance and locomotion. *Neuroscientist, 10,* 247–259.

Moscovitch, M. (1994). Memory and working-with-memory: A component process model based on modules and central systems. In D. L. Schacter & E. Tulving (Eds.), *Memory systems 1994.* Cambridge, MA: MIT Press.

Moscovitch, M. (1995). Confabulation. In D. Schacter (Ed.), *Memory distortions: How minds, brains, and societies reconstruct the past* (pp. 226–251). Cambridge, MA: Harvard University Press.

Moscovitch, M., Nadel, L., Winocur, G., Gilboa, A., & Rosenbaum, R. S. (2006). The cognitive neuroscience of remote episodic, semantic and spatial memory. *Current Opinion in Neurobiology, 16,* 179–190.

Moscovitch, M., Westmacott, R., Gilboa, A., Addis, D. R., Rosenbaum, R. S., Viskontas, I., et al. (2005). Hippocampal complex contributions to retention and retrieval of recent and remote episodic and semantic memories: Evidence from behavioural and neuroimaging studies of normal and brain-damaged people. In N. Ohta, C. M. MacLeod, & B. Uttl (Eds.), *Dynamic cognitive processes* (pp. 333–380). Tokyo: Springer-Verlag.

Moscovitch, M., Winocur, G., & Behrmann, M. (1997). What is special about face recognition? Nineteen experiments on a person with visual object agnosia and dyslexia but normal face recognition. *Journal of Cognitive Neuroscience, 9,* 555–604.

Moser, E. I., & Moser, M.-B. (2008). A metric for space. *Hippocampus, 18,* 1142–1156.

Moser, E. I., Kropff, E., & Moser, M.-B. (2008). Place cells, grid cells, and the brain's spatial representation system. *Annual Review of Neuroscience, 31,* 69–89.

Motter, B. C., & Mountcastle, V. B. (1981). The functional properties of light-sensitive neurons of the posterior parietal cortex studies in waking monkeys: Foveal sparing and opponent vector organization. *Journal of Neuroscience, 1,* 3–26.

Mountcastle, V. B., Lynch, J. C., Georgopoulos, A., Sakata, H., & Acuna, C. (1975). Posterior parietal association cortex of the monkey: Command functions for operations within extrapersonal space. *Journal of Neurophysiology, 38,* 871–908.

Moussavi, S., Chatterji, S., Verdes, E., Tandon, A., Patel, V., & Ustun, B. (2007). Depression, chronic disease, and decrements in health: Results from the World Health Surveys. *Lancet, 370,* 851–858.

Mowry, E. M., Beheshtian, A., Waubant, E., Goodin, D. S., Cree, B. A., Qualley, P., Lincoln, R., George, M. F., Gomez, R., Hauser, S. L., Okuda, D. T., & Pelletier, J. (2009). Quality of life in multiple sclerosis is associated with lesion burden and brain volume measures. *Neurology, 72,* 1760–1765.

Moya, K. L., Benowitz, L. I., Levine, D. N., & Finklestein, S. (1986). Covariant defects in visuospatial abilities and recall of verbal narrative after right hemisphere stroke. *Cortex, 22,* 381–397.

Mozer, M. C., & Sitton, M. (1998). Computational modeling of spatial attention. In H. Pashler (Ed.), *Attention* (pp. 341–395). Hove, East Essex: Psychology Press.

Mozer, M. C., Halligan, P. W., & Marshall, J. C. (1997). The end of the line for a brain-damaged model of unilateral neglect. *Journal of Cognitive Neuroscience, 9*(2), 171–190.

MTA Cooperative Group. (1999). A 14-month randomized clinical trial of treatment strategies for attention-deficit/hyperactivity disorder. *Archives of General Psychiatry, 56,* 1073–1086.

Mueser, K. T., & McGurk, S. R. (2004). Schizophrenia. *Lancet, 363,* 2063–2072.

Muggleton, N. G., Cowey, A., & Walsh, V. (2008). The role of the angular gyrus in visual conjunction search investigated using signal detection analysis and transcranial magnetic stimulation. *Neuropsychologia, 46,* 2198–2202.

Muller, R. U., Kubie, J. L., & Ranck, Jr., J. B. (1987). Spatial firing patterns of hippocampal complex spike cells in a fixed environment. *Journal of Neuroscience, 7,* 1935–1950.

Mullette-Gillman, O. A., Cohen, Y. E., & Groh, J. M. (2005). Eye-centered, head-centered, and complex coding of visual and auditory targets in the intraparietal sulcus. *Journal of Neurophysiology, 94,* 2331–2352.

Mulliken, G. H., Musallam, S., & Andersen, R. A. (2008). Decoding trajectories from posterior parietal cortex ensembles. *Journal of Neuroscience, 28,* 12913–12926.

Mumenthaler, M. S., Taylor, J. L., O'Hara, R., & Yesavage, J. A. (1998). Influence of nicotine on simulator flight performance in non-smokers. *Psychopharmacology, 140,* 38–41.

Munoz-Cespedes, J. M., Rios-Lago, M., Paul, N., & Maestu, F. (2005). Functional neuroimaging studies of cognitive recovery after acquired brain damage in adults. *Neuropsychology Review, 15,* 169–183.

Murphy, F. C., Michael, A., Robbins, T. W., & Sahakian, B. J. (2003). Neuropsychological impairment in patients with major depressive disorder: The effects of feedback on task performance. *Psychological Medicine, 33,* 455–467.

Murray, E. A. (2007). The amygdala, reward, and emotion. *Trends in Cognitive Sciences, 11,* 489–497.

Musallam, S., Corneil, B. D., Greger, B., Scherberger, H., & Andersen, R. A. (2004). Cognitive control signals for neural prosthetics. *Science, 304,* 258–262.

Näätanen, R., Gaillard, A. W. K., & Mantysalo, S. (1978). The N_1 effect of selective attention reinterpreted. *Acta Psychologica (Amsterdam), 42,* 313–329.

Nachev, P., Kennard, C., & Husain, M. (2008). Functional role of the supplementary and pre-supplementary motor areas. *Nature Reviews Neuroscience, 9,* 856–869.

Nadel, L., & Moscovitch, M. (1997). Memory consolidation, retrograde amnesia and the hippocampal complex. *Current Opinion in Neurobiology, 7,* 217–227.

Nader, K., & LeDoux, J. (1999). Inhibition of the mesoamygdala dopaminergic pathway impairs the retrieval of conditioned fear associations. *Behavioral Neuroscience, 113,* 891–901.

Naeser, M. A., & Borod, J. C. (1986). Aphasia in left-handers: Lesion site, lesion side and hemispheric asymmetries on CT. *Neurology, 36,* 471–488.

Nagahama, Y., Okada, T., Katsumi, Y., Hayashi, T., Yamauchi, H., Oyanagi, C., et al. (2001). Dissociable mechanisms of attentional control within the human prefrontal cortex. *Cerebral Cortex, 11,* 85–92.

Nagano-Saito, A., Leyton, M., Monchi, O., Goldberg, Y. K., He, Y., & Dagher, A. (2008). Dopamine depletion impairs frontostriatal functional connectivity during a set-shifting task. *Journal of Neuroscience, 28,* 3697–3706.

Nagy, Z., Esiri, M. M., Jobst, K. A., Morris, J. H., King, E. M. F., McDonald, B., et al. (1995). Relative roles of plaques and tangles in the dementia of Alzheimer's disease: Correlations using three sets of neuropathological criteria. *Dementia, 6,* 21–31.

Nagy, Z., Westerberg, H., & Klingberg, T. (2004). Maturation of white matter is associated with the development of cognitive functions during childhood. *Journal of Cognitive Neuroscience, 16,* 1227–1233.

Nakatani, E., Nakgawa, A., Ohara, Y., Goto, S., Uozumi, N., Iwakiri, M., et al. (2003). Effects of behavior therapy on regional cerebral blood flow in obsessive-compulsive disorder. *Psychiatry Research-Neuroimaging, 124,* 113–120.

Naqvi, N. H., Rudrauf, D., Damasio, H., & Bechara, A. (2007). Damage to the insula disrupts addiction to cigarette smoking. *Science, 315,* 531–534.

Narayana, S., Fox, P., Zhang, W., Franklin, C., Robin, D., Vogel, D., & Ramig, L. (2010). Neural correlates of efficacy of voice therapy in Parkinson's disease identified by performance-correlation analysis. *Human Brain Mapping, 31*(2), 222–236.

Narr, K. L., Thompson, P. M., Sharma, T., Moussai, J., Cannestra, A. F., & Toga, A. W. (2000). Mapping morphology of the corpus callosum in schizophrenia. *Cerebral Cortex, 10,* 40–49.

Nassi, J. J., & Callaway, E. M. (2009). Parallel processing strategies of the primate visual system. *Nature Reviews Neuroscience, 10,* 360–372.

Navia, B. A., Cho, E., Petito, C. K., & Price, R. W. (1986). The AIDS dementia complex: II. Neuropathology. *Annals of Neurology, 19,* 525–535.

Navia, B. A., Jordan, B. D., & Price, R. W. (1986). The AIDS dementia complex: I. Clinical features. *Annals of Neurology, 19,* 517–524.

Neary, J. T., & Bu, Y. (1999). Hypericum LI 160 inhibits uptake of serotonin and norepinephrine in astrocytes. *Brain Research, 816,* 358–363.

Nebel, K., Wiese, H., Stude, P., de Greiff, A., Diener, H. C., & Keidel, M. (2005). On the neural basis of focused and divided attention. *Cognitive Brain Research, 25,* 760–776.

Nee, D. E., Wager, T. D., & Jonides, J. (2007). Interference resolution: Insights from a meta-analysis of neuroimaging tasks. *Cognitive, Affective, & Behavioral Neuroscience, 7,* 1–17.

Nelson III, C. A., Zeanah, C. H., Fox, N. A., Marshall, P. J., Smyke, A. T., & Guthrie, D. (2007). Cognitive recovery in socially deprived young children: The Bucharest Early Intervention Project. *Science, 318,* 1937–1940.

Nelson, A. P., & O'Connor, M. G. (2008). Mild cognitive impairment: A neuropsychological perspective. *CNS Spectrums, 13,* 56–64.

Nelson, H. E. (1982). *National Adult Reading Test: Test manual.* Windsor, UK: NFER-Nelson.

Nemetz, P. N., Leibson, C., Naessens, J. M., Beard, M., Kokmen, E., Annegers, J. F., & Kurland, L. T. (1999). Traumatic brain injury and the time to onset of Alzheimer's disease: A population-based study. *American Journal of Epidemiology, 149,* 32–40.

Nestler, E. J. (2009). Cellular and molecular mechanisms of drug addiction. In D. S. Charney & E. J. Nestler (Eds.), *Neurobiology of mental illness* (3d ed.; pp. 775–785). Oxford, UK: Oxford University Press.

Nestler, E. J., & Carlezon, W. A. (2006). The mesolimbic dopamine reward circuit in depression. *Biological Psychiatry, 59,* 1151–1159.

Nestor, S. M., Rupsingh, R., Borrie, M., Smith, M., Accomazzi, V., Wells, J. L., et al. (2008). Ventricular enlargement as a possible measure of Alzheimer's disease progression validated using the Alzheimer's disease neuroimaging initiative database. *Brain, 131,* 2443–2454.

Neville, H. J. (1990). Intermodal competition and compensation in development: Evidence from studies of the visual system in congenitally deaf adults. *Annals of the New York Academy of Sciences, 608,* 71–91.

Neville, H. J., & Lawson, D. (1987a). Attention to central and peripheral visual space in movement detection task: An event-related potential and behavioral study. I. Normal hearing adults. *Brain Research, 405,* 253–267.

Neville, H. J., & Lawson, D. (1987b). Attention to central and peripheral visual space in movement detection task: An event-related potential and behavioral study. II. Congenitally deaf adults. *Brain Research, 405,* 268–283.

Neville, H. J., & Lawson, D. (1987c). Attention to central and peripheral visual space in movement detection task: An event-related potential and behavioral study. III. Separate effects of auditory deprivation and acquisition of a visual language. *Brain Research, 405,* 284–294.

Neville, H. J., Bavelier, D., Corina, D., Rauschecker, J., Karni, A., Lalwani, A., et al. (1998). Cerebral organization for language in deaf and hearing subjects: Biological constraints and effects of experience. *Proceedings of the National Academy of Sciences, USA, 95,* 922–929.

Newcombe, F. (1969). *Missile wounds of the brain: A study of psychological deficits.* Oxford, UK: Oxford University Press.

Newman, A. J., Bavelier, D., Corina, D., Jezzard, P., & Neville, H. J. (2002). A critical period for right hemisphere recruitment in American Sign Language processing. *Nature Neuroscience, 5*(1), 76–80.

Newport, E. L., Bavelier, D., & Neville, H. J. (2001). Critical thinking about critical periods: Perspectives on a critical period for language acquisition. In E. Dupoux (Ed.), *Language, brain, and cognitive development* (pp. 481–502). Cambridge, MA: MIT Press.

Newsome, W. T., & Pare, E. B. (1988). A selective impairment of motion perception following lesions of the middle temporal visual area (MT). *Journal of Neuroscience, 8,* 2201–2211.

Ng, V. W. K., Bullmore, E. T., de Zubicaray, G. I., Cooper, A., Suckling, J., & Williams, S. C. R. (2001). Identifying rate-limiting nodes in large-scale cortical networks for visuospatial processing: An illustration using fMRI. *Journal of Cognitive Neuroscience, 13,* 537–545.

Nichelli, P., Grafman, J., Pietrini, P., Clark, K., Lee, K. Y., & Miletich, R. (1995). Where the brain appreciates the moral of a story. *NeuroReport, 6,* 2309–2313.

Nicholls, M. E. R., Clode, D., Wood, S. J., & Wood, A. G. (1999). Laterality of expression in portraiture: Putting your best cheek forward. *Proceedings of the Royal Society of London B, 266,* 1517–1522.

Nichols, M. E., Meador, K. J., & Loring, D. W. (1993). Neuropsychological effects of antiepileptic drugs: A current perspective. *Clinical Neuropharmacology, 16,* 471–484.

Nichols, M. J., & Newsome, W. T. (2002). Middle temporal visual area microstimulation influences veridical judgments of motion direction. *Journal of Neuroscience, 22,* 9530–9540.

Nicolelis, M. A. L., & Lebedev, M. A. (2009). Principles of neural ensemble physiology underlying the operation of brain-machine interfaces. *Nature Reviews Neuroscience, 10,* 530–540.

Nierenberg, J., Salisbury, D. F., Levitt, J. J., David, E. A., McCarley, R. W., & Shenton, M. E. (2005). Reduced left angular gyrus volume in first-episode schizophrenia. *American Journal of Psychiatry, 162,* 1539–1541.

Nieuwenhuis, S., Ridderinkhof, K. R., Blom, J., Band, G. P. H., & Kok, A. (2001). Error-related brain potentials are differentially related to awareness of response errors: Evidence from an anti-saccade task. *Psychophysiology, 38*(5), 752–60.

NIH Consensus Development Panel on Rehabilitation of Persons With Traumatic Brain Injury (1999). Rehabilitation of Persons With Traumatic Brain Injury. *JAMA, 282*, 974–983.

Niogi, S. N., Mukherjee, P., Ghajar, J., Johnson, C., Kolster, R. A., Sarkar, R., et al. (2008). Extent of microstructural white matter injury in postconcussive syndrome correlates with impaired cognitive reaction time: A 3T diffusion tensor imaging study of mild traumatic brain injury. *American Journal of Neuroradiology, 29*, 967–973.

Nitschke, J. B., Heller, W., & Miller, G. A. (2000). The neuropsychology of anxiety. In J. C. Borod (Ed.), *The neuropsychology of emotion* (pp. 298–319). New York: Oxford University Press.

Nitschke, J. B., Heller, W., Etienne, M. A., & Miller, G. A. (2004). Prefrontal cortex activity differentiates processes affecting memory in depression. *Biological Psychology, 67*, 125–143.

Noble, K. G., Wolmetz, M. E., Ochs, L. G., Farah, M. J., & McCandliss, B. D. (2006). Brain-behavior relationships in reading acquisition are modulated by socioeconomic factors. *Developmental Science.*

Nobre, A. C., Gitelman, D. R., Sebestyen, G. N., Meyer, J., Frackowiak, R. S. J., Frith, C. D., & Mesulam, M. M. (1997). Functional localization of the system for visuospatial attention using positron emission tomography. *Brain, 120*, 515–553.

Nolen-Hoeksema, S. (2007). *Abnormal psychology* (4th ed.). New York: McGraw-Hill.

Noonan, W. C. W., Kathman, S. J., & White, C. M. C. (2002). Prevalence estimates for MS in the United States and evidence of an increasing trend for women. *Neurology, 58*, 136–138.

Nordahl, T. E., Carter, C. S., Salo, R. E., Kraft, L., Baldo, J., Salamat, S., et al. (2001). Anterior cingulate metabolism correlates with Stroop errors in paranoid schizophrenia patients. *Neuropsychopharmacology, 25*, 139–148.

Norton, A., Zipse, L., Marchina, S., & Schlaug, G. (2009). Melodic intonation therapy: Shared insights on how it is done and why it might help. *Annals of the New York Academy of Sciences, 1169*, 431–436.

Nottebohm, F. (1971). Neural lateralization of vocal control in a Passerine bird. I. Song. *Journal of Experimental Zoology, 177*, 229–261.

Nottebohm, F. (1977). Asymmetries in neural control of vocalization in the canary. In S. Harnad, R. W. Doty, L. Goldstein, J. Jaynes, & G. Krauthamer (Eds.), *Lateralization of the nervous system* (pp. 23–44). New York: Academic Press.

Noulhaine, M., Piolino, P., Hasboun, D., Clemenceau, S., Baulac, M., & Samson, S. (2007). Autobiographical memory after temporal lobe resection: Neuropsychological and MRI volumetric findings. *Brain, 130*(12), 3184.

Novelly, R. A. (1992). The debt of neuropsychology to the epilepsies. *American Psychologist, 47*, 1126–1129.

Nudo, R. J. (2006). Mechanisms for recovery of motor function following cortical damage. *Current Opinion in Neurobiology, 16*, 638–644.

Nudo, R. J., Milliken, G. W., Jenkins, W. M., & Merzenich, M. M. (1996). Use-dependent alterations of movement representations in primary motor cortex of adult squirrel monkeys. *Journal of Neuroscience, 16*(2), 785–807.

Nyberg, L., Habib, R., McIntosh, A. R., & Tulving, E. (2000). Reactivation of encoding-related brain activity during memory retrieval. *Proceedings of the National Academy of Sciences, USA, 97*(20), 11120–11124.

Nyhus, E., & Barceló, F. (2009). The Wisconsin Card Sorting Test and the cognitive assessment of prefrontal executive functions: A critical update. *Brain & Cognition, 71*, 437–451.

O'Boyle, M. W., Van Wyhe-Lawler, F., & Miller, D. A. (1987). Recognition of letters traced in the right and left palms: Evidence for a process-oriented tactile asymmetry. *Brain and Cognition, 6*, 474–494.

O'Connor, D. H., Fukui, M. M., Pinsk, M. A., & Kastner, S. (2002). Attention modulates responses in the human lateral geniculate nucleus. *Nature Neuroscience, 5*, 1203–1209.

O'Craven, K., Downing, P., & Kanwisher, N. (1999). fMRI evidence for objects as the units of attentional selection. *Nature, 401*, 584–587.

O'Doherty, J., Kringelbach, M. L., Rolls, E. T., Hornak, J., & Andrews, C. (2001). Abstract reward and punishment representations in the human orbitofrontal cortex. *Nature Neuroscience, 4*, 95–102.

O'Dougherty, M., Wright, F. S., Loewenson, R. B., & Torres, F. (1985). Cerebral dysfunction after chronic hypoxia in children. *Neurology, 35*, 42–46.

O'Keefe, J., & Burgess, N. (1996). Geometric determinants of the place fields of hippocampal neurons. *Nature, 381*(6581), 425–428.

O'Keefe, J., & Dostrovsky, J. (1971). The hippocampus as a spatial map. Preliminary evidence from unit activity in the freely-moving rat. *Brain Research, 34*(1), 171–175.

O'Keefe, J., & Nadel, L. (1978). *The hippocampus as a cognitive map.* Oxford, UK: Oxford University Press.

O'Reilly, R. C., & Munakata, Y. (2000). *Computational explorations in cognitive neuroscience: Understanding the mind by simulating the brain.* Cambridge, MA: MIT Press.

O'Reilly, R. C., & Norman, K. A. (2002). Hippocampal and neocortical contributions to memory: Advances in the complementary learning systems framework. *Trends in Cognitive Sciences, 6*, 505–510.

O'Reilly, R. C., & Rudy, J. W. (2000). Computational principles of learning in the neocortex and hippocampus. *Hippocampus, 10*(4), 389–397.

O'Reilly, R. C., & Rudy, J. W. (2001). Conjunctive representations in learning and memory: Principles of cortical and hippocampal function. *Psychological Review, 108*(2), 311–345.

Oberman, L. M., & Ramachandran, V. S. (2007). The simulating social mind: The role of the mirror neuron system and simulation in the social and communicative deficits of autism spectrum disorders. *Psychological Bulletin, 133*, 310–327.

Ochsner, K. N., Bunge, S. A., Gross, J. J., & Gabrieli, J. D. E. (2002). Rethinking feelings: An fMRI study of the cognitive regulation of emotion. *Journal of Cognitive Neuroscience, 14*, 1215–1229.

Ochsner, K. N., Ray, R. D., Cooper, J. C., Robertson, E. R., Chopra, S., Gabrieli, J. D. E., & Gross, J. J. (2004). For better or for worse: Neural systems supporting the cognitive down- and up-regulation of negative emotion. *NeuroImage, 23*, 483–499.

Ogden, J. A. (1985). Antero-posterior interhemispheric differences in the loci of lesions producing visual hemineglect. *Brain & Cognition, 4*, 59–75.

Ohkura, T., Isse, K., Akazawa, K., Hamamoto, M., Yaoi, Y., & Hagino, N. (1994). Evaluation of estrogen treatment in female patients with dementia of the Alzheimer type. *Endocrine Journal, 41*, 361–371.

Ojemann, G. A. (1983). Brain organization for language from the perspective of electrical stimulation mapping. *Behavioral and Brain Sciences, 6*, 189–230.

Oke, A., Keller, R., Mefford, I., & Adams, R. (1978). Lateralization of norepinephrine in human thalamus. *Science, 200*, 1411–1413.

Oksenberg, J. R., Baranzini, S. E., Sawcer, S., & Hauser, S. L. (2008). The genetics of multiple sclerosis: SNPs to pathways to pathogenesis. *Nature Reviews Genetics, 9*, 516–526.

Olanow, C. W., Stern, M. B., & Sethi, K. (2009). The scientific and clinical basis for the treatment of Parkinson disease. *Neurology, 72*(Suppl. 4), S1–S136.

Olds, J., & Milner, P. (1954). Positive reinforcement produced by electrical stimulation of septal area and other regions of rat brain. *Journal of Comparative & Physiological Psychology, 47*, 419–427.

Oliver, C., & Holland, A. J. (1986). Down's syndrome and Alzheimer's disease: A review. *Psychological Medicine, 16*, 307–322.

Oliveri, M., & Caltagirone, C. (2006). Suppression of extension with TMS in humans: From healthy controls to patients. *Behavioural Neurology, 17*, See 163–167.

Oliveri, M., & Vallar, G. (2009). Parietal vs. temporal lobe components in spatial cognition: Setting the mid-point of a horizontal line. *Journal of Neuropsychology, 3*, 201–211.

Oliveri, M., Bisiach, E., Brighina, F., Piazza, A., La Bua, V., Buffa, D., & Fierro, B. (2001). rTMS of the unaffected hemisphere transiently reduces contralesional visuospatial hemineglect. *Neurology, 57*, 1338–1340.

Olsson, A., & Phelps, E. A. (2007). Social learning of fear. *Nature Neuroscience, 10*, 1095–1102.

Olsson, A., Ebert, J. P., Banaji, M. R., & Phelps, E. A. (2005). The role of social groups in the persistence of learned fear. *Science, 309*, 785–787.

Olvera-Cortés, M. E., Anguiano-Rodriguez, P., López-Vázquez, M. A., & Alfaro, J. M. C. (2008). Serotonin/dopamine interaction in learning. *Progress in Brain Research, 172*, 567–602.

Op de Beeck, H., & Vogels, R. (2000). Spatial sensitivity of macaque inferior temporal neurons. *Journal of Comparative Neurology, 426*, 505–518.

Orban, G. A., Janssen, P., & Vogels, R. (2006). Extracting 3D structure from disparity. *Trends in Neurosciences, 29*, 466–473.

Orsini, D. L., Van Gorp, W. G., & Boone, K. B. (1988). *The neuropsychology casebook*. New York: Springer-Verlag.

Orton, S. T. (1937). *Reading, writing and speech problems in children*. New York: Norton.

Osterhout, L., & Holcomb, P. J. (1992). Event-related potentials elicited by syntactic anomaly. *Journal of Memory & Language, 31*, 785–806.

Osterhout, L., McLaughlin, J., & Bersick, M. (1997). Event-related brain potentials and human language. *Trends in Cognitive Sciences, 1*, 203–209.

Ota, H., Fujii, T., Suzuki, K., Fukatsu, R., & Yamadori, A. (2001). Dissociation of body-centered and stimulus-centered representations in unilateral neglect. *Neurology, 57*, 2064–2069.

Owen, A. M., & Coleman, M. R. (2008). Functional neuroimaging of the vegetative state. *Nature Reviews Neuroscience, 9*, 235–243.

Owen, A. M., Coleman, M. R., Boly, M., Davis, M. H., Laureys, S., & Pickard, J. D. (2006). Detecting awareness in the vegetative state. *Science, 313*, 1402.

Owen, A. M., Doyon, J., Petrides, M., & Evans, A. (1996). Planning and spatial working memory: A PET study in humans. *European Journal of Neuroscience, 8*, 353–364.

Owen, A. M., Roberts, A. C., Hodges, J. R., Summers, A. B. A., Polkey, C. E., & Robbins, T. W. (1993). Contrasting mechanisms of impaired attentional set-shifting in patients with frontal lobe damage or Parkinson's disease. *Brain, 116*(5), 1159–1175.

Owen, A. M., Roberts, A. C., Polkey, C. E., Sahakian, B. J., & Robbins, T. W. (1991). Extra-dimensional versus intradimensional set shifting performance following frontal lobe excisions, temporal lobe excisions or amygdalohippocampectomy in man. *Neuropsychologia, 29*, 993–1006.

Packard, M. G., & McGaugh, J. L. (1996). Inactivation of hippocampus or caudate nucleus with lidocaine differentially affects expression of place and response learning. *Neurobiology of Learning & Memory, 65*(1), 65–72.

Packard, M., & Knowlton, B. (2002). Learning and memory functions of the basal ganglia. *Annual Review in Neuroscience, 25*, 563–593.

Paller, K. A., Kutas, M., & Mayes, R. A. R. (1987). Neural correlates of encoding in an incidental learning paradigm. *Electroencephalography & Clinical Neurophysiology, 67*(4), 360–371.

Paniak, C., MacDonald, J., Toller-Lobe, G., Durand, A., & Nagy, J. (1998). A preliminary normative profile of mild traumatic brain injury diagnostic criteria. *Journal of Clinical & Experimental Neuropsychology, 20*(6), 852–855.

Pantelis, C., Velakoulis, D., McGorry, P. D., Wood, S. J., Suckling, J., Phillips, L. J., et al. (2003). Neuroanatomical abnormalities before and after onset of psychosis: A cross-sectional and longitudinal MRI comparison. *Lancet, 361*, 281–288.

Paolicchi, J. M. (2008). Is the Wada test still relevant? Yes. *Archives of Neurology, 65*, 838–840.

Papez, J. W. (1937). A proposed mechanism of emotion. *Archives of Neurological Psychiatry, 38*, 725–743.

Pappalardo, A., Ciancio, M. R., Reggio, E., & Patti, F. (2004). Posterior alien hand syndrome: Case report and rehabilitative treatment. *Neurorehabilitation and Neural Repair, 18*, 176–181.

Paradis, M., Hagiwara, H., & Hildebrandt, N. (1985). *Neurolinguistic aspects of the Japanese writing system*. New York: Academic Press.

Parellada, E., Catarineu, S., Catafau, A., Bernardo, M., & Lomeña, F. (2000). Psychopathology and Wisconsin card sorting task performance in young unmedicated schizophrenic patients. *Psychopathology, 33*, 14–18.

Park, D. C., & Reuter-Lorenz, P. (2009). The adaptive brain: Aging and neurocognitive scaffolding. *Annual Review of Psychology, 60*, 173–196.

Park, D. C., Polk, T. A., Park, R., Minear, M., Savage, A., & Smith, M. R. (2004). Aging reduced neural specialization in ventral visual cortex. *Proceedings of the National Academy of Sciences, USA, 101*, 13091–13095.

Park, N. W., & Ingles, J. L. (2001). Effectiveness of attention rehabilitation after an acquired brain injury: A meta-analysis. *Neuropsychology, 15*, 199–210.

Parker, A. J. (2007). Binocular depth perception and the cerebral cortex. *Nature Reviews Neuroscience, 8*, 379–391.

Parker, S. W., & Nelson, C. A. (2005). The impact of early institutional rearing on the ability to discriminate facial expressions of emotion: An event-related potential study. *Child Development, 76*, 54–72.

Parker, S. W., Nelson, C. A., & Bucharest Early Intervention Project Core Group. (2007). Erratum: An event-related potential study of the impact of institutional rearing on face recognition. *Development & Psychopathology, 19*, 623–625.

Parkin, A. J., Walter, B. M., & Hunkin, N. M. (1995). Relationships between normal aging, frontal lobe function, and memory for temporal and spatial information. *Neuropsychology, 9*, 304–312.

Parnetti, L., Senin, U., & Mecocci, P. (1997). Cognitive enhancement therapy for Alzheimer's disease. *Drugs, 53*, 752–768.

Pascual, A., Huang, K.-L., Neveu, J., & Préat, T. (2004). Brain asymmetry and long-term memory. *Nature, 427*, 605–606.

Pascual-Leone, A., Gates, J. R., & Dhuna, A. (1991). Induction of speech arrest and counting errors with rapid rate transcranial magnetic stimulation. *Neurology, 41*, 697–702.

Pascual-Leone, A., Grafman, J., Clark, K., Stewart, M., Massaquoi, S., Lou, J. S., & Hallett, M. (1993). Procedural learning in Parkinson's disease and cerebellar degeneration. *Annals of Neurology, 34*(4), 594–602.

Passarotti, A. M., Smith, J., DeLano, M., & Huang, J. (2007). Developmental differences in the neural bases of the face inversion effect show progressive tuning of face-selective regions to the upright orientation. *Neuroimage, 34*, 1708–1722.

Patterson, K. (1982). Reading and phonological coding. In A. W. Ellis (Ed.), *Normality and pathology in cognitive functions* (pp. 77–112). New York: Academic Press.

Patterson, K. E., & Kay, J. (1982). Letter-by-letter reading: Psychological descriptions of a neurological syndrome. *Quarterly Journal of Experimental Psychology, 34A*, 411–441.

Patterson, K. E., Seidenberg, M. S., & McClelland, J. L. (1989). Connections and disconnections: Acquired dyslexia in a computational model of reading processes. In R. G. M. Morris (Ed.), *Parallel distributed processing: Implications for psychology and neurobiology* (pp. 131–181). Oxford, UK: Oxford University Press.

Patterson, K., Nestor, P. J., & Rogers, T. T. (2007). Where do you know what you know? The representation of semantic knowledge in the human brain. *Nature Reviews Neuroscience, 8*(12), 976–987.

Paulesu, E., Demonet, J.-F., Fazio, F., McCrory, E., Chanoine, V., Brunswick, N., et al. (2001). Dyslexia: Cultural diversity and biological unity. *Science, 291*, 2165–2167.

Paulesu, E., McCrory, E., Fazio, F., Menoncello, L., Brunswick, N., Cappa, S. F., et al. (2000). A cultural effect on brain function. *Nature Neuroscience, 3*, 91–96.

Paus, T. (1996). Location and function of the human frontal eye-field: A selective review. *Neuropsychologia, 34*, 475–483.

Paus, T. (2001). Primate anterior cingulate cortex: Where motor control, drive and cognition interface. *Nature Reviews Neuroscience, 2*, 417–424.

Paus, T. (2005). Mapping brain maturation and cognitive development during adolescence. *Trends in Cognitive Sciences, 9*, 60–68.

Paus, T., & Barrett, J. (2004). Transcranial magnetic stimulation (TMS) of the human frontal cortex: Implications for repetitive

TMS treatment of depression. *Journal of Psychiatry & Neuroscience, 29,* 268–279.

Paus, T., Castro-Alamancos, M. A., & Petrides, M. (2001). Cortico-cortical connectivity of the human mid-dorsolateral frontal cortex and its modulation by repetitive transcranial magnetic stimulation. *European Journal of Neuroscience, 14,* 1405–1411.

Paus, T., Kalina, M., Patockova, L., Angerova, Y., Cerny, R., Mecir, P., et al. (1991). Medial versus lateral frontal lobe lesions and differential impairment of central-gaze fixation maintenance in man. *Brain, 114,* 2051–2067.

Paus, T., Koski, L., Caramanos, Z., & Westbury, C. (1998). Regional differences in the effects of task difficulty and motor output on blood flow response in the human anterior cingulate cortex: A review of 107 PET activation studies. *NeuroReport, 9,* R37–R47.

Paus, T., Petrides, M., Evans, A. C., & Meyer, E. (1993). Role of the human anterior cingulate cortex in the control of oculomotor, manual, and speech responses: A positron emission tomography study. *Journal of Neurophysiology, 70,* 1–18.

Paus, T., Zatorre, R. J., Hofle, N., Caramanos, Z., Gotman, J., Petrides, M., & Evans, A. C. (1997). Time-related changes in neural systems underlying attention and arousal during the performance of an auditory vigilance task. *Journal of Cognitive Neuroscience, 9,* 392–408.

Paus, T., Zijdenbos, A., Worsley, K., Collins, D. L., Blumenthal, J., Geidd, J. N., Rapoport, J. L., & Evans, A. C. (1999). Structural maturation of neural pathways in children and adolescents: In vivo study. *Science, 293,* 1908–1911.

Pavani, F., Làdavas, E., & Driver, J. (2003). Auditory and multisensory aspects of visuospatial neglect. *Trends in Cognitive Sciences, 7,* 407–414.

Pavlides, C., & Winson, J. (1989). Influences of hippocampal place cell firing in the awake state on the activity of these cells during subsequent sleep episodes. *Journal of Neuroscience, 9(8),* 2907–2918.

Peña, M., Maki, A., Kovacic, D., Dehaene-Lambertz, G., Koizumi, H., et al. (2003). Sounds and silence: An optical topography study of language recognition at birth. *Proceedings of the National Academy of Sciences, 100,* 11702–11705.

Pedersen, J. R., Johannsen, P., Bak, C. K., Kofoed, B., Saermark, K., & Gjedde, A. (1998). Origin of human motor readiness field linked to left middle frontal gyrus by MEG and PET. *NeuroImage, 8,* 214–220.

Peelen, M. V., & Downing, P. E. (2005). Selectivity for the human body in the fusiform gyrus. *Journal of Neurophysiology, 93,* 603–608.

Peelen, M. V., & Downing, P. E. (2007). The neural basis of visual body perception. *Nature Reviews Neuroscience, 8,* 636–648.

Peissig, J. J., & Tarr, M. J. (2007). Visual object recognition: Do we know more now than we did 20 years ago? *Annual Review of Psychology, 58,* 75–96.

Pell, M. D. (1999). Fundamental frequency encoding of linguistic and emotional prosody by right hemisphere-damaged speakers. *Brain & Language, 69,* 161–192.

Pell, M. D. (2006). Cerebral mechanisms for understanding emotional prosody in speech. *Brain & Language, 96,* 221–234.

Pell, M. D. (2006). Judging emotion and attitudes from prosody following brain damage. *Progress in Brain Research, 156,* 303–317.

Pelphrey, K. A., Morris, J. P., & McCarthy, G. (2005). Neural basis of eye gaze processing deficits in autism. *Brain, 128,* 1038–1048.

Pelphrey, K. A., Singerman, J. D., Allison, T., & McCarthy, G. (2003). Brain activation evoked by perception of gaze shifts: The influence of context. *Neuropsychologia, 41,* 156–170.

Penfield, W., & Faulk, M. E. (1955). The insula: Further observations on its function. *Brain, 78,* 445–470.

Penfield, W., & Rasmussen, T. (1950). *The cerebral cortex of man: A clinical study of localization of function.* New York: Macmillan.

Perani, D., & Abutalebi, J. (2005). The neural basis of first and second language processing. *Current Opinions in Neurobiology, 15,* 202–206.

Perani, D., Cappa, S. F., Bettinardi, V., Bressi, S., Gorno-Tempini, M., Matarrese, M., & Fazio, F. (1995). Different neural systems for the recognition of animals and manmade tools. *NeuroReport, 6,* 1637–1641.

Perenin, M.-T., & Vighetto, A. (1988). Optic ataxia: A specific disruption in visuomotor mechanisms. I. Different aspects of the deficit in reaching for objects. *Brain, 111,* 643–674.

Peres, M., Van De Moortele, P. F., Pierard, C., Lehericy, S., Le Bihan, D., & Guezennec, C. Y. (2000). Functional magnetic resonance imaging of mental strategy in a simulated aviation performance task. *Aviation, Space, & Environmental Medicine, 71,* 1218–1231.

Peretz, I., & Zatorre, R. J. (2005). Brain organization for music processing. *Annual Review of Psychology, 56,* 89–114.

Perlstein, W. M., Carter, C. S., Noll, D. C., & Cohen, J. D. (2001). Relation of prefrontal cortex dysfunction to working memory and symptoms in schizophrenia. *American Journal of Psychiatry, 158,* 1105–1113.

Perlstein, W. M., Dixit, N. K., Carter, C. S., Noll, D. C., & Cohen, J. D. (2003). Prefrontal cortex dysfunction mediates deficits in working memory and prepotent responding in schizophrenia. *Biological Psychiatry, 53,* 25–38.

Perrett, D. I., & Mistlin, A. J. (1990). Perception of facial attributes. In W. C. Stebbins & M. A. Berkley (Eds.), *Comparative perception, complex signals, Vol. 2* (pp. 187–215). New York: Wiley.

Perrett, D. I., Mistlin, A. J., & Chitty, A. J. (1987). Visual neurones responsive to faces. *Trends in Neurosciences, 10,* 358–364.

Perrett, D. I., Smith, P. A. J., Potter, D. D., Mistlin, A. J., Head, A. S., Milner, A. D., & Jeeves, M. A. (1985). Visual cells in the temporal cortex sensitive to face view and gaze direction. *Proceedings of the Royal Society of London, B, 223,* 293–317.

Perrine, K., & Kiolbasa, T. (1999). Cognitive deficits in epilepsy and contribution to psychopathology. *Neurology, 53*(Suppl. 2), S39–S48.

Perry, N., Court, G., Bidet, N., & Court, J. (1996). European herbs with cholinergic activities: Potential in dementia therapy. *International Journal of Geriatric Psychiatry, 11,* 1063–1069.

Persico, A. M., & Bourgeron, T. (2006). Searching for ways out of the autism maze: Genetic, epigenetic and environmental clues. *Trends in Neurosciences, 29,* 349–358.

Peru, A., & Avesani, R. (2008). To know what it is for, but not how it is: Semantic dissociations in a case of visual agnosia. *Neurocase, 14,* 249–263.

Pessoa, L., Japee, S., Sturman, D., & Ungerleider, L. G. (2006). Target visibility and visual awareness modulate amygdala responses to fearful faces. *Cerebral Cortex, 16,* 366–375.

Petersen, E. T., Zimine, I., Ho, Y.-C., L., & Golay, X. (2006). Non-invasive measurement of perfusion: A critical review of arterial spin labelling techniques. *British Journal of Radiology, 79,* 688–701.

Petersen, R. C. & Negash, S. (2008). Mild cognitive impairment: An overview. *CNS Spectrums, 13,* 45–53.

Petersen, S. E., Fox, P. T., Posner, M. I., Mintun, M., & Raichle, M. E. (1988). Positron emission tomographic studies of the cortical anatomy of single-word processing. *Nature, 331,* 585–589.

Petersen, S. E., Fox, P. T., Snyder, A. Z., & Raichle, M. E. (1990). Activation of extrastriate and frontal cortical areas by visual words and word-like stimuli. *Science, 249,* 1041–1044.

Petito, L. A., Zatorre, R. J., Gauna, K., Nikelski, E. J., Dostie, D., & Evans, A. C. (2000). Speech-like cerebral activity in profoundly deaf people processing signed languages: Implications for the neural basis of human language. *Proceedings of the National Academy of Sciences, USA, 97,* 13961–13966.

Petreska, B., Adriani, M., Blanke, O., & Billard, A. G. (2007). Apraxia: A review. *Progress in Brain Research, 164,* 61–83.

Petrides, M. (2007). The orbitofrontal cortex: Novelty, deviation from expectation, and memory. *Annals of the New York Academy of Sciences, 1121,* 33–53.

Petrides, M., & Milner, B. (1982). Deficits on subject-ordered tasks after frontal- and temporal-lobe lesions in man. *Neuropsychologia, 20,* 249–262.

Petry, N. M. (2001). Pathological gamblers, with and without substance use disorders, discount delayed rewards at high rates. *Journal of Abnormal Psychology, 110,* 482–487.

Peyser, J. M., & Poser, C. M. (1986). Neuropsychological correlates of multiple sclerosis. In S. B. Filskov & T. J. Boll (Eds.), *Handbook of clinical neuropsychology* (pp. 364–398). New York: John Wiley & Sons.

Pezawas, L., Meyer-Lindenberg, A., Drabant, E. M., Verchinksi, B. A., Munoz, K. E., Kolachana, B. S., et al. (2005). 5-HTTLPR polymorphism impacts human cingulate-amygdala interactions: A genetic susceptibility mechanism for depression. *Nature Neuroscience, 8,* 828–834.

Pfeiffer, B. E., & Huber, K. M. (2009). The state of synapses in Fragile X syndrome. *Neuroscientist, 15,* 549–567.

Phan, K. L., Fitzgerald, D. A., Nathan, P. J., & Tancer, M. E. (2006). Association between amygdala hyperactivity to harsh faces and severity of social anxiety in generalized social phobia. *Biological Psychiatry, 59,* 424–429.

Phan, K. L., Wager, T., Taylor, S. F., & Liberzon, I. (2002). Functional neuroanatomy of emotion: A meta-analysis of emotion activation studies in PET and fMRI. *NeuroImage, 16,* 331–348.

Phelps, E. A. (2004). Human emotion and memory: Interactions of the amygdala and hippocampal complex. *Current Opinion in Neurobiology, 14,* 198–202.

Phelps, E. A., Cannistraci, C. J., & Cunningham, W. A. (2003). Intact performance on an indirect measure of race bias following amygdala damage. *Neuropsychologia, 41,* 203–208.

Phelps, E. A., Delgado, M. R., Nearing, K. I., & LeDoux, J. E. (2004). Extinction learning in humans: Role of the amygdala and vmPFC. *Neuron, 43,* 897–905.

Phelps, E. A., O'Connor, K. J., Cunningham, W. A., Funayama, E. S., Gatenby, J. C., Gore, J. C., & Banaji, M. R. (2000). Performance on indirect measures of race evaluation predicts amygdala activation. *Journal of Cognitive Neuroscience, 12,* 729–738.

Phelps, E. A., O'Connor, K. J., Gatenby, J. C., Gore, J. C., Grillon, C., & Davis, M. (2001). Activation of the left amygdala to a cognitive representation of fear. *Nature Neuroscience, 4,* 437–441.

Phillips, J. A., Noppeney, U., Humphreys, G. W., & Price, C. J. (2002). Can segregation within the semantic system account for category-specific deficits? *Brain, 125,* 2067–2080.

Phillips, M. L., Drevets, W. C., Rauch, S. L., & Lane, R. (2003). Neurobiology of emotion perception II: Implications for major psychiatric disorders. *Biological Psychiatry, 54,* 515–528.

Phillips, W., Shannon, K. M., & Barker, R. A. (2008). The current clinical management of Huntington's disease. *Movement Disorders, 23,* 1491–1504.

Pierce, K. A., Müller, R.-A, Ambrose, J., Allen, G., & Courchesne, E. (2001). Face processing occurs outside the fusiform "face area" in autism: Evidence from functional MRI. *Brain, 124,* 2059–2073.

Pierce, K., & Courchesne, E. (2001). Evidence for a cerebellar role in reduced exploration and stereotyped behavior in autism. *Biological Psychiatry, 49,* 655–664.

Pietrzak, R. H., Mollica, C. M., Maruff, P., & Snyder, P. J. (2006). Cognitive effects of immediate-release methylphenidate in children with attention-deficit/hyperactivity disorder. *Neuroscience & Biobehavioral Reviews, 30,* 1225–1245.

Pigott, S., & Milner, B. (1993). Memory for different aspects of complex visual scenes after unilateral temporalor frontal-lobe resection. *Neuropsychologia, 31,* 1–15.

Pigott, S., & Milner, B. (1994). Capacity of visual short-term memory after unilateral frontal or anterior temporal-lobe resection. *Neuropsychologia, 32,* 969–981.

Pillon, B., Deweer, B., Agid, Y., & Dubois, B. (1993). Explicit memory in Alzheimer's, Huntington's, and Parkinson's diseases. *Archives of Neurology, 50,* 374–379.

Pinek, B., Duhamel, J.-R., Cave, C., & Brouchon, M. (1989). Audiospatial deficits in humans: Differential effects associated with left versus right hemisphere parietal damage. *Cortex, 25,* 175–186.

Pinsk, M. A., DeSimone, K., Moore, T., Gross, C. G., & Kastner, S. (2005). Representations of faces and body parts in macaque temporal cortex: A functional MRI study. *Proceedings of the National Academy of Sciences, 102,* 6996–7001.

Pissiota, A., Frans, O., Fernandez, M., von Knorring, L., Fischer, H., & Fredrikson, M. (2002). Neurofunctional correlates of posttraumatic stress disorder: A PET symptom provocation study. *European Archives of Psychiatry & Clinical Neurosciences, 252,* 68–75.

Pitchford, N. J., Funnell, E., De Haan, B., & Morgan, P. S. (2007). Right-hemisphere reading in a case of developmental deep dyslexia. *Quarterly Journal of Experimental Psychology, 60,* 1187–1196.

Pitman, R. K., Gilbertson, M. W., Gurvits, T. V., May, F. S., Lasko, N. B., Metzger, L. J., et al. (2006). Clarifying the origins of biological abnormalities in PTSD through the study of identical twins discordant for combat exposure. *Annals of the New York Academy of Sciences, 1071,* 242–254.

Pizzagalli, D., Pascual-Marqui, R. D., Nitschke, J. B., Oakes, T. R., Larson, C. L., Abercrombie, H. C., et al. (2001). Anterior cingulate activity as a predictor of degree of treatment response in major depression: Evidence from brain electrical tomography analysis. *American Journal of Psychiatry, 158,* 405–415.

Plaut, D. C. (2003). Interpreting double dissociations in connectionist network. *Cortex, 39,* 138–141.

Plihal, W., & Born, J. (1997). Effects of early and late nocturnal sleep on declarative and procedural memory. *Journal of Cognitive Neuroscience, 9,* 534–547.

Plihal, W., & Born, J. (1999). Effects of early and late nocturnal sleep on priming and spatial memory. *Psychophysiology, 36,* 571–582.

Pliszka, S. R., Glahn, D. C., Semrud-Clikeman, M., Franklin, C., Perez, R., Xiong, J., & Liotti, M. (2006). Neuroimaging of inhibitory control areas in children with attention deficit hyperactivity disorder who were treatment naïve or in long-term treatment. *American Journal of Psychiatry, 163,* 1052–1060.

Podzebenko, K., Egan, G. F., & Watson, J. D. G. (2005). Real and imaginary rotary motion processing: Functional parcellation of the human parietal lobe revealed by fMRI. *Journal of Cognitive Neuroscience, 17,* 24–36.

Poeck, K. (1986). The clinical examination for motor apraxia. *Neuropsychologia, 24,* 129–134.

Poizner, H., Klima, E. S., & Bellugi, U. (1987). *What the hands reveal about the brain.* Cambridge, MA: MIT Press.

Pol, H. H., & Kahn, R. (2008). What happens after the first episode? A review of progressive brain changes in chronically ill patients with schizophrenia. *Schizophrenia Bulletin, 34,* 354–366.

Poldrack, R. A., & Gabrieli, J. D. (2001). Characterizing the neural mechanisms of skill learning and repetition priming: Evidence from mirror reading. *Brain, 124*(Pt. 1), 67–82.

Poldrack, R. A., & Gabrieli, J. D. E. (1998). Memory and the brain: What's right and what's left? *Cell, 93,*1091–1093.

Poldrack, R. A., Desmond, J. E., Glover, G. H., & Gabrieli, J. D. (1998). The neural basis of visual skill learning: An fMRI study of mirror reading. *Cerebral Cortex, 8,* 1–10.

Poldrack, R. A., Prabhakaran, V., Seger, C. A., & Gabrieli, J. D. E. (1999). Striatal activation during acquisition of a cognitive skill. *Neuropsychology, 13,* 564–574.

Poldrack, R., & Packard, M. (2003). Competition among multiple memory systems: Converging evidence from animal and human brain studies. *Neuropsychologia, 41,* 245–251.

Polonsky, A., Blake, R., Braun, J., & Heeger, D. J. (2000). Neuronal activity in human primary visual cortex correlates with perception during binocular rivalry. *Nature Neuroscience, 3,* 1153–1159.

Pomarol-Clotet, E., Oh, T. M. S. S., Laws, K. R., & McKenna, P. J. (2008). Semantic priming in schizophrenia: Systematic review and meta-analysis. *British Journal of Psychiatry, 192,* 92–97.

Poorthuis, R., Goriounova, N., Couey, J., & Mansvelder, H. (2009). Nicotinic actions on neuronal networks for cognition: General principles and long-term consequences. *Biochemical Pharmacology, 78,* 668–676.

Poremba, A., Malloy, M., Saunders, R. C., Carson, R. E., Herscovitch, P., & Mishkin, M. (2004). Species-specific calls evoke asymmetric activity in the monkey's temporal poles. *Nature, 427,* 448–451.

Portas, C. M., Rees, G., Howseman, A. M., Josephs, O., Turner, R., & Frith, C. D. (1998). A specific role for the thalamus in mediating the interaction of attention and arousal in humans. *Journal of Neuroscience, 18,* 8979–8989.

Posner, M. I., & Raichle, M. E. (1994). *Images of mind.* New York: Freeman.

Posner, M. I., & Rothbart, M. K. (2007). Research on attention networks as a model for the integration of psychological science. *Annual Review of Psychology, 58,* 1–23.

Posner, M. I., Walker, J. A., Friedrich, F. J., & Rafal, R. D. (1984). Effects of parietal injury on covert orienting of attention. *Journal of Neuroscience, 4,* 1863–1874.

Postle, B. R., Druzgal, T. J., & D'Esposito, M. (2003). Seeking the neural substrates of visual working memory storage. *Cortex, 39,* 927–946.

Postle, R. B. R., Jonides, J., Smith, E. E., Corkin, S., & Growdon, J. H. (1997). Spatial, but not object, delayed response is impaired in early Parkinson's disease. *Neuropsychology, 11,* 171–179.

Pothuizen, H. H. J., Aggleton, J. P., & Vann, S. D. (2008). Do rats with retrosplenial cortex lesions lack direction? *European Journal of Neuroscience, 28,* 2486–2498.

Potts, G. F., Liotti, M., Tucker, D. M., & Posner, M. I. (1996). Frontal and inferior temporal cortical activity in visual target detection: Evidence from high spatially sampled event-related potentials. *Brain Topography, 9*(1), 3–14.

Pouget, A., Dayan, P., & Zemel, R. (2000). Information processing population codes. *Nature Reviews Neuroscience, 1,* 125–132.

Pourtois, G., Peelen, M. V., Spinelli, L., Seeck, M., & Vuilleumier, P. (2007). Direct intracranial recording of body-selective responses in human extrastriate cortex. *Neuropsychologia, 45,* 262–265.

Povinelli, D. J., & Vonk, J. (2003). Chimpanzee minds: Suspiciously human? *Trends in Cognitive Sciences, 7,* 157–160.

Powell, H. W. R., Koepp, M. J., Symms, M. R., Boulby, P. A., Salek-Haddadi, A., Thompson, P. J., et al. (2005). Material-specific lateralization of memory encoding in the medial temporal lobe: Blocked versus event-related design. *NeuroImage, 27,* 231–239.

Powell, J. W., & Barber-Foss, K. D. (1999). Traumatic brain injury in high school athletes. *JAMA, 282,* 958–963.

Prather, S. C., Votaw, J. R., & Sathian, K. (2004). Task-specific recruitment of dorsal and ventral visual areas during tactile perception. *Neuropsychologia, 42,* 1079–1087.

Praticó, D. (2008). Oxidative stress in Alzheimer's disease: A reappraisal. *Trends in Pharmacological Sciences, 29,* 609–615.

Price, C. J. (1998). The functional anatomy of word comprehension and production. *Trends in Cognitive Sciences, 2,* 281–288.

Price, C. J., Gorno-Tempini, M. L., Graham, K. S., Biggio, N., Mechelli, A., Patterson, K., & Noppeney, U. (2003). Normal and pathological reading: Converging data from lesion and imaging studies. *NeuroImage, 20*(Suppl. I), S30–S41.

Price, C. J., Moore, C. J., Humphreys, G. W., & Wise, R. J. S. (1997). Segregating semantic from phonological processes during reading. *Journal of Cognitive Neuroscience, 9,* 727–733.

Price, C. J., Wise, R. J. S., Watson, J. D. G., Patterson, K., Howard, D., & Frackowiak, R. S. J. (1994). Brain activity during reading: The effects of exposure duration and task. *Brain, 117,* 1255–1269.

Prigatano, G. P., Altman, I. M., & O'Brien, K. P. (1990). Behavioral limitations that traumatic-brain-injured patients tend to underestimate. *Clinical Neuropsychologist, 4,* 163–176.

Prikryl, R., Kasparek, T., Skotakova, S., Ustohal, L., Kucerova, H., & Ceskova, E. (2007). Treatment of negative symptoms of schizophrenia using repetitive transcranial magnetic stimulation in a double-blind, randomized controlled study. *Schizophrenia Research, 95,* 151–157.

Proksch, J., & Bavelier, D. (2002). Changes in the spatial distribution of visual attention after early deafness. *Journal of Cognitive Neuroscience, 14,* 687–701.

Provins, K. A. (1997). Handedness and speech: A critical reappraisal of the role of genetic and environmental factors in the cerebral lateralization of function. *Psychological Review, 104,* 554–571.

Ptito, A., & Leh, S. E. (2007). Neural substrates of blindsight after hemispherectomy. *Neuroscientist, 13,* 506–518.

Puce, A., & Allison, T. (1999). Differential processing of mobile and static faces by temporal cortex. *NeuroImage, 9,* S801.

Pugh, K. R., Shaywitz, B. A., Shaywitz, S. E., Constable, R. T., Skudlarksi, P., Fulbright, R. K., et al. (1996). Cerebral organization for component processes in reading. *Brain, 119,* 1221–1238.

Pylyshyn, Z. W. (1973). What the mind's eye tells the mind's brain: A critique of mental imagery. *Psychological Bulletin, 80,* 1–24.

Pylyshyn, Z. W. (1981). The imagery debate: Analogue media versus tacit knowledge. *Psychological Review, 87,* 16–45.

Qian, N. (1995). Generalization and analysis of the Lisberger-Sejnowski VOR model. *Neural Computation, 7*(4), 735–752.

Qiu, J., Li, H., Chen, A., & Zhang, Q. (2008). The neural basis of analogical reasoning: An event-related potential study. *Neuropsychologia, 46,* 3006–3013.

Querbes, O., Aubury, F., Pariente, J., Lotterie, J.-A., Démonet, J.-F., Duret, V., et al. (2009). Early diagnosis of Alzheimer's disease using cortical thickness: Impact of cognitive reserve. *Brain, 132,* 2036–2047.

Quiroga, R. Q., Reddy, L., Kreiman, G., Koch, C., & Fried, I. (2005). Invariant visual representation by single neurons in the human brain. *Nature, 435,* 1102–1107.

Rämä, P., Poremba, A., Sala, J. B., Yee, L., Malloy, M., Mishkin, M., & Courtney, S. M. (2004). Dissociable functional cortical topographies for working memory maintenance of voice identity and location. *Cerebral Cortex, 14,* 768–780.

Röder, B., Rösler, F., & Neville, H. J. (2001). Auditory memory in congenitally blind adults: A behavioral-electrophysiological investigation. *Cognitive Brain Research, 11,* 289–303.

Röder, B., Stock, O., Bien, S., Neville, H., & Rösler, F. (2002). Speech processing activates visual cortex in congenitally blind humans. *European Journal of Neuroscience, 16,* 930–936.

Rabe, S., Debener, S., Brocke, B., & Beauducel, A. (2005). Depression and its relation to posterior cortical activity during performance of neuropsychological verbal and spatial tasks. *Personality & Individual Differences, 39,* 601–611.

Radoeva, P. D., Prasad, S., Brainard, D. H., & Aguirre, G. K. (2008). Neural activity within area V1 reflects unconscious visual performance in a case of blindsight. *Journal of Cognitive Neuroscience, 20,* 1927–1939.

Rafal, R., & Posner, M. I. (1987). Deficits in human visual spatial attention following thalamic lesions. *Proceedings of the National Academy of Sciences, USA, 84,* 7349–7353.

Rafal, R. D., Posner, M. I., Friedman, J. H., Inhoff, A. W., & Bernstein, E. (1988). Orienting of visual attention in progressive supranuclear palsy. *Brain, 111,* 267–280.

Rafal, R., Henik, A., & Smith, J. (1991). Extrageniculate contributions to reflex visual orientating in normal humans: A temporal hemifield advantage. *Journal of Cognitive Neuroscience, 3,* 322–328.

Raff, M. (1998). Cell suicide for beginners. *Nature, 396,* 119–122.

Ragozzino, M. E. (2007). The contribution of the medial prefrontal cortex, orbitofrontal cortex, and dorsomedial striatum to behavioral flexibility. *Annals of the New York Academy of Sciences, 1121,* 355–375.

Raichle, M. (2001). A default mode of brain function. *Proceedings of the National Academy of Sciences, 98,* 676–682.

Raichle, M. E., Fiez, J. A., Videen, T. O., MacLeod, A.-M. K., Pardo, J. V., Fox, P. T., & Petersen, S. E. (1994). Practice-related changes in human brain functional anatomy during nonmotor learning. *Cerebral Cortex, 4*(1), 8–26.

Rakic, P. (1991). Plasticity of cortical development. In S. E. Brauth, W. S. Hall, & R. J. Dooling (Eds.), *Plasticity of development* (pp. 127–161). Cambridge, MA: MIT Press.

Ramachandran, V. S., & Hirstein, W. (1998). The perception of phantom limbs. *Brain, 121,* 1603–1630.

Ramachandran, V. S., Rogers-Ramachandran, D., & Steward, M. (1992). Perceptual correlates of massive cortical reorganization. *Science, 258,* 1159–1160.

Ramnani, N., & Owen, A. M. (2004). Anterior prefrontal cortex: Insights into function from anatomy and neuroimaging. *Nature Reviews Neuroscience, 5,* 184–194.

Ramus, F. (2004). Neurobiology of dyslexia: A reinterpretation of the data. *Trends in Neurosciences, 27,* 720–726.

Randolph, C., Braun, A. R., Goldberg, T. E., & Chase, T. N. (1993). Semantic fluency in Alzheimer's, Parkinson's and Huntington's disease: Dissociation of storage and retrieval failures. *Neuropsychology, 7,* 82–88.

Ranscht, B. (2000). Cadherins: Molecular codes for axon guidance and synapse formation. *International Journal of Developmental Neuroscience, 18,* 643–651.

Rao, S. (1986). Neuropsychology of multiple sclerosis: A critical review. *Journal of Clinical & Experimental Neuropsychology, 8,* 503–542.

Rao, S. M., Leo, G. J., Bernardin, L., & Unverzagt, F. (1991). Cognitive dysfunction in multiple sclerosis: 1. Frequency, patterns, and prediction. *Neurology, 41,* 685–691.

Rapcsak, S. Z., Henry, M. L., Teague, S. L., Carnahan, S. D., & Beeson, P. M. (2007). Do dual-route models accurately predict reading and spelling performance in individuals with acquired alexia and agraphia? *Neuropsychologia, 45,* 2519–2524.

Rapoport, J. L., Addington, A. M., Frangou, S., & MRC Psych. (2005). The neurodevelopmental model of schizophrenia: Update 2005. *Molecular Psychiatry, 10,* 443–449.

Rasmussen, T., & Milner, B. (1977). The role of early left-brain injury in determining lateralization of cerebral speech functions. In S. Dimond & D. Blizzard (Eds.), *Evolution and lateralization of function in the brain.* New York: New York Academy of Sciences.

Rasmussen, T., & Milner, B. (1977a). The role of early left-brain injury in determining lateralization of cerebral speech function. *Annals of the New York Academy of Sciences, 299,* 355–369.

Ratcliff, G., & Davies-Jones, G. A. B. (1972). Defective visual localization in focal brain wounds. *Brain, 95,* 49–60.

Ratcliff, G., & Newcombe, F. (1973). Spatial orientation in man: Effects of left, right, and bilateral cerebral lesions. *Journal of Neurology, Neurosurgery & Psychiatry, 36,* 448–454.

Ratcliff, G., & Newcombe, F. (1982). Object recognition: Some deductions from the clinical evidence. In A. W. Ellis (Ed.), *Normality and pathology in cognitive functions* (pp. 147–171). London: Academic Press.

Rauch, S. L., van der Kolk, B. A., Fisler, R. E., Alpert, N. M., Orr, S. P., Savage, A. J., et al. (1996). A symptom provocation study of post-traumatic stress disorder using positron emission tomography and script-driven imagery. *Archives of General Psychiatry, 53,* 380–387.

Rauch, S. L., Whalen, P. J., Shin, L. M., McInerney, S. C., Macklin, M. L., Lasko, N. B., et al. (2000). Exaggerated amygdala response to masked facial stimuli in posttraumatic stress disorder: A functional MRI study. *Biological Psychiatry, 47,* 769–776.

Rauschecker, J. P., & Tian, B. (2000). Mechanisms and streams for processing of "what" and "where" in auditory cortex. *Proceedings of the National Academy of Sciences, 97,* 11800–11806.

Ravizza, S. M., & Carter, C. S. (2008). Shifting set about task switching: Behavioral and neural evidence for distinct forms of cognitive flexibility. *Neuropsychologia, 46,* 2924–2935.

Raymond, C. R. (2007). LTP forms 1, 2 and 3: Different mechanisms for the "long" in long-term potentiation. *Trends in Neurosciences, 30,* 167–175.

Raz, N., Lindenberger, U., Rodrigue, K. M., Kennedy, K. M., Head, D., Williamson, A., et al. (2005). Regional brain changes in aging healthy adults: General trends, individual differences and modifiers. *Cerebral Cortex, 15,* 1676–1689.

Raz, N., Torres, I. J., Spencer, W. D., Baertschie, J. C., Millman, D., & Sarpel, G. (1993). Neuroanatomical correlates of age-sensitive and age-invariant cognitive abilities: An in vivo MRI investigation. *Intelligence, 17,* 407–422.

Recanzone, G. H., & Sutter, M. L. (2008). The biological basis of audition. *Annual Review of Psychology, 59,* 119–142.

Recanzone, G. H., Merzenich, M. M., & Jenkins, W. M. (1992). Frequency discrimination training engaging a restricted skin surface results in an emergence of a cutaneous response zone in cortical area 3a. *Journal of Neurophysiology, 67*(5), 1071–1091.

Recanzone, G. H., Schreiner, C. E., & Merzenich, M. M. (1993). Plasticity in the frequency representation of primary auditory cortex following discrimination training in adult owl monkeys. *Journal of Neuroscience, 13*(1), 87–103.

Redcay, E., & Courchesne, E. (2005). When is the brain enlarged in autism? A meta-analysis of all brain size reports. *Biological Psychiatry, 58,* 1–9.

Reddihough, D. S., & Collins, K. J. (2003). The epidemiology and causes of cerebral palsy. *Australian Journal of Physiotherapy, 49,* 7–12.

Reddy, L., & Kanwisher, N. (2006). Coding of visual objects in the ventral stream. *Current Opinion in Neurobiology, 16,* 408–414.

Reddy, L., Kanwisher, N. G., & Vanrullen, R. (2009). Attention and biased competition in multi-voxel object representations. *Proceedings of the National Academy of Sciences USA, 106,* 21447–21452.

Reder, L. M., Park, H., & Kieffaber, P. D. (2009). Memory systems do not divide on consciousness: Reinterpreting memory in terms of activation and binding. *Psychological Bulletin, 135,* 23–49.

Redmond, D. E., Bjugstad, K. B., Teng, Y. D., Ourednik, V., Ourednik, J., Wakeman, D. R., et al. (2007). Behavioral improvement in a primate Parkinson's model is associated with multiple homeostatic effects of human neural stem cells. *Proceedings of the National Academy of Sciences, 104,* 12175–12180.

Reed, C. L., & Caselli, R. J. (1994). The nature of tactile agnosia: A case study. *Neuropsychologia, 32,* 527–539.

Reed, C. L., Caselli, R. J., & Farah, M. J. (1996). Tactile agnosia: Underlying impairment and implications for normal tactile recognition. *Brain, 199,* 875–888.

Reed, C. L., Klatzky, R. L., & Halgren, E. (2005). What vs. where in touch: An fMRI study. *Neuroimage, 25,* 718–726.

Reed, C. L., Stone, V. E., Bozova, S., & Tanaka, J. (2003). The body-inversion effect. *Psychological Science, 14,* 302–308.

Reed, C. L., Stone, V. E., Grubb, J. D., & McGoldrick, J. E. (2006). Turning configural processing upside down: Part and whole body postures. *Journal of Experimental Psychology: Human Perception and Performance, 32,* 73–87.

Reed, J. M., & Squire, L. R. (1998). Retrograde amnesia for facts and events: Findings from four new cases. *Journal of Neuroscience, 18*(10), 3943–3954.

Rees, G., Frith, C. D., & Lavie, N. (1997). Modulating irrelevant motion perception by varying attentional load in an unrelated task. *Science, 278,* 1616–1619.

Rees, G., Wojciulik, E., Clarke, K., Husain, M., Frith, C., & Driver, J. (2000). Unconscious activation of visual cortex in the damaged right hemisphere of a parietal patient with extinction. *Brain, 123,* 1624–1633.

Rees, G., Wojciulik, E., Clarke, K., Husain, M., Frith, C., & Driver, J. (2002). Neural correlates of conscious and unconscious vision in parietal extinction. *Neurocase, 8,* 387–393.

Rehak, A., Kaplan, J. A., & Gardner, H. (1992). Sensitivity to conversational deviance in right-hemisphere-damaged patients. *Brain & Language, 42,* 203–217.

Reid, S. A., Duke, L. M., & Allen, J. J. B. (1998). Resting frontal electroencephalographic asymmetry in depression: Inconsistencies suggest the need to identify mediating factors. *Psychophysiology, 35,* 389–404.

Reisberg, B., Ferris, S. H., deLeon, M. J., & Crook, T. (1988). Global Deterioration Scale (GDS). *Psychopharmacology Bulletin, 24,* 661–663.

Reisberg, B., Ferris, S. H., deLeon, M. J., Kluger, A., Franssen, E., Borenstein, J., & Alba, R. C. (1989). The stage-specific temporal course of Alzheimer's disease: Functional and behavioral concomitants based upon cross-sectional and longitudinal observation. *Progress in Clinical & Biological Research, 317,* 23–41.

Reisenhuber, M., & Poggio, T. (2000). Models of object recognition. *Nature Neuroscience, 3,* 1199–1204.

Reist, C., Duffy, J. G., Fujimoto, K., & Cahill, L. (2001). Beta-adrenergic blockade and emotional memory in PTSD. *International Journal of Neuropsychopharmacology, 4,* 377–383.

Reite, M., Adams, M., Simon, J., Teale, P., Sheeder, J., Richardson, D., & Grabbe, R. (1994). Auditory M100 component 1: Relationship to Heschl's gyri. *Cognitive Brain Research, 2,* 13–20.

Reite, M., Sheeder, J., Teale, P., Adams, M., Richardson, D., Simon, J., Jones, R., & Rojas, D. (1997). Magnetic source imaging evidence of sex differences in cerebral lateralization in schizophrenia. *Archives of General Psychiatry, 54,* 433–440.

Repov, G., & Baddeley, A. D. (2006). The multi-component model of working memory: Explorations in experimental cognitive psychology. *Neuroscience, 139,* 5–21.

Ressel, V., Wilke, M., Lidzba, K., Preissl, H., Krägeloh-Mann, I., & Lutzenberger, W. (2006). Language lateralization in magneto-encephalography: Two tasks to investigate hemispheric dominance. *Neuroreport, 17,* 1209–1213.

Ressler, K. J., & Mayberg, H. S. (2007). Targeting abnormal neural circuits in mood and anxiety disorders: From the laboratory to the clinic. *Nature Neuroscience, 10,* 1116–1124.

Ressler, K. J., Rothbaum, B. O., Tannenbaum, L., Anderson, P., Graap, K., Zimand, E., et al. (2004). Cognitive enhancers as adjuncts to psychotherapy: Use of D-cycloserine in phobic individuals to facilitate extinction of fear. *Archives of General Psychiatry, 61,* 1136–1144.

Reuter-Lorenz, P. A. (2002). New visions of the aging mind and brain. *Trends in Cognitive Sciences, 6,* 394–400.

Reuter-Lorenz, P. A., & Miller, A. C. (1998). The cognitive neuroscience of human laterality: Lessons from the bisected brain. *Current Directions in Psychological Science, 7,* 15–20.

Reuter-Lorenz, P. A., & Posner, M. I. (1990). Components of neglect from right-hemisphere damage: An analysis of line bisection. *Neuropsychologia, 28,* 327–333.

Reuter-Lorenz, P. A., Kinsbourne, M., & Moscovitch, M. (1990). Hemispheric control of spatial attention. *Brain & Cognition, 12,* 240–266.

Reuter-Lorenz, P. A., Marshuetz, C., Jones, J., Smith, E. E., Hartley, A., & Koeppe, R. (2001). Neurocognitive ageing of storage and executive processes. *European Journal of Cognitive Psychology, 13,* 257–278.

Reuter-Lorenz, P. A., Stanczak, L. M., & Miller, A. C. (1999). Neural recruitment and cognitive aging: Two hemispheres are better than one, especially as you age. *Psychological Science, 10*(6), 494–500.

Reverberi, C., D'Agostini, S., Skrap, M., & Shallice, T. (2005). Generation and recognition of abstract rules in different frontal lobe subgroups. *Neuropsychologia, 43,* 1924–1937.

Reverberi, C., Laiacona, M., & Capitani, E. (2006). Qualitative features of semantic fluency performance in medial and lateral frontal patients. *Neuropsychologia, 44,* 469–478.

Reverberi, C., Toraldo, A., D'Agostini, S., & Skrap, M. (2005). Better without (lateral) frontal cortex? Insight problems solved by frontal patients. *Brain, 128,* 2882–2890.

Reynolds, J. H., Chelazzi, L., & Desimone, R. (1999). Competitive mechanisms subserve attention in macaque areas V2 and V4. *Journal of Neuroscience, 19,* 1736–1753.

Rhodes, G., Tan, S., Brake, S., & Taylor, K. (1989). Expertise and configural coding in face recognition. *British Journal of Psychology, 80,* 313–331.

Ribot, T. (1881/1882). *Diseases of memory.* New York: Appleton.

Richardson, F. M., & Price, C. J. (2009). Structural MRI studies of language function in the undamaged brain. *Brain Structure & Function, 213,* 511–523.

Richter, W., Somorjai, R., Summers, R., Jarmasz, M., Menon, R. S., Gati, J. S., et al. (2000). Motor area activity during mental rotation studied by time-resolved single-trial fMRI. *Journal of Cognitive Neuroscience, 12*(2), 310–320.

Riddoch, M. J., & Humphreys, G. W. (1983). The effect of cueing on unilateral neglect. *Neuropsychologia, 21,* 589–599.

Riedel, W. M., Klaassen, T., Deutz, N. E. P., van Someren, A., & van Praag, H. M. (1999). Tryptophan depletion in normal volunteers produces selective impairment in memory consolidation. *Psychopharmacology, 141,* 362–369.

Riesenhuber, M., & Poggio, T. (2000). Models of object recognition. *Nature Neuroscience, 3*(Suppl.), 1199–1204.

Riggio, S., & Wong, M. (2009). Neurobehavioral sequelae of traumatic brain injury. *Mount Sinai Journal of Medicine, 76,* 163–172.

Rilling, J. K., Glasser, M. F., Preuss, T. M., Ma, X., Zhao, T., Hu, X., & Behrens, T. E. (2008). The evolution of the arcuate fasciculus revealed with comparative DTI. *Nature Neuroscience, 11,* 426–428.

Ringo, J. L., Doty, R. W., Demeter, S., & Simard, P. Y. (1994). Time is of the essence: A conjecture that hemispheric specialization arises from interhemispheric conduction delay. *Cerebral Cortex, 4,* 331–343.

Risch, N., Herrell, R., Lehner, T., Liang, K.-Y., Eaves, L., Hoh, J., et al. (2009). Interaction between the serotonin transporter gene (5-HTTLPR), stressful life events, and risk of depression. *JAMA, 301,* 2462–2471.

Ritsner, M. S. (2007). Predicting quality of life impairment in chronic schizophrenia from cognitive variables. *Quality of Life Research, 16,* 929–937.

Rivlin-Etzion, M., Marmor, O., Heimer, G., Raz, A., Nini, A., & Bergman, H. (2006). Basal ganglia oscillations and pathophysiology of movement disorders. *Current Opinion in Neurobiology, 16,* 629–637.

Rizzolatti, G., & Fabbri-Destro, M. (2008). The mirror system and its role in social cognition. *Current Opinion in Neurobiology, 18,* 179–184.

Rizzolatti, G., & Lupino, G. (2001). The cortical motor system. *Neuron, 31,* 889–901.

Robbins, R., & McKone, E. (2007). No face-like processing for objects-of-expertise in three behavioural tasks. *Cognition, 103,* 34–79.

Roberts, A. C. (2006). Primate orbitofrontal cortex and adaptive behaviour. *Trends in Cognitive Sciences, 10,* 83–90.

Robertson, E. M., Théoret, H., & Pascual-Leone, A. (2003). Studies in cognition: The problems solved and created by transcranial magnetic stimulation. *Journal of Cognitive Neuroscience, 15,* 948–960.

Robertson, K., Liner, J., & Heaton, R. (2009). Neuropsychological assessment of HIV-infected populations in international settings. *Neuropsychology Review, 19,* 232–249.

Robertson, L. C., & Ivry, R. (2000). Hemispheric asymmetries: Attention to visual and auditory primitives. *Current Directions in Psychological Science, 9,* 59–63.

Robertson, L. C., & Lamb, M. R. (1991). Neuropsychological contributions to part-whole organization. *Cognitive Psychology, 23,* 299–332.

Robertson, L. C., Lamb, M. R., & Knight, R. T. (1988). Effects of lesions of temporal-parietal junction on perceptual and attentional processing in humans. *Journal of Neuroscience, 8,* 3757–3769.

Robichon, F., & Habib, M. (1998). Abnormal callosal morphology in male adult dyslexics: Relationships to handedness and phonological ability. *Brain & Language, 62,* 127–146.

Robinson, R. G., & Szetela, B. (1981). Mood change following left hemisphere brain injury. *Annals of Neurology, 9,* 447–453.

Rode, G., Charles, N., Perenin, M. T., Vighetto, A., Trillet, M., & Aimard, G. (1992). Partial remission of hemiplegia and somatoparaphrenia through vestibular stimulation in a case of unilateral neglect. *Cortex, 28*(2), 203–208.

Rodel, M., Cook, N. D., Regard, M., & Landis, T. (1992). Hemispheric dissociation in judging semantic relations: Complementarity for close and distant associates. *Brain & Language, 43,* 448–459.

Roenker, D. L., Cissell, G. M., Ball, K. K., Wadley, V. G., & Edwards, J. D. (2003). Speed-of-processing and driving simulator training result in improved driving performance. *Human Factors, 45,* 218–233.

Roffman, J. L., Marci, C. D., Glick, D. M., Dougherty, D. D., & Rauch, S. L. (2005). Neuroimaging and the functional neuroanatomy of psychotherapy. *Psychological Medicine, 35,* 1385–1398.

Rogers, L. J., Zucca, P., & Vallortigara, G. (2004). Advantage of having a lateralized brain. *Proceedings of the Royal Society of London B (Suppl.): Biology Letters, 271,* 420–422.

Rogers, R. D., Andrews, T. C., Grasby, P. M., Brooks, D. J., & Robbins, T. W. (2000). Contrasting cortical and subcortical activations produced by attentional-set shifting and reversal learning in humans. *Journal of Cognitive Neuroscience, 12,* 142–162.

Rogers, R.D., Sahakian, B.J., Hodges, J.R., Polkey, C.E., Kennard, C., & Robbins, T.W. (1998). Dissociating executive mechanisms of task control following frontal lobe damage and Parkinson's disease. *Brain, 121,* 815–842.

Roland, P. E., Larsen, B., Lassen, N. A., & Skinhøj, E. (1980). Supplementary motor area and other cortical areas in organization of voluntary movements in man. *Journal of Neurophysiology, 43,* 118–136.

Rolls, E. T. (1999). *The brain and emotion.* Oxford, UK: Oxford University Press.

Rolls, E. T. (2004). Invariant object and face recognition. In L. M. Chalupa & J. S. Werner (Eds.), *The visual neurosciences* (pp. 1165–1178). Cambridge, MA: MIT Press.

Rolls, E. T., Hornak, J., Wade, D., & McGrath, J. (1994). Emotion-related learning in patients with social and emotional changes associated with frontal lobe damage. *Journal of Neurology, Neurosurgery, & Psychiatry, 57,* 1518–1524.

Romanski, L. M. (2007). Representation and integration of auditory and visual stimuli in the primate ventral lateral prefrontal cortex. *Cerebral Cortex, 17,* i61–i69.

Romanski, L. M., & Averbeck, B. B. (2009). The primate cortical auditory system and neural representation of conspecific vocalizations. *Annual Review of Neuroscience, 32,* 315–346.

Rorden, C., & Karnath, H. O. (2004). Using human brain lesions to infer function: A relic from a past era in the fMRI age? *Nature Reviews Neuroscience, 5,* 813–819.

Rosas, H. D., Salat, D. H., Lee, S. Y., Zaleta, A. K., Pappu, V., Fischl, B., et al. (2008). Cerebral cortex and the clinical expression of Huntington's disease: Complexity and heterogeneity. *Brain,* 131, 1057–1068.

Rosen, A. C., Prull, M. W., O'Hara, R., Race, E., Desmond, J. E., Glover, G. H., et al. (2002). Variable effects of aging on frontal lobe contributions to memory. *NeuroReport, 13,* 2425–2428.

Rosenzweig, M. R., Bennett, E. L., & Diamond, M. C. (1972). Brain changes in response to experience. *Scientific American, 226,* 22–29.

Ross, A. J., & Sachdev, P.S. (2004). Magnetic resonance spectroscopy in cognitive research. *Brain Research: Brain Research Reviews, 44,* 83–102.

Ross, C. A., McInnis, M. G., Margolis, R. L., & Li, S. (1993). Genes with triplet repeats: Candidate mediators of neuropsychiatric disorders. *Trends in Neurosciences, 16(7),* 254–260.

Ross, E. D. (1981). The aprosodias: Functional-anatomic organization of the affective components of language in the right hemisphere. *Archives of Neurology, 38,* 561–569.

Ross, E. D. (2006). The aprosodias. In M. J. Farah & T. E. Feinberg (Eds.), *Patient-based approaches to cognitive neuroscience* (2d ed.; pp. 259–269). Cambridge, MA: MIT Press.

Ross, E. D., & Monnot, M. (2008). Neurology of affective prosody and its functional-anatomic organization in right hemisphere. *Brain & Language, 104,* 51–74.

Ross, R. G., Olincy, A., Harris, J. G., Radant, A., Adler, L. E., & Freedman, R. (1998). Anticipatory saccades during smooth pursuit eye movements and familial transmission of schizophrenia. *Biological Psychiatry, 44,* 690–697.

Rossetti, Y., Rode, G., Pisella, L., Farné, A., Li, L., Boisson, D., & Perenin, M. T. (1998). Prism adaptation to a rightward optical deviation rehabilitates left hemispatial neglect. *Nature, 395,* 166–169.

Rougier, N. P., Noelle, D. C., Braver, T. S., Cohen, J. D., & O'Reilly, R. (2005). Prefrontal cortex and flexible cognitive control: Rules without symbols. *Proceedings of the National Academy of Sciences, USA, 102,* 7338–7343.

Rovaris, M., Judica, E., Gallo, A., Benedetti, B., Sormani, M. P., Caputo, D., et al. (2006). Grey matter damage predicts the evolution of primary progressive multiple sclerosis at 5 years. *Brain, 129,* 2628–2634,

Rowe, J. B., Sakai, K., Lund, T. E., Ramsøy, T., Christensen, M. S., Baare, W. F., et al. (2007). Is the prefrontal cortex necessary for establishing cognitive sets? *Journal of Neuroscience, 48,* 13303–13310.

Rowland, L.P. (2006). Why haven't we banned boxing? *Neurology Today, 6,* 5–6.

Rozzi, S., Ferrari, P. F., Bonini, L., Rizzolatti, G., & Fogassi, L. (2008). Functional organization of inferior parietal lobule convexity in the macaque monkey: Electrophysiological characterization of motor, sensory, and mirror responses and their correlation with cytoarchitectonic areas. *European Journal of Neuroscience, 28,* 1569–1588.

Rubens, A. B. (1985). Caloric stimulation and unilateral visual neglect. *Neurology, 35,* 1019–1024.

Rubens, A. B., Geschwind, N., Mahowald, M. W., & Mastri, A. (1977). Posttraumatic cerebral hemispheric disconnection syndrome. *Archives of Neurology, 34,* 750–755.

Rubens, A. B., Mahowald, M. W., & Hutton, J. T. (1976). Asymmetry of lateral (Sylvian) fissure in man. *Neurology, 26,* 620–624.

Ruchsow, M., Grön, G., Reuter, K., Spitzer, M., Hermle, L., & Kiefer, M. (2005). Error-related brain activity in patients with obsessive-compulsive disorder and in healthy controls. *Journal of Psychophysiology, 19,* 298–304.

Rueda, M. R., Rothbart, M. K., McCandliss, B. D., Saccamanno, L., & Posner, M. I. (2005). Training, maturation, and genetic influences on the development of executive attention. *Proceedings of the National Academy of Sciences, 102,* 14931–14935.

Ruff, R. M., Hersh, N. A., & Pribram, K. H. (1981). Auditory spatial deficits in the personal and extrapersonal frames of reference due to cortical lesions. *Neuropsychologia, 19,* 435–443.

Ruge, H., Braver, T., & Meiran, N. (2009). Attention, intention, and strategy in preparatory control. *Neuropsychologia, 47,* 1670–1685.

Rugg, M. D., & Curran, T. (2007). Event-related potentials and recognition memory. *Trends in Cognitive Sciences, 11,* 251–257.

Rumi, D. O., Gattaz, W. F., Rigonatti, S. P., Rosa, M. A., Fregni, F., Rosa, M. A., et al. (2005). Transcranial magnetic stimulation accelerates the antidepressant effect of amitriptyline in severe depression: A double-blind placebo-controlled study. *Biological Psychiatry, 57,* 162–166.

Rumsey, J. M., Horwitz, B., Donohue, B. C., Nace, K., Maisog, J. M., & Andreason, P. (1997). Phonological and orthographic components of word recognition: A PET-rCBF study. *Brain, 120,* 739–759.

Rush, A. J., George, M. S., Sackeim, H. A., Marangell, L. B., Husain, M. M., Giller, C., et al. (2000). Vagus nerve stimulation (VNS) for treatment-resistant depressions: A multicenter study. *Biological Psychiatry, 47,* 276–286.

Rush, A. J., Marangell, L. B., Sackeim, H. A., George, M. S., Brannan, S. K., Davis, S. M., et al. (2005). Vagus nerve stimulation for treatment-resistant depression: A randomized, controlled acute phase trial. *Biological Psychiatry, 58,* 347–354.

Rush, A. J., Sackeim, H. A., Marangell, L. B., George, M. S., Brannan, S. K., Davis, S. M., et al. (2005). Effects of 12 months of vagus nerve stimulation in treatment-resistant depression: A naturalistic study. *Biological Psychiatry, 58,* 355–363.

Rushworth, M. F. (2008). Intention, choice, and the medial frontal cortex. *Annals of the New York Academy of Sciences, 1124,* 181–207.

Rushworth, M. F. S., Paus, T., & Sipila, P. K. (2001). Attention systems and the organization of the human parietal cortex. *Journal of Neuroscience, 21,* 5262–5271.

Rushworth, M. F. S., Walton, M. E., Kennerley, S. W., & Bannerman, D. M. (2004). Action sets and decisions in medial frontal cortex. *Trends in Cognitive Sciences, 8,* 410–417.

Rushworth, M., Buckley, M., Behrens, T., Walton, M., & Bannerman, D. (2007). Functional organization of the medial frontal cortex. *Current Opinion in Neurobiology, 17,* 220–227.

Russo, M. B., Stetz, M. C., & Thomas, M. L. (2005). Monitoring and predicting cognitive state and performance via physiological correlates of neuronal signals. *Aviation, Space, & Environmental Medicine, 76,* C59–C63.

Rutherford, A., Stephens, R., & Potter, D. (2003). The neuropsychology of heading and head trauma in association football (soccer): A review. *Neuropsychology Review, 13,* 153–179.

Rutherford, A., Stephens, R., Potter, D., & Fernie, G. (2005). Neuropsychological impairment as a consequence of football (soccer) play and football heading: Preliminary analyses and report on university footballers. *Journal of Clinical & Experimental Neuropsychology, 27,* 299–319.

Rutland-Brown, W., Langlois, J. A., Thomas, K. E., & Xi, Y. L. (2006). Incidence of traumatic brain injury in the United States, 2003. *Journal of Head Trauma Rehabilitation, 6,* 544–548.

Rutter, M. (1983). Cognitive deficits in the pathogenesis of autism. *Journal of Child Psychology & Psychiatry, 24,* 513–531.

Rutter, M., Caspi, A., Fergusson, D., Horwood, L. J., Goodman, R., Maughan, B., et al. (2004). Sex differences in developmental reading disability. *JAMA, 291,* 2007–2012.

Ryan, J. D., Althoff, R. R., Whitlow, S., & Cohen, N. J. (2000). Amnesia is a deficit in relational memory. *Psychological Science, 11(6),* 454–461.

Ryan, L., Cox, C., Hayes, S. M., & Nadel, L. (2008). Hippocampal activation during episodic and semantic memory retrieval: Comparing category production and category cued recall. *Neuropsychologia, 46,* 2109–2121.

Rypma, B., Eldreth, D. A., & Rebbechi, D. (2007). Age-related differences in activation-performance relations in delayed-response tasks: A multiple component analysis. *Cortex, 43,* 65–76.

Ryu, S. I., & Shenoy, K. V. (2009). Human cortical prostheses: Lost in translation? *Neurological Focus, 27,* E5.

Söderlund, G., Sikström, S., & Smart, A. (2007). Listen to the noise: Noise is beneficial for cognitive performance in ADHD. *Journal of Child Psychology & Psychiatry & Allied Disciplines, 48,* 840–847.

Saalmann, Y. B., Pigarev, I. N., & Vidyasagar, T. R. (2007). Neural mechanisms of visual attention: How top-down feedback highlights relevant locations. *Science, 316,* 1612–1615.

Sackheim, H. A., Gur, R. C., & Saucy, M. C. (1978). Emotions are expressed more intensely on the left side of the face. *Science, 202,* 434.

Sacks, O. (1995). *An anthropologist on Mars: Seven paradoxical tales.* New York: Alfred A. Knopf.

Sadato, N., Pascual-Leone, A., Grafman, J., Deiber, M.-P., Ibañez, V., & Hallett, M. (1998). Neural networks for Braille reading by the blind. *Brain, 121,* 1213–1229.

Sadato, N., Pascual-Leone, A., Grafman, J., Ibanez, V., Deiber, M.-P., Dold, G., & Hallett, M. (1996). Activation of the primary visual cortex by Braille reading in blind subjects. *Nature, 380,* 526–528.

Sadek, J. R., Johnson, S. A., White, D. A., Salmon, D. P., Taylor, K. I., Delapena, J. H., et al. (2004). Retrograde amnesia in dementia: Comparison of HIV-associated dementia, Alzheimer's disease, and Huntington's disease. *Neuropsychology, 18*(4), 692–699.

Sahakian, B. J., & Coull, J. T. (1994). Nicotine and tetrahydroaminoarcridine: Evidence for improved attention in patients with dementia of the Alzheimer's type. *Drug Development Research, 31,* 80–88.

Saito, H. A., Yukic, M., Tanaka, K., Hikosaka, K., Fukada, Y., & Iwai, E. (1986). Integration of direction signals of image motion in the superior temporal sulcus of the macaque monkey macaca-fuscafa. *Journal of Neuroscience, 6,* 147–157.

Sakai, K. L., Nauchi, A., Tatsuno, Y., Hirano, K., Muraishi, Y., Kimura, M., Bostwick, M., & Yusa, N. (2009). Distinct roles of left inferior frontal regions that explain individual differences in second language acquisition. *Human Brain Mapping, 30,* 2440–2452.

Sakai, K., & Miyashita, Y. (1991). Neural organization for the long-term memory of paired associates. *Nature, 354,* 152–155.

Sakata, H., Shibutani, H., Kawano, K., & Harrington, T. L. (1985). Neural mechanism of space vision in the parietal association cortex of the monkey. *Vision Research, 25,* 453–463.

Sakata, H., Taira, M., Kusunoki, M., Murata, A., & Tanaka, Y. (1997). The parietal association cortex in depth perception and visual control of hand action. *Trends in Neurosciences, 20,* 350–357.

Sakurai, Y., Momose, T., Iwata, M., Sudo, Y., Ohtomo, K., & Kanazawa, I. (2000). Different cortical activity in reading Kanji words, Kana words and Kana nonwords. *Cognitive Brain Research, 9*(1), 111–115.

Salamy, A. (1978). Commissural transmission: Maturational changes in humans. *Science, 200,* 1409–1411.

Salcido, R., & Costich, J. F. (1992). Recurrent traumatic brain injury. *Brain Injury, 6,* 293–298.

Salisbury, D. F., Shenton, M. E., Sherwood, A. R., Fischer, I. A., Yurgelun-Todd, D. A., Tohen, M., & McCarley, R. W. (1998). First-episode schizophrenic psychosis differs from first-episode affective psychosis and controls in P300 amplitude over left temporal lobe. *Archives of General Psychiatry, 55,* 173–180.

Salmelin, R., & Kujala, J. (2006). Neural representation of language: Activation versus long-range connectivity. *Trends in Cognitive Sciences, 10,* 519–525.

Salmon, D. P., & Butters, N. (1995). Neurobiology of skill and habit learning. *Current Opinion in Neurobiology, 5*(2), 184–190.

Salmond, C. H., Menon, D. K., Chatfield, D. A., Williams, G. B., Pena, A., Sahakian, B. J., & Pickard, J. D. (2006). Diffusion tensor imaging in chronic head injury survivors: Correlations with learning and memory indices. *NeuroImage, 29,* 117–124.

Salthouse, T. A. (1996). The processing-speed theory of adult age differences in cognition. *Psychological Review, 103,* 403–428.

Sampaio, R. C., & Truwit, C. L. (2001). Myelination in the developing human brain. In C. A. Nelson & M. Luciana (Eds.), *Handbook of developmental cognitive neuroscience* (pp. 35–44). Cambridge, MA: MIT Press.

Samuelsson, H., Hjelmquist, E., Jensen, C., Ekholm, S., & Blomstrand, C. (1998). Nonlateralized attentional deficits: An important component behind persisting visuospatial neglect? *Journal of Clinical & Experimental Neuropsychology, 20,* 73–88.

Sanders, A. L., Wheeler, M. E., & Buckner, R. L. (2000). Episodic recognition modulates frontal and parietal cortex activity. *Journal of Cognitive Neuroscience, (Suppl.),* 50A.

Sandman, C. A., O'Halloran, J. P., & Isenhart, R. (1984). Is there an evoked vascular response? *Science, 224,* 1355–1367.

Sandrini, M., Rossini, P., & Miniussi, C. (2008). Lateralized contribution of prefrontal cortex in controlling task-irrelevant information during verbal and spatial working memory tasks: rTMS evidence. *Neuropsychologia, 46*(7), 2056–2063.

Santarelli, L., Saxe, M., Gross, C., Surget, A., Battaglia, F., Dulawa, S., et al. (2003). Requirement of hippocampal neurogenesis for the behavioral effects of antidepressants. *Science, 301,* 805–809.

Sapolsky, R. M. (2004). Is impaired neurogenesis relevant to the affective symptoms of depression? *Biological Psychiatry, 56,* 137–139.

Sara, S. J. (2009). The locus coeruleus and noradrenergic modulation of cognition. *Nature Reviews Neuroscience, 10,* 211–223.

Sargolini, F., Fyhn, M., Hafting, T., McNaughton, B. L., Witter, M. P., Moser, M.-B., & Moser, E. I. (2006). Conjunctive representation of position, direction, and velocity in entorhinal cortex. *Science, 312,* 758–762.

Saron, C. D., & Davidson, R. J. (1989). Visual evoked potential measures of interhemispheric transfer time in humans. *Behavioral Neuroscience, 103,* 1115–1138.

Sarter, M., Givens, B., & Bruno, J. P. (2001). The cognitive neuroscience of sustained attention: Where top-down meets bottom-up. *Brain Research Reviews, 35,* 146–160.

Sarter, M., Hasselmo, M. E., Bruno, J. P., & Givens, B. (2005). Unraveling the attentional functions of cortical cholinergic inputs: Interactions between signal-driven and cognitive modulation of signal detection. *Brain Research Reviews, 48,* 98–111.

Sasanuma, S. (1980). Acquired dyslexia in Japanese: Clinical features and underlying mechanisms. In M. Coltheart, K. E. Patterson, & J. C. Marshall (Eds.), *Deep dyslexia* (pp. 91–118). London: Routledge & Kegan Paul.

Sato, T., Uchida, G., & Tanifuji, M. (2009). Cortical columnar organization is reconsidered in inferior temporal cortex. *Cerebral Cortex, 19,* 1870–1888.

Saur, D., Lange, R., Baumgaertner, A., Schraknepper, V., Willmes, K., Rijntjes, M., & Weiller, C. (2006). Dynamics of language reorganization after stroke. *Brain, 129,* 1371–1384.

Savazzi, S. (2003). Object-based versus object-centred neglect in reading words. *Neurocase, 9,* 203–212.

Savazzi, S., Mancini, F., Veronesi, G., & Posteraro, L. (2009). Repetita iuvant: Object-centered neglect with non-verbal visual stimuli induced by repetition. *Cortex, 45,* 863–869.

Sawaguchi, T., & Goldman-Rakic, P. S. (1991). D1 dopamine receptors in prefrontal cortex: Involvement in working memory. *Science, 251,* 947–950.

Saxe, R. (2006). Uniquely human social cognition. *Current Opinion in Neurobiology, 16,* 235–239.

Saxe, R., Carey, S., & Kanwisher, N. (2004). Understanding other minds: Linking developmental psychology and functional neuroimaging. *Annual Review of Psychology, 55,* 87–124.

Saxena, S., Brody, A. L., Maidment, K. M., Dunkin, J. J., Colgan, M., Alborzian, S., et al. (1999). Localized orbitofrontal and subcortical metabolic changes and predictors of response to paroxetine treatment in obsessive-compulsive disorder. *Neuropsychopharmacology, 21,* 683–693.

Sayres, R., & Grill-Spector, K. (2008). Relating retinotopic and object-selective responses in human lateral occipital cortex. *Journal of Neurophysiology, 100,* 249–267.

Scalf, P. E., Colcombe, S. J., McCarley, J. S., Erickson, K. I., Alvarado, M., Kim, J. S., et al. (2007). The neural correlates of an expanded functional field of view. *Journals of Gerontology Series B, Psychological Sciences & Social Sciences, 62*(Spec No. 1), 32–44.

Scarmeas, N., Luchsinger, J. A., Mayeux, R., & Stern, Y. (2007). Mediterranean diet and Alzheimer disease mortality. *Neurology, 69,* 1084–1093.

Scarmeas, N., Luchsinger, J. A., Schupf, N., Brickman, A. M., Cosentino, S., Tang, M. X., & Stern, Y. (2009). Physical activity, diet, and risk of Alzheimer disease. *JAMA, 302,* 627–637.

Scarmeas, N., Stern, Y., Mayeux, R., Manly, J., Schupf, N., & Luchsinger, J. A. (2009). Mediterranean diet and mild cognitive impairment. *Archives of Neurology, 66,* 216–225.

Schön, D., Anton, J. L., Roth, M., & Besson, M. (2002). An fMRI study of music sight-reading. *NeuroReport, 13,* 2285–2289.

Schacter, D. L. (1987). Implicit memory: History and current status. *Journal of Experimental Psychology: Learning, Memory, & Cognition, 13,* 501–518.

Schacter, D. L., & Tulving, E. (1994). Memory, amnesia, and the episodic/semantic distinction. In R. L. Isaacson & N. E. Spear (Eds.), *Expressions of knowledge.* New York: Plenum Press.

Schacter, D. L., & Wagner, A. D. (1999). Medial temporal lobe activations in fMRI and PET studies of episodic encoding and retrieval. *Hippocampus, 9*(1), 7–24.

Schacter, D. L., Curran, T., Galluccio, L., Milberg, W. P., & Bates, J. F. (1996). False recognition and the right frontal lobe: A case study. *Neuropsychologia, 34*(8), 793–808.

Schaffer, C. E., Davidson, R. J., & Saron, C. (1983). Frontal and parietal electroencephalogram asymmetry in depressed and nondepressed subjects. *Biological Psychiatry, 18,* 753–762.

Schaie, K. W. (1994). The course of adult intellectual development. *American Psychologist, 49,* 304–313.

Schall, J. D., & Boucher, L. (2007). Executive control of gaze by the frontal lobes. *Cognitive, Affective & Behavioral Neuroscience, 7,* 396–412.

Schapira, A. H. V. (2009). Neurobiology and treatment of Parkinson's disease. *Trends in Pharmacological Sciences, 30,* 41–47.

Scheffers, M. K., Coles, M. G. H., Bernstein, P., Gehring, W. J., & Donchin, E. (1996). Event-related brain potentials and error-related processing: An analysis of incorrect responses to go and no-go stimuli. *Psychophysiology, 33,* 42–53.

Scheibel, A. B. (1984). A dendritic correlate of human speech. In N. Geschwind & A. M. Galaburda (Eds.), *Cerebral dominance: The biological foundations* (pp. 43–52). Cambridge, MA: Harvard University Press.

Schenck, F., & Morris, R. G. M. (1985). Dissociation between components of spatial memory in rats after recovery from the effects of retrohippocampal lesions. *Experimental Brain Research, 58,* 11–28.

Schenk, T., Ellison, A., Rice, N., & Milner, A. D. (2005). The role of V5/MT1 in the control of catching movements: An rTMS study. *Neuropsychologia, 43,* 189–198.

Scherberger, H., & Andersen, R. A. (2004). Sensorimotor transformation in the posterior parietal cortex. In L. M. Chalupa & J. S. Werner (Eds.), *The visual neurosciences* (pp. 1324–1336). Cambridge, MA: MIT Press.

Scherg, M. (1992). Functional imaging and localization of electromagnetic brain activity. *Brain Topography, 5,* 103–111.

Schienle, A., Schafer, A., & Vaitl, D. (2008). Individual differences in disgust imagery: A functional magnetic resonance imaging study. *NeuroReport, 19,* 527–530.

Schiff, N. D. (2008). Central thalamic contributions to arousal regulation and neurological disorders of consciousness. *Annals of the New York Academy of Sciences, 1129,* 105–118.

Schiff, N. D., Giacino, J. T., Kalmar, K., Victor, J. D., Baker, K., Gerber, M., et al. (2007). Behavioural improvements with thalamic stimulation after severe traumatic brain injury. *Nature, 448,* 600–603.

Schiff, N. D., Rodriguez-Moreno, D., Kamal, A., Kim, K. H. S., Giacino, J. T., Plum, F., & Hirsch, J. (2005). fMRI reveals large-scale network activation in minimally conscious patients. *Neurology, 64,* 514–523.

Schiller, P. H., Logothetis, N. K., & Charles, E. R. (1990). Functions of the colour-opponent and broad-band channels of the visual system. *Nature, 343,* 68–70.

Schiller, P. H., Sandell, J. H., & Maunsell, J. H. R. (1987). The effect of frontal eye field and superior colliculus lesions on saccadic latencies in the rhesus monkey. *Journal of Neurophysiology, 57,* 1033–1049.

Schiller, P. H., True, S. D., & Conway, J. L. (1980). Deficits in eye movements following frontal eye field and superior colliculus ablations. *Journal of Neurophysiology, 44,* 1175–1189.

Schindler, I., Rice, N. J., McIntosh, R. D., Rossetti, Y., Vighetto, A., & Milner, A.D. (2004). Automatic avoidance of obstacles is a dorsal stream function: Evidence from optic ataxia. *Nature Neuroscience, 7,* 779–784.

Schlaepfer, T. E., Cohen, M. X., Frick, C., Kosel, M., Brodesser, D., Axmacher, N., et al. (2008). Deep brain stimulation to reward circuitry alleviates anhedonia in refractory major depression. *Neuropsychopharmacology, 33,* 368–377.

Schlag-Rey, M., Schlag, J., & Dassonville, P. (1992). How the frontal eye field can impose a saccade goal on superior colliculus neurons. *Journal of Neurophysiology, 67,* 1003–1005.

Schmidt, R. H., & Grady, M. S. (1995). Loss of forebrain cholinergic neurons following fluid percussion injury. *Journal of Neurosurgery, 83,* 496–502.

Schmitt, J. A. J., Wingen, M., Ramaekers, J. G., Evers, E. A. T., & Riedel, W. J. (2006). Serotonin and human cognitive performance. *Current Pharmaceutical Design, 12,* 2473–2486.

Schneider, F., Weiss, U., Kessler, C., Müller-Gärtner, H.-W., Posse, S., Salloum, J., et al. (1999). Subcortical correlates of differential classical conditioning of aversive emotional reactions in social phobia. *Biological Psychiatry, 45,* 863–871.

Schneider, K. A., & Kastner, S. (2009). Effects of sustained spatial attention in the human lateral geniculate nucleus and superior colliculus. *Journal of Neuroscience, 29,* 1784–1795.

Schneiderman, E. I., Murasugi, K. G., & Saddy, J. D. (1992). Story arrangement ability in right brain-damaged patients. *Brain & Language, 43,* 107–120.

Schnupp, J. W. H., & Carr, C. E. (2009). On hearing with more than one ear: Lessons from evolution. *Nature Neuroscience, 12,* 692–697.

Schoenbaum, G., Roesch, M. R., & Stalnaker, T. A. (2006). Orbitofrontal cortex, decision-making and drug addiction. *Trends in Neurosciences, 29,* 116–124.

Schoenbaum, G., Saddoris, M. P., Ramus, S. J., Shaham, Y., & Setlow, B. (2004). Cocaine-experienced rats exhibit learning deficits in a task sensitive to orbitofrontal cortex lesions. *European Journal of Neuroscience, 19,* 1997–2002.

Schoups, A., Vogels, R., Qian, N., & Orban, G. (2001). Practising orientation identification improves orientation coding in V1 neurons. *Nature, 412,* 549–553.

Schretlen, D. J., & Shapiro, A. M. (2003). A quantitative review of the effects of traumatic brain injury on cognitive functioning. *International Review of Psychiatry, 15,* 341–349.

Schuff, N., Woerner, N., Boreat, L., Kornfield, T., Shaw, L. M., Trojanowski, J. Q., et al. (2009). MRI of hippocampal volume loss in early Alzheimer's disease in relation to ApoE genotype and biomarkers. *Brain, 132,* 1067–1077.

Schutter, D. J. (2009). Antidepressant efficacy of high-frequency transcranial magnetic stimulation over the left dorsolateral prefrontal cortex in double-blind sham-controlled designs: A meta-analysis. *Psychological Medicine, 39*(1), 65–75.

Schwarz, A. (2009a, October 3). Congress to hold hearings on N.F.L. head injuries. *New York Times*

Schwarz, A. (2009b, September 30). Dementia risk seen in players in N.F.L. study. *New York Times*

Schwarzlose, R. F., Baker, C. I., & Kanwisher, N. (2005). Separate face and body selectivity on the fusiform gyrus. *Journal of Neuroscience, 25,* 11055–11059.

Scott, R. B., Harrison, J., Boulton, C., Wilson, J., Gregory, R., Parkin, S., et al. (2002). Global attentional-executive sequelae following surgical lesions to globus pallidus interna. *Brain, 125,* 562–574.

Scott, S. H. (2000). Population vectors and motor cortex: Neural coding or epiphenomenon? *Nature Neuroscience, 3,* 307–308.

Scott, S. H. (2008). Inconvenient truths about neural processing in primary motor cortex. *Journal of Physiology, 586,* 1217–1224.

Scoville, W. B., & Milner, B. (1957). Loss of recent memory after bilateral hippocampal lesions. *Journal of Neurology, Neurosurgery & Psychiatry, 20,* 11–15.

Scully, R. E. (1986). Case records of the Massachusetts General Hospital. Case 16–1986. *New England Journal of Medicine, 314,* 1101–1111.

Segalowitz, S., & Gruber, F. (Eds.). (1977). *Language development and neurological theory.* New York: Academic Press.

Seidenberg, M. S., & McClelland, J. L. (1989). A distributed, developmental model of word recognition and naming. *Psychological Review, 96*(4), 523–568.

Seidman, L. J., Thermenos, H. W., Poldrack, R. A., Peace, N. K., Koch, J. K., Faraone, S. V., & Tsuang, M. T. (2006). Altered brain activation in dorsolateral prefrontal cortex in adolescents and young adults at genetic risk for schizophrenia: An fMRI study of working memory. *Schizophrenia Research, 85,* 58–72.

Seidman, L. J., Valera, E. M., & Makris, N. (2005). Structural brain imaging of attention-deficit/hyperactivity disorder. *Biological Psychiatry, 57,* 1263–1272.

Seitz, R. J., & Roland, E. (1992). Learning of sequential finger movements in man: A combined kinematic and positron emission tomography (PET) study. *European Journal of Neuroscience, 4,* 154–165.

Semmes, J. (1968). Hemispheric specialization: A possible clue to mechanism. *Neuropsychologia, 6,* 11–26.

Semmes, J., Weinstein, S., Ghent, L., & Teuber, H.-L. (1955). Spatial orientation: 1. Analysis of locus of lesion. *Journal of Psychology, 39,* 227–244.

Semmes, J., Weinstein, S., Ghent, L., & Teuber, H.-L. (1963). Impaired orientation in personal and extrapersonal space. *Brain, 86,* 747–772.

Serences, J., Schwarzbach, J., Courtney, S., Golay, X., & Yantis, S. (2004). Control of object-based attention in human cortex. *Cerebral Cortex, 14,* 1346–1357.

Sereno, M. I., & Huang, R.-S. (2006). A human parietal face area contains aligned head-centered visual and tactile maps. *Nature Neuroscience, 9,* 1337–1343.

Sergeant, J. A. (2005). Modeling attention-deficit/hyperactivity disorder: A critical appraisal of the cognitive-energetic model. *Biological Psychiatry, 57,* 1248–1255.

Sergent, J. (1983). The role of the input in visual hemispheric asymmetries. *Psychological Bulletin, 93,* 481–514.

Sergent, J. (1990). Furtive incursions into bicameral minds. *Brain, 113,* 537–568.

Sergent, J. (1994). Brain-imaging studies of cognitive functions. *Trends in Neurosciences, 17*(6), 221–227.

Sergent, J., & Signoret, J.-L. (1992). Varieties of functional deficits in prosopagnosia. *Cerebral Cortex, 2,* 375–388.

Sergent, J., Ohta, S., & MacDonald, B. (1992). Functional neuroanatomy of face and object processing. *Brain, 115,* 15–36.

Sergent, J., Zuck, E., Terriah, S., &. Macdonald, B. (1992). Distributed neural network underlying musical sight-reading and keyboard performance. *Science, 257,* 106–109.

Serino, A., Angeli, V., Frassinetti, F., & Ládavas, E. (2006). Mechanisms underlying neglect recovery after prism adaptation. *Neuropsychologia, 44,* 1068–1078.

Serino, A., Barbiani, M., Rinaldesi, M. L., & Ládavas, E. (2009). Effectiveness of prism adaptation in neglect rehabilitation: A controlled trial study. *Stroke, 40,* 1392–1398.

Shadmehr, R., & Krakauer, J. W. (2008). A computational neuroanatomy for motor control. *Experimental Brain Research, 185,* 359–381.

Shallice, T. (1981). Phonological agraphia and the lexical route in writing. *Brain, 104,* 413–429.

Shallice, T. (1982). Specific impairments of planning. *Philosophical Transactions of the Royal Society of London, B298,* 199–209.

Shallice, T. (1988). *From neuropsychology to mental structure.* Cambridge, UK: Cambridge University Press.

Shallice, T., & Burgess, P. (1996). The domain of supervisory processes and temporal organization of behaviour. *Philosophical Transactions of the Royal Society of London Series B, Biological Sciences, 351,* 1405–1411.

Shallice, T., & Evans, M. E. (1978). The involvement of frontal lobes in cognitive estimation. *Cortex, 13,* 294–303.

Shallice, T., & Warrington, E. K. (1970). Independent functioning of verbal memory stores: A neuropsychological study. *Quarterly Journal of Experimental Psychology, 22,* 261–273.

Shallice, T., & Warrington, E. K. (1977). The possible role of selective attention in acquired dyslexia. *Neuropsychologia, 15,* 31–41.

Shallice, T., & Warrington, E. K. (1979). Auditory-verbal short-term memory impairment and conduction aphasia. *Brain & Language, 4,* 479–491.

Shallice, T., Warrington, E. K., & McCarthy, R. (*1983*). Reading without semantics. *Quarterly Journal of Experimental Psychology, 35A,* 111–138.

Shankman, S. A., Klein, D. N., Tenke, C. E., & Bruder, G. E. (2007). Reward sensitivity in depression: A biobehavioral study. *Journal of Abnormal Psychology, 116,* 95–104.

Shapiro, M. L., Heikki, T., & Eichenbaum, H. (1997). Cues that hippocampal place cells encode: Dynamic and hierarchical representation of local and distal stimuli. *Hippocampus, 7*(6), 624–642.

Shaw, P., Greenstein, D., Lerch, J., Clasen, L., Lenroot, R., Gogtay, N., et al. (2006). Intellectual ability and cortical development in children and adolescents. *Nature, 440,* 676–679.

Shaw, P., Lerch, J., Greenstein, D., Sharp, W., Clasen, L., Evans, A., et al. (2006). Longitudinal mapping of cortical thickness and clinical outcome in children and adolescents with attention-deficit/hyperactivity disorder. *Archives of General Psychiatry, 63,* 540–549.

Shaywitz, B. A., Shaywitz, S. E., Pugh, K. R., Constable, R. T., Skudlarski, P., Fulbright, R. K., et al. (1995). Sex differences in the functional organization of the brain for language. *Nature, 373,* 607–609.

Shaywitz, S. E., & Shaywitz, B. A. (2003). Dyslexia (specific reading disability). *Pediatrics in Review, 24,* 147–153.

Shelton, R. C., Keller, M. B., Gelenberg, A., Dunner, D. L., Hirschfeld, R., Thase, M. E., et al. (2001). Effectiveness of St. John's wort in major depression. *JAMA, 285,* 1978–1986.

Shen, L., & Alexander, G. E. (1997). Neural correlates of a spatial sensory-to-motor transformation in the primary motor cortex. *Journal of Neurophysiology, 77,* 1171–1194.

Shenton, M. E., Dickey, C. C., Frumin, M., & McCarley, R. W. (2001). A review of MRI findings in schizophrenia. *Schizophrenia Research, 49,* 1–52.

Shepard, R. (1988). The role of transformations in spatial cognition. In J. Stiles-Davis, M. Kritchevsky, & U. Bellugi (Eds.), *Spatial cognition: Brain bases and development* (pp. 81–110). Hillsdale, NJ: Erlbaum.

Sherman, S. M., & Guillery, R. W. (2004). The visual relays in the thalamus. In L. M. Chalupa & J. S. Werner (Eds.), *The visual neurosciences* (pp. 565–591). Cambridge, MA: MIT Press.

Sherrington, R., Rogaev, E. I., Liang, Y., Rogacva, E. A., Levesque, G., Ikeda, M., et al. (1995). Cloning of a gene bearing missense mutations in early onset familial Alzheimers disease. *Nature, 375,* 754–760.

Shibata, M., Abe, J., Terao, A., & Miyamoto, T. (2007). Neural mechanisms involved in the comprehension of metaphoric and literal sentences: An fMRI study. *Brain Research, 1166,* 92–102.

Shima, K., & Tanji, J. (2000). Neuronal activity in the supplementary and presupplementary motor areas for temporal organization of multiple movements. *Journal of Neurophysiology, 84,* 2148–2160.

Shimamura, A. P., Salmon, D. P., Squire, L. R., & Butters, N. (1987). Memory dysfunction and word priming in dementia and amnesia. *Behavioral Neuroscience, 101,* 347–351.

Shin, L. M., Dougherty, D. D., Orr, S. P., Pitman, R. K., Lasko, M., Macklin, M. L., et al. (2000). Activation of anterior paralimbic structures during guilt-related script-driven imagery. *Biological Psychiatry, 48,* 43–50.

Shin, L. M., Kosslyn, S. M., McNally, R. J., Alpert, N. M., Thompson, W. L., Rauch, S. L., et al. (1997). Visual imagery and perception in posttraumatic stress disorder: A positron emission tomographic investigation. *Archives of General Psychiatry, 54,* 233–241.

Shindo, K., Sugiyama, K., Huabao, L., Nishjima, K., Kondo, T., & Izumi, S.-I. (2006). Long-term effect of low-frequency repetitive transcranial magnetic stimulation over the unaffected posterior parietal cortex in patients with unilateral spatial neglect. *Journal of Rehabilitation Medicine, 38,* 65–67.

Shipp, S. (2004). The brain circuitry of attention. *Trends in Cognitive Sciences, 8,* 223–230.

Shirani, P., Thorn, J., Davis, C., Heidler-Gary, J., Newhart, M., Gottesman, R. F., & Hillis, A. E. (2009). Severity of hypoperfusion in distinct brain regions predicts severity of hemispatial neglect in different reference frames. *Stroke, 40,* 3563–3566.

Shohamy, D., Myers, C. E., Grossman, S., Sage, J., Gluck, M. A., & Poldrack, R. A. (2004). Cortico-striatal contributions to feedback-based learning: Converging data from neuroimaging and neuropsychology. *Brain, 127,* 851–859.

Shomstein, S., & Yantis, S. (2006). Parietal cortex mediates voluntary control of spatial and nonspatial auditory attention. *Journal of Neuroscience, 26,* 435–439.

Shumake, J., & Gonzalez-Lima, F. (2003). Brain systems underlying susceptibility to helplessness and depression. *Behavioral & Cognitive Neuroscience Reviews, 2,* 198–220.

Sidtis, J. J., Volpe, B. T., Watson, D. H., Rayport, M., & Gazzaniga, M. S. (1981). Variability in right hemisphere language after callosal section: Evidence for a continuum of generative capacity. *Journal of Neuroscience, 1,* 323–331.

Siebner, H. R., & Rothwell, J. (2003). Transcranial magnetic stimulation: New insights into representational cortical plasticity. *Experimental Brain Research, 148,* 1–16.

Siegal, M., & Blades, M. (2003). Language and auditory processing in autism. *Trends in Cognitive Sciences, 7,* 378–380.

Siegert, R. J., & Abernethy, D. A. (2005). Depression in multiple sclerosis: A review. *Journal of Neurology, Neurosurgery, & Psychiatry, 76,* 469–475.

Siegle, G. J., Carter, C. S., & Thase, M. E. (2006). Use of fMRI to predict recovery from unipolar depression with cognitive behavior therapy. *American Journal of Psychiatry, 163,* 735–738.

Siegle, G. J., Steinhauer, S. R., Thase, M. E., Stenger, A. V., & Carter, C. S. (2002). Can't shake that feeling: Event-related fMRI assessment of sustained amygdala activity in response to emotional information in depressed individuals. *Biological Psychiatry, 51,* 693–707.

Siegle, G. J., Thompson, W., Carter, C. S., Steinhauer, S. R., & Thase, M. E. (2007). Increased amygdala and decreased dorsolateral prefrontal BOLD responses in unipolar depression: Related and independent features. *Biological Psychiatry, 61,* 198–209.

Sigala, N., & Logothetis, N. K. (2002). Visual categorization shapes feature selectivity in the primate temporal cortex. *Nature, 415,* 318–320.

Sikström, S., & Söderlund, G. (2007). Stimulus-dependent dopamine release in attention-deficit/hyperactivity disorder. *Psychological Review, 114,* 1047–1075.

Sillito, A. M., & Jones, H. E. (2004). Feedback systems in visual processing. In L. M. Chalupa & J. S. Werner (Eds.), *The visual neurosciences* (pp. 609–624). Cambridge, MA: MIT Press.

Sillito, A. M., Cudeiro, J., & Jones, H. E. (2006). Always returning: Feedback and sensory processing in visual cortex and thalamus. *Trends in Neurosciences, 29,* 307–316.

Simmonds, D. J., Pekar, J. J., & Mostofsky, S. H. (2008). Meta-analysis of Go/No-go tasks demonstrating that fMRI activation associated with response inhibition is task-dependent. *Neuropsychologia, 46,* 224–232.

Sincich, L. C., & Horton, J. C. (2005). The circuitry of V1 and V2: Integration of color, form, and motion. *Annual Review of Neuroscience, 28,* 303–326.

Sincich, L. C., Park, K. F., Wohlgemuth, M. J., & Horton, J. C. (2004). Bypassing Vi: A direct geniculate input to area MT. *Nature Neuroscience, 7,* 1123–1128.

Singer, H. S. (2005). Tourette's syndrome: From behaviour to biology. *Lancet Neurology, 4,* 149–159.

Singer, T., Seymour, B., O'Doherty, J., Kaube, H., Dolan, R. J., & Frith, C. D. (2004). Empathy for pain involves the affective but not sensory components of pain. *Science, 303,* 1157–1162.

Sirigu, A., Duhamel, J.-R., Cohen, L., Pillon, B., Dubois, B., & Agid, Y. (1996). The mental representation of hand movements after parietal cortex damage. *Science, 273,* 1564–1568.

Sirovich, L., & Uglesich, R. (2004). The organization of orientation and spatial frequency in primary visual cortex. *Proceedings of the National Academy of Sciences, 101,* 16941–16946.

Sirviö, J. (1999). Strategies that support declining cholinergic neurotransmission in Alzheimer's disease patients. *Gerontology, 45* (Suppl. 1), 3–14.

Sisk, C., & Foster, D. (2004). The neural basis of puberty and adolescence. *Nature Neuroscience, 7,* 1040–1047.

Sitaram, N., Weingartner, H., & Gillin, J. C. (1978). Human serial learning: Enhancement with arechline and choline and impairment with scopolamine. *Science, 201,* 274–276.

Skaggs, W. E., & McNaughton, B. L. (1996). Replay of neuronal firing sequences in rat hippocampus during sleep following spatial experience. *Science, 271*(5257), 1870–1873.

Skinner, E. I., & Fernandes, M. A. (2007). Neural correlates of recollection and familiarity: A review of neuroimaging and patient data. *Neuropsychologia, 45,* 2163–2179.

Slagter, H. A., Weissman, D. H., Giesbrecht, B., Kenemans, J. L., Mangun, G. R., Kok, A., & Woldorff, M. G. (2006). Brain regions activated by endogenous preparatory set-shifting as revealed by fMRI. *Cognitive, Affective, & Behavioral Neuroscience, 6*(3), 175–189.

Slotnick, S. D., & Moo, L. R. (2006). Prefrontal cortex hemispheric specialization for categorical and coordinate visual spatial memory. *Neuropsychologia, 44,* 1560–1568.

Slotnick, S. D., Moo, L. R., Tesoro, M. A., & Hart, J. (2001). Hemispheric asymmetry in categorical versus coordinate visuospatial processing revealed by temporary cortical deactivation. *Journal of Cognitive Neuroscience, 13,* 1088–1096.

Slotnick, S. D., Thompson, W. L., & Kosslyn, S. M. (2005). Visual mental imagery induces retinotopically organized activation of early visual areas. *Cerebral Cortex, 15,* 1570–1583.

Small, D. M., Gregory, M. D., Mak, Y. E., Gitelman, D., Mesulam, M. M., & Parrish, T. (2003). Dissociation of neural representation of intensity and affective valuation in human gustation. *Neuron, 39,* 701–711.

Small, D. M., Zatorre, R. J., Dagher, A., Evans, A. C., & Jones-Gotman, M. (2001). Changes in brain activity related to eating chocolate: From pleasure to aversion. *Brain, 124,* 1720–1733.

Smith, A. B., Taylor, E., Brammer, M., Toone, B., & Rubia, K. (2006). Task-specific hypoactivation in prefrontal and temporoparietal brain regions during motor inhibition and task switching in medication-naïve children and adolescents with attention deficit hyperactivity disorder. *American Journal of Psychiatry, 163,* 1044–1051.

Smith, A. S., Boutrous, N. N., & Schwarzkopf, S. B. (1994). Reliability of P50 auditory event-related potential indices of sensory gating. *Psychophysiology, 31,* 495–502.

Smith, A. T., Singh, K. D., Williams, A. L., & Greenlee, M. W. (2001). Estimating receptive field size from fMRI data in human striate and extrastriate visual cortex. *Cerebral Cortex, 11,* 1182–1190.

Smith, A., & Nutt, D. (1996). Noradrenaline and attention lapses. *Nature, 380,* 291.

Smith, C. N., & Squire, L. R. (2008). Experience-dependent eye movements reflect hippocampus-dependent (aware) memory. *Journal of Neuroscience, 28,* 12825–12833.

Smith, M. L., & Milner, B. (1984). Differential effects of frontal-lobe lesions on cognitive estimation and spatial memory. *Neuropsychologia, 22,* 697–705.

Smith, M. L., & Milner, B. (1988). Estimation of frequency of occurrence of abstract designs after frontal or temporal lobectomy. *Neuropsychologia, 26*(2), 297–306.

Snow, J. C., Allen, H. A., Rafal, R. D., & Humphreys, G. W. (2009). Impaired attentional selection following lesions to the human pulvinar: Evidence for homology between human and monkey. *Proceedings of the National Academy of Sciences, USA, 106,* 4054–4059.

Snowdon, D. A., Kemper, S. J., Mortimer, J. A., Greiner, L. H., Wekstein, D. R., & Markesbery, W. R. (1996). Linguistic ability in early life and cognitive function and Alzheimer's Disease in late life: Findings from the Nun Study. *JAMA, 275,* 528–532.

Snyder, H. R., Feigenson, K., & Thompson-Schill, S. L. (2007). Prefrontal cortical response to conflict during semantic and phonological tasks. *Journal of Cognitive Neuroscience, 19,* 761–775.

Snyder, L. H., Batista, A. P., & Andersen, R. A. (1997). Coding of intention in the posterior parietal cortex. *Nature, 386,* 167–170.

Snyder, L. H., Grieve, K. L., Brotchie, P., & Andersen, R. A. (1998). Separate body- and world-reference representations of visual space in parietal cortex. *Nature, 394,* 887–891.

Solomon, P. R., Adams, F., Silver, A., Zimmer, J., & DeVeaux, R. (2002). Ginkgo for memory enhancement: A randomized controlled trial. *JAMA, 288,* 835–840.

Somerville, L. H., Heatherton, T. F., & Kelley, W. M. (2006). Anterior cingulate cortex responds differentially to expectancy violation and social rejection. *Nature Neuroscience, 9,* 1007–1008.

Sommer, M. A., & Wurtz, R. H. (2004). The dialogue between cerebral cortex and superior colliculus: Implications for saccadic target selection and corollary discharge. In L. M. Chalupa & J. S. Werner (Eds.), *The visual neurosciences* (pp. 1466–1484). Cambridge, MA: MIT Press.

Sommer, M. A., & Wurtz, R. H. (2008). Brain circuits for the internal monitoring of movements. *Annual Review of Neuroscience, 31,* 317–338.

Sotres-Bayon, F., Bush, D. E. A., & LeDoux, J. E. (2004). Emotional perseveration: An update on prefrontal-amygdala interactions in fear extinction. *Learning & Memory, 11,* 525–535.

Spanagel, R., & Weiss, F. (1999). The dopamine hypothesis of reward: Past and current status. *Trends in Neurosciences, 22,* 521–527.

Spaniol, J., Davidson, P. S., Kim, A. S., Han, H., Moscovitch, M., & Grady, C. L. (2009). Event-related fMRI studies of episodic encoding and retrieval: Meta-analyses using activation likelihood estimation. *Neuropsychologia, 47*(8–9), 1765–1779.

Speer, A. M., Kimbrell, T. A., Wassermann, E. M., Repella, J. D., Willis, M. W., Herscovitch, P., & Post, R. M. (2000). Opposite effects of high and low frequency rTMS on regional brain activity in depressed patients. *Biological Psychiatry, 48,* 1133–1141.

Spencer, K. A., & Slocomb, D. L. (2007). The neural basis of ataxic dysarthria. *Cerebellum, 6,* 58–65.

Spencer, K. M., Dien, J., & Donchin, E. (1999). A componential analysis of the ERP elicited by novel events using a dense electrode array. *Psychophysiology, 36*(3), 409–414.

Spencer, K. M., Nestor, P. G., Niznikiewicz, M. A., Salisbury, D. F., Shenton, M. E., & McCarley, R. W. (2003). Abnormal neural synchrony in schizophrenia. *Journal of Neuroscience, 23,* 7407–7411.

Sperling, A. J., Lu, Z.-L., Manis, F. R., & Seidenberg, M. S. (2005). Deficits in perceptual noise exclusion in developmental dyslexia. *Nature Neuroscience, 8,* 862–863.

Sperry, R. W. (1974). Lateral specialization in the surgically separated hemispheres. In F. Schmitt & F. Worden (Eds.), *The neurosciences: Third study program.* Cambridge, MA: MIT Press.

Sperry, R. W., Zaidel, E., & Zaidel, D. (1979). Self-recognition and social awareness in the deconnected minor hemisphere. *Neuropsychologia, 17,* 153–166.

Spezio, M. L., Adolphs, R., Hurley, R. S. E., & Piven, J. (2007). Analysis of face gaze in autism using "Bubbles." *Neuropsychologia, 45,* 144–151.

Spillane, J. A., White, P., Goodhardt, W. J., Flack, R. H., Bowen, D. M., & Davison, A. N. (1977). Selective vulnerability of neurones in organic dementia. *Nature, 266,* 558–559.

Spillantini, M. G., Bird, T. D., & Ghetti, B. (1998). Frontotemporal dementia and parkinsonism linked to chromosome 17: A new group of tauopathies. *Brain Pathology, 8,* 387–402.

Spillmann, L., Otte, T., Hamburger, K., & Magnussen, S. (2006). Perceptual filling-in from the edge of the blind spot. *Vision Research, 46,* 4252–4257.

Spires-Jones, T. L., Stoothoff, W. H., de Calignon, A., Jones, P. B., & Hyman, B. T. (2009). Tau pathophysiology in neurodegeneration: A tangled issue. *Trends in Neurosciences, 32,* 150–159.

Sprecht, K., Lie, C. H., Shah, N. J., & Fink, G. R. (2009). Disentangling the prefrontal network for rule selection by means of a non-verbal variant of the Wisconsin Card Sorting Test. *Human Brain Mapping, 30,* 1734–1743.

Spreen, O., Tupper, D., Risser, A., Tuokko, H., & Edgell, D. (1984). *Human developmental neuropsychology.* New York: Oxford University Press.

Springer, J. A., Binder, J. R., Hammeke, T. A., Swanson, S. J., Frost, J. A., Bellgowan, P. S. F., et al. (1999). Language dominance in neurologically normal and epilepsy subjects: A functional MRI study. *Brain, 122,* 2033–2045.

Squire, L. R. (1987). *Memory and brain.* New York: Oxford University Press.

Squire, L. R. (1992). Memory and the hippocampus: A synthesis from findings with rats, monkeys, and humans. *Psychological Review, 99*(2), 195–231.

Squire, L. R. (2009a). The legacy of patient H.M. for neuroscience. *Neuron, 61,* 6–9.

Squire, L. R. (2009b). Memory and brain systems: 1969–2009. *Journal of Neuroscience, 29,* 12711–12716.

Squire, L. R., & Alvarez, P. (1995). Retrograde amnesia and memory consolidation: A neurobiological perspective. *Current Opinion in Neurobiology, 5,* 169–177.

Squire, L. R., & Bayley, P. J. (2007). The neuroscience of remote memory. *Current Opinion in Neurobiology, 17,* 185–196.

Squire, L. R., & Cohen, N. J. (1979). Memory and amnesia: Resistance to disruption develops for years after learning. *Behavioral & Neural Biology, 25,* 115–125.

Squire, L. R., Stark, C. E., & Clark, R. E. (2004). The medial temporal lobe. *Annual Review of Neuroscience, 27,* 279–306.

Squire, L. R., Wixted, J., & Clark, R. E. (2007). Recognition memory and the medial temporal lobe: A new perspective. *Nature Reviews Neuroscience, 8*(11), 872–883.

St. George, M., Kutas, M., Martinez, A., & Sereno, M. I. (1999). Semantic integration in reading: Engagement on the right hemisphere during discourse processing. *Brain, 122,* 1317–1325.

Stanford, A. D., Sharif, Z., Corcoran, C., Urban, N., Malaspina, D., & Lisanby, S. H. (2008). rTMS strategies for the study and treatment of schizophrenia: A review. *International Journal of Neuropsychopharmacology, 11,* 563–576.

Stanford, T. R., Quessy, S., & Stein, B. E. (2005). Evaluating the operations underlying multisensory integration in the cat superior colliculus. *Journal of Neuroscience, 25,* 6499–6508.

Stanwood, G. D., & Levitt, P. (2001). The effects of cocaine on the developing nervous system. In C. A. Nelson & M. Luciana (Eds.), *Handbook of developmental cognitive neuroscience* (pp. 519–536). Cambridge, MA: MIT Press.

Stark, R., Zimmerman, M., Kagerer, S., Schienle, A., Walter, B., Weygandt, M., & Vaitl, D. (2007). Hemodynamic brain correlates of disgust and fear ratings. *NeuroImage, 37,* 663–673.

Starkstein, S. E., Brandt, J., Folstein, S., Strauss, M., Berthier, M. L., Pearlson, G. D., et al. (1988). Neuropsychological and neuroradiological correlates in Huntington's disease. *Journal of Neurology, Neurosurgery & Psychiatry, 51,* 1259–1263.

Steele, J. D., Kumar, P., & Ebmeier, K. P. (2007). Blunted response to feedback information in depressive illness. *Brain, 130,* 2367–2374.

Stehr-Green, P., Tull, P., Stellfeld, M., Mortenson, P.-B., & Simpson, D. (2003). Autism and thimerosal-containing vaccines: Lack of consistent evidence for an association. *American Journal of Preventive Medicine, 25,* 101–106.

Stein, J., Talcott, J., & Walsh, V. (2000). Controversy about the visual magnocellular deficit in developmental dyslexics. *Trends in Cognitive Sciences, 4,* 209–211.

Steinberg, L. (2005). Cognitive and affective development in adolescence. *Trends in Cognitive Sciences, 9,* 69–74.

Steinberg, L. (2008). A social neuroscience perspective on adolescent risk-taking. *Developmental Review, 28,* 78–106.

Steinvorth, S., Levine, B., & Corkin, S. (2005). Medial temporal lobe structures are needed to re-experience remote autobiographical memories: Evidence from H.M. and W.R. *Neuropsychologia, 43,* 470–496.

Sterling, P. (2004). How retinal circuits optimize the transfer of visual information. In L. M. Chalupa & J. S. Werner (Eds.), *The visual neurosciences* (pp. 234–259). Cambridge, MA: MIT Press.

Stern, Y., Gurland, B., Tatemichi, K., Tang, M. X., Wilder, D., & Mayeux, R. (1994). Influence of education and occupation on the incidence of Alzheimer's disease. *JAMA, 271,* 1004–1010.

Sternberg, S. S., Monsell, S., Knoll, R. L., & Wright, C. E. (1978). The latency and duration of rapid movement sequences: Comparisons of speech and type-writing. In G. E. Stelmach (Ed.), *Information processing in motor control and learning* (pp. 118–152). New York: Academic Press.

Stevens, B. (2003). Glia: Much more than the neuron's side-kick. *Current Biology, 13*(12), R469–472.

Stevens, M. C., Kiehl, K. A., Pearlson, G. D., & Calhoun, V. D. (2009). Brain networks during error commission. *Human Brain Mapping, 30,* 24–37.

Stewart, L. (2005). A neurocognitive approach to music reading. *Annals of the New York Academy of Sciences, 1060,* 377–386.

Stewart, L., von Kriegstein, K., Warren, J. D., & Griffiths, T. D. (2006). Music and the brain: Disorders of musical listening. *Brain, 129,* 2533–2553.

Stewart, R. (1998). Cardiovascular factors in Alzheimer's disease. *Journal of Neurology, Neurosurgery and Psychiatry, 65,* 143–147.

Stickgold, R. (2005). Sleep-dependent memory consolidation. *Nature, 437,* 1272–1278.

Stickgold, R. (2009). The simplest way to reboot your brain. *Harvard Business Review, 87,* 36.

Stiles, J., Reilly, J., Paul, B., & Moses, P. (2005). Cognitive development following early brain injury: Evidence for neural adaptation. *Trends in Cognitive Sciences, 9,* 136–143.

Stoerig, P. (1993). Sources of blindsight. *Science, 261,* 493.

Stoerig, P., Kleinschmidt, A., & Frahm, J. (1998). No visual responses in denervated V1: High-resolution functional magnetic resonance imaging of a blindsight patient. *Neuroreport, 9,* 21–25.

Stokes, A., Banich, M. T., & Elledge, V. C. (1991). Testing the tests: An empirical evaluation of screening tests for the detection of cognitive impairment in aviators. *Aviation Space & Environmental Medicine, 62,* 783–788.

Stokes, M., Thompson, R., Cusack, R., & Duncan, J. (2009). Top-down activation of shape-specific population codes in visual cortex during mental imagery. *Journal of Neuroscience, 29,* 1565–1572.

Stone, J., Davis, J., Leucht, S., & Pilowsky, L. (2009). Cortical dopamine D2/D3 receptors are a common site of action for antipsychotic drugs: An original patient data meta-analysis of the SPECT and PET in vivo receptor imaging literature. *Schizophrenia Bulletin, 35(4),* 789–797.

Stoodley, C. J., & Schmahmann, J. D. (2009). Functional topography in the human cerebellum: A meta-analysis of neuroimaging studies. *Neuroimage, 44,* 489–501.

Strafella, A. P., Paus, T., Barrett, J., & Dagher, A. (2001). Repetitive transcranial magnetic stimulation of the human prefrontal cortex induces dopamine release in the caudate nucleus. *Journal of Neuroscience, 21,* RC157(1–4).

Strauss, E., & Moscovitch, M. (1981). Perception of facial expressions. *Brain & Language, 13,* 308–332.

Strayer, D. L., Drews, F. A., & Crouch, D. J. (2006). A comparison of the cellphone driver and the drunk driver. *Human Factors, 48,* 381–391.

Stromswold, K., Caplan, D., Alpert, N., & Rauch, S. (1996). Localization of syntactic comprehension by positron emission tomography. *Brain & Language, 52,* 452–473.

Studdert-Kennedy, M., & Shankweiler, D. (1970). Hemispheric specialization for speech perception. *Journal of the Acoustical Society of America, 48,* 579–594.

Sturm, W., de Simone, A., Krause, B. J., Specht, K., Hesselmann, V., Radermacher, I., et al. (1999). Functional anatomy of intrinsic alertness: Evidence for a fronto-parietal-thalamic-brainstem network in the right hemisphere. *Neuropsychologia, 37,* 797–805.

Sturm, W., Longoni, F., Fimm, B., Dietrich, T., Weis, S., Kemna, S., et al. (2004). Network for auditory intrinsic alertness: A PET study. *Neuropsychologia, 42,* 563–568.

Stuss, D. T. (1987). Contribution of frontal lobe injury to cognitive impairment after closed head injury: Methods of assessment and recent findings. In H. S. Levin, J. Grafman, & H. M. Eisenberg (Eds.), *Neurobehavioral recovery from head injury* (pp. 166–177). New York: Oxford University Press.

Stuss, D. T., & Alexander, M. P. (2007). Is there a dysexecutive syndrome? *Philosophical Transactions of the Royal Society of London, Series B, Biological Sciences, 362,* 901–915.

Stuss, D. T., & Benson, D. F. (1986). *The frontal lobes.* New York: Raven Press.

Sugihara, T., Diltz, M. D., Averbeck, B. B., & Romanski, L. M. (2006). Integration of auditory and visual communication information in the primate ventrolateral prefrontal cortex. *Journal of Neuroscience, 26,* 11138–11147.

Sultana, R., Perluigi, M., & Butterfield, D. A. (2009). Oxidatively modified proteins in Alzheimer's disease (AD), mild cognitive impairment and animal models of AD: Role of Abeta in pathogenesis. *Acta Neuropathologica, 118,* 131–150.

Sun, T., Patoine, C., Abu-Khalil, A., Visvader, J., Sum, E., Cherry, T. J., et al. (2005). Early asymmetry of gene transcription in embryonic human left and right cerebral cortex. *Science, 308,* 1794–1798.

Sutherland, R. J., Whishaw, I. Q., & Kolb, B. (1983). A behavioral analysis of spatial localization following electrolytic, kainate- or colchicine-induced damage to the hippocampal formation in the rat. *Behavioral Brain Research, 7,* 133–153.

Sutton, S. K. (2002). Incentive and threat reactivity: Relations with anterior cortical activity. In D. Cervone & W. Mischel (Eds.), *Advances in personality science* (pp. 127–150). New York: Guilford Press.

Sylvester, R., Josephs, O., Driver, J., & Rees, G. (2007). Visual fMRI responses in human superior colliculus show a temporal-nasal asymmetry that is absent in lateral geniculate and visual cortex. *Journal of Neurophysiology, 97,* 1495–1502.

Symonds, G. P. (1937). Mental disorder following head injury. *Proceedings of the Royal Society of Medicine, 30,* 1081–1094.

Tajfel, H. (1970). Experiments in intergroup discrimination. *Scientific American, 223,* 96–102.

Talamini, L. M., Nieuwenhuis, I. L., Takashima, A., & Jensen, O. (2008). Sleep directly following learning benefits consolidation of spatial associative memory. *Learning & Memory, 15,* 233–237.

Tallal, P., Miller, S. L., Bedi, G., Byma, G., Wang, X., Nagarajan, S. S., et al. (1996). Language comprehension in language-learning impaired children improved with acoustically modified speech. *Science, 271,* 81–84.

Tamm, L., Menon, V., & Reiss, A. L. (2006). Parietal attentional system aberrations during target detection in adolescents with attention deficit hyperactivity disorder: Event-related fMRI evidence. *American Journal of Psychiatry, 163,* 1033–1043.

Tamminga, C. A. (2009). Principles of the pharmacotherapy of schizophrenia. In D. S. Charney & E. J. Nestler (Eds.), *Neurobiology of mental illness* (pp. 329–347). Oxford, UK: Oxford University Press.

Tamura, H., Kaneko, H., & Fujita, I. (2005). Quantitative analysis of functional clustering of neurons in the macaque inferior temporal cortex. *Neuroscience Research, 52,* 311–322.

Tanabe, J., Tregellas, J., Dalwani, M., Thompson, L., Owen, E., Crowley, T., & Banich, M. (2009). Medial orbitofrontal cortex gray matter is reduced in abstinent substance-dependent individuals. *Biological Psychiatry, 65,* 160–164.

Tanabe, J., Tregellas, J., Miller, D., Ross, R. G., & Freedman, R. (2002). Brain activation during smooth-pursuit eye movements. *NeuroImage, 17,* 1315–1324.

Tanji, J., Taniguchi, K., & Saga, T. (1980). Supplementary motor area: Neuronal response to motor instructions. *Journal of Neurophysiology, 43,* 60–68.

Tarkiainen, A., Helenius, P., Hansen, P. C., Cornelissen, P. L., & Salmelin, R. (1999). Dynamics of letter string perception in the human occipitotemporal cortex. *Brain, 122,* 2119–2131.

Tarr, M. J., & Bülthoff, H. H. (1998). Image-based object recognition in man, monkey, and machine. *Cognition, 67,* 1–20.

Tarr, M. J., & Gauthier, I. (2000). FFA: A flexible fusiform area for subordinate-level visual processing automatized by expertise. *Nature Neuroscience, 3(8),* 764–769.

Tatsuno, Y., & Sakai, K. L. (2005). Language-related activations in the left prefrontal regions are differentially modulated by age, proficiency, and task demands. *Journal of Neuroscience, 25(7),* 1637–1644.

Taub, E., & Uswatte, G. (2000). Constraint-induced movement therapy based on behavioral neuroscience. In R. G. Frank & T. R. Elliott (Eds.), *Handbook of rehabilitation psychology* (pp. 475–496). Washington, DC: American Psychological Association.

Taylor, K. S., Seminowicz, D. A., & Davis, K. D. (2009). Two systems of resting state connectivity between the insula and cingulate cortex. *Human Brain Mapping, 30,* 2731–45.

Taylor, P. C. J., Walsh, V., & Eimer, M. (2008). Combining TMS and EEG to study cognitive function and cortico-cortico interactions. *Behavioral Brain Research, 191,* 141–147.

Taylor, P. C., Nobre, A. C., & Rushworth, M. F. (2007). Subsecond changes in top down control exerted by human medial frontal cortex during conflict and action selection: A combined transcranial magnetic stimulation electroencephalography study. *Journal of Neuroscience, 27,* 11343–11353.

Taylor, S. E., Way, B. M., Welch, W. T., Hilmert, C. J., Lehman, B. J., & Eisenberger, N. I. (2006). Early family environment, current adversity, the serotonin transporter promoter polymorphism, and depressive symptomatology. *Biological Psychiatry, 60,* 671–676.

Taylor, S. F., Martis, B., Fitzgerald, K. D., Welsh, R. C., Abelson, J. L., Liberzon, I., et al. (2006). Medial frontal cortex activity and loss-related responses to errors. *Journal of Neuroscience, 26*(15), 4063–4070.

Taylor, S. F., Stern, E. R., & Gehring, W. J. (2007). Neural systems for error monitoring: Recent findings and theoretical perspectives. *Neuroscientist, 13,* 160–172.

Teasdale, G., & Jennett, B. (1974). Assessment of coma and impaired consciousness: A practical scale. *Lancet, 2,* 81–84.

Temple, E. (2002). Brain mechanisms in normal and dyslexic readers. *Current Opinion in Neurobiology, 12,* 178–183.

Teuber, H. L. (1955). Physiological psychology. *Annual Review of Psychology, 6,* 267–296.

Teuber, H. L., & Rudel, R. G. (1962). Behavior after cerebral lesions in children and adults. *Developmental Medicine & Child Neurology, 3,* 3–20.

Thibodeau, R., Jorgensen, R. S., & Kim, S. (2006). Depression, anxiety, and resting frontal EEG asymmetry: A meta-analytic review. *Journal of Abnormal Psychology, 115,* 715–729.

Thiel, C. M. (2003). Cholinergic modulation of learning and memory in the human brain as detected with functional neuroimaging. *Neurobiology of Learning and Memory, 80,* 234–244.

Thierry, G., Martin, C. D., Downing, P., & Pegna, A. J. (2007a). Controlling for interstimulus perceptual variance abolishes N170 face selectivity. *Nature Neuroscience, 10,* 505–511.

Thierry, G., Martin, C. D., Downing, P., & Pegna, A. J. (2007b). Is the N170 sensitive to the human face or to several intertwined perceptual and conceptual factors? *Nature Neuroscience, 10,* 802–803.

Thimm, M., Fink, G. R., Küst, J., Karbe, H., & Sturm, W. (2006). Impact of alertness training on spatial neglect: A behavioural and fMRI study *Neuropsychologia, 44,* 1230–1246.

Thimm, M., Fink, G. R., Küst, J., Karbe, H., Willmes, K., & Sturm, W. (2009). Recovery from hemineglect: Differential neurobiological effects of optokinetic stimulation and alertness training. *Cortex, 45,* 850–862.

Thoma, R. J., Hanlon, F. M., Moses, S. N., Edgar, J. C., Huang, M., Weisend, M. P., et al. (2003). Lateralization of auditory sensory gating and neuropsychological dysfunction in schizophrenia. *American Journal of Psychiatry, 160,* 1595–1605.

Thoma, R. J., Hanlon, F. M., Moses, S. N., Ricker, D., Huang, M., Edgar, C., et al. (2005). M50 sensory gating predicts negative symptoms in schizophrenia. *Schizophrenia Research, 73,* 311–328.

Thomas, J. D., & Trexler, L. E. (1982). Behavioral and cognitive deficits in cerebrovascular accident and closed head injury: Implications for cognitive rehabilitation. In L. E. Trexler (Ed.), *Cognitive rehabilitation: Conceptualization and intervention* (pp. 27–62). New York: Plenum Press.

Thomas-Antérion, C., Koenig, O., Navez, M., & Laurent, B. (1999). Midazolam effects on implicit and explicit memory processes in healthy subjects. *Psychopharmacology, 145,* 139–143.

Thompson, P. J., & Trimble, M. R. (1996). Neuropsychological aspects of epilepsy. In G. Igor & K. M. Adams (Eds.), *Neuropsychological assessment of neuropsychiatric disorders* (2d ed.; pp. 263–287). New York: Oxford University Press.

Thompson, P. M., Giedd, J. N., Woods, R. P., MacDonald, D., Evans, A. C., & Toga, A. W. (2000). Growth patterns in the developing brain detected by using continuum mechanical tensor maps. *Nature, 404,* 190–193.

Thompson, P. M., Vidal, C., Giedd, J. N., Gochman, P., Blumenthal, J., Nicolson, R., et al. (2001). Mapping adolescent brain change reveals dynamic wave of accelerated gray matter loss in very early-onset schizophrenia. *Proceedings of the National Academy of Sciences, 98,* 11650–11655.

Thompson-Schill, S. L., Aguirre, G. K., D'Esposito, M., & Farah, M. J. (1999). A neural basis of category and modality specificity of semantic knowledge. *Neuropsychologia, 37,* 671–676.

Thompson-Schill, S. L., Ramscar, M., & Chrysikou, E. G. (2009). Cognition without control: When a little frontal lobe goes a long way. *Current Directions in Psychological Science, 18,* 259–263.

Thurstone, L., & Thurstone, T. (1943). *The Chicago tests of primary mental abilities.* Chicago: Science Research Associates.

Tian, B., Reser, D., Durham, A., Kustov, A., & Rauschecker, J. P. (2001). Functional specialization in rhesus monkey auditory cortex. *Science, 292,* 290–293.

Tian, J. R., Zee, D. S., Lasker, A. G., & Folstein, S. E. (1991). Saccades in Huntington's disease: Predictive tracking and interaction between release of fixation and initiation of saccades. *Neurology, 41,* 875–881.

Tillfors, M., Furmark, T., Marteinsdottir, I., Fischer, H., Pissiota, A., Långström, B., & Fredrikson, M. (2001). Cerebral blood flow in subjects with social phobia during stressful speaking tasks: A PET study. *American Journal of Psychiatry, 158,* 1220–1226.

Tison, F., Dartigues, J. F., Auriacombe, S., Letenneur, L., Boller, F., & Alperovitch, A. (1995). Dementia in Parkinson's disease: A population-based study in ambulatory and institutionalized individuals. *Neurology, 45,* 705–708.

Todorov, E., & Jordan, M. I. (2002). Optimal feedback control as a theory of motor coordination. *Nature Neuroscience, 5,* 1226–1235.

Toga, A. W., & Thompson, P. M. (2003). Mapping brain asymmetry. *Nature Reviews Neuroscience, 4,* 37–48.

Toga, A. W., Thompson, P. M., & Sowell, E. R. (2006). Mapping brain maturation. *Trends in Neurosciences, 29,* 148–159.

Tognola, G., & Vignolo, L. A. (1980). Brain lesions associated with oral apraxia in stroke patients: A cliniconeuroradiological investigation with CT scan. *Neuropsychologia, 18,* 257–272.

Tomarken, A. J., Dichter, G. S., Garber, J., & Simien, C. (2004). Resting frontal brain activity: Linkages to maternal depression and socio-economic status among adolescents. *Biological Psychology, 67,* 77–102.

Tomasello, M., Call, J., & Hare, B. (2003). Chimpanzees understand psychological states—the question is which ones and to what extent. *Trends in Cognitive Sciences, 7,* 153–156.

Tomlinson, B. E. (1980). The structural and quantitative aspects of the dementias. In P. Roberts (Ed.), *Biochemistry of dementia* (pp. 15–52). London: Wiley.

Tomlinson, B. E. (1982). Plaques, tangles and Alzheimer's disease. *Psychological Medicine, 12,* 449–459.

Tong, F., & Engel, S. (2001). Interocular rivalry revealed in the human cortical blind spot representation. *Nature, 411,* 195–199.

Tonnaer, J. A., & Dekker, W. C. (1994). Nerve growth factor, neurotrophic agents and dementia. In D. G. Nicholson (Ed.), *Antidementia agents: Research and prospects for therapy* (pp. 139–165). London: Academic Press.

Tootell, R. B. H., Nelissen, K., Vanduffel, W., & Orban, G. A. (2004). Search for color "center(s)" in macaque visual cortex. *Cerebral Cortex, 14,* 353–363.

Tootell, R. B. H., Reppas, J. B., Kwong, K. K., Malach, R., Born, R. T., Brady, T. J., Rosen, B. R., & Belliveau, J. W. (1995). Functional analysis of human MT and related visual cortical areas using magnetic resonance imaging. *Journal of Neuroscience, 15,* 3215–3230.

Toth, C. (2008). The epidemiology of injuries to the nervous system resulting from sport and recreation. *Neurologic Clinic, 26,* 1–31.

Tovar-Spinoza, Z. S., Ochi, A., Rutka, J. T., Go, C., & Otsubo, H. (2008). The role of magnetoencephalography in epilepsy surgery. *Neurosurgical Focus, 25,* E16.

Tracey, I. (2005). Nociceptive processing in the human brain. *Current Opinion in Neurobiology, 15,* 478–487.

Tranel, D., & Damasio, A. R. (1988). Non-conscious face recognition in patients with face agnosia. *Behavioral Brain Research, 30,* 235–249.

Tranel, D., Damasio, A. R., & Damasio, H. (1988). Intact recognition of facial expression, gender, and age in patients with impaired recognition of face identity. *Neurology, 38,* 690–696.

Tranel, D., Damasio, H., & Damasio, A. R. (1997). A neural basis for the retrieval of conceptual knowledge. *Neuropsychologia, 35,* 1319–1327.

Trapp, B. D., & Nave, K. A. (2008). Multiple sclerosis: An immune or neurodegenerative disorder? *Annual Review of Neuroscience, 31,* 247–269.

Tregellas, J. R., Tanabe, J. L., Miller, D. E., Ross, R. G., Olincy, A., & Freedman, R. (2004). Neurobiology of smooth pursuit eye movement deficits in schizophrenia: An fMRI study. *American Journal of Psychiatry, 161,* 315–321.

Treisman, A. M., & Schmidt, H. (1982). Illusory conjunctions in the perception of objects. *Cognitive Psychology, 14,* 107–141.

Treisman, A., & Gelade, G. (1980). A feature integration theory of attention. *Cognitive Psychology, 12,* 97–136.

Trojano, L., Fragassi, N. A., Chicacchio, L., Izzo, O., Izzo, G., Di Cesare, G., Cristinzio, C., & Grossi, D. (2004). Relationships between constructional and visuospatial abilities in normal subjects and in focal brain-damaged patients. *Journal of Clinical & Experimental Neuropsychology, 26,* 1103–1112.

Ts'o, D. Y., Zarella, M., & Burkitt, G. (2009). Whither the hypercolumn? *Journal of Physiology, 587,* 2791–2805.

Tsao, D. Y., Freiwald, W. A., Knutsen, T. A., Mandeville, J. B., & Tootell, R. B. H. (2003). Faces and objects in macaque cerebral cortex. *Nature Neuroscience, 6,* 989–995.

Tsao, D. Y., Freiwald, W. A., Tootell, R. B. H., & Livingstone, M. S. (2006). A cortical region consisting entirely of face-selective cells. *Science, 311,* 670–674.

Tse, C.-Y., Lee, C.-L., Sullivan, J., Garnsey, S. M., Dell, G. S., Fabiani, M., & Gratton, G. (2007). Imaging cortical dynamics of language processing with the event-related optical signal. *Proceedings of the National Academy of Sciences, U.S.A., 104,* 17157–17162.

Tsuang, M. T., Boor, M., & Fleming, J. A. (1985). Psychiatric aspects of traffic accidents. *American Journal of Psychiatry, 142,* 538–546.

Tucker, D. M., Watson, R. T., & Heilman, K. M. (1977). Discrimination and evocation of affectively intoned speech in patients with right parietal disease. *Neurology, 27,* 947–958.

Tucker, D., & Williamson, P. (1984). Asymmetric neural control systems in human self-regulation. *Psychological Review, 91*(2), 185–215.

Tucker, M. A., Hirota, Y., Wamsley, E. J., Lau, H., Chaklader, A., & Fishbein, W. (2006). A daytime nap containing solely non-REM sleep enhances declarative but not procedural memory. *Neurobiology of Learning & Memory, 86,* 241–247.

Tulving, E. (1972). Episodic and semantic memory. In E. Tulving & W. Donaldson (Eds.), *Organization of memory* (pp. 381–403). New York: Academic Press.

Tulving, E. (1985). Memory and consciousness. *Canadian Psychologist, 25,* 1–12.

Tunik, E., Frey, S. H., & Grafton, S. T. (2005). Virtual lesions of the anterior intraparietal area disrupt goal-dependent on-line adjustments of grasp. *Nature Neuroscience, 8,* 505–511.

Turner, A. M., & Greenough, W. T. (1985). Differential rearing effects on rat visual cortex synapses: I. Synaptic and neuronal density and synapses per neuron. *Brain Research, 329,* 195–203.

Tyler, T. J., & DiScenna, P. (1986). The hippocampus memory indexing theory. *Behavioral Neuroscience, 100,* 147–152.

Udekwu, P., Kromhout-Schiro, S., Vaslef, S., Baker, C., & Oller, D. (2004). Glasgow Coma Scale score, mortality, and functional outcome in head-injured patients. *Journal of Trauma Injury, Infection, & Critical Care, 56,* 1084–1089.

Ungerleider, L. G. (1995). Functional brain imaging studies of cortical mechanisms for memory. *Science, 270*(5237), 769–775.

Ungerleider, L. G., & Mishkin, M. (1982). Two cortical visual systems. In D. J. Ingle, M. A. Goodale, & R. J. W. Mansfield (Eds.), *Analysis of visual behavior* (pp. 549–586). Cambridge, MA: MIT Press.

Ungerleider, L. G., & Mishkin, M. (1982). Two cortical visual systems. In D. J. Ingle, R. J. W. Mansfield, & M. S. Goodale (Eds.), *The analysis of visual behavior* (pp. 549–586). Cambridge, MA: MIT Press.

Ungerleider, L. G., & Pasternak, T. (2004). Ventral and dorsal processing streams. In L. M. Chalupa & J. S. Werner (Eds.), *The visual neurosciences* (pp. 541–562). Cambridge, MA: MIT Press.

Unterrainer, J., Rahm, B., Kaller, C., Quiske, K., Hoppe-Seyler, K., Meier, C., et al. (2004). Planning abilities and the Tower of London: Is this task measuring a discrete cognitive function? *Journal of Clinical & Experimental Neuropsychology, 26,* 846–856.

Upton, N., Chuang, T. T., Hunter, A. J., & Virley, D. J. (2008). 5-HT6 receptor antagonists as novel cognitive enhancing agents for Alzheimer's disease. *Neurotherapeutics, 5,* 458–469.

Urgesi, C., Candidi, M., Ionta, S., & Aglioti, S. M. (2007). Representation of body identity and body actions in extrastriate body area and ventral premotor cortex. *Nature Neuroscience, 10,* 30–31.

Usui, K., Ikeda, A., Nagamine, T., Matsuhashi, M., Kinoshita, M., Mikuni, N., et al. (2009). Temporal dynamics of Japanese morphogram and syllabogram processing in the left basal temporal area studied by event-related potentials. *Journal of Clinical Neurophysiology, 26,* 160–166.

Uttara, B., Singh, A. V., Zamboni, P., & Mahajan, R. T. (2009). Oxidative stress and neurodegenerative diseases: A review of upstream and downstream antioxidant therapeutic options. *Current Neuropharmacology, 7,* 65–74.

Utter, A. A., & Basso, M. A. (2008). The basal ganglia: An overview of circuits and function. *Neuroscience and Biobehavioral Reviews, 32,* 333–342.

Vaina, L.M., Lemay, M., Bienfang, D.C., Choi, A.Y., & Nakayama, K. (1990). Intact "biological motion" and "structure from motion" perception in a patient with impaired motion mechanisms: A case study. *Visual Neuroscience, 5,* 353–369.

Valera, E. M., Faraone, S. V., Murray, K. E., & Seidman, L. J. (2007). Meta-analysis of structural brain imaging findings in attention-deficit/hyperactivity disorder. *Biological Psychiatry, 61,* 1361–1369.

Vallar, G., & Baddeley, A. (1984). Phonological short-term store, phonological processing, and sentence comprehension: A neuropsychological case study. *Cognitive Neuropsychology, 1,* 121–141.

Vallar, G., & Perani, D. (1986). The anatomy of unilateral neglect after right-hemisphere stroke lesions. A clinical CT/scan study in man. *Neuropsychologia, 24,* 609–622.

Vallar, G., Guariglia, C., & Rusconi, M. L. (1997). Modulation of neglect syndrome by sensory stimulation. In P. Their & H. O. Karnath (Eds.), *Parietal lobe contributions to orientation in 3D-space* (pp. 401–429). Heidelberg: Springer-Verlag.

Vallar, G., Guariglia, C., Nico, D., & Pizzamiglio, L. (1997). Motor deficits and optokinetic stimulation in patients with left hemineglect. *Neurology, 49,* 1364–1370.

Vallar, G., Sterai, R., Bottini, G., Cappa, S., & Rusconi, M. L. (1990). Temporary remission of left hemi-anesthesia after vestibular stimulation: A sensory neglect phenomenon. *Cortex, 26,* 121–131.

Vallortigara, G. (2000). Comparative neuropsychology of the dual brain: A stroll through animals' left and right perceptual worlds. *Brain and Language, 73,* 189–219.

Vallortigara, G., & Bisazza, A. (2002). How ancient is brain lateralization? In L. J. Rogers & R. J. Andrew (Eds.), *Comparative vertebrate lateralization* (pp. 9–69). Cambridge, UK: Cambridge University Press.

Vallortigara, G., & Rogers, L. J. (2005). Survival with an asymmetrical brain: Advantages and disadvantages of cerebral lateralization. *Behavioral and Brain Sciences, 28,* 575–633.

Vallortigara, G., Rogers, L. J., Bisazza, A., Lippolis, G., & Robins, A. (1998). Complementary right and left hemifield use for predatory and agonistic behaviour in toads. *NeuroReport, 9,* 3341–3344.

Van Bavel, J. J., Packer, D. J., & Cunningham, W. A. (2008). The neural substrates of in-group bias. *Psychological Science, 19,* 1131–1139.

van Boxtel, M. P., Paas, F. G., Houx, P. J., Adam, J. J., Teeken, J. C., & Jolles, J. (1997). Aerobic capacity and cognitive performance in a cross-sectional aging study. *Medicine & Science in Sports & Exercise, 29*, 1357–1365.

van den Heuvel, O. A., Groenewegen, H. J., Barkhof, F., Lazeron, R. H., van Dyck, R., & Veltman, D. J., (2003). Frontostriatal system in planning complexity: A parametric functional magnetic resonance version of Tower of London Task. *NeuroImage, 18*, 367–374.

van der Ham, I. J. M., van Wezel, R. J. A., Oleksiak, A., & Postma, A. (2007). The time course of hemispheric differences in categorical and coordinate spatial processing. *Neuropsychologia, 45*, 2492–2498.

Van Der Werf, J., Jensen, O., Fries, P., & Medendorp, W. P. (2008). Gamma-band activity in human posterior parietal cortex encodes the motor goal during delayed prosaccades and antisaccades. *Journal of Neuroscience, 28*, 8397–8405.

van Donkelaar, P., Langan, J., Rodriguez, E., Drew, A., Halterman, C., Osternig, L. R., & Chou, L.-S. (2005). Attentional deficits in concussion. *Brain Injury, 19*, 1031–1039.

van Heuven, W. J., Schriefers, H., Dijkstra, T., & Hagoort, P. (2008). Language conflict in the bilingual brain. *Cerebral Cortex, 18*, 2706–2716.

Van Lancker, D., & Sidtis, J. J. (1992). The identification of affective-prosodic stimuli by left and right brain damaged subjects: All errors are not created equal. *Journal of Speech & Hearing Research, 35*, 963–970.

Van Petten, C., & Luka, B. J. (2006). Neural localization of semantic context effects in electromagnetic and hemodynamic studies. *Brain & Language, 97*, 279–293.

van Praag, H., Kempermann, G., & Gage, F. H. (1999). Running increases cell proliferation and neurogenesis in the adult mouse dentate gyrus. *Nature Neuroscience, 2*, 266–270.

van Schie, H. T., Mars, R. B., Coles, M. G. H., & Bekkering, H. (2004). Modulation of activity in medial frontal and motor cortices during error observation. *Nature Neuroscience, 7*, 549–554.

van Veen, V., & Carter, C. S. (2002). The timing of action-monitoring processes in the anterior cingulate cortex. *Journal of Cognitive Neuroscience, 14*, 593–602.

Van Voorhis, S., & Hillyard, S. A. (1977). Visual evoked potentials and selective attention to points in space. *Perception & Psychophysics, 22*, 54–62.

Vandenberghe, R., & Gillebert, C. R. (2009). Parcellation of parietal cortex: Convergence between lesion-symptom mapping and mapping of the intact functioning brain. *Behavioural Brain Research, 199*, 171–182.

Vargha-Khadem, F., Gadian, D. G., Watkins, K. E., Connelly, A., Van Paesschen, W., & Mishkin, M. (1997). Different effects of early hippocampal pathology on episodic and semantic memory. *Science, 277*, 376–380.

Vellas, B., Andrieu, S., Ousset, P. J., Ouzid, M., Mathiex-Fortunet, H., & GuidAge Study Group. (2006). The GuidAge study: Methodological issues. A 5-year double-blind randomized trial of the efficacy of EGb 761 for prevention of Alzheimer disease in patients over 70 with a memory complaint. *Neurology, 67* (Suppl 3), S6–S11.

Verhagen, J. V. (2007). The neurocognitive bases of human multimodal food perception: Consciousness. *Brain Research Reviews, 53*, 271–286.

Verma, A. (2000). Opportunities for neuroprotection in traumatic brain injury. *Journal of Head Trauma Rehabilitation, 15*, 1149–1161.

Videbech, P., & Ravnkilde, B. (2004). Hippocampal volume and depression: A meta-analysis of MRI studies. *American Journal of Psychiatry, 161*, 1957–1966.

Vigneau, M., Beaucousin, V., Hervé, P. Y., Duffau, H., Crivello, F., Houdé, O., Mazoyer, B., & Tzourio-Mazoyer, N. (2006). Meta-analyzing left hemisphere language areas: Phonology, semantics, and sentence processing. *NeuroImage, 30*, 1414–1432.

Vilberg, K. L., & Rugg, M. D. (2008). Memory retrieval and the parietal cortex: A review of evidence from a dual-process perspective. *Neuropsychologia, 46*(7), 1787–1799.

Vilberg, K. L., & Rugg, M. D. (2009). Functional significance of retrieval-related activity in lateral parietal cortex: Evidence from fMRI and ERPs. *Human Brain Mapping, 30*(5), 1490–1501.

Voeller, K. K. S. (2006). Mental retardation. In M. J. Farah & T. E. Feinberg (Eds.), *Patient-based approaches to cognitive neuroscience* (2d ed.; pp. 397–406). Cambridge, MA: MIT Press.

Vogt, B. A., Finch, D. M., & Olson, C. R. (1992). Functional heterogeneity in cingulate cortex: The anterior executive and posterior evaluative regions. *Cerebral Cortex, 2*, 435–443.

Vohn, R., Fimm, B., Weber, J., Schnitker, R., Thron, A., Spijkers, W., et al. (2007). Management of attentional resources in within-modal and cross-modal divided attention tasks: An fMRI study. *Human Brain Mapping, 28*, 1267–1275.

Volkow, N. D., & Fowler, J. S. (2000). Addiction, a disease of compulsion and drive: Involvement of the orbitofrontal cortex. *Cerebral Cortex, 10*, 318–325.

von Helmholtz, H. (1910/1925). *Treatise on physiological optics.* English translation: Optical Society of America, Dover Publications.

von Kriegstein, K., Kleinschmidt, A., Sterzer, P., & Giraud, A.-L. (2005). Interaction of face and voice areas during speaker recognition. *Journal of Cognitive Neuroscience, 17*, 367–376.

von Plessen, K., Lundervold, A., Duta, N., Heiervang, E., Klauschen, F., Smievoll, A. I., et al. (2002). Less developed corpus callosum in dyslexic subjects: A structural MRI study. *Neuropsychologia, 40*, 1035–1044.

von Stockert, T. R., & Bader, A. L. (1976). Some relations of grammar and lexicon in aphasia. *Cortex, 12*, 49–60.

Vuilleumier, P. (2005). How brains beware: Neural mechanisms of emotional attention. *Trends in Cognitive Sciences, 9*, 585–594.

Vuilleumier, P., Sagiv, N., Hazeltine, E., Poldrack, R. A., Swick, D., Rafal, R. D., & Gabrieli, J. D. E. (2001). Neural fate of seen and unseen faces in visuospatial neglect: A combined event-related functional MRI and event-related potential study. *Proceedings of the National Academy of Sciences, USA, 98*, 3495–3500.

Wada, J. A., Clarke, R., & Hamm, A. (1975). Cerebral hemispheric asymmetry in humans. *Archives of Neurology, 32*, 239–246.

Wager, T. D., Jonides, J., Smith, E. E., & Nichols, T. E. (2005). Toward a taxonomy of attention shifting: Individual differences in fMRI during multiple shift types. *Cognitive, Affective & Behavioral Neuroscience, 5*, 127–143.

Wager, T., & Smith, E. (2003). Neuroimaging studies of working memory: A meta-analysis. *Cognitive, Affective & Behavioral Neuroscience, 3*, 255–274.

Wagner, A. D. (1999). Working-memory contributions to human learning and remembering. *Neuron, 22*(1), 19–22.

Wagner, A. D., Desmond, J. E., Glover, G. H., & Gabrieli, J. D. (1998). Prefrontal cortex and recognition memory. Functional-MRI evidence for context-dependent retrieval processes. *Brain, 121*(10), 1985–2002.

Wagner, A. D., Shannon, B. J., Kahn, I., & Buckner, R. L. (2005). Parietal lobe contributions to episodic memory retrieval. *Trends in Cognitive Science, 9*, 445–453.

Wagner, G., Koch, K., Reichenbach, J. R., Sauer, H., & Schlösser, R. G. (2006). The special involvement of the rostrolateral prefrontal cortex in planning abilities: An event-related fMRI study with the Tower of London paradigm. *Neuropsychologia, 44*, 2337–2347.

Wagner, H. N., Burns, D. H., Dannais, R. F., Wong, D. F., Langstrom, B., Duefler, T., et al. (1983). Imaging dopamine receptors in the human brain by positron tomography. *Science, 221*, 1264–1266.

Wahlin, T.-B. R., Lundin, A., & Dear, K. (2007). Early cognitive deficits in Swedish gene carriers of Huntington's disease. *Neuropsychology, 21*, 31–44.

Wake, G., Court, J., Pickering, A., Lewis, R., Wilkins, R., & Perry, E. (2000). CNS acetylcholine receptor activity in European medicinal plants traditionally used to improve failing memory. *Journal of Ethnopharmacology, 69*, 105–114.

Waldman, I. D., & Gizer, I. R. (2006). The genetics of attention deficit hyperactivity disorder. *Clinical Psychology Review, 26*, 396–432.

Walker, D. L., Ressler, K. J., Lu, K.-T., & Davis, M. (2002). Facilitation of conditioned fear extinction by systemic administration or intra-amygdala infusions of D-cycloserine as assessed with fear-potentiated startle in rats. *Journal of Neuroscience, 22*, 2343–2351.

Walker, E. F., Savoie, T., & Davis, D. (1994). Neuromotor precursors of schizophrenia. *Schizophrenia Bulletin, 20*, 441–451.

Walker, E., & Bollini, A. M. (2002). Pubertal neurodevelopment and the emergence of psychotic symptoms. *Schizophrenia Research, 54*, 17–53.

Walker, F. O. (2007). Huntington's disease. *Seminars in Neurology, 27*, 143–150.

Walker, J. P., Daigle, T., & Buzzard, M. (2002). Hemispheric specialization in processing prosodic structures: Revisited. *Aphasiology, 16*, 1155–1172.

Walterfang, M., Wood, S. J., Velakoulis, D., & Pantelis, C. (2006). Neuropathological, neurogenetic and neuroimaging evidence for white matter pathology in schizophrenia. *Neuroscience & Biobehavioral Reviews, 30*, 918–948.

Wandell, B. A., & Wade, A. R. (2003). Functional imaging of the visual pathways. *Neurologic Clinics of North America, 21*, 417–443.

Wang, L., Hosakere, M., Trein, J. C. L., Miller, A., Ratnanather, J. T., Barch, D. M., et al. (2007). Abnormalities of cingulate gyrus neuroanatomy in schizophrenia. *Schizophrenia Research, 93*, 66–78.

Wang, X., Zhang, M., Cohen, I. S., & Goldberg, M. E. (2007). The proprioceptive representation of eye position in monkey primary somatosensory cortex. *Nature Neuroscience, 10*, 640–646.

Wang, Y., Celebrini, S., Trotter, Y., & Barone, P. (2008). Visuo-auditory interactions in the primary visual cortex of the behaving monkey: Electrophysiological evidence. *BMC Neuroscience, 9*, 79.

Warburton, E., Price, C. J., Swinburn, K., & Wise, R. J. S. (1999). Mechanisms of recovery from aphasia: Evidence from positron emission tomography studies. *Journal of Neurology, Neurosurgery, & Psychiatry, 66*, 155–161.

Wardak, C., Ibos, G., Duhamel, J. R., & Olivier, E. (2006). Contribution of the monkey frontal eye field to covert visual attention. *Journal of Neuroscience, 26*, 4228–4235.

Warren, S. T., & Nelson, D. L. (1994). Advances in molecular analysis of fragile X syndrome. *JAMA, 271*(7), 536–542.

Warrington, E. K. (1975). The selective impairment of semantic memory. *Quarterly Journal of Experimental Psychology, 27*, 187–199.

Warrington, E. K. (1982). Neuropsychological studies of object recognition. *Philosophical Transactions of the Royal Society of London, B298*, 15–33.

Warrington, E. K. (1996). Studies of retrograde memory: A long-term view. *Proceedings of the National Academy of Science, 93*, 13523–13526.

Warrington, E. K., & James, M. (1988). Visual apperceptive agnosia: A clinico-anatomical study of three cases. *Cortex, 24*, 13–32.

Warrington, E. K., & McCarthy, R. A. (1987). Categories of knowledge: Further fractionations and an attempted integration. *Brain, 110*, 1273–1296.

Warrington, E. K., & Rabin, P. (1970). Perceptual matching in patients with cerebral lesions. *Neuropsychologia, 8*, 475–487.

Warrington, E. K., & Sanders, H. I. (1971). The fate of old memories. *Quarterly Journal of Experimental Psychology, 23*, 432–442.

Warrington, E. K., & Shallice, T. (1980). Word-form dyslexia. *Brain, 103*, 99–112.

Warrington, E. K., & Shallice, T. (1984). Category specific semantic impairments. *Brain, 107*, 829–854.

Warrington, E. K., & Taylor, A. M. (1973). The contribution of the right parietal lobe to object recognition. *Cortex, 9*, 152–164.

Warrington, E. K., & Taylor, A. M. (1978). Two categorical stages of object recognition. *Perception, 7*, 695–705.

Warrington, E. K., & Weiskrantz, L. (1968). A new method of testing long-term retention with special reference to amnesic patients. *Nature, 217*, 972–974.

Warrington, E. K., & Weiskrantz, L. (1970). The amnesic syndrome: Consolidation or retrieval? *Nature, 228*, 628–630.

Wartenburger, I., Heekeren, H. R., Burchert, F., De Bleser, R., & Villringer, A. (2003). Grammaticality judgments on sentences with and without movement of phrasal constituents: An event-related fMRI study. *Journal of Neurolinguistics, 16*, 301–314.

Wasserman, E. M. (1998). Risk and safety of repetitive transcranial magnetic stimulation: Report and suggested guidelines from the International Workshop on the Safety of Repetitive Transcranial Magnetic Stimulation, June 5–7, 1996. *Electroencephalography and Clinical Neurophysiology, 198*, 1–16.

Wasserman, E. M., Cohen, L. G., Flitman, S. S., Chen, R., & Hallett, M. (1996). Seizure in healthy people with repeated "safe" trains of transcranial magnetic stimulation. *Lancet, 347*, 825–826.

Watkins, K., & Paus, T. (2004). Modulation of motor excitability during speech perception: The role of Broca's area. *Journal of Cognitive Neuroscience, 16*, 978–987.

Watson, R. T., Valenstein, E., & Heilman, K. M. (1981). Thalamic neglect. *Archives of Neurology, 38*, 501–506.

Weaver, B., Bédard, M., McAuliffe, J., & Parkkari, M. (2009). Using the Attention Network Test to predict driving test scores. *Accident; Analysis & Prevention, 41*, 76–83.

Weaver, F. M., Follett, K., Stern, M., Hur, K., Harris, C., Marks, M. J., et al. (2009). Bilateral deep brain stimulation vs. best medical therapy for patients with advanced Parkinson disease: A randomized controlled trial. *JAMA, 301*, 63–73.

Wechsler, D. (2002). *Wechsler Preschool and Primary Scale of Intelligence, Third Edition,* Upper Saddle River, N.J.: Pearson Education.

Wechsler, D. (2003). *Wechsler Intelligence Scale for Children, Fourth Edition.* Upper Saddle River, N.J.: Pearson Education.

Wechsler, D. (2008). *Wechsler Adult Intelligence Scale—Fourth Edition.* Upper Saddle River, N.J.: Pearson Education.

Wechsler, D., & Naglieri, J. A. (2006). *Wechsler Nonverbal Scale of Ability.* Upper Saddle River, N.J.: Pearson Education.

Weinberger, D. R. (1987). Implications of normal brain development for the pathogenesis of schizophrenia. *Archives of General Psychiatry, 44*, 660–669.

Weingartner, H., Kaye, W., Smallberg, S. A., Ebert, M. H., Gillin, J. C., & Sitaram, N. (1981). Memory failures in progressive idiopathic dementia. *Journal of Abnormal Psychology, 90*, 187–196.

Weintraub, S., & Mesulam, M. (1987). Right cerebral dominance in spatial attention. *Archives of Neurology, 44*, 621–625.

Weintraub, S., Mesulam, M.-M., & Kramer, L. (1981). Disturbances in prosody: A right hemisphere contribution to language. *Archives of Neurology, 38*, 742–744.

Weiskrantz, L. (1986). *Blindsight: A case study and implications.* Oxford, UK: Oxford University Press.

Weiskrantz, L. (2004). Blindsight. In L. M. Chalupa & J. S. Werner (Eds.), *The visual neurosciences* (pp. 657–669). Cambridge, MA: MIT Press.

Weissman, D. H., Roberts, K. C., Visscher, K. M., & Woldorff, M. G. (2006). The neural bases of momentary lapses in attention. *Nature Neuroscience, 9*, 971–978.

Welsh, K. A., Butters, N., Hughes, J., Mohs, R., & Heyman, A. (1991). Detection of abnormal memory decline in mild cases of Alzheimer's disease using CERAD neuropsychological measures. *Archives of Neurology, 48*, 278–281.

Wendelken, C. & Bunge, S. A. (2010). Transitive inference: Distinct contributions of rostrolateral prefrontal cortex and the hippocampus. *Journal of Cognitive Neuroscience, 22*(5), 837–847.

Wesnes, K., & Warburton, D. M. (1984). Effects of scopolamine and nicotine on human rapid information-processing performance. *Psychopharmacology, 82*(3), 147–150.

Wessberg, J., Stambaugh, C. R., Kralik, J. D., Beck, P. D., Laubach, M., Chapin, J. K., Kim, J., Biggs, S. J., Srinivasan, M. A., & Nicolelis, M. A. (2000). Real-time prediction of hand trajectory by ensembles of cortical neurons in primates. *Nature, 408*, 361–365.

Westwood, D. A., Schweizer, T. A., Heath, M. D., Roy, E. A., Dixon, M. J., & Black, S. (2001). Transitive gesture production in apraxia: Visual and nonvisual sensory contributions. *Brain & Cognition, 46*, 300–304.

Wettstein, A. (2000). Cholinesterase inhibitors and Ginkgo extracts—Are they comparable in the treatment of dementia? Comparison of published placebo-controlled efficacy studies of at least six months' duration. *Phytomedicine, 6*, 393–401.

Wexler, B. E., Gottschalk, C. H., Fulbright, R. K., Prohovnik, I., Lacadie, C. M., Rounsaville, B. J., & Gore, J. C. (2001). Functional magnetic imaging of cocaine craving. *American Journal of Psychiatry, 158*, 86–95.

Whalen, P. J., Kagan, J., Cook, R. G., Davis, F. C., Kim, H., Polis, S., et al. (2004). Human amygdala responsivity to masked fearful eye whites. *Science, 306,* 2061.

Whalen, P. J., Rauch, S. L., Etcoff, N. L., McInerney, S. C., Lee, M. B., & Jenike, M. A. (1998). Masked presentations of emotional facial expressions modulate amygdala activity without explicit knowledge. *Journal of Neuroscience, 18,* 411–418.

Wheeler, M. A., Stuss, D. T., & Tulving, E. (1995). Frontal lobe damage produces episodic memory impairment. *Journal of the International Neuropsychological Society, 1*(6), 525–536.

Wheeler, M. E., Petersen, S. E., & Buckner, R. L. (2000). Memory's echo: Vivid remembering reactivates sensory-specific cortex. *Proceedings of the National Academy of Science, USA, 97*(20), 11125–11129.

Whishaw, I. Q., Cassel, J. C., & Jarrad, L. E. (1995). Rats with fimbria-fornix lesions display a place response in a swimming pool: A dissociation between getting there and knowing where. *Journal of Neuroscience, 15*(8), 5779–5788.

White, D., Heaton, R. K., Monsch, A. U., & the HNRC Group. (1995). Neuropsychological studies of asymptomatic human immunodeficiency virus-type-1 infected individuals. *Journal of the International Neuropsychological Society, 1,* 304–315.

White, N. M., & McDonald, R. J. (1993). Acquisition of a spatial conditioned place preference is impaired by amygdala lesions and improved by fornix lesions. *Behavioral Brain Research, 55*(2), 269–281.

Whitehouse, P. J., Price, D. L., Clark, A. W., Coyle, J. T., & DeLong, M. R. (1981). Alzheimer disease: Evidence for selective loss of cholinergic neurons in the nucleus basalis. *Annals of Neurology, 10,* 122–126.

Whitehouse, P. J., Price, D. L., Stubble, R. G., Clark, A. W., Coyle, J. T., & DeLong, M. R. (1982). Alzheimer's disease and senile dementia: Loss of neurons in the basal forebrain. *Science, 215,* 1237–1239.

Whitney, D., Ellison, A., Rice, N. J., Arnold, D., Goodale, M., Walsh, V., & Milner, D. (2007). Visually guided reaching depends on motion area MT1. *Cerebral Cortex, 17,* 2644–2649.

Whitwell, J. L., Przybelski, S., Weigand, S. D., Knopman, D. S., Boeve, B. F., Petersen, R. C., & Jack, C. R. (2007). 3D maps from multiple MRI illustrate changing atrophy patterns as subjects progress from MCI to AD. *Brain, 130,* 1777–1786.

Wichmann, T., & Soares, J. (2006). Neuronal firing before and after burst discharges in the monkey basal ganglia is predictably patterned in the normal state and altered in Parkinsonism. *Journal of Neurophysiology, 95,* 2120–2133.

Wickens, C. D. (1980). The structure of attentional resources. In R. Nickerson & R. Pew (Eds.), *Attention and performance VIII.* Hillsdale, NJ: Erlbaum.

Wickens, C. D. (2002). Situation awareness and workload in aviation. *Current Directions in Psychological Science, 11,* 128–133.

Wickens, C. D., & Prevett, T. T. (1995). Exploring the dimensions of egocentricity in aircraft navigation displays. *Journal of Experimental Psychology: Applied, 1,* 110–135.

Wickens, C., Kramer, A., Vanasse, L., & Donchin, E. (1983). Performance of concurrent tasks: A psychophysiological analysis of the reciprocity of information-processing resources. *Science, 221,* 1080–1082.

Wicker, B., Keysers, C., Plailly, J., Royet, J., Gallese, V., & Rizzolatti, G. (2003). Both of us disgusted in my insula: The common neural basis of seeing and feeling disgust. *Neuron, 40,* 655–664.

Wieloch, T., & Nikolich, K. (2006). Mechanisms of neural plasticity following brain injury. *Current Opinion in Neurobiology, 16,* 258–264.

Wiesel, T. N., & Hubel, D. H. (1963). Single-cell response in striate cortex of kittens deprived of vision in one eye. *Journal of Neurophysiology, 26,* 1003–1017.

Wieser, H. G., Schindler, K., & Zumsteg, D. (2006). EEG in Creutzfeldt-Jakob disease. *Clinical Neurophysiology, 117,* 935–951.

Wigstrom, H., & Gustafsson, B. (1985). On long-lasting potentiation in the hippocampus: A proposed mechanism for its dependence on pre- and postsynaptic activity. *Acta Psychologia Scandinavica, 123,* 519–522.

Wilcock, G. K., Esiri, M. M., Bowen, D. M., & Smith, C. C. T. (1982). Alzheimer's disease: Correlation of cortical choline acetyltransferase activity with the severity of dementia and histological abnormalities. *Journal of Neurological Sciences, 57,* 407–417.

Wilke, M., Lidzba, K., Staudt, M., Buchenau, K., Grodd, W., & Krageloh-Mann, I. (2006). An fMRI task battery for assessing hemispheric language dominance in children. *NeuroImage, 32,* 400–410.

Wilkins, W. K., & Wakefield, J. (1995). Brain evolution and neurolinguistic preconditions. *Behavioral & Brain Sciences Special Issue: Second Annual "Controversies in Neuroscience" Conference, 18*(1), 161–226.

Will, B., Galani, R., Kelche, C., & Rosenzweig, M. R. (2004). Recovery from brain injury in animals: Relative efficacy of environmental enrichment, physical exercise or formal training (1990–2002). *Progress in Neurobiology, 72,* 167–182.

Will, R. G., & Matthews, W. B. (1984). A retrospective study of Creutzfeldt-Jakob disease in England and Wales, 1970–1979. I. Clinical features. *Journal of Neurology, Neurosurgery & Psychiatry, 47,* 134–140.

Willcutt, E. G., Doyle, A. E., Nigg, J. T., Faraone, S. V., & Pennington, B. F. (2005). Validity of the executive function theory of attention-deficit/hyperactivity disorder. *Biological Psychiatry, 57,* 1336–1346.

Williams, B. M., Luo, Y., Ward, C., Redd, K., Gibson, R., Kuczaj, S. A., & McCoy, J. G. (2001). Environmental enrichment: Effects on spatial memory and hippocampal CREB immunoreactivity. *Physiology & Behavior, 73,* 649–658.

Williams, M. A., Morris, A. P., McGlone, F., Abbott, D. F., & Mattingley, J. B. (2004). Amygdala responses to fearful and happy facial expressions under conditions of binocular suppression. *Journal of Neuroscience, 24,* 2898–2904.

Willingham, D. B., & Koroshetz, W. J. (1993). Evidence for dissociable motor skills in Huntington's disease patients. *Psychobiology, 21*(3), 173–182.

Wilson, M. A., & McNaughton, B. L. (1994). Reactivation of hippocampal ensemble memories during sleep. *Science, 265*(5172), 676–679.

Wilson, R. S., Bacon, L. D., Fox, J. H., & Kaszniak, A. W. (1983). Primary memory and secondary memory in dementia of the Alzheimer type. *Journal of Clinical Neuropsychology, 5,* 337–344.

Wilson, S. J., Sayette, M. A., & Fiez, J. A. (2004). Prefrontal responses to drug cues: A neurocognitive analysis. *Nature Neuroscience, 7,* 211–214.

Wilson, T. W., Hernandez, O. O., Asherin, R. M., Teale, P. D., Reite, M. L., & Rojas, D. C. (2008). Cortical gamma generators suggest abnormal auditory circuitry in early-onset psychosis. *Cerebral Cortex, 18,* 371–378.

Winner, E., & Gardner, H. (1977). The comprehension of metaphor in brain-damaged patients. *Brain, 100,* 719–727.

Winterer, G., & Weinberger, D. R. (2004). Genes, dopamine and cortical signal-to-noise ratio in schizophrenia. *Trends in Neurosciences, 27,* 683–690.

Wise, R. A., & Gardner, E. L. (2004). Animal models of addiction. In D. S. Charney & E. J. Nestler (Eds.), *Neurobiology of mental illness* (2d ed.; pp. 683–697). Oxford, UK: Oxford University Press.

Wisneski, K. J., Anderson, N., Schalk, G. Smyth, M., Moran, D., & Leuthardt, E. C. (2008). Unique cortical physiology associated with ipsilateral hand movements and neuroprosthetic implications. *Stroke, 39,* 3351–3359.

Wisniewski, K. E., Wisniewski, H. M., & Wen, G.Y. (1985). Occurrence of neuropathological changes and dementia of Alzheimer's disease in Down's syndrome. *Annals of Neurology, 17,* 278–282.

Witelson, S. F. (1974). Hemisphere specialization for linguistic and nonlinguistic tactual perception using a dichotomous stimulation technique. *Cortex, 10,* 3–17.

Witelson, S. F. (1977). Early hemisphere specialization and interhemispheric plasticity: An empirical and theoretical review. In S. J. Segalowitz & F. A. Gruber (Eds.), *Language development and neurological theory* (pp. 213–289). New York: Academic Press.

Witelson, S. F., & Goldsmith, C. H. (1991). The relationship of hand preference to anatomy of the corpus callosum in men. *Brain Research, 545,* 175–182.

Witelson, S. F., & Pallie, W. (1973). Left hemisphere specialization in the newborn: Anatomical evidence of asymmetry. *Brain, 96,* 641–646.

Witte, E. A., Davidson, M. C., & Marrocco, R. T. (1997). Effects of altering brain cholinergic activity on covert orienting of attention: Comparison of monkey and human performance. *Psychopharmacology, 132,* 324–334.

Wittling, W. (1990). Psychophysiological correlates of human brain asymmetry: Blood pressure changes during lateralized presentation of an emotionally laden film. *Neuropsychologia, 28,* 457–470.

Wittling, W., & Pflüger, M. (1990). Neuroendocrine hemisphere asymmetries: Salivary cortisol secretion during lateralized viewing of emotion-related and neutral films. *Brain & Cognition, 14,* 243–265.

Wittling, W., Block, A., Schweiger, E., & Genzel, S. (1998). Hemisphere asymmetry in sympathetic control of the human myocardium. *Brain & Cognition, 38,* 17–35.

Woelk, H. (2000). Comparison of St. John's wort and imipramine for treating depression: Randomised controlled trial. *British Medical Journal, 321,* 536–539.

Wojciulik, E., & Kanwisher, N. (1999). The generality of parietal involvement in visual attention. *Neuron, 23,* 747–764.

Wolf, R. C., Vasic, N., Schönfeldt-Lecuona, C., Landwehrmeyer, G. B., & Ecker, D. (2007). Dorsolateral prefrontal cortex dysfunction in presymptomatic Huntington's disease: Evidence from event-related fMRI. *Brain, 130,* 2845–2857.

Wolfe, J. M. (1994). Guided search 2.0: A revised model of visual search. *Psychonomic Bulletin & Review, 1*(2), 202–238.

Wolpert, D. M., & Ghahramani, Z. (2000). Computational principles of movement neuroscience. *Nature Neuroscience, 3*(Suppl), 1212–1217.

Wong, A. H. C., & Van Tol, H. H. M. (2003). Schizophrenia: From phenomenology to neurobiology. *Neuroscience & Biobehavioral Reviews, 27,* 269–306.

Wong, D. F., Wagner, H. N., Tune, L. E., Dannals, R. F., et al. (1986). Positron emission tomography revealed elevated D2 receptors in drug-naive schizophrenics. *Science, 234,* 1558–1563.

Wood, E. R., Dudchenko, P. A., & Eichenbaum, H. (1999). The global record of memory in hippocampal neuronal activity. *Nature, 397*(6720), 613–616.

Woods, S. P., Moore, D. J., Weber, E., & Grant, I. (2009). Cognitive neuropsychology of HIV-associated neurocognitive disorders. *Neuropsychology Review, 19,* 152–168.

World Health Organization. (2001). *The World Health Report 2001: Mental health: New understanding, new hope.* Geneva: Author.

Wright, B. A., Bowen, R. W., & Zecker, S. G. (2000). Nonlinguistic perceptual deficits associated with reading and language disorders. *Current Opinion in Neurobiology, 10,* 482–486.

Wright, C. E. (1990). Controlling sequential motor activity. In D. N. Osherson, S. M. Kosslyn, & J. M. Hollerbach (Eds.), *Visual cognition and action* (pp. 285–316). Cambridge, MA: MIT Press.

Wurtz, R. H. (2009). Recounting the impact of Hubel and Wiesel. *Journal of Physiology, 587,* 2817–2823.

Wurtz, R. H., & Goldberg, M. E. (1972). Activity of superior colliculus in behaving monkey: III. Cells discharging before eye movements. *Journal of Neurophysiology, 35,* 575–586.

Wurtz, R. H., & Goldberg, M. E. (Eds.). (1988). *The neurobiology of saccadic eye movements.* Amsterdam: Elsevier.

Wylie, E., Luders, H., & Murphy, D. (1990). Intracarotid amobarbital (Wada) test for language dominance: Correlation with results of cortical stimulation. *Epilepsia, 31*(2), 156–161.

Xu, Y. (2005). Revisiting the role of the fusiform face area in visual expertise. *Cerebral Cortex, 15,* 1234–1242.

Yamaguchi, S., & Knight, R. T. (1991). Anterior and posterior association cortex contributions to the somatosensory P300. *Journal of Neuroscience, 11,* 2039–2054.

Yamane, Y., Tsunoda, K., Matsumoto, M., Phillips, A. N., & Tanifuji, M. (2006). Representation of the spatial relationship among object parts by neurons in macaque inferotemporal cortex. *Journal of Neurophysiology, 96,* 3147–3156.

Yantis, S., & Serences, J. T. (2003). Cortical mechanisms of space-based and object-based attentional control. *Current Opinion in Neurobiology, 13,* 187–193.

Yantis, S., Schwarzbach, J., Serences, J. T., Carlson, R. L., Steinmetz, M. A., Pekar, J. J., & Courtney, S. M. (2002). Transient neural activity in human parietal cortex during spatial attention shifts. *Nature Neuroscience, 5,* 995–1002.

Yee, C. M., Nuechterlein, K. H., Morris, S. E., & White, P. M. (1998). P50 suppression in recent-onset schizophrenia: Clinical correlates and risperidone effects. *Journal of Abnormal Psychology, 107,* 691–698.

Yin, R. K. (1970). Face recognition by brain-injured patients: A dissociable ability? *Neuropsychologia, 8,* 395–402.

Yokoyama, K., Jennings, R., Ackles, P., Hood, P., & Boller, F. (1987). Lack of heart rate changes during an attention-demanding task after right hemisphere lesions. *Neurology, 37,* 624–630.

Yonelinas, A. P. (2001). Components of episodic memory: The contribution of recollection and familiarity. *Philosophical Transactions of the Royal Society of London, Series B—Biological Science, 356,* 1363–1374.

Yoshor, D., Bosking, W. H., Ghose, G. M., & Maunsell, J. H. R. (2007). Receptive fields in human visual cortex mapped with surface electrodes. *Cerebral Cortex, 17,* 2293–2302.

Young, A. W., DeHaan, E. H. F., Newcombe, F., & Hay, D. C. (1990). Facial neglect. *Neuropsychologia, 28,* 391–415.

Young, A. W., Hellawell, D. J., & Welch, J. (1992). Neglect and visual recognition. *Brain, 115,* 51–71.

Young, A. W., Newcombe, F., de Haan, E. H. F., Small, M., & Hay, D. C. (1993). Face perception after brain injury: Selective impairments affecting identity and expression. *Brain, 116,* 941–959.

Young, G. B. (2009). Coma. *Annals of the New York Academy of Sciences, 1157,* 32–47.

Yovel, G., & Kanwisher, N. (2004). Face perception: Domain specific, not process specific. *Neuron, 44,* 889–898.

Yurgelun-Todd, D. (2007). Emotional and cognitive changes during adolescence. *Current Opinion in Neurobiology, 17,* 251–257.

Zacks, J. M. (2008). Neuroimaging studies of mental rotation: A meta-analysis and review. *Journal of Cognitive Neuroscience, 20,* 1–19.

Zahrt, J., Taylor, J. R., Mathew, R. G., & Arnsten, A. F. T. (1997). Supranormal stimulation of dopamine D1 receptors in the rodent prefrontal cortex impairs spatial working memory performance. *Journal of Neuroscience, 17,* 8525–8535.

Zaidel, E. (1978). Auditory language comprehension in the right hemisphere following cerebral commissurotomy and hemispherectomy: A comparison with child language and aphasia. In A. Caramazza & E. B. Zurif (Eds.), *Language acquisition and language breakdown: Parallels and divergencies* (pp. 229–275). Baltimore, MD: Johns Hopkins University Press.

Zaidel, E. (1983a). Disconnection syndrome as a model for laterality effects in the normal brain. In J. B. Hellige (Ed.), *Cerebral hemisphere asymmetry: Method, theory and application* (pp. 95–151). New York: Praeger.

Zaidel, E. (1983b). A response to Gazzaniga: Language in the right hemisphere, convergent perspectives. *American Psychologist, 38,* 542–546.

Zaidel, E. (1990). The saga of right-hemisphere reading. In C. Trevarthen (Ed.), *Brain circuits and functions of the mind: Essays in honor of Roger W. Sperry* (pp. 304–319). Cambridge, UK: Cambridge University Press.

Zakzanis, K. K., Campbell, Z., & Jovanovski, D. (2007). The neuropsychology of ecstasy (MDMA) use: A quantitative review. *Human Psychopharmacology, 22,* 427–435.

Zald, D. H. (2003). The human amygdala and the emotional evaluation of sensory stimuli. *Brain Research Reviews, 41,* 88–123.

Zangenehpour, S., & Chaudhuri, A. (2001). Neural activity profiles of the neocortex and superior colliculus after bimodal sensory stimulation. *Cerebral Cortex, 11,* 924–935.

Zangenehpour, S., & Chaudhuri, A. (2005). Patchy organization and asymmetric distribution of the neural correlates of face processing in monkey inferotemporal cortex. *Current Biology, 15,* 993–1005.

Zangwill, O. L. (1960). La problème de l'apraxie idéatoire [The problem of ideational apraxia]. *Revue Neurologique (Paris), 102,* 595–603.

Zatorre, R. J., Bouffard, M., Ahad, P., & Belin, P. (2002). Where is "where" in the human auditory cortex? *Nature Neuroscience, 5,* 905–909.

Zatorre, R. J., Evans, A. C., Meyer, E., & Gjedde, A. (1992). Lateralization of phonetic and pitch discrimination in speech processing. *Science, 256,* 846–849.

Zatorre, R. J., Meyer, E., Gjedde, A., & Evans, A. C. (1996). PET studies of phonetic processing of speech: Review, replication, and reanalysis. *Cerebral Cortex, 6,* 21–30.

Zeki, S. (1973). Colour coding in rhesus monkey prestriate cortex. *Brain Research, 53,* 422–427.

Zeki, S. (1983). Colour coding in the cerebral cortex: The responses of wavelength-selective and colour-coded cells in monkey visual cortex to changes in wavelength composition. *Neuroscience, 9,* 767–781.

Zeki, S. M. (1974). Functional organization of a visual area in the posterior bank of the superior temporal sulcus of the rhesus monkey. *Journal of Physiology, 236,* 549–573.

Zeki, S., & Shipp, S. (1988). The functional logic of cortical connections. *Nature, 335,* 311–317.

Zeki, S., Watson, J. D. G., Lueck, C. J., Friston, K. J., Kennard, C., & Frackowiak, R. S. J. (1991). A direct demonstration of functional specialization in human visual cortex. *Journal of Neuroscience, 11,* 641–649.

Zeman, A. (1997). Persistent vegetative state. *Lancet, 350,* 795–799.

Zemper, E. (1994). Analysis of cerebral concussion frequency with the most commonly used models of football helmets. *Journal of Athletic Training, 29,* 33–50.

Zerr, I., Kallenberg, K., Summers, D. M., Romero, C., Taratuto, A., Heinemann, U., et al. (2009). Updated clinical diagnostic criteria for sporadic Creutzfeldt-Jakob disease. *Brain, 132,* 2659–2668.

Zhang, M., & Barash, S. (2000). Neuronal switching of sensorimotor transformations for antisaccades. *Nature, 408,* 971–975.

Zhang, W., & Luck, S. J. (2009). Feature-based attention modulates feedforward visual processing. *Nature Neuroscience, 12,* 24–25.

Zhang, Y., Schuff, N., Du, A.-T., Rosen, H. J., Kramer, J. H., Gorno-Tempini, M. L., et al. (2009). White matter damage in frontotemporal dementia and Alzheimer's disease measured by diffusion MRI. *Brain, 132,* 2579–2592.

Zhao, C., Deng, W., & Gage, F. H. (2008). Mechanisms and functional implications of adult neurogenesis. *Cell, 132,* 645–660.

Zhu, Q., Ma, J., Yu, L. & Yuan, C. (2009). Grafted neural stem cells migrate to substantia nigra and improve behavior in Parkinsonian rats. *Neuroscience Letters, 462,* 213–218.

Ziegler, D., Piguet, O., Salat, D., Prince, K., Connally, E., & Corkin, S. (2008). Cognitive ability in healthy aging is related to regional white matter integrity, but not cortical thickness. *Neurobiology of Aging,* Epub ahead of print.

Ziegler, J. C., & Goswami, U. (2005). Reading acquisition, vdevelopmental dyslexia, and skilled reading across languages: A psycholinguistic grain size theory. *Psychological Bulletin, 131,* 3–29.

Zigmond, M. J., Abercrombie, E. D., Berger, T. W., Grace, A. A., et al. (1990). Compensations after lesions of central dopaminergic neurons: Some clinical and basic implications. *Trends in Neurosciences, 13,* 290–296.

Zihl, J., Von Cramon, D., & Mai, N. (1983). Selective disturbance of movement vision after bilateral brain damage. *Brain, 106,* 313–340.

Zilbovicius, M., Meresse, I., Chabane, N., Brunelle, F., Samson, Y., & Boddaert, N. (2006). Autism, the superior temporal sulcus and social perception. *Trends in Neurosciences, 29,* 359–366.

Zipser, D., & Andersen, R. A. (1988). A backpropagation programmed network that simulates response properties of a subset of posterior parietal neurons. *Nature, 331,* 679–684.

Zoccolotti, P., Matan, A., Deloche, G., Cantagallo, A., Passadori, A., Leclercq, M., et al. (2000). Patterns of attentional impairment following closed head injury: A collaborative European study. *Cortex, 36,* 93–107.

Zola-Morgan, S., & Squire, L. R. (1985). Medial temporal lesions in monkeys impair memory on a variety of tasks sensitive to human amnesia. *Behavioral Neuroscience, 99,* 22–34.

Zurif, E. B., Gardner, J., & Brownell, H. H. (1989). The case against the case against group studies. *Brain and Cognition, 10,* 237–255.

Name Index

Subject Index